PhET SIMULATIONS

Available in the Pearson eText and in the Study Area of MasteringPhysics

Extended Edition includes Chapters 1–44. Standard Edition includes Chapters 1–37.
Three-volume edition: Volume 1 includes Chapters 1–20, Volume 2 includes Chapters 21–37, and Volume 3 includes Chapters 37–44.

*Indicates an associated tutorial available in the MasteringPhysics Item Library.

ActivPhysics OnLine™ ACTIVITIES

(MP) www.masteringphysics.com

SEARS AND ZEMANSKY'S

UNIVERSITY PHYSICS

VOLUME 2
13TH EDITION

HUGH D. YOUNG
CARNEGIE MELLON
UNIVERSITY

ROGER A. FREEDMAN
UNIVERSITY
OF CALIFORNIA,
SANTA BARBARA

CONTRIBUTING AUTHOR
A. LEWIS FORD
TEXAS A&M UNIVERSITY

Addison-Wesley

Boston   Columbus   Indianapolis
New York   San Francisco   Upper Saddle River
Amsterdam   Cape Town   Dubai   London
Madrid   Milan   Munich   Paris   Montréal   Toronto
Delhi   Mexico City   São Paulo   Sydney
Hong Kong   Seoul   Singapore   Taipei   Tokyo

Publisher: Jim Smith
Executive Editor: Nancy Whilton
Project Editor: Chandrika Madhavan
Director of Development: Michael Gillespie
Editorial Manager: Laura Kenney
Senior Development Editor: Margot Otway
Editorial Assistant: Steven Le
Associate Media Producer: Kelly Reed
Managing Editor: Corinne Benson
Production Project Manager: Beth Collins
Production Management and Composition: Nesbitt Graphics
Copyeditor: Carol Reitz
Interior Designer: Elm Street Publishing Services
Cover Designer: Jodi Notowitz
Illustrators: Rolin Graphics
Senior Art Editor: Donna Kalal
Photo Researcher: Eric Shrader
Manufacturing Buyer: Jeff Sargent
Senior Marketing Manager: Kerry Chapman

If you purchased this book within the United States or Canada you should be aware that it has been imported without the approval of the Publisher or the Author.

ISBN 13: 978-0-321-71000-0; ISBN 10: 0-321-71000-2

Addison-Wesley
is an imprint of

1 2 3 4 5 6 7 8 9 10—VHC—14 13 12 11 10

BRIEF CONTENTS

Build **Skills**

Learn basic and advanced skills that help solve a broad range of physics problems.

Problem-Solving Strategies coach students in how to approach specific types of problems.

▼

This text's **uniquely extensive set** of Examples enables students to explore problem-solving challenges in exceptional detail.

Consistent
The **Identify / Set Up / Execute / Evaluate** format, used in all Examples, encourages students to tackle problems thoughtfully rather than skipping to the math.

Focused
All Examples and Problem-Solving Strategies are revised to be more concise and focused.

Visual
Most Examples employ a diagram—often a **pencil sketch** that shows what a student should draw.

Problem-Solving Strategy 5.2 Newton's Second Law: Dynamics of Particles

IDENTIFY the relevant concepts: You have to use Newton's second law for *any* problem that involves forces acting on an accelerating ... accelerate in different directions, you can use a different set of axes for each body.

Example 5.17 Toboggan ride with friction II

The same toboggan with the same coefficient of friction as in Example 5.16 *accelerates* down a steeper hill. Derive an expression for the acceleration in terms of g, α, μ_k, and w.

SOLUTION

IDENTIFY and SET UP: The toboggan is accelerating, so we must use Newton's second law as given in Eqs. (5.4). Our target variable is the downhill acceleration.

Our sketch and free-body diagram (Fig. 5.23) are almost the same as for Example 5.16. The toboggan's y-component of acceleration a_y is still zero but the x-component a_x is not, so we've drawn the downhill component of weight as a longer vector than the (uphill) friction force.

EXECUTE: It's convenient to express the weight as $w = mg$. Then Newton's second law in component form says

$$\sum F_x = mg \sin \alpha + (-f_k) = ma_x$$
$$\sum F_y = n + (-mg \cos \alpha) = 0$$

5.23 Our sketches for this problem.

(a) The situation   (b) Free-body diagram for toboggan

From the second equation and Eq. (5.5) we get an expression for f_k:

$$n = mg \cos \alpha$$
$$f_k = \mu_k n = \mu_k mg \cos \alpha$$

We substitute this into the x-component equation and solve for a_x:

$$mg \sin \alpha + (-\mu_k mg \cos \alpha) = ma_x$$
$$a_x = g(\sin \alpha - \mu_k \cos \alpha)$$

EVALUATE: As for the frictionless toboggan in Example 5.10, the acceleration doesn't depend on the mass m of the toboggan. That's because all of the forces that act on the toboggan (weight, normal force, and kinetic friction force) are proportional to m.

Let's check some special cases. If the hill is vertical ($\alpha = 90°$) so that $\sin \alpha = 1$ and $\cos \alpha = 0$, we have $a_x = g$ (the toboggan falls freely). For a certain value of α the acceleration is zero; this happens if

$$\sin \alpha = \mu_k \cos \alpha \qquad \text{and} \qquad \mu_k = \tan \alpha$$

This agrees with our result for the constant-velocity toboggan in Example 5.16. If the angle is even smaller, $\mu_k \cos \alpha$ is greater than $\sin \alpha$ and a_x is *negative*; if we give the toboggan an initial downhill push to start it moving, it will slow down and stop. Finally, if the hill is frictionless so that $\mu_k = 0$, we retrieve the result of Example 5.10: $a_x = g \sin \alpha$.

Notice that we started with a simple problem (Example 5.10) and extended it to more and more general situations. The general result we found in this example includes *all* the previous ones as special cases. Don't memorize this result, but do make sure you understand how we obtained it and what it means.

Suppose instead we give the toboggan an initial push *up* the hill. The direction of the kinetic friction force is now reversed, so the acceleration is different from the downhill value. It turns out that the expression for a_x is the same as for downhill motion except that the minus sign becomes plus. Can you show this?

Example 1.1 Converting speed units

The world land speed record is 763.0 mi/h, set on October 15, 1997, by Andy Green in the jet-engine car *Thrust SSC*. Express this speed in meters per second.

Identify: mi/h → m/s   mi → m   h → s

Set up: 1 mi = 1.609 km   1 km = 1000 m
1 h = 3600 s

Execute
763.0 mi/h = $\left(763.0 \dfrac{mi}{h}\right)\left(\dfrac{1.609 \, km}{1 \, mi}\right)\left(\dfrac{1000 \, m}{1 \, km}\right)\left(\dfrac{1 \, h}{3600 \, s}\right)$

= 341.018611 m/s = 341.0 m/s

▲

NEW! Video Tutor Solution for Every Example
Each Example is explained and solved by an instructor in a Video Tutor solution provided in the Study Area of MasteringPhysics® and in the Pearson eText.

NEW! Mathematics Review Tutorials
MasteringPhysics offers an extensive set of assignable mathematics review tutorials—covering differential and integral calculus as well as algebra and trigonometry.

Build Confidence

Develop problem-solving confidence through a range of practice options—from guided to unguided.

NEW! Bridging Problems
At the start of each problem set, a Bridging Problem helps students make the leap from routine exercises to challenging problems with confidence and ease.

Each Bridging Problem poses a moderately difficult, multi-concept problem, which often draws on earlier chapters. In place of a full solution, it provides a skeleton solution guide consisting of questions and hints.

A full solution is explained in a Video Tutor, provided in the Study Area of MasteringPhysics® and in the Pearson eText.

BRIDGING PROBLEM   Billiard Physics

A cue ball (a uniform solid sphere of mass m and radius R) is at rest on a level pool table. Using a pool cue, you give the ball a sharp, horizontal hit of magnitude F at a height h above the center of the ball (Fig. 10.37). The force of the hit is much greater than the friction force f that the table surface exerts on the ball. The hit lasts for a short time Δt. (a) For what value of h will the ball roll without slipping? (b) If you hit the ball dead center ($h = 0$), the ball will slide across the table for a while, but eventually it will roll without slipping. What will the speed of its center of mass be then?

SOLUTION GUIDE

See MasteringPhysics® study area for a Video Tutor solution.

IDENTIFY and SET UP
1. Draw a free-body diagram for the ball for the situation in part (a), including your choice of coordinate axes. Note that the cue exerts both an impulsive force on the ball and an impulsive torque around the center of mass.
2. The cue force applied for a time Δt gives the ball's center of mass a speed v_{cm}, and the cue torque applied for that same time gives the ball an angular speed ω. What must be the relationship between v_{cm} and ω for the ball to roll without slipping?

3. Draw two free-body diagrams for the ball in part (b): one showing the forces during the hit and the other showing the forces after the hit but before the ball is rolling without slipping.
4. What is the angular speed of the ball in part (b) just after the hit? While the ball is sliding, does v_{cm} increase or decrease? Does ω increase or decrease? What is the relationship between v_{cm} and ω when the ball is finally rolling without slipping?

EXECUTE
5. In part (a), use the impulse–momentum theorem to find the speed of the ball's center of mass immediately after the hit. Then use the rotational version of the impulse–momentum theorem to find the angular speed immediately after the hit. (*Hint:* To write down the rotational version of the impulse–momentum theorem, remember that the relationship between torque and angular momentum is the same as that between force and linear momentum.)
6. Use your results from step 5 to find the value of h that will cause the ball to roll without slipping immediately after the hit.
7. In part (b), again find the ball's center-of-mass speed and angular speed immediately after the hit. Then write Newton's second law for the translational motion and rotational motion of the ball as it is sliding. Use these equations to write expressions for v_{cm} and ω as functions of the elapsed time t since the hit.
8. Using your results from step 7, find the time t when v_{cm} and ω have the correct relationship for rolling without slipping. Then find the value of v_{cm} at this time.

EVALUATE
9. If you have access to a pool table, test out the results of parts (a) and (b) for yourself!
10. Can you show that if you used a hollow cylinder rather than a solid ball, you would have to hit the top of the cylinder to cause rolling without slipping as in part (a)?

10.37

14.95 • CP In Fig. P14.95 the upper ball is released from rest, collides with the stationary lower ball, and sticks to it. The strings are both 50.0 cm long. The upper ball has mass 2.00 kg, and it is initially 10.0 cm higher than the lower ball, which has mass 3.00 kg. Find the frequency and maximum angular displacement of the motion after the collision.

Figure **P14.95**

10.0 cm

14.96 •• CP BIO *T. rex.* Model the leg of the *T. rex* in Example 14.10 (Section 14.6) as two uniform rods, each 1.55 m long, joined rigidly end to end. Let the lower rod have mass M and the upper rod mass $2M$. The composite object is pivoted about the top of the upper rod. Compute the oscillation period of this object for small-amplitude oscillations. Compare your result to that of Example 14.10.

14.97 •• CALC A slender, uniform, metal rod with mass M is pivoted without friction about an axis through its midpoint and perpendicular to the rod. A horizontal spring with force constant k is attached to the lower end of the rod, with the other end of the spring attached to a rigid support. If the rod is displaced by a small angle Θ from the vertical (Fig. P14.97) and released, show that it moves in angular SHM and calculate the period. (*Hint:* Assume that the angle Θ is small enough for the approximations $\sin \Theta \approx \Theta$ and $\cos \Theta \approx 1$ to be valid. The motion is simple harmonic if $d^2\theta/dt^2 = -\omega^2\theta$, and the period is then $T = 2\pi/\omega$.)

Figure **P14.97**

In response to professors, the **Problem Sets** now include more biomedically oriented problems (BIO), more difficult problems requiring calculus (CALC), and more cumulative problems that draw on earlier chapters (CP).

About 20% of problems are new or revised. These revisions are driven by detailed student-performance data gathered nationally through MasteringPhysics.

Problem difficulty is now indicated by a three-dot ranking system based on data from MasteringPhysics.

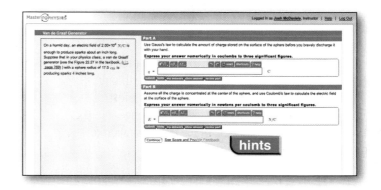

NEW! Enhanced End-of-Chapter Problems in MasteringPhysics
Select end-of-chapter problems will now offer additional support such as problem-solving strategy hints, relevant math review and practice, and links to the eText. These new enhanced problems bridge the gap between guided tutorials and traditional homework problems.

Bring Physics to Life

Deepen knowledge of physics by building connections to the real world.

Application Moment of Inertia of a Bird's Wing
When a bird flaps its wings, it rotates the wings up and down around the shoulder. A hummingbird has small wings with a small moment of inertia, so the bird can make its wings move rapidly (up to 70 beats per second). By contrast, the Andean condor (*Vultur gryphus*) has immense wings that are hard to move due to their large moment of inertia. Condors flap their wings at about one beat per second on takeoff, but at most times prefer to soar while holding their wings steady.

Application Tendons Are Nonideal Springs
Muscles exert forces via the tendons that attach them to bones. A tendon consists of long, stiffly elastic collagen fibers. The graph shows how the tendon from the hind leg of a wallaby (a small kangaroo) stretches in response to an applied force. The tendon does not exhibit the simple, straight-line behavior of an ideal spring, so the work it does has to be found by integration [Eq. (6.7)]. Note that the tendon exerts less force while relaxing than while stretching. As a result, the relaxing tendon does only about 93% of the work that was done to stretch it.

NEW! Applications of Physics
Throughout the text, free-standing captioned photos apply physics to real situations, with particular emphasis on applications of biomedical and general interest. ▶

Application Listening for Turbulent Flow
Normal blood flow in the human aorta is laminar, but a small disturbance such as a heart pathology can cause the flow to become turbulent. Turbulence makes noise, which is why listening to blood flow with a stethoscope is a useful diagnostic technique.

◀ **NEW! PhET Simulations and Tutorials**
Sixteen assignable PhET Tutorials enable students to make connections between real-life phenomena and the underlying physics. 76 PhET simulations are provided in the Study Area of MasteringPhysics® and in the Pearson eText.

The comprehensive library of ActivPhysics applets and applet-based tutorials is also available.

NEW! Video Tutor Demonstrations and Tutorials
"Pause and predict" demonstration videos of key physics concepts engage students by asking them to submit a prediction before seeing the outcome. These videos are available through the Study Area of MasteringPhysics and in the Pearson eText. A set of assignable tutorials based on these videos challenge students to transfer their understanding of the demonstration to a related problem situation.

Biomedically Based End-of-Chapter Problems ▶
To serve biosciences students, the text adds a substantial number of problems based on biological and biomedical situations.

Figure **E21.23**

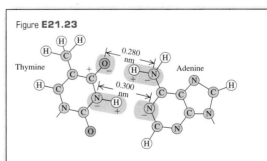

21.24 •• **BIO** **Base Pairing in DNA, II.** Refer to Exercise 21.23. Figure E21.24 shows the bonding of the cytosine and guanine molecules. The O—H and H—N distances are each 0.110 nm. In this case, assume that the bonding is due only to the forces along the O—H—O, N—H—N, and O—H—N combinations, and assume also that these three combinations are parallel to each other. Calculate the *net* force that cytosine exerts on guanine due to the preceding three combinations. Is this force attractive or repulsive?

Make a Difference with MasteringPhysics®

www.masteringphysics.com

MasteringPhysics is the most effective and widely used online science tutorial, homework, and assessment system available.

NEW! Pre-Built Assignments ▶

For every chapter in the book, MasteringPhysics now provides pre-built assignments that cover the material with a tested mix of tutorials and end-of-chapter problems of graded difficulty. Professors may use these assignments as-is or take them as a starting point for modification.

◀ Gradebook

- Every assignment is graded automatically.
- Shades of red highlight vulnerable students and challenging assignments.

Class Performance on Assignment ▶

Click on a problem to see which step your students struggled with most, and even their most common wrong answers. Compare results at every stage with the national average or with your previous class.

◀ Gradebook Diagnostics

This screen provides your favorite weekly diagnostics. With a single click, charts summarize the most difficult problems, vulnerable students, grade distribution, and even improvement in scores over the course.

ABOUT THE AUTHORS

Hugh D. Young is Emeritus Professor of Physics at Carnegie Mellon University. He earned both his undergraduate and graduate degrees from that university. He earned his Ph.D. in fundamental particle theory under the direction of the late Richard Cutkosky. He joined the faculty of Carnegie Mellon in 1956 and retired in 2004. He also had two visiting professorships at the University of California, Berkeley.

Dr. Young's career has centered entirely on undergraduate education. He has written several undergraduate-level textbooks, and in 1973 he became a coauthor with Francis Sears and Mark Zemansky for their well-known introductory texts. In addition to his role on Sears and Zemansky's *University Physics,* he is also author of Sears and Zemansky's *College Physics.*

Dr. Young earned a bachelor's degree in organ performance from Carnegie Mellon in 1972 and spent several years as Associate Organist at St. Paul's Cathedral in Pittsburgh. He has played numerous organ recitals in the Pittsburgh area. Dr. Young and his wife, Alice, usually travel extensively in the summer, especially overseas and in the desert canyon country of southern Utah.

Roger A. Freedman is a Lecturer in Physics at the University of California, Santa Barbara. Dr. Freedman was an undergraduate at the University of California campuses in San Diego and Los Angeles, and did his doctoral research in nuclear theory at Stanford University under the direction of Professor J. Dirk Walecka. He came to UCSB in 1981 after three years teaching and doing research at the University of Washington.

At UCSB, Dr. Freedman has taught in both the Department of Physics and the College of Creative Studies, a branch of the university intended for highly gifted and motivated undergraduates. He has published research in nuclear physics, elementary particle physics, and laser physics. In recent years, he has worked to make physics lectures a more interactive experience through the use of classroom response systems.

In the 1970s Dr. Freedman worked as a comic book letterer and helped organize the San Diego Comic-Con (now the world's largest popular culture convention) during its first few years. Today, when not in the classroom or slaving over a computer, Dr. Freedman can be found either flying (he holds a commercial pilot's license) or driving with his wife, Caroline, in their 1960 Nash Metropolitan convertible.

A. Lewis Ford is Professor of Physics at Texas A&M University. He received a B.A. from Rice University in 1968 and a Ph.D. in chemical physics from the University of Texas at Austin in 1972. After a one-year postdoc at Harvard University, he joined the Texas A&M physics faculty in 1973 and has been there ever since. Professor Ford's research area is theoretical atomic physics, with a specialization in atomic collisions. At Texas A&M he has taught a variety of undergraduate and graduate courses, but primarily introductory physics.

HOW TO SUCCEED IN PHYSICS BY REALLY TRYING

Mark Hollabaugh *Normandale Community College*

Physics encompasses the large and the small, the old and the new. From the atom to galaxies, from electrical circuitry to aerodynamics, physics is very much a part of the world around us. You probably are taking this introductory course in calculus-based physics because it is required for subsequent courses you plan to take in preparation for a career in science or engineering. Your professor wants you to learn physics and to enjoy the experience. He or she is very interested in helping you learn this fascinating subject. That is part of the reason your professor chose this textbook for your course. That is also the reason Drs. Young and Freedman asked me to write this introductory section. We want you to succeed!

The purpose of this section of *University Physics* is to give you some ideas that will assist your learning. Specific suggestions on how to use the textbook will follow a brief discussion of general study habits and strategies.

Preparation for This Course

If you had high school physics, you will probably learn concepts faster than those who have not because you will be familiar with the language of physics. If English is a second language for you, keep a glossary of new terms that you encounter and make sure you understand how they are used in physics. Likewise, if you are farther along in your mathematics courses, you will pick up the mathematical aspects of physics faster. Even if your mathematics is adequate, you may find a book such as Arnold D. Pickar's *Preparing for General Physics: Math Skill Drills and Other Useful Help (Calculus Version)* to be useful. Your professor may actually assign sections of this math review to assist your learning.

Learning to Learn

Each of us has a different learning style and a preferred means of learning. Understanding your own learning style will help you to focus on aspects of physics that may give you difficulty and to use those components of your course that will help you overcome the difficulty. Obviously you will want to spend more time on those aspects that give you the most trouble. If you learn by hearing, lectures will be very important. If you learn by explaining, then working with other students will be useful to you. If solving problems is difficult for you, spend more time learning how to solve problems. Also, it is important to understand and develop good study habits. Perhaps the most important thing you can do for yourself is to set aside adequate, regularly scheduled study time in a distraction-free environment.

Answer the following questions for yourself:
- Am I able to use fundamental mathematical concepts from algebra, geometry and trigonometry? (If not, plan a program of review with help from your professor.)
- In similar courses, what activity has given me the most trouble? (Spend more time on this.) What has been the easiest for me? (Do this first; it will help to build your confidence.)

- Do I understand the material better if I read the book before or after the lecture? (You may learn best by skimming the material, going to lecture, and then undertaking an in-depth reading.)
- Do I spend adequate time in studying physics? (A rule of thumb for a class like this is to devote, on the average, 2.5 hours out of class for each hour in class. For a course meeting 5 hours each week, that means you should spend about 10 to 15 hours per week studying physics.)
- Do I study physics every day? (Spread that 10 to 15 hours out over an entire week!) At what time of the day am I at my best for studying physics? (Pick a specific time of the day and stick to it.)
- Do I work in a quiet place where I can maintain my focus? (Distractions will break your routine and cause you to miss important points.)

Working with Others

Scientists or engineers seldom work in isolation from one another but rather work cooperatively. You will learn more physics and have more fun doing it if you work with other students. Some professors may formalize the use of cooperative learning or facilitate the formation of study groups. You may wish to form your own informal study group with members of your class who live in your neighborhood or dorm. If you have access to e-mail, use it to keep in touch with one another. Your study group is an excellent resource when reviewing for exams.

Lectures and Taking Notes

An important component of any college course is the lecture. In physics this is especially important because your professor will frequently do demonstrations of physical principles, run computer simulations, or show video clips. All of these are learning activities that will help you to understand the basic principles of physics. Don't miss lectures, and if for some reason you do, ask a friend or member of your study group to provide you with notes and let you know what happened.

Take your class notes in outline form, and fill in the details later. It can be very difficult to take word for word notes, so just write down key ideas. Your professor may use a diagram from the textbook. Leave a space in your notes and just add the diagram later. After class, edit your notes, filling in any gaps or omissions and noting things you need to study further. Make references to the textbook by page, equation number, or section number.

Make sure you ask questions in class, or see your professor during office hours. Remember the only "dumb" question is the one that is not asked. Your college may also have teaching assistants or peer tutors who are available to help you with difficulties you may have.

Examinations

Taking an examination is stressful. But if you feel adequately prepared and are well-rested, your stress will be lessened. Preparing for an exam is a continual process; it begins the moment the last exam is over. You should immediately go over the exam and understand any mistakes you made. If you worked a problem and made substantial errors, try this: Take a piece of paper and divide it down the middle with a line from top to bottom. In one column, write the proper solution to the problem. In the other column, write what you did and why, if you know, and why your solution was incorrect. If you are uncertain why you made your mistake, or how to avoid making it again, talk with your professor. Physics continually builds on fundamental ideas and it is important to correct any misunderstandings immediately. *Warning:* While cramming at the last minute may get you through the present exam, you will not adequately retain the concepts for use on the next exam.

PREFACE

This book is the product of more than six decades of leadership and innovation in physics education. When the first edition of *University Physics* by Francis W. Sears and Mark W. Zemansky was published in 1949, it was revolutionary among calculus-based physics textbooks in its emphasis on the fundamental principles of physics and how to apply them. The success of *University Physics* with generations of several million students and educators around the world is a testament to the merits of this approach, and to the many innovations it has introduced subsequently.

In preparing this new Thirteenth Edition, we have further enhanced and developed *University Physics* to assimilate the best ideas from education research with enhanced problem-solving instruction, pioneering visual and conceptual pedagogy, the first systematically enhanced problems, and the most pedagogically proven and widely used online homework and tutorial system in the world.

New to This Edition

- Included in each chapter, **Bridging Problems** provide a transition between the single-concept Examples and the more challenging end-of-chapter problems. Each Bridging Problem poses a difficult, multiconcept problem, which often incorporates physics from earlier chapters. In place of a full solution, it provides a skeleton **Solution Guide** consisting of questions and hints, which helps train students to approach and solve challenging problems with confidence.
- **All Examples, Conceptual Examples, and Problem-Solving Strategies are revised** to enhance conciseness and clarity for today's students.
- The **core modern physics chapters** (Chapters 38–41) are revised extensively to provide a more idea-centered, less historical approach to the material. Chapters 42–44 are also revised significantly.
- **The fluid mechanics chapter now precedes the chapters on gravitation and periodic motion,** so that the latter immediately precedes the chapter on mechanical waves.
- **Additional bioscience applications** appear throughout the text, mostly in the form of marginal photos with explanatory captions, to help students see how physics is connected to many breakthroughs and discoveries in the biosciences.
- The **text has been streamlined** for tighter and more focused language.
- **Using data from MasteringPhysics, changes to the end-of-chapter content** include the following:
  - **15%–20% of problems are new.**
  - The number and level of **calculus-requiring problems** has been increased.
  - Most chapters include **five to seven biosciences-related problems.**
  - The number of **cumulative problems** (those incorporating physics from earlier chapters) has been increased.
- **Over 70 PhET simulations** are linked to the Pearson eText and provided in the Study Area of the MasteringPhysics website (with icons in the print text). These powerful simulations allow students to interact productively with the physics concepts they are learning. PhET clicker questions are also included on the Instructor Resource DVD.
- **Video Tutors bring key content to life throughout the text:**
  - Dozens of Video Tutors feature "pause-and-predict" demonstrations of **key physics concepts** and incorporate assessment as the student progresses to actively engage the student in understanding the key conceptual ideas underlying the physics principles.

Standard, Extended, and Three-Volume Editions

With MasteringPhysics:
- **Standard Edition:** Chapters 1–37 (ISBN 978-0-321-69688-5)
- **Extended Edition:** Chapters 1–44 (ISBN 978-0-321-67546-0)

Without MasteringPhysics:
- **Standard Edition:** Chapters 1–37 (ISBN 978-0-321-69689-2)
- **Extended Edition:** Chapters 1–44 (ISBN 978-0-321-69686-1)
- **Volume 1:** Chapters 1–20 (ISBN 978-0-321-73338-2)
- **Volume 2:** Chapters 21–37 (ISBN 978-0-321-75121-8)
- **Volume 3:** Chapters 37–44 (ISBN 978-0-321-75120-1)

- **Every Worked Example in the book is accompanied by a Video Tutor Solution** that walks students through the problem-solving process, providing a virtual teaching assistant on a round-the-clock basis.
- **All of these Video Tutors play directly through links within the Pearson eText.** Many also appear in the Study Area within MasteringPhysics.

Key Features of *University Physics*

- Deep and extensive **problem sets** cover a wide range of difficulty and exercise both physical understanding and problem-solving expertise. Many problems are based on complex real-life situations.
- This text offers a larger number of **Examples** and **Conceptual Examples** than any other leading calculus-based text, allowing it to explore problem-solving challenges not addressed in other texts.
- A research-based **problem-solving approach (Identify, Set Up, Execute, Evaluate)** is used not just in every Example but also in the Problem-Solving Strategies and throughout the Student and Instructor Solutions Manuals and the Study Guide. This consistent approach teaches students to tackle problems thoughtfully rather than cutting straight to the math.
- **Problem-Solving Strategies** coach students in how to approach specific types of problems.
- The **Figures** use a simplified graphical style to focus on the physics of a situation, and they incorporate **explanatory annotation.** Both techniques have been demonstrated to have a strong positive effect on learning.
- Figures that illustrate Example solutions often take the form of black-and-white **pencil sketches,** which directly represent what a student should draw in solving such a problem.
- The popular **Caution paragraphs** focus on typical misconceptions and student problem areas.
- End-of-section **Test Your Understanding** questions let students check their grasp of the material and use a multiple-choice or ranking-task format to probe for common misconceptions.
- **Visual Summaries** at the end of each chapter present the key ideas in words, equations, and thumbnail pictures, helping students to review more effectively.

Instructor Supplements

Note: For convenience, all of the following instructor supplements (except for the Instructor Resource DVD) can be downloaded from the Instructor Area, accessed via the left-hand navigation bar of MasteringPhysics (www.masteringphysics.com).

Instructor Solutions, prepared by A. Lewis Ford (Texas A&M University) and Wayne Anderson, contain complete and detailed solutions to all end-of-chapter problems. All solutions follow consistently the same Identify/Set Up/Execute/Evaluate problem-solving framework used in the textbook. Download only from the MasteringPhysics Instructor Area or from the Instructor Resource Center (www.pearsonhighered.com/irc).

The cross-platform **Instructor Resource DVD** (ISBN 978-0-321-69661-8) provides a comprehensive library of more than 420 applets from ActivPhysics OnLine as well as all line figures from the textbook in JPEG format. In addition, all the key equations, problem-solving strategies, tables, and chapter summaries are provided in editable Word format. In-class weekly multiple-choice questions for use with various Classroom Response Systems (CRS) are also provided, based on the Test Your Understanding questions in the text. Lecture outlines in PowerPoint are also included along with over 70 PhET simulations.

MasteringPhysics® (www.masteringphysics.com) is the most advanced, educationally effective, and widely used physics homework and tutorial system in the world. Eight years in development, it provides instructors with a library of extensively pre-tested end-of-chapter problems and rich, multipart, multistep tutorials that incorporate a wide variety of answer types, wrong answer feedback, individualized help (comprising hints or simpler sub-problems upon request), all driven by the largest metadatabase of student problem-solving in the world. NSF-sponsored published research (and subsequent studies) show that Mastering-Physics has dramatic educational results. MasteringPhysics allows instructors to build wide-ranging homework assignments of just the right difficulty and length and provides them with efficient tools to analyze both class trends, and the work of any student in unprecedented detail.

MasteringPhysics routinely provides instant and individualized feedback and guidance to more than 100,000 students every day. A wide range of tools and support make MasteringPhysics fast and easy for instructors and students to learn to use. Extensive class tests show that by the end of their course, an unprecedented eight of nine students recommend MasteringPhysics as their preferred way to study physics and do homework.

MasteringPhysics enables instructors to:
- Quickly build homework assignments that combine regular end-of-chapter problems and tutoring (through additional multi-step tutorial problems that offer wrong-answer feedback and simpler problems upon request).
- Expand homework to include the widest range of automatically graded activities available—from numerical problems with randomized values, through algebraic answers, to free-hand drawing.
- Choose from a wide range of nationally pre-tested problems that provide accurate estimates of time to complete and difficulty.
- After an assignment is completed, quickly identify not only the problems that were the trickiest for students but the individual problem types where students had trouble.
- Compare class results against the system's worldwide average for each problem assigned, to identify issues to be addressed with just-in-time teaching.
- Check the work of an individual student in detail, including time spent on each problem, what wrong answers they submitted at each step, how much help they asked for, and how many practice problems they worked.

ActivPhysics OnLine™ (which is accessed through the Study Area within www.masteringphysics.com) provides a comprehensive library of more than 420 tried and tested ActivPhysics applets updated for web delivery using the latest online technologies. In addition, it provides a suite of highly regarded applet-based tutorials developed by education pioneers Alan Van Heuvelen and Paul D'Alessandris. Margin icons throughout the text direct students to specific exercises that complement the textbook discussion.

The online exercises are designed to encourage students to confront misconceptions, reason qualitatively about physical processes, experiment quantitatively, and learn to think critically. The highly acclaimed ActivPhysics OnLine companion workbooks help students work through complex concepts and understand them more clearly. More than 420 applets from the ActivPhysics OnLine library are also available on the Instructor Resource DVD for this text.

The **Test Bank** contains more than 2,000 high-quality problems, with a range of multiple-choice, true/false, short-answer, and regular homework-type questions. Test files are provided both in TestGen (an easy-to-use, fully networkable program for creating and editing quizzes and exams) and Word format. Download only from the MasteringPhysics Instructor Area or from the Instructor Resource Center (www.pearsonhighered.com/irc).

Five Easy Lessons: Strategies for Successful Physics Teaching (ISBN 978-0-805-38702-5) by Randall D. Knight (California Polytechnic State University, San Luis Obispo) is packed with creative ideas on how to enhance any physics course. It is an invaluable companion for both novice and veteran physics instructors.

Student Supplements

The **Study Guide** by Laird Kramer reinforces the text's emphasis on problem-solving strategies and student misconceptions. The *Study Guide for Volume 1* (ISBN 978-0-321-69665-6) covers Chapters 1–20, and the *Study Guide for Volumes 2 and 3* (ISBN 978-0-321-69669-4) covers Chapters 21–44.

The **Student Solutions Manual** by Lewis Ford (Texas A&M University) and Wayne Anderson contains detailed, step-by-step solutions to more than half of the odd-numbered end-of-chapter problems from the textbook. All solutions follow consistently the same Identify/Set Up/Execute/Evaluate problem-solving framework used in the textbook. The *Student Solutions Manual for Volume 1* (ISBN 978-0-321-69668-7) covers Chapters 1–20, and the *Student Solutions Manual for Volumes 2 and 3* (ISBN 978-0-321-69667-0) covers Chapters 21–44.

 MasteringPhysics® (www.masteringphysics.com) is a homework, tutorial, and assessment system based on years of research into how students work physics problems and precisely where they need help. Studies show that students who use MasteringPhysics significantly increase their scores compared to hand-written homework. MasteringPhysics achieves this improvement by providing students with instantaneous feedback specific to their wrong answers, simpler sub-problems upon request when they get stuck, and partial credit for their method(s). This individualized, 24/7 Socratic tutoring is recommended by nine out of ten students to their peers as the most effective and time-efficient way to study.

Pearson eText is available through MasteringPhysics, either automatically when MasteringPhysics is packaged with new books, or available as a purchased upgrade online. Allowing students access to the text wherever they have access to the Internet, Pearson eText comprises the full text, including figures that can be enlarged for better viewing. With eText, students are also able to pop up definitions and terms to help with vocabulary and the reading of the material. Students can also take notes in eText using the annotation feature at the top of each page.

Pearson Tutor Services (www.pearsontutorservices.com). Each student's subscription to MasteringPhysics also contains complimentary access to Pearson Tutor Services, powered by Smarthinking, Inc. By logging in with their MasteringPhysics ID and password, students will be connected to highly qualified e-instructors who provide additional interactive online tutoring on the major concepts of physics. Some restrictions apply; offer subject to change.

 ActivPhysics OnLine™ (which is accessed through the Study Area within www.masteringphysics.com) provides students with a suite of highly regarded applet-based tutorials (see above). The following workbooks help students work through complex concepts and understand them more clearly.

> **ActivPhysics OnLine Workbook, Volume 1: Mechanics * Thermal Physics * Oscillations & Waves** (978-0-805-39060-5)

> **ActivPhysics OnLine Workbook, Volume 2: Electricity & Magnetism * Optics * Modern Physics** (978-0-805-39061-2)

Acknowledgments

We would like to thank the hundreds of reviewers and colleagues who have offered valuable comments and suggestions over the life of this textbook. The continuing success of *University Physics* is due in large measure to their contributions.

Edward Adelson (Ohio State University), Ralph Alexander (University of Missouri at Rolla), J. G. Anderson, R. S. Anderson, Wayne Anderson (Sacramento City College), Alex Azima (Lansing Community College), Dilip Balamore (Nassau Community College), Harold Bale (University of North Dakota), Arun Bansil (Northeastern University), John Barach (Vanderbilt University), J. D. Barnett, H. H. Barschall, Albert Bartlett (University of Colorado), Marshall Bartlett (Hollins University), Paul Baum (CUNY, Queens College), Frederick Becchetti (University of Michigan), B. Bederson, David Bennum (University of Nevada, Reno), Lev I. Berger (San Diego State University), Robert Boeke (William Rainey Harper College), S. Borowitz, A. C. Braden, James Brooks (Boston University), Nicholas E. Brown (California Polytechnic State University, San Luis Obispo), Tony Buffa (California Polytechnic State University, San Luis Obispo), A. Capecelatro, Michael Cardamone (Pennsylvania State University), Duane Carmony (Purdue University), Troy Carter (UCLA), P. Catranides, John Cerne (SUNY at Buffalo), Tim Chupp (University of Michigan), Shinil Cho (La Roche College), Roger Clapp (University of South Florida), William M. Cloud (Eastern Illinois University), Leonard Cohen (Drexel University), W. R. Coker (University of Texas, Austin), Malcolm D. Cole (University of Missouri at Rolla), H. Conrad, David Cook (Lawrence University), Gayl Cook (University of Colorado), Hans Courant (University of Minnesota), Bruce A. Craver (University of Dayton), Larry Curtis (University of Toledo), Jai Dahiya (Southeast Missouri State University), Steve Detweiler (University of Florida), George Dixon (Oklahoma State University), Donald S. Duncan, Boyd Edwards (West Virginia University), Robert Eisenstein (Carnegie Mellon University), Amy Emerson Missourn (Virginia Institute of Technology), William Faissler (Northeastern University), William Fasnacht (U.S. Naval Academy), Paul Feldker (St. Louis Community College), Carlos Figueroa (Cabrillo College), L. H. Fisher, Neil Fletcher (Florida State University), Robert Folk, Peter Fong (Emory University), A. Lewis Ford (Texas A&M University), D. Frantszog, James R. Gaines (Ohio State University), Solomon Gartenhaus (Purdue University), Ron Gautreau (New Jersey Institute of Technology), J. David Gavenda (University of Texas, Austin), Dennis Gay (University of North Florida), James Gerhart (University of Washington), N. S. Gingrich, J. L. Glathart, S. Goodwin, Rich Gottfried (Frederick Community College), Walter S. Gray (University of Michigan), Paul Gresser (University of Maryland), Benjamin Grinstein (UC San Diego), Howard Grotch (Pennsylvania State University), John Gruber (San Jose State University), Graham D. Gutsche (U.S. Naval Academy), Michael J. Harrison (Michigan State University), Harold Hart (Western Illinois University), Howard Hayden (University of Connecticut), Carl Helrich (Goshen College), Laurent Hodges (Iowa State University), C. D. Hodgman, Michael Hones (Villanova University), Keith Honey (West Virginia Institute of Technology), Gregory Hood (Tidewater Community College), John Hubisz (North Carolina State University), M. Iona, John Jaszczak (Michigan Technical University), Alvin Jenkins (North Carolina State University), Robert P. Johnson (UC Santa Cruz), Lorella Jones (University of Illinois), John Karchek (GMI Engineering & Management Institute), Thomas Keil (Worcester Polytechnic Institute), Robert Kraemer (Carnegie Mellon University), Jean P. Krisch (University of Michigan), Robert A. Kromhout, Andrew Kunz (Marquette University), Charles Lane (Berry College), Thomas N. Lawrence (Texas State University), Robert J. Lee, Alfred Leitner (Rensselaer Polytechnic University), Gerald P. Lietz (De Paul University), Gordon Lind (Utah State University), S. Livingston, Elihu Lubkin (University of Wisconsin, Milwaukee), Robert Luke (Boise State University), David Lynch (Iowa State University), Michael Lysak (San Bernardino Valley College), Jeffrey Mallow (Loyola University), Robert Mania (Kentucky State University), Robert Marchina (University of Memphis), David Markowitz (University of Connecticut), R. J. Maurer, Oren Maxwell (Florida International University), Joseph L. McCauley (University of Houston), T. K. McCubbin, Jr. (Pennsylvania State University), Charles McFarland (University of Missouri at Rolla), James Mcguire (Tulane University), Lawrence McIntyre (University of Arizona), Fredric Messing (Carnegie-Mellon University), Thomas Meyer (Texas A&M University), Andre Mirabelli (St. Peter's College, New Jersey), Herbert Muether (S.U.N.Y., Stony Brook), Jack Munsee (California State University, Long Beach), Lorenzo Narducci (Drexel University), Van E. Neie (Purdue University), David A. Nordling (U. S. Naval Academy), Benedict Oh (Pennsylvania State University), L. O. Olsen, Jim Pannell (DeVry Institute of Technology), W. F. Parks (University of Missouri), Robert Paulson (California State University, Chico), Jerry Peacher (University of Missouri at Rolla), Arnold Perlmutter (University of Miami), Lennart Peterson (University of Florida), R. J. Peterson (University of Colorado, Boulder), R. Pinkston, Ronald Poling (University of Minnesota), J. G. Potter, C. W. Price (Millersville University), Francis Prosser (University of Kansas), Shelden H. Radin, Roberto Ramos (Drexel University), Michael Rapport (Anne Arundel Community College), R. Resnick, James A. Richards, Jr., John S. Risley (North Carolina State University), Francesc Roig (University of California, Santa Barbara), T. L. Rokoske, Richard Roth (Eastern Michigan University), Carl Rotter (University of West Virginia), S. Clark Rowland (Andrews University), Rajarshi Roy (Georgia Institute of Technology), Russell A. Roy (Santa Fe Community College), Dhiraj Sardar (University of Texas, San Antonio), Bruce Schumm (UC Santa Cruz), Melvin Schwartz (St. John's University), F. A. Scott, L. W. Seagondollar, Paul Shand (University of Northern Iowa), Stan Shepherd (Pennsylvania State University), Douglas Sherman (San Jose State), Bruce Sherwood (Carnegie Mellon University), Hugh Siefkin (Greenville College), Tomasz Skwarnicki (Syracuse University), C. P. Slichter, Charles W. Smith (University of Maine, Orono), Malcolm Smith (University of Lowell), Ross Spencer (Brigham Young University), Julien Sprott (University of Wisconsin), Victor Stanionis (Iona College), James Stith (American Institute of Physics), Chuck Stone (North Carolina A&T State

University), Edward Strother (Florida Institute of Technology), Conley Stutz (Bradley University), Albert Stwertka (U.S. Merchant Marine Academy), Kenneth Szpara-DeNisco (Harrisburg Area Community College), Martin Tiersten (CUNY, City College), David Toot (Alfred University), Somdev Tyagi (Drexel University), F. Verbrugge, Helmut Vogel (Carnegie Mellon University), Robert Webb (Texas A & M), Thomas Weber (Iowa State University), M. Russell Wehr, (Pennsylvania State University), Robert Weidman (Michigan Technical University), Dan Whalen (UC San Diego), Lester V. Whitney, Thomas Wiggins (Pennsylvania State University), David Willey (University of Pittsburgh, Johnstown), George Williams (University of Utah), John Williams (Auburn University), Stanley Williams (Iowa State University), Jack Willis, Suzanne Willis (Northern Illinois University), Robert Wilson (San Bernardino Valley College), L. Wolfenstein, James Wood (Palm Beach Junior College), Lowell Wood (University of Houston), R. E. Worley, D. H. Ziebell (Manatee Community College), George O. Zimmerman (Boston University)

In addition, we both have individual acknowledgments we would like to make.

I want to extend my heartfelt thanks to my colleagues at Carnegie Mellon, especially Professors Robert Kraemer, Bruce Sherwood, Ruth Chabay, Helmut Vogel, and Brian Quinn, for many stimulating discussions about physics pedagogy and for their support and encouragement during the writing of several successive editions of this book. I am equally indebted to the many generations of Carnegie Mellon students who have helped me learn what good teaching and good writing are, by showing me what works and what doesn't. It is always a joy and a privilege to express my gratitude to my wife Alice and our children Gretchen and Rebecca for their love, support, and emotional sustenance during the writing of several successive editions of this book. May all men and women be blessed with love such as theirs. — H. D. Y.

I would like to thank my past and present colleagues at UCSB, including Rob Geller, Carl Gwinn, Al Nash, Elisabeth Nicol, and Francesc Roig, for their whole-hearted support and for many helpful discussions. I owe a special debt of gratitude to my early teachers Willa Ramsay, Peter Zimmerman, William Little, Alan Schwettman, and Dirk Walecka for showing me what clear and engaging physics teaching is all about, and to Stuart Johnson for inviting me to become a co-author of *University Physics* beginning with the 9th edition. I want to express special thanks to the editorial staff at Addison-Wesley and their partners: to Nancy Whilton for her editorial vision; to Margot Otway for her superb graphic sense and careful development of this edition; to Peter Murphy for his contributions to the worked examples; to Jason J. B. Harlow for his careful reading of the page proofs; and to Chandrika Madhavan, Steven Le, and Cindy Johnson for keeping the editorial and production pipeline flowing. Most of all, I want to express my gratitude and love to my wife Caroline, to whom I dedicate my contribution to this book. Hey, Caroline, the new edition's done at last — let's go flying! — R. A. F.

Please Tell Us What You Think!

We welcome communications from students and professors, especially concerning errors or deficiencies that you find in this edition. We have devoted a lot of time and effort to writing the best book we know how to write, and we hope it will help you to teach and learn physics. In turn, you can help us by letting us know what still needs to be improved! Please feel free to contact us either electronically or by ordinary mail. Your comments will be greatly appreciated.

December 2010

Hugh D. Young
Department of Physics
Carnegie Mellon University
Pittsburgh, PA 15213
hdy@andrew.cmu.edu

Roger A. Freedman
Department of Physics
University of California, Santa Barbara
Santa Barbara, CA 93106-9530
airboy@physics.ucsb.edu
http://www.physics.ucsb.edu/~airboy/

DETAILED CONTENTS

The Biot-Savart Law

APPENDICES

ELECTRIC CHARGE AND ELECTRIC FIELD

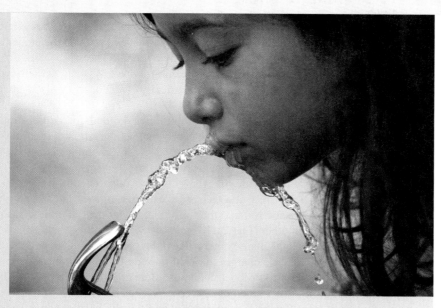

? Water makes life possible: The cells of your body could not function without water in which to dissolve essential biological molecules. What electrical properties of water make it such a good solvent?

In Chapter 5 we mentioned the four kinds of fundamental forces. To this point the only one of these forces that we have examined in any detail is gravity. Now we are ready to examine the force of *electromagnetism,* which encompasses both electricity and magnetism. Electromagnetic phenomena will occupy our attention for most of the remainder of this book.

Electromagnetic interactions involve particles that have a property called *electric charge,* an attribute that is as fundamental as mass. Just as objects with mass are accelerated by gravitational forces, so electrically charged objects are accelerated by electric forces. The shock you feel when you scuff your shoes across a carpet and then reach for a metal doorknob is due to charged particles leaping between your finger and the doorknob. Electric currents are simply streams of charged particles flowing within wires in response to electric forces. Even the forces that hold atoms together to form solid matter, and that keep the atoms of solid objects from passing through each other, are fundamentally due to electric interactions between the charged particles within atoms.

We begin our study of electromagnetism in this chapter by examining the nature of electric charge. We'll find that charge is quantized and obeys a conservation principle. When charges are at rest in our frame of reference, they exert *electrostatic* forces on each other. These forces are of tremendous importance in chemistry and biology and have many technological applications. Electrostatic forces are governed by a simple relationship known as *Coulomb's law* and are most conveniently described by using the concept of *electric field.* In later chapters we'll expand our discussion to include electric charges in motion. This will lead us to an understanding of magnetism and, remarkably, of the nature of light.

While the key ideas of electromagnetism are conceptually simple, applying them to practical problems will make use of many of your mathematical skills, especially your knowledge of geometry and integral calculus. For this reason you may find this chapter and those that follow to be more mathematically demanding than earlier chapters. The reward for your extra effort will be a deeper understanding of principles that are at the heart of modern physics and technology.

21.1 Electric Charge

The ancient Greeks discovered as early as 600 B.C. that after they rubbed amber with wool, the amber could attract other objects. Today we say that the amber has acquired a net **electric charge,** or has become *charged.* The word "electric" is derived from the Greek word *elektron,* meaning amber. When you scuff your shoes across a nylon carpet, you become electrically charged, and you can charge a comb by passing it through dry hair.

Plastic rods and fur (real or fake) are particularly good for demonstrating **electrostatics,** the interactions between electric charges that are at rest (or nearly so). After we charge both plastic rods in Fig. 21.1a by rubbing them with the piece of fur, we find that the rods repel each other.

When we rub glass rods with silk, the glass rods also become charged and repel each other (Fig. 21.1b). But a charged plastic rod *attracts* a charged glass rod; furthermore, the plastic rod and the fur attract each other, and the glass rod and the silk attract each other (Fig. 21.1c).

These experiments and many others like them have shown that there are exactly two kinds of electric charge: the kind on the plastic rod rubbed with fur and the kind on the glass rod rubbed with silk. Benjamin Franklin (1706–1790) suggested calling these two kinds of charge *negative* and *positive,* respectively, and these names are still used. The plastic rod and the silk have negative charge; the glass rod and the fur have positive charge.

Two positive charges or two negative charges repel each other. A positive charge and a negative charge attract each other.

CAUTION **Electric attraction and repulsion** The attraction and repulsion of two charged objects are sometimes summarized as "Like charges repel, and opposite charges attract." But keep in mind that the phrase "like charges" does *not* mean that the two charges are exactly identical, only that both charges have the same algebraic *sign* (both positive or both negative). "Opposite charges" means that both objects have an electric charge, and those charges have different signs (one positive and the other negative).

21.1 Experiments in electrostatics. (a) Negatively charged objects repel each other. (b) Positively charged objects repel each other. (c) Positively charged objects and negatively charged objects attract each other.

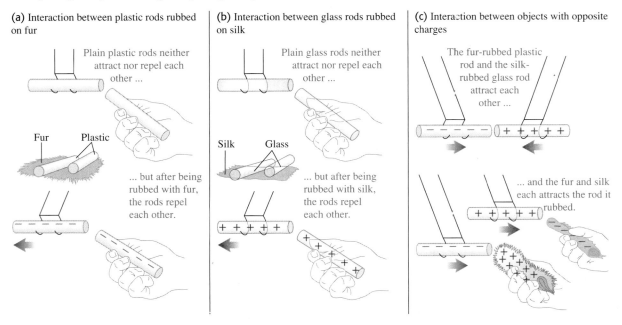

(a) Interaction between plastic rods rubbed on fur

Plain plastic rods neither attract nor repel each other ...

Fur   Plastic

... but after being rubbed with fur, the rods repel each other.

(b) Interaction between glass rods rubbed on silk

Plain glass rods neither attract nor repel each other ...

Silk   Glass

... but after being rubbed with silk, the rods repel each other.

(c) Interaction between objects with opposite charges

The fur-rubbed plastic rod and the silk-rubbed glass rod attract each other ...

... and the fur and silk each attracts the rod it rubbed.

21.2 Schematic diagram of the operation of a laser printer.

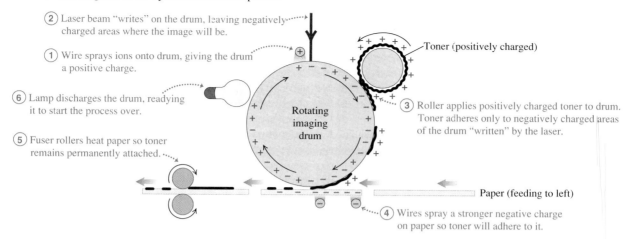

2 Laser beam "writes" on the drum, leaving negatively
charged areas where the image will be.

1 Wire sprays ions onto drum, giving the drum
a positive charge.

6 Lamp discharges the drum, readying
it to start the process over.

5 Fuser rollers heat paper so toner
remains permanently attached.

Toner (positively charged)

3 Roller applies positively charged toner to drum.
Toner adheres only to negatively charged areas
of the drum "written" by the laser.

Rotating
imaging
drum

Paper (feeding to left)

4 Wires spray a stronger negative charge
on paper so toner will adhere to it.

One application of forces between charged bodies is in a laser printer (Fig. 21.2). The printer's light-sensitive imaging drum is given a positive charge. As the drum rotates, a laser beam shines on selected areas of the drum, leaving those areas with a *negative* charge. Positively charged particles of toner adhere only to the areas of the drum "written" by the laser. When a piece of paper is placed in contact with the drum, the toner particles stick to the paper and form an image.

Electric Charge and the Structure of Matter

When you charge a rod by rubbing it with fur or silk as in Fig. 21.1, there is no visible change in the appearance of the rod. What, then, actually happens to the rod when you charge it? To answer this question, we must look more closely at the structure of atoms, the building blocks of ordinary matter.

The structure of atoms can be described in terms of three particles: the negatively charged **electron**, the positively charged **proton,** and the uncharged **neutron** (Fig. 21.3). The proton and neutron are combinations of other entities called *quarks*, which have charges of $\pm\frac{1}{3}$ and $\pm\frac{2}{3}$ times the electron charge. Isolated quarks have not been observed, and there are theoretical reasons to believe that it is impossible in principle to observe a quark in isolation.

The protons and neutrons in an atom make up a small, very dense core called the **nucleus,** with dimensions of the order of 10^{-15} m. Surrounding the nucleus are the electrons, extending out to distances of the order of 10^{-10} m from the nucleus. If an atom were a few kilometers across, its nucleus would be the size of a tennis ball. The negatively charged electrons are held within the atom by the attractive electric forces exerted on them by the positively charged nucleus. (The protons and neutrons are held within stable atomic nuclei by an attractive interaction, called the *strong nuclear force,* that overcomes the electric repulsion of the protons. The strong nuclear force has a short range, and its effects do not extend far beyond the nucleus.)

The masses of the individual particles, to the precision that they are presently known, are

$$\text{Mass of electron} = m_e = 9.10938215(45) \times 10^{-31} \text{ kg}$$

$$\text{Mass of proton} = m_p = 1.672621637(83) \times 10^{-27} \text{ kg}$$

$$\text{Mass of neutron} = m_n = 1.674927211(84) \times 10^{-27} \text{ kg}$$

The numbers in parentheses are the uncertainties in the last two digits. Note that the masses of the proton and neutron are nearly equal and are roughly 2000 times

21.3 The structure of an atom. The particular atom depicted here is lithium (see Fig. 21.4a).

Atom

Most of the atom's volume is occupied sparsely by electrons.

$\leftarrow\!\sim\!10^{-10}$ m $\rightarrow$

Nucleus

Tiny compared with the rest of the atom, the nucleus contains over 99.9% of the atom's mass.

$\sim\!10^{-15}$ m

+ **Proton:** Positive charge
Mass = 1.673×10^{-27} kg

Neutron: No charge
Mass = 1.675×10^{-27} kg

− **Electron:** Negative charge
Mass = 9.109×10^{-31} kg

The charges of the electron and proton are equal in magnitude.

21.4 (a) A neutral atom has as many electrons as it does protons. (b) A positive ion has a deficit of electrons. (c) A negative ion has an excess of electrons. (The electron "shells" are a schematic representation of the actual electron distribution, a diffuse cloud many times larger than the nucleus.)

● Protons (+)   ○ Neutrons
   ◎ Electrons (−)

(a) **Neutral lithium atom (Li):**
3 protons (3+)
4 neutrons
3 electrons (3−)

Electrons equal protons:
Zero net charge

(b) **Positive lithium ion (Li⁺):**
3 protons (3+)
4 neutrons
2 electrons (2−)

Fewer electrons than protons:
Positive net charge

(c) **Negative lithium ion (Li⁻):**
3 protons (3+)
4 neutrons
4 electrons (4−)

More electrons than protons:
Negative net charge

the mass of the electron. Over 99.9% of the mass of any atom is concentrated in its nucleus.

The negative charge of the electron has (within experimental error) *exactly* the same magnitude as the positive charge of the proton. In a neutral atom the number of electrons equals the number of protons in the nucleus, and the net electric charge (the algebraic sum of all the charges) is exactly zero (Fig. 21.4a). The number of protons or electrons in a neutral atom of an element is called the **atomic number** of the element. If one or more electrons are removed from an atom, what remains is called a **positive ion** (Fig. 21.4b). A **negative ion** is an atom that has *gained* one or more electrons (Fig. 21.4c). This gain or loss of electrons is called **ionization.**

When the total number of protons in a macroscopic body equals the total number of electrons, the total charge is zero and the body as a whole is electrically neutral. To give a body an excess negative charge, we may either *add negative* charges to a neutral body or *remove positive* charges from that body. Similarly, we can create an excess positive charge by either *adding positive* charge or *removing negative* charge. In most cases, negatively charged (and highly mobile) electrons are added or removed, and a "positively charged body" is one that has lost some of its normal complement of electrons. When we speak of the charge of a body, we always mean its *net* charge. The net charge is always a very small fraction (typically no more than 10^{-12}) of the total positive charge or negative charge in the body.

Electric Charge Is Conserved

Implicit in the foregoing discussion are two very important principles. First is the **principle of conservation of charge:**

The algebraic sum of all the electric charges in any closed system is constant.

If we rub together a plastic rod and a piece of fur, both initially uncharged, the rod acquires a negative charge (since it takes electrons from the fur) and the fur acquires a positive charge of the *same* magnitude (since it has lost as many electrons as the rod has gained). Hence the total electric charge on the two bodies together does not change. In any charging process, charge is not created or destroyed; it is merely *transferred* from one body to another.

Conservation of charge is thought to be a *universal* conservation law. No experimental evidence for any violation of this principle has ever been observed. Even in high-energy interactions in which particles are created and destroyed, such as the creation of electron–positron pairs, the total charge of any closed system is exactly constant.

The second important principle is:

The magnitude of charge of the electron or proton is a natural unit of charge.

Every observable amount of electric charge is always an integer multiple of this basic unit. We say that charge is *quantized*. A familiar example of quantization is money. When you pay cash for an item in a store, you have to do it in one-cent increments. Cash can't be divided into amounts smaller than one cent, and electric charge can't be divided into amounts smaller than the charge of one electron or proton. (The quark charges, $\pm\frac{1}{3}$ and $\pm\frac{2}{3}$ of the electron charge, are probably not observable as isolated charges.) Thus the charge on any macroscopic body is always either zero or an integer multiple (negative or positive) of the electron charge.

Understanding the electric nature of matter gives us insight into many aspects of the physical world (Fig. 21.5). The chemical bonds that hold atoms together to form molecules are due to electric interactions between the atoms. They include the strong ionic bonds that hold sodium and chlorine atoms together to make table salt and the relatively weak bonds between the strands of DNA that record your body's genetic code. The normal force exerted on you by the chair in which you're sitting arises from electric forces between charged particles in the atoms of your seat and in the atoms of your chair. The tension force in a stretched string and the adhesive force of glue are likewise due to the electric interactions of atoms.

Test Your Understanding of Section 21.1 (a) Strictly speaking, does the plastic rod in Fig. 21.1 weigh more, less, or the same after rubbing it with fur? (b) What about the glass rod after rubbing it with silk? What about (c) the fur and (d) the silk? ▮

21.2 Conductors, Insulators, and Induced Charges

Some materials permit electric charge to move easily from one region of the material to another, while others do not. For example, Fig. 21.6a shows a copper wire supported by a nylon thread. Suppose you touch one end of the wire to a charged plastic rod and attach the other end to a metal ball that is initially uncharged; you then remove the charged rod and the wire. When you bring another charged body up close to the ball (Figs. 21.6b and 21.6c), the ball is attracted or repelled, showing that the ball has become electrically charged. Electric charge has been transferred through the copper wire between the ball and the surface of the plastic rod.

The copper wire is called a **conductor** of electricity. If you repeat the experiment using a rubber band or nylon thread in place of the wire, you find that *no* charge is transferred to the ball. These materials are called **insulators.** Conductors permit the easy movement of charge through them, while insulators do not. (The supporting nylon threads shown in Fig. 21.6 are insulators, which prevents charge from leaving the metal ball and copper wire.)

As an example, carpet fibers on a dry day are good insulators. As you walk across a carpet, the rubbing of your shoes against the fibers causes charge to build up on you, and this charge remains on you because it can't flow through the insulating fibers. If you then touch a conducting object such as a doorknob, a rapid charge transfer takes place between your finger and the doorknob, and you feel a shock. One way to prevent this is to wind some of the carpet fibers around conducting cores so that any charge that builds up on you can be transferred harmlessly to the carpet. Another solution is to coat the carpet fibers with an anti-static layer that does not easily transfer electrons to or from your shoes; this prevents any charge from building up on you in the first place.

21.5 Most of the forces on this water skier are electric. Electric interactions between adjacent molecules give rise to the force of the water on the ski, the tension in the tow rope, and the resistance of the air on the skier's body. Electric interactions also hold the atoms of the skier's body together. Only one wholly nonelectric force acts on the skier: the force of gravity.

Mastering**PHYSICS**

PhET: Balloons and Static Electricity
PhET: John Travoltage

21.6 Copper is a good conductor of electricity; nylon is a good insulator. **(a)** The copper wire conducts charge between the metal ball and the charged plastic rod to charge the ball negatively. Afterward, the metal ball is **(b)** repelled by a negatively charged plastic rod and **(c)** attracted to a positively charged glass rod.

(a)

The wire conducts charge from the negatively charged plastic rod to the metal ball.

(b)

A negatively charged plastic rod now repels the ball ...

Charged plastic rod

(c)

... and a positively charged glass rod attracts the ball.

Charged glass rod

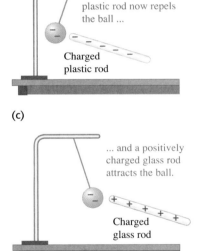

Most metals are good conductors, while most nonmetals are insulators. Within a solid metal such as copper, one or more outer electrons in each atom become detached and can move freely throughout the material, just as the molecules of a gas can move through the spaces between the grains in a bucket of sand. The other electrons remain bound to the positively charged nuclei, which themselves are bound in nearly fixed positions within the material. In an insulator there are no, or very few, free electrons, and electric charge cannot move freely through the material. Some materials called *semiconductors* are intermediate in their properties between good conductors and good insulators.

Charging by Induction

We can charge a metal ball using a copper wire and an electrically charged plastic rod, as in Fig. 21.6a. In this process, some of the excess electrons on the rod are transferred from it to the ball, leaving the rod with a smaller negative charge. But there is a different technique in which the plastic rod can give another body a charge of *opposite* sign without losing any of its own charge. This process is called charging by **induction.**

Figure 21.7 shows an example of charging by induction. An uncharged metal ball is supported on an insulating stand (Fig. 21.7a). When you bring a negatively charged rod near it, without actually touching it (Fig. 21.7b), the free electrons in the metal ball are repelled by the excess electrons on the rod, and they shift toward the right, away from the rod. They cannot escape from the ball because the supporting stand and the surrounding air are insulators. So we get excess negative charge at the right surface of the ball and a deficiency of negative charge (that is, a net positive charge) at the left surface. These excess charges are called **induced charges.**

Not all of the free electrons move to the right surface of the ball. As soon as any induced charge develops, it exerts forces toward the *left* on the other free electrons. These electrons are repelled by the negative induced charge on the right and attracted toward the positive induced charge on the left. The system reaches an equilibrium state in which the force toward the right on an electron, due to the charged rod, is just balanced by the force toward the left due to the induced charge. If we remove the charged rod, the free electrons shift back to the left, and the original neutral condition is restored.

What happens if, while the plastic rod is nearby, you touch one end of a conducting wire to the right surface of the ball and the other end to the earth (Fig. 21.7c)? The earth is a conductor, and it is so large that it can act as a practically infinite source of extra electrons or sink of unwanted electrons. Some of the negative charge flows through the wire to the earth. Now suppose you disconnect the wire (Fig. 21.7d) and then remove the rod (Fig. 21.7e); a net positive charge is left on the ball. The charge on the negatively charged rod has not changed during this process. The earth acquires a negative charge that is equal in magnitude to the induced positive charge remaining on the ball.

21.7 Charging a metal ball by induction.

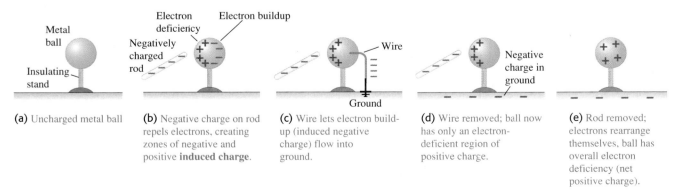

(a) Uncharged metal ball

(b) Negative charge on rod repels electrons, creating zones of negative and positive **induced charge**.

(c) Wire lets electron build-up (induced negative charge) flow into ground.

(d) Wire removed; ball now has only an electron-deficient region of positive charge.

(e) Rod removed; electrons rearrange themselves, ball has overall electron deficiency (net positive charge).

21.8 The charges within the molecules of an insulating material can shift slightly. As a result, a comb with either sign of charge attracts a neutral insulator. By Newton's third law the neutral insulator exerts an equal-magnitude attractive force on the comb.

(a) A charged comb picking up uncharged pieces of plastic

(b) How a negatively charged comb attracts an insulator

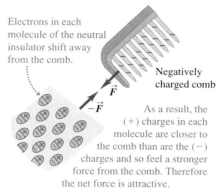

Electrons in each molecule of the neutral insulator shift away from the comb.

Negatively charged comb

$\vec{F}$

$-\vec{F}$

As a result, the (+) charges in each molecule are closer to the comb than are the (−) charges and so feel a stronger force from the comb. Therefore the net force is attractive.

(c) How a positively charged comb attracts an insulator

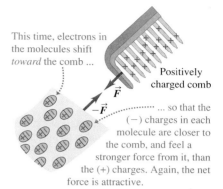

This time, electrons in the molecules shift *toward* the comb ...

Positively charged comb

$\vec{F}$

$-\vec{F}$

... so that the (−) charges in each molecule are closer to the comb, and feel a stronger force from it, than the (+) charges. Again, the net force is attractive.

Electric Forces on Uncharged Objects

Finally, we note that a charged body can exert forces even on objects that are *not* charged themselves. If you rub a balloon on the rug and then hold the balloon against the ceiling, it sticks, even though the ceiling has no net electric charge. After you electrify a comb by running it through your hair, you can pick up uncharged bits of paper or plastic with the comb (Fig. 21.8a). How is this possible?

This interaction is an induced-charge effect. Even in an insulator, electric charges can shift back and forth a little when there is charge nearby. This is shown in Fig. 21.8b; the negatively charged plastic comb causes a slight shifting of charge within the molecules of the neutral insulator, an effect called *polarization*. The positive and negative charges in the material are present in equal amounts, but the positive charges are closer to the plastic comb and so feel an attraction that is stronger than the repulsion felt by the negative charges, giving a net attractive force. (In Section 21.3 we will study how electric forces depend on distance.) Note that a neutral insulator is also attracted to a *positively* charged comb (Fig. 21.8c). Now the charges in the insulator shift in the opposite direction; the negative charges in the insulator are closer to the comb and feel an attractive force that is stronger than the repulsion felt by the positive charges in the insulator. Hence a charged object of *either* sign exerts an attractive force on an uncharged insulator. Figure 21.9 shows an industrial application of this effect.

Test Your Understanding of Section 21.2 You have two lightweight metal spheres, each hanging from an insulating nylon thread. One of the spheres has a net negative charge, while the other sphere has no net charge. (a) If the spheres are close together but do not touch, will they (i) attract each other, (ii) repel each other, or (iii) exert no force on each other? (b) You now allow the two spheres to touch. Once they have touched, will the two spheres (i) attract each other, (ii) repel each other, or (iii) exert no force on each other?

21.9 The electrostatic painting process (compare Figs. 21.7b and 21.7c). A metal object to be painted is connected to the earth ("ground"), and the paint droplets are given an electric charge as they exit the sprayer nozzle. Induced charges of the opposite sign appear in the object as the droplets approach, just as in Fig. 21.7b, and they attract the droplets to the surface. This process minimizes overspray from clouds of stray paint particles and gives a particularly smooth finish.

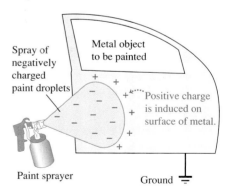

Spray of negatively charged paint droplets

Metal object to be painted

Positive charge is induced on surface of metal.

Paint sprayer

Ground

21.3 Coulomb's Law

Charles Augustin de Coulomb (1736–1806) studied the interaction forces of charged particles in detail in 1784. He used a torsion balance (Fig. 21.10a) similar to the one used 13 years later by Cavendish to study the much weaker gravitational interaction, as we discussed in Section 13.1. For **point charges,** charged

MasteringPHYSICS

ActivPhysics 11.1: Electric Force: Coulomb's Law
ActivPhysics 11.2: Electric Force: Superposition Principle
ActivPhysics 11.3: Electric Force: Superposition (Quantitative)

Application Electric Forces, Sweat, and Cystic Fibrosis

One way to test for the genetic disease cystic fibrosis (CF) is by measuring the salt content of a person's sweat. Sweat is a mixture of water and ions, including the sodium (Na^+) and chloride (Cl^-) ions that make up ordinary salt (NaCl). When sweat is secreted by epithelial cells, some of the Cl^- ions flow from the sweat back into these cells (a process called reabsorption). The electric attraction between negative and positive charges pulls Na^+ ions along with the Cl^-. Water molecules cannot flow back into the epithelial cells, so sweat on the skin has a low salt content. However, in persons with CF the reabsorption of Cl^- ions is blocked. Hence the sweat of persons with CF is unusually salty, with up to four times the normal concentration of Cl^- and Na^+.

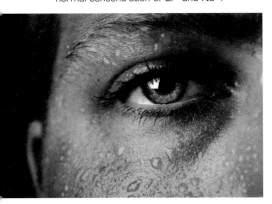

bodies that are very small in comparison with the distance r between them, Coulomb found that the electric force is proportional to $1/r^2$. That is, when the distance r doubles, the force decreases to one-quarter of its initial value; when the distance is halved, the force increases to four times its initial value.

The electric force between two point charges also depends on the quantity of charge on each body, which we will denote by q or Q. To explore this dependence, Coulomb divided a charge into two equal parts by placing a small charged spherical conductor into contact with an identical but uncharged sphere; by symmetry, the charge is shared equally between the two spheres. (Note the essential role of the principle of conservation of charge in this procedure.) Thus he could obtain one-half, one-quarter, and so on, of any initial charge. He found that the forces that two point charges q_1 and q_2 exert on each other are proportional to each charge and therefore are proportional to the *product* q_1q_2 of the two charges.

Thus Coulomb established what we now call **Coulomb's law:**

The magnitude of the electric force between two point charges is directly proportional to the product of the charges and inversely proportional to the square of the distance between them.

In mathematical terms, the magnitude F of the force that each of two point charges q_1 and q_2 a distance r apart exerts on the other can be expressed as

$$F = k\frac{|q_1q_2|}{r^2} \qquad (21.1)$$

where k is a proportionality constant whose numerical value depends on the system of units used. The absolute value bars are used in Eq. (21.1) because the charges q_1 and q_2 can be either positive or negative, while the force magnitude F is always positive.

The directions of the forces the two charges exert on each other are always along the line joining them. When the charges q_1 and q_2 have the same sign, either both positive or both negative, the forces are repulsive; when the charges have opposite signs, the forces are attractive (Fig. 21.10b). The two forces obey Newton's third law; they are always equal in magnitude and opposite in direction, even when the charges are not equal in magnitude.

21.10 (a) Measuring the electric force between point charges. (b) The electric forces between point charges obey Newton's third law: $\vec{F}_{1\text{ on }2} = -\vec{F}_{2\text{ on }1}$.

(a) A torsion balance of the type used by Coulomb to measure the electric force

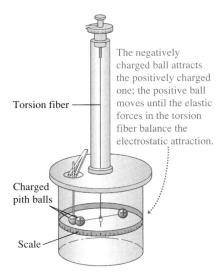

Torsion fiber

The negatively charged ball attracts the positively charged one; the positive ball moves until the elastic forces in the torsion fiber balance the electrostatic attraction.

Charged pith balls

Scale

(b) Interactions between point charges

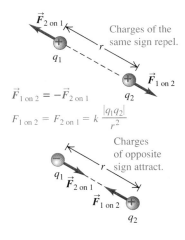

Charges of the same sign repel.

$\vec{F}_{1\text{ on }2} = -\vec{F}_{2\text{ on }1}$

$F_{1\text{ on }2} = F_{2\text{ on }1} = k\dfrac{|q_1q_2|}{r^2}$

Charges of opposite sign attract.

The proportionality of the electric force to $1/r^2$ has been verified with great precision. There is no reason to suspect that the exponent is different from precisely 2. Thus the form of Eq. (21.1) is the same as that of the law of gravitation. But electric and gravitational interactions are two distinct classes of phenomena. Electric interactions depend on electric charges and can be either attractive or repulsive, while gravitational interactions depend on mass and are always attractive (because there is no such thing as negative mass).

Fundamental Electric Constants

The value of the proportionality constant k in Coulomb's law depends on the system of units used. In our study of electricity and magnetism we will use SI units exclusively. The SI electric units include most of the familiar units such as the volt, the ampere, the ohm, and the watt. (There is *no* British system of electric units.) The SI unit of electric charge is called one **coulomb** (1 C). In SI units the constant k in Eq. (21.1) is

$$k = 8.987551787 \times 10^9 \, \text{N} \cdot \text{m}^2/\text{C}^2 \cong 8.988 \times 10^9 \, \text{N} \cdot \text{m}^2/\text{C}^2$$

The value of k is known to such a large number of significant figures because this value is closely related to the speed of light in vacuum. (We will show this in Chapter 32 when we study electromagnetic radiation.) As we discussed in Section 1.3, this speed is *defined* to be exactly $c = 2.99792458 \times 10^8$ m/s. The numerical value of k is defined in terms of c to be precisely

$$k = (10^{-7} \, \text{N} \cdot \text{s}^2/\text{C}^2)c^2$$

You should check this expression to confirm that k has the right units.

In principle we can measure the electric force F between two equal charges q at a measured distance r and use Coulomb's law to determine the charge. Thus we could regard the value of k as an operational definition of the coulomb. For reasons of experimental precision it is better to define the coulomb instead in terms of a unit of electric *current* (charge per unit time), the *ampere,* equal to 1 coulomb per second. We will return to this definition in Chapter 28.

In SI units we usually write the constant k in Eq. (21.1) as $1/4\pi\epsilon_0$, where ϵ_0 ("epsilon-nought" or "epsilon-zero") is another constant. This appears to complicate matters, but it actually simplifies many formulas that we will encounter in later chapters. From now on, we will usually write Coulomb's law as

$$F = \frac{1}{4\pi\epsilon_0} \frac{|q_1 q_2|}{r^2} \qquad \text{(Coulomb's law: force between two point charges)} \qquad (21.2)$$

The constants in Eq. (21.2) are approximately

$$\epsilon_0 = 8.854 \times 10^{-12} \, \text{C}^2/\text{N} \cdot \text{m}^2 \quad \text{and} \quad \frac{1}{4\pi\epsilon_0} = k = 8.988 \times 10^9 \, \text{N} \cdot \text{m}^2/\text{C}^2$$

In examples and problems we will often use the approximate value

$$\frac{1}{4\pi\epsilon_0} = 9.0 \times 10^9 \, \text{N} \cdot \text{m}^2/\text{C}^2$$

which is within about 0.1% of the correct value.

As we mentioned in Section 21.1, the most fundamental unit of charge is the magnitude of the charge of an electron or a proton, which is denoted by e. The most precise value available as of the writing of this book is

$$e = 1.602176487(40) \times 10^{-19} \, \text{C}$$

One coulomb represents the negative of the total charge of about 6×10^{18} electrons. For comparison, a copper cube 1 cm on a side contains about 2.4×10^{24}

electrons. About 10^{19} electrons pass through the glowing filament of a flashlight bulb every second.

In electrostatics problems (that is, problems that involve charges at rest), it's very unusual to encounter charges as large as 1 coulomb. Two 1-C charges separated by 1 m would exert forces on each other of magnitude 9×10^9 N (about 1 million tons)! The total charge of all the electrons in a copper one-cent coin is even greater, about 1.4×10^5 C, which shows that we can't disturb electric neutrality very much without using enormous forces. More typical values of charge range from about 10^{-9} to about 10^{-6} C. The microcoulomb ($1 \ \mu\text{C} = 10^{-6} \text{C}$) and the nanocoulomb ($1 \ \text{nC} = 10^{-9} \text{C}$) are often used as practical units of charge.

Example 21.1   **Electric force versus gravitational force**

An α particle (the nucleus of a helium atom) has mass $m = 6.64 \times 10^{-27}$ kg and charge $q = +2e = 3.2 \times 10^{-19}$ C. Compare the magnitude of the electric repulsion between two α ("alpha") particles with that of the gravitational attraction between them.

SOLUTION

IDENTIFY and SET UP: This problem involves Newton's law for the gravitational force F_g between particles (see Section 13.1) and Coulomb's law for the electric force F_e between point charges. To compare these forces, we make our target variable the ratio F_e/F_g. We use Eq. (21.2) for F_e and Eq. (13.1) for F_g.

21.11 Our sketch for this problem.

$$q = 3.2 \times 10^{-19} \ C$$
$$m = 6.64 \times 10^{-27} \ kg$$

EXECUTE: Figure 21.11 shows our sketch. From Eqs. (21.2) and (13.1),

$$F_e = \frac{1}{4\pi\epsilon_0}\frac{q^2}{r^2} \qquad F_g = G\frac{m^2}{r^2}$$

These are both inverse-square forces, so the r^2 factors cancel when we take the ratio:

$$\frac{F_e}{F_g} = \frac{1}{4\pi\epsilon_0 G}\frac{q^2}{m^2}$$

$$= \frac{9.0 \times 10^9 \ \text{N} \cdot \text{m}^2/\text{C}^2}{6.67 \times 10^{-11} \ \text{N} \cdot \text{m}^2/\text{kg}^2}\frac{(3.2 \times 10^{-19} \ \text{C})^2}{(6.64 \times 10^{-27} \ \text{kg})^2}$$

$$= 3.1 \times 10^{35}$$

EVALUATE: This astonishingly large number shows that the gravitational force in this situation is completely negligible in comparison to the electric force. This is always true for interactions of atomic and subnuclear particles. But within objects the size of a person or a planet, the positive and negative charges are nearly equal in magnitude, and the net electric force is usually much *smaller* than the gravitational force.

Superposition of Forces

Coulomb's law as we have stated it describes only the interaction of two *point* charges. Experiments show that when two charges exert forces simultaneously on a third charge, the total force acting on that charge is the *vector sum* of the forces that the two charges would exert individually. This important property, called the **principle of superposition of forces,** holds for any number of charges. By using this principle, we can apply Coulomb's law to *any* collection of charges. Two of the examples at the end of this section use the superposition principle.

Strictly speaking, Coulomb's law as we have stated it should be used only for point charges *in a vacuum.* If matter is present in the space between the charges, the net force acting on each charge is altered because charges are induced in the molecules of the intervening material. We will describe this effect later. As a practical matter, though, we can use Coulomb's law unaltered for point charges in air. At normal atmospheric pressure, the presence of air changes the electric force from its vacuum value by only about one part in 2000.

Problem-Solving Strategy 21.1 Coulomb's Law

IDENTIFY *the relevant concepts:* Coulomb's law describes the electric force between charged particles.

SET UP *the problem* using the following steps:
1. Sketch the locations of the charged particles and label each particle with its charge.
2. If the charges do not all lie on a single line, set up an *xy*-coordinate system.
3. The problem will ask you to find the electric force on one or more particles. Identify which these are.

EXECUTE *the solution* as follows:
1. For each particle that exerts an electric force on a given particle of interest, use Eq. (21.2) to calculate the magnitude of that force.
2. Using those magnitudes, sketch a free-body diagram showing the electric force vectors acting on each particle of interest. The force exerted by particle 1 on particle 2 points from particle 2 toward particle 1 if the charges have opposite signs, but points from particle 2 directly away from particle 1 if the charges have the same sign.
3. Use the principle of superposition to calculate the total electric force—a *vector* sum—on each particle of interest. (Review the

vector algebra in Sections 1.7 through 1.9. The method of components is often helpful.)
4. Use consistent units; SI units are completely consistent. With $1/4\pi\epsilon_0 = 9.0 \times 10^9 \text{ N} \cdot \text{m}^2/\text{C}^2$, distances must be in meters, charges in coulombs, and forces in newtons.
5. Some examples and problems in this and later chapters involve *continuous* distributions of charge along a line, over a surface, or throughout a volume. In these cases the vector sum in step 3 becomes a vector *integral*. We divide the charge distribution into infinitesimal pieces, use Coulomb's law for each piece, and integrate to find the vector sum. Sometimes this can be done without actual integration.
6. Exploit any symmetries in the charge distribution to simplify your problem solving. For example, two identical charges q exert zero net electric force on a charge Q midway between them, because the forces on Q have equal magnitude and opposite direction.

EVALUATE *your answer:* Check whether your numerical results are reasonable. Confirm that the direction of the net electric force agrees with the principle that charges of the same sign repel and charges of opposite sign attract.

Example 21.2 Force between two point charges

Two point charges, $q_1 = +25$ nC and $q_2 = -75$ nC, are separated by a distance $r = 3.0$ cm (Fig. 21.12a). Find the magnitude and direction of the electric force (a) that q_1 exerts on q_2 and (b) that q_2 exerts on q_1.

SOLUTION

IDENTIFY and SET UP: This problem asks for the electric forces that two charges exert on each other. We use Coulomb's law, Eq. (21.2), to calculate the magnitudes of the forces. The signs of the charges will determine the directions of the forces.

EXECUTE: (a) After converting the units of r to meters and the units of q_1 and q_2 to coulombs, Eq. (21.2) gives us

$$F_{1 \text{ on } 2} = \frac{1}{4\pi\epsilon_0} \frac{|q_1 q_2|}{r^2}$$

$$= (9.0 \times 10^9 \text{ N} \cdot \text{m}^2/\text{C}^2) \frac{|(+25 \times 10^{-9} \text{ C})(-75 \times 10^{-9} \text{ C})|}{(0.030 \text{ m})^2}$$

$$= 0.019 \text{ N}$$

The charges have opposite signs, so the force is attractive (to the left in Fig. 21.12b); that is, the force that acts on q_2 is directed toward q_1 along the line joining the two charges.

21.12 What force does q_1 exert on q_2, and what force does q_2 exert on q_1? Gravitational forces are negligible.

(a) The two charges   (b) Free-body diagram for charge q_2 (c) Free-body diagram for charge q_1

(b) Proceeding as in part (a), we have

$$F_{1 \text{ on } 2} = \frac{1}{4\pi\epsilon_0} \frac{|q_2 q_1|}{r^2} = F_{2 \text{ on } 1} = 0.019 \text{ N}$$

The attractive force that acts on q_1 is to the right, toward q_2 (Fig. 21.12c).

EVALUATE: Newton's third law applies to the electric force. Even though the charges have different magnitudes, the magnitude of the force that q_2 exerts on q_1 is the same as the magnitude of the force that q_1 exerts on q_2, and these two forces are in opposite directions.

Example 21.3 Vector addition of electric forces on a line

Two point charges are located on the *x*-axis of a coordinate system: $q_1 = 1.0$ nC is at $x = +2.0$ cm, and $q_2 = -3.0$ nC is at $x = +4.0$ cm. What is the total electric force exerted by q_1 and q_2 on a charge $q_3 = 5.0$ nC at $x = 0$?

SOLUTION

IDENTIFY and SET UP: Figure 21.13a shows the situation. To find the total force on q_3, our target variable, we find the vector sum of the two electric forces on it.

Continued

EXECUTE: Figure 21.13b is a free-body diagram for q_3, which is repelled by q_1 (which has the same sign) and attracted to q_2 (which has the opposite sign): $\vec{F}_{1\text{ on }3}$ is in the $-x$-direction and $\vec{F}_{2\text{ on }3}$ is in the $+x$-direction. After unit conversions, we have from Eq. (21.2)

$$F_{1\text{ on }3} = \frac{1}{4\pi\epsilon_0}\frac{|q_1 q_3|}{r_{13}^2}$$

$$= (9.0 \times 10^9 \text{ N}\cdot\text{m}^2/\text{C}^2)\frac{(1.0 \times 10^{-9}\text{ C})(5.0 \times 10^{-9}\text{ C})}{(0.020\text{ m})^2}$$

$$= 1.12 \times 10^{-4}\text{ N} = 112\ \mu\text{N}$$

In the same way you can show that $F_{2\text{ on }3} = 84\ \mu\text{N}$. We thus have $\vec{F}_{1\text{ on }3} = (-112\ \mu\text{N})\hat{\imath}$ and $\vec{F}_{2\text{ on }3} = (84\ \mu\text{N})\hat{\imath}$. The net force on q_3 is

$$\vec{F}_3 = \vec{F}_{1\text{ on }3} + \vec{F}_{2\text{ on }3} = (-112\ \mu\text{N})\hat{\imath} + (84\ \mu\text{N})\hat{\imath} = (-28\ \mu\text{N})\hat{\imath}$$

21.13 Our sketches for this problem.

(a) Our diagram of the situation

(b) Free-body diagram for q_3

EVALUATE: As a check, note that the magnitude of q_2 is three times that of q_1, but q_2 is twice as far from q_3 as q_1. Equation (21.2) then says that $F_{2\text{ on }3}$ must be $3/2^2 = 3/4 = 0.75$ as large as $F_{1\text{ on }3}$. This agrees with our calculated values: $F_{2\text{ on }3}/F_{1\text{ on }3} = (84\ \mu\text{N})/(112\ \mu\text{N}) = 0.75$. Because $F_{2\text{ on }3}$ is the weaker force, the direction of the net force is that of $\vec{F}_{1\text{ on }3}$—that is, in the negative x-direction.

Example 21.4 Vector addition of electric forces in a plane

Two equal positive charges $q_1 = q_2 = 2.0\ \mu\text{C}$ are located at $x = 0$, $y = 0.30$ m and $x = 0$, $y = -0.30$ m, respectively. What are the magnitude and direction of the total electric force that q_1 and q_2 exert on a third charge $Q = 4.0\ \mu\text{C}$ at $x = 0.40$ m, $y = 0$?

SOLUTION

IDENTIFY and SET UP: As in Example 21.3, we must compute the force that each charge exerts on Q and then find the vector sum of those forces. Figure 21.14 shows the situation. Since the three charges do not all lie on a line, the best way to calculate the forces is to use components.

21.14 Our sketch for this problem.

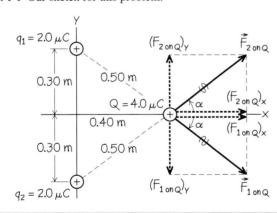

EXECUTE: Figure 21.14 shows the forces $\vec{F}_{1\text{ on }Q}$ and $\vec{F}_{2\text{ on }Q}$ due to the identical charges q_1 and q_2, which are at equal distances from Q. From Coulomb's law, *both* forces have magnitude

$$F_{1\text{ or }2\text{ on }Q} = (9.0 \times 10^9\text{ N}\cdot\text{m}^2/\text{C}^2)$$

$$\times \frac{(4.0 \times 10^{-6}\text{ C})(2.0 \times 10^{-6}\text{ C})}{(0.50\text{ m})^2} = 0.29\text{ N}$$

The x-components of the two forces are equal:

$$(F_{1\text{ or }2\text{ on }Q})_x = (F_{1\text{ or }2\text{ on }Q})\cos\alpha = (0.29\text{ N})\frac{0.40\text{ m}}{0.50\text{ m}} = 0.23\text{ N}$$

From symmetry we see that the y-components of the two forces are equal and opposite. Hence their sum is zero and the total force $\vec{F}$ on Q has only an x-component $F_x = 0.23\text{ N} + 0.23\text{ N} = 0.46\text{ N}$. The total force on Q is in the $+x$-direction, with magnitude 0.46 N.

EVALUATE: The total force on Q points neither directly away from q_1 nor directly away from q_2. Rather, this direction is a compromise that points away from the *system* of charges q_1 and q_2. Can you see that the total force would *not* be in the $+x$-direction if q_1 and q_2 were not equal or if the geometrical arrangement of the charges were not so symmetric?

Test Your Understanding of Section 21.3 Suppose that charge q_2 in Example 21.4 were $-2.0\ \mu\text{C}$. In this case, the total electric force on Q would be (i) in the positive x-direction; (ii) in the negative x-direction; (iii) in the positive y-direction; (iv) in the negative y-direction; (v) zero; (vi) none of these.

21.4 Electric Field and Electric Forces

When two electrically charged particles in empty space interact, how does each one know the other is there? We can begin to answer this question, and at the same time reformulate Coulomb's law in a very useful way, by using the concept of *electric field*.

Electric Field

To introduce this concept, let's look at the mutual repulsion of two positively charged bodies A and B (Fig. 21.15a). Suppose B has charge q_0, and let $\vec{F}_0$ be the electric force of A on B. One way to think about this force is as an "action-at-a-distance" force—that is, as a force that acts across empty space without needing any matter (such as a push rod or a rope) to transmit it through the intervening space. (Gravity can also be thought of as an "action-at-a-distance" force.) But a more fruitful way to visualize the repulsion between A and B is as a two-stage process. We first envision that body A, as a result of the charge that it carries, somehow *modifies the properties of the space around it*. Then body B, as a result of the charge that *it* carries, senses how space has been modified at its position. The response of body B is to experience the force $\vec{F}_0$.

To elaborate how this two-stage process occurs, we first consider body A by itself: We remove body B and label its former position as point P (Fig. 21.15b). We say that the charged body A produces or causes an **electric field** at point P (and at all other points in the neighborhood). This electric field is present at P even if there is no charge at P; it is a consequence of the charge on body A only. If a point charge q_0 is then placed at point P, it experiences the force $\vec{F}_0$. We take the point of view that this force is exerted on q_0 *by the field* at P (Fig. 21.15c). Thus the electric field is the intermediary through which A communicates its presence to q_0. Because the point charge q_0 would experience a force at *any* point in the neighborhood of A, the electric field that A produces exists at all points in the region around A.

We can likewise say that the point charge q_0 produces an electric field in the space around it and that this electric field exerts the force $-\vec{F}_0$ on body A. For each force (the force of A on q_0 and the force of q_0 on A), one charge sets up an electric field that exerts a force on the second charge. We emphasize that this is an *interaction* between *two* charged bodies. A single charge produces an electric field in the surrounding space, but this electric field cannot exert a net force on the charge that created it; as we discussed in Section 4.3, a body cannot exert a net force on itself. (If this wasn't true, you would be able to lift yourself to the ceiling by pulling up on your belt!)

> **The electric force on a charged body is exerted by the electric field created by *other* charged bodies.**

To find out experimentally whether there is an electric field at a particular point, we place a small charged body, which we call a **test charge,** at the point (Fig. 21.15c). If the test charge experiences an electric force, then there is an electric field at that point. This field is produced by charges other than q_0.

Force is a vector quantity, so electric field is also a vector quantity. (Note the use of vector signs as well as boldface letters and plus, minus, and equals signs in the following discussion.) We define the *electric field* $\vec{E}$ at a point as the electric force $\vec{F}_0$ experienced by a test charge q_0 at the point, divided by the charge q_0. That is, the electric field at a certain point is equal to the *electric force per unit charge* experienced by a charge at that point:

$$\vec{E} = \frac{\vec{F}_0}{q_0} \qquad \text{(definition of electric field as electric force per unit charge)} \qquad (21.3)$$

In SI units, in which the unit of force is 1 N and the unit of charge is 1 C, the unit of electric field magnitude is 1 newton per coulomb (1 N/C).

If the field $\vec{E}$ at a certain point is known, rearranging Eq. (21.3) gives the force $\vec{F}_0$ experienced by a point charge q_0 placed at that point. This force is just equal to the electric field $\vec{E}$ produced at that point by charges other than q_0, multiplied by the charge q_0:

$$\vec{F}_0 = q_0\vec{E} \qquad \text{(force exerted on a point charge } q_0 \text{ by an electric field } \vec{E}) \qquad (21.4)$$

21.15 A charged body creates an electric field in the space around it.

(a) *A* and *B* exert electric forces on each other.

(b) Remove body *B* ...

... and label its former position as *P*.

(c) Body *A* sets up an electric field $\vec{E}$ at point *P*.

$\vec{E}$ is the force per unit charge exerted by *A* on a test charge at *P*.

Application **Sharks and the "Sixth Sense"**
Sharks have the ability to locate prey (such as flounder and other bottom-dwelling fish) that are completely hidden beneath the sand at the bottom of the ocean. They do this by sensing the weak electric fields produced by muscle contractions in their prey. Sharks derive their sensitivity to electric fields (a "sixth sense") from jelly-filled canals in their bodies. These canals end in pores on the shark's skin (shown in this photograph). An electric field as weak as 5×10^{-7} N/C causes charge flow within the canals and triggers a signal in the shark's nervous system. Because the shark has canals with different orientations, it can measure different components of the electric-field vector and hence determine the direction of the field.

21.16 The force $\vec{F}_0 = q_0 \vec{E}$ exerted on a point charge q_0 placed in an electric field $\vec{E}$.

The force on a positive test charge q_0 points in the direction of the electric field.

The force on a negative test charge q_0 points opposite to the electric field.

ActivPhysics 11.4: Electric Field: Point Charge
ActivPhysics 11.9: Motion of a Charge in an Electric Field: Introduction
ActivPhysics 11.10: Motion in an Electric Field: Problems

The charge q_0 can be either positive or negative. If q_0 is *positive*, the force $\vec{F}_0$ experienced by the charge is the same direction as $\vec{E}$; if q_0 is *negative*, $\vec{F}_0$ and $\vec{E}$ are in opposite directions (Fig. 21.16).

While the electric field concept may be new to you, the basic idea—that one body sets up a field in the space around it and a second body responds to that field—is one that you've actually used before. Compare Eq. (21.4) to the familiar expression for the gravitational force $\vec{F}_g$ that the earth exerts on a mass m_0:

$$\vec{F}_g = m_0 \vec{g} \qquad (21.5)$$

In this expression, $\vec{g}$ is the acceleration due to gravity. If we divide both sides of Eq. (21.5) by the mass m_0, we obtain

$$\vec{g} = \frac{\vec{F}_g}{m_0}$$

Thus $\vec{g}$ can be regarded as the gravitational force per unit mass. By analogy to Eq. (21.3), we can interpret $\vec{g}$ as the *gravitational field*. Thus we treat the gravitational interaction between the earth and the mass m_0 as a two-stage process: The earth sets up a gravitational field $\vec{g}$ in the space around it, and this gravitational field exerts a force given by Eq. (21.5) on the mass m_0 (which we can regard as a *test mass*). The gravitational field $\vec{g}$, or gravitational force per unit mass, is a useful concept because it does not depend on the mass of the body on which the gravitational force is exerted; likewise, the electric field $\vec{E}$, or electric force per unit charge, is useful because it does not depend on the charge of the body on which the electric force is exerted.

CAUTION $\vec{F}_0 = q_0 \vec{E}_0$ **is for *point* test charges only** The electric force experienced by a test charge q_0 can vary from point to point, so the electric field can also be different at different points. For this reason, Eq. (21.4) can be used only to find the electric force on a *point* charge. If a charged body is large enough in size, the electric field $\vec{E}$ may be noticeably different in magnitude and direction at different points on the body, and calculating the net electric force on the body can become rather complicated.

Electric Field of a Point Charge

If the source distribution is a point charge q, it is easy to find the electric field that it produces. We call the location of the charge the **source point,** and we call the point P where we are determining the field the **field point.** It is also useful to introduce a *unit vector* $\hat{r}$ that points along the line from source point to field point (Fig. 21.17a). This unit vector is equal to the displacement vector $\vec{r}$ from the source point to the field point, divided by the distance $r = |\vec{r}|$ between these two points; that is, $\hat{r} = \vec{r}/r$. If we place a small test charge q_0 at the field point P, at a

21.17 The electric field $\vec{E}$ produced at point P by an isolated point charge q at S. Note that in both (b) and (c), $\vec{E}$ is *produced* by q [see Eq. (21.7)] but *acts* on the charge q_0 at point P [see Eq. (21.4)].

(a)

Unit vector $\hat{r}$ points from source point S to field point P.

(b)

At each point P, the electric field set up by an isolated *positive* point charge q points directly *away* from the charge in the *same* direction as $\hat{r}$.

(c)

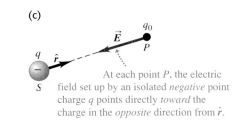

At each point P, the electric field set up by an isolated *negative* point charge q points directly *toward* the charge in the *opposite* direction from $\hat{r}$.

distance r from the source point, the magnitude F_0 of the force is given by Coulomb's law, Eq. (21.2):

$$F_0 = \frac{1}{4\pi\epsilon_0} \frac{|qq_0|}{r^2}$$

From Eq. (21.3) the magnitude E of the electric field at P is

$$E = \frac{1}{4\pi\epsilon_0} \frac{|q|}{r^2} \quad \text{(magnitude of electric field of a point charge)} \quad (21.6)$$

Using the unit vector $\hat{r}$, we can write a *vector* equation that gives both the magnitude and direction of the electric field $\vec{E}$:

$$\vec{E} = \frac{1}{4\pi\epsilon_0} \frac{q}{r^2}\hat{r} \quad \text{(electric field of a point charge)} \quad (21.7)$$

By definition, the electric field of a point charge always points *away from* a positive charge (that is, in the same direction as $\hat{r}$; see Fig. 21.17b) but *toward* a negative charge (that is, in the direction opposite $\hat{r}$; see Fig. 21.17c).

We have emphasized calculating the electric field $\vec{E}$ at a certain point. But since $\vec{E}$ can vary from point to point, it is not a single vector quantity but rather an *infinite* set of vector quantities, one associated with each point in space. This is an example of a **vector field.** Figure 21.18 shows a number of the field vectors produced by a positive or negative point charge. If we use a rectangular (x, y, z) coordinate system, each component of $\vec{E}$ at any point is in general a function of the coordinates (x, y, z) of the point. We can represent the functions as $E_x(x, y, z)$, $E_y(x, y, z)$, and $E_z(x, y, z)$. Vector fields are an important part of the language of physics, not just in electricity and magnetism. One everyday example of a vector field is the velocity $\vec{v}$ of wind currents; the magnitude and direction of $\vec{v}$, and hence its vector components, vary from point to point in the atmosphere.

In some situations the magnitude and direction of the field (and hence its vector components) have the same values everywhere throughout a certain region; we then say that the field is *uniform* in this region. An important example of this is the electric field inside a *conductor.* If there is an electric field within a conductor, the field exerts a force on every charge in the conductor, giving the free charges a net motion. By definition an electrostatic situation is one in which the charges have *no* net motion. We conclude that *in electrostatics the electric field at every point within the material of a conductor must be zero.* (Note that we are not saying that the field is necessarily zero in a *hole* inside a conductor.)

In summary, our description of electric interactions has two parts. First, a given charge distribution acts as a source of electric field. Second, the electric field exerts a force on any charge that is present in the field. Our analysis often has two corresponding steps: first, calculating the field caused by a source charge distribution; second, looking at the effect of the field in terms of force and motion. The second step often involves Newton's laws as well as the principles of electric interactions. In the next section we show how to calculate fields caused by various source distributions, but first here are three examples of calculating the field due to a point charge and of finding the force on a charge due to a given field $\vec{E}$.

21.18 A point charge q produces an electric field $\vec{E}$ at *all* points in space. The field strength decreases with increasing distance.

(a) The field produced by a positive point charge points *away from* the charge.

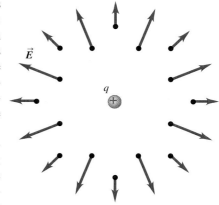

(b) The field produced by a negative point charge points *toward* the charge.

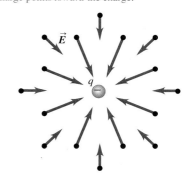

Example 21.5 **Electric-field magnitude for a point charge**

What is the magnitude of the electric field $\vec{E}$ at a field point 2.0 m from a point charge $q = 4.0$ nC?

SOLUTION

IDENTIFY and SET UP: This problem concerns the electric field due to a point charge. We are given the magnitude of the charge

Continued

and the distance from the charge to the field point, so we use Eq. (21.6) to calculate the field magnitude E.

EXECUTE: From Eq. (21.6),

$$E = \frac{1}{4\pi\epsilon_0}\frac{|q|}{r^2} = (9.0 \times 10^9 \text{ N} \cdot \text{m}^2/\text{C}^2)\frac{4.0 \times 10^{-9} \text{ C}}{(2.0 \text{ m})^2}$$

$$= 9.0 \text{ N/C}$$

EVALUATE: Our result $E = 9.0$ N/C means that if we placed a 1.0-C charge at a point 2.0 m from q, it would experience a 9.0-N force. The force on a 2.0-C charge at that point would be $(2.0 \text{ C})(9.0 \text{ N/C}) = 18$ N, and so on.

Example 21.6 Electric-field vector for a point charge

A point charge $q = -8.0$ nC is located at the origin. Find the electric-field vector at the field point $x = 1.2$ m, $y = -1.6$ m.

SOLUTION

IDENTIFY and SET UP: We must find the electric-field *vector* $\vec{E}$ due to a point charge. Figure 21.19 shows the situation. We use Eq. (21.7); to do this, we must find the distance r from the source point S (the position of the charge q, which in this example is at the origin O) to the field point P, and we must obtain an expression for the unit vector $\hat{r} = \vec{r}/r$ that points from S to P.

EXECUTE: The distance from S to P is

$$r = \sqrt{x^2 + y^2} = \sqrt{(1.2 \text{ m})^2 + (-1.6 \text{ m})^2} = 2.0 \text{ m}$$

The unit vector $\hat{r}$ is then

$$\hat{r} = \frac{\vec{r}}{r} = \frac{x\hat{i} + y\hat{j}}{r}$$

$$= \frac{(1.2 \text{ m})\hat{i} + (-1.6 \text{ m})\hat{j}}{2.0 \text{ m}} = 0.60\hat{i} - 0.80\hat{j}$$

Then, from Eq. (21.7),

$$\vec{E} = \frac{1}{4\pi\epsilon_0}\frac{q}{r^2}\hat{r}$$

$$= (9.0 \times 10^9 \text{ N} \cdot \text{m}^2/\text{C}^2)\frac{(-8.0 \times 10^{-9} \text{ C})}{(2.0 \text{ m})^2}(0.60\hat{i} - 0.80\hat{j})$$

$$= (-11 \text{ N/C})\hat{i} + (14 \text{ N/C})\hat{j}$$

EVALUATE: Since q is negative, $\vec{E}$ points from the field point to the charge (the source point), in the direction opposite to $\hat{r}$ (compare Fig. 21.17c). We leave the calculation of the magnitude and direction of $\vec{E}$ to you (see Exercise 21.36).

21.19 Our sketch for this problem.

Example 21.7 Electron in a uniform field

When the terminals of a battery are connected to two parallel conducting plates with a small gap between them, the resulting charges on the plates produce a nearly uniform electric field $\vec{E}$ between the plates. (In the next section we'll see why this is.) If the plates are 1.0 cm apart and are connected to a 100-volt battery as shown in Fig. 21.20, the field is vertically upward and has magnitude

21.20 A uniform electric field between two parallel conducting plates connected to a 100-volt battery. (The separation of the plates is exaggerated in this figure relative to the dimensions of the plates.)

The thin arrows represent the uniform electric field.

$E = 1.00 \times 10^4$ N/C. (a) If an electron (charge $-e = -1.60 \times 10^{-19}$ C, mass $m = 9.11 \times 10^{-31}$ kg) is released from rest at the upper plate, what is its acceleration? (b) What speed and kinetic energy does it acquire while traveling 1.0 cm to the lower plate? (c) How long does it take to travel this distance?

SOLUTION

IDENTIFY and SET UP: This example involves the relationship between electric field and electric force. It also involves the relationship between force and acceleration, the definition of kinetic energy, and the kinematic relationships among acceleration, distance, velocity, and time. Figure 21.20 shows our coordinate system. We are given the electric field, so we use Eq. (21.4) to find the force on the electron and Newton's second law to find its acceleration. Because the field is uniform, the force is constant and we can use the constant-acceleration formulas from Chapter 2 to find the electron's velocity and travel time. We find the kinetic energy using $K = \frac{1}{2}mv^2$.

EXECUTE: (a) Although $\vec{E}$ is upward (in the $+y$-direction), $\vec{F}$ is downward (because the electron's charge is negative) and so F_y is negative. Because F_y is constant, the electron's acceleration is constant:

$$a_y = \frac{F_y}{m} = \frac{-eE}{m} = \frac{(-1.60 \times 10^{-19}\ C)(1.00 \times 10^4\ N/C)}{9.11 \times 10^{-31}\ kg}$$

$$= -1.76 \times 10^{15}\ m/s^2$$

(b) The electron starts from rest, so its motion is in the y-direction only (the direction of the acceleration). We can find the electron's speed at any position y using the constant-acceleration Eq. (2.13), $v_y^2 = v_{0y}^2 + 2a_y(y - y_0)$. We have $v_{0y} = 0$ and $y_0 = 0$, so at $y = -1.0\ cm = -1.0 \times 10^{-2}\ m$ we have

$$|v_y| = \sqrt{2a_y y} = \sqrt{2(-1.76 \times 10^{15}\ m/s^2)(-1.0 \times 10^{-2}\ m)}$$

$$= 5.9 \times 10^6\ m/s$$

The velocity is downward, so $v_y = -5.9 \times 10^6\ m/s$. The electron's kinetic energy is

$$K = \tfrac{1}{2}mv^2 = \tfrac{1}{2}(9.11 \times 10^{-31}\ kg)(5.9 \times 10^6\ m/s)^2$$

$$= 1.6 \times 10^{-17}\ J$$

(c) From Eq. (2.8) for constant acceleration, $v_y = v_{0y} + a_y t$,

$$t = \frac{v_y - v_{0y}}{a_y} = \frac{(-5.9 \times 10^6\ m/s) - (0\ m/s)}{-1.76 \times 10^{15}\ m/s^2}$$

$$= 3.4 \times 10^{-9}\ s$$

EVALUATE: Our results show that in problems concerning subatomic particles such as electrons, many quantities—including acceleration, speed, kinetic energy, and time—will have *very* different values from those typical of everyday objects such as baseballs and automobiles.

Test Your Understanding of Section 21.4 (a) A negative point charge moves along a straight-line path directly toward a stationary positive point charge. Which aspect(s) of the electric force on the negative point charge will remain constant as it moves? (i) magnitude; (ii) direction; (iii) both magnitude and direction; (iv) neither magnitude nor direction. (b) A negative point charge moves along a circular orbit around a positive point charge. Which aspect(s) of the electric force on the negative point charge will remain constant as it moves? (i) magnitude; (ii) direction; (iii) both magnitude and direction; (iv) neither magnitude nor direction.

21.5 Electric-Field Calculations

ActivPhysics 11.5: Electric Field Due to a Dipole
ActivPhysics 11.6: Electric Field: Problems

Equation (21.7) gives the electric field caused by a single point charge. But in most realistic situations that involve electric fields and forces, we encounter charge that is *distributed* over space. The charged plastic and glass rods in Fig. 21.1 have electric charge distributed over their surfaces, as does the imaging drum of a laser printer (Fig. 21.2). In this section we'll learn to calculate electric fields caused by various distributions of electric charge. Calculations of this kind are of tremendous importance for technological applications of electric forces. To determine the trajectories of atomic nuclei in an accelerator for cancer radiotherapy or of charged particles in a semiconductor electronic device, you have to know the detailed nature of the electric field acting on the charges.

The Superposition of Electric Fields

To find the field caused by a charge distribution, we imagine the distribution to be made up of many point charges $q_1, q_2, q_3, \ldots$. (This is actually quite a realistic description, since we have seen that charge is carried by electrons and protons that are so small as to be almost pointlike.) At any given point P, each point charge produces its own electric field $\vec{E}_1, \vec{E}_2, \vec{E}_3, \ldots$, so a test charge q_0 placed at P experiences a force $\vec{F}_1 = q_0\vec{E}_1$ from charge q_1, a force $\vec{F}_2 = q_0\vec{E}_2$ from charge q_2, and so on. From the principle of superposition of forces discussed in Section 21.3, the *total* force $\vec{F}_0$ that the charge distribution exerts on q_0 is the vector sum of these individual forces:

$$\vec{F}_0 = \vec{F}_1 + \vec{F}_2 + \vec{F}_3 + \cdots = q_0\vec{E}_1 + q_0\vec{E}_2 + q_0\vec{E}_3 + \cdots$$

The combined effect of all the charges in the distribution is described by the *total* electric field $\vec{E}$ at point P. From the definition of electric field, Eq. (21.3), this is

$$\vec{E} = \frac{\vec{F}_0}{q_0} = \vec{E}_1 + \vec{E}_2 + \vec{E}_3 + \cdots$$

21.21 Illustrating the principle of superposition of electric fields.

The total electric field $\vec{E}$ at point P is the vector sum of $\vec{E}_1$ and $\vec{E}_2$.

The total electric field at P is the vector sum of the fields at P due to each point charge in the charge distribution (Fig. 21.21). This is the **principle of superposition of electric fields.**

When charge is distributed along a line, over a surface, or through a volume, a few additional terms are useful. For a line charge distribution (such as a long, thin, charged plastic rod), we use λ (the Greek letter lambda) to represent the **linear charge density** (charge per unit length, measured in C/m). When charge is distributed over a surface (such as the surface of the imaging drum of a laser printer), we use σ (sigma) to represent the **surface charge density** (charge per unit area, measured in C/m^2). And when charge is distributed through a volume, we use ρ (rho) to represent the **volume charge density** (charge per unit volume, C/m^3).

Some of the calculations in the following examples may look fairly intricate. After you've worked through the examples one step at a time, the process will seem less formidable. We will use many of the calculational techniques in these examples in Chapter 28 to calculate the *magnetic* fields caused by charges in motion.

Problem-Solving Strategy 21.2   **Electric-Field Calculations**

IDENTIFY *the relevant concepts:* Use the principle of superposition to calculate the electric field due to a discrete or continuous charge distribution.

SET UP *the problem* using the following steps:
1. Make a drawing showing the locations of the charges and your choice of coordinate axes.
2. On your drawing, indicate the position of the *field point P* (the point at which you want to calculate the electric field $\vec{E}$).

EXECUTE *the solution* as follows:
1. Use consistent units. Distances must be in meters and charge must be in coulombs. If you are given centimeters or nano-coulombs, don't forget to convert.
2. Distinguish between the source point S and the field point P. The field produced by a point charge always points from S to P if the charge is positive, and from P to S if the charge is negative.
3. Use *vector* addition when applying the principle of superposition; review the treatment of vector addition in Chapter 1 if necessary.

4. Simplify your calculations by exploiting any symmetries in the charge distribution.
5. If the charge distribution is continuous, define a small element of charge that can be considered as a point, find its electric field at P, and find a way to add the fields of all the charge elements by doing an integral. Usually it is easiest to do this for each component of $\vec{E}$ separately, so you may need to evaluate more than one integral. Ensure that the limits on your integrals are correct; especially when the situation has symmetry, don't count a charge twice.

EVALUATE *your answer:* Check that the direction of $\vec{E}$ is reasonable. If your result for the electric-field magnitude E is a function of position (say, the coordinate x), check your result in any limits for which you know what the magnitude should be. When possible, check your answer by calculating it in a different way.

Example 21.8   **Field of an electric dipole**

Point charges $q_1 = +12$ nC and $q_2 = -12$ nC are 0.100 m apart (Fig. 21.22). (Such pairs of point charges with equal magnitude and opposite sign are called *electric dipoles*.) Compute the electric field caused by q_1, the field caused by q_2, and the total field (a) at point a; (b) at point b; and (c) at point c.

SOLUTION

IDENTIFY and SET UP: We must find the total electric field at various points due to two point charges. We use the principle of super-position: $\vec{E} = \vec{E}_1 + \vec{E}_2$. Figure 21.22 shows the coordinate system and the locations of the field points a, b, and c.

EXECUTE: At each field point, $\vec{E}$ depends on $\vec{E}_1$ and $\vec{E}_2$ there; we first calculate the magnitudes E_1 and E_2 at each field point. At a the magnitude of the field $\vec{E}_{1a}$ caused by q_1 is

$$E_{1a} = \frac{1}{4\pi\epsilon_0}\frac{|q_1|}{r^2} = (9.0 \times 10^9 \text{ N}\cdot\text{m}^2/\text{C}^2)\frac{12 \times 10^{-9} \text{ C}}{(0.060 \text{ m})^2}$$
$$= 3.0 \times 10^4 \text{ N/C}$$

We calculate the other field magnitudes in a similar way. The results are

$$E_{1a} = 3.0 \times 10^4 \text{ N/C} \qquad E_{1b} = 6.8 \times 10^4 \text{ N/C}$$
$$E_{1c} = 6.39 \times 10^3 \text{ N/C}$$

$$E_{2a} = 6.8 \times 10^4 \text{ N/C} \qquad E_{2b} = 0.55 \times 10^4 \text{ N/C}$$
$$E_{2c} = E_{1c} = 6.39 \times 10^3 \text{ N/C}$$

The *directions* of the corresponding fields are in all cases *away* from the positive charge q_1 and *toward* the negative charge q_2.

21.22 Electric field at three points, a, b, and c, set up by charges q_1 and q_2, which form an electric dipole.

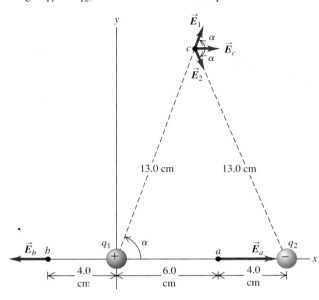

(a) At a, $\vec{E}_{1a}$ and $\vec{E}_{2a}$ are both directed to the right, so

$$\vec{E}_a = E_{1a}\hat{\imath} + E_{2a}\hat{\imath} = (9.8 \times 10^4 \text{ N/C})\hat{\imath}$$

(b) At b, $\vec{E}_{1b}$ is directed to the left and $\vec{E}_{2b}$ is directed to the right, so

$$\vec{E}_b = -E_{1b}\hat{\imath} + E_{2b}\hat{\imath} = (-6.2 \times 10^4 \text{ N/C})\hat{\imath}$$

(c) Figure 21.22 shows the directions of $\vec{E}_1$ and $\vec{E}_2$ at c. Both vectors have the same x-component:

$$E_{1cx} = E_{2cx} = E_{1c}\cos\alpha = (6.39 \times 10^3 \text{ N/C})\left(\tfrac{5}{13}\right)$$
$$= 2.46 \times 10^3 \text{ N/C}$$

From symmetry, E_{1y} and E_{2y} are equal and opposite, so their sum is zero. Hence

$$\vec{E}_c = 2(2.46 \times 10^3 \text{ N/C})\hat{\imath} = (4.9 \times 10^3 \text{ N/C})\hat{\imath}$$

EVALUATE: We can also find $\vec{E}_c$ using Eq. (21.7) for the field of a point charge. The displacement vector $\vec{r}_1$ from q_1 to point c is $\vec{r}_1 = r\cos\alpha\hat{\imath} + r\sin\alpha\hat{\jmath}$. Hence the unit vector that points from q_1 to point c is $\hat{r}_1 = \vec{r}_1/r = \cos\alpha\hat{\imath} + \sin\alpha\hat{\jmath}$. By symmetry, the unit vector that points from q_2 to point c has the opposite x-component but the same y-component: $\hat{r}_2 = -\cos\alpha\hat{\imath} + \sin\alpha\hat{\jmath}$. We can now use Eq. (21.7) to write the fields $\vec{E}_{1c}$ and $\vec{E}_{2c}$ at c in vector form, then find their sum. Since $q_2 = -q_1$ and the distance r to c is the same for both charges,

$$\vec{E}_c = \vec{E}_{1c} + \vec{E}_{2c} = \frac{1}{4\pi\epsilon_0}\frac{q_1}{r^2}\hat{r}_1 + \frac{1}{4\pi\epsilon_0}\frac{q_2}{r^2}\hat{r}_2$$
$$= \frac{1}{4\pi\epsilon_0 r^2}(q_1\hat{r}_1 + q_2\hat{r}_2) = \frac{q_1}{4\pi\epsilon_0 r^2}(\hat{r}_1 - \hat{r}_2)$$
$$= \frac{1}{4\pi\epsilon_0}\frac{q_1}{r^2}(2\cos\alpha\hat{\imath})$$
$$= 2(9.0 \times 10^9 \text{ N}\cdot\text{m}^2/\text{C}^2)\frac{12 \times 10^{-9} \text{ C}}{(0.13 \text{ m})^2}\left(\tfrac{5}{13}\right)\hat{\imath}$$
$$= (4.9 \times 10^3 \text{ N/C})\hat{\imath}$$

This is the same as we calculated in part (c).

Example 21.9   **Field of a ring of charge**

Charge Q is uniformly distributed around a conducting ring of radius a (Fig. 21.23). Find the electric field at a point P on the ring axis at a distance x from its center.

SOLUTION

IDENTIFY and SET UP: This is a problem in the superposition of electric fields. Each bit of charge around the ring produces an electric field at an arbitrary point on the x-axis; our target variable is the total field at this point due to all such bits of charge.

21.23 Calculating the electric field on the axis of a ring of charge. In this figure, the charge is assumed to be positive.

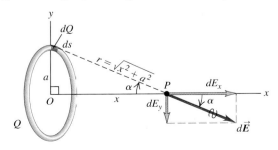

EXECUTE: We divide the ring into infinitesimal segments ds as shown in Fig. 21.23. In terms of the linear charge density $\lambda = Q/2\pi a$, the charge in a segment of length ds is $dQ = \lambda\,ds$. Consider two identical segments, one as shown in the figure at $y = a$ and another halfway around the ring at $y = -a$. From Example 21.4, we see that the net force $d\vec{F}$ they exert on a point test charge at P, and thus their net field $d\vec{E}$, are directed along the x-axis. The same is true for any such pair of segments around the ring, so the *net* field at P is along the x-axis: $\vec{E} = E_x\hat{\imath}$.

To calculate E_x, note that the square of the distance r from a single ring segment to the point P is $r^2 = x^2 + a^2$. Hence the magnitude of this segment's contribution $d\vec{E}$ to the electric field at P is

$$dE = \frac{1}{4\pi\epsilon_0}\frac{dQ}{x^2 + a^2}$$

The x-component of this field is $dE_x = dE\cos\alpha$. We know $dQ = \lambda\,ds$ and Fig. 21.23 shows that $\cos\alpha = x/r = x/(x^2 + a^2)^{1/2}$, so

$$dE_x = dE\cos\alpha = \frac{1}{4\pi\epsilon_0}\frac{dQ}{x^2 + a^2}\frac{x}{\sqrt{x^2 + a^2}}$$
$$= \frac{1}{4\pi\epsilon_0}\frac{\lambda x}{(x^2 + a^2)^{3/2}}ds$$

Continued

To find E_x we integrate this expression over the entire ring—that is, for s from 0 to $2\pi a$ (the circumference of the ring). The integrand has the same value for all points on the ring, so it can be taken outside the integral. Hence we get

$$E_x = \int dE_x = \frac{1}{4\pi\epsilon_0} \frac{\lambda x}{(x^2 + a^2)^{3/2}} \int_0^{2\pi a} ds$$

$$= \frac{1}{4\pi\epsilon_0} \frac{\lambda x}{(x^2 + a^2)^{3/2}}(2\pi a)$$

$$\vec{E} = E_x\hat{\imath} = \frac{1}{4\pi\epsilon_0} \frac{Qx}{(x^2 + a^2)^{3/2}}\hat{\imath} \qquad (21.8)$$

EVALUATE: Equation (21.8) shows that $\vec{E} = 0$ at the center of the ring ($x = 0$). This makes sense; charges on opposite sides of the ring push in opposite directions on a test charge at the center, and the vector sum of each such pair of forces is zero. When the field point P is much farther from the ring than the ring's radius, we have $x \gg a$ and the denominator in Eq. (21.8) becomes approximately equal to x^3. In this limit the electric field at P is

$$\vec{E} = \frac{1}{4\pi\epsilon_0} \frac{Q}{x^2}\hat{\imath}$$

That is, when the ring is so far away that its radius is negligible in comparison to the distance x, its field is the same as that of a point charge.

Example 21.10 | Field of a charged line segment

Positive charge Q is distributed uniformly along the y-axis between $y = -a$ and $y = +a$. Find the electric field at point P on the x-axis at a distance x from the origin.

SOLUTION

IDENTIFY and SET UP: Figure 21.24 shows the situation. As in Example 21.9, we must find the electric field due to a continuous distribution of charge. Our target variable is an expression for the electric field at P as a function of x. The x-axis is a perpendicular bisector of the segment, so we can use a symmetry argument.

EXECUTE: We divide the line charge of length $2a$ into infinitesimal segments of length dy. The linear charge density is $\lambda = Q/2a$, and the charge in a segment is $dQ = \lambda\,dy = (Q/2a)dy$. The distance r from a segment at height y to the field point P is $r = (x^2 + y^2)^{1/2}$, so the magnitude of the field at P due to the segment at height y is

$$dE = \frac{1}{4\pi\epsilon_0} \frac{dQ}{r^2} = \frac{1}{4\pi\epsilon_0} \frac{Q}{2a} \frac{dy}{(x^2 + y^2)}$$

Figure 21.24 shows that the x- and y-components of this field are $dE_x = dE\cos\alpha$ and $dE_y = -dE\sin\alpha$, where $\cos\alpha = x/r$ and $\sin\alpha = y/r$. Hence

$$dE_x = \frac{1}{4\pi\epsilon_0} \frac{Q}{2a} \frac{x\,dy}{(x^2 + y^2)^{3/2}}$$

$$dE_y = \frac{1}{4\pi\epsilon_0} \frac{Q}{2a} \frac{y\,dy}{(x^2 + y^2)^{3/2}}$$

To find the total field at P, we must sum the fields from all segments along the line—that is, we must integrate from $y = -a$ to $y = +a$. You should work out the details of the integration (a table of integrals will help). The results are

$$E_x = \frac{1}{4\pi\epsilon_0} \frac{Q}{2a} \int_{-a}^{+a} \frac{x\,dy}{(x^2 + y^2)^{3/2}} = \frac{Q}{4\pi\epsilon_0} \frac{1}{x\sqrt{x^2 + a^2}}$$

$$E_y = \frac{1}{4\pi\epsilon_0} \frac{Q}{2a} \int_{-a}^{+a} \frac{y\,dy}{(x^2 + y^2)^{3/2}} = 0$$

or, in vector form,

$$\vec{E} = \frac{1}{4\pi\epsilon_0} \frac{Q}{x\sqrt{x^2 + a^2}}\hat{\imath} \qquad (21.9)$$

21.24 Our sketch for this problem.

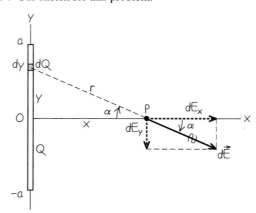

$\vec{E}$ points away from the line of charge if λ is positive and toward the line of charge if λ is negative.

EVALUATE: Using a symmetry argument as in Example 21.9, we could have guessed that E_y would be zero; if we place a positive test charge at P, the upper half of the line of charge pushes downward on it, and the lower half pushes up with equal magnitude. Symmetry also tells us that the upper and lower halves of the segment contribute equally to the total field at P.

If the segment is very *short* (or the field point is very far from the segment) so that $x \gg a$, we can neglect a in the denominator of Eq. (21.9). Then the field becomes that of a point charge, just as in Example 21.9:

$$\vec{E} = \frac{1}{4\pi\epsilon_0} \frac{Q}{x^2}\hat{\imath}$$

To see what happens if the segment is very *long* (or the field point is very close to it) so that $a \gg x$, we first rewrite Eq. (21.9) slightly:

$$\vec{E} = \frac{1}{2\pi\epsilon_0} \frac{\lambda}{x\sqrt{(x^2/a^2) + 1}}\hat{\imath} \qquad (21.10)$$

In the limit $a \gg x$ we can neglect x^2/a^2 in the denominator of Eq. (21.10), so

$$\vec{E} = \frac{\lambda}{2\pi\epsilon_0 x}\hat{\imath}$$

This is the field of an *infinitely long* line of charge. At any point P at a perpendicular distance r from the line in *any* direction, $\vec{E}$ has magnitude

$$E = \frac{\lambda}{2\pi\epsilon_0 r} \qquad \text{(infinite line of charge)}$$

Note that this field is proportional to $1/r$ rather than to $1/r^2$ as for a point charge.

There's really no such thing in nature as an infinite line of charge. But when the field point is close enough to the line, there's very little difference between the result for an infinite line and the real-life finite case. For example, if the distance r of the field point from the center of the line is 1% of the length of the line, the value of E differs from the infinite-length value by less than 0.02%.

Example 21.11   Field of a uniformly charged disk

A nonconducting disk of radius R has a uniform positive surface charge density σ. Find the electric field at a point along the axis of the disk a distance x from its center. Assume that x is positive.

SOLUTION

IDENTIFY and SET UP: Figure 21.25 shows the situation. We represent the charge distribution as a collection of concentric rings of charge dQ. In Example 21.9 we obtained Eq. (21.8) for the field on the axis of a single uniformly charged ring, so all we need do here is integrate the contributions of our rings.

EXECUTE: A typical ring has charge dQ, inner radius r, and outer radius $r + dr$. Its area is approximately equal to its width dr times its circumference $2\pi r$, or $dA = 2\pi r\, dr$. The charge per unit area is $\sigma = dQ/dA$, so the charge of the ring is $dQ = \sigma\, dA = 2\pi\sigma r\, dr$. We use dQ in place of Q in Eq. (21.8), the expression for the field due to a ring that we found in Example 21.9, and replace the ring radius a with r. Then the field component dE_x at point P due to this ring is

$$dE_x = \frac{1}{4\pi\epsilon_0}\frac{2\pi\sigma rx\, dr}{(x^2 + r^2)^{3/2}}$$

21.25 Our sketch for this problem.

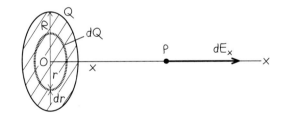

To find the total field due to all the rings, we integrate dE_x over r from $r = 0$ to $r = R$ (*not* from $-R$ to R):

$$E_x = \int_0^R \frac{1}{4\pi\epsilon_0}\frac{(2\pi\sigma r\, dr)x}{(x^2 + r^2)^{3/2}} = \frac{\sigma x}{4\epsilon_0}\int_0^R \frac{2r\, dr}{(x^2 + r^2)^{3/2}}$$

You can evaluate this integral by making the substitution $t = x^2 + r^2$ (which yields $dt = 2r\, dr$); you can work out the details. The result is

$$E_x = \frac{\sigma x}{2\epsilon_0}\left[-\frac{1}{\sqrt{x^2 + R^2}} + \frac{1}{x}\right]$$

$$= \frac{\sigma}{2\epsilon_0}\left[1 - \frac{1}{\sqrt{(R^2/x^2) + 1}}\right] \qquad (21.11)$$

EVALUATE: If the disk is very large (or if we are very close to it), so that $R \gg x$, the term $1/\sqrt{(R^2/x^2) + 1}$ in Eq. (21.11) is very much less than 1. Then Eq. (21.11) becomes

$$E = \frac{\sigma}{2\epsilon_0} \qquad (21.12)$$

Our final result does not contain the distance x from the plane. Hence the electric field produced by an *infinite* plane sheet of charge is *independent of the distance from the sheet*. The field direction is everywhere perpendicular to the sheet, away from it. There is no such thing as an infinite sheet of charge, but if the dimensions of the sheet are much larger than the distance x of the field point P from the sheet, the field is very nearly given by Eq. (21.12).

If P is to the *left* of the plane $(x < 0)$, the result is the same except that the direction of $\vec{E}$ is to the left instead of the right. If the surface charge density is negative, the directions of the fields on both sides of the plane are toward it rather than away from it.

Example 21.12   Field of two oppositely charged infinite sheets

Two infinite plane sheets with uniform surface charge densities $+\sigma$ and $-\sigma$ are placed parallel to each other with separation d (Fig. 21.26). Find the electric field between the sheets, above the upper sheet, and below the lower sheet.

SOLUTION

IDENTIFY and SET UP: Equation (21.12) gives the electric field due to a single infinite plane sheet of charge. To find the field due to *two* such sheets, we combine the fields using the principle of superposition (Fig. 21.26).

21.26 Finding the electric field due to two oppositely charged infinite sheets. The sheets are seen edge-on; only a portion of the infinite sheets can be shown!

Continued

EXECUTE: From Eq. (21.12), both $\vec{E}_1$ and $\vec{E}_2$ have the same magnitude at all points, independent of distance from either sheet:

$$E_1 = E_2 = \frac{\sigma}{2\epsilon_0}$$

From Example 21.11, $\vec{E}_1$ is everywhere directed away from sheet 1, and $\vec{E}_2$ is everywhere directed toward sheet 2.

Between the sheets, $\vec{E}_1$ and $\vec{E}_2$ reinforce each other; above the upper sheet and below the lower sheet, they cancel each other. Thus the total field is

$$\vec{E} = \vec{E}_1 + \vec{E}_2 = \begin{cases} 0 & \text{above the upper sheet} \\ \dfrac{\sigma}{\epsilon_0}\hat{j} & \text{between the sheets} \\ 0 & \text{below the lower sheet} \end{cases}$$

EVALUATE: Because we considered the sheets to be infinite, our result does not depend on the separation d. Our result shows that the field between oppositely charged plates is essentially uniform if the plate separation is much smaller than the dimensions of the plates. We actually used this result in Example 21.7 (Section 21.4).

CAUTION **Electric fields are not "flows"** You may have thought that the field $\vec{E}_1$ of sheet 1 would be unable to "penetrate" sheet 2, and that field $\vec{E}_2$ caused by sheet 2 would be unable to "penetrate" sheet 1. You might conclude this if you think of the electric field as some kind of physical substance that "flows" into or out of charges. But in fact there is no such substance, and the electric fields $\vec{E}_1$ and $\vec{E}_2$ depend only on the individual charge distributions that create them. The *total* field at every point is just the vector sum of $\vec{E}_1$ and $\vec{E}_2$.

Test Your Understanding of Section 21.5 Suppose that the line of charge in Fig. 21.25 (Example 21.11) had charge $+Q$ distributed uniformly between $y = 0$ and $y = +a$ and had charge $-Q$ distributed uniformly between $y = 0$ and $y = -a$. In this situation, the electric field at P would be (i) in the positive x-direction; (ii) in the negative x-direction; (iii) in the positive y-direction; (iv) in the negative y-direction; (v) zero; (vi) none of these.

21.6 Electric Field Lines

21.27 The direction of the electric field at any point is tangent to the field line through that point.

PhET: Charges and Fields
PhET: Electric Field of Dreams
PhET: Electric Field Hockey

The concept of an electric field can be a little elusive because you can't see an electric field directly. Electric field *lines* can be a big help for visualizing electric fields and making them seem more real. An **electric field line** is an imaginary line or curve drawn through a region of space so that its tangent at any point is in the direction of the electric-field vector at that point. Figure 21.27 shows the basic idea. (We used a similar concept in our discussion of fluid flow in Section 12.5. A *streamline* is a line or curve whose tangent at any point is in the direction of the velocity of the fluid at that point. However, the similarity between electric field lines and fluid streamlines is a mathematical one only; there is nothing "flowing" in an electric field.) The English scientist Michael Faraday (1791–1867) first introduced the concept of field lines. He called them "lines of force," but the term "field lines" is preferable.

Electric field lines show the direction of $\vec{E}$ at each point, and their spacing gives a general idea of the *magnitude* of $\vec{E}$ at each point. Where $\vec{E}$ is strong, we draw lines bunched closely together; where $\vec{E}$ is weaker, they are farther apart. At any particular point, the electric field has a unique direction, so only one field line can pass through each point of the field. In other words, *field lines never intersect.*

Figure 21.28 shows some of the electric field lines in a plane containing (a) a single positive charge; (b) two equal-magnitude charges, one positive and one negative (a dipole); and (c) two equal positive charges. Diagrams such as these are sometimes called *field maps;* they are cross sections of the actual three-dimensional patterns. The direction of the total electric field at every point in each diagram is along the tangent to the electric field line passing through the point. Arrowheads indicate the direction of the $\vec{E}$-field vector along each field line. The actual field vectors have been drawn at several points in each pattern. Notice that in general, the magnitude of the electric field is different at different points on a given field line; a field line is *not* a curve of constant electric-field magnitude!

Figure 21.28 shows that field lines are directed *away* from positive charges (since close to a positive point charge, $\vec{E}$ points away from the charge) and

21.28 Electric field lines for three different charge distributions. In general, the magnitude of $\vec{E}$ is different at different points along a given field line.

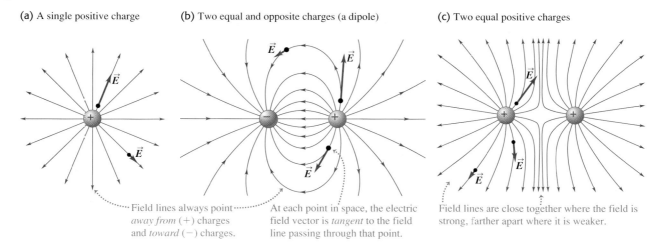

(a) A single positive charge

(b) Two equal and opposite charges (a dipole)

(c) Two equal positive charges

Field lines always point *away from* (+) charges and *toward* (−) charges.

At each point in space, the electric field vector is *tangent* to the field line passing through that point.

Field lines are close together where the field is strong, farther apart where it is weaker.

toward negative charges (since close to a negative point charge, $\vec{E}$ points toward the charge). In regions where the field magnitude is large, such as between the positive and negative charges in Fig. 21.28b, the field lines are drawn close together. In regions where the field magnitude is small, such as between the two positive charges in Fig. 21.28c, the lines are widely separated. In a *uniform* field, the field lines are straight, parallel, and uniformly spaced, as in Fig. 21.20.

Figure 21.29 is a view from above of a demonstration setup for visualizing electric field lines. In the arrangement shown here, the tips of two positively charged wires are inserted in a container of insulating liquid, and some grass seeds are floated on the liquid. The grass seeds are electrically neutral insulators, but the electric field of the two charged wires causes *polarization* of the grass seeds; there is a slight shifting of the positive and negative charges within the molecules of each seed, like that shown in Fig. 21.8. The positively charged end of each grass seed is pulled in the direction of $\vec{E}$ and the negatively charged end is pulled opposite $\vec{E}$. Hence the long axis of each grass seed tends to orient parallel to the electric field, in the direction of the field line that passes through the position of the seed (Fig. 21.29b).

> **CAUTION** **Electric field lines are not the same as trajectories** It's a common misconception that if a charged particle of charge q is in motion where there is an electric field, the particle must move along an electric field line. Because $\vec{E}$ at any point is tangent to the field line that passes through that point, it is indeed true that the *force* $\vec{F} = q\vec{E}$ on the particle, and hence the particle's acceleration, are tangent to the field line. But we learned in Chapter 3 that when a particle moves on a curved path, its acceleration *cannot* be tangent to the path. So in general, the trajectory of a charged particle is *not* the same as a field line. ∎

Test Your Understanding of Section 21.6   Suppose the electric field lines in a region of space are straight lines. If a charged particle is released from rest in that region, will the trajectory of the particle be along a field line? ∎

21.7 Electric Dipoles

An **electric dipole** is a pair of point charges with equal magnitude and opposite sign (a positive charge q and a negative charge $-q$) separated by a distance d. We introduced electric dipoles in Example 21.8 (Section 21.5); the concept is worth exploring further because many physical systems, from molecules to TV antennas, can be described as electric dipoles. We will also use this concept extensively in our discussion of dielectrics in Chapter 24.

21.29 (a) Electric field lines produced by two equal point charges. The pattern is formed by grass seeds floating on a liquid above two charged wires. Compare this pattern with Fig. 21.28c. (b) The electric field causes polarization of the grass seeds, which in turn causes the seeds to align with the field.

(a)

(b)

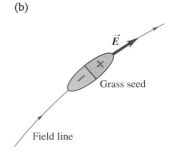

21.30 (a) A water molecule is an example of an electric dipole. (b) Each test tube contains a solution of a different substance in water. The large electric dipole moment of water makes it an excellent solvent.

(a) A water molecule, showing positive charge as red and negative charge as blue

The electric dipole moment $\vec{p}$ is directed from the negative end to the positive end of the molecule.

(b) Various substances dissolved in water

21.31 The net force on this electric dipole is zero, but there is a torque directed into the page that tends to rotate the dipole clockwise.

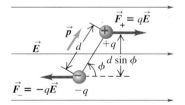

Figure 21.30 a shows a molecule of water (H_2O), which in many ways behaves like an electric dipole. The water molecule as a whole is electrically neutral, but the chemical bonds within the molecule cause a displacement of charge; the result is a net negative charge on the oxygen end of the molecule and a net positive charge on the hydrogen end, forming an electric dipole. The effect is equivalent to shifting one electron only about 4×10^{-11} m (about the radius of a hydrogen atom), but the consequences of this shift are profound. Water is an excellent solvent for ionic substances such as table salt (sodium chloride, NaCl) precisely because the water molecule is an electric dipole (Fig. 21.30b). When dissolved in water, salt dissociates into a positive sodium ion (Na^+) and a negative chlorine ion (Cl^-), which tend to be attracted to the negative and positive ends, respectively, of water molecules; this holds the ions in solution. If water molecules were not electric dipoles, water would be a poor solvent, and almost all of the chemistry that occurs in aqueous solutions would be impossible. This includes all of the biochemical reactions that occur in all of the life on earth. In a very real sense, your existence as a living being depends on electric dipoles!

We examine two questions about electric dipoles. First, what forces and torques does an electric dipole experience when placed in an external electric field (that is, a field set up by charges outside the dipole)? Second, what electric field does an electric dipole itself produce?

Force and Torque on an Electric Dipole

To start with the first question, let's place an electric dipole in a *uniform* external electric field $\vec{E}$, as shown in Fig. 21.31. The forces $\vec{F}_+$ and $\vec{F}_-$ on the two charges both have magnitude qE, but their directions are opposite, and they add to zero. *The net force on an electric dipole in a uniform external electric field is zero.*

However, the two forces don't act along the same line, so their *torques* don't add to zero. We calculate torques with respect to the center of the dipole. Let the angle between the electric field $\vec{E}$ and the dipole axis be ϕ; then the lever arm for both $\vec{F}_+$ and $\vec{F}_-$ is $(d/2)\sin\phi$. The torque of $\vec{F}_+$ and the torque of $\vec{F}_-$ both have the same magnitude of $(qE)(d/2)\sin\phi$, and both torques tend to rotate the dipole clockwise (that is, $\vec{\tau}$ is directed into the page in Fig. 21.31). Hence the magnitude of the net torque is twice the magnitude of either individual torque:

$$\tau = (qE)(d\sin\phi) \qquad (21.13)$$

where $d\sin\phi$ is the perpendicular distance between the lines of action of the two forces.

The product of the charge q and the separation d is the magnitude of a quantity called the **electric dipole moment,** denoted by p:

$$p = qd \qquad \text{(magnitude of electric dipole moment)} \qquad (21.14)$$

The units of p are charge times distance ($C \cdot m$). For example, the magnitude of the electric dipole moment of a water molecule is $p = 6.13 \times 10^{-30}\ C \cdot m$.

CAUTION **The symbol p has multiple meanings** Be careful not to confuse dipole moment with momentum or pressure. There aren't as many letters in the alphabet as there are physical quantities, so some letters are used several times. The context usually makes it clear what we mean, but be careful.

We further define the electric dipole moment to be a *vector* quantity $\vec{p}$. The magnitude of $\vec{p}$ is given by Eq. (21.14), and its direction is along the dipole axis from the negative charge to the positive charge as shown in Fig. 21.31.

In terms of p, Eq. (21.13) for the magnitude τ of the torque exerted by the field becomes

$$\tau = pE \sin\phi \qquad \text{(magnitude of the torque on an electric dipole)} \qquad (21.15)$$

Since the angle ϕ in Fig. 21.31 is the angle between the directions of the vectors $\vec{p}$ and $\vec{E}$, this is reminiscent of the expression for the magnitude of the *vector product* discussed in Section 1.10. (You may want to review that discussion.) Hence we can write the torque on the dipole in vector form as

$$\vec{\tau} = \vec{p} \times \vec{E} \qquad \text{(torque on an electric dipole, in vector form)} \qquad (21.16)$$

You can use the right-hand rule for the vector product to verify that in the situation shown in Fig. 21.31, $\vec{\tau}$ is directed into the page. The torque is greatest when $\vec{p}$ and $\vec{E}$ are perpendicular and is zero when they are parallel or antiparallel. The torque always tends to turn $\vec{p}$ to line it up with $\vec{E}$. The position $\phi = 0$, with $\vec{p}$ parallel to $\vec{E}$, is a position of stable equilibrium, and the position $\phi = \pi$, with $\vec{p}$ and $\vec{E}$ antiparallel, is a position of unstable equilibrium. The polarization of a grass seed in the apparatus of Fig. 21.29b gives it an electric dipole moment; the torque exerted by $\vec{E}$ then causes the seed to align with $\vec{E}$ and hence with the field lines.

Potential Energy of an Electric Dipole

When a dipole changes direction in an electric field, the electric-field torque does *work* on it, with a corresponding change in potential energy. The work dW done by a torque τ during an infinitesimal displacement $d\phi$ is given by Eq. (10.19): $dW = \tau\, d\phi$. Because the torque is in the direction of decreasing ϕ, we must write the torque as $\tau = -pE \sin\phi$, and

$$dW = \tau\, d\phi = -pE \sin\phi\, d\phi$$

In a finite displacement from ϕ_1 to ϕ_2 the total work done on the dipole is

$$W = \int_{\phi_1}^{\phi_2} (-pE \sin\phi)\, d\phi$$

$$= pE \cos\phi_2 - pE \cos\phi_1$$

The work is the negative of the change of potential energy, just as in Chapter 7: $W = U_1 - U_2$. So a suitable definition of potential energy U for this system is

$$U(\phi) = -pE \cos\phi \qquad (21.17)$$

In this expression we recognize the *scalar product* $\vec{p} \cdot \vec{E} = pE \cos\phi$, so we can also write

$$U = -\vec{p} \cdot \vec{E} \qquad \text{(potential energy for a dipole in an electric field)} \qquad (21.18)$$

The potential energy has its minimum (most negative) value $U = -pE$ at the stable equilibrium position, where $\phi = 0$ and $\vec{p}$ is parallel to $\vec{E}$. The potential energy is maximum when $\phi = \pi$ and $\vec{p}$ is antiparallel to $\vec{E}$; then $U = +pE$. At $\phi = \pi/2$, where $\vec{p}$ is perpendicular to $\vec{E}$, U is zero. We could define U differently so that it is zero at some other orientation of $\vec{p}$, but our definition is simplest.

Equation (21.18) gives us another way to look at the effect shown in Fig. 21.29. The electric field $\vec{E}$ gives each grass seed an electric dipole moment, and the grass seed then aligns itself with $\vec{E}$ to minimize the potential energy.

Mastering**PHYSICS**

PhET: Microwaves

Example 21.13   Force and torque on an electric dipole

Figure 21.32a shows an electric dipole in a uniform electric field of magnitude 5.0×10^5 N/C that is directed parallel to the plane of the figure. The charges are $\pm 1.6 \times 10^{-19}$ C; both lie in the plane and are separated by 0.125 nm $= 0.125 \times 10^{-9}$ m. Find (a) the net force exerted by the field on the dipole; (b) the magnitude and

Continued

21.32 (a) An electric dipole. (b) Directions of the electric dipole moment, electric field, and torque ($\vec{\tau}$ points out of the page).

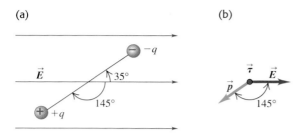

direction of the electric dipole moment; (c) the magnitude and direction of the torque; (d) the potential energy of the system in the position shown.

SOLUTION

IDENTIFY and SET UP: This problem uses the ideas of this section about an electric dipole placed in an electric field. We use the relationship $\vec{F} = q\vec{E}$ for each point charge to find the force on the dipole as a whole. Equation (21.14) gives the dipole moment, Eq. (21.16) gives the torque on the dipole, and Eq. (21.18) gives the potential energy of the system.

EXECUTE: (a) The field is uniform, so the forces on the two charges are equal and opposite. Hence the total force on the dipole is zero.

(b) The magnitude p of the electric dipole moment $\vec{p}$ is

$$p = qd = (1.6 \times 10^{-19}\ \text{C})(0.125 \times 10^{-9}\ \text{m})$$
$$= 2.0 \times 10^{-29}\ \text{C} \cdot \text{m}$$

The direction of $\vec{p}$ is from the negative to the positive charge, 145° clockwise from the electric-field direction (Fig. 21.32b).

(c) The magnitude of the torque is

$$\tau = pE\sin\phi = (2.0 \times 10^{-29}\ \text{C})(5.0 \times 10^5\ \text{N/C})(\sin 145°)$$
$$= 5.7 \times 10^{-24}\ \text{N} \cdot \text{m}$$

From the right-hand rule for vector products (see Section 1.10), the direction of the torque $\vec{\tau} = \vec{p} \times \vec{E}$ is out of the page. This corresponds to a counterclockwise torque that tends to align $\vec{p}$ with $\vec{E}$.

(d) The potential energy

$$U = -pE\cos\phi$$
$$= -(2.0 \times 10^{-29}\ \text{C} \cdot \text{m})(5.0 \times 10^5\ \text{N/C})(\cos 145°)$$
$$= 8.2 \times 10^{-24}\ \text{J}$$

EVALUATE: The charge magnitude, the distance between the charges, the dipole moment, and the potential energy are all very small, but are all typical of molecules.

In this discussion we have assumed that $\vec{E}$ is uniform, so there is no net force on the dipole. If $\vec{E}$ is not uniform, the forces at the ends may not cancel completely, and the net force may not be zero. Thus a body with zero net charge but an electric dipole moment can experience a net force in a nonuniform electric field. As we mentioned in Section 21.1, an uncharged body can be polarized by an electric field, giving rise to a separation of charge and an electric dipole moment. This is how uncharged bodies can experience electrostatic forces (see Fig. 21.8).

Field of an Electric Dipole

Now let's think of an electric dipole as a *source* of electric field. What does the field look like? The general shape of things is shown by the field map of Fig. 21.28b. At each point in the pattern the total $\vec{E}$ field is the vector sum of the fields from the two individual charges, as in Example 21.8 (Section 21.5). Try drawing diagrams showing this vector sum for several points.

To get quantitative information about the field of an electric dipole, we have to do some calculating, as illustrated in the next example. Notice the use of the principle of superposition of electric fields to add up the contributions to the field of the individual charges. Also notice that we need to use approximation techniques even for the relatively simple case of a field due to two charges. Field calculations often become very complicated, and computer analysis is typically used to determine the field due to an arbitrary charge distribution.

Example 21.14 **Field of an electric dipole, revisited**

An electric dipole is centered at the origin, with $\vec{p}$ in the direction of the +y-axis (Fig. 21.33). Derive an approximate expression for the electric field at a point P on the y-axis for which y is much larger than d. To do this, use the binomial expansion $(1 + x)^n \cong 1 + nx + n(n - 1)x^2/2 + \cdots$ (valid for the case $|x| < 1$).

SOLUTION

IDENTIFY and SET UP: We use the principle of superposition: The total electric field is the vector sum of the field produced by the positive charge and the field produced by the negative charge. At the field point P shown in Fig. 21.33, the field $\vec{E}_+$ of the positive charge has a positive (upward) y-component and the field $\vec{E}_-$ of

21.33 Finding the electric field of an electric dipole at a point on its axis.

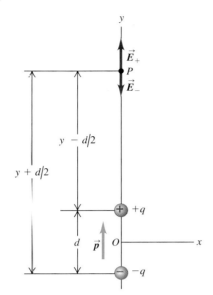

the negative charge has a negative (downward) y-component. We add these components to find the total field and then apply the approximation that y is much greater than d.

EXECUTE: The total y-component E_y of electric field from the two charges is

$$E_y = \frac{q}{4\pi\epsilon_0}\left[\frac{1}{(y - d/2)^2} - \frac{1}{(y + d/2)^2}\right]$$

$$= \frac{q}{4\pi\epsilon_0 y^2}\left[\left(1 - \frac{d}{2y}\right)^{-2} - \left(1 + \frac{d}{2y}\right)^{-2}\right]$$

We used this same approach in Example 21.8 (Section 21.5). Now the approximation: When we are far from the dipole compared to its size, so $y \gg d$, we have $d/2y \ll 1$. With $n = -2$ and with $d/2y$ replacing x in the binomial expansion, we keep only the first two terms (the terms we discard are much smaller). We then have

$$\left(1 - \frac{d}{2y}\right)^{-2} \cong 1 + \frac{d}{y} \quad \text{and} \quad \left(1 + \frac{d}{2y}\right)^{-2} \cong 1 - \frac{d}{y}$$

Hence E_y is given approximately by

$$E_y \cong \frac{q}{4\pi\epsilon_0 y^2}\left[1 + \frac{d}{y} - \left(1 - \frac{d}{y}\right)\right] = \frac{qd}{2\pi\epsilon_0 y^3} = \frac{p}{2\pi\epsilon_0 y^3}$$

EVALUATE: An alternative route to this result is to put the fractions in the first expression for E_y over a common denominator, add, and then approximate the denominator $(y - d/2)^2(y + d/2)^2$ as y^4. We leave the details to you (see Exercise 21.60).

For points P off the coordinate axes, the expressions are more complicated, but at *all* points far away from the dipole (in any direction) the field drops off as $1/r^3$. We can compare this with the $1/r^2$ behavior of a point charge, the $1/r$ behavior of a long line charge, and the independence of r for a large sheet of charge. There are charge distributions for which the field drops off even more quickly. At large distances, the field of an *electric quadrupole*, which consists of two equal dipoles with opposite orientation, separated by a small distance, drops off as $1/r^4$.

Test Your Understanding of Section 21.7 An electric dipole is placed in a region of uniform electric field $\vec{E}$, with the electric dipole moment $\vec{p}$, pointing in the direction opposite to $\vec{E}$. Is the dipole (i) in stable equilibrium, (ii) in unstable equilibrium, or (iii) neither? (*Hint:* You many want to review Section 7.5.)

Electric charge, conductors, and insulators: The fundamental quantity in electrostatics is electric charge. There are two kinds of charge, positive and negative. Charges of the same sign repel each other; charges of opposite sign attract. Charge is conserved; the total charge in an isolated system is constant.

All ordinary matter is made of protons, neutrons, and electrons. The positive protons and electrically neutral neutrons in the nucleus of an atom are bound together by the nuclear force; the negative electrons surround the nucleus at distances much greater than the nuclear size. Electric interactions are chiefly responsible for the structure of atoms, molecules, and solids.

Conductors are materials in which charge moves easily; in insulators, charge does not move easily. Most metals are good conductors; most nonmetals are insulators.

Coulomb's law: For charges q_1 and q_2 separated by a distance r, the magnitude of the electric force on either charge is proportional to the product q_1q_2 and inversely proportional to r^2. The force on each charge is along the line joining the two charges—repulsive if q_1 and q_2 have the same sign, attractive if they have opposite signs. In SI units the unit of electric charge is the coulomb, abbreviated C. (See Examples 21.1 and 21.2.)

When two or more charges each exert a force on a charge, the total force on that charge is the vector sum of the forces exerted by the individual charges. (See Examples 21.3 and 21.4.)

$$F = \frac{1}{4\pi\epsilon_0} \frac{|q_1q_2|}{r^2} \quad (21.2)$$

$$\frac{1}{4\pi\epsilon_0} = 8.988 \times 10^9 \, \text{N} \cdot \text{m}^2/\text{C}^2$$

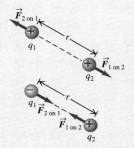

Electric field: Electric field $\vec{E}$, a vector quantity, is the force per unit charge exerted on a test charge at any point. The electric field produced by a point charge is directed radially away from or toward the charge. (See Examples 21.5–21.7.)

$$\vec{E} = \frac{\vec{F}_0}{q_0} \quad (21.3)$$

$$\vec{E} = \frac{1}{4\pi\epsilon_0} \frac{q}{r^2}\hat{r} \quad (21.7)$$

Superposition of electric fields: The electric field $\vec{E}$ of any combination of charges is the vector sum of the fields caused by the individual charges. To calculate the electric field caused by a continuous distribution of charge, divide the distribution into small elements, calculate the field caused by each element, and then carry out the vector sum, usually by integrating. Charge distributions are described by linear charge density λ, surface charge density σ, and volume charge density ρ. (See Examples 21.8–21.12.)

Electric field lines: Field lines provide a graphical representation of electric fields. At any point on a field line, the tangent to the line is in the direction of $\vec{E}$ at that point. The number of lines per unit area (perpendicular to their direction) is proportional to the magnitude of $\vec{E}$ at the point.

Electric dipoles: An electric dipole is a pair of electric charges of equal magnitude q but opposite sign, separated by a distance d. The electric dipole moment $\vec{p}$ has magnitude $p = qd$. The direction of $\vec{p}$ is from negative toward positive charge. An electric dipole in an electric field $\vec{E}$ experiences a torque $\vec{\tau}$ equal to the vector product of $\vec{p}$ and $\vec{E}$. The magnitude of the torque depends on the angle ϕ between $\vec{p}$ and $\vec{E}$. The potential energy U for an electric dipole in an electric field also depends on the relative orientation of $\vec{p}$ and $\vec{E}$. (See Examples 21.13 and 21.14.)

$$\tau = pE \sin\phi \quad (21.15)$$

$$\vec{\tau} = \vec{p} \times \vec{E} \quad (21.16)$$

$$U = -\vec{p} \cdot \vec{E} \quad (21.18)$$

BRIDGING PROBLEM | Calculating Electric Field: Half a Ring of Charge

Positive charge Q is uniformly distributed around a semicircle of radius a as shown in Fig. 21.34. Find the magnitude and direction of the resulting electric field at point P, the center of curvature of the semicircle.

SOLUTION GUIDE

See MasteringPhysics® study area for a Video Tutor solution.

IDENTIFY and SET UP

1. The target variables are the components of the electric field at P.
2. Divide the semicircle into infinitesimal segments, each of which is a short circular arc of radius a and angle $d\theta$. What is the length of such a segment? How much charge is on a segment?

21.34

3. Consider an infinitesimal segment located at an angular position θ on the semicircle, measured from the lower right corner of the semicircle at $x = a$, $y = 0$. (Thus $\theta = \pi/2$ at $x = 0$, $y = a$ and $\theta = \pi$ at $x = -a$, $y = 0$.) What are the x- and y-components of the electric field at P (dE_x and dE_y) produced by just this segment?

EXECUTE

4. Integrate your expressions for dE_x and dE_y from $\theta = 0$ to $\theta = \pi$. The results will be the x-component and y-component of the electric field at P.
5. Use your results from step 4 to find the magnitude and direction of the field at P.

EVALUATE

6. Does your result for the electric-field magnitude have the correct units?
7. Explain how you could have found the x-component of the electric field using a symmetry argument.
8. What would be the electric field at P if the semicircle were extended to a full circle centered at P?

Problems

For instructor-assigned homework, go to www.masteringphysics.com

•, ••, •••: Problems of increasing difficulty. **CP**: Cumulative problems incorporating material from earlier chapters. **CALC**: Problems requiring calculus. **BIO**: Biosciences problems.

DISCUSSION QUESTIONS

Q21.1 If you peel two strips of transparent tape off the same roll and immediately let them hang near each other, they will repel each other. If you then stick the sticky side of one to the shiny side of the other and rip them apart, they will attract each other. Give a plausible explanation, involving transfer of electrons between the strips of tape, for this sequence of events.

Q21.2 Two metal spheres are hanging from nylon threads. When you bring the spheres close to each other, they tend to attract. Based on this information alone, discuss all the possible ways that the spheres could be charged. Is it possible that after the spheres touch, they will cling together? Explain.

Q21.3 The electric force between two charged particles becomes weaker with increasing distance. Suppose instead that the electric force were *independent* of distance. In this case, would a charged comb still cause a neutral insulator to become polarized as in Fig. 21.8? Why or why not? Would the neutral insulator still be attracted to the comb? Again, why or why not?

Q21.4 Your clothing tends to cling together after going through the dryer. Why? Would you expect more or less clinging if all your clothing were made of the same material (say, cotton) than if you dried different kinds of clothing together? Again, why? (You may want to experiment with your next load of laundry.)

Q21.5 An uncharged metal sphere hangs from a nylon thread. When a positively charged glass rod is brought close to the metal sphere, the sphere is drawn toward the rod. But if the sphere touches the rod, it suddenly flies away from the rod. Explain why the sphere is first attracted and then repelled.

Q21.6 The free electrons in a metal are gravitationally attracted toward the earth. Why, then, don't they all settle to the bottom of the conductor, like sediment settling to the bottom of a river?

Q21.7 • Figure Q21.7 shows some of the electric field lines due to three point charges arranged along the vertical axis. All three charges have the same magnitude. (a) What are the signs of the three charges? Explain your reasoning. (b) At what point(s) is the magnitude of the electric field the smallest? Explain your reasoning. Explain how the fields produced by each individual point charge combine to give a small net field at this point or points.

Figure **Q21.7**

Q21.8 Good electrical conductors, such as metals, are typically good conductors of heat; electrical insulators, such as wood, are typically poor conductors of heat. Explain why there should be a relationship between electrical conduction and heat conduction in these materials.

Q21.9 • Suppose the charge shown in Fig. 21.28a is fixed in position. A small, positively charged particle is then placed at some point in the figure and released. Will the trajectory of the particle follow an electric field line? Why or why not? Suppose instead that the particle is placed at some point in Fig. 21.28b and released (the positive and negative charges shown in the figure are fixed in position). Will its trajectory follow an electric field line? Again, why or why not? Explain any differences between your answers for the two different situations.

Q21.10 Two identical metal objects are mounted on insulating stands. Describe how you could place charges of opposite sign but exactly equal magnitude on the two objects.

Q21.11 You can use plastic food wrap to cover a container by stretching the material across the top and pressing the overhanging material against the sides. What makes it stick? (*Hint:* The answer involves the electric force.) Does the food wrap stick to itself with equal tenacity? Why or why not? Does it work with metallic containers? Again, why or why not?

Q21.12 If you walk across a nylon rug and then touch a large metal object such as a doorknob, you may get a spark and a shock. Why does this tend to happen more on dry days than on humid days? (*Hint:* See Fig. 21.30.) Why are you less likely to get a shock if you touch a *small* metal object, such as a paper clip?

Q21.13 You have a negatively charged object. How can you use it to place a net negative charge on an insulated metal sphere? To place a net positive charge on the sphere?

Q21.14 When two point charges of equal mass and charge are released on a frictionless table, each has an initial acceleration a_0. If instead you keep one fixed and release the other one, what will be its initial acceleration: a_0, $2a_0$, or $a_0/2$? Explain.

Q21.15 A point charge of mass m and charge Q and another point charge of mass m but charge $2Q$ are released on a frictionless table. If the charge Q has an initial acceleration a_0, what will be the acceleration of $2Q$: a_0, $2a_0$, $4a_0$, $a_0/2$, or $a_0/4$? Explain.

Q21.16 A proton is placed in a uniform electric field and then released. Then an electron is placed at this same point and released. Do these two particles experience the same force? The same acceleration? Do they move in the same direction when released?

Q21.17 In Example 21.1 (Section 21.3) we saw that the electric force between two α particles is of the order of 10^{35} times as strong as the gravitational force. So why do we readily feel the gravity of the earth but no electrical force from it?

Q21.18 What similarities do electrical forces have with gravitational forces? What are the most significant differences?

Q21.19 Two irregular objects A and B carry charges of opposite sign. Figure Q21.19 shows the electric field lines near each of these objects. (a) Which object is positive, A or B? How do you know? (b) Where is the electric field stronger, close to A or close to B? How do you know?

Figure **Q21.19**

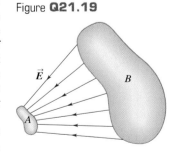

Q21.20 Atomic nuclei are made of protons and neutrons. This shows that there must be another kind of interaction in addition to gravitational and electric forces. Explain.

Q21.21 Sufficiently strong electric fields can cause atoms to become positively ionized—that is, to lose one or more electrons. Explain how this can happen. What determines how strong the field must be to make this happen?

Q21.22 The electric fields at point P due to the positive charges q_1 and q_2 are shown in Fig. Q21.22. Does the fact that they cross each other violate the statement in Section 21.6 that electric field lines never cross? Explain.

Figure **Q21.22**

Q21.23 The air temperature and the velocity of the air have different values at different places in the earth's atmosphere. Is the air velocity a vector field? Why or why not? Is the air temperature a vector field? Again, why or why not?

EXERCISES

Section 21.3 Coulomb's Law

21.1 •• Excess electrons are placed on a small lead sphere with mass 8.00 g so that its net charge is -3.20×10^{-9} C. (a) Find the number of excess electrons on the sphere. (b) How many excess electrons are there per lead atom? The atomic number of lead is 82, and its atomic mass is 207 g/mol.

21.2 • Lightning occurs when there is a flow of electric charge (principally electrons) between the ground and a thundercloud. The maximum rate of charge flow in a lightning bolt is about 20,000 C/s; this lasts for 100 μs or less. How much charge flows between the ground and the cloud in this time? How many electrons flow during this time?

21.3 •• **BIO** Estimate how many electrons there are in your body. Make any assumptions you feel are necessary, but clearly state what they are. (*Hint:* Most of the atoms in your body have equal numbers of electrons, protons, and neutrons.) What is the combined charge of all these electrons?

21.4 • **Particles in a Gold Ring.** You have a pure (24-karat) gold ring with mass 17.7 g. Gold has an atomic mass of 197 g/mol and an atomic number of 79. (a) How many protons are in the ring, and what is their total positive charge? (b) If the ring carries no net charge, how many electrons are in it?

21.5 • **BIO Signal Propagation in Neurons.** *Neurons* are components of the nervous system of the body that transmit signals as electrical impulses travel along their length. These impulses propagate when charge suddenly rushes into and then out of a part of the neuron called an *axon*. Measurements have shown that, during the inflow part of this cycle, approximately 5.6×10^{11} Na$^+$ (sodium ions) per meter, each with charge $+e$, enter the axon. How many coulombs of charge enter a 1.5-cm length of the axon during this process?

21.6 • Two small spheres spaced 20.0 cm apart have equal charge. How many excess electrons must be present on each sphere if the magnitude of the force of repulsion between them is 4.57×10^{-21} N?

21.7 •• An average human weighs about 650 N. If two such generic humans each carried 1.0 coulomb of excess charge, one positive and one negative, how far apart would they have to be for the electric attraction between them to equal their 650-N weight?

21.8 •• Two small aluminum spheres, each having mass 0.0250 kg, are separated by 80.0 cm. (a) How many electrons does each sphere contain? (The atomic mass of aluminum is 26.982 g/mol, and its atomic number is 13.) (b) How many electrons would have to be removed from one sphere and added to the other to cause an attractive force between the spheres of magnitude 1.00×10^{4} N (roughly 1 ton)? Assume that the spheres may be treated as point charges. (c) What fraction of all the electrons in each sphere does this represent?

21.9 •• Two small plastic spheres are given positive electrical charges. When they are 15.0 cm apart, the repulsive force between them has magnitude 0.220 N. What is the charge on each sphere (a) if the two charges are equal and (b) if one sphere has four times the charge of the other?

21.10 •• **What If We Were Not Neutral?** A 75-kg person holds out his arms so that his hands are 1.7 m apart. Typically, a person's hand makes up about 1.0% of his or her body weight. For round numbers, we shall assume that all the weight of each hand is due to the calcium in the bones, and we shall treat the hands as point charges. One mole of Ca contains 40.18 g, and each atom has 20 protons and 20 electrons. Suppose that only 1.0% of the positive charges in each hand were unbalanced by negative charge. (a) How many Ca atoms does each hand contain? (b) How many coulombs of unbalanced charge does each hand contain? (c) What force would the person's arms have to exert on his hands to prevent them from flying off? Does it seem likely that his arms are capable of exerting such a force?

21.11 •• Two very small 8.55-g spheres, 15.0 cm apart from center to center, are charged by adding equal numbers of electrons to each of them. Disregarding all other forces, how many electrons would you have to add to each sphere so that the two spheres will accelerate at $25.0g$ when released? Which way will they accelerate?

21.12 •• **Just How Strong Is the Electric Force?** Suppose you had two small boxes, each containing 1.0 g of protons. (a) If one were placed on the moon by an astronaut and the other were left on the earth, and if they were connected by a very light (and very long!) string, what would be the tension in the string? Express your answer in newtons and in pounds. Do you need to take into account the gravitational forces of the earth and moon on the protons? Why? (b) What gravitational force would each box of protons exert on the other box?

21.13 • In an experiment in space, one proton is held fixed and another proton is released from rest a distance of 2.50 mm away. (a) What is the initial acceleration of the proton after it is released? (b) Sketch qualitative (no numbers!) acceleration–time and velocity–time graphs of the released proton's motion.

21.14 • A negative charge of $-0.550~\mu\text{C}$ exerts an upward 0.200-N force on an unknown charge 0.300 m directly below it. (a) What is the unknown charge (magnitude and sign)? (b) What are the magnitude and direction of the force that the unknown charge exerts on the -0.550-μC charge?

21.15 •• Three point charges are arranged on a line. Charge $q_3 = +5.00$ nC and is at the origin. Charge $q_2 = -3.00$ nC and is at $x = +4.00$ cm. Charge q_1 is at $x = +2.00$ cm. What is q_1 (magnitude and sign) if the net force on q_3 is zero?

21.16 •• In Example 21.4, suppose the point charge on the y-axis at $y = -0.30$ m has negative charge $-2.0~\mu\text{C}$, and the other charges remain the same. Find the magnitude and direction of the net force on Q. How does your answer differ from that in Example 21.4? Explain the differences.

21.17 •• In Example 21.3, calculate the net force on charge q_1.

21.18 •• In Example 21.4, what is the net force (magnitude and direction) on charge q_1 exerted by the other two charges?

21.19 •• Three point charges are arranged along the x-axis. Charge $q_1 = +3.00~\mu\text{C}$ is at the origin, and charge $q_2 = -5.00~\mu\text{C}$ is at $x = 0.200$ m. Charge $q_3 = -8.00~\mu\text{C}$. Where is q_3 located if the net force on q_1 is 7.00 N in the $-x$-direction?

21.20 •• Repeat Exercise 21.19 for $q_3 = +8.00~\mu\text{C}$.

21.21 •• Two point charges are located on the y-axis as follows: charge $q_1 = -1.50$ nC at $y = -0.600$ m, and charge $q_2 = +3.20$ nC at the origin ($y = 0$). What is the total force (magnitude and direction) exerted by these two charges on a third charge $q_3 = +5.00$ nC located at $y = -0.400$ m?

21.22 •• Two point charges are placed on the x-axis as follows: Charge $q_1 = +4.00$ nC is located at $x = 0.200$ m, and charge $q_2 = +5.00$ nC is at $x = -0.300$ m. What are the magnitude and direction of the total force exerted by these two charges on a negative point charge $q_3 = -6.00$ nC that is placed at the origin?

21.23 •• **BIO Base Pairing in DNA, I.** The two sides of the DNA double helix are connected by pairs of bases (adenine, thymine, cytosine, and guanine). Because of the geometric shape of these molecules, adenine bonds with thymine and cytosine bonds with guanine. Figure E21.23 shows the thymine–adenine bond. Each charge shown is $\pm e$, and the H—N distance is 0.110 nm. (a) Calculate the *net* force that thymine exerts on adenine. Is it attractive or repulsive? To keep the calculations fairly simple, yet reasonable, consider only the forces due to the O—H—N and the N—H—N combinations, assuming that these two combinations are parallel to each other. Remember, however, that in the O—H—N set, the O^- exerts a force on both the H^+ and the N^-, and likewise along the N—H—N set. (b) Calculate the force on the electron in the hydrogen atom, which is 0.0529 nm from the proton. Then compare the strength of the bonding force of the electron in hydrogen with the bonding force of the adenine–thymine molecules.

Figure **E21.23**

21.24 •• **BIO Base Pairing in DNA, II.** Refer to Exercise 21.23. Figure E21.24 shows the bonding of the cytosine and guanine molecules. The O—H and H—N distances are each 0.110 nm. In this case, assume that the bonding is due only to the forces along the O—H—O, N—H—N, and O—H—N combinations, and assume also that these three combinations are parallel to each other. Calculate the *net* force that cytosine exerts on guanine due to the preceding three combinations. Is this force attractive or repulsive?

Figure **E21.24**

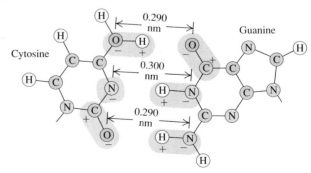

Section 21.4 Electric Field and Electric Forces

21.25 • **CP** A proton is placed in a uniform electric field of 2.75×10^3 N/C. Calculate: (a) the magnitude of the electric force felt by the proton; (b) the proton's acceleration; (c) the proton's speed after 1.00 μs in the field, assuming it starts from rest.

21.26 • A particle has charge -3.00 nC. (a) Find the magnitude and direction of the electric field due to this particle at a point 0.250 m directly above it. (b) At what distance from this particle does its electric field have a magnitude of 12.0 N/C?

21.27 • **CP** A proton is traveling horizontally to the right at 4.50×10^6 m/s. (a) Find the magnitude and direction of the weakest electric field that can bring the proton uniformly to rest over a distance of 3.20 cm. (b) How much time does it take the proton to stop after entering the field? (c) What minimum field (magnitude and direction) would be needed to stop an electron under the conditions of part (a)?

21.28 • **CP** An electron is released from rest in a uniform electric field. The electron accelerates vertically upward, traveling 4.50 m in the first 3.00 μs after it is released. (a) What are the magnitude and direction of the electric field? (b) Are we justified in ignoring the effects of gravity? Justify your answer quantitatively.

21.29 •• (a) What must the charge (sign and magnitude) of a 1.45-g particle be for it to remain stationary when placed in a downward-directed electric field of magnitude 650 N/C? (b) What is the magnitude of an electric field in which the electric force on a proton is equal in magnitude to its weight?

21.30 •• A point charge is placed at each corner of a square with side length a. The charges all have the same magnitude q. Two of the charges are positive and two are negative, as shown in Fig. E21.30. What is the direction of the net electric field at the center of the square due to the four charges, and what is its magnitude in terms of q and a?

Figure **E21.30**

21.31 • Two point charges are separated by 25.0 cm (Fig. E21.31). Find the net electric field these charges produce at (a) point A and (b) point B. (c) What would be the magnitude and direction of the electric force this combination of charges would produce on a proton at A?

Figure **E21.31**

21.32 •• **Electric Field of the Earth.** The earth has a net electric charge that causes a field at points near its surface equal to 150 N/C and directed in toward the center of the earth. (a) What magnitude and sign of charge would a 60-kg human have to acquire to overcome his or her weight by the force exerted by the earth's electric field? (b) What would be the force of repulsion between two people each with the charge calculated in part (a) and separated by a distance of 100 m? Is use of the earth's electric field a feasible means of flight? Why or why not?

21.33 •• **CP** An electron is projected with an initial speed $v_0 = 1.60 \times 10^6$ m/s into the uniform field between the parallel plates in Fig. E21.33. Assume that the field between the plates is uniform and directed vertically downward, and that the field outside the plates is zero. The electron enters the field at a point

Figure **E21.33**

midway between the plates. (a) If the electron just misses the upper plate as it emerges from the field, find the magnitude of the electric field. (b) Suppose that in Fig. E21.33 the electron is replaced by a proton with the same initial speed v_0. Would the proton hit one of the plates? If the proton would not hit one of the plates, what would be the magnitude and direction of its vertical displacement as it exits the region between the plates? (c) Compare the paths traveled by the electron and the proton and explain the differences. (d) Discuss whether it is reasonable to ignore the effects of gravity for each particle.

21.34 •• Point charge $q_1 = -5.00$ nC is at the origin and point charge $q_2 = +3.00$ nC is on the x-axis at $x = 3.00$ cm. Point P is on the y-axis at $y = 4.00$ cm. (a) Calculate the electric fields $\vec{E}_1$ and $\vec{E}_2$ at point P due to the charges q_1 and q_2. Express your results in terms of unit vectors (see Example 21.6). (b) Use the results of part (a) to obtain the resultant field at P, expressed in unit vector form.

21.35 •• **CP** In Exercise 21.33, what is the speed of the electron as it emerges from the field?

21.36 • (a) Calculate the magnitude and direction (relative to the $+x$-axis) of the electric field in Example 21.6. (b) A -2.5-nC point charge is placed at point P in Fig. 21.19. Find the magnitude and direction of (i) the force that the -8.0-nC charge at the origin exerts on this charge and (ii) the force that this charge exerts on the -8.0-nC charge at the origin.

21.37 •• If two electrons are each 1.50×10^{-10} m from a proton, as shown in Fig. E21.37, find the magnitude and direction of the net electric force they will exert on the proton.

Figure **E21.37**

21.38 •• **CP** A uniform electric field exists in the region between two oppositely charged plane parallel plates. A proton is released from rest at the surface of the positively charged plate and strikes the surface of the opposite plate, 1.60 cm distant from the first, in a time interval of 1.50×10^{-6} s. (a) Find the magnitude of the electric field. (b) Find the speed of the proton when it strikes the negatively charged plate.

21.39 • A point charge is at the origin. With this point charge as the source point, what is the unit vector $\hat{r}$ in the direction of (a) the field point at $x = 0$, $y = -1.35$ m; (b) the field point at $x = 12.0$ cm, $y = 12.0$ cm; (c) the field point at $x = -1.10$ m, $y = 2.60$ m? Express your results in terms of the unit vectors $\hat{i}$ and $\hat{j}$.

21.40 •• A $+8.75$-μC point charge is glued down on a horizontal frictionless table. It is tied to a -6.50-μC point charge by a light, nonconducting 2.50-cm wire. A uniform electric field of magnitude 1.85×10^8 N/C is directed parallel to the wire, as shown in Fig. E21.40. (a) Find the tension in the wire. (b) What would the tension be if both charges were negative?

Figure **E21.40**

21.41 •• (a) An electron is moving east in a uniform electric field of 1.50 N/C directed to the west. At point A, the velocity of the electron is 4.50×10^5 m/s toward the east. What is the speed of the electron when it reaches point B, 0.375 m east of point A? (b) A proton is moving in the uniform electric field of part (a). At point A, the velocity of the proton is 1.90×10^4 m/s, east. What is the speed of the proton at point B?

Section 21.5 Electric-Field Calculations

21.42 • Two point charges Q and $+q$ (where q is positive) produce the net electric field shown at point P in Fig. E21.42. The field points parallel to the line connecting the two charges. (a) What can you conclude about the sign and magnitude of Q? Explain your reasoning. (b) If the lower charge were negative instead, would it be possible for the field to have the direction shown in the figure? Explain your reasoning.

Figure **E21.42**

21.43 •• Two positive point charges q are placed on the x-axis, one at $x = a$ and one at $x = -a$. (a) Find the magnitude and direction of the electric field at $x = 0$. (b) Derive an expression for the electric field at points on the x-axis. Use your result to graph the x-component of the electric field as a function of x, for values of x between $-4a$ and $+4a$.

21.44 • The two charges q_1 and q_2 shown in Fig. E21.44 have equal magnitudes. What is the direction of the net electric field due to these two charges at points A (midway between the charges), B, and C if (a) both charges are negative, (b) both charges are positive, (c) q_1 is positive and q_2 is negative.

Figure **E21.44**

21.45 • A $+2.00$-nC point charge is at the origin, and a second -5.00-nC point charge is on the x-axis at $x = 0.800$ m. (a) Find the electric field (magnitude and direction) at each of the following points on the x-axis: (i) $x = 0.200$ m; (ii) $x = 1.20$ m; (iii) $x = -0.200$ m. (b) Find the net electric force that the two charges would exert on an electron placed at each point in part (a).

21.46 •• Repeat Exercise 21.44, but now let $q_1 = -4.00$ nC.

21.47 • Three negative point charges lie along a line as shown in Fig. E21.47. Find the magnitude and direction of the electric field this combination of charges produces at point P, which lies 6.00 cm from the -2.00-μC charge measured perpendicular to the line connecting the three charges.

Figure **E21.47**

21.48 •• BIO **Electric Field of Axons.** A nerve signal is transmitted through a neuron when an excess of Na^+ ions suddenly enters the axon, a long cylindrical part of the neuron. Axons are approximately 10.0 μm in diameter, and measurements show that about 5.6×10^{11} Na^+ ions per meter (each of charge $+e$) enter during this process. Although the axon is a long cylinder, the charge does not all enter everywhere at the same time. A plausible model would be a series of point charges moving along the axon. Let us look at a 0.10-mm length of the axon and model it as a point charge. (a) If the charge that enters each meter of the axon gets distributed uniformly along it, how many coulombs of charge enter a 0.10-mm length of the axon? (b) What electric field (magnitude and direction) does the sudden influx of charge produce at the surface of the body if the axon is 5.00 cm below the skin? (c) Certain sharks can respond to electric fields as weak as 1.0 μN/C.

How far from this segment of axon could a shark be and still detect its electric field?

21.49 • In a rectangular coordinate system a positive point charge $q = 6.00 \times 10^{-9}$ C is placed at the point $x = +0.150$ m, $y = 0$, and an identical point charge is placed at $x = -0.150$ m, $y = 0$. Find the x- and y-components, the magnitude, and the direction of the electric field at the following points: (a) the origin; (b) $x = 0.300$ m, $y = 0$; (c) $x = 0.150$ m, $y = -0.400$ m; (d) $x = 0$, $y = 0.200$ m.

21.50 •• A point charge $q_1 = -4.00$ nC is at the point $x = 0.600$ m, $y = 0.800$ m, and a second point charge $q_2 = +6.00$ nC is at the point $x = 0.600$ m, $y = 0$. Calculate the magnitude and direction of the net electric field at the origin due to these two point charges.

21.51 •• Repeat Exercise 21.49 for the case where the point charge at $x = +0.150$ m, $y = 0$ is positive and the other is negative, each with magnitude 6.00×10^{-9} C.

21.52 •• A very long, straight wire has charge per unit length 1.50×10^{-10} C/m. At what distance from the wire is the electric-field magnitude equal to 2.50 N/C?

21.53 • A ring-shaped conductor with radius $a = 2.50$ cm has a total positive charge $Q = +0.125$ nC uniformly distributed around it, as shown in Fig. 21.23. The center of the ring is at the origin of coordinates O. (a) What is the electric field (magnitude and direction) at point P, which is on the x-axis at $x = 40.0$ cm? (b) A point charge $q = -2.50$ μC is placed at the point P described in part (a). What are the magnitude and direction of the force exerted *by* the charge q *on* the ring?

21.54 •• A straight, nonconducting plastic wire 8.50 cm long carries a charge density of $+175$ nC/m distributed uniformly along its length. It is lying on a horizontal tabletop. (a) Find the magnitude and direction of the electric field this wire produces at a point 6.00 cm directly above its midpoint. (b) If the wire is now bent into a circle lying flat on the table, find the magnitude and direction of the electric field it produces at a point 6.00 cm directly above its center.

21.55 •• A charge of -6.50 nC is spread uniformly over the surface of one face of a nonconducting disk of radius 1.25 cm. (a) Find the magnitude and direction of the electric field this disk produces at a point P on the axis of the disk a distance of 2.00 cm from its center. (b) Suppose that the charge were all pushed away from the center and distributed uniformly on the outer rim of the disk. Find the magnitude and direction of the electric field at point P. (c) If the charge is all brought to the center of the disk, find the magnitude and direction of the electric field at point P. (d) Why is the field in part (a) stronger than the field in part (b)? Why is the field in part (c) the strongest of the three fields?

Section 21.7 Electric Dipoles

21.56 • The ammonia molecule (NH_3) has a dipole moment of 5.0×10^{-30} C$\cdot$m. Ammonia molecules in the gas phase are placed in a uniform electric field $\vec{E}$ with magnitude 1.6×10^6 N/C. (a) What is the change in electric potential energy when the dipole moment of a molecule changes its orientation with respect to $\vec{E}$ from parallel to perpendicular? (b) At what absolute temperature T is the average translational kinetic energy $\frac{3}{2}kT$ of a molecule equal to the change in potential energy calculated in part (a)? (*Note:* Above this temperature, thermal agitation prevents the dipoles from aligning with the electric field.)

21.57 • Point charges $q_1 = -4.5$ nC and $q_2 = +4.5$ nC are separated by 3.1 mm, forming an electric dipole. (a) Find the electric dipole moment (magnitude and direction). (b) The charges are in a uniform electric field whose direction makes an angle of 36.9° with the line connecting the charges. What is the magnitude of this field if the torque exerted on the dipole has magnitude 7.2×10^{-9} N·m?

21.58 • The dipole moment of the water molecule (H_2O) is 6.17×10^{-30} C·m. Consider a water molecule located at the origin whose dipole moment $\vec{p}$ points in the $+x$-direction. A chlorine ion (Cl^-), of charge -1.60×10^{-19} C, is located at $x = 3.00 \times 10^{-9}$ m. Find the magnitude and direction of the electric force that the water molecule exerts on the chlorine ion. Is this force attractive or repulsive? Assume that x is much larger than the separation d between the charges in the dipole, so that the approximate expression for the electric field along the dipole axis derived in Example 21.14 can be used.

21.59 • **Torque on a Dipole.** An electric dipole with dipole moment $\vec{p}$ is in a uniform electric field $\vec{E}$. (a) Find the orientations of the dipole for which the torque on the dipole is zero. (b) Which of the orientations in part (a) is stable, and which is unstable? (*Hint:* Consider a small displacement away from the equilibrium position and see what happens.) (c) Show that for the stable orientation in part (b), the dipole's own electric field tends to oppose the external field.

21.60 •• Consider the electric dipole of Example 21.14. (a) Derive an expression for the magnitude of the electric field produced by the dipole at a point on the x-axis in Fig. 21.33. What is the direction of this electric field? (b) How does the electric field at points on the x-axis depend on x when x is very large?

21.61 • Three charges are at the corners of an isosceles triangle as shown in Fig. E21.61. The ± 5.00-μC charges form a dipole. (a) Find the force (magnitude and direction) the -10.00-μC charge exerts on the dipole. (b) For an axis perpendicular to the line connecting the ± 5.00-μC charges at the midpoint of this line, find the torque (magnitude and direction) exerted on the dipole by the -10.00-μC charge.

Figure **E21.61**

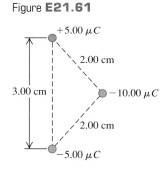

+5.00 μC

2.00 cm

3.00 cm

-10.00 μC

2.00 cm

-5.00 μC

21.62 • A dipole consisting of charges $\pm e$, 220 nm apart, is placed between two very large (essentially infinite) sheets carrying equal but opposite charge densities of 125 μC/m². (a) What is the maximum potential energy this dipole can have due to the sheets, and how should it be oriented relative to the sheets to attain this value? (b) What is the maximum torque the sheets can exert on the dipole, and how should it be oriented relative to the sheets to attain this value? (c) What net force do the two sheets exert on the dipole?

PROBLEMS

21.63 ••• Four identical charges Q are placed at the corners of a square of side L. (a) In a free-body diagram, show all of the forces that act on one of the charges. (b) Find the magnitude and direction of the total force exerted on one charge by the other three charges.

21.64 ••• Two charges, one of 2.50 μC and the other of -3.50 μC, are placed on the x-axis, one at the origin and the other at $x = 0.600$ m, as shown in Fig. P21.64. Find the position on the x-axis where the net force on a small charge $+q$ would be zero.

Figure **P21.64**

$+2.50$ μC -3.50 μC

x (m)

0   0.600 m

21.65 •• Three point charges are arranged along the x-axis. Charge $q_1 = -4.50$ nC is located at $x = 0.200$ m, and charge $q_2 = +2.50$ nC is at $x = -0.300$ m. A positive point charge q_3 is located at the origin. (a) What must the value of q_3 be for the net force on this point charge to have magnitude 4.00 μN? (b) What is the direction of the net force on q_3? (c) Where along the x-axis can q_3 be placed and the net force on it be zero, other than the trivial answers of $x = +\infty$ and $x = -\infty$?

21.66 •• A charge $q_1 = +5.00$ nC is placed at the origin of an xy-coordinate system, and a charge $q_2 = -2.00$ nC is placed on the positive x-axis at $x = 4.00$ cm. (a) If a third charge $q_3 = +6.00$ nC is now placed at the point $x = 4.00$ cm, $y = 3.00$ cm, find the x- and y-components of the total force exerted on this charge by the other two. (b) Find the magnitude and direction of this force.

21.67 •• **CP** Two positive point charges Q are held fixed on the x-axis at $x = a$ and $x = -a$. A third positive point charge q, with mass m, is placed on the x-axis away from the origin at a coordinate x such that $|x| \ll a$. The charge q, which is free to move along the x-axis, is then released. (a) Find the frequency of oscillation of the charge q. (*Hint:* Review the definition of simple harmonic motion in Section 14.2. Use the binomial expansion $(1 + z)^n = 1 + nz + n(n-1)z^2/2 + \cdots$, valid for the case $|z| < 1$.) (b) Suppose instead that the charge q were placed on the y-axis at a coordinate y such that $|y| \ll a$, and then released. If this charge is free to move anywhere in the xy-plane, what will happen to it? Explain your answer.

21.68 •• **CP** Two identical spheres with mass m are hung from silk threads of length L, as shown in Fig. P21.68. Each sphere has the same charge, so $q_1 = q_2 = q$. The radius of each sphere is very small compared to the distance between the spheres, so they may be treated as point charges. Show that if the angle θ is small, the equilibrium separation d between the spheres is $d = (q^2L/2\pi\epsilon_0 mg)^{1/3}$. (*Hint:* If θ is small, then $\tan\theta \cong \sin\theta$.)

Figure **P21.68**

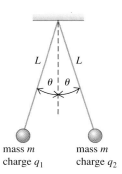

L L

θ θ

mass m mass m
charge q_1 charge q_2

21.69 ••• **CP** Two small spheres with mass $m = 15.0$ g are hung by silk threads of length $L = 1.20$ m from a common point (Fig. P21.68). When the spheres are given equal quantities of negative charge, so that $q_1 = q_2 = q$, each thread hangs at $\theta = 25.0°$ from the vertical. (a) Draw a diagram showing the forces on each sphere. Treat the spheres as point charges. (b) Find the magnitude of q. (c) Both threads are now shortened to length $L = 0.600$ m, while the charges q_1 and q_2 remain unchanged. What new angle will each thread make with the vertical? (*Hint:* This part of the problem can be solved numerically by using trial values for θ and adjusting the values of θ until a self-consistent answer is obtained.)

21.70 •• **CP** Two identical spheres are each attached to silk threads of length $L = 0.500$ m and hung from a common point (Fig. P21.68). Each sphere has mass $m = 8.00$ g. The radius of each sphere is very small compared to the distance between the spheres, so they may be treated as point charges. One sphere is given positive charge q_1, and the other a different positive charge q_2; this causes the spheres to separate so that when the spheres are in equilibrium, each thread makes an angle $\theta = 20.0°$ with the vertical. (a) Draw a free-body diagram for each sphere when in equilibrium, and label all the forces that act on each sphere. (b) Determine the magnitude of the electrostatic force that acts on each sphere, and determine the tension in each thread. (c) Based on the information you have been given, what can you say about the magnitudes of q_1 and q_2? Explain your answers. (d) A small wire is now connected between the spheres, allowing charge to be transferred from one sphere to the other until the two spheres have equal charges; the wire is then removed. Each thread now makes an angle of $30.0°$ with the vertical. Determine the original charges. (*Hint:* The total charge on the pair of spheres is conserved.)

21.71 •• Sodium chloride (NaCl, ordinary table salt) is made up of positive sodium ions (Na^+) and negative chloride ions (Cl^-). (a) If a point charge with the same charge and mass as all the Na^+ ions in 0.100 mol of NaCl is 2.00 cm from a point charge with the same charge and mass as all the Cl^- ions, what is the magnitude of the attractive force between these two point charges? (b) If the positive point charge in part (a) is held in place and the negative point charge is released from rest, what is its initial acceleration? (See Appendix D for atomic masses.) (c) Does it seem reasonable that the ions in NaCl could be separated in this way? Why or why not? (In fact, when sodium chloride dissolves in water, it breaks up into Na^+ and Cl^- ions. However, in this situation there are additional electric forces exerted by the water molecules on the ions.)

21.72 •• A -5.00-nC point charge is on the x-axis at $x = 1.20$ m. A second point charge Q is on the x-axis at -0.600 m. What must be the sign and magnitude of Q for the resultant electric field at the origin to be (a) 45.0 N/C in the $+x$-direction, (b) 45.0 N/C in the $-x$-direction?

21.73 •• **CP** A small 12.3-g plastic ball is tied to a very light 28.6-cm string that is attached to the vertical wall of a room (Fig. P21.73). A uniform horizontal electric field exists in this room. When the ball has been given an excess charge of $-1.11\ \mu C$, you observe that it remains suspended, with the string making an angle of $17.4°$ with the wall. Find the magnitude and direction of the electric field in the room.

Figure **P21.73**

17.4°

21.74 •• **CP** At $t = 0$ a very small object with mass 0.400 mg and charge $+9.00\ \mu C$ is traveling at 125 m/s in the $-x$-direction. The charge is moving in a uniform electric field that is in the $+y$-direction and that has magnitude $E = 895$ N/C. The gravitational force on the particle can be neglected. How far is the particle from the origin at $t = 7.00$ ms?

21.75 •• Two particles having charges $q_1 = 0.500$ nC and $q_2 = 8.00$ nC are separated by a distance of 1.20 m. At what point along the line connecting the two charges is the total electric field due to the two charges equal to zero?

21.76 ••• Two point charges q_1 and q_2 are held in place 4.50 cm apart. Another point charge $Q = -1.75\ \mu C$ of mass 5.00 g is initially located 3.00 cm from each of these charges (Fig. P21.76) and released from rest. You observe that the initial acceleration of Q is 324 m/s² upward, parallel to the line connecting the two point charges. Find q_1 and q_2.

Figure **P21.76**

21.77 • Three identical point charges q are placed at each of three corners of a square of side L. Find the magnitude and direction of the net force on a point charge $-3q$ placed (a) at the center of the square and (b) at the vacant corner of the square. In each case, draw a free-body diagram showing the forces exerted on the $-3q$ charge by each of the other three charges.

21.78 ••• Three point charges are placed on the y-axis: a charge q at $y = a$, a charge $-2q$ at the origin, and a charge q at $y = -a$. Such an arrangement is called an electric quadrupole. (a) Find the magnitude and direction of the electric field at points on the positive x-axis. (b) Use the binomial expansion to find an approximate expression for the electric field valid for $x \gg a$. Contrast this behavior to that of the electric field of a point charge and that of the electric field of a dipole.

21.79 •• **CP** **Strength of the Electric Force.** Imagine two 1.0-g bags of protons, one at the earth's north pole and the other at the south pole. (a) How many protons are in each bag? (b) Calculate the gravitational attraction and the electrical repulsion that each bag exerts on the other. (c) Are the forces in part (b) large enough for you to feel if you were holding one of the bags?

21.80 • **Electric Force Within the Nucleus.** Typical dimensions of atomic nuclei are of the order of 10^{-15} m (1 fm). (a) If two protons in a nucleus are 2.0 fm apart, find the magnitude of the electric force each one exerts on the other. Express the answer in newtons and in pounds. Would this force be large enough for a person to feel? (b) Since the protons repel each other so strongly, why don't they shoot out of the nucleus?

21.81 •• **If Atoms Were Not Neutral . . .** Because the charges on the electron and proton have the same absolute value, atoms are electrically neutral. Suppose this were not precisely true, and the absolute value of the charge of the electron were less than the charge of the proton by 0.00100%. (a) Estimate what the net charge of this textbook would be under these circumstances. Make any assumptions you feel are justified, but state clearly what they are. (*Hint:* Most of the atoms in this textbook have equal numbers of electrons, protons, and neutrons.) (b) What would be the magnitude of the electric force between two textbooks placed 5.0 m apart? Would this force be attractive or repulsive? Estimate what the acceleration of each book would be if the books were 5.0 m apart and there were no non-electric forces on them. (c) Discuss how the fact that ordinary matter is stable shows that the absolute values of the charges on the electron and proton must be identical to a *very* high level of accuracy.

21.82 ••• **CP** Two tiny spheres of mass 6.80 mg carry charges of equal magnitude,

Figure **P21.82**

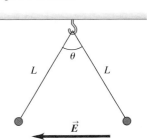

72.0 nC, but opposite sign. They are tied to the same ceiling hook by light strings of length 0.530 m. When a horizontal uniform electric field E that is directed to the left is turned on, the spheres hang at rest with the angle θ between the strings equal to 50.0° (Fig. P21.82). (a) Which ball (the one on the right or the one on the left) has positive charge? (b) What is the magnitude E of the field?

21.83 ·· **CP** Consider a model of a hydrogen atom in which an electron is in a circular orbit of radius $r = 5.29 \times 10^{-11}$ m around a stationary proton. What is the speed of the electron in its orbit?

21.84 ·· **CP** A small sphere with mass $9.00\ \mu g$ and charge $-4.30\ \mu C$ is moving in a circular orbit around a stationary sphere that has charge $+7.50\ \mu C$. If the speed of the small sphere is 5.90×10^3 m/s, what is the radius of its orbit? Treat the spheres as point charges and ignore gravity.

21.85 ·· Two small copper spheres each have radius 1.00 mm. (a) How many atoms does each sphere contain? (b) Assume that each copper atom contains 29 protons and 29 electrons. We know that electrons and protons have charges of exactly the same magnitude, but let's explore the effect of small differences (see also Problem 21.81). If the charge of a proton is $+e$ and the magnitude of the charge of an electron is 0.100% smaller, what is the net charge of each sphere and what force would one sphere exert on the other if they were separated by 1.00 m?

21.86 ··· **CP Operation of an Inkjet Printer.** In an inkjet printer, letters are built up by squirting drops of ink at the paper from a rapidly moving nozzle. The ink drops, which have a mass of 1.4×10^{-8} g each, leave the nozzle and travel toward the paper at 20 m/s, passing through a charging unit that gives each drop a positive charge q by removing some electrons from it. The drops then pass between parallel deflecting plates 2.0 cm long where there is a uniform vertical electric field with magnitude 8.0×10^4 N/C. If a drop is to be deflected 0.30 mm by the time it reaches the end of the deflection plates, what magnitude of charge must be given to the drop?

21.87 ·· **CP** A proton is projected into a uniform electric field that points vertically upward and has magnitude E. The initial velocity of the proton has a magnitude v_0 and is directed at an angle α below the horizontal. (a) Find the maximum distance h_{max} that the proton descends vertically below its initial elevation. You can ignore gravitational forces. (b) After what horizontal distance d does the proton return to its original elevation? (c) Sketch the trajectory of the proton. (d) Find the numerical values of h_{max} and d if $E = 500$ N/C, $v_0 = 4.00 \times 10^5$ m/s, and $\alpha = 30.0°$.

21.88 · A negative point charge $q_1 = -4.00$ nC is on the x-axis at $x = 0.60$ m. A second point charge q_2 is on the x-axis at $x = -1.20$ m. What must the sign and magnitude of q_2 be for the net electric field at the origin to be (a) 50.0 N/C in the $+x$-direction and (b) 50.0 N/C in the $-x$-direction?

21.89 ·· **CALC** Positive charge Q is distributed uniformly along the x-axis from $x = 0$ to $x = a$. A positive point charge q is located on the positive x-axis at $x = a + r$, a distance r to the right of the end of Q (Fig. P21.89). (a) Calculate the x- and y-components of the electric field produced by the charge distribution Q at points on the positive x-axis where $x > a$. (b) Calculate the force (magnitude and direction) that the charge distribution Q exerts on q. (c) Show that if $r \gg a$, the magnitude of the force in part (b) is approximately $Qq/4\pi\epsilon_0 r^2$. Explain why this result is obtained.

Figure **P21.89**

21.90 ·· **CALC** Positive charge Q is distributed uniformly along the positive y-axis between $y = 0$ and $y = a$. A negative point charge $-q$ lies on the positive x-axis, a distance x from the origin (Fig. P21.90). (a) Calculate the x- and y-components of the electric field produced by the charge distribution Q at points on the positive x-axis. (b) Calculate the x- and y-components of the force that the charge distribution Q exerts on q. (c) Show that if $x \gg a$, $F_x \cong -Qq/4\pi\epsilon_0 x^2$ and $F_y \cong +Qqa/8\pi\epsilon_0 x^3$. Explain why this result is obtained.

Figure **P21.90**

21.91 ·· A charged line like that shown in Fig. 21.24 extends from $y = 2.50$ cm to $y = -2.50$ cm. The total charge distributed uniformly along the line is -7.00 nC. (a) Find the electric field (magnitude and direction) on the x-axis at $x = 10.0$ cm. (b) Is the magnitude of the electric field you calculated in part (a) larger or smaller than the electric field 10.0 cm from a point charge that has the same total charge as this finite line of charge? In terms of the approximation used to derive $E = Q/4\pi\epsilon_0 x^2$ for a point charge from Eq. (21.9), explain why this is so. (c) At what distance x does the result for the finite line of charge differ by 1.0% from that for the point charge?

21.92 · **CP A Parallel Universe.** Imagine a parallel universe in which the electric force has the same properties as in our universe but there is no gravity. In this parallel universe, the sun carries charge Q, the earth carries charge $-Q$, and the electric attraction between them keeps the earth in orbit. The earth in the parallel universe has the same mass, the same orbital radius, and the same orbital period as in our universe. Calculate the value of Q. (Consult Appendix F as needed.)

21.93 ··· A uniformly charged disk like the disk in Fig. 21.25 has radius 2.50 cm and carries a total charge of 7.0×10^{-12} C. (a) Find the electric field (magnitude and direction) on the x-axis at $x = 20.0$ cm. (b) Show that for $x \gg R$, Eq. (21.11) becomes $E = Q/4\pi\epsilon_0 x^2$, where Q is the total charge on the disk. (c) Is the magnitude of the electric field you calculated in part (a) larger or smaller than the electric field 20.0 cm from a point charge that has the same total charge as this disk? In terms of the approximation used in part (b) to derive $E = Q/4\pi\epsilon_0 x^2$ for a point charge from Eq. (21.11), explain why this is so. (d) What is the percent difference between the electric fields produced by the finite disk and by a point charge with the same charge at $x = 20.0$ cm and at $x = 10.0$ cm?

21.94 ·· **BIO Electrophoresis.** Electrophoresis is a process used by biologists to separate different biological molecules (such as proteins) from each other according to their ratio of charge to size. The materials to be separated are in a viscous solution that produces a drag force F_D proportional to the size and speed of the molecule. We can express this relationship as $F_D = KRv$, where R is the radius of the molecule (modeled as being spherical), v is its speed, and K is a constant that depends on the viscosity of the

Figure **P21.94**

solution. The solution is placed in an external electric field E so that the electric force on a particle of charge q is $F = qE$. (a) Show that when the electric field is adjusted so that the two forces (electric and viscous drag) just balance, the ratio of q to R is Kv/E. (b) Show that if we leave the electric field on for a time T, the distance x that the molecule moves during that time is $x = (ET/k)(q/R)$. (c) Suppose you have a sample containing three different biological molecules for which the molecular ratio q/R for material 2 is twice that of material 1 and the ratio for material 3 is three times that of material 1. Show that the distances migrated by these molecules after the same amount of time are $x_2 = 2x_1$ and $x_3 = 3x_1$. In other words, material 2 travels twice as far as material 1, and material 3 travels three times as far as material 1. Therefore, we have separated these molecules according to their ratio of charge to size. In practice, this process can be carried out in a special gel or paper, along which the biological molecules migrate. (Fig. P21.94). The process can be rather slow, requiring several hours for separations of just a centimeter or so.

21.95 • **CALC** Positive charge $+Q$ is distributed uniformly along the $+x$-axis from $x = 0$ to $x = a$. Negative charge $-Q$ is distributed uniformly along the $-x$-axis from $x = 0$ to $x = -a$. (a) A positive point charge q lies on the positive y-axis, a distance y from the origin. Find the force (magnitude and direction) that the positive and negative charge distributions together exert on q. Show that this force is proportional to y^{-3} for $y \gg a$. (b) Suppose instead that the positive point charge q lies on the positive x-axis, a distance $x > a$ from the origin. Find the force (magnitude and direction) that the charge distribution exerts on q. Show that this force is proportional to x^{-3} for $x \gg a$.

21.96 •• **CP** A small sphere with mass m carries a positive charge q and is attached to one end of a silk fiber of length L. The other end of the fiber is attached to a large vertical insulating sheet that has a positive surface charge density σ. Show that when the sphere is in equilibrium, the fiber makes an angle equal to arctan $(q\sigma/2mg\epsilon_0)$ with the vertical sheet.

21.97 •• **CALC** Negative charge $-Q$ is distributed uniformly around a quarter-circle of radius a that lies in the first quadrant, with the center of curvature at the origin. Find the x- and y-components of the net electric field at the origin.

21.98 •• **CALC** A semicircle of radius a is in the first and second quadrants, with the center of curvature at the origin. Positive charge $+Q$ is distributed uniformly around the left half of the semicircle, and negative charge $-Q$ is distributed uniformly around the right half of the semicircle (Fig. P21.98). What are the magnitude and direction of the net electric field at the origin produced by this distribution of charge?

Figure **P21.98**

21.99 •• Two 1.20-m nonconducting wires meet at a right angle. One segment carries $+2.50\ \mu C$ of charge distributed uniformly along its length, and the other carries $-2.50\ \mu C$ distributed uniformly along it, as shown in Fig. P21.99.

Figure **P21.99**

(a) Find the magnitude and direction of the electric field these wires produce at point P, which is 60.0 cm from each wire. (b) If an electron is released at P, what are the magnitude and direction of the net force that these wires exert on it?

21.100 • Two very large parallel sheets are 5.00 cm apart. Sheet A carries a uniform surface charge density of $-9.50\mu C/m^2$, and sheet B, which is to the right of A, carries a uniform charge density of $-11.6\ \mu C/m^2$. Assume the sheets are large enough to be treated as infinite. Find the magnitude and direction of the net electric field these sheets produce at a point (a) 4.00 cm to the right of sheet A; (b) 4.00 cm to the left of sheet A; (c) 4.00 cm to the right of sheet B.

21.101 • Repeat Problem 21.100 for the case where sheet B is positive.

21.102 • Two very large horizontal sheets are 4.25 cm apart and carry equal but opposite uniform surface charge densities of magnitude σ. You want to use these sheets to hold stationary in the region between them an oil droplet of mass 324 μg that carries an excess of five electrons. Assuming that the drop is in vacuum, (a) which way should the electric field between the plates point, and (b) what should σ be?

21.103 •• An infinite sheet with positive charge per unit area σ lies in the xy-plane. A second infinite sheet with negative charge per unit area $-\sigma$ lies in the yz-plane. Find the net electric field at all points that do not lie in either of these planes. Express your answer in terms of the unit vectors $\hat{i}, \hat{j}$, and $\hat{k}$.

21.104 •• **CP** A thin disk with a circular hole at its center, called an *annulus*, has inner radius R_1 and outer radius R_2 (Fig. P21.104). The disk has a uniform positive surface charge density σ on its surface. (a) Determine the total electric charge on the annulus. (b) The annulus lies in the yz-plane, with its center at the origin. For an arbitrary point on the x-axis (the axis of the annulus), find the magnitude and direction of the electric field $\vec{E}$. Consider points both above and below the annulus in Fig. P21.104. (c) Show that at points on the x-axis that are sufficiently close to the origin, the magnitude of the electric field is approximately proportional to the distance between the center of the annulus and the point. How close is "sufficiently close"? (d) A point particle with mass m and negative charge $-q$ is free to move along the x-axis (but cannot move off the axis). The particle is originally placed at rest at $x = 0.01R_1$ and released. Find the frequency of oscillation of the particle. (*Hint:* Review Section 14.2. The annulus is held stationary.)

Figure **P21.104**

CHALLENGE PROBLEMS

21.105 ••• Three charges are placed as shown in Fig. P21.105. The magnitude of q_1 is 2.00 μC, but its sign and the value of the charge q_2 are not known. Charge q_3 is $+4.00\ \mu C$, and the net force $\vec{F}$ on q_3 is entirely in the negative x-direction. (a) Considering the different possible signs of q_1, there are four possible force diagrams representing the forces $\vec{F}_1$ and $\vec{F}_2$ that q_1 and q_2 exert on q_3. Sketch these four possible force configurations.

Figure **P21.105**

(b) Using the sketches from part (a) and the direction of $\vec{F}$, deduce the signs of the charges q_1 and q_2. (c) Calculate the magnitude of q_2. (d) Determine F, the magnitude of the net force on q_3.

21.106 ••• Two charges are placed as shown in Fig. P21.106. The magnitude of q_1 is 3.00 μC, but its sign and the value of the charge q_2 are not known. The direction of the net electric field $\vec{E}$ at point P is entirely in the negative y-direction. (a) Considering the different possible signs of q_1 and q_2, there are four possible diagrams that could represent the electric fields $\vec{E}_1$ and $\vec{E}_2$ produced by q_1 and q_2. Sketch the four possible electric-field configurations. (b) Using the sketches from part (a) and the direction of $\vec{E}$, deduce the signs of q_1 and q_2. (c) Determine the magnitude of $\vec{E}$.

Figure **P21.106**

P

5.0 cm   12.0 cm

$\vec{E}$

q_1 13.0 cm q_2

21.107 ••• **CALC** Two thin rods of length L lie along the x-axis, one between $x = a/2$ and $x = a/2 + L$ and the other between $x = -a/2$ and $x = -a/2 - L$. Each rod has positive charge Q distributed uniformly along its length. (a) Calculate the electric field produced by the second rod at points along the positive x-axis. (b) Show that the magnitude of the force that one rod exerts on the other is

$$F = \frac{Q^2}{4\pi\epsilon_0 L^2} \ln\left[\frac{(a + L)^2}{a(a + 2L)}\right]$$

(c) Show that if $a \gg L$, the magnitude of this force reduces to $F = Q^2/4\pi\epsilon_0 a^2$. (*Hint:* Use the expansion $\ln(1 + z) = z - z^2/2 + z^3/3 - \cdots$, valid for $|z| \ll 1$. Carry *all* expansions to at least order L^2/a^2.) Interpret this result.

Answers

Chapter Opening Question ?

Water molecules have a permanent electric dipole moment: One end of the molecule has a positive charge and the other end has a negative charge. These ends attract negative and positive ions, respectively, holding the ions apart in solution. Water is less effective as a solvent for materials whose molecules do not ionize (called *nonionic* substances), such as oils.

Test Your Understanding Questions

21.1 Answers: (a) the plastic rod weighs more, (b) the glass rod weighs less, (c) the fur weighs less, (d) the silk weighs more The plastic rod gets a negative charge by taking electrons from the fur, so the rod weighs a little more and the fur weighs a little less after the rubbing. By contrast, the glass rod gets a positive charge by giving electrons to the silk. Hence, after they are rubbed together, the glass rod weighs a little less and the silk weighs a little more. The weight change is *very* small: The number of electrons transferred is a small fraction of a mole, and a mole of electrons has a mass of only $(6.02 \times 10^{23}$ electrons$)(9.11 \times 10^{-31}$ kg/electron$) = 5.48 \times 10^{-7}$ kg $= 0.548$ milligram!

21.2 Answers: (a) (i), (b) (ii) Before the two spheres touch, the negatively charged sphere exerts a repulsive force on the electrons in the other sphere, causing zones of positive and negative induced charge (see Fig. 21.7b). The positive zone is closer to the negatively charged sphere than the negative zone, so there is a net force of attraction that pulls the spheres together, like the comb and insulator in Fig. 21.8b. Once the two metal spheres touch, some of the excess electrons on the negatively charged sphere will flow onto the other sphere (because metals are conductors). Then both spheres will have a net negative charge and will repel each other.

21.3 Answer: (iv) The force exerted by q_1 on Q is still as in Example 21.4. The magnitude of the force exerted by q_2 on Q is still equal to $F_{1 \text{ on } Q}$, but the direction of the force is now *toward* q_2 at an angle α below the x-axis. Hence the x-components of the two forces cancel while the (negative) y-components add together, and the total electric force is in the negative y-direction.

21.4 Answers: (a) (ii), (b) (i) The electric field $\vec{E}$ produced by a positive point charge points directly away from the charge (see Fig. 21.18a) and has a magnitude that depends on the distance r from the charge to the field point. Hence a second, negative point charge $q < 0$ will feel a force $\vec{F} = q\vec{E}$ that points directly toward the positive charge and has a magnitude that depends on the distance r between the two charges. If the negative charge moves directly toward the positive charge, the direction of the force remains the same but the force magnitude increases as the distance r decreases. If the negative charge moves in a circle around the positive charge, the force magnitude stays the same (because the distance r is constant) but the force direction changes.

21.5 Answer: (iv) Think of a pair of segments of length dy, one at coordinate $y > 0$ and the other at coordinate $-y < 0$. The upper segment has a positive charge and produces an electric field $d\vec{E}$ at P that points away from the segment, so this $d\vec{E}$ has a positive x-component and a negative y-component, like the vector $d\vec{E}$ in Fig. 21.24. The lower segment has the same amount of negative charge. It produces a $d\vec{E}$ that has the same magnitude but points *toward* the lower segment, so it has a negative x-component and a negative y-component. By symmetry, the two x-components are equal but opposite, so they cancel. Thus the total electric field has only a negative y-component.

21.6 Answer: yes If the field lines are straight, $\vec{E}$ must point in the same direction throughout the region. Hence the force $\vec{F} = q\vec{E}$ on a particle of charge q is always in the same direction. A particle released from rest accelerates in a straight line in the direction of $\vec{F}$, and so its trajectory is a straight line along a field line.

21.7 Answer: (ii) Equations (21.17) and (21.18) tell us that the potential energy for a dipole in an electric field is $U = -\vec{p} \cdot \vec{E} = -pE \cos\phi$, where ϕ is the angle between the directions of $\vec{p}$ and $\vec{E}$. If $\vec{p}$ and $\vec{E}$ point in opposite directions, so that $\phi = 180°$, we have $\cos\phi = -1$ and $U = +pE$. This is the maximum value that U can have. From our discussion of energy diagrams in Section 7.5, it follows that this is a situation of unstable equilibrium.

Bridging Problem

Answer: $E = 2kQ/\pi a^2$ in the $-y$-direction

GAUSS'S LAW

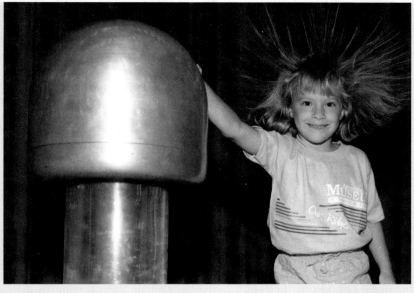

? This child acquires an electric charge by touching the charged metal sphere. The charged hairs on the child's head repel and stand out. If the child stands *inside* a large, charged metal sphere, will her hair stand on end?

Often, there are both an easy way and a hard way to do a job; the easy way may involve nothing more than using the right tools. In physics, an important tool for simplifying problems is the *symmetry properties* of systems. Many physical systems have symmetry; for example, a cylindrical body doesn't look any different after you've rotated it around its axis, and a charged metal sphere looks just the same after you've turned it about any axis through its center.

Gauss's law is part of the key to using symmetry considerations to simplify electric-field calculations. For example, the field of a straight-line or plane-sheet charge distribution, which we derived in Section 21.5 using some fairly strenuous integrations, can be obtained in a few lines with the help of Gauss's law. But Gauss's law is more than just a way to make certain calculations easier. Indeed, it is a fundamental statement about the relationship between electric charges and electric fields. Among other things, Gauss's law can help us understand how electric charge distributes itself over conducting bodies.

Here's what Gauss's law is all about. Given any general distribution of charge, we surround it with an imaginary surface that encloses the charge. Then we look at the electric field at various points on this imaginary surface. Gauss's law is a relationship between the field at *all* the points on the surface and the total charge enclosed within the surface. This may sound like a rather indirect way of expressing things, but it turns out to be a tremendously useful relationship. Above and beyond its use as a calculational tool, Gauss's law can help us gain deeper insights into electric fields. We will make use of these insights repeatedly in the next several chapters as we pursue our study of electromagnetism.

22.1 Charge and Electric Flux

In Chapter 21 we asked the question, "Given a charge distribution, what is the electric field produced by that distribution at a point *P*?" We saw that the answer could be found by representing the distribution as an assembly of point charges,

The discussion of Gauss's law in this section is based on and inspired by the innovative ideas of Ruth W. Chabay and Bruce A. Sherwood in *Electric and Magnetic Interactions* (John Wiley & Sons, 1994).

22.1 How can you measure the charge inside a box without opening it?

(a) A box containing an unknown amount of charge

(b) Using a test charge outside the box to probe the amount of charge inside the box

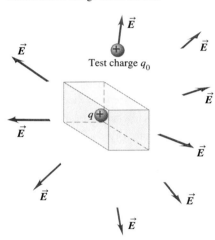

each of which produces an electric field $\vec{E}$ given by Eq. (21.7). The total field at P is then the vector sum of the fields due to all the point charges.

But there is an alternative relationship between charge distributions and electric fields. To discover this relationship, let's stand the question of Chapter 21 on its head and ask, "If the electric field pattern is known in a given region, what can we determine about the charge distribution in that region?"

Here's an example. Consider the box shown in Fig. 22.1a, which may or may not contain electric charge. We'll imagine that the box is made of a material that has no effect on any electric fields; it's of the same breed as the massless rope and the frictionless incline. Better still, let the box represent an *imaginary* surface that may or may not enclose some charge. We'll refer to the box as a **closed surface** because it completely encloses a volume. How can you determine how much (if any) electric charge lies within the box?

Knowing that a charge distribution produces an electric field and that an electric field exerts a force on a test charge, you move a test charge q_0 around the vicinity of the box. By measuring the force $\vec{F}$ experienced by the test charge at different positions, you make a three-dimensional map of the electric field $\vec{E} = \vec{F}/q_0$ outside the box. In the case shown in Fig. 22.1b, the map turns out to be the same as that of the electric field produced by a positive point charge (Fig. 21.28a). From the details of the map, you can find the exact value of the point charge inside the box.

To determine the contents of the box, we actually need to measure $\vec{E}$ only on the *surface* of the box. In Fig. 22.2a there is a single *positive* point charge inside the box, and in Fig. 22.2b there are two such charges. The field patterns on the surfaces of the boxes are different in detail, but in each case the electric field points *out* of the box. Figures 22.2c and 22.2d show cases with one and two *negative* point charges, respectively, inside the box. Again, the details of $\vec{E}$ are different for the two cases, but the electric field points *into* each box.

Electric Flux and Enclosed Charge

In Section 21.4 we mentioned the analogy between electric-field vectors and the velocity vectors of a fluid in motion. This analogy can be helpful, even though an electric field does not actually "flow." Using this analogy, in Figs. 22.2a and 22.2b, in which the electric field vectors point out of the surface, we say that there is an *outward* **electric flux.** (The word "flux" comes from a Latin word meaning "flow.") In Figs. 22.2c and 22.2d the $\vec{E}$ vectors point into the surface, and the electric flux is *inward*.

Figure 22.2 suggests a simple relationship: Positive charge inside the box goes with an outward electric flux through the box's surface, and negative charge inside goes with an inward electric flux. What happens if there is *zero* charge

22.2 The electric field on the surface of boxes containing **(a)** a single positive point charge, **(b)** two positive point charges, **(c)** a single negative point charge, or **(d)** two negative point charges.

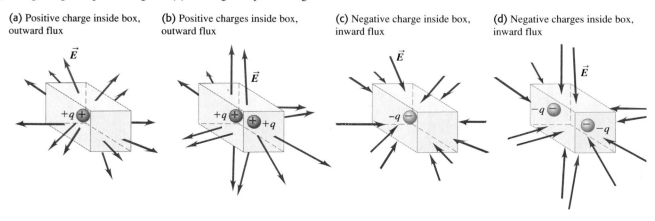

(a) Positive charge inside box, outward flux

(b) Positive charges inside box, outward flux

(c) Negative charge inside box, inward flux

(d) Negative charges inside box, inward flux

inside the box? In Fig. 22.3a the box is empty and $\vec{E} = 0$ everywhere, so there is no electric flux into or out of the box. In Fig. 22.3b, one positive and one negative point charge of equal magnitude are enclosed within the box, so the *net* charge inside the box is zero. There is an electric field, but it "flows into" the box on half of its surface and "flows out of" the box on the other half. Hence there is no *net* electric flux into or out of the box.

The box is again empty in Fig. 22.3c. However, there is charge present *outside* the box; the box has been placed with one end parallel to a uniformly charged infinite sheet, which produces a uniform electric field perpendicular to the sheet (as we learned in Example 21.11 of Section 21.5). On one end of the box, $\vec{E}$ points into the box; on the opposite end, $\vec{E}$ points out of the box; and on the sides, $\vec{E}$ is parallel to the surface and so points neither into nor out of the box. As in Fig. 22.3b, the inward electric flux on one part of the box exactly compensates for the outward electric flux on the other part. So in all of the cases shown in Fig. 22.3, there is no *net* electric flux through the surface of the box, and no *net* charge is enclosed in the box.

Figures 22.2 and 22.3 demonstrate a connection between the *sign* (positive, negative, or zero) of the *net* charge enclosed by a closed surface and the sense (outward, inward, or none) of the net electric flux through the surface. There is also a connection between the *magnitude* of the net charge inside the closed surface and the *strength* of the net "flow" of $\vec{E}$ over the surface. In both Figs. 22.4a and 22.4b there is a single point charge inside the box, but in Fig. 22.4b the magnitude of the charge is twice as great, and so $\vec{E}$ is everywhere twice as great in magnitude as in Fig. 22.4a. If we keep in mind the fluid-flow analogy, this means that the net outward electric flux is also twice as great in Fig. 22.4b as in Fig. 22.4a. This suggests that the net electric flux through the surface of the box is *directly proportional* to the magnitude of the net charge enclosed by the box.

This conclusion is independent of the size of the box. In Fig. 22.4c the point charge $+q$ is enclosed by a box with twice the linear dimensions of the box in Fig. 22.4a. The magnitude of the electric field of a point charge decreases with distance according to $1/r^2$, so the average magnitude of $\vec{E}$ on each face of the large box in Fig. 22.4c is just $\frac{1}{4}$ of the average magnitude on the corresponding face in Fig. 22.4a. But each face of the large box has exactly four times the area of the corresponding face of the small box. Hence the outward electric flux is the *same* for the two boxes if we *define* electric flux as follows: For each face of the box, take the product of the average perpendicular component of $\vec{E}$ and the area of that face; then add up the results from all faces of the box. With this definition the net electric flux due to a single point charge inside the box is independent of the size of the box and depends only on the net charge inside the box.

22.3 Three cases in which there is zero *net* charge inside a box and no net electric flux through the surface of the box. (a) An empty box with $\vec{E} = 0$. (b) A box containing one positive and one equal-magnitude negative point charge. (c) An empty box immersed in a uniform electric field.

(a) No charge inside box, zero flux

(b) Zero *net* charge inside box, inward flux cancels outward flux.

(c) No charge inside box, inward flux cancels outward flux.

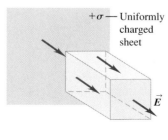

22.4 (a) A box enclosing a positive point charge $+q$. (b) Doubling the charge causes the magnitude of $\vec{E}$ to double, and it doubles the electric flux through the surface. (c) If the charge stays the same but the dimensions of the box are doubled, the flux stays the same. The magnitude of $\vec{E}$ on the surface decreases by a factor of $\frac{1}{4}$, but the area through which $\vec{E}$ "flows" increases by a factor of 4.

(a) A box containing a charge

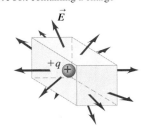

(b) Doubling the enclosed charge doubles the flux.

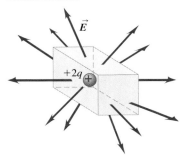

(c) Doubling the box dimensions *does not change* the flux.

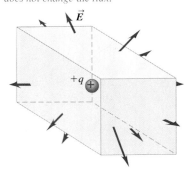

To summarize, for the special cases of a closed surface in the shape of a rectangular box and charge distributions made up of point charges or infinite charged sheets, we have found:

1. Whether there is a net outward or inward electric flux through a closed surface depends on the sign of the enclosed charge.
2. Charges *outside* the surface do not give a net electric flux through the surface.
3. The net electric flux is directly proportional to the net amount of charge enclosed within the surface but is otherwise independent of the size of the closed surface.

These observations are a qualitative statement of *Gauss's law.*

Do these observations hold true for other kinds of charge distributions and for closed surfaces of arbitrary shape? The answer to these questions will prove to be yes. But to explain why this is so, we need a precise mathematical statement of what we mean by electric flux. We develop this in the next section.

Test Your Understanding of Section 22.1 If all of the dimensions of the box in Fig. 22.2a are increased by a factor of 3, what effect will this change have on the electric flux through the box? (i) The flux will be $3^2 = 9$ times greater; (ii) the flux will be 3 times greater; (iii) the flux will be unchanged; (iv) the flux will be $\frac{1}{3}$ as great; (v) the flux will be $\left(\frac{1}{3}\right)^2 = \frac{1}{9}$ as great; (vi) not enough information is given to decide.

22.2 Calculating Electric Flux

In the preceding section we introduced the concept of *electric flux.* We used this to give a rough qualitative statement of Gauss's law: The net electric flux through a closed surface is directly proportional to the net charge inside that surface. To be able to make full use of this law, we need to know how to *calculate* electric flux. To do this, let's again make use of the analogy between an electric field $\vec{E}$ and the field of velocity vectors $\vec{v}$ in a flowing fluid. (Again, keep in mind that this is only an analogy; an electric field is *not* a flow.)

Flux: Fluid-Flow Analogy

Figure 22.5 shows a fluid flowing steadily from left to right. Let's examine the volume flow rate dV/dt (in, say, cubic meters per second) through the wire rectangle with area A. When the area is perpendicular to the flow velocity $\vec{v}$ (Fig. 22.5a) and the flow velocity is the same at all points in the fluid, the volume flow rate dV/dt is the area A multiplied by the flow speed v:

$$\frac{dV}{dt} = vA$$

When the rectangle is tilted at an angle ϕ (Fig. 22.5b) so that its face is not perpendicular to $\vec{v}$, the area that counts is the silhouette area that we see when we look in the direction of $\vec{v}$. This area, which is outlined in red and labeled $A_\perp$ in Fig. 22.5b, is the *projection* of the area A onto a surface perpendicular to $\vec{v}$. Two sides of the projected rectangle have the same length as the original one, but the other two are foreshortened by a factor of $\cos\phi$, so the projected area $A_\perp$ is equal to $A\cos\phi$. Then the volume flow rate through A is

$$\frac{dV}{dt} = vA\cos\phi$$

If $\phi = 90°$, $dV/dt = 0$; the wire rectangle is edge-on to the flow, and no fluid passes through the rectangle.

Also, $v\cos\phi$ is the component of the vector $\vec{v}$ perpendicular to the plane of the area A. Calling this component $v_\perp$, we can rewrite the volume flow rate as

$$\frac{dV}{dt} = v_\perp A$$

We can express the volume flow rate more compactly by using the concept of *vector area* $\vec{A}$, a vector quantity with magnitude A and a direction perpendicular to the plane of the area we are describing. The vector area $\vec{A}$ describes both the size of an area and its orientation in space. In terms of $\vec{A}$, we can write the volume flow rate of fluid through the rectangle in Fig. 22.5b as a scalar (dot) product:

$$\frac{dV}{dt} = \vec{v} \cdot \vec{A}$$

Flux of a Uniform Electric Field

Using the analogy between electric field and fluid flow, we now define electric flux in the same way as we have just defined the volume flow rate of a fluid; we simply replace the fluid velocity $\vec{v}$ by the electric field $\vec{E}$. The symbol that we use for electric flux is Φ_E (the capital Greek letter phi; the subscript E is a reminder that this is *electric* flux). Consider first a flat area A perpendicular to a uniform electric field $\vec{E}$ (Fig. 22.6a). We define the electric flux through this area to be the product of the field magnitude E and the area A:

$$\Phi_E = EA$$

Roughly speaking, we can picture Φ_E in terms of the field lines passing through A. Increasing the area means that more lines of $\vec{E}$ pass through the area, increasing the flux; a stronger field means more closely spaced lines of $\vec{E}$ and therefore more lines per unit area, so again the flux increases.

If the area A is flat but not perpendicular to the field $\vec{E}$, then fewer field lines pass through it. In this case the area that counts is the silhouette area that we see when looking in the direction of $\vec{E}$. This is the area $A_\perp$ in Fig. 22.6b and is equal to $A\cos\phi$ (compare to Fig. 22.5b). We generalize our definition of electric flux for a uniform electric field to

$$\Phi_E = EA\cos\phi \qquad \text{(electric flux for uniform } \vec{E}\text{, flat surface)} \qquad (22.1)$$

Since $E\cos\phi$ is the component of $\vec{E}$ perpendicular to the area, we can rewrite Eq. (22.1) as

$$\Phi_E = E_\perp A \qquad \text{(electric flux for uniform } \vec{E}\text{, flat surface)} \qquad (22.2)$$

In terms of the vector area $\vec{A}$ perpendicular to the area, we can write the electric flux as the scalar product of $\vec{E}$ and $\vec{A}$:

$$\Phi_E = \vec{E} \cdot \vec{A} \qquad \text{(electric flux for uniform } \vec{E}\text{, flat surface)} \qquad (22.3)$$

Equations (22.1), (22.2), and (22.3) express the electric flux for a *flat* surface and a *uniform* electric field in different but equivalent ways. The SI unit for electric flux is $1\ \text{N} \cdot \text{m}^2/\text{C}$. Note that if the area is edge-on to the field, $\vec{E}$ and $\vec{A}$ are perpendicular and the flux is zero (Fig. 22.6c).

We can represent the direction of a vector area $\vec{A}$ by using a *unit vector* $\hat{n}$ perpendicular to the area; $\hat{n}$ stands for "normal." Then

$$\vec{A} = A\hat{n} \qquad (22.4)$$

A surface has two sides, so there are two possible directions for $\hat{n}$ and $\vec{A}$. We must always specify which direction we choose. In Section 22.1 we related the charge inside a *closed* surface to the electric flux through the surface. With a closed surface we will always choose the direction of $\hat{n}$ to be *outward*, and we

22.5 The volume flow rate of fluid through the wire rectangle (a) is vA when the area of the rectangle is perpendicular to $\vec{v}$ and (b) is $vA\cos\phi$ when the rectangle is tilted at an angle ϕ.

(a) A wire rectangle in a fluid

(b) The wire rectangle tilted by an angle ϕ

Application Flux Through a Basking Shark's Mouth

Unlike aggressive carnivorous sharks such as great whites, a basking shark feeds passively on plankton in the water that passes through the shark's gills as it swims. To survive on these tiny organisms requires a huge flux of water through a basking shark's immense mouth, which can be up to a meter across. The water flux—the product of the shark's speed through the water and the area of its mouth—can be up to $0.5\ \text{m}^3/\text{s}$ (500 liters per second, or almost 5×10^5 gallons per hour). In a similar way, the flux of electric field through a surface depends on the magnitude of the field and the area of the surface (as well as the relative orientation of the field and surface).

22.6 A flat surface in a uniform electric field. The electric flux Φ_E through the surface equals the scalar product of the electric field $\vec{E}$ and the area vector $\vec{A}$.

(a) Surface is face-on to electric field:
- $\vec{E}$ and $\vec{A}$ are parallel (the angle between $\vec{E}$ and $\vec{A}$ is $\phi = 0$).
- The flux $\Phi_E = \vec{E} \cdot \vec{A} = EA$.

(b) Surface is tilted from a face-on orientation by an angle ϕ:
- The angle between $\vec{E}$ and $\vec{A}$ is ϕ.
- The flux $\Phi_E = \vec{E} \cdot \vec{A} = EA \cos \phi$.

(c) Surface is edge-on to electric field:
- $\vec{E}$ and $\vec{A}$ are perpendicular (the angle between $\vec{E}$ and $\vec{A}$ is $\phi = 90°$).
- The flux $\Phi_E = \vec{E} \cdot \vec{A} = EA \cos 90° = 0$.

will speak of the flux *out of* a closed surface. Thus what we called "outward electric flux" in Section 22.1 corresponds to a *positive* value of Φ_E, and what we called "inward electric flux" corresponds to a *negative* value of Φ_E.

Flux of a Nonuniform Electric Field

What happens if the electric field $\vec{E}$ isn't uniform but varies from point to point over the area A? Or what if A is part of a curved surface? Then we divide A into many small elements dA, each of which has a unit vector $\hat{n}$ perpendicular to it and a vector area $d\vec{A} = \hat{n}\, dA$. We calculate the electric flux through each element and integrate the results to obtain the total flux:

$$\Phi_E = \int E \cos \phi \, dA = \int E_\perp \, dA = \int \vec{E} \cdot d\vec{A} \quad \begin{array}{l}\text{(general definition}\\ \text{of electric flux)}\end{array} \quad (22.5)$$

We call this integral the **surface integral** of the component $E_\perp$ over the area, or the surface integral of $\vec{E} \cdot d\vec{A}$. In specific problems, one form of the integral is sometimes more convenient than another. Example 22.3 at the end of this section illustrates the use of Eq. (22.5).

In Eq. (22.5) the electric flux $\int E_\perp \, dA$ is equal to the *average* value of the perpendicular component of the electric field, multiplied by the area of the surface. This is the same definition of electric flux that we were led to in Section 22.1, now expressed more mathematically. In the next section we will see the connection between the total electric flux through *any* closed surface, no matter what its shape, and the amount of charge enclosed within that surface.

Example 22.1 **Electric flux through a disk**

A disk of radius 0.10 m is oriented with its normal unit vector $\hat{n}$ at 30° to a uniform electric field $\vec{E}$ of magnitude $2.0 \times 10^3 \, \text{N/C}$ (Fig. 22.7). (Since this isn't a closed surface, it has no "inside" or "outside." That's why we have to specify the direction of $\hat{n}$ in the figure.) (a) What is the electric flux through the disk? (b) What is the flux through the disk if it is turned so that $\hat{n}$ is perpendicular to $\vec{E}$? (c) What is the flux through the disk if $\hat{n}$ is parallel to $\vec{E}$?

22.7 The electric flux Φ_E through a disk depends on the angle between its normal $\hat{n}$ and the electric field $\vec{E}$.

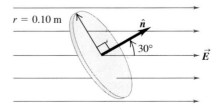

SOLUTION

IDENTIFY and SET UP: This problem is about a flat surface in a uniform electric field, so we can apply the ideas of this section. We calculate the electric flux using Eq. (22.1).

EXECUTE: (a) The area is $A = \pi(0.10 \text{ m})^2 = 0.0314 \text{ m}^2$ and the angle between $\vec{E}$ and $\vec{A} = A\hat{n}$ is $\phi = 30°$, so from Eq. (22.1),

$$\Phi_E = EA\cos\phi = (2.0 \times 10^3 \text{ N/C})(0.0314 \text{ m}^2)(\cos 30°)$$
$$= 54 \text{ N} \cdot \text{m}^2/\text{C}$$

(b) The normal to the disk is now perpendicular to $\vec{E}$, so $\phi = 90°$, $\cos\phi = 0$, and $\Phi_E = 0$.

(c) The normal to the disk is parallel to $\vec{E}$, so $\phi = 0$ and $\cos\phi = 1$:

$$\Phi_E = EA\cos\phi = (2.0 \times 10^3 \text{ N/C})(0.0314 \text{ m}^2)(1)$$
$$= 63 \text{ N} \cdot \text{m}^2/\text{C}$$

EVALUATE: As a check on our results, note that our answer to part (b) is smaller than that to part (a), which is in turn smaller than that to part (c). Is all this as it should be?

Example 22.2   Electric flux through a cube

An imaginary cubical surface of side L is in a region of uniform electric field $\vec{E}$. Find the electric flux through each face of the cube and the total flux through the cube when (a) it is oriented with two of its faces perpendicular to $\vec{E}$ (Fig. 22.8a) and (b) the cube is turned by an angle θ about a vertical axis (Fig. 22.8b).

SOLUTION

IDENTIFY and SET UP: Since $\vec{E}$ is uniform and each of the six faces of the cube is flat, we find the flux Φ_{Ei} through each face using Eqs. (22.3) and (22.4). The total flux through the cube is the sum of the six individual fluxes.

EXECUTE: (a) Figure 22.8a shows the unit vectors $\hat{n}_1$ through $\hat{n}_6$ for each face; each unit vector points *outward* from the cube's closed surface. The angle between $\vec{E}$ and $\hat{n}_1$ is 180°, the angle between $\vec{E}$

22.8 Electric flux of a uniform field $\vec{E}$ through a cubical box of side L in two orientations.

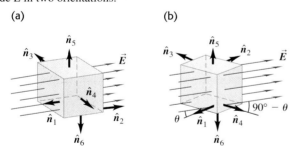

(a)   (b)

and $\hat{n}_2$ is 0°, and the angle between $\vec{E}$ and each of the other four unit vectors is 90°. Each face of the cube has area L^2, so the fluxes through the faces are

$$\Phi_{E1} = \vec{E} \cdot \hat{n}_1 A = EL^2\cos 180° = -EL^2$$
$$\Phi_{E2} = \vec{E} \cdot \hat{n}_2 A = EL^2\cos 0° = +EL^2$$
$$\Phi_{E3} = \Phi_{E4} = \Phi_{E5} = \Phi_{E6} = EL^2\cos 90° = 0$$

The flux is negative on face 1, where $\vec{E}$ is directed into the cube, and positive on face 2, where $\vec{E}$ is directed out of the cube. The total flux through the cube is

$$\Phi_E = \Phi_{E1} + \Phi_{E2} + \Phi_{E3} + \Phi_{E4} + \Phi_{E5} + \Phi_{E6}$$
$$= -EL^2 + EL^2 + 0 + 0 + 0 + 0 = 0$$

(b) The field $\vec{E}$ is directed into faces 1 and 3, so the fluxes through them are negative; $\vec{E}$ is directed out of faces 2 and 4, so the fluxes through them are positive. We find

$$\Phi_{E1} = \vec{E} \cdot \hat{n}_1 A = EL^2\cos(180° - \theta) = -EL^2\cos\theta$$
$$\Phi_{E2} = \vec{E} \cdot \hat{n}_2 A = +EL^2\cos\theta$$
$$\Phi_{E3} = \vec{E} \cdot \hat{n}_3 A = EL^2\cos(90° + \theta) = -EL^2\sin\theta$$
$$\Phi_{E4} = \vec{E} \cdot \hat{n}_4 A = EL^2\cos(90° - \theta) = +EL^2\sin\theta$$
$$\Phi_{E5} = \Phi_{E6} = EL^2\cos 90° = 0$$

The total flux $\Phi_E = \Phi_{E1} + \Phi_{E2} + \Phi_{E3} + \Phi_{E4} + \Phi_{E5} + \Phi_{E6}$ through the surface of the cube is again zero.

EVALUATE: We came to the same conclusion in our discussion of Fig. 22.3c: There is zero net flux of a uniform electric field through a closed surface that contains no electric charge.

Example 22.3   Electric flux through a sphere

A point charge $q = +3.0 \text{ }\mu\text{C}$ is surrounded by an imaginary sphere of radius $r = 0.20 \text{ m}$ centered on the charge (Fig. 22.9). Find the resulting electric flux through the sphere.

SOLUTION

IDENTIFY and SET UP: The surface is not flat and the electric field is not uniform, so to calculate the electric flux (our target variable)

we must use the general definition, Eq. (22.5). We use Eq. (22.5) to calculate the electric flux (our target variable). Because the sphere is centered on the point charge, at any point on the spherical surface, $\vec{E}$ is directed out of the sphere perpendicular to the surface. The positive direction for both $\hat{n}$ and $E_\perp$ is outward, so $E_\perp = E$ and the flux through a surface element dA is $\vec{E} \cdot d\vec{A} = E \, dA$. This greatly simplifies the integral in Eq. (22.5).

Continued

22.9 Electric flux through a sphere centered on a point charge.

EXECUTE: We must evaluate the integral of Eq. (22.5), $\Phi_E = \int E \, dA$. At any point on the sphere of radius r the electric field has the same magnitude $E = q/4\pi\epsilon_0 r^2$. Hence E can be taken outside the integral, which becomes $\Phi_E = E\int dA = EA$, where A is the area of the spherical surface: $A = 4\pi r^2$. Hence the total flux through the sphere is

$$\Phi_E = EA = \frac{q}{4\pi\epsilon_0 r^2} 4\pi r^2 = \frac{q}{\epsilon_0}$$

$$= \frac{3.0 \times 10^{-6} \text{ C}}{8.85 \times 10^{-12} \text{ C}^2/\text{N} \cdot \text{m}^2} = 3.4 \times 10^5 \text{ N} \cdot \text{m}^2/\text{C}$$

EVALUATE: The radius r of the sphere cancels out of the result for Φ_E. We would have obtained the same flux with a sphere of radius 2.0 m or 200 m. We came to essentially the same conclusion in our discussion of Fig. 22.4 in Section 22.1, where we considered rectangular closed surfaces of two different sizes enclosing a point charge. There we found that the flux of $\vec{E}$ was independent of the size of the surface; the same result holds true for a spherical surface. Indeed, the flux through *any* surface enclosing a single point charge is independent of the shape or size of the surface, as we'll soon see.

Test Your Understanding of Section 22.2 Rank the following surfaces in order from most positive to most negative electric flux. (i) a flat rectangular surface with vector area $\vec{A} = (6.0 \text{ m}^2)\hat{\imath}$ in a uniform electric field $\vec{E} = (4.0 \text{ N/C})\hat{\jmath}$; (ii) a flat circular surface with vector area $\vec{A} = (3.0 \text{ m}^2)\hat{\jmath}$ in a uniform electric field $\vec{E} = (4.0 \text{ N/C})\hat{\imath} + (2.0 \text{ N/C})\hat{\jmath}$; (iii) a flat square surface with vector area $\vec{A} = (3.0 \text{ m}^2)\hat{\imath} + (7.0 \text{ m}^2)\hat{\jmath}$ in a uniform electric field $\vec{E} = (4.0 \text{ N/C})\hat{\imath} - (2.0 \text{ N/C})\hat{\jmath}$; (iv) a flat oval surface with vector area $\vec{A} = (3.0 \text{ m}^2)\hat{\imath} - (7.0 \text{ m}^2)\hat{\jmath}$ in a uniform electric field $\vec{E} = (4.0 \text{ N/C})\hat{\imath} - (2.0 \text{ N/C})\hat{\jmath}$.

22.3 Gauss's Law

22.10 Carl Friedrich Gauss helped develop several branches of mathematics, including differential geometry, real analysis, and number theory. The "bell curve" of statistics is one of his inventions. Gauss also made state-of-the-art investigations of the earth's magnetism and calculated the orbit of the first asteroid to be discovered.

Gauss's law is an alternative to Coulomb's law. While completely equivalent to Coulomb's law, Gauss's law provides a different way to express the relationship between electric charge and electric field. It was formulated by Carl Friedrich Gauss (1777–1855), one of the greatest mathematicians of all time (Fig. 22.10).

Point Charge Inside a Spherical Surface

Gauss's law states that the total electric flux through any closed surface (a surface enclosing a definite volume) is proportional to the total (net) electric charge inside the surface. In Section 22.1 we observed this relationship qualitatively for certain special cases; now we'll develop it more rigorously. We'll start with the field of a single positive point charge q. The field lines radiate out equally in all directions. We place this charge at the center of an imaginary spherical surface with radius R. The magnitude E of the electric field at every point on the surface is given by

$$E = \frac{1}{4\pi\epsilon_0} \frac{q}{R^2}$$

At each point on the surface, $\vec{E}$ is perpendicular to the surface, and its magnitude is the same at every point, just as in Example 22.3 (Section 22.2). The total electric flux is the product of the field magnitude E and the total area $A = 4\pi R^2$ of the sphere:

$$\Phi_E = EA = \frac{1}{4\pi\epsilon_0} \frac{q}{R^2} (4\pi R^2) = \frac{q}{\epsilon_0} \tag{22.6}$$

The flux is independent of the radius R of the sphere. It depends only on the charge q enclosed by the sphere.

We can also interpret this result in terms of field lines. Figure 22.11 shows two spheres with radii R and $2R$ centered on the point charge q. Every field line that passes through the smaller sphere also passes through the larger sphere, so the total flux through each sphere is the same.

What is true of the entire sphere is also true of any portion of its surface. In Fig. 22.11 an area dA is outlined on the sphere of radius R and then projected onto the sphere of radius $2R$ by drawing lines from the center through points on the boundary of dA. The area projected on the larger sphere is clearly $4\ dA$. But since the electric field due to a point charge is inversely proportional to r^2, the field magnitude is $\frac{1}{4}$ as great on the sphere of radius $2R$ as on the sphere of radius R. Hence the electric flux is the same for both areas and is independent of the radius of the sphere.

Point Charge Inside a Nonspherical Surface

This projection technique shows us how to extend this discussion to nonspherical surfaces. Instead of a second sphere, let us surround the sphere of radius R by a surface of irregular shape, as in Fig. 22.12a. Consider a small element of area dA on the irregular surface; we note that this area is *larger* than the corresponding element on a spherical surface at the same distance from q. If a normal to dA makes an angle ϕ with a radial line from q, two sides of the area projected onto the spherical surface are foreshortened by a factor $\cos\phi$ (Fig. 22.12b). The other two sides are unchanged. Thus the electric flux through the spherical surface element is equal to the flux $E\ dA\cos\phi$ through the corresponding irregular surface element.

We can divide the entire irregular surface into elements dA, compute the electric flux $E\ dA\cos\phi$ for each, and sum the results by integrating, as in Eq. (22.5). Each of the area elements projects onto a corresponding spherical surface element. Thus the *total* electric flux through the irregular surface, given by any of the forms of Eq. (22.5), must be the same as the total flux through a sphere, which Eq. (22.6) shows is equal to q/ϵ_0. Thus, for the irregular surface,

$$\Phi_E = \oint \vec{E}\cdot d\vec{A} = \frac{q}{\epsilon_0} \qquad (22.7)$$

Equation (22.7) holds for a surface of *any* shape or size, provided only that it is a *closed* surface enclosing the charge q. The circle on the integral sign reminds us that the integral is always taken over a *closed* surface.

The area elements $d\vec{A}$ and the corresponding unit vectors $\hat{n}$ always point *out of* the volume enclosed by the surface. The electric flux is then positive in areas

22.11 Projection of an element of area dA of a sphere of radius R onto a concentric sphere of radius $2R$. The projection multiplies each linear dimension by 2, so the area element on the larger sphere is $4\ dA$.

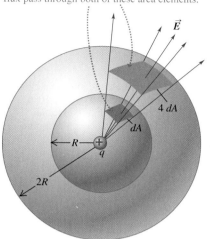

The same number of field lines and the same flux pass through both of these area elements.

22.12 Calculating the electric flux through a nonspherical surface.

(a) The outward normal to the surface makes an angle ϕ with the direction of $\vec{E}$.

(b)

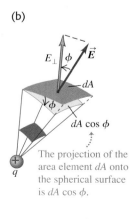

The projection of the area element dA onto the spherical surface is $dA\cos\phi$.

where the electric field points out of the surface and negative where it points inward. Also, $E_\perp$ is positive at points where $\vec{E}$ points out of the surface and negative at points where $\vec{E}$ points into the surface.

If the point charge in Fig. 22.12 is negative, the $\vec{E}$ field is directed radially *inward;* the angle ϕ is then greater than 90°, its cosine is negative, and the integral in Eq. (22.7) is negative. But since q is also negative, Eq. (22.7) still holds.

For a closed surface enclosing *no* charge,

$$\Phi_E = \oint \vec{E} \cdot d\vec{A} = 0$$

22.13 A point charge *outside* a closed surface that encloses no charge. If an electric field line from the external charge enters the surface at one point, it must leave at another.

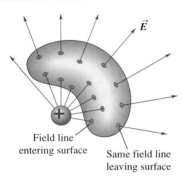

Field line entering surface
Same field line leaving surface

$\vec{E}$

This is the mathematical statement that when a region contains no charge, any field lines caused by charges *outside* the region that enter on one side must leave again on the other side. (In Section 22.1 we came to the same conclusion by considering the special case of a rectangular box in a uniform field.) Figure 22.13 illustrates this point. *Electric field lines can begin or end inside a region of space only when there is charge in that region.*

General Form of Gauss's Law

Now comes the final step in obtaining the general form of Gauss's law. Suppose the surface encloses not just one point charge q but several charges q_1, q_2, q_3, ... The total (resultant) electric field $\vec{E}$ at any point is the vector sum of the $\vec{E}$ fields of the individual charges. Let Q_{encl} be the *total* charge enclosed by the surface: $Q_{\text{encl}} = q_1 + q_2 + q_3 + \cdots$. Also let $\vec{E}$ be the *total* field at the position of the surface area element $d\vec{A}$, and let $E_\perp$ be its component perpendicular to the plane of that element (that is, parallel to $d\vec{A}$). Then we can write an equation like Eq. (22.7) for each charge and its corresponding field and add the results. When we do, we obtain the general statement of Gauss's law:

$$\Phi_E = \oint \vec{E} \cdot d\vec{A} = \frac{Q_{\text{encl}}}{\epsilon_0} \qquad \text{(Gauss's law)} \qquad (22.8)$$

The total electric flux through a closed surface is equal to the total (net) electric charge inside the surface, divided by ϵ_0.

CAUTION **Gaussian surfaces are imaginary** Remember that the closed surface in Gauss's law is *imaginary;* there need not be any material object at the position of the surface. We often refer to a closed surface used in Gauss's law as a **Gaussian surface.**

Using the definition of Q_{encl} and the various ways to express electric flux given in Eq. (22.5), we can express Gauss's law in the following equivalent forms:

$$\Phi_E = \oint E \cos \phi \, dA = \oint E_\perp \, dA = \oint \vec{E} \cdot d\vec{A} = \frac{Q_{\text{encl}}}{\epsilon_0} \quad \begin{array}{l} \text{(various forms} \\ \text{of Gauss's law)} \end{array} \quad (22.9)$$

As in Eq. (22.5), the various forms of the integral all express the same thing, the total electric flux through the Gaussian surface, in different terms. One form is sometimes more convenient than another.

As an example, Fig. 22.14a shows a spherical Gaussian surface of radius r around a positive point charge $+q$. The electric field points out of the Gaussian surface, so at every point on the surface $\vec{E}$ is in the same direction as $d\vec{A}$, $\phi = 0$, and $E_\perp$ is equal to the field magnitude $E = q/4\pi\epsilon_0 r^2$. Since E is the same at all points

(a) Gaussian surface around positive charge: positive (outward) flux

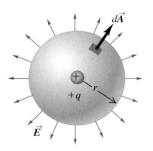

(b) Gaussian surface around negative charge: negative (inward) flux

22.14 Spherical Gaussian surfaces around **(a)** a positive point charge and **(b)** a negative point charge.

on the surface, we can take it outside the integral in Eq. (22.9). Then the remaining integral is $\int dA = A = 4\pi r^2$, the area of the sphere. Hence Eq. (22.9) becomes

$$\Phi_E = \oint E_\perp \, dA = \oint \left(\frac{q}{4\pi\epsilon_0 r^2} \right) dA = \frac{q}{4\pi\epsilon_0 r^2} \oint dA = \frac{q}{4\pi\epsilon_0 r^2} 4\pi r^2 = \frac{q}{\epsilon_0}$$

The enclosed charge Q_{encl} is just the charge $+q$, so this agrees with Gauss's law. If the Gaussian surface encloses a *negative* point charge as in Fig. 22.14b, then $\vec{E}$ points *into* the surface at each point in the direction opposite $d\vec{A}$. Then $\phi = 180°$ and $E_\perp$ is equal to the negative of the field magnitude: $E_\perp = -E = -|-q|/4\pi\epsilon_0 r^2 = -q/4\pi\epsilon_0 r^2$. Equation (22.9) then becomes

$$\Phi_E = \oint E_\perp \, dA = \oint \left(\frac{-q}{4\pi\epsilon_0 r^2} \right) dA = \frac{-q}{4\pi\epsilon_0 r^2} \oint dA = \frac{-q}{4\pi\epsilon_0 r^2} 4\pi r^2 = \frac{-q}{\epsilon_0}$$

This again agrees with Gauss's law because the enclosed charge in Fig. 22.14b is $Q_{encl} = -q$.

In Eqs. (22.8) and (22.9), Q_{encl} is always the algebraic sum of all the positive and negative charges enclosed by the Gaussian surface, and $\vec{E}$ is the *total* field at each point on the surface. Also note that in general, this field is caused partly by charges inside the surface and partly by charges outside. But as Fig. 22.13 shows, the outside charges do *not* contribute to the total (net) flux through the surface. So Eqs. (22.8) and (22.9) are correct even when there are charges outside the surface that contribute to the electric field at the surface. When $Q_{encl} = 0$, the total flux through the Gaussian surface must be zero, even though some areas may have positive flux and others may have negative flux (see Fig. 22.3b).

Gauss's law is the definitive answer to the question we posed at the beginning of Section 22.1: "If the electric field pattern is known in a given region, what can we determine about the charge distribution in that region?" It provides a relationship between the electric field on a closed surface and the charge distribution within that surface. But in some cases we can use Gauss's law to answer the reverse question: "If the charge distribution is known, what can we determine about the electric field that the charge distribution produces?" Gauss's law may seem like an unappealing way to address this question, since it may look as though evaluating the integral in Eq. (22.8) is a hopeless task. Sometimes it is, but other times it is surprisingly easy. Here's an example in which *no* integration is involved at all; we'll work out several more examples in the next section.

Conceptual Example 22.4   **Electric flux and enclosed charge**

Figure 22.15 shows the field produced by two point charges $+q$ and $-q$ (an electric dipole). Find the electric flux through each of the closed surfaces A, B, C, and D.

SOLUTION

Gauss's law, Eq. (22.8), says that the total electric flux through a closed surface is equal to the total enclosed charge divided by ϵ_0. In

Continued

Fig. 22.15, surface A (shown in red) encloses the positive charge, so $Q_{encl} = +q$; surface B (in blue) encloses the negative charge, so $Q_{encl} = -q$; surface C (in purple) encloses *both* charges, so $Q_{encl} = +q + (-q) = 0$; and surface D (in yellow) encloses no charges, so $Q_{encl} = 0$. Hence, without having to do any integration, we have $\Phi_{EA} = +q/\epsilon_0$, $\Phi_{EB} = -q/\epsilon_0$, and $\Phi_{EC} = \Phi_{ED} = 0$. These results depend only on the charges enclosed within each Gaussian surface, not on the precise shapes of the surfaces.

We can draw similar conclusions by examining the electric field lines. All the field lines that cross surface A are directed out of the surface, so the flux through A must be positive. Similarly, the flux through B must be negative since all of the field lines that cross that surface point inward. For both surface C and surface D, there are as many field lines pointing into the surface as there are field lines pointing outward, so the flux through each of these surfaces is zero.

22.15 The net number of field lines leaving a closed surface is proportional to the total charge enclosed by that surface.

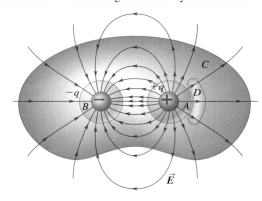

22.16 Five Gaussian surfaces and six point charges.

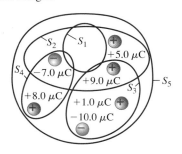

Test Your Understanding of Section 22.3 Figure 22.16 shows six point charges that all lie in the same plane. Five Gaussian surfaces—S_1, S_2, S_3, S_4, and S_5—each enclose part of this plane, and Fig. 22.16 shows the intersection of each surface with the plane. Rank these five surfaces in order of the electric flux through them, from most positive to most negative.

22.4 Applications of Gauss's Law

Gauss's law is valid for *any* distribution of charges and for *any* closed surface. Gauss's law can be used in two ways. If we know the charge distribution, and if it has enough symmetry to let us evaluate the integral in Gauss's law, we can find the field. Or if we know the field, we can use Gauss's law to find the charge distribution, such as charges on conducting surfaces.

In this section we present examples of both kinds of applications. As you study them, watch for the role played by the symmetry properties of each system. We will use Gauss's law to calculate the electric fields caused by several simple charge distributions; the results are collected in a table in the chapter summary.

In practical problems we often encounter situations in which we want to know the electric field caused by a charge distribution on a conductor. These calculations are aided by the following remarkable fact: *When excess charge is placed on a solid conductor and is at rest, it resides entirely on the surface, not in the interior of the material.* (By *excess* we mean charges other than the ions and free electrons that make up the neutral conductor.) Here's the proof. We know from Section 21.4 that in an electrostatic situation (with all charges at rest) the electric field $\vec{E}$ at every point in the interior of a conducting material is zero. If $\vec{E}$ were *not* zero, the excess charges would move. Suppose we construct a Gaussian surface inside the conductor, such as surface A in Fig. 22.17. Because $\vec{E} = 0$ everywhere on this surface, Gauss's law requires that the net charge inside the surface is zero. Now imagine shrinking the surface like a collapsing balloon until it encloses a region so small that we may consider it as a point P; then the charge at that point must be zero. We can do this anywhere inside the conductor, so *there can be no excess charge at any point within a solid conductor; any excess charge must reside on the conductor's surface.* (This result is for a *solid* conductor. In the next section we'll discuss what can happen if the conductor has cavities in its interior.) We will make use of this fact frequently in the examples that follow.

22.17 Under electrostatic conditions (charges not in motion), any excess charge on a solid conductor resides entirely on the conductor's surface.

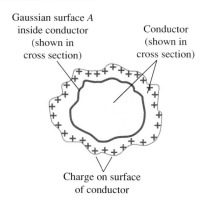

Problem-Solving Strategy 22.1 Gauss's Law

IDENTIFY *the relevant concepts:* Gauss's law is most useful when the charge distribution has spherical, cylindrical, or planar symmetry. In these cases the symmetry determines the direction of $\vec{E}$. Then Gauss's law yields the magnitude of $\vec{E}$ if we are given the charge distribution, and vice versa. In either case, begin the analysis by asking the question: What is the symmetry?

SET UP *the problem* using the following steps:
1. List the known and unknown quantities and identify the target variable.
2. Select the appropriate closed, imaginary Gaussian surface. For spherical symmetry, use a concentric spherical surface. For cylindrical symmetry, use a coaxial cylindrical surface with flat ends perpendicular to the axis of symmetry (like a soup can). For planar symmetry, use a cylindrical surface (like a tuna can) with its flat ends parallel to the plane.

EXECUTE *the solution* as follows:
1. Determine the appropriate size and placement of your Gaussian surface. To evaluate the field magnitude at a particular point, the surface must include that point. It may help to place one end of a can-shaped surface within a conductor, where $\vec{E}$ and therefore Φ are zero, or to place its ends equidistant from a charged plane.
2. Evaluate the integral $\oint E_{\perp}\, dA$ in Eq. (22.9). In this equation $E_{\perp}$ is the perpendicular component of the *total* electric field at each point on the Gaussian surface. A well-chosen Gaussian surface should make integration trivial or unnecessary. If the surface comprises several separate surfaces, such as the sides and ends

of a cylinder, the integral $\oint E_{\perp}\, dA$ over the entire closed surface is the sum of the integrals $\int E_{\perp}\, dA$ over the separate surfaces. Consider points 3–6 as you work.
3. If $\vec{E}$ is *perpendicular* (normal) at every point to a surface with area A, if it points *outward* from the interior of the surface, and if it has the same *magnitude* at every point on the surface, then $E_{\perp} = E = $ constant, and $\int E_{\perp}\, dA$ over that surface is equal to EA. (If $\vec{E}$ is inward, then $E_{\perp} = -E$ and $\int E_{\perp}\, dA = -EA$.) This should be the case for part or all of your Gaussian surface. If $\vec{E}$ is tangent to a surface at every point, then $E_{\perp} = 0$ and the integral over that surface is zero. This may be the case for parts of a cylindrical Gaussian surface. If $\vec{E} = 0$ at every point on a surface, the integral is zero.
4. Even when there is *no* charge within a Gaussian surface, the field at any given point on the surface is not necessarily zero. In that case, however, the total electric flux through the surface is always zero.
5. The flux integral $\oint E_{\perp}\, dA$ can be approximated as the difference between the numbers of electric lines of force leaving and entering the Gaussian surface. In this sense the flux gives the sign of the enclosed charge, but is only proportional to it; zero flux corresponds to zero enclosed charge.
6. Once you have evaluated $\oint E_{\perp}\, dA$, use Eq. (22.9) to solve for your target variable.

EVALUATE *your answer:* If your result is a *function* that describes how the magnitude of the electric field varies with position, ensure that it makes sense.

Example 22.5 Field of a charged conducting sphere

We place a total positive charge q on a solid conducting sphere with radius R (Fig. 22.18). Find $\vec{E}$ at any point inside or outside the sphere.

22.18 Calculating the electric field of a conducting sphere with positive charge q. Outside the sphere, the field is the same as if all of the charge were concentrated at the center of the sphere.

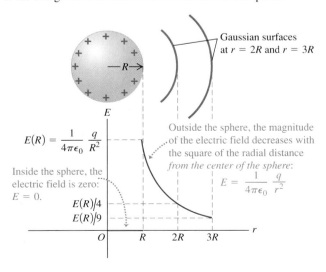

$$E(R) = \frac{1}{4\pi\epsilon_0}\frac{q}{R^2}$$

Inside the sphere, the electric field is zero: $E = 0$.

Outside the sphere, the magnitude of the electric field decreases with the square of the radial distance *from the center of the sphere:*

$$E = \frac{1}{4\pi\epsilon_0}\frac{q}{r^2}$$

SOLUTION

IDENTIFY and SET UP: As we discussed earlier in this section, all of the charge must be on the surface of the sphere. The charge is free to move on the conductor, and there is no preferred position on the surface; the charge is therefore distributed *uniformly* over the surface, and the system is spherically symmetric. To exploit this symmetry, we take as our Gaussian surface a sphere of radius r centered on the conductor. We can calculate the field inside or outside the conductor by taking $r < R$ or $r > R$, respectively. In either case, the point at which we want to calculate $\vec{E}$ lies on the Gaussian surface.

EXECUTE: The spherical symmetry means that the direction of the electric field must be radial; that's because there is no preferred direction parallel to the surface, so $\vec{E}$ can have no component parallel to the surface. There is also no preferred orientation of the sphere, so the field magnitude E can depend only on the distance r from the center and must have the same value at all points on the Gaussian surface.

For $r > R$ the entire conductor is within the Gaussian surface, so the enclosed charge is q. The area of the Gaussian surface is $4\pi r^2$, and $\vec{E}$ is uniform over the surface and perpendicular to it at each point. The flux integral $\oint E_{\perp}\, dA$ is then just $E(4\pi r^2)$, and Eq. (22.8) gives

Continued

$$E(4\pi r^2) = \frac{q}{\epsilon_0} \quad \text{and}$$

$$E = \frac{1}{4\pi\epsilon_0} \frac{q}{r^2} \quad \begin{array}{l}\text{(outside a charged} \\ \text{conducting sphere)}\end{array}$$

This expression is the same as that for a point charge; outside the charged sphere, its field is the same as though the entire charge were concentrated at its center. Just outside the surface of the sphere, where $r = R$,

$$E = \frac{1}{4\pi\epsilon_0} \frac{q}{R^2} \quad \text{(at the surface of a charged conducting sphere)}$$

CAUTION Flux can be positive or negative Remember that we have chosen the charge q to be *positive*. If the charge is negative, the electric field is radially *inward* instead of radially outward, and the electric flux through the Gaussian surface is negative. The electric-field magnitudes outside and at the surface of the sphere are given by the same expressions as above, except that q denotes the *magnitude* (absolute value) of the charge.

For $r < R$ we again have $E(4\pi r^2) = Q_{encl}/\epsilon_0$. But now our Gaussian surface (which lies entirely within the conductor)

encloses *no* charge, so $Q_{encl} = 0$. The electric field inside the conductor is therefore zero.

EVALUATE: We already knew that $\vec{E} = 0$ inside a solid conductor (whether spherical or not) when the charges are at rest. Figure 22.18 shows E as a function of the distance r from the center of the sphere. Note that in the limit as $R \rightarrow 0$, the sphere becomes a point charge; there is then only an "outside," and the field is everywhere given by $E = q/4\pi\epsilon_0 r^2$. Thus we have deduced Coulomb's law from Gauss's law. (In Section 22.3 we deduced Gauss's law from Coulomb's law; the two laws are equivalent.)

We can also use this method for a conducting spherical *shell* (a spherical conductor with a concentric spherical hole inside) if there is no charge inside the hole. We use a spherical Gaussian surface with radius r less than the radius of the hole. If there *were* a field inside the hole, it would have to be radial and spherically symmetric as before, so $E = Q_{encl}/4\pi\epsilon_0 r^2$. But now there is no enclosed charge, so $Q_{encl} = 0$ and $E = 0$ inside the hole.

Can you use this same technique to find the electric field in the region between a charged sphere and a concentric hollow conducting sphere that surrounds it?

Example 22.6 Field of a uniform line charge

Electric charge is distributed uniformly along an infinitely long, thin wire. The charge per unit length is λ (assumed positive). Find the electric field using Gauss's law.

SOLUTION

IDENTIFY and SET UP: We found in Example 21.10 (Section 21.5) that the field $\vec{E}$ of a uniformly charged, infinite wire is radially outward if λ is positive and radially inward if λ is negative, and that the field magnitude E depends only on the radial distance from the wire. This suggests that we use a *cylindrical* Gaussian surface, of radius r and arbitrary length l, coaxial with the wire and with its ends perpendicular to the wire (Fig. 22.19).

EXECUTE: The flux through the flat ends of our Gaussian surface is zero because the radial electric field is parallel to these ends, and so $\vec{E} \cdot \hat{n} = 0$. On the cylindrical part of our surface we have $\vec{E} \cdot \hat{n} = E_\perp = E$ everywhere. (If λ were negative, we would have

22.19 A coaxial cylindrical Gaussian surface is used to find the electric field outside an infinitely long, charged wire.

$\vec{E} \cdot \hat{n} = E_\perp = -E$ everywhere.) The area of the cylindrical surface is $2\pi rl$, so the flux through it—and hence the total flux Φ_E through the Gaussian surface—is $EA = 2\pi rlE$. The total enclosed charge is $Q_{encl} = \lambda l$, and so from Gauss's law, Eq. (22.8),

$$\Phi_E = 2\pi rlE = \frac{\lambda l}{\epsilon_0} \quad \text{and}$$

$$E = \frac{1}{2\pi\epsilon_0} \frac{\lambda}{r} \quad \text{(field of an infinite line of charge)}$$

We found this same result in Example 21.10 with *much* more effort.

If λ is *negative,* $\vec{E}$ is directed radially inward, and in the above expression for E we must interpret λ as the absolute value of the charge per unit length.

EVALUATE: We saw in Example 21.10 that the *entire* charge on the wire contributes to the field at any point, and yet we consider only that part of the charge $Q_{encl} = \lambda l$ within the Gaussian surface when we apply Gauss's law. There's nothing inconsistent here; it takes the entire charge to give the field the properties that allow us to calculate Φ_E so easily, and Gauss's law always applies to the enclosed charge only. If the wire is short, the symmetry of the infinite wire is lost, and E is not uniform over a coaxial, cylindrical Gaussian surface. Gauss's law then *cannot* be used to find Φ_E; we must solve the problem the hard way, as in Example 21.10.

We can use the Gaussian surface in Fig. 22.19 to show that the field outside a long, uniformly charged cylinder is the same as though all the charge were concentrated on a line along its axis (see Problem 22.42). We can also calculate the electric field in the space between a charged cylinder and a coaxial hollow conducting cylinder surrounding it (see Problem 22.39).

Example 22.7 Field of an infinite plane sheet of charge

Use Gauss's law to find the electric field caused by a thin, flat, infinite sheet with a uniform positive surface charge density σ.

SOLUTION

IDENTIFY and SET UP: In Example 21.11 (Section 21.5) we found that the field $\vec{E}$ of a uniformly charged infinite sheet is normal to the sheet, and that its magnitude is independent of the distance from the sheet. To take advantage of these symmetry properties, we use a cylindrical Gaussian surface with ends of area A and with its axis perpendicular to the sheet of charge (Fig. 22.20).

22.20 A cylindrical Gaussian surface is used to find the field of an infinite plane sheet of charge.

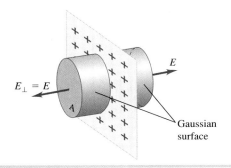

EXECUTE: The flux through the cylindrical part of our Gaussian surface is zero because $\vec{E} \cdot \hat{n} = 0$ everywhere. The flux through each flat end of the surface is $+EA$ because $\vec{E} \cdot \hat{n} = E_\perp = E$ everywhere, so the total flux through both ends—and hence the total flux Φ_E through the Gaussian surface—is $+2EA$. The total enclosed charge is $Q_{encl} = \sigma A$, and so from Gauss's law,

$$2EA = \frac{\sigma A}{\epsilon_0} \quad \text{and}$$

$$E = \frac{\sigma}{2\epsilon_0} \quad \text{(field of an infinite sheet of charge)}$$

In Example 21.11 we found this same result using a much more complex calculation.

If σ is negative, $\vec{E}$ is directed *toward* the sheet, the flux through the Gaussian surface in Fig. 22.20 is negative, and σ in the expression $E = \sigma/2\epsilon_0$ denotes the magnitude (absolute value) of the charge density.

EVALUATE: Again we see that, given favorable symmetry, we can deduce electric fields using Gauss's law much more easily than using Coulomb's law.

Example 22.8 Field between oppositely charged parallel conducting plates

Two large plane parallel conducting plates are given charges of equal magnitude and opposite sign; the surface charge densities are $+\sigma$ and $-\sigma$. Find the electric field in the region between the plates.

SOLUTION

IDENTIFY and SET UP: Figure 22.21a shows the field. Because opposite charges attract, most of the charge accumulates at the opposing faces of the plates. A small amount of charge resides on the *outer* surfaces of the plates, and there is some spreading or "fringing" of

the field at the edges. But if the plates are very large in comparison to the distance between them, the amount of charge on the outer surfaces is negligibly small, and the fringing can be neglected except near the edges. In this case we can assume that the field is uniform in the interior region between the plates, as in Fig. 22.21b, and that the charges are distributed uniformly over the opposing surfaces. To exploit this symmetry, we can use the shaded Gaussian surfaces S_1, S_2, S_3, and S_4. These surfaces are cylinders with flat ends of area A; one end of each surface lies *within* a plate.

22.21 Electric field between oppositely charged parallel plates.

(a) Realistic drawing

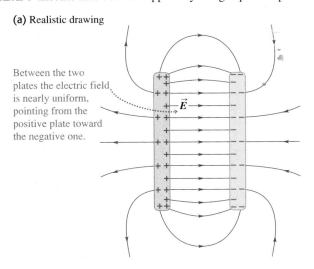

Between the two plates the electric field is nearly uniform, pointing from the positive plate toward the negative one.

(b) Idealized model

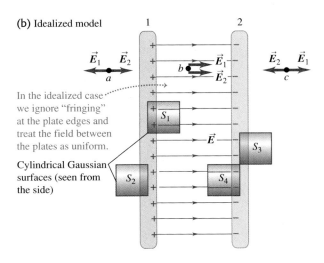

In the idealized case we ignore "fringing" at the plate edges and treat the field between the plates as uniform.

Cylindrical Gaussian surfaces (seen from the side)

Continued

EXECUTE: The left-hand end of surface S_1 is within the positive plate 1. Since the field is zero within the volume of any solid conductor under electrostatic conditions, there is no electric flux through this end. The electric field between the plates is perpendicular to the right-hand end, so on that end, $E_\perp$ is equal to E and the flux is EA; this is positive, since $\vec{E}$ is directed out of the Gaussian surface. There is no flux through the side walls of the cylinder, since these walls are parallel to $\vec{E}$. So the total flux integral in Gauss's law is EA. The net charge enclosed by the cylinder is σA, so Eq. (22.8) yields $EA = \sigma A/\epsilon_0$; we then have

$$E = \frac{\sigma}{\epsilon_0} \quad \text{(field between oppositely charged conducting plates)}$$

The field is uniform and perpendicular to the plates, and its magnitude is independent of the distance from either plate. The Gaussian surface S_4 yields the same result. Surfaces S_2 and S_3 yield $E = 0$ to the left of plate 1 and to the right of plate 2, respectively. We leave these calculations to you (see Exercise 22.29).

EVALUATE: We obtained the same results in Example 21.11 by using the principle of superposition of electric fields. The fields due to the two sheets of charge (one on each plate) are $\vec{E}_1$ and $\vec{E}_2$; from Example 22.7, both of these have magnitude $\sigma/2\epsilon_0$. The total electric field at any point is the vector sum $\vec{E} = \vec{E}_1 + \vec{E}_2$. At points a and c in Fig. 22.21b, $\vec{E}_1$ and $\vec{E}_2$ point in opposite directions, and their sum is zero. At point b, $\vec{E}_1$ and $\vec{E}_2$ are in the same direction; their sum has magnitude $E = \sigma/\epsilon_0$, just as we found above using Gauss's law.

Example 22.9 Field of a uniformly charged sphere

Positive electric charge Q is distributed uniformly *throughout the volume* of an *insulating* sphere with radius R. Find the magnitude of the electric field at a point P a distance r from the center of the sphere.

SOLUTION

IDENTIFY and SET UP: As in Example 22.5, the system is spherically symmetric. Hence we can use the conclusions of that example about the direction and magnitude of $\vec{E}$. To make use of the spherical symmetry, we choose as our Gaussian surface a sphere with radius r, concentric with the charge distribution.

EXECUTE: From symmetry, the direction of $\vec{E}$ is radial at every point on the Gaussian surface, so $E_\perp = E$ and the field magnitude E is the same at every point on the surface. Hence the total electric flux through the Gaussian surface is the product of E and the total area of the surface $A = 4\pi r^2$—that is, $\Phi_E = 4\pi r^2 E$.

The amount of charge enclosed within the Gaussian surface depends on r. To find E *inside* the sphere, we choose $r < R$. The volume charge density ρ is the charge Q divided by the volume of the entire charged sphere of radius R:

$$\rho = \frac{Q}{4\pi R^3/3}$$

The volume V_{encl} enclosed by the Gaussian surface is $\frac{4}{3}\pi r^3$, so the total charge Q_{encl} enclosed by that surface is

$$Q_{encl} = \rho V_{encl} = \left(\frac{Q}{4\pi R^3/3}\right)\left(\tfrac{4}{3}\pi r^3\right) = Q\frac{r^3}{R^3}$$

Then Gauss's law, Eq. (22.8), becomes

$$4\pi r^2 E = \frac{Q}{\epsilon_0}\frac{r^3}{R^3} \quad \text{or}$$

$$E = \frac{1}{4\pi\epsilon_0}\frac{Qr}{R^3} \quad \text{(field inside a uniformly charged sphere)}$$

The field magnitude is proportional to the distance r of the field point from the center of the sphere (see the graph of E versus r in Fig. 22.22).

To find E *outside* the sphere, we take $r > R$. This surface encloses the entire charged sphere, so $Q_{encl} = Q$, and Gauss's law gives

$$4\pi r^2 E = \frac{Q}{\epsilon_0} \quad \text{or}$$

$$E = \frac{1}{4\pi\epsilon_0}\frac{Q}{r^2} \quad \text{(field outside a uniformly charged sphere)}$$

22.22 The magnitude of the electric field of a uniformly charged insulating sphere. Compare this with the field for a conducting sphere (see Fig. 22.18).

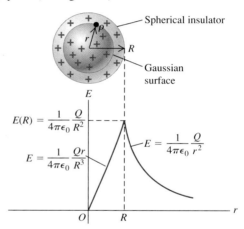

The field outside *any* spherically symmetric charged body varies as $1/r^2$, as though the entire charge were concentrated at the center. This is graphed in Fig. 22.22.

If the charge is *negative*, $\vec{E}$ is radially *inward* and in the expressions for E we interpret Q as the absolute value of the charge.

EVALUATE: Notice that if we set $r = R$ in either expression for E, we get the same result $E = Q/4\pi\epsilon_0 R^2$ for the magnitude of the field at the surface of the sphere. This is because the magnitude E is a *continuous* function of r. By contrast, for the charged conducting sphere of Example 22.5 the electric-field magnitude is *discontinuous* at $r = R$ (it jumps from $E = 0$ just inside the sphere to $E = Q/4\pi\epsilon_0 R^2$ just outside the sphere). In general, the electric field $\vec{E}$ is discontinuous in magnitude, direction, or both wherever there is a *sheet* of charge, such as at the surface of a charged conducting sphere (Example 22.5), at the surface of an infinite charged sheet (Example 22.7), or at the surface of a charged conducting plate (Example 22.8).

The approach used here can be applied to *any* spherically symmetric distribution of charge, even if it is not radially uniform, as it was here. Such charge distributions occur within many atoms and atomic nuclei, so Gauss's law is useful in atomic and nuclear physics.

Example 22.10 **Charge on a hollow sphere**

A thin-walled, hollow sphere of radius 0.250 m has an unknown charge distributed uniformly over its surface. At a distance of 0.300 m from the center of the sphere, the electric field points radially inward and has magnitude 1.80×10^2 N/C. How much charge is on the sphere?

SOLUTION

IDENTIFY and SET UP: The charge distribution is spherically symmetric. As in Examples 22.5 and 22.9, it follows that the electric field is radial everywhere and its magnitude is a function only of the radial distance r from the center of the sphere. We use a spherical Gaussian surface that is concentric with the charge distribution and has radius $r = 0.300$ m. Our target variable is $Q_{\text{encl}} = q$.

EXECUTE: The charge distribution is the same as if the charge were on the surface of a 0.250-m-radius conducting sphere. Hence we can borrow the results of Example 22.5. We note that the electric

field here is directed toward the sphere, so that q must be *negative*. Furthermore, the electric field is directed into the Gaussian surface, so that $E_\perp = -E$ and $\Phi_E = \oint E_\perp \, dA = -E(4\pi r^2)$.

By Gauss's law, the flux is equal to the charge q on the sphere (all of which is enclosed by the Gaussian surface) divided by ϵ_0. Solving for q, we find

$$q = -E(4\pi\epsilon_0 r^2) = -(1.80 \times 10^2 \text{ N/C})(4\pi)$$
$$\times (8.854 \times 10^{-12} \text{ C}^2/\text{N} \cdot \text{m}^2)(0.300 \text{ m})^2$$
$$= -1.80 \times 10^{-9} \text{ C} = -1.80 \text{ nC}$$

EVALUATE: To determine the charge, we had to know the electric field at *all* points on the Gaussian surface so that we could calculate the flux integral. This was possible here because the charge distribution is highly symmetric. If the charge distribution is irregular or lacks symmetry, Gauss's law is not very useful for calculating the charge distribution from the field, or vice versa.

Test Your Understanding of Section 22.4 You place a known amount of charge Q on the irregularly shaped conductor shown in Fig. 22.17. If you know the size and shape of the conductor, can you use Gauss's law to calculate the electric field at an arbitrary position outside the conductor?

22.5 Charges on Conductors

We have learned that in an electrostatic situation (in which there is no net motion of charge) the electric field at every point within a conductor is zero and that any excess charge on a solid conductor is located entirely on its surface (Fig. 22.23a). But what if there is a *cavity* inside the conductor (Fig. 22.23b)? If there is no charge within the cavity, we can use a Gaussian surface such as A (which lies completely within the material of the conductor) to show that the *net* charge on the *surface of the cavity* must be zero, because $\vec{E} = 0$ everywhere on the Gaussian surface. In fact, we can prove in this situation that there can't be any charge *anywhere* on the cavity surface. We will postpone detailed proof of this statement until Chapter 23.

Suppose we place a small body with a charge q inside a cavity within a conductor (Fig. 22.23c). The conductor is uncharged and is insulated from the charge q. Again $\vec{E} = 0$ everywhere on surface A, so according to Gauss's law the *total* charge inside this surface must be zero. Therefore there must be a charge $-q$ distributed on the surface of the cavity, drawn there by the charge q inside the cavity. The *total* charge on the conductor must remain zero, so a charge $+q$ must appear

Application **Charge Distribution Inside a Nerve Cell**

The interior of a human nerve cell contains both positive potassium ions (K^+) and negatively charged protein molecules (Pr^-). Potassium ions can flow out of the cell through the cell membrane, but the much larger protein molecules cannot. The result is that the interior of the cell has a net negative charge. (The fluid outside the cell has a positive charge that balances this.) The fluid within the cell is a good conductor, so the Pr^- molecules distribute themselves on the outer surface of the fluid—that is, on the inner surface of the cell membrane, which is an insulator. This is true no matter what the shape of the cell.

22.23 Finding the electric field within a charged conductor.

(a) Solid conductor with charge q_C

The charge q_C resides entirely on the surface of the conductor. The situation is electrostatic, so $\vec{E} = 0$ within the conductor.

(b) The same conductor with an internal cavity

Because $\vec{E} = 0$ at all points within the conductor, the electric field at all points on the Gaussian surface must be zero.

(c) An isolated charge q placed in the cavity

For $\vec{E}$ to be zero at all points on the Gaussian surface, the surface of the cavity must have a total charge $-q$.

either on its outer surface or inside the material. But we showed that in an electrostatic situation there can't be any excess charge within the material of a conductor. So we conclude that the charge $+q$ must appear on the outer surface. By the same reasoning, if the conductor originally had a charge q_C, then the total charge on the outer surface must be $q_C + q$ after the charge q is inserted into the cavity.

Conceptual Example 22.11   **A conductor with a cavity**

A solid conductor with a cavity carries a total charge of $+7$ nC. Within the cavity, insulated from the conductor, is a point charge of -5 nC. How much charge is on each surface (inner and outer) of the conductor?

SOLUTION

Figure 22.24 shows the situation. If the charge in the cavity is $q = -5$ nC, the charge on the inner cavity surface must be $-q = -(-5 \text{ nC}) = +5$ nC. The conductor carries a *total* charge of $+7$ nC, none of which is in the interior of the material. If $+5$ nC is on the inner surface of the cavity, then there must be $(+7 \text{ nC}) - (+5 \text{ nC}) = +2$ nC on the outer surface of the conductor.

22.24 Our sketch for this problem. There is zero electric field inside the bulk conductor and hence zero flux through the Gaussian surface shown, so the charge on the cavity wall must be the opposite of the point charge.

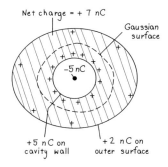

Testing Gauss's Law Experimentally

We can now consider a historic experiment, shown in Fig. 22.25. We mount a conducting container on an insulating stand. The container is initially uncharged. Then we hang a charged metal ball from an insulating thread (Fig. 22.25a), lower it into the container, and put the lid on (Fig. 22.25b). Charges are induced on the walls of the container, as shown. But now we let the ball *touch* the inner wall (Fig. 22.25c). The surface of the ball becomes part of the cavity surface. The situation is now the same as Fig. 22.23b; if Gauss's law is correct, the net charge on the cavity surface must be zero. Thus the ball must lose all its charge. Finally, we pull the ball out; we find that it has indeed lost all its charge.

This experiment was performed in the 19th century by the English scientist Michael Faraday, using a metal icepail with a lid, and it is called **Faraday's icepail experiment.** The result confirms the validity of Gauss's law and therefore of

22.25 (a) A charged conducting ball suspended by an insulating thread outside a conducting container on an insulating stand. (b) The ball is lowered into the container, and the lid is put on. (c) The ball is touched to the inner surface of the container.

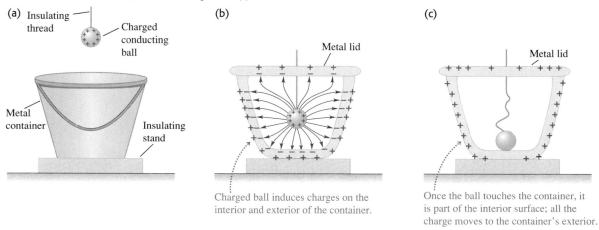

22.26 Cutaway view of the essential parts of a Van de Graaff electrostatic generator. The electron sink at the bottom draws electrons from the belt, giving it a positive charge; at the top the belt attracts electrons away from the conducting shell, giving the shell a positive charge.

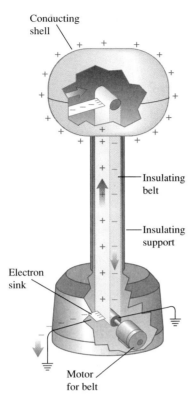

Coulomb's law. Faraday's result was significant because Coulomb's experimental method, using a torsion balance and dividing of charges, was not very precise; it is very difficult to confirm the $1/r^2$ dependence of the electrostatic force by direct force measurements. By contrast, experiments like Faraday's test the validity of Gauss's law, and therefore of Coulomb's law, with much greater precision. Modern versions of this experiment have shown that the exponent 2 in the $1/r^2$ of Coulomb's law does not differ from precisely 2 by more than 10^{-16}. So there is no reason to believe it is anything other than exactly 2.

The same principle behind Faraday's icepail experiment is used in a *Van de Graaff electrostatic generator* (Fig. 22.26). A charged belt continuously carries charge to the inside of a conducting shell. By Gauss's law, there can never be any charge on the inner surface of this shell, so the charge is immediately carried away to the outside surface of the shell. As a result, the charge on the shell and the electric field around it can become very large very rapidly. The Van de Graaff generator is used as an accelerator of charged particles and for physics demonstrations.

This principle also forms the basis for *electrostatic shielding*. Suppose we have a very sensitive electronic instrument that we want to protect from stray electric fields that might cause erroneous measurements. We surround the instrument with a conducting box, or we line the walls, floor, and ceiling of the room with a conducting material such as sheet copper. The external electric field redistributes the free electrons in the conductor, leaving a net positive charge on the outer surface in some regions and a net negative charge in others (Fig. 22.27). This charge distribution causes an additional electric field such that the *total* field at every point inside the box is zero, as Gauss's law says it must be. The charge distribution on the box also alters the shapes of the field lines near the box, as the figure shows. Such a setup is often called a *Faraday cage*. The same physics tells

22.27 (a) A conducting box (a Faraday cage) immersed in a uniform electric field. The field of the induced charges on the box combines with the uniform field to give zero total field inside the box. (b) This person is inside a Faraday cage, and so is protected from the powerful electric discharge.

(a)

(b)

you that one of the safest places to be in a lightning storm is inside an automobile; if the car is struck by lightning, the charge tends to remain on the metal skin of the vehicle, and little or no electric field is produced inside the passenger compartment.

Field at the Surface of a Conductor

Finally, we note that there is a direct relationship between the $\vec{E}$ field at a point just outside any conductor and the surface charge density σ at that point. In general, σ varies from point to point on the surface. We will show in Chapter 23 that at any such point, the direction of $\vec{E}$ is always *perpendicular* to the surface. (You can see this effect in Fig. 22.27a.)

To find a relationship between σ at any point on the surface and the perpendicular component of the electric field at that point, we construct a Gaussian surface in the form of a small cylinder (Fig. 22.28). One end face, with area A, lies within the conductor and the other lies just outside. The electric field is zero at all points within the conductor. Outside the conductor the component of $\vec{E}$ perpendicular to the side walls of the cylinder is zero, and over the end face the perpendicular component is equal to $E_\perp$. (If σ is positive, the electric field points out of the conductor and $E_\perp$ is positive; if σ is negative, the field points inward and $E_\perp$ is negative.) Hence the total flux through the surface is $E_\perp A$. The charge enclosed within the Gaussian surface is σA, so from Gauss's law,

22.28 The field just outside a charged conductor is perpendicular to the surface, and its perpendicular component $E_\perp$ is equal to σ/ϵ_0.

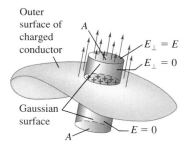

Outer surface of charged conductor

$E_\perp = E$

$E_\perp = 0$

Gaussian surface

$E = 0$

$$E_\perp A = \frac{\sigma A}{\epsilon_0} \quad \text{and} \quad E_\perp = \frac{\sigma}{\epsilon_0} \qquad \text{(field at the surface of a conductor)} \qquad (22.10)$$

We can check this with the results we have obtained for spherical, cylindrical, and plane surfaces.

We showed in Example 22.8 that the field magnitude between two infinite flat oppositely charged conducting plates also equals σ/ϵ_0. In this case the field magnitude E is the same at *all* distances from the plates, but in all other cases E decreases with increasing distance from the surface.

Conceptual Example 22.12 Field at the surface of a conducting sphere

Verify Eq. (22.10) for a conducting sphere with radius R and total charge q.

SOLUTION

In Example 22.5 (Section 22.4) we showed that the electric field just outside the surface is

$$E = \frac{1}{4\pi\epsilon_0}\frac{q}{R^2}$$

The surface charge density is uniform and equal to q divided by the surface area of the sphere:

$$\sigma = \frac{q}{4\pi R^2}$$

Comparing these two expressions, we see that $E = \sigma/\epsilon_0$, which verifies Eq. (22.10).

Example 22.13 Electric field of the earth

The earth (a conductor) has a net electric charge. The resulting electric field near the surface has an average value of about 150 N/C, directed toward the center of the earth. (a) What is the corresponding surface charge density? (b) What is the *total* surface charge of the earth?

SOLUTION

IDENTIFY and SET UP: We are given the electric-field magnitude at the surface of the conducting earth. We can calculate the surface charge density σ using Eq. (22.10). The total charge Q on the earth's surface is then the product of σ and the earth's surface area.

EXECUTE: (a) The direction of the field means that σ is negative (corresponding to $\vec{E}$ being directed *into* the surface, so $E_\perp$ is negative). From Eq. (22.10),

$$\sigma = \epsilon_0 E_\perp = (8.85 \times 10^{-12}\ \text{C}^2/\text{N}\cdot\text{m}^2)(-150\ \text{N/C})$$
$$= -1.33 \times 10^{-9}\ \text{C/m}^2 = -1.33\ \text{nC/m}^2$$

(b) The earth's surface area is $4\pi R_E^2$, where $R_E = 6.38 \times 10^6$ m is the radius of the earth (see Appendix F). The total charge Q is the product $4\pi R_E^2 \sigma$, or

$$Q = 4\pi(6.38 \times 10^6\ \text{m})^2(-1.33 \times 10^{-9}\ \text{C/m}^2)$$
$$= -6.8 \times 10^5\ \text{C} = -680\ \text{kC}$$

EVALUATE: You can check our result in part (b) using the result of Example 22.5. Solving for Q, we find

$$Q = 4\pi\epsilon_0 R^2 E_\perp$$
$$= \frac{1}{9.0 \times 10^9\ \text{N}\cdot\text{m}^2/\text{C}^2}(6.38 \times 10^6\ \text{m})^2\,(-150\ \text{N/C})$$
$$= -6.8 \times 10^5\ \text{C}$$

One electron has a charge of -1.60×10^{-19} C. Hence this much excess negative electric charge corresponds to there being $(-6.8 \times 10^5\ \text{C})/(-1.60 \times 10^{-19}\ \text{C}) = 4.2 \times 10^{24}$ excess electrons on the earth, or about 7 moles of excess electrons. This is compensated by an equal *deficiency* of electrons in the earth's upper atmosphere, so the combination of the earth and its atmosphere is electrically neutral.

Test Your Understanding of Section 22.5 A hollow conducting sphere has no net charge. There is a positive point charge q at the center of the spherical cavity within the sphere. You connect a conducting wire from the outside of the sphere to ground. Will you measure an electric field outside the sphere?

Electric flux: Electric flux is a measure of the "flow" of electric field through a surface. It is equal to the product of an area element and the perpendicular component of $\vec{E}$, integrated over a surface. (See Examples 22.1–22.3.)

$$\Phi_E = \int E\cos\phi\, dA$$

$$= \int E_\perp\, dA = \int \vec{E} \cdot d\vec{A} \quad (22.5)$$

Gauss's law: Gauss's law states that the total electric flux through a closed surface, which can be written as the surface integral of the component of $\vec{E}$ normal to the surface, equals a constant times the total charge Q_{encl} enclosed by the surface. Gauss's law is logically equivalent to Coulomb's law, but its use greatly simplifies problems with a high degree of symmetry. (See Examples 22.4–22.10.)

When excess charge is placed on a conductor and is at rest, it resides entirely on the surface, and $\vec{E} = \mathbf{0}$ everywhere in the material of the conductor. (See Examples 22.11–22.13.)

$$\Phi_E = \oint E\cos\phi\, dA$$

$$= \oint E_\perp\, dA = \oint \vec{E} \cdot d\vec{A}$$

$$= \frac{Q_{encl}}{\epsilon_0} \quad (22.8), (22.9)$$

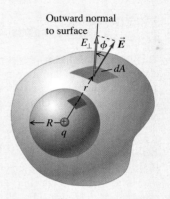

Electric field of various symmetric charge distributions: The following table lists electric fields caused by several symmetric charge distributions. In the table, q, Q, λ, and σ refer to the *magnitudes* of the quantities.

Charge Distribution	Point in Electric Field	Electric Field Magnitude
Single point charge q	Distance r from q	$E = \dfrac{1}{4\pi\epsilon_0}\dfrac{q}{r^2}$
Charge q on surface of conducting sphere with radius R	Outside sphere, $r > R$	$E = \dfrac{1}{4\pi\epsilon_0}\dfrac{q}{r^2}$
	Inside sphere, $r < R$	$E = 0$
Infinite wire, charge per unit length λ	Distance r from wire	$E = \dfrac{1}{2\pi\epsilon_0}\dfrac{\lambda}{r}$
Infinite conducting cylinder with radius R, charge per unit length λ	Outside cylinder, $r > R$	$E = \dfrac{1}{2\pi\epsilon_0}\dfrac{\lambda}{r}$
	Inside cylinder, $r < R$	$E = 0$
Solid insulating sphere with radius R, charge Q distributed uniformly throughout volume	Outside sphere, $r > R$	$E = \dfrac{1}{4\pi\epsilon_0}\dfrac{Q}{r^2}$
	Inside sphere, $r < R$	$E = \dfrac{1}{4\pi\epsilon_0}\dfrac{Qr}{R^3}$
Infinite sheet of charge with uniform charge per unit area σ	Any point	$E = \dfrac{\sigma}{2\epsilon_0}$
Two oppositely charged conducting plates with surface charge densities $+\sigma$ and $-\sigma$	Any point between plates	$E = \dfrac{\sigma}{\epsilon_0}$
Charged conductor	Just outside the conductor	$E = \dfrac{\sigma}{\epsilon_0}$

BRIDGING PROBLEM | Electric Field Inside a Hydrogen Atom

A hydrogen atom is made up of a proton of charge $+Q = 1.60 \times 10^{-19}$ C and an electron of charge $-Q = -1.60 \times 10^{-19}$ C. The proton may be regarded as a point charge at $r = 0$, the center of the atom. The motion of the electron causes its charge to be "smeared out" into a spherical distribution around the proton, so that the electron is equivalent to a charge per unit volume of $\rho(r) = -(Q/\pi a_0^3)e^{-2r/a_0}$, where $a_0 = 5.29 \times 10^{-11}$ m is called the *Bohr radius*. (a) Find the total amount of the hydrogen atom's charge that is enclosed within a sphere with radius r centered on the proton. (b) Find the electric field (magnitude and direction) caused by the charge of the hydrogen atom as a function of r. (c) Make a graph as a function of r of the ratio of the electric-field magnitude E to the magnitude of the field due to the proton alone.

SOLUTION GUIDE

See MasteringPhysics® study area for a Video Tutor solution.

IDENTIFY and SET UP

1. The charge distribution in this problem is spherically symmetric, just as in Example 22.9, so you can solve it using Gauss's law.
2. The charge within a sphere of radius r includes the proton charge $+Q$ plus the portion of the electron charge distribution that lies within the sphere. The difference from Example 22.9 is that the electron charge distribution is *not* uniform, so the charge enclosed within a sphere of radius r is *not* simply the charge density multiplied by the volume $4\pi r^3/3$ of the sphere. Instead, you'll have to do an integral.

3. Consider a thin spherical shell centered on the proton, with radius r' and infinitesimal thickness dr'. Since the shell is so thin, every point within the shell is at essentially the same radius from the proton. Hence the amount of electron charge within this shell *is* equal to the electron charge density $\rho(r')$ at this radius multiplied by the volume dV of the shell. What is dV in terms of r'?
4. The total electron charge within a radius r equals the integral of $\rho(r')dV$ from $r' = 0$ to $r' = r$. Set up this integral (but don't solve it yet), and use it to write an expression for the total charge (including the proton) within a sphere of radius r.

EXECUTE

5. Integrate your expression from step 4 to find the charge within radius r. *Hint:* Integrate by substitution: Change the integration variable from r' to $x = 2r'/a_0$. You can calculate the integral $\int x^2 e^{-x}\,dx$ using integration by parts, or you can look it up in a table of integrals or on the World Wide Web.
6. Use Gauss's law and your results from step 5 to find the electric field at a distance r from the proton.
7. Find the ratio referred to in part (c) and graph it versus r. (You'll actually find it simplest to graph this function versus the quantity r/a_0.)

EVALUATE

8. How do your results for the enclosed charge and the electric-field magnitude behave in the limit $r \to 0$? In the limit $r \to \infty$? Explain your results.

Problems

For instructor-assigned homework, go to www.masteringphysics.com

•, ••, •••: Problems of increasing difficulty. **CP**: Cumulative problems incorporating material from earlier chapters. **CALC**: Problems requiring calculus. **BIO**: Biosciences problems.

DISCUSSION QUESTIONS

Q22.1 A rubber balloon has a single point charge in its interior. Does the electric flux through the balloon depend on whether or not it is fully inflated? Explain your reasoning.

Q22.2 Suppose that in Fig. 22.15 both charges were positive. What would be the fluxes through each of the four surfaces in the example?

Q22.3 In Fig. 22.15, suppose a third point charge were placed outside the purple Gaussian surface C. Would this affect the electric flux through any of the surfaces A, B, C, or D in the figure? Why or why not?

Q22.4 A certain region of space bounded by an imaginary closed surface contains no charge. Is the electric field always zero everywhere on the surface? If not, under what circumstances is it zero on the surface?

Q22.5 A spherical Gaussian surface encloses a point charge q. If the point charge is moved from the center of the sphere to a point away from the center, does the electric field at a point on the surface change? Does the total flux through the Gaussian surface change? Explain.

Q22.6 You find a sealed box on your doorstep. You suspect that the box contains several charged metal spheres packed in insulating material. How can you determine the total net charge inside the box without opening the box? Or isn't this possible?

Q22.7 A solid copper sphere has a net positive charge. The charge is distributed uniformly over the surface of the sphere, and the electric field inside the sphere is zero. Then a negative point charge outside the sphere is brought close to the surface of the sphere. Is all the net charge on the sphere still on its surface? If so, is this charge still distributed uniformly over the surface? If it is not uniform, how is it distributed? Is the electric field inside the sphere still zero? In each case justify your answers.

Q22.8 If the electric field of a point charge were proportional to $1/r^3$ instead of $1/r^2$, would Gauss's law still be valid? Explain your reasoning. (*Hint:* Consider a spherical Gaussian surface centered on a single point charge.)

Q22.9 In a conductor, one or more electrons from each atom are free to roam throughout the volume of the conductor. Does this contradict the statement that any excess charge on a solid conductor must reside on its surface? Why or why not?

Q22.10 You charge up the van de Graaff generator shown in Fig. 22.26, and then bring an identical but uncharged hollow conducting sphere near it, without letting the two spheres touch. Sketch the distribution of charges on the second sphere. What is the net flux through the second sphere? What is the electric field inside the second sphere?

Q22.11 A lightning rod is a rounded copper rod mounted on top of a building and welded to a heavy copper cable running down into the ground. Lightning rods are used to protect houses and barns from lightning; the lightning current runs through the copper rather than through the building. Why? Why should the end of the rod be rounded?

Q22.12 A solid conductor has a cavity in its interior. Would the presence of a point charge inside the cavity affect the electric field outside the conductor? Why or why not? Would the presence of a point charge outside the conductor affect the electric field inside the cavity? Again, why or why not?

Q22.13 Explain this statement: "In a static situation, the electric field at the surface of a conductor can have no component parallel to the surface because this would violate the condition that the charges on the surface are at rest." Would this same statement be valid for the electric field at the surface of an *insulator*? Explain your answer and the reason for any differences between the cases of a conductor and an insulator.

Q22.14 In a certain region of space, the electric field $\vec{E}$ is uniform. (a) Use Gauss's law to prove that this region of space must be electrically neutral; that is, the volume charge density ρ must be zero. (b) Is the converse true? That is, in a region of space where there is no charge, must $\vec{E}$ be uniform? Explain.

Q22.15 (a) In a certain region of space, the volume charge density ρ has a uniform positive value. Can $\vec{E}$ be uniform in this region? Explain. (b) Suppose that in this region of uniform positive ρ there is a "bubble" within which $\rho = 0$. Can $\vec{E}$ be uniform within this bubble? Explain.

EXERCISES

Section 22.2 Calculating Electric Flux

22.1 • A flat sheet of paper of area 0.250 m² is oriented so that the normal to the sheet is at an angle of 60° to a uniform electric field of magnitude 14 N/C. (a) Find the magnitude of the electric flux through the sheet. (b) Does the answer to part (a) depend on the shape of the sheet? Why or why not? (c) For what angle ϕ between the normal to the sheet and the electric field is the magnitude of the flux through the sheet (i) largest and (ii) smallest? Explain your answers.

22.2 •• A flat sheet is in the shape of a rectangle with sides of lengths 0.400 m and 0.600 m. The sheet is immersed in a uniform electric field of magnitude 75.0 N/C that is directed at 20° from the plane of the sheet (Fig. E22.2). Find the magnitude of the electric flux through the sheet.

Figure **E22.2**

22.3 • You measure an electric field of 1.25×10^6 N/C at a distance of 0.150 m from a point charge. There is no other source of electric field in the region other than this point charge. (a) What is the electric flux through the surface of a sphere that has this charge at its center and that has radius 0.150 m? (b) What is the magnitude of this charge?

22.4 • It was shown in Example 21.11 (Section 21.5) that the electric field due to an infinite line of charge is perpendicular to the line and has magnitude $E = \lambda/2\pi\epsilon_0 r$. Consider an imaginary cylinder with radius $r = 0.250$ m and length $l = 0.400$ m that has an infinite line of positive charge running along its axis. The charge per unit length on the line is $\lambda = 3.00\ \mu\text{C/m}$. (a) What is the electric flux through the cylinder due to this infinite line of charge? (b) What is the flux through the cylinder if its radius is increased to $r = 0.500$ m? (c) What is the flux through the cylinder if its length is increased to $l = 0.800$ m?

22.5 •• A hemispherical surface with radius r in a region of uniform electric field $\vec{E}$ has its axis aligned parallel to the direction of the field. Calculate the flux through the surface.

22.6 • The cube in Fig. E22.6 has sides of length $L = 10.0$ cm. The electric field is uniform, has magnitude $E = 4.00 \times 10^3$ N/C, and is parallel to the xy-plane at an angle of 53.1° measured from the $+x$-axis toward the $+y$-axis. (a) What is the electric flux through each of the six cube faces S_1, S_2, S_3, S_4, S_5, and S_6? (b) What is the total electric flux through all faces of the cube?

Figure **E22.6**

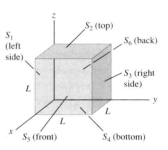

Section 22.3 Gauss's Law

22.7 • **BIO** As discussed in Section 22.5, human nerve cells have a net negative charge and the material in the interior of the cell is a good conductor. If a cell has a net charge of -8.65 pC, what are the magnitude and direction (inward or outward) of the net flux through the cell boundary?

22.8 • The three small spheres shown in Fig. E22.8 carry charges $q_1 = 4.00$ nC, $q_2 = -7.80$ nC, and $q_3 = 2.40$ nC. Find the net electric flux through each of the following closed surfaces shown in cross section in the figure: (a) S_1; (b) S_2; (c) S_3; (d) S_4; (e) S_5. (f) Do your answers to parts (a)–(e) depend on how the charge is distributed over each small sphere? Why or why not?

Figure **E22.8**

Surface	What it encloses
S_1	q_1
S_2	q_2
S_3	q_1 and q_2
S_4	q_1 and q_3
S_5	q_1 and q_2 and q_3

22.9 •• A charged paint is spread in a very thin uniform layer over the surface of a plastic sphere of diameter 12.0 cm, giving it a charge of $-35.0\ \mu\text{C}$. Find the electric field (a) just inside the paint layer; (b) just outside the paint layer; (c) 5.00 cm outside the surface of the paint layer.

22.10 • A point charge $q_1 = 4.00$ nC is located on the x-axis at $x = 2.00$ m, and a second point charge $q_2 = -6.00$ nC is on the y-axis at $y = 1.00$ m. What is the total electric flux due to these two point charges through a spherical surface centered at the origin and with radius (a) 0.500 m, (b) 1.50 m, (c) 2.50 m?

22.11 • A 6.20-μC point charge is at the center of a cube with sides of length 0.500 m. (a) What is the electric flux through one of the six faces of the cube? (b) How would your answer to part (a) change if the sides were 0.250 m long? Explain.

22.12 • **Electric Fields in an Atom.** The nuclei of large atoms, such as uranium, with 92 protons, can be modeled as spherically symmetric spheres of charge. The radius of the uranium nucleus is approximately 7.4×10^{-15} m. (a) What is the electric field this nucleus produces just outside its surface? (b) What magnitude of electric field does it produce at the distance of the electrons, which is about 1.0×10^{-10} m? (c) The electrons can be modeled as forming a uniform shell of negative charge. What net electric field do they produce at the location of the nucleus?

22.13 • A point charge of $+5.00 \, \mu$C is located on the x-axis at $x = 4.00$ m, next to a spherical surface of radius 3.00 m centered at the origin. (a) Calculate the magnitude of the electric field at $x = 3.00$ m. (b) Calculate the magnitude of the electric field at $x = -3.00$ m. (c) According to Gauss's law, the net flux through the sphere is zero because it contains no charge. Yet the field due to the external charge is much stronger on the near side of the sphere (i.e., at $x = 3.00$ m) than on the far side (at $x = -3.00$ m). How, then, can the flux into the sphere (on the near side) equal the flux out of it (on the far side)? Explain. A sketch will help.

Section 22.4 Applications of Gauss's Law and
Section 22.5 Charges on Conductors

22.14 •• A solid metal sphere with radius 0.450 m carries a net charge of 0.250 nC. Find the magnitude of the electric field (a) at a point 0.100 m outside the surface of the sphere and (b) at a point inside the sphere, 0.100 m below the surface.

22.15 •• Two very long uniform lines of charge are parallel and are separated by 0.300 m. Each line of charge has charge per unit length $+5.20 \, \mu$C/m. What magnitude of force does one line of charge exert on a 0.0500-m section of the other line of charge?

22.16 • Some planetary scientists have suggested that the planet Mars has an electric field somewhat similar to that of the earth, producing a net electric flux of 3.63×10^{16} N·m²/C at the planet's surface, directed toward the center of the planet. Calculate: (a) the total electric charge on the planet; (b) the electric field at the planet's surface (refer to the astronomical data inside the back cover); (c) the charge density on Mars, assuming all the charge is uniformly distributed over the planet's surface.

22.17 •• How many excess electrons must be added to an isolated spherical conductor 32.0 cm in diameter to produce an electric field of 1150 N/C just outside the surface?

22.18 •• The electric field 0.400 m from a very long uniform line of charge is 840 N/C. How much charge is contained in a 2.00-cm section of the line?

22.19 •• A very long uniform line of charge has charge per unit length 4.80 μC/m and lies along the x-axis. A second long uniform line of charge has charge per unit length $-2.40 \, \mu$C/m and is parallel to the x-axis at $y = 0.400$ m. What is the net electric field (magnitude and direction) at the following points on the y-axis: (a) $y = 0.200$ m and (b) $y = 0.600$ m?

22.20 • (a) At a distance of 0.200 cm from the center of a charged conducting sphere with radius 0.100 cm, the electric field is 480 N/C. What is the electric field 0.600 cm from the center of the sphere? (b) At a distance of 0.200 cm from the axis of a very long charged conducting cylinder with radius 0.100 cm, the electric field is 480 N/C. What is the electric field 0.600 cm from the axis of the cylinder? (c) At a distance of 0.200 cm from a large uniform sheet of charge, the electric field is 480 N/C. What is the electric field 1.20 cm from the sheet?

22.21 •• A hollow, conducting sphere with an outer radius of 0.250 m and an inner radius of 0.200 m has a uniform surface charge density of $+6.37 \times 10^{-6}$ C/m². A charge of $-0.500 \, \mu$C is now introduced into the cavity inside the sphere. (a) What is the new charge density on the outside of the sphere? (b) Calculate the strength of the electric field just outside the sphere. (c) What is the electric flux through a spherical surface just inside the inner surface of the sphere?

22.22 •• A point charge of $-2.00 \, \mu$C is located in the center of a spherical cavity of radius 6.50 cm inside an insulating charged solid. The charge density in the solid is $\rho = 7.35 \times 10^{-4}$ C/m³. Calculate the electric field inside the solid at a distance of 9.50 cm from the center of the cavity.

22.23 •• The electric field at a distance of 0.145 m from the surface of a solid insulating sphere with radius 0.355 m is 1750 N/C. (a) Assuming the sphere's charge is uniformly distributed, what is the charge density inside it? (b) Calculate the electric field inside the sphere at a distance of 0.200 m from the center.

22.24 •• CP A very small object with mass 8.20×10^{-9} kg and positive charge 6.50×10^{-9} C is projected directly toward a very large insulating sheet of positive charge that has uniform surface charge density 5.90×10^{-8} C/m². The object is initially 0.400 m from the sheet. What initial speed must the object have in order for its closest distance of approach to the sheet to be 0.100 m?

22.25 •• CP At time $t = 0$ a proton is a distance of 0.360 m from a very large insulating sheet of charge and is moving parallel to the sheet with speed 9.70×10^2 m/s. The sheet has uniform surface charge density 2.34×10^{-9} C/m². What is the speed of the proton at $t = 5.00 \times 10^{-8}$ s?

22.26 •• CP An electron is released from rest at a distance of 0.300 m from a large insulating sheet of charge that has uniform surface charge density $+2.90 \times 10^{-12}$ C/m². (a) How much work is done on the electron by the electric field of the sheet as the electron moves from its initial position to a point 0.050 m from the sheet? (b) What is the speed of the electron when it is 0.050 m from the sheet?

22.27 ••• CP CALC An insulating sphere of radius $R = 0.160$ m has uniform charge density $\rho = +7.20 \times 10^{-9}$ C/m³. A small object that can be treated as a point charge is released from rest just outside the surface of the sphere. The small object has positive charge $q = 3.40 \times 10^{-6}$ C. How much work does the electric field of the sphere do on the object as the object moves to a point very far from the sphere?

22.28 • A conductor with an inner cavity, like that shown in Fig. 22.23c, carries a total charge of $+5.00$ nC. The charge within the cavity, insulated from the conductor, is -6.00 nC. How much charge is on (a) the inner surface of the conductor and (b) the outer surface of the conductor?

22.29 • Apply Gauss's law to the Gaussian surfaces S_2, S_3, and S_4 in Fig. 22.21b to calculate the electric field between and outside the plates.

22.30 • A square insulating sheet 80.0 cm on a side is held horizontally. The sheet has 7.50 nC of charge spread uniformly over its area. (a) Calculate the electric field at a point 0.100 mm above the center of the sheet. (b) Estimate the electric field at a point 100 m above the center of the sheet. (c) Would the answers to parts (a) and (b) be different if the sheet were made of a conducting material? Why or why not?

22.31 • An infinitely long cylindrical conductor has radius R and uniform surface charge density σ. (a) In terms of σ and R, what is the charge per unit length λ for the cylinder? (b) In terms of σ, what is the magnitude of the electric field produced by the charged cylinder at a distance $r > R$ from its axis? (c) Express the result of part (b) in terms of λ and show that the electric field outside the cylinder is the same as if all the charge were on the axis. Compare your result to the result for a line of charge in Example 22.6 (Section 22.4).

22.32 • Two very large, nonconducting plastic sheets, each 10.0 cm thick, carry uniform charge densities σ_1, σ_2, σ_3, and σ_4 on their surfaces, as shown in Fig. E22.32. These surface charge densities have the values $\sigma_1 = -6.00\ \mu C/m^2$, $\sigma_2 = +5.00\ \mu C/m^2$, $\sigma_3 = +2.00\ \mu C/m^2$, and $\sigma_4 = +4.00\ \mu C/m^2$. Use Gauss's law to find the magnitude and direction of the electric field at the following points, far from the edges of these sheets: (a) point A, 5.00 cm from the left face of the left-hand sheet; (b) point B, 1.25 cm from the inner surface of the right-hand sheet; (c) point C, in the middle of the right-hand sheet.

Figure **E22.32**

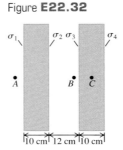

22.33 • A negative charge $-Q$ is placed inside the cavity of a hollow metal solid. The outside of the solid is grounded by connecting a conducting wire between it and the earth. (a) Is there any excess charge induced on the inner surface of the piece of metal? If so, find its sign and magnitude. (b) Is there any excess charge on the outside of the piece of metal? Why or why not? (c) Is there an electric field in the cavity? Explain. (d) Is there an electric field within the metal? Why or why not? Is there an electric field outside the piece of metal? Explain why or why not. (e) Would someone outside the solid measure an electric field due to the charge $-Q$? Is it reasonable to say that the grounded conductor has *shielded* the region from the effects of the charge $-Q$? In principle, could the same thing be done for gravity? Why or why not?

PROBLEMS

22.34 •• A cube has sides of length $L = 0.300$ m. It is placed with one corner at the origin as shown in Fig. E22.6. The electric field is not uniform but is given by $\vec{E} = (-5.00\ \text{N/C} \cdot \text{m})x\hat{\imath} + (3.00\ \text{N/C} \cdot \text{m})z\hat{k}$. (a) Find the electric flux through each of the six cube faces S_1, S_2, S_3, S_4, S_5, and S_6. (b) Find the total electric charge inside the cube.

22.35 • The electric field $\vec{E}$ in Fig. P22.35 is everywhere parallel to the x-axis, so the components E_y and E_z are zero. The x-component of the field E_x depends on x but not on y and z. At points in the yz-plane (where $x = 0$), $E_x = 125$ N/C. (a) What is the electric flux through surface I in Fig. P22.35? (b) What is the electric flux through surface II? (c) The volume shown in the figure is a small section of a very large insulating slab 1.0 m thick. If there is a total charge of -24.0 nC within the volume shown, what are the magnitude and direction of $\vec{E}$ at the face opposite surface I? (d) Is the electric field produced only by charges within the slab, or is the field also due to charges outside the slab? How can you tell?

Figure **P22.35**

22.36 •• **CALC** In a region of space there is an electric field $\vec{E}$ that is in the z-direction and that has magnitude $E = (964\ \text{N}/(\text{C} \cdot \text{m}))x$. Find the flux for this field through a square in the xy-plane at $z = 0$ and with side length 0.350 m. One side of the square is along the $+x$-axis and another side is along the $+y$-axis.

22.37 •• The electric field $\vec{E}_1$ at one face of a parallelepiped is uniform over the entire face and is directed out of the face. At the opposite face, the electric field $\vec{E}_2$ is also uniform over the entire face and is directed into that face (Fig. P22.37). The two faces in question are inclined at 30.0° from the horizontal, while $\vec{E}_1$ and $\vec{E}_2$ are both horizontal; $\vec{E}_1$ has a magnitude of 2.50×10^4 N/C, and $\vec{E}_2$ has a magnitude of 7.00×10^4 N/C. (a) Assuming that no other electric field lines cross the surfaces of the parallelepiped, determine the net charge contained within. (b) Is the electric field produced only by the charges within the parallelepiped, or is the field also due to charges outside the parallelepiped? How can you tell?

Figure **P22.37**

22.38 • A long line carrying a uniform linear charge density $+50.0\ \mu C/m$ runs parallel to and 10.0 cm from the surface of a large, flat plastic sheet that has a uniform surface charge density of $-100\ \mu C/m^2$ on one side. Find the location of all points where an α particle would feel no force due to this arrangement of charged objects.

22.39 • **The Coaxial Cable.** A long coaxial cable consists of an inner cylindrical conductor with radius a and an outer coaxial cylinder with inner radius b and outer radius c. The outer cylinder is mounted on insulating supports and has no net charge. The inner cylinder has a uniform positive charge per unit length λ. Calculate the electric field (a) at any point between the cylinders a distance r from the axis and (b) at any point outside the outer cylinder. (c) Graph the magnitude of the electric field as a function of the distance r from the axis of the cable, from $r = 0$ to $r = 2c$. (d) Find the charge per unit length on the inner surface and on the outer surface of the outer cylinder.

22.40 • A very long conducting tube (hollow cylinder) has inner radius a and outer radius b. It carries charge per unit length $+\alpha$, where α is a positive constant with units of C/m. A line of charge lies along the axis of the tube. The line of charge has charge per unit length $+\alpha$. (a) Calculate the electric field in terms of α and the distance r from the axis of the tube for (i) $r < a$; (ii) $a < r < b$; (iii) $r > b$. Show your results in a graph of E as a function of r. (b) What is the charge per unit length on (i) the inner surface of the tube and (ii) the outer surface of the tube?

22.41 • Repeat Problem 22.40, but now let the conducting tube have charge per unit length $-\alpha$. As in Problem 22.40, the line of charge has charge per unit length $+\alpha$.

22.42 • A very long, solid cylinder with radius R has positive charge uniformly distributed throughout it, with charge per unit volume ρ. (a) Derive the expression for the electric field inside the volume at a distance r from the axis of the cylinder in terms of the charge density ρ. (b) What is the electric field at a point outside the volume in terms of the charge per unit length λ in the cylinder? (c) Compare the answers to parts (a) and (b) for $r = R$. (d) Graph the electric-field magnitude as a function of r from $r = 0$ to $r = 3R$.

22.43 •• **CP** A small sphere with a mass of 4.00×10^{-6} kg and carrying a charge of 5.00×10^{-8} C hangs from a thread near a very large, charged insulating

Figure **P22.43**

sheet, as shown in Fig. P22.43. The charge density on the surface of the sheet is uniform and equal to 2.50×10^{-9} C/m². Find the angle of the thread.

22.44 · **A Sphere in a Sphere.** A solid conducting sphere carrying charge q has radius a. It is inside a concentric hollow conducting sphere with inner radius b and outer radius c. The hollow sphere has no net charge. (a) Derive expressions for the electric-field magnitude in terms of the distance r from the center for the regions $r < a$, $a < r < b$, $b < r < c$, and $r > c$. (b) Graph the magnitude of the electric field as a function of r from $r = 0$ to $r = 2c$. (c) What is the charge on the inner surface of the hollow sphere? (d) On the outer surface? (e) Represent the charge of the small sphere by four plus signs. Sketch the field lines of the system within a spherical volume of radius $2c$.

22.45 · A solid conducting sphere with radius R that carries positive charge Q is concentric with a very thin insulating shell of radius $2R$ that also carries charge Q. The charge Q is distributed uniformly over the insulating shell. (a) Find the electric field (magnitude and direction) in each of the regions $0 < r < R$, $R < r < 2R$, and $r > 2R$. (b) Graph the electric-field magnitude as a function of r.

22.46 · A conducting spherical shell with inner radius a and outer radius b has a positive point charge Q located at its center. The total charge on the shell is $-3Q$, and it is insulated from its surroundings (Fig. P22.46). (a) Derive expressions for the electric-field magnitude in terms of the distance r from the center for the regions $r < a$, $a < r < b$, and $r > b$. (b) What is the surface charge density on the inner surface of the conducting shell? (c) What is the surface charge density on the outer surface of the conducting shell? (d) Sketch the electric field lines and the location of all charges. (e) Graph the electric-field magnitude as a function of r.

Figure
P22.46

22.47 · **Concentric Spherical Shells.** A small conducting spherical shell with inner radius a and outer radius b is concentric with a larger conducting spherical shell with inner radius c and outer radius d (Fig. P22.47). The inner shell has total charge $+2q$, and the outer shell has charge $+4q$. (a) Calculate the electric field (magnitude and direction) in terms of q and the distance r from the common center of the two shells for (i) $r < a$; (ii) $a < r < b$; (iii) $b < r < c$; (iv) $c < r < d$; (v) $r > d$. Show your results in a graph of the radial component of $\vec{E}$ as a function of r. (b) What is the total charge on the (i) inner surface of the small shell; (ii) outer surface of the small shell; (iii) inner surface of the large shell; (iv) outer surface of the large shell?

Figure **P22.47**

22.48 · Repeat Problem 22.47, but now let the outer shell have charge $-2q$. As in Problem 22.47, the inner shell has charge $+2q$.

22.49 · Repeat Problem 22.47, but now let the outer shell have charge $-4q$. As in Problem 22.47, the inner shell has charge $+2q$.

22.50 · A solid conducting sphere with radius R carries a positive total charge Q. The sphere is surrounded by an insulating shell with inner radius R and outer radius $2R$. The insulating shell has a uniform charge density ρ. (a) Find the value of ρ so that the net charge of the entire system is zero. (b) If ρ has the value found in part (a), find the electric field (magnitude and direction) in each of the regions $0 < r < R$, $R < r < 2R$, and $r > 2R$. Show your results in a graph of the radial component of $\vec{E}$ as a function of r. (c) As a general rule, the electric field is discontinuous only at locations where there is a thin sheet of charge. Explain how your results in part (b) agree with this rule.

22.51 · Negative charge $-Q$ is distributed uniformly over the surface of a thin spherical insulating shell with radius R. Calculate the force (magnitude and direction) that the shell exerts on a positive point charge q located (a) a distance $r > R$ from the center of the shell (outside the shell) and (b) a distance $r < R$ from the center of the shell (inside the shell).

22.52 ·· (a) How many excess electrons must be distributed uniformly within the volume of an isolated plastic sphere 30.0 cm in diameter to produce an electric field of 1390 N/C just outside the surface of the sphere? (b) What is the electric field at a point 10.0 cm outside the surface of the sphere?

22.53 ··· CALC An insulating hollow sphere has inner radius a and outer radius b. Within the insulating material the volume charge density is given by $\rho(r) = \frac{\alpha}{r}$, where α is a positive constant. (a) In terms of α and a, what is the magnitude of the electric field at a distance r from the center of the shell, where $a < r < b$? (b) A point charge q is placed at the center of the hollow space, at $r = 0$. In terms of α and a, what value must q have (sign and magnitude) in order for the electric field to be constant in the region $a < r < b$, and what then is the value of the constant field in this region?

22.54 ·· CP **Thomson's Model of the Atom.** In the early years of the 20th century, a leading model of the structure of the atom was that of the English physicist J. J. Thomson (the discoverer of the electron). In Thomson's model, an atom consisted of a sphere of positively charged material in which were embedded negatively charged electrons, like chocolate chips in a ball of cookie dough. Consider such an atom consisting of one electron with mass m and charge $-e$, which may be regarded as a point charge, and a uniformly charged sphere of charge $+e$ and radius R. (a) Explain why the equilibrium position of the electron is at the center of the nucleus. (b) In Thomson's model, it was assumed that the positive material provided little or no resistance to the motion of the electron. If the electron is displaced from equilibrium by a distance less than R, show that the resulting motion of the electron will be simple harmonic, and calculate the frequency of oscillation. (*Hint:* Review the definition of simple harmonic motion in Section 14.2. If it can be shown that the net force on the electron is of this form, then it follows that the motion is simple harmonic. Conversely, if the net force on the electron does not follow this form, the motion is not simple harmonic.) (c) By Thomson's time, it was known that excited atoms emit light waves of only certain frequencies. In his model, the frequency of emitted light is the same as the oscillation frequency of the electron or electrons in the atom. What would the radius of a Thomson-model atom have to be for it to produce red light of frequency 4.57×10^{14} Hz? Compare your answer to the radii of real atoms, which are of the order of 10^{-10} m (see Appendix F for data about the electron). (d) If the electron were displaced from equilibrium by a distance greater than R, would the electron oscillate? Would its motion be simple harmonic? Explain your reasoning. (*Historical note:* In 1910, the atomic nucleus was discovered, proving the Thomson model to be incorrect. An atom's positive charge is not spread over its volume as Thomson supposed, but is concentrated in the tiny nucleus of radius 10^{-14} to 10^{-15} m.)

22.55 · **Thomson's Model of the Atom, Continued.** Using Thomson's (outdated) model of the atom described in Problem 22.54, consider an atom consisting of two electrons, each of charge $-e$, embedded in a sphere of charge $+2e$ and radius R. In

Figure **P22.55**

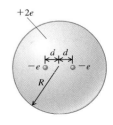

equilibrium, each electron is a distance d from the center of the atom (Fig. P22.55). Find the distance d in terms of the other properties of the atom.

22.56 • **A Uniformly Charged Slab.** A slab of insulating material has thickness $2d$ and is oriented so that its faces are parallel to the yz-plane and given by the planes $x = d$ and $x = -d$. The y- and z-dimensions of the slab are very large compared to d and may be treated as essentially infinite. The slab has a uniform positive charge density ρ. (a) Explain why the electric field due to the slab is zero at the center of the slab ($x = 0$). (b) Using Gauss's law, find the electric field due to the slab (magnitude and direction) at all points in space.

22.57 • **CALC A Nonuniformly Charged Slab.** Repeat Problem 22.56, but now let the charge density of the slab be given by $\rho(x) = \rho_0(x/d)^2$, where ρ_0 is a positive constant.

22.58 • **CALC** A nonuniform, but spherically symmetric, distribution of charge has a charge density $\rho(r)$ given as follows:

$$\rho(r) = \rho_0(1 - 4r/3R) \qquad \text{for } r \leq R$$
$$\rho(r) = 0 \qquad \text{for } r \geq R$$

where ρ_0 is a positive constant. (a) Find the total charge contained in the charge distribution. (b) Obtain an expression for the electric field in the region $r \geq R$. (c) Obtain an expression for the electric field in the region $r \leq R$. (d) Graph the electric-field magnitude E as a function of r. (e) Find the value of r at which the electric field is maximum, and find the value of that maximum field.

22.59 • **CP CALC Gauss's Law for Gravitation.** The gravitational force between two point masses separated by a distance r is proportional to $1/r^2$, just like the electric force between two point charges. Because of this similarity between gravitational and electric interactions, there is also a Gauss's law for gravitation. (a) Let $\vec{g}$ be the acceleration due to gravity caused by a point mass m at the origin, so that $\vec{g} = -(Gm/r^2)\hat{r}$. Consider a spherical Gaussian surface with radius r centered on this point mass, and show that the flux of $\vec{g}$ through this surface is given by

$$\oint \vec{g} \cdot d\vec{A} = -4\pi Gm$$

(b) By following the same logical steps used in Section 22.3 to obtain Gauss's law for the electric field, show that the flux of $\vec{g}$ through *any* closed surface is given by

$$\oint \vec{g} \cdot d\vec{A} = -4\pi GM_{encl}$$

where M_{encl} is the total mass enclosed within the closed surface.

22.60 • **CP Applying Gauss's Law for Gravitation.** Using Gauss's law for gravitation (derived in part (b) of Problem 22.59), show that the following statements are true: (a) For any spherically symmetric mass distribution with total mass M, the acceleration due to gravity outside the distribution is the same as though all the mass were concentrated at the center. (*Hint:* See Example 22.5 in Section 22.4.) (b) At any point inside a spherically symmetric shell of mass, the acceleration due to gravity is zero. (*Hint:* See Example 22.5.) (c) If we could drill a hole through a spherically symmetric planet to its center, and if the density were uniform, we would find that the magnitude of $\vec{g}$ is directly proportional to the distance r from the center. (*Hint:* See Example 22.9 in Section 22.4.) We proved these results in Section 13.6 using some fairly strenuous analysis; the proofs using Gauss's law for gravitation are *much* easier.

22.61 • (a) An insulating sphere with radius a has a uniform charge density ρ. The sphere is not centered at the origin but at $\vec{r} = \vec{b}$. Show that the electric field inside the sphere is given by

$\vec{E} = \rho(\vec{r} - \vec{b})/3\epsilon_0$. (b) An insulating sphere of radius R has a spherical hole of radius a located within its volume and centered a distance b from the center of the sphere, where $a < b < R$ (a cross section of the sphere is shown in Fig. P22.61). The solid part of the sphere has a uniform volume charge density ρ. Find the magnitude and direction of the electric field $\vec{E}$ inside the hole, and show that $\vec{E}$ is uniform over the entire hole. [*Hint:* Use the principle of superposition and the result of part (a).]

Figure **P22.61**

Charge density ρ

22.62 • A very long, solid insulating cylinder with radius R has a cylindrical hole with radius a bored along its entire length. The axis of the hole is a distance b from the axis of the cylinder, where $a < b < R$ (Fig. P22.62). The solid material of the cylinder has a uniform volume charge density ρ. Find the magnitude and direction of the electric field $\vec{E}$ inside the hole, and show that $\vec{E}$ is uniform over the entire hole. (*Hint:* See Problem 22.61.)

Figure **P22.62**

Charge density ρ

22.63 • Positive charge Q is distributed uniformly over each of two spherical volumes with radius R. One sphere of charge is centered at the origin and the other at $x = 2R$ (Fig. P22.63). Find the magnitude and direction of the net electric field due to these two distributions of charge at the following points on the x-axis: (a) $x = 0$; (b) $x = R/2$; (c) $x = R$; (d) $x = 3R$.

Figure **P22.63**

22.64 • Repeat Problem 22.63, but now let the left-hand sphere have positive charge Q and let the right-hand sphere have negative charge $-Q$.

22.65 •• **CALC** A nonuniform, but spherically symmetric, distribution of charge has a charge density $\rho(r)$ given as follows:

$$\rho(r) = \rho_0(1 - r/R) \qquad \text{for } r \leq R$$
$$\rho(r) = 0 \qquad \text{for } r \geq R$$

where $\rho_0 = 3Q/\pi R^3$ is a positive constant. (a) Show that the total charge contained in the charge distribution is Q. (b) Show that the electric field in the region $r \geq R$ is identical to that produced by a point charge Q at $r = 0$. (c) Obtain an expression for the electric field in the region $r \leq R$. (d) Graph the electric-field magnitude E as a function of r. (e) Find the value of r at which the electric field is maximum, and find the value of that maximum field.

CHALLENGE PROBLEMS

22.66 ••• **CP CALC** A region in space contains a total positive charge Q that is distributed spherically such that the volume charge density $\rho(r)$ is given by

$$\rho(r) = \alpha \qquad \text{for } r \leq R/2$$
$$\rho(r) = 2\alpha(1 - r/R) \qquad \text{for } R/2 \leq r \leq R$$
$$\rho(r) = 0 \qquad \text{for } r \geq R$$

Here α is a positive constant having units of C/m^3. (a) Determine α in terms of Q and R. (b) Using Gauss's law, derive an expression for the magnitude of $\vec{E}$ as a function of r. Do this separately for all three regions. Express your answers in terms of the total charge Q. Be sure to check that your results agree on the boundaries of the regions. (c) What fraction of the total charge is contained within the region $r \leq R/2$? (d) If an electron with charge $q' = -e$ is oscillating back and forth about $r = 0$ (the center of the distribution) with an amplitude less than $R/2$, show that the motion is simple harmonic. (*Hint:* Review the discussion of simple harmonic motion in Section 14.2. If, and only if, the net force on the electron is proportional to its displacement from equilibrium, then the motion is simple harmonic.) (e) What is the period of the motion in part (d)? (f) If the amplitude of the motion described in part (e) is greater than $R/2$, is the motion still simple harmonic? Why or why not?

22.67 ••• **CP CALC** A region in space contains a total positive charge Q that is distributed spherically such that the volume charge density $\rho(r)$ is given by

$$\rho(r) = 3\alpha r/(2R) \qquad \text{for } r \leq R/2$$
$$\rho(r) = \alpha[1 - (r/R)^2] \qquad \text{for } R/2 \leq r \leq R$$
$$\rho(r) = 0 \qquad \text{for } r \geq R$$

Here α is a positive constant having units of C/m^3. (a) Determine α in terms of Q and R. (b) Using Gauss's law, derive an expression for the magnitude of the electric field as a function of r. Do this separately for all three regions. Express your answers in terms of the total charge Q. (c) What fraction of the total charge is contained within the region $R/2 \leq r \leq R$? (d) What is the magnitude of $\vec{E}$ at $r = R/2$? (e) If an electron with charge $q' = -e$ is released from rest at any point in any of the three regions, the resulting motion will be oscillatory but not simple harmonic. Why? (See Challenge Problem 22.66.)

Answers

Chapter Opening Question ?

No. The electric field inside a cavity within a conductor is zero, so there is no electric effect on the child. (See Section 22.5.)

Test Your Understanding Questions

22.1 Answer: (iii) Each part of the surface of the box will be three times farther from the charge $+q$, so the electric field will be $\left(\frac{1}{3}\right)^2 = \frac{1}{9}$ as strong. But the area of the box will increase by a factor of $3^2 = 9$. Hence the electric flux will be multiplied by a factor of $\left(\frac{1}{9}\right)(9) = 1$. In other words, the flux will be unchanged.

22.2 Answer: (iv), (ii), (i), (iii) In each case the electric field is uniform, so the flux is $\Phi_E = \vec{E} \cdot \vec{A}$. We use the relationships for the scalar products of unit vectors: $\hat{\imath} \cdot \hat{\imath} = \hat{\jmath} \cdot \hat{\jmath} = 1$, $\hat{\imath} \cdot \hat{\jmath} = 0$. In case (i) we have $\Phi_E = (4.0 \text{ N/C})(6.0 \text{ m}^2)\hat{\imath} \cdot \hat{\jmath} = 0$ (the electric field and vector area are perpendicular, so there is zero flux). In case (ii) we have $\Phi_E = [(4.0 \text{ N/C})\hat{\imath} + (2.0 \text{ N/C})\hat{\jmath}] \cdot (3.0 \text{ m}^2)\hat{\jmath} = (2.0 \text{ N/C}) \cdot (3.0 \text{ m}^2) = 6.0 \text{ N} \cdot \text{m}^2/\text{C}$. Similarly, in case (iii) we have $\Phi_E = [(4.0 \text{ N/C})\hat{\imath} - (2.0 \text{ N/C})\hat{\jmath}] \cdot [(3.0 \text{ m}^2)\hat{\imath} + (7.0 \text{ m}^2)\hat{\jmath}] = (4.0 \text{ N/C})(3.0 \text{ m}^2) - (2.0 \text{ N/C})(7.0 \text{ m}^2) = -2 \text{ N} \cdot \text{m}^2/\text{C}$, and in case (iv) we have $\Phi_E = [(4.0 \text{ N/C})\hat{\imath} - (2.0 \text{ N/C})\hat{\jmath}] \cdot [(3.0 \text{ m}^2)\hat{\imath} - (7.0 \text{ m}^2)\hat{\jmath}] = (4.0 \text{ N/C})(3.0 \text{ m}^2) + (2.0 \text{ N/C}) \cdot (7.0 \text{ m}^2) = 26 \text{ N} \cdot \text{m}^2/\text{C}$.

22.3 Answer: S_2, S_5, S_4, S_1 and S_3 (tie) Gauss's law tells us that the flux through a closed surface is proportional to the amount of charge enclosed within that surface. So an ordering of these surfaces by their fluxes is the same as an ordering by the amount of enclosed charge. Surface S_1 encloses no charge, surface S_2 encloses $9.0 \ \mu\text{C} + 5.0 \ \mu\text{C} + (-7.0 \ \mu\text{C}) = 7.0 \ \mu\text{C}$, surface S_3 encloses $9.0 \ \mu\text{C} + 1.0 \ \mu\text{C} + (-10.0 \ \mu\text{C}) = 0$, surface S_4 encloses $8.0 \ \mu\text{C} + (-7.0 \ \mu\text{C}) = 1.0 \ \mu\text{C}$, and surface S_5 encloses $8.0 \ \mu\text{C} + (-7.0 \ \mu\text{C}) + (-10.0 \ \mu\text{C}) + (1.0 \ \mu\text{C}) + (9.0 \ \mu\text{C}) + (5.0 \ \mu\text{C}) = 6.0 \ \mu\text{C}$.

22.4 Answer: no You might be tempted to draw a Gaussian surface that is an enlarged version of the conductor, with the same shape and placed so that it completely encloses the conductor.

While you know the flux through this Gaussian surface (by Gauss's law, it's $\Phi_E = Q/\epsilon_0$), the direction of the electric field need not be perpendicular to the surface and the magnitude of the field need not be the same at all points on the surface. It's not possible to do the flux integral $\oint E_\perp \, dA$, and we can't calculate the electric field. Gauss's law is useful for calculating the electric field only when the charge distribution is *highly* symmetric.

22.5 Answer: no Before you connect the wire to the sphere, the presence of the point charge will induce a charge $-q$ on the inner surface of the hollow sphere and a charge q on the outer surface (the net charge on the sphere is zero). There will be an electric field outside the sphere due to the charge on the outer surface. Once you touch the conducting wire to the sphere, however, electrons will flow from ground to the outer surface of the sphere to neutralize the charge there (see Fig. 21.7c). As a result the sphere will have no charge on its outer surface and no electric field outside.

Bridging Problem

Answers: (a) $Q(r) = Qe^{-2r/a_0}[2(r/a_0)^2 + 2(r/a_0) + 1]$

(b) $E = \dfrac{kQe^{-2r/a_0}}{r^2}[2(r/a_0)^2 + 2(r/a_0) + 1]$

(c)

23 ELECTRIC POTENTIAL

? In one type of welding, electric charge flows between the welding tool and the metal pieces that are to be joined together. This produces a glowing arc whose high temperature fuses the pieces together. Why must the tool be held close to the pieces being welded?

This chapter is about energy associated with electrical interactions. Every time you turn on a light, listen to an MP3 player, or talk on a mobile phone, you are using electrical energy, an indispensable ingredient of our technological society. In Chapters 6 and 7 we introduced the concepts of *work* and *energy* in the context of mechanics; now we'll combine these concepts with what we've learned about electric charge, electric forces, and electric fields. Just as we found for many problems in mechanics, using energy ideas makes it easier to solve a variety of problems in electricity.

When a charged particle moves in an electric field, the field exerts a force that can do *work* on the particle. This work can always be expressed in terms of electric potential energy. Just as gravitational potential energy depends on the height of a mass above the earth's surface, electric potential energy depends on the position of the charged particle in the electric field. We'll describe electric potential energy using a new concept called *electric potential,* or simply *potential.* In circuits, a difference in potential from one point to another is often called *voltage.* The concepts of potential and voltage are crucial to understanding how electric circuits work and have equally important applications to electron beams used in cancer radiotherapy, high-energy particle accelerators, and many other devices.

23.1 Electric Potential Energy

The concepts of work, potential energy, and conservation of energy proved to be extremely useful in our study of mechanics. In this section we'll show that these concepts are just as useful for understanding and analyzing electrical interactions.

Let's begin by reviewing three essential points from Chapters 6 and 7. First, when a force $\vec{F}$ acts on a particle that moves from point a to point b, the work $W_{a \to b}$ done by the force is given by a *line integral:*

$$W_{a \to b} = \int_a^b \vec{F} \cdot d\vec{l} = \int_a^b F \cos\phi \, dl \quad \text{(work done by a force)} \tag{23.1}$$

where $d\vec{l}$ is an infinitesimal displacement along the particle's path and ϕ is the angle between $\vec{F}$ and $d\vec{l}$ at each point along the path.

Second, if the force $\vec{F}$ is *conservative,* as we defined the term in Section 7.3, the work done by $\vec{F}$ can always be expressed in terms of a **potential energy** U. When the particle moves from a point where the potential energy is U_a to a point where it is U_b, the change in potential energy is $\Delta U = U_b - U_a$ and the work $W_{a \to b}$ done by the force is

$$W_{a \to b} = U_a - U_b = -(U_b - U_a) = -\Delta U \quad \begin{array}{l}\text{(work done by a}\\\text{conservative force)}\end{array} \tag{23.2}$$

When $W_{a \to b}$ is positive, U_a is greater than U_b, ΔU is negative, and the potential energy *decreases.* That's what happens when a baseball falls from a high point (a) to a lower point (b) under the influence of the earth's gravity; the force of gravity does positive work, and the gravitational potential energy decreases (Fig. 23.1). When a tossed ball is moving upward, the gravitational force does negative work during the ascent, and the potential energy increases.

Third, the work–energy theorem says that the change in kinetic energy $\Delta K = K_b - K_a$ during a displacement equals the *total* work done on the particle. If only conservative forces do work, then Eq. (23.2) gives the total work, and $K_b - K_a = -(U_b - U_a)$. We usually write this as

$$K_a + U_a = K_b + U_b \tag{23.3}$$

That is, the total mechanical energy (kinetic plus potential) is *conserved* under these circumstances.

23.1 The work done on a baseball moving in a uniform gravitational field.

Object moving in a uniform gravitational field

$\vec{w} = m\vec{g}$

The work done by the gravitational force is the same for any path from a to b: $W_{a \to b} = -\Delta U = mgh$

Electric Potential Energy in a Uniform Field

Let's look at an electrical example of these basic concepts. In Fig. 23.2 a pair of charged parallel metal plates sets up a uniform, downward electric field with magnitude E. The field exerts a downward force with magnitude $F = q_0 E$ on a positive test charge q_0. As the charge moves downward a distance d from point a to point b, the force on the test charge is constant and independent of its location. So the work done by the electric field is the product of the force magnitude and the component of displacement in the (downward) direction of the force:

$$W_{a \to b} = Fd = q_0 Ed \tag{23.4}$$

This work is positive, since the force is in the same direction as the net displacement of the test charge.

The y-component of the electric force, $F_y = -q_0 E$, is constant, and there is no x- or z-component. This is exactly analogous to the gravitational force on a mass m near the earth's surface; for this force, there is a constant y-component $F_y = -mg$ and the x- and z-components are zero. Because of this analogy, we can conclude that the force exerted on q_0 by the uniform electric field in Fig. 23.2 is *conservative,* just as is the gravitational force. This means that the work $W_{a \to b}$ done by the field is independent of the path the particle takes from a to b. We can represent this work with a *potential-energy* function U, just as we did for gravitational potential energy

23.2 The work done on a point charge moving in a uniform electric field. Compare with Fig. 23.1.

Point charge moving in a uniform electric field

$\vec{E}$

q_0

$\vec{F} = q_0 \vec{E}$

The work done by the electric force is the same for any path from a to b: $W_{a \to b} = -\Delta U = q_0 Ed$

23.3 A positive charge moving (a) in the direction of the electric field $\vec{E}$ and (b) in the direction opposite $\vec{E}$.

(a) Positive charge moves in the direction of $\vec{E}$:
• Field does *positive* work on charge.
• *U decreases.*

(b) Positive charge moves opposite $\vec{E}$:
• Field does *negative* work on charge.
• *U increases.*

in Section 7.1. The potential energy for the gravitational force $F_y = -mg$ was $U = mgy$; hence the potential energy for the electric force $F_y = -q_0 E$ is

$$U = q_0 E y \qquad (23.5)$$

When the test charge moves from height y_a to height y_b, the work done on the charge by the field is given by

$$W_{a \rightarrow b} = -\Delta U = -(U_b - U_a) = -(q_0 E y_b - q_0 E y_a) = q_0 E(y_a - y_b) \quad (23.6)$$

When y_a is greater than y_b (Fig. 23.3a), the positive test charge q_0 moves downward, in the same direction as $\vec{E}$; the displacement is in the same direction as the force $\vec{F} = q_0 \vec{E}$, so the field does positive work and U decreases. [In particular, if $y_a - y_b = d$ as in Fig. 23.2, Eq. (23.6) gives $W_{a \rightarrow b} = q_0 E d$, in agreement with Eq. (23.4).] When y_a is less than y_b (Fig. 23.3b), the positive test charge q_0 moves upward, in the opposite direction to $\vec{E}$; the displacement is opposite the force, the field does negative work, and U increases.

If the test charge q_0 is *negative,* the potential energy increases when it moves with the field and decreases when it moves against the field (Fig. 23.4).

Whether the test charge is positive or negative, the following general rules apply: *U increases* if the test charge q_0 moves in the direction *opposite* the electric force $\vec{F} = q_0 \vec{E}$ (Figs. 23.3b and 23.4a); *U decreases* if q_0 moves in the *same*

23.4 A negative charge moving (a) in the direction of the electric field $\vec{E}$ and (b) in the direction opposite $\vec{E}$. Compare with Fig. 23.3.

(a) Negative charge moves in the direction of $\vec{E}$:
• Field does *negative* work on charge.
• *U increases.*

(b) Negative charge moves opposite $\vec{E}$:
• Field does *positive* work on charge.
• *U decreases.*

direction as $\vec{F} = q_0\vec{E}$ (Figs. 23.3a and 23.4b). This is the same behavior as for gravitational potential energy, which increases if a mass m moves upward (opposite the direction of the gravitational force) and decreases if m moves downward (in the same direction as the gravitational force).

CAUTION **Electric potential energy** The relationship between electric potential energy change and motion in an electric field is an important one that we'll use often, but that takes some effort to truly understand. Take the time to carefully study the preceding paragraph as well as Figs. 23.3 and 23.4. Doing so now will help you tremendously later!

Electric Potential Energy of Two Point Charges

The idea of electric potential energy isn't restricted to the special case of a uniform electric field. Indeed, we can apply this concept to a point charge in *any* electric field caused by a static charge distribution. Recall from Chapter 21 that we can represent any charge distribution as a collection of point charges. Therefore it's useful to calculate the work done on a test charge q_0 moving in the electric field caused by a single, stationary point charge q.

We'll consider first a displacement along the *radial* line in Fig. 23.5. The force on q_0 is given by Coulomb's law, and its radial component is

$$F_r = \frac{1}{4\pi\epsilon_0}\frac{qq_0}{r^2} \qquad (23.7)$$

If q and q_0 have the same sign ($+$ or $-$) the force is repulsive and F_r is positive; if the two charges have opposite signs, the force is attractive and F_r is negative. The force is *not* constant during the displacement, and we have to integrate to calculate the work $W_{a\to b}$ done on q_0 by this force as q_0 moves from a to b:

$$W_{a\to b} = \int_{r_a}^{r_b} F_r\,dr = \int_{r_a}^{r_b}\frac{1}{4\pi\epsilon_0}\frac{qq_0}{r^2}\,dr = \frac{qq_0}{4\pi\epsilon_0}\left(\frac{1}{r_a} - \frac{1}{r_b}\right) \qquad (23.8)$$

The work done by the electric force for this particular path depends only on the endpoints.

Now let's consider a more general displacement (Fig. 23.6) in which a and b do *not* lie on the same radial line. From Eq. (23.1) the work done on q_0 during this displacement is given by

$$W_{a\to b} = \int_{r_a}^{r_b} F\cos\phi\,dl = \int_{r_a}^{r_b}\frac{1}{4\pi\epsilon_0}\frac{qq_0}{r^2}\cos\phi\,dl$$

But Fig. 23.6 shows that $\cos\phi\,dl = dr$. That is, the work done during a small displacement $d\vec{l}$ depends only on the change dr in the distance r between the charges, which is the *radial component* of the displacement. Thus Eq. (23.8) is valid even for this more general displacement; the work done on q_0 by the electric field $\vec{E}$ produced by q depends only on r_a and r_b, not on the details of the path. Also, if q_0 returns to its starting point a by a different path, the total work done in the round-trip displacement is zero (the integral in Eq. (23.8) is from r_a back to r_a). These are the needed characteristics for a conservative force, as we defined it in Section 7.3. Thus the force on q_0 is a *conservative* force.

We see that Eqs. (23.2) and (23.8) are consistent if we define the potential energy to be $U_a = qq_0/4\pi\epsilon_0 r_a$ when q_0 is a distance r_a from q, and to be $U_b = qq_0/4\pi\epsilon_0 r_b$ when q_0 is a distance r_b from q. Thus the potential energy U when the test charge q_0 is at *any* distance r from charge q is

$$U = \frac{1}{4\pi\epsilon_0}\frac{qq_0}{r} \qquad \begin{array}{l}\text{(electric potential energy of}\\ \text{two point charges } q \text{ and } q_0)\end{array} \qquad (23.9)$$

23.5 Test charge q_0 moves along a straight line extending radially from charge q. As it moves from a to b, the distance varies from r_a to r_b.

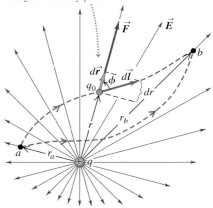

23.6 The work done on charge q_0 by the electric field of charge q does not depend on the path taken, but only on the distances r_a and r_b.

Test charge q_0 moves from a to b along an arbitrary path.

23.7 Graphs of the potential energy U of two point charges q and q_0 versus their separation r.

(a) q and q_0 have the same sign.

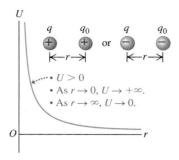

- $U > 0$
- As $r \to 0$, $U \to +\infty$.
- As $r \to \infty$, $U \to 0$.

(b) q and q_0 have opposite signs.

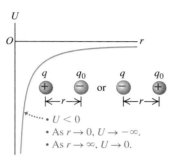

- $U < 0$
- As $r \to 0$, $U \to -\infty$.
- As $r \to \infty$, $U \to 0$.

Equation (23.9) is valid no matter what the signs of the charges q and q_0. The potential energy is positive if the charges q and q_0 have the same sign (Fig. 23.7a) and negative if they have opposite signs (Fig. 23.7b).

CAUTION **Electric potential energy vs. electric force** Don't confuse Eq. (23.9) for the potential energy of two point charges with the similar expression in Eq. (23.7) for the radial component of the electric force that one charge exerts on the other. Potential energy U is proportional to $1/r$, while the force component F_r is proportional to $1/r^2$.

Potential energy is always defined relative to some reference point where $U = 0$. In Eq. (23.9), U is zero when q and q_0 are infinitely far apart and $r = \infty$. Therefore U represents the work that would be done on the test charge q_0 by the field of q if q_0 moved from an initial distance r to infinity. If q and q_0 have the same sign, the interaction is repulsive, this work is positive, and U is positive at any finite separation (Fig. 23.7a). If the charges have opposite signs, the interaction is attractive, the work done is negative, and U is negative (Fig. 23.7b).

We emphasize that the potential energy U given by Eq. (23.9) is a *shared* property of the two charges. If the distance between q and q_0 is changed from r_a to r_b, the change in potential energy is the same whether q is held fixed and q_0 is moved or q_0 is held fixed and q is moved. For this reason, we never use the phrase "the electric potential energy *of* a point charge." (Likewise, if a mass m is at a height h above the earth's surface, the gravitational potential energy is a shared property of the mass m and the earth. We emphasized this in Sections 7.1 and 13.3.)

Equation (23.9) also holds if the charge q_0 is outside a spherically symmetric charge *distribution* with total charge q; the distance r is from q_0 to the center of the distribution. That's because Gauss's law tells us that the electric field outside such a distribution is the same as if all of its charge q were concentrated at its center (see Example 22.9 in Section 22.4).

Example 23.1 Conservation of energy with electric forces

A positron (the electron's antiparticle) has mass 9.11×10^{-31} kg and charge $q_0 = +e = +1.60 \times 10^{-19}$ C. Suppose a positron moves in the vicinity of an α (alpha) particle, which has charge $q = +2e = 3.20 \times 10^{-19}$ C and mass 6.64×10^{-27} kg. The α particle's mass is more than 7000 times that of the positron, so we assume that the α particle remains at rest. When the positron is 1.00×10^{-10} m from the α particle, it is moving directly away from the α particle at 3.00×10^6 m/s. (a) What is the positron's speed when the particles are 2.00×10^{-10} m apart? (b) What is the positron's speed when it is very far from the α particle? (c) Suppose the initial conditions are the same but the moving particle is an electron (with the same mass as the positron but charge $q_0 = -e$). Describe the subsequent motion.

SOLUTION

IDENTIFY and SET UP: The electric force between a positron (or an electron) and an α particle is conservative, so mechanical energy (kinetic plus potential) is conserved. Equation (23.9) gives the potential energy U at any separation r: The potential-energy function for parts (a) and (b) looks like that of Fig. 23.7a, and the function for part (c) looks like that of Fig. 23.7b. We are given the positron speed $v_a = 3.00 \times 10^6$ m/s when the separation between the particles is $r_a = 1.00 \times 10^{-10}$ m. In parts (a) and (b) we use Eqs. (23.3) and (23.9) to find the speed for $r = r_b = 2.00 \times 10^{-10}$ m and $r = r_c \to \infty$, respectively. In part (c) we replace the positron with an electron and reconsider the problem.

EXECUTE: (a) Both particles have positive charge, so the positron speeds up as it moves away from the α particle. From the energy-conservation equation, Eq. (23.3), the final kinetic energy is

$$K_b = \tfrac{1}{2}mv_b^2 = K_a + U_a - U_b$$

In this expression,

$$K_a = \tfrac{1}{2}mv_a^2 = \tfrac{1}{2}(9.11 \times 10^{-31} \text{ kg})(3.00 \times 10^6 \text{ m/s})^2$$
$$= 4.10 \times 10^{-18} \text{ J}$$

$$U_a = \frac{1}{4\pi\epsilon_0}\frac{qq_0}{r_a} = (9.0 \times 10^9 \text{ N} \cdot \text{m}^2/\text{C}^2)$$
$$\times \frac{(3.20 \times 10^{-19} \text{ C})(1.60 \times 10^{-19} \text{ C})}{1.00 \times 10^{-10} \text{ m}}$$
$$= 4.61 \times 10^{-18} \text{ J}$$

$$U_b = \frac{1}{4\pi\epsilon_0}\frac{qq_0}{r_b} = 2.30 \times 10^{-18} \text{ J}$$

Hence the positron kinetic energy and speed at $r = r_b = 2.00 \times 10^{-10}$ m are

$$K_b = \tfrac{1}{2}mv_b^2 = 4.10 \times 10^{-18} \text{ J} + 4.61 \times 10^{-18} \text{ J} - 2.30 \times 10^{-18} \text{ J}$$
$$= 6.41 \times 10^{-18} \text{ J}$$

$$v_b = \sqrt{\frac{2K_b}{m}} = \sqrt{\frac{2(6.41 \times 10^{-18} \text{ J})}{9.11 \times 10^{-31} \text{ kg}}} = 3.8 \times 10^6 \text{ m/s}$$

(b) When the positron and α particle are very far apart so that $r = r_c \to \infty$, the final potential energy U_c approaches zero. Again from energy conservation, the final kinetic energy and speed of the positron in this case are

$$K_c = K_a + U_a - U_c = 4.10 \times 10^{-18}\,\text{J} + 4.61 \times 10^{-18}\,\text{J} - 0$$
$$= 8.71 \times 10^{-18}\,\text{J}$$

$$v_c = \sqrt{\frac{2K_c}{m}} = \sqrt{\frac{2(8.71 \times 10^{-18}\,\text{J})}{9.11 \times 10^{-31}\,\text{kg}}} = 4.4 \times 10^6\,\text{m/s}$$

(c) The electron and α particle have opposite charges, so the force is attractive and the electron slows down as it moves away. Changing the moving particle's sign from $+e$ to $-e$ means that the initial potential energy is now $U_a = -4.61 \times 10^{-18}\,\text{J}$, which makes the total mechanical energy *negative*:

$$K_a + U_a = (4.10 \times 10^{-18}\,\text{J}) - (4.61 \times 10^{-18}\,\text{J})$$
$$= -0.51 \times 10^{-18}\,\text{J}$$

The total mechanical energy would have to be positive for the electron to move infinitely far away from the α particle. Like a rock thrown upward at low speed from the earth's surface, it will reach a maximum separation $r = r_d$ from the α particle before reversing direction. At this point its speed and its kinetic energy K_d are zero, so at separation r_d we have

$$U_d = K_a + U_a - K_d = (-0.51 \times 10^{-18}\,\text{J}) - 0$$
$$U_d = \frac{1}{4\pi\epsilon_0}\frac{qq_0}{r_d} = -0.51 \times 10^{-18}\,\text{J}$$
$$r_d = \frac{1}{U_d}\frac{qq_0}{4\pi\epsilon_0}$$
$$= \frac{(9.0 \times 10^9\,\text{N}\cdot\text{m}^2/\text{C}^2)}{-0.51 \times 10^{-18}\,\text{J}}(3.20 \times 10^{-19}\,\text{C})(-1.60 \times 10^{-19}\,\text{C})$$
$$= 9.0 \times 10^{-10}\,\text{m}$$

For $r_b = 2.00 \times 10^{-10}\,\text{m}$ we have $U_b = -2.30 \times 10^{-18}\,\text{J}$, so the electron kinetic energy and speed at this point are

$$K_b = \tfrac{1}{2}mv_b^2 = 4.10 \times 10^{-18}\,\text{J} + (-4.61 \times 10^{-18}\,\text{J})$$
$$- (-2.30 \times 10^{-18}\,\text{J}) = 1.79 \times 10^{-18}\,\text{J}$$
$$v_b = \sqrt{\frac{2K_b}{m}} = \sqrt{\frac{2(1.79 \times 10^{-18}\,\text{J})}{9.11 \times 10^{-31}\,\text{kg}}} = 2.0 \times 10^6\,\text{m/s}$$

EVALUATE: Both particles behave as expected as they move away from the α particle: The positron speeds up, and the electron slows down and eventually turns around. How fast would an electron have to be moving at $r_a = 1.00 \times 10^{-10}\,\text{m}$ to travel infinitely far from the α particle? (*Hint:* See Example 13.4 in Section 13.3.)

Electric Potential Energy with Several Point Charges

Suppose the electric field $\vec{E}$ in which charge q_0 moves is caused by *several* point charges $q_1, q_2, q_3, \ldots$ at distances $r_1, r_2, r_3, \ldots$ from q_0, as in Fig. 23.8. For example, q_0 could be a positive ion moving in the presence of other ions (Fig. 23.9). The total electric field at each point is the *vector sum* of the fields due to the individual charges, and the total work done on q_0 during any displacement is the sum of the contributions from the individual charges. From Eq. (23.9) we conclude that the potential energy associated with the test charge q_0 at point a in Fig. 23.8 is the *algebraic* sum (*not* a vector sum):

23.8 The potential energy associated with a charge q_0 at point a depends on the other charges q_1, q_2, and q_3 and on their distances r_1, r_2, and r_3 from point a.

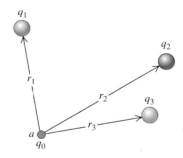

$$U = \frac{q_0}{4\pi\epsilon_0}\left(\frac{q_1}{r_1} + \frac{q_2}{r_2} + \frac{q_3}{r_3} + \cdots\right) = \frac{q_0}{4\pi\epsilon_0}\sum_i \frac{q_i}{r_i} \quad \begin{array}{l}\text{(point charge } q_0 \\ \text{and collection} \quad \text{(23.10)} \\ \text{of charges } q_i)\end{array}$$

When q_0 is at a different point b, the potential energy is given by the same expression, but $r_1, r_2, \ldots$ are the distances from $q_1, q_2, \ldots$ to point b. The work done on charge q_0 when it moves from a to b along any path is equal to the difference $U_a - U_b$ between the potential energies when q_0 is at a and at b.

We can represent *any* charge distribution as a collection of point charges, so Eq. (23.10) shows that we can always find a potential-energy function for *any* static electric field. It follows that **for every electric field due to a static charge distribution, the force exerted by that field is conservative.**

Equations (23.9) and (23.10) define U to be zero when all the distances $r_1, r_2, \ldots$ are infinite—that is, when the test charge q_0 is very far away from all the charges that produce the field. As with any potential-energy function, the point where $U = 0$ is arbitrary; we can always add a constant to make U equal zero at any point we choose. In electrostatics problems it's usually simplest to choose this point to be at infinity. When we analyze electric circuits in Chapters 25 and 26, other choices will be more convenient.

23.9 This ion engine for spacecraft uses electric forces to eject a stream of positive xenon ions (Xe^+) at speeds in excess of 30 km/s. The thrust produced is very low (about 0.09 newton) but can be maintained continuously for days, in contrast to chemical rockets, which produce a large thrust for a short time (see Fig. 8.33). Such ion engines have been used for maneuvering interplanetary spacecraft.

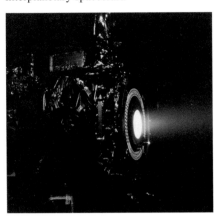

Equation (23.10) gives the potential energy associated with the presence of the test charge q_0 in the $\vec{E}$ field produced by $q_1, q_2, q_3, \dots$. But there is also potential energy involved in assembling these charges. If we start with charges $q_1, q_2, q_3, \dots$ all separated from each other by infinite distances and then bring them together so that the distance between q_i and q_j is r_{ij}, the *total* potential energy U is the sum of the potential energies of interaction for each pair of charges. We can write this as

$$U = \frac{1}{4\pi\epsilon_0} \sum_{i<j} \frac{q_i q_j}{r_{ij}} \qquad (23.11)$$

This sum extends over all *pairs* of charges; we don't let $i = j$ (because that would be an interaction of a charge with itself), and we include only terms with $i < j$ to make sure that we count each pair only once. Thus, to account for the interaction between q_3 and q_4, we include a term with $i = 3$ and $j = 4$ but not a term with $i = 4$ and $j = 3$.

Interpreting Electric Potential Energy

As a final comment, here are two viewpoints on electric potential energy. We have defined it in terms of the work done *by the electric field* on a charged particle moving in the field, just as in Chapter 7 we defined potential energy in terms of the work done by gravity or by a spring. When a particle moves from point a to point b, the work done on it by the electric field is $W_{a \to b} = U_a - U_b$. Thus the potential-energy difference $U_a - U_b$ equals *the work that is done by the electric force when the particle moves from a to b.* When U_a is greater than U_b, the field does positive work on the particle as it "falls" from a point of higher potential energy (a) to a point of lower potential energy (b).

An alternative but equivalent viewpoint is to consider how much work we would have to do to "raise" a particle from a point b where the potential energy is U_b to a point a where it has a greater value U_a (pushing two positive charges closer together, for example). To move the particle slowly (so as not to give it any kinetic energy), we need to exert an additional external force $\vec{F}_{ext}$ that is equal and opposite to the electric-field force and does positive work. The potential-energy difference $U_a - U_b$ is then defined as *the work that must be done by an external force to move the particle slowly from b to a against the electric force.* Because $\vec{F}_{ext}$ is the negative of the electric-field force and the displacement is in the opposite direction, this definition of the potential difference $U_a - U_b$ is equivalent to that given above. This alternative viewpoint also works if U_a is less than U_b, corresponding to "lowering" the particle; an example is moving two positive charges away from each other. In this case, $U_a - U_b$ is again equal to the work done by the external force, but now this work is negative.

We will use both of these viewpoints in the next section to interpret what is meant by electric *potential,* or potential energy per unit charge.

Example 23.2 | **A system of point charges**

Two point charges are located on the x-axis, $q_1 = -e$ at $x = 0$ and $q_2 = +e$ at $x = a$. (a) Find the work that must be done by an external force to bring a third point charge $q_3 = +e$ from infinity to $x = 2a$. (b) Find the total potential energy of the system of three charges.

SOLUTION

IDENTIFY and SET UP: Figure 23.10 shows the final arrangement of the three charges. In part (a) we need to find the work W that must be done on q_3 by an external force $\vec{F}_{ext}$ to bring q_3 in from

infinity to $x = 2a$. We do this by using Eq. (23.10) to find the potential energy associated with q_3 in the presence of q_1 and q_2. In part (b) we use Eq. (23.11), the expression for the potential energy of a collection of point charges, to find the total potential energy of the system.

23.10 Our sketch of the situation after the third charge has been brought in from infinity.

$$q_1 = -e \qquad q_2 = +e \qquad q_3 = +e$$

$$\ominus \qquad \oplus \qquad \oplus \qquad x$$
$$x = 0 \qquad x = a \qquad x = 2a$$

EXECUTE: (a) The work W equals the difference between (i) the potential energy U associated with q_3 when it is at $x = 2a$ and (ii) the potential energy when it is infinitely far away. The second of these is zero, so the work required is equal to U. The distances between the charges are $r_{13} = 2a$ and $r_{23} = a$, so from Eq. (23.10),

$$W = U = \frac{q_3}{4\pi\epsilon_0}\left(\frac{q_1}{r_{13}} + \frac{q_2}{r_{23}}\right) = \frac{+e}{4\pi\epsilon_0}\left(\frac{-e}{2a} + \frac{+e}{a}\right) = \frac{+e^2}{8\pi\epsilon_0 a}$$

This is positive, just as we should expect. If we bring q_3 in from infinity along the $+x$-axis, it is attracted by q_1 but is repelled more strongly by q_2. Hence we must do positive work to push q_3 to the position at $x = 2a$.

(b) From Eq. (23.11), the total potential energy of the three-charge system is

$$U = \frac{1}{4\pi\epsilon_0}\sum_{i<j}\frac{q_i q_j}{r_{ij}} = \frac{1}{4\pi\epsilon_0}\left(\frac{q_1 q_2}{r_{12}} + \frac{q_1 q_3}{r_{13}} + \frac{q_2 q_3}{r_{23}}\right)$$

$$= \frac{1}{4\pi\epsilon_0}\left[\frac{(-e)(e)}{a} + \frac{(-e)(e)}{2a} + \frac{(e)(e)}{a}\right] = \frac{-e^2}{8\pi\epsilon_0 a}$$

EVALUATE: Our negative result in part (b) means that the system has lower potential energy than it would if the three charges were infinitely far apart. An external force would have to do *negative* work to bring the three charges from infinity to assemble this entire arrangement and would have to do *positive* work to move the three charges back to infinity.

Test Your Understanding of Section 23.1 Consider the system of three point charges in Example 21.4 (Section 21.3) and shown in Fig. 21.14. (a) What is the sign of the total potential energy of this system? (i) positive; (ii) negative; (iii) zero. (b) What is the sign of the total amount of work you would have to do to move these charges infinitely far from each other? (i) positive; (ii) negative; (iii) zero. ∎

23.2 Electric Potential

In Section 23.1 we looked at the potential energy U associated with a test charge q_0 in an electric field. Now we want to describe this potential energy on a "per unit charge" basis, just as electric field describes the force per unit charge on a charged particle in the field. This leads us to the concept of *electric potential*, often called simply *potential*. This concept is very useful in calculations involving energies of charged particles. It also facilitates many electric-field calculations because electric potential is closely related to the electric field $\vec{E}$. When we need to determine an electric field, it is often easier to determine the potential first and then find the field from it.

Potential is *potential energy per unit charge*. We define the potential V at any point in an electric field as the potential energy U *per unit charge* associated with a test charge q_0 at that point:

$$V = \frac{U}{q_0} \quad \text{or} \quad U = q_0 V \qquad (23.12)$$

Potential energy and charge are both scalars, so potential is a scalar. From Eq. (23.12) its units are the units of energy divided by those of charge. The SI unit of potential, called one **volt** (1 V) in honor of the Italian electrical experimenter Alessandro Volta (1745–1827), equals 1 joule per coulomb:

$$1 \text{ V} = 1 \text{ volt} = 1 \text{ J/C} = 1 \text{ joule/coulomb}$$

Let's put Eq. (23.2), which equates the work done by the electric force during a displacement from a to b to the quantity $-\Delta U = -(U_b - U_a)$, on a "work per unit charge" basis. We divide this equation by q_0, obtaining

$$\frac{W_{a\to b}}{q_0} = -\frac{\Delta U}{q_0} = -\left(\frac{U_b}{q_0} - \frac{U_a}{q_0}\right) = -(V_b - V_a) = V_a - V_b \qquad (23.13)$$

where $V_a = U_a/q_0$ is the potential energy per unit charge at point a and similarly for V_b. We call V_a and V_b the *potential at point a* and *potential at point b*, respectively. Thus the work done per unit charge by the electric force when a charged body moves from a to b is equal to the potential at a minus the potential at b.

Mastering**PHYSICS**

PhET: Charges and Fields
ActivPhysics 11.13: Electrical Potential Energy and Potential

23.11 The voltage of this battery equals the difference in potential $V_{ab} = V_a - V_b$ between its positive terminal (point *a*) and its negative terminal (point *b*).

Point *a* (positive terminal)

$V_{ab} = 1.5$ volts

Point *b* (negative terminal)

The difference $V_a - V_b$ is called the *potential of a with respect to b*; we sometimes abbreviate this difference as $V_{ab} = V_a - V_b$ (note the order of the subscripts). This is often called the potential difference between *a* and *b*, but that's ambiguous unless we specify which is the reference point. In electric circuits, which we will analyze in later chapters, the potential difference between two points is often called **voltage** (Fig. 23.11). Equation (23.13) then states: V_{ab}, **the potential of *a* with respect to *b*, equals the work done by the electric force when a UNIT charge moves from *a* to *b*.**

Another way to interpret the potential difference V_{ab} in Eq. (23.13) is to use the alternative viewpoint mentioned at the end of Section 23.1. In that viewpoint, $U_a - U_b$ is the amount of work that must be done by an *external* force to move a particle of charge q_0 slowly from *b* to *a* against the electric force. The work that must be done *per unit charge* by the external force is then $(U_a - U_b)/q_0 = V_a - V_b = V_{ab}$. In other words: V_{ab}, **the potential of *a* with respect to *b*, equals the work that must be done to move a UNIT charge slowly from *b* to *a* against the electric force.**

An instrument that measures the difference of potential between two points is called a *voltmeter*. (In Chapter 26 we'll discuss how these devices work.) Voltmeters that can measure a potential difference of 1 μV are common, and sensitivities down to 10^{-12} V can be attained.

Calculating Electric Potential

To find the potential V due to a single point charge q, we divide Eq. (23.9) by q_0:

$$V = \frac{U}{q_0} = \frac{1}{4\pi\epsilon_0}\frac{q}{r} \quad \text{(potential due to a point charge)} \quad \text{(23.14)}$$

where r is the distance from the point charge q to the point at which the potential is evaluated. If q is positive, the potential that it produces is positive at all points; if q is negative, it produces a potential that is negative everywhere. In either case, V is equal to zero at $r = \infty$, an infinite distance from the point charge. Note that potential, like electric field, is independent of the test charge q_0 that we use to define it.

Similarly, we divide Eq. (23.10) by q_0 to find the potential due to a collection of point charges:

$$V = \frac{U}{q_0} = \frac{1}{4\pi\epsilon_0}\sum_i \frac{q_i}{r_i} \quad \begin{array}{l}\text{(potential due to a collection}\\\text{of point charge)}\end{array} \quad \text{(23.15)}$$

In this expression, r_i is the distance from the ith charge, q_i, to the point at which V is evaluated. Just as the electric field due to a collection of point charges is the *vector* sum of the fields produced by each charge, the electric potential due to a collection of point charges is the *scalar* sum of the potentials due to each charge. When we have a continuous distribution of charge along a line, over a surface, or through a volume, we divide the charge into elements dq, and the sum in Eq. (23.15) becomes an integral:

$$V = \frac{1}{4\pi\epsilon_0}\int \frac{dq}{r} \quad \begin{array}{l}\text{(potential due to a continuous}\\\text{distribution of charge)}\end{array} \quad \text{(23.16)}$$

where r is the distance from the charge element dq to the field point where we are finding V. We'll work out several examples of such cases. The potential defined by Eqs. (23.15) and (23.16) is zero at points that are infinitely far away from *all* the charges. Later we'll encounter cases in which the charge distribution itself

Application Electrocardiography

The electrodes used in an electrocardiogram—EKG or ECG for short—measure the potential differences (typically no greater than 1 mV = 10^{-3} V) between different parts of the patient's skin. These are indicative of the potential differences between regions of the heart, and so provide a sensitive way to detect any abnormalities in the electrical activity that drives cardiac function.

extends to infinity. We'll find that in such cases we cannot set $V = 0$ at infinity, and we'll need to exercise care in using and interpreting Eqs. (23.15) and (23.16).

CAUTION **What is electric potential?** Before getting too involved in the details of how to calculate electric potential, you should stop and remind yourself what potential is. The electric *potential* at a certain point is the potential energy that would be associated with a *unit* charge placed at that point. That's why potential is measured in joules per coulomb, or volts. Keep in mind, too, that there doesn't have to be a charge at a given point for a potential V to exist at that point. (In the same way, an electric field can exist at a given point even if there's no charge there to respond to it.) ▌

Finding Electric Potential from Electric Field

When we are given a collection of point charges, Eq. (23.15) is usually the easiest way to calculate the potential V. But in some problems in which the electric field is known or can be found easily, it is easier to determine V from $\vec{E}$. The force $\vec{F}$ on a test charge q_0 can be written as $\vec{F} = q_0\vec{E}$, so from Eq. (23.1) the work done by the electric force as the test charge moves from a to b is given by

$$W_{a \to b} = \int_a^b \vec{F} \cdot d\vec{l} = \int_a^b q_0 \vec{E} \cdot d\vec{l}$$

If we divide this by q_0 and compare the result with Eq. (23.13), we find

$$V_a - V_b = \int_a^b \vec{E} \cdot d\vec{l} = \int_a^b E \cos\phi \, dl \qquad \text{(potential difference as an integral of } \vec{E}) \qquad (23.17)$$

The value of $V_a - V_b$ is independent of the path taken from a to b, just as the value of $W_{a \to b}$ is independent of the path. To interpret Eq. (23.17), remember that $\vec{E}$ is the electric force per unit charge on a test charge. If the line integral $\int_a^b \vec{E} \cdot d\vec{l}$ is positive, the electric field does positive work on a positive test charge as it moves from a to b. In this case the electric potential energy decreases as the test charge moves, so the potential energy per unit charge decreases as well; hence V_b is less than V_a and $V_a - V_b$ is positive.

As an illustration, consider a positive point charge (Fig. 23.12a). The electric field is directed away from the charge, and $V = q/4\pi\epsilon_0 r$ is positive at any finite distance from the charge. If you move away from the charge, in the direction of $\vec{E}$, you move toward lower values of V; if you move toward the charge, in the direction opposite $\vec{E}$, you move toward greater values of V. For the negative point charge in Fig. 23.12b, $\vec{E}$ is directed toward the charge and $V = q/4\pi\epsilon_0 r$ is negative at any finite distance from the charge. In this case, if you move toward the charge, you are moving in the direction of $\vec{E}$ and in the direction of decreasing (more negative) V. Moving away from the charge, in the direction opposite $\vec{E}$, moves you toward increasing (less negative) values of V. The general rule, valid for *any* electric field, is: Moving *with* the direction of $\vec{E}$ means moving in the direction of *decreasing* V, and moving *against* the direction of $\vec{E}$ means moving in the direction of *increasing* V.

Also, a positive test charge q_0 experiences an electric force in the direction of $\vec{E}$, toward lower values of V; a negative test charge experiences a force opposite $\vec{E}$, toward higher values of V. Thus a positive charge tends to "fall" from a high-potential region to a lower-potential region. The opposite is true for a negative charge.

Notice that Eq. (23.17) can be rewritten as

$$V_a - V_b = -\int_b^a \vec{E} \cdot d\vec{l} \qquad (23.18)$$

This has a negative sign compared to the integral in Eq. (23.17), and the limits are reversed; hence Eqs. (23.17) and (23.18) are equivalent. But Eq. (23.18) has a slightly different interpretation. To move a unit charge slowly against the electric

23.12 If you move in the direction of $\vec{E}$, electric potential V decreases; if you move in the direction opposite $\vec{E}$, V increases.

(a) A positive point charge

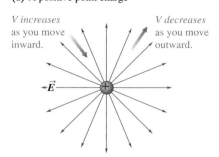

V increases as you move inward.   *V decreases* as you move outward.

(b) A negative point charge

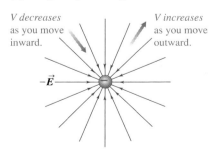

V decreases as you move inward.   *V increases* as you move outward.

force, we must apply an *external* force per unit charge equal to $-\vec{E}$, equal and opposite to the electric force per unit charge $\vec{E}$. Equation (23.18) says that $V_a - V_b = V_{ab}$, the potential of *a* with respect to *b*, equals the work done per unit charge by this external force to move a unit charge from *b* to *a*. This is the same alternative interpretation we discussed under Eq. (23.13).

Equations (23.17) and (23.18) show that the unit of potential difference (1 V) is equal to the unit of electric field (1 N/C) multiplied by the unit of distance (1 m). Hence the unit of electric field can be expressed as 1 *volt per meter* (1 V/m), as well as 1 N/C:

$$1 \text{ V/m} = 1 \text{ volt/meter} = 1 \text{ N/C} = 1 \text{ newton/coulomb}$$

In practice, the volt per meter is the usual unit of electric-field magnitude.

Electron Volts

The magnitude *e* of the electron charge can be used to define a unit of energy that is useful in many calculations with atomic and nuclear systems. When a particle with charge *q* moves from a point where the potential is V_b to a point where it is V_a, the change in the potential energy *U* is

$$U_a - U_b = q(V_a - V_b) = qV_{ab}$$

If the charge *q* equals the magnitude *e* of the electron charge, 1.602×10^{-19} C, and the potential difference is $V_{ab} = 1$ V, the change in energy is

$$U_a - U_b = (1.602 \times 10^{-19} \text{ C})(1 \text{ V}) = 1.602 \times 10^{-19} \text{ J}$$

This quantity of energy is defined to be 1 **electron volt** (1 eV):

$$1 \text{ eV} = 1.602 \times 10^{-19} \text{ J}$$

The multiples meV, keV, MeV, GeV, and TeV are often used.

CAUTION **Electron volts vs. volts** Remember that the electron volt is a unit of energy, *not* a unit of potential or potential difference! ▌

When a particle with charge *e* moves through a potential difference of 1 volt, the change in potential *energy* is 1 eV. If the charge is some multiple of *e*—say *Ne*—the change in potential energy in electron volts is *N* times the potential difference in volts. For example, when an alpha particle, which has charge 2*e*, moves between two points with a potential difference of 1000 V, the change in potential energy is 2(1000 eV) = 2000 eV. To confirm this, we write

$$U_a - U_b = qV_{ab} = (2e)(1000 \text{ V}) = (2)(1.602 \times 10^{-19} \text{ C})(1000 \text{ V})$$

$$= 3.204 \times 10^{-16} \text{ J} = 2000 \text{ eV}$$

Although we have defined the electron volt in terms of *potential* energy, we can use it for *any* form of energy, such as the kinetic energy of a moving particle. When we speak of a "one-million-electron-volt proton," we mean a proton with a kinetic energy of one million electron volts (1 MeV), equal to $(10^6)(1.602 \times 10^{-19} \text{ J}) = 1.602 \times 10^{-13}$ J. The Large Hadron Collider near Geneva, Switzerland, is designed to accelerate protons to a kinetic energy of 7 TeV (7×10^{12} eV).

Example 23.3 **Electric force and electric potential**

A proton (charge $+e = 1.602 \times 10^{-19}$ C) moves a distance $d = 0.50$ m in a straight line between points *a* and *b* in a linear accelerator. The electric field is uniform along this line, with magnitude $E = 1.5 \times 10^7$ V/m $= 1.5 \times 10^7$ N/C in the direction from *a* to *b*. Determine (a) the force on the proton; (b) the work done on it by the field; (c) the potential difference $V_a - V_b$.

IDENTIFY and SET UP: This problem uses the relationship between electric field and electric force. It also uses the relationship among force, work, and potential-energy difference. We are given the electric field, so it is straightforward to find the electric force on the proton. Calculating the work is also straightforward because $\vec{E}$ is uniform, so the force on the proton is constant. Once the work is known, we find $V_a - V_b$ using Eq. (23.13).

EXECUTE: (a) The force on the proton is in the same direction as the electric field, and its magnitude is

$$F = qE = (1.602 \times 10^{-19}\,\text{C})(1.5 \times 10^7\,\text{N/C})$$
$$= 2.4 \times 10^{-12}\,\text{N}$$

(b) The force is constant and in the same direction as the displacement, so the work done on the proton is

$$W_{a \to b} = Fd = (2.4 \times 10^{-12}\,\text{N})(0.50\,\text{m}) = 1.2 \times 10^{-12}\,\text{J}$$

$$= (1.2 \times 10^{-12}\,\text{J})\frac{1\,\text{eV}}{1.602 \times 10^{-19}\,\text{J}}$$

$$= 7.5 \times 10^6\,\text{eV} = 7.5\,\text{MeV}$$

(c) From Eq. (23.13) the potential difference is the work per unit charge, which is

$$V_a - V_b = \frac{W_{a \to b}}{q} = \frac{1.2 \times 10^{-12}\,\text{J}}{1.602 \times 10^{-19}\,\text{C}}$$

$$= 7.5 \times 10^6\,\text{J/C} = 7.5 \times 10^6\,\text{V}$$

$$= 7.5\,\text{MV}$$

We can get this same result even more easily by remembering that 1 electron volt equals 1 volt multiplied by the charge e. The work done is 7.5×10^6 eV and the charge is e, so the potential difference is $(7.5 \times 10^6\,\text{eV})/e = 7.5 \times 10^6$ V.

EVALUATE: We can check our result in part (c) by using Eq. (23.17) or Eq. (23.18). The angle ϕ between the constant field $\vec{E}$ and the displacement is zero, so Eq. (23.17) becomes

$$V_a - V_b = \int_a^b E \cos \phi \, dl = \int_a^b E \, dl = E \int_a^b dl$$

The integral of dl from a to b is just the distance d, so we again find

$$V_a - V_b = Ed = (1.5 \times 10^7\,\text{V/m})(0.50\,\text{m}) = 7.5 \times 10^6\,\text{V}$$

Example 23.4 **Potential due to two point charges**

An electric dipole consists of point charges $q_1 = +12$ nC and $q_2 = -12$ nC placed 10.0 cm apart (Fig. 23.13). Compute the electric potentials at points a, b, and c.

IDENTIFY and SET UP: This is the same arrangement as in Example 21.8, in which we calculated the electric *field* at each point by doing a *vector* sum. Here our target variable is the electric *potential* V at three points, which we find by doing the *algebraic* sum in Eq. (23.15).

EXECUTE: At point a we have $r_1 = 0.060$ m and $r_2 = 0.040$ m, so Eq. (23.15) becomes

$$V_a = \frac{1}{4\pi\epsilon_0}\sum_i \frac{q_i}{r_i} = \frac{1}{4\pi\epsilon_0}\frac{q_1}{r_1} + \frac{1}{4\pi\epsilon_0}\frac{q_2}{r_2}$$

$$= (9.0 \times 10^9\,\text{N}\cdot\text{m}^2/\text{C}^2)\frac{12 \times 10^{-9}\,\text{C}}{0.060\,\text{m}}$$

$$+ (9.0 \times 10^9\,\text{N}\cdot\text{m}^2/\text{C}^2)\frac{(-12 \times 10^{-9}\,\text{C})}{0.040\,\text{m}}$$

$$= 1800\,\text{N}\cdot\text{m/C} + (-2700\,\text{N}\cdot\text{m/C})$$

$$= 1800\,\text{V} + (-2700\,\text{V}) = -900\,\text{V}$$

In a similar way you can show that the potential at point b (where $r_1 = 0.040$ m and $r_2 = 0.140$ m) is $V_b = 1930$ V and that the potential at point c (where $r_1 = r_2 = 0.130$ m) is $V_c = 0$.

EVALUATE: Let's confirm that these results make sense. Point a is closer to the -12-nC charge than to the $+12$-nC charge, so the potential at a is negative. The potential is positive at point b, which

23.13 What are the potentials at points a, b, and c due to this electric dipole?

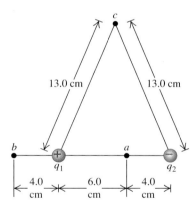

is closer to the $+12$-nC charge than the -12-nC charge. Finally, point c is equidistant from the $+12$-nC charge and the -12-nC charge, so the potential there is zero. (The potential is also equal to zero at a point infinitely far from both charges.)

Comparing this example with Example 21.8 shows that it's much easier to calculate electric potential (a scalar) than electric field (a vector). We'll take advantage of this simplification whenever possible.

Example 23.5 **Potential and potential energy**

Compute the potential energy associated with a +4.0-nC point charge if it is placed at points a, b, and c in Fig. 23.13.

SOLUTION

IDENTIFY and SET UP: The potential energy U associated with a point charge q at a location where the electric potential is V is $U = qV$. We use the values of V from Example 23.4.

EXECUTE: At the three points we find

$$U_a = qV_a = (4.0 \times 10^{-9}\,\text{C})(-900\,\text{J/C}) = -3.6 \times 10^{-6}\,\text{J}$$
$$U_b = qV_b = (4.0 \times 10^{-9}\,\text{C})(1930\,\text{J/C}) = 7.7 \times 10^{-6}\,\text{J}$$
$$U_c = qV_c = 0$$

All of these values correspond to U and V being zero at infinity.

EVALUATE: Note that *zero* net work is done on the 4.0-nC charge if it moves from point c to infinity *by any path*. In particular, let the path be along the perpendicular bisector of the line joining the other two charges q_1 and q_2 in Fig. 23.13. As shown in Example 21.8 (Section 21.5), at points on the bisector, the direction of $\vec{E}$ is perpendicular to the bisector. Hence the force on the 4.0-nC charge is perpendicular to the path, and no work is done in any displacement along it.

Example 23.6 **Finding potential by integration**

By integrating the electric field as in Eq. (23.17), find the potential at a distance r from a point charge q.

SOLUTION

IDENTIFY and SET UP: We let point a in Eq. (23.17) be at distance r and let point b be at infinity (Fig. 23.14). As usual, we choose the potential to be zero at an infinite distance from the charge q.

EXECUTE: To carry out the integral, we can choose any path we like between points a and b. The most convenient path is a radial line as shown in Fig. 23.14, so that $d\vec{l}$ is in the radial direction and has magnitude dr. Writing $d\vec{l} = \hat{r}\,dr$, we have from Eq. (23.17)

$$V - 0 = V = \int_r^{\infty} \vec{E} \cdot d\vec{l}$$
$$= \int_r^{\infty} \frac{1}{4\pi\epsilon_0}\frac{q}{r^2}\hat{r} \cdot \hat{r}\,dr = \int_r^{\infty} \frac{q}{4\pi\epsilon_0 r^2}\,dr$$
$$= -\frac{q}{4\pi\epsilon_0 r}\Big|_r^{\infty} = 0 - \left(-\frac{q}{4\pi\epsilon_0 r}\right)$$
$$V = \frac{q}{4\pi\epsilon_0 r}$$

23.14 Calculating the potential by integrating $\vec{E}$ for a single point charge.

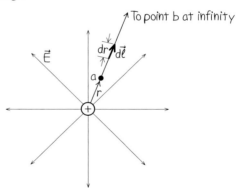

EVALUATE: Our result agrees with Eq. (23.14) and is correct for positive or negative q.

Example 23.7 **Moving through a potential difference**

In Fig. 23.15 a dust particle with mass $m = 5.0 \times 10^{-9}$ kg $= 5.0\,\mu$g and charge $q_0 = 2.0$ nC starts from rest and moves in a straight line from point a to point b. What is its speed v at point b?

SOLUTION

IDENTIFY and SET UP: Only the conservative electric force acts on the particle, so mechanical energy is conserved: $K_a + U_a = K_b + U_b$. We get the potential energies U from the

23.15 The particle moves from point a to point b; its acceleration is not constant.

corresponding potentials V using Eq. (23.12): $U_a = q_0V_a$ and $U_b = q_0V_b$.

EXECUTE: We have $K_a = 0$ and $K_b = \frac{1}{2}mv^2$. We substitute these and our expressions for U_a and U_b into the energy-conservation equation, then solve for v. We find

$$0 + q_0 V_a = \frac{1}{2}mv^2 + q_0 V_b$$

$$v = \sqrt{\frac{2q_0(V_a - V_b)}{m}}$$

We calculate the potentials using Eq. (23.15), $V = q/4\pi\epsilon_0 r$:

$$V_a = (9.0 \times 10^9 \text{ N} \cdot \text{m}^2/\text{C}^2)\left(\frac{3.0 \times 10^{-9} \text{ C}}{0.010 \text{ m}}\right.$$

$$\left. + \frac{(-3.0 \times 10^{-9} \text{ C})}{0.020 \text{ m}}\right)$$

$$= 1350 \text{ V}$$

$$V_b = (9.0 \times 10^9 \text{ N} \cdot \text{m}^2/\text{C}^2)\left(\frac{3.0 \times 10^{-9} \text{ C}}{0.020 \text{ m}}\right.$$

$$\left. + \frac{(-3.0 \times 10^{-9} \text{ C})}{0.010 \text{ m}}\right)$$

$$= -1350 \text{ V}$$

$$V_a - V_b = (1350 \text{ V}) - (-1350 \text{ V}) = 2700 \text{ V}$$

Finally,

$$v = \sqrt{\frac{2(2.0 \times 10^{-9} \text{ C})(2700 \text{ V})}{5.0 \times 10^{-9} \text{ kg}}} = 46 \text{ m/s}$$

EVALUATE: Our result makes sense: The positive test charge speeds up as it moves away from the positive charge and toward the negative charge. To check unit consistency in the final line of the calculation, note that 1 V = 1 J/C, so the numerator under the radical has units of J or $kg \cdot m^2/s^2$.

Test Your Understanding of Section 23.2 If the electric *potential* at a certain point is zero, does the electric *field* at that point have to be zero? (*Hint:* Consider point c in Example 23.4 and Example 21.8.) ❙

23.3 Calculating Electric Potential

When calculating the potential due to a charge distribution, we usually follow one of two routes. If we know the charge distribution, we can use Eq. (23.15) or (23.16). Or if we know how the electric field depends on position, we can use Eq. (23.17), defining the potential to be zero at some convenient place. Some problems require a combination of these approaches.

As you read through these examples, compare them with the related examples of calculating electric *field* in Section 21.5. You'll see how much easier it is to calculate scalar electric potentials than vector electric fields. The moral is clear: Whenever possible, solve problems using an energy approach (using electric potential and electric potential energy) rather than a dynamics approach (using electric fields and electric forces).

Problem-Solving Strategy 23.1 **Calculating Electric Potential**

IDENTIFY *the relevant concepts:* Remember that electric potential is *potential energy per unit charge*.

SET UP *the problem* using the following steps:
1. Make a drawing showing the locations and values of the charges (which may be point charges or a continuous distribution of charge) and your choice of coordinate axes.
2. Indicate on your drawing the position of the point at which you want to calculate the electric potential V. Sometimes this position will be an arbitrary one (say, a point a distance r from the center of a charged sphere).

EXECUTE *the solution* as follows:
1. To find the potential due to a collection of point charges, use Eq. (23.15). If you are given a continuous charge distribution, devise a way to divide it into infinitesimal elements and use Eq. (23.16). Carry out the integration, using appropriate limits to include the entire charge distribution.
2. If you are given the electric field, or if you can find it using any of the methods presented in Chapter 21 or 22, it may be

easier to find the potential difference between points a and b using Eq. (23.17) or (23.18). When appropriate, make use of your freedom to define V to be zero at some convenient place, and choose this place to be point b. (For point charges, this will usually be at infinity. For other distributions of charge—especially those that themselves extend to infinity—it may be necessary to define V_b to be zero at some finite distance from the charge distribution.) Then the potential at any other point, say a, can by found from Eq. (23.17) or (23.18) with $V_b = 0$.
3. Although potential V is a *scalar* quantity, you may have to use components of the vectors $\vec{E}$ and $d\vec{l}$ when you use Eq. (23.17) or (23.18) to calculate V.

EVALUATE *your answer:* Check whether your answer agrees with your intuition. If your result gives V as a function of position, graph the function to see whether it makes sense. If you know the electric field, you can make a rough check of your result for V by verifying that V decreases if you move in the direction of $\vec{E}$.

Example 23.8 | **A charged conducting sphere**

A solid conducting sphere of radius R has a total charge q. Find the electric potential everywhere, both outside and inside the sphere.

SOLUTION

IDENTIFY and SET UP: In Example 22.5 (Section 22.4) we used Gauss's law to find the electric *field* at all points for this charge distribution. We can use that result to determine the corresponding potential.

EXECUTE: From Example 22.5, the field *outside* the sphere is the same as if the sphere were removed and replaced by a point charge q. We take $V = 0$ at infinity, as we did for a point charge. Then the potential at a point outside the sphere at a distance r from its center is the same as that due to a point charge q at the center:

$$V = \frac{1}{4\pi\epsilon_0}\frac{q}{r}$$

The potential at the surface of the sphere is $V_{surface} = q/4\pi\epsilon_0 R$.

Inside the sphere, $\vec{E}$ is zero everywhere. Hence no work is done on a test charge that moves from any point to any other point inside the sphere. This means that the potential is the same at every point inside the sphere and is equal to its value $q/4\pi\epsilon_0 R$ at the surface.

EVALUATE: Figure 23.16 shows the field and potential for a positive charge q. In this case the electric field points radially away

from the sphere. As you move away from the sphere, in the direction of $\vec{E}$, V decreases (as it should).

23.16 Electric-field magnitude E and potential V at points inside and outside a positively charged spherical conductor.

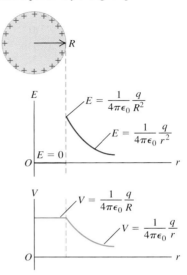

Ionization and Corona Discharge

The results of Example 23.8 have numerous practical consequences. One consequence relates to the maximum potential to which a conductor in air can be raised. This potential is limited because air molecules become *ionized,* and air becomes a conductor, at an electric-field magnitude of about 3×10^6 V/m. Assume for the moment that q is positive. When we compare the expressions in Example 23.8 for the potential $V_{surface}$ and field magnitude $E_{surface}$ at the surface of a charged conducting sphere, we note that $V_{surface} = E_{surface}R$. Thus, if E_m represents the electric-field magnitude at which air becomes conductive (known as the *dielectric strength* of air), then the maximum potential V_m to which a spherical conductor can be raised is

$$V_m = RE_m$$

For a conducting sphere 1 cm in radius in air, $V_m = (10^{-2}\text{ m})(3 \times 10^6\text{ V/m}) = 30,000$ V. No amount of "charging" could raise the potential of a conducting sphere of this size in air higher than about 30,000 V; attempting to raise the potential further by adding extra charge would cause the surrounding air to become ionized and conductive, and the extra added charge would leak into the air.

To attain even higher potentials, high-voltage machines such as Van de Graaff generators use spherical terminals with very large radii (see Fig. 22.26 and the photograph that opens Chapter 22). For example, a terminal of radius $R = 2$ m has a maximum potential $V_m = (2\text{ m})(3 \times 10^6\text{ V/m}) = 6 \times 10^6$ V $= 6$ MV.

Our result in Example 23.8 also explains what happens with a charged conductor with a very *small* radius of curvature, such as a sharp point or thin wire. Because the maximum potential is proportional to the radius, even relatively small potentials applied to sharp points in air produce sufficiently high fields just outside the point to ionize the surrounding air, making it become a conductor. The resulting current and its associated glow (visible in a dark room) are called *corona*. Laser printers and photocopying machines use corona from fine wires to spray charge on the imaging drum (see Fig. 21.2).

A large-radius conductor is used in situations where it's important to *prevent* corona. An example is the metal ball at the end of a car radio antenna, which prevents the static that would be caused by corona. Another example is the blunt end of a metal lightning rod (Fig. 23.17). If there is an excess charge in the atmosphere, as happens during thunderstorms, a substantial charge of the opposite sign can build up on this blunt end. As a result, when the atmospheric charge is discharged through a lightning bolt, it tends to be attracted to the charged lightning rod rather than to other nearby structures that could be damaged. (A conducting wire connecting the lightning rod to the ground then allows the acquired charge to dissipate harmlessly.) A lightning rod with a sharp end would allow less charge buildup and hence would be less effective.

23.17 The metal mast at the top of the Empire State Building acts as a lightning rod. It is struck by lightning as many as 500 times each year.

Example 23.9 Oppositely charged parallel plates

Find the potential at any height y between the two oppositely charged parallel plates discussed in Section 23.1 (Fig. 23.18).

SOLUTION

IDENTIFY and SET UP: We discussed this situation in Section 23.1. From Eq. (23.5), we know the electric *potential energy U* for a test charge q_0 is $U = q_0 Ey$. (We set $y = 0$ and $U = 0$ at the bottom plate.) We use Eq. (23.12), $U = q_0 V$, to find the electric *potential V* as a function of y.

EXECUTE: The potential $V(y)$ at coordinate y is the potential energy per unit charge:

$$V(y) = \frac{U(y)}{q_0} = \frac{q_0 Ey}{q_0} = Ey$$

The potential decreases as we move in the direction of $\vec{E}$ from the upper to the lower plate. At point a, where $y = d$ and $V(y) = V_a$,

$$V_a - V_b = Ed \quad \text{and} \quad E = \frac{V_a - V_b}{d} = \frac{V_{ab}}{d}$$

where V_{ab} is the potential of the positive plate with respect to the negative plate. That is, the electric field equals the potential difference between the plates divided by the distance between them. For a given potential difference V_{ab}, the smaller the distance d between the two plates, the greater the magnitude E of the electric field. (This relationship between E and V_{ab} holds *only* for the planar geometry

23.18 The charged parallel plates from Fig. 23.2.

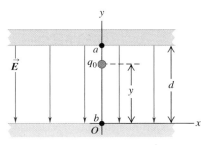

we have described. It does *not* work for situations such as concentric cylinders or spheres in which the electric field is not uniform.)

EVALUATE: Our result shows that $V = 0$ at the bottom plate (at $y = 0$). This is consistent with our choice that $U = q_0 V = 0$ for a test charge placed at the bottom plate.

CAUTION **"Zero potential" is arbitrary** You might think that if a conducting body has zero potential, it must necessarily also have zero net charge. But that just isn't so! As an example, the plate at $y = 0$ in Fig. 23.18 has zero potential ($V = 0$) but has a nonzero charge per unit area $-\sigma$. There's nothing particularly special about the place where potential is zero; we can *define* this place to be wherever we want it to be.

Example 23.10 An infinite line charge or charged conducting cylinder

Find the potential at a distance r from a very long line of charge with linear charge density (charge per unit length) λ.

SOLUTION

IDENTIFY and SET UP: In both Example 21.10 (Section 21.5) and Example 22.6 (Section 22.4) we found that the electric field at a

radial distance r from a long straight-line charge (Fig. 23.19a) has only a radial component given by $E_r = \lambda/2\pi\epsilon_0 r$. We use this expression to find the potential by integrating $\vec{E}$ as in Eq. (23.17).

EXECUTE: Since the field has only a radial component, we have $\vec{E} \cdot d\vec{l} = E_r \, dr$. Hence from Eq. (23.17) the potential of any point a

Continued

with respect to any other point b, at radial distances r_a and r_b from the line of charge, is

$$V_a - V_b = \int_a^b \vec{E} \cdot d\vec{l} = \int_a^b E_r \, dr = \frac{\lambda}{2\pi\epsilon_0} \int_{r_a}^{r_b} \frac{dr}{r} = \frac{\lambda}{2\pi\epsilon_0} \ln \frac{r_b}{r_a}$$

If we take point b at infinity and set $V_b = 0$, we find that V_a is *infinite* for any finite distance r_a from the line charge: $V_a = (\lambda/2\pi\epsilon_0) \ln (\infty/r_a) = \infty$. This is *not* a useful way to define V for this problem! The difficulty is that the charge distribution itself extends to infinity.

Instead, as recommended in Problem-Solving Strategy 23.1, we set $V_b = 0$ at point b at an arbitrary but *finite* radial distance r_0. Then the potential $V = V_a$ at point a at a radial distance r is given by $V - 0 = (\lambda/2\pi\epsilon_0) \ln (r_0/r)$, or

$$V = \frac{\lambda}{2\pi\epsilon_0} \ln \frac{r_0}{r}$$

EVALUATE: According to our result, if λ is positive, then V decreases as r increases. This is as it should be: V decreases as we move in the direction of $\vec{E}$.

From Example 22.6, the expression for E_r with which we started also applies outside a long, charged conducting cylinder with charge per unit length λ (Fig. 23.19b). Hence our result also gives the potential for such a cylinder, but only for values

23.19 Electric field outside **(a)** a long, positively charged wire and **(b)** a long, positively charged cylinder.

of r (the distance from the cylinder axis) equal to or greater than the radius R of the cylinder. If we choose r_0 to be the cylinder radius R, so that $V = 0$ when $r = R$, then at any point for which $r > R$,

$$V = \frac{\lambda}{2\pi\epsilon_0} \ln \frac{R}{r}$$

Inside the cylinder, $\vec{E} = 0$, and V has the same value (zero) as on the cylinder's surface.

Example 23.11 A ring of charge

Electric charge Q is distributed uniformly around a thin ring of radius a (Fig. 23.20). Find the potential at a point P on the ring axis at a distance x from the center of the ring.

SOLUTION

IDENTIFY and SET UP: We divide the ring into infinitesimal segments and use Eq. (23.16) to find V. All parts of the ring (and therefore all elements of the charge distribution) are at the same distance from P.

EXECUTE: Figure 23.20 shows that the distance from each charge element dq to P is $r = \sqrt{x^2 + a^2}$. Hence we can take the factor $1/r$ outside the integral in Eq. (23.16), and

$$V = \frac{1}{4\pi\epsilon_0} \int \frac{dq}{r} = \frac{1}{4\pi\epsilon_0} \frac{1}{\sqrt{x^2 + a^2}} \int dq = \frac{1}{4\pi\epsilon_0} \frac{Q}{\sqrt{x^2 + a^2}}$$

EVALUATE: When x is much larger than a, our expression for V becomes approximately $V = Q/4\pi\epsilon_0 x$, which is the potential at a distance x from a point charge Q. Very far away from a charged

23.20 All the charge in a ring of charge Q is the same distance r from a point P on the ring axis.

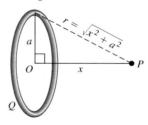

ring, its electric potential looks like that of a point charge. We drew a similar conclusion about the electric *field* of a ring in Example 21.9 (Section 21.5).

We know the electric field at all points along the x-axis from Example 21.9 (Section 21.5), so we can also find V along this axis by integrating $\vec{E} \cdot d\vec{l}$ as in Eq. (23.17).

Example 23.12 Potential of a line of charge

Positive electric charge Q is distributed uniformly along a line of length $2a$ lying along the y-axis between $y = -a$ and $y = +a$ (Fig. 23.21). Find the electric potential at a point P on the x-axis at a distance x from the origin.

SOLUTION

IDENTIFY and SET UP: This is the same situation as in Example 21.10 (Section 21.5), where we found an expression for the electric field $\vec{E}$ at an arbitrary point on the *x*-axis. We can find *V* at point *P* by integrating over the charge distribution using Eq. (23.16). Unlike the situation in Example 23.11, each charge element *dQ* is a *different* distance from point *P*, so the integration will take a little more effort.

EXECUTE: As in Example 21.10, the element of charge *dQ* corresponding to an element of length *dy* on the rod is $dQ = (Q/2a)dy$. The distance from *dQ* to *P* is $\sqrt{x^2 + y^2}$, so the contribution *dV* that the charge element makes to the potential at *P* is

$$dV = \frac{1}{4\pi\epsilon_0} \frac{Q}{2a} \frac{dy}{\sqrt{x^2 + y^2}}$$

To find the potential at *P* due to the entire rod, we integrate *dV* over the length of the rod from $y = -a$ to $y = a$:

$$V = \frac{1}{4\pi\epsilon_0} \frac{Q}{2a} \int_{-a}^{a} \frac{dy}{\sqrt{x^2 + y^2}}$$

You can look up the integral in a table. The final result is

$$V = \frac{1}{4\pi\epsilon_0} \frac{Q}{2a} \ln\left(\frac{\sqrt{a^2 + x^2} + a}{\sqrt{a^2 + x^2} - a}\right)$$

23.21 Our sketch for this problem.

EVALUATE: We can check our result by letting *x* approach infinity. In this limit the point *P* is infinitely far from all of the charge, so we expect *V* to approach zero; you can verify that it does.

We know the electric field at all points along the *x*-axis from Example 21.10. We invite you to use this information to find *V* along this axis by integrating $\vec{E}$ as in Eq. (23.17).

Test Your Understanding of Section 23.3 If the electric *field* at a certain point is zero, does the electric *potential* at that point have to be zero? (*Hint:* Consider the center of the ring in Example 23.11 and Example 21.9.) ❙

23.4 Equipotential Surfaces

Field lines (see Section 21.6) help us visualize electric fields. In a similar way, the potential at various points in an electric field can be represented graphically by *equipotential surfaces*. These use the same fundamental idea as topographic maps like those used by hikers and mountain climbers (Fig. 23.22). On a topographic map, contour lines are drawn through points that are all at the same elevation. Any number of these could be drawn, but typically only a few contour lines are shown at equal spacings of elevation. If a mass *m* is moved over the terrain along such a contour line, the gravitational potential energy *mgy* does not change because the elevation *y* is constant. Thus contour lines on a topographic map are really curves of constant gravitational potential energy. Contour lines are close together where the terrain is steep and there are large changes in elevation over a small horizontal distance; the contour lines are farther apart where the terrain is gently sloping. A ball allowed to roll downhill will experience the greatest downhill gravitational force where contour lines are closest together.

By analogy to contour lines on a topographic map, an **equipotential surface** is a three-dimensional surface on which the *electric potential V* is the same at every point. If a test charge q_0 is moved from point to point on such a surface, the *electric potential energy* q_0V remains constant. In a region where an electric field is present, we can construct an equipotential surface through any point. In diagrams we usually show only a few representative equipotentials, often with equal potential differences between adjacent surfaces. No point can be at two different potentials, so equipotential surfaces for different potentials can never touch or intersect.

23.22 Contour lines on a topographic map are curves of constant elevation and hence of constant gravitational potential energy.

Equipotential Surfaces and Field Lines

Because potential energy does not change as a test charge moves over an equipotential surface, the electric field can do no work on such a charge. It follows that $\vec{E}$ must be perpendicular to the surface at every point so that the electric force $q_0\vec{E}$ is always perpendicular to the displacement of a charge moving on the surface.

23.23 Cross sections of equipotential surfaces (blue lines) and electric field lines (red lines) for assemblies of point charges. There are equal potential differences between adjacent surfaces. Compare these diagrams to those in Fig. 21.28, which showed only the electric field lines.

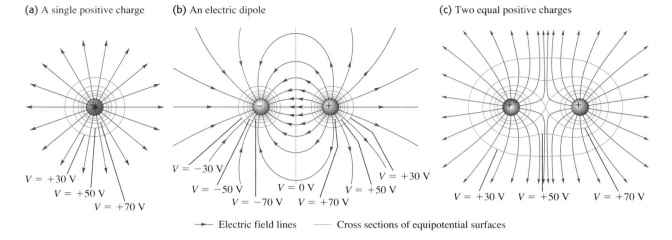

(a) A single positive charge   (b) An electric dipole   (c) Two equal positive charges

Electric field lines ——— Cross sections of equipotential surfaces

Field lines and equipotential surfaces are always mutually perpendicular. In general, field lines are curves, and equipotentials are curved surfaces. For the special case of a *uniform* field, in which the field lines are straight, parallel, and equally spaced, the equipotentials are parallel *planes* perpendicular to the field lines.

Figure 23.23 shows three arrangements of charges. The field lines in the plane of the charges are represented by red lines, and the intersections of the equipotential surfaces with this plane (that is, cross sections of these surfaces) are shown as blue lines. The actual equipotential surfaces are three-dimensional. At each crossing of an equipotential and a field line, the two are perpendicular.

In Fig. 23.23 we have drawn equipotentials so that there are equal potential differences between adjacent surfaces. In regions where the magnitude of $\vec{E}$ is large, the equipotential surfaces are close together because the field does a relatively large amount of work on a test charge in a relatively small displacement. This is the case near the point charge in Fig. 23.23a or between the two point charges in Fig. 23.23b; note that in these regions the field lines are also closer together. This is directly analogous to the downhill force of gravity being greatest in regions on a topographic map where contour lines are close together. Conversely, in regions where the field is weaker, the equipotential surfaces are farther apart; this happens at larger radii in Fig. 23.23a, to the left of the negative charge or the right of the positive charge in Fig. 23.23b, and at greater distances from both charges in Fig. 23.23c. (It may appear that two equipotential surfaces intersect at the center of Fig. 23.23c, in violation of the rule that this can never happen. In fact this is a single figure-8–shaped equipotential surface.)

CAUTION   *E need not be constant over an equipotential surface* On a given equipotential surface, the potential *V* has the same value at every point. In general, however, the electric-field magnitude *E* is *not* the same at all points on an equipotential surface. For instance, on the equipotential surface labeled "$V = -30$ V" in Fig. 23.23b, the magnitude *E* is less to the left of the negative charge than it is between the two charges. On the figure-8–shaped equipotential surface in Fig. 23.23c, $E = 0$ at the middle point halfway between the two charges; at any other point on this surface, *E* is nonzero.

Equipotentials and Conductors

Here's an important statement about equipotential surfaces: **When all charges are at rest, the surface of a conductor is always an equipotential surface.**

Since the electric field $\vec{E}$ is always perpendicular to an equipotential surface, we can prove this statement by proving that **when all charges are at rest, the electric field just outside a conductor must be perpendicular to the surface at every point** (Fig. 23.24). We know that $\vec{E} = 0$ everywhere inside the conductor; otherwise, charges would move. In particular, at any point just inside the surface the component of $\vec{E}$ tangent to the surface is zero. It follows that the tangential component of $\vec{E}$ is also zero just *outside* the surface. If it were not, a charge could move around a rectangular path partly inside and partly outside (Fig. 23.25) and return to its starting point with a net amount of work having been done on it. This would violate the conservative nature of electrostatic fields, so the tangential component of $\vec{E}$ just outside the surface must be zero at every point on the surface. Thus $\vec{E}$ is perpendicular to the surface at each point, proving our statement.

It also follows that **when all charges are at rest, the entire solid volume of a conductor is at the same potential.** Equation (23.17) states that the potential difference between two points a and b within the conductor's solid volume, $V_a - V_b$, is equal to the line integral $\int_a^b \vec{E} \cdot d\vec{l}$ of the electric field from a to b. Since $\vec{E} = 0$ everywhere inside the conductor, the integral is guaranteed to be zero for any two such points a and b. Hence the potential is the same for any two points within the solid volume of the conductor. We describe this by saying that the solid volume of the conductor is an *equipotential volume.*

Finally, we can now prove a theorem that we quoted without proof in Section 22.5. The theorem is as follows: In an electrostatic situation, if a conductor contains a cavity and if no charge is present inside the cavity, then there can be no net charge *anywhere* on the surface of the cavity. This means that if you're inside a charged conducting box, you can safely touch any point on the inside walls of the box without being shocked. To prove this theorem, we first prove that *every point in the cavity is at the same potential.* In Fig. 23.26 the conducting surface A of the cavity is an equipotential surface, as we have just proved. Suppose point P in the cavity is at a different potential; then we can construct a different equipotential surface B including point P.

Now consider a Gaussian surface, shown in Fig. 23.26, between the two equipotential surfaces. Because of the relationship between $\vec{E}$ and the equipotentials, we know that the field at every point between the equipotentials is from A toward B, or else at every point it is from B toward A, depending on which equipotential surface is at higher potential. In either case the flux through this Gaussian surface is certainly not zero. But then Gauss's law says that the charge enclosed by the Gaussian surface cannot be zero. This contradicts our initial assumption that there is *no* charge in the cavity. So the potential at P *cannot* be different from that at the cavity wall.

The entire region of the cavity must therefore be at the same potential. But for this to be true, *the electric field inside the cavity must be zero everywhere.* Finally, Gauss's law shows that the electric field at any point on the surface of a conductor is proportional to the surface charge density σ at that point. We conclude that *the surface charge density on the wall of the cavity is zero at every point.* This chain of reasoning may seem tortuous, but it is worth careful study.

CAUTION Equipotential surfaces vs. Gaussian surfaces Don't confuse equipotential surfaces with the Gaussian surfaces we encountered in Chapter 22. Gaussian surfaces have relevance only when we are using Gauss's law, and we can choose *any* Gaussian surface that's convenient. We are *not* free to choose the shape of equipotential surfaces; the shape is determined by the charge distribution.

Test Your Understanding of Section 23.4 Would the shapes of the equipotential surfaces in Fig. 23.23 change if the sign of each charge were reversed?

23.24 When charges are at rest, a conducting surface is always an equipotential surface. Field lines are perpendicular to a conducting surface.

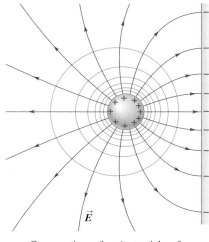

—— Cross sections of equipotential surfaces
→— Electric field lines

23.25 At all points on the surface of a conductor, the electric field must be perpendicular to the surface. If $\vec{E}$ had a tangential component, a net amount of work would be done on a test charge by moving it around a loop as shown here—which is impossible because the electric force is conservative.

An impossible electric field
If the electric field just outside a conductor had a tangential component $E_\parallel$, a charge could move in a loop with net work done.

23.26 A cavity in a conductor. If the cavity contains no charge, every point in the cavity is at the same potential, the electric field is zero everywhere in the cavity, and there is no charge anywhere on the surface of the cavity.

23.5 Potential Gradient

Electric field and potential are closely related. Equation (23.17), restated here, expresses one aspect of that relationship:

$$V_a - V_b = \int_a^b \vec{E} \cdot d\vec{l}$$

If we know $\vec{E}$ at various points, we can use this equation to calculate potential differences. In this section we show how to turn this around; if we know the potential V at various points, we can use it to determine $\vec{E}$. Regarding V as a function of the coordinates (x, y, z) of a point in space, we will show that the components of $\vec{E}$ are related to the *partial derivatives* of V with respect to x, y, and z.

In Eq. (23.17), $V_a - V_b$ is the potential of a with respect to b—that is, the change of potential encountered on a trip from b to a. We can write this as

$$V_a - V_b = \int_b^a dV = -\int_a^b dV$$

where dV is the infinitesimal change of potential accompanying an infinitesimal element $d\vec{l}$ of the path from b to a. Comparing to Eq. (23.17), we have

$$-\int_a^b dV = \int_a^b \vec{E} \cdot d\vec{l}$$

These two integrals must be equal for *any* pair of limits a and b, and for this to be true the *integrands* must be equal. Thus, for *any* infinitesimal displacement $d\vec{l}$,

$$-dV = \vec{E} \cdot d\vec{l}$$

To interpret this expression, we write $\vec{E}$ and $d\vec{l}$ in terms of their components: $\vec{E} = \hat{\imath} E_x + \hat{\jmath} E_y + \hat{k} E_z$ and $d\vec{l} = \hat{\imath}\, dx + \hat{\jmath}\, dy + \hat{k}\, dz$. Then we have

$$-dV = E_x\, dx + E_y\, dy + E_z\, dz$$

Suppose the displacement is parallel to the x-axis, so $dy = dz = 0$. Then $-dV = E_x\, dx$ or $E_x = -(dV/dx)_{y,\,z\text{ constant}}$, where the subscript reminds us that only x varies in the derivative; recall that V is in general a function of x, y, and z. But this is just what is meant by the partial derivative $\partial V/\partial x$. The y- and z-components of $\vec{E}$ are related to the corresponding derivatives of V in the same way, so we have

$$E_x = -\frac{\partial V}{\partial x} \qquad E_y = -\frac{\partial V}{\partial y} \qquad E_z = -\frac{\partial V}{\partial z} \qquad \begin{matrix}\text{(components of } \vec{E} \\ \text{in terms of } V\text{)}\end{matrix} \qquad \text{(23.19)}$$

This is consistent with the units of electric field being V/m. In terms of unit vectors we can write $\vec{E}$ as

$$\vec{E} = -\left(\hat{\imath}\frac{\partial V}{\partial x} + \hat{\jmath}\frac{\partial V}{\partial y} + \hat{k}\frac{\partial V}{\partial z} \right) \qquad (\vec{E} \text{ in terms of } V) \qquad \text{(23.20)}$$

In vector notation the following operation is called the **gradient** of the function f:

$$\vec{\nabla}f = \left(\hat{\imath}\frac{\partial}{\partial x} + \hat{\jmath}\frac{\partial}{\partial y} + \hat{k}\frac{\partial}{\partial z} \right)f \qquad \text{(23.21)}$$

The operator denoted by the symbol $\vec{\nabla}$ is called "grad" or "del." Thus in vector notation,

$$\vec{E} = -\vec{\nabla}V \qquad \text{(23.22)}$$

This is read "$\vec{E}$ is the negative of the gradient of V" or "$\vec{E}$ equals negative grad V." The quantity $\vec{\nabla}V$ is called the *potential gradient*.

Application Potential Gradient Across a Cell Membrane
The interior of a human cell is at a lower electric potential V than the exterior. (The potential difference when the cell is inactive is about -70 mV in neurons and about -95 mV in skeletal muscle cells.) Hence there is a potential gradient $\vec{\nabla}V$ that points from the *interior* to the *exterior* of the cell membrane, and an electric field $\vec{E} = -\vec{\nabla}V$ that points from the *exterior* to the *interior*. This field affects how ions flow into or out of the cell through special channels in the membrane.

Calcium (Ca)
Potassium (K)
Sodium (Na)

At each point, the potential gradient points in the direction in which V *increases* most rapidly with a change in position. Hence at each point the direction of $\vec{E}$ is the direction in which V *decreases* most rapidly and is always perpendicular to the equipotential surface through the point. This agrees with our observation in Section 23.2 that moving in the direction of the electric field means moving in the direction of decreasing potential.

Equation (23.22) doesn't depend on the particular choice of the zero point for V. If we were to change the zero point, the effect would be to change V at every point by the same amount; the derivatives of V would be the same.

If $\vec{E}$ is radial with respect to a point or an axis and r is the distance from the point or the axis, the relationship corresponding to Eqs. (23.19) is

$$E_r = -\frac{\partial V}{\partial r} \quad \text{(radial electric field)} \tag{23.23}$$

Often we can compute the electric field caused by a charge distribution in either of two ways: directly, by adding the $\vec{E}$ fields of point charges, or by first calculating the potential and then taking its gradient to find the field. The second method is often easier because potential is a *scalar* quantity, requiring at worst the integration of a scalar function. Electric field is a *vector* quantity, requiring computation of components for each element of charge and a separate integration for each component. Thus, quite apart from its fundamental significance, potential offers a very useful computational technique in field calculations. Below, we present two examples in which a knowledge of V is used to find the electric field.

We stress once more that if we know $\vec{E}$ as a function of position, we can calculate V using Eq. (23.17) or (23.18), and if we know V as a function of position, we can calculate $\vec{E}$ using Eq. (23.19), (23.20), or (23.23). Deriving V from $\vec{E}$ requires integration, and deriving $\vec{E}$ from V requires differentiation.

Example 23.13 | **Potential and field of a point charge**

From Eq. (23.14) the potential at a radial distance r from a point charge q is $V = q/4\pi\epsilon_0 r$. Find the vector electric field from this expression for V.

SOLUTION

IDENTIFY and SET UP: This problem uses the general relationship between the electric potential as a function of position and the electric-field vector. By symmetry, the electric field here has only a radial component E_r. We use Eq. (23.23) to find this component.

EXECUTE: From Eq. (23.23),

$$E_r = -\frac{\partial V}{\partial r} = -\frac{\partial}{\partial r}\left(\frac{1}{4\pi\epsilon_0}\frac{q}{r}\right) = \frac{1}{4\pi\epsilon_0}\frac{q}{r^2}$$

so the vector electric field is

$$\vec{E} = \hat{r}E_r = \frac{1}{4\pi\epsilon_0}\frac{q}{r^2}\hat{r}$$

EVALUATE: Our result agrees with Eq. (21.7), as it must.

An alternative approach is to ignore the radial symmetry, write the radial distance as $r = \sqrt{x^2 + y^2 + z^2}$, and take the derivatives of V with respect to x, y, and z as in Eq. (23.20). We find

$$\frac{\partial V}{\partial x} = \frac{\partial}{\partial x}\left(\frac{1}{4\pi\epsilon_0}\frac{q}{\sqrt{x^2+y^2+z^2}}\right) = -\frac{1}{4\pi\epsilon_0}\frac{qx}{(x^2+y^2+z^2)^{3/2}}$$

$$= -\frac{qx}{4\pi\epsilon_0 r^3}$$

and similarly

$$\frac{\partial V}{\partial y} = -\frac{qy}{4\pi\epsilon_0 r^3} \qquad \frac{\partial V}{\partial z} = -\frac{qz}{4\pi\epsilon_0 r^3}$$

Then from Eq. (23.20),

$$\vec{E} = -\left[\hat{i}\left(-\frac{qx}{4\pi\epsilon_0 r^3}\right) + \hat{j}\left(-\frac{qy}{4\pi\epsilon_0 r^3}\right) + \hat{k}\left(-\frac{qz}{4\pi\epsilon_0 r^3}\right)\right]$$

$$= \frac{1}{4\pi\epsilon_0}\frac{q}{r^2}\left(\frac{x\hat{i} + y\hat{j} + z\hat{k}}{r}\right) = \frac{1}{4\pi\epsilon_0}\frac{q}{r^2}\hat{r}$$

This approach gives us the same answer, but with more effort. Clearly it's best to exploit the symmetry of the charge distribution whenever possible.

Example 23.14 **Potential and field of a ring of charge**

In Example 23.11 (Section 23.3) we found that for a ring of charge with radius a and total charge Q, the potential at a point P on the ring's symmetry axis a distance x from the center is

$$V = \frac{1}{4\pi\epsilon_0} \frac{Q}{\sqrt{x^2 + a^2}}$$

Find the electric field at P.

SOLUTION

IDENTIFY and SET UP: Figure 23.20 shows the situation. We are given V as a function of x along the x-axis, and we wish to find the electric field at a point on this axis. From the symmetry of the charge distribution, the electric field along the symmetry (x-) axis of the ring can have only an x-component. We find it using the first of Eqs. (23.19).

EXECUTE: The x-component of the electric field is

$$E_x = -\frac{\partial V}{\partial x} = \frac{1}{4\pi\epsilon_0} \frac{Qx}{(x^2 + a^2)^{3/2}}$$

EVALUATE: This agrees with our result in Example 21.9.

CAUTION **Don't use expressions where they don't apply** In this example, V is not a function of y or z on the ring axis, so that $\partial V/\partial y = \partial V/\partial z = 0$ and $E_y = E_z = 0$. But that does not mean that it's true *everywhere*; our expressions for V and E_x are valid *only on the ring axis*. If we had an expression for V valid at *all* points in space, we could use it to find the components of $\vec{E}$ at any point using Eqs. (23.19).

Test Your Understanding of Section 23.5 In a certain region of space the potential is given by $V = A + Bx + Cy^3 + Dxy$, where A, B, C, and D are positive constants. Which of these statements about the electric field $\vec{E}$ in this region of space is correct? (There may be more than one correct answer.) (i) Increasing the value of A will increase the value of $\vec{E}$ at all points; (ii) increasing the value of A will decrease the value of $\vec{E}$ at all points; (iii) $\vec{E}$ has no z-component; (iv) the electric field is zero at the origin ($x = 0$, $y = 0$, $z = 0$).

Electric potential energy: The electric force caused by any collection of charges at rest is a conservative force. The work W done by the electric force on a charged particle moving in an electric field can be represented by the change in a potential-energy function U.

The electric potential energy for two point charges q and q_0 depends on their separation r. The electric potential energy for a charge q_0 in the presence of a collection of charges q_1, q_2, q_3 depends on the distance from q_0 to each of these other charges. (See Examples 23.1 and 23.2.)

$$W_{a \to b} = U_a - U_b \qquad (23.2)$$

$$U = \frac{1}{4\pi\epsilon_0} \frac{q q_0}{r} \qquad (23.9)$$

(two point charges)

$$U = \frac{q_0}{4\pi\epsilon_0} \left(\frac{q_1}{r_1} + \frac{q_2}{r_2} + \frac{q_3}{r_3} + \cdots \right)$$

$$= \frac{q_0}{4\pi\epsilon_0} \sum_i \frac{q_i}{r_i} \qquad (23.10)$$

(q_0 in presence of other point charges)

$$U = \frac{q_0}{4\pi\epsilon_0} \left(\frac{q_1}{r_1} + \frac{q_2}{r_2} + \frac{q_3}{r_3} \right)$$

Electric potential: Potential, denoted by V, is potential energy per unit charge. The potential difference between two points equals the amount of work that would be required to move a unit positive test charge between those points. The potential V due to a quantity of charge can be calculated by summing (if the charge is a collection of point charges) or by integrating (if the charge is a distribution). (See Examples 23.3, 23.4, 23.5, 23.7, 23.11, and 23.12.)

The potential difference between two points a and b, also called the potential of a with respect to b, is given by the line integral of $\vec{E}$. The potential at a given point can be found by first finding $\vec{E}$ and then carrying out this integral. (See Examples 23.6, 23.8, 23.9, and 23.10.)

$$V = \frac{U}{q_0} = \frac{1}{4\pi\epsilon_0} \frac{q}{r} \qquad (23.14)$$

(due to a point charge)

$$V = \frac{U}{q_0} = \frac{1}{4\pi\epsilon_0} \sum_i \frac{q_i}{r_i} \qquad (23.15)$$

(due to a collection of point charges)

$$V = \frac{1}{4\pi\epsilon_0} \int \frac{dq}{r} \qquad (23.16)$$

(due to a charge distribution)

$$V_a - V_b = \int_a^b \vec{E} \cdot d\vec{l} = \int_a^b E \cos\phi \, dl \qquad (23.17)$$

$$V = \frac{1}{4\pi\epsilon_0} \left(\frac{q_1}{r_1} + \frac{q_2}{r_2} + \frac{q_3}{r_3} \right)$$

Equipotential surfaces: An equipotential surface is a surface on which the potential has the same value at every point. At a point where a field line crosses an equipotential surface, the two are perpendicular. When all charges are at rest, the surface of a conductor is always an equipotential surface and all points in the interior of a conductor are at the same potential. When a cavity within a conductor contains no charge, the entire cavity is an equipotential region and there is no surface charge anywhere on the surface of the cavity.

Electric field line

Cross section of equipotential surface

Finding electric field from electric potential: If the potential V is known as a function of the coordinates x, y, and z, the components of electric field $\vec{E}$ at any point are given by partial derivatives of V. (See Examples 23.13 and 23.14.)

$$E_x = -\frac{\partial V}{\partial x} \quad E_y = -\frac{\partial V}{\partial y} \quad E_z = -\frac{\partial V}{\partial z} \qquad (23.19)$$

$$\vec{E} = -\left(\hat{i}\frac{\partial V}{\partial x} + \hat{j}\frac{\partial V}{\partial y} + \hat{k}\frac{\partial V}{\partial z} \right) \qquad (23.20)$$

(vector form)

BRIDGING PROBLEM **A Point Charge and a Line of Charge**

Positive electric charge Q is distributed uniformly along a thin rod of length $2a$. The rod lies along the x-axis between $x = -a$ and $x = +a$. Calculate how much work you must do to bring a positive point charge q from infinity to the point $x = +L$ on the x-axis, where $L > a$.

SOLUTION GUIDE

See MasteringPhysics® study area for a Video Tutor solution.

IDENTIFY and SET UP

1. In this problem you must first calculate the potential V at $x = +L$ due to the charged rod. You can then find the change in potential energy involved in bringing the point charge q from infinity (where $V = 0$) to $x = +L$.

2. To find V, divide the rod into infinitesimal segments of length dx'. How much charge is on such a segment? Consider one such segment located at $x = x'$, where $-a \le x' \le a$. What is the potential dV at $x = +L$ due to this segment?

3. The total potential at $x = +L$ is the integral of dV, including contributions from all of the segments for x' from $-a$ to $+a$. Set up this integral.

EXECUTE

4. Integrate your expression from step 3 to find the potential V at $x = +L$. A simple, standard substitution will do the trick; use a table of integrals only as a last resort.

5. Use your result from step 4 to find the potential energy for a point charge q placed at $x = +L$.

6. Use your result from step 5 to find the work you must do to bring the point charge from infinity to $x = +L$.

EVALUATE

7. What does your result from step 5 become in the limit $a \to 0$? Does this make sense?

8. Suppose the point charge q were negative rather than positive. How would this affect your result in step 4? In step 5?

Problems

For instructor-assigned homework, go to www.masteringphysics.com

•, ••, •••: Problems of increasing difficulty. **CP**: Cumulative problems incorporating material from earlier chapters. **CALC**: Problems requiring calculus. **BIO**: Biosciences problems.

DISCUSSION QUESTIONS

Q23.1 A student asked, "Since electrical potential is always proportional to potential energy, why bother with the concept of potential at all?" How would you respond?

Q23.2 The potential (relative to a point at infinity) midway between two charges of equal magnitude and opposite sign is zero. Is it possible to bring a test charge from infinity to this midpoint in such a way that no work is done in any part of the displacement? If so, describe how it can be done. If it is not possible, explain why.

Q23.3 Is it possible to have an arrangement of two point charges separated by a finite distance such that the electric potential energy of the arrangement is the same as if the two charges were infinitely far apart? Why or why not? What if there are three charges? Explain your reasoning.

Q23.4 Since potential can have any value you want depending on the choice of the reference level of zero potential, how does a voltmeter know what to read when you connect it between two points?

Q23.5 If $\vec{E}$ is zero everywhere along a certain path that leads from point A to point B, what is the potential difference between those two points? Does this mean that $\vec{E}$ is zero everywhere along *any* path from A to B? Explain.

Q23.6 If $\vec{E}$ is zero throughout a certain region of space, is the potential necessarily also zero in this region? Why or why not? If not, what *can* be said about the potential?

Q23.7 If you carry out the integral of the electric field $\int \vec{E} \cdot d\vec{l}$ for a *closed* path like that shown in Fig. Q23.7, the integral will *always* be equal to zero, independent of the shape of the

Figure **Q23.7**

path and independent of where charges may be located relative to the path. Explain why.

Q23.8 The potential difference between the two terminals of an AA battery (used in flashlights and portable stereos) is 1.5 V. If two AA batteries are placed end to end with the positive terminal of one battery touching the negative terminal of the other, what is the potential difference between the terminals at the exposed ends of the combination? What if the two positive terminals are touching each other? Explain your reasoning.

Q23.9 It is easy to produce a potential difference of several thousand volts between your body and the floor by scuffing your shoes across a nylon carpet. When you touch a metal doorknob, you get a mild shock. Yet contact with a power line of comparable voltage would probably be fatal. Why is there a difference?

Q23.10 If the electric potential at a single point is known, can $\vec{E}$ at that point be determined? If so, how? If not, why not?

Q23.11 Because electric field lines and equipotential surfaces are always perpendicular, two equipotential surfaces can never cross; if they did, the direction of $\vec{E}$ would be ambiguous at the crossing points. Yet two equipotential surfaces appear to cross at the center of Fig. 23.23c. Explain why there is no ambiguity about the direction of $\vec{E}$ in this particular case.

Q23.12 A uniform electric field is directed due east. Point B is 2.00 m west of point A, point C is 2.00 m east of point A, and point D is 2.00 m south of A. For each point, B, C, and D, is the potential at that point larger, smaller, or the same as at point A? Give the reasoning behind your answers.

Q23.13 We often say that if point A is at a higher potential than point B, A is at positive potential and B is at negative potential. Does it necessarily follow that a point at positive potential is positively charged, or that a point at negative potential is negatively charged? Illustrate your answers with clear, simple examples.

Q23.14 A conducting sphere is to be charged by bringing in positive charge a little at a time until the total charge is Q. The total work required for this process is alleged to be proportional to Q^2. Is this correct? Why or why not?

Q23.15 Three pairs of parallel metal plates (A, B, and C) are connected as shown in Fig. Q23.15, and a battery maintains a potential of 1.5 V across ab. What can you say about the potential difference across each pair of plates? Why?

Figure **Q23.15**

Q23.16 A conducting sphere is placed between two charged parallel plates such as those shown in Fig. 23.2. Does the electric field inside the sphere depend on precisely where between the plates the sphere is placed? What about the electric potential inside the sphere? Do the answers to these questions depend on whether or not there is a net charge on the sphere? Explain your reasoning.

Q23.17 A conductor that carries a net charge Q has a hollow, empty cavity in its interior. Does the potential vary from point to point within the material of the conductor? What about within the cavity? How does the potential inside the cavity compare to the potential within the material of the conductor?

Q23.18 A high-voltage dc power line falls on a car, so the entire metal body of the car is at a potential of 10,000 V with respect to the ground. What happens to the occupants (a) when they are sitting in the car and (b) when they step out of the car? Explain your reasoning.

Q23.19 When a thunderstorm is approaching, sailors at sea sometimes observe a phenomenon called "St. Elmo's fire," a bluish flickering light at the tips of masts. What causes this? Why does it occur at the tips of masts? Why is the effect most pronounced when the masts are wet? (*Hint:* Seawater is a good conductor of electricity.)

Q23.20 A positive point charge is placed near a very large conducting plane. A professor of physics asserted that the field caused by this configuration is the same as would be obtained by removing the plane and placing a negative point charge of equal magnitude in the mirror-image position behind the initial position of the plane. Is this correct? Why or why not? (*Hint:* Inspect Fig. 23.23b.)

Q23.21 In electronics it is customary to define the potential of ground (thinking of the earth as a large conductor) as zero. Is this consistent with the fact that the earth has a net electric charge that is not zero? (Refer to Exercise 21.32.)

EXERCISES

Section 23.1 Electric Potential Energy

23.1 •• A point charge $q_1 = +2.40 \ \mu C$ is held stationary at the origin. A second point charge $q_2 = -4.30 \ \mu C$ moves from the point $x = 0.150$ m, $y = 0$ to the point $x = 0.250$ m, $y = 0.250$ m. How much work is done by the electric force on q_2?

23.2 • A point charge q_1 is held stationary at the origin. A second charge q_2 is placed at point a, and the electric potential energy of the pair of charges is $+5.4 \times 10^{-8}$ J. When the second charge is moved to point b, the electric force on the charge does -1.9×10^{-8} J of work. What is the electric potential energy of the pair of charges when the second charge is at point b?

23.3 •• **Energy of the Nucleus.** How much work is needed to assemble an atomic nucleus containing three protons (such as Be) if we model it as an equilateral triangle of side 2.00×10^{-15} m

with a proton at each vertex? Assume the protons started from very far away.

23.4 •• (a) How much work would it take to push two protons very slowly from a separation of 2.00×10^{-10} m (a typical atomic distance) to 3.00×10^{-15} m (a typical nuclear distance)? (b) If the protons are both released from rest at the closer distance in part (a), how fast are they moving when they reach their original separation?

23.5 •• A small metal sphere, carrying a net charge of $q_1 = -2.80 \ \mu C$, is held in a stationary position by insulating supports. A second small metal sphere, with a net charge of $q_2 = -7.80 \ \mu C$ and mass 1.50 g, is projected toward q_1. When the two spheres are 0.800 m apart, q_2 is moving toward q_1 with speed 22.0 m/s (Fig. E23.5). Assume that the two spheres can be treated as point charges. You can ignore the force of gravity. (a) What is the speed of q_2 when the spheres are 0.400 m apart? (b) How close does q_2 get to q_1?

Figure **E23.5**

23.6 •• **BIO** **Energy of DNA Base Pairing, I.** (See Exercise 21.23.) (a) Calculate the electric potential energy of the adenine–thymine bond, using the same combinations of molecules ($O - H - N$ and $N - H - N$) as in Exercise 21.23. (b) Compare this energy with the potential energy of the proton–electron pair in the hydrogen atom.

23.7 •• **BIO** **Energy of DNA Base Pairing, II.** (See Exercise 21.24.) Calculate the electric potential energy of the guanine–cytosine bond, using the same combinations of molecules ($O - H - O$, $N - H - N$, and $O - H - N$) as in Exercise 21.24.

23.8 •• Three equal 1.20-μC point charges are placed at the corners of an equilateral triangle whose sides are 0.500 m long. What is the potential energy of the system? (Take as zero the potential energy of the three charges when they are infinitely far apart.)

23.9 •• Two protons are released from rest when they are 0.750 nm apart. (a) What is the maximum speed they will reach? When does this speed occur? (b) What is the maximum acceleration they will achieve? When does this acceleration occur?

23.10 •• Four electrons are located at the corners of a square 10.0 nm on a side, with an alpha particle at its midpoint. How much work is needed to move the alpha particle to the midpoint of one of the sides of the square?

23.11 •• Three point charges, which initially are infinitely far apart, are placed at the corners of an equilateral triangle with sides d. Two of the point charges are identical and have charge q. If zero net work is required to place the three charges at the corners of the triangle, what must the value of the third charge be?

23.12 •• Starting from a separation of several meters, two protons are aimed directly toward each other by a cyclotron accelerator with speeds of 1000 km/s, measured relative to the earth. Find the maximum electrical force that these protons will exert on each other.

Section 23.2 Electric Potential

23.13 • A small particle has charge $-5.00 \ \mu C$ and mass 2.00×10^{-4} kg. It moves from point A, where the electric potential is $V_A = +200$ V, to point B, where the electric potential is $V_B = +800$ V. The electric force is the only force acting on the particle. The particle has speed 5.00 m/s at point A. What is its speed at point B? Is it moving faster or slower at B than at A? Explain.

23.14 • A particle with a charge of $+4.20$ nC is in a uniform electric field $\vec{E}$ directed to the left. It is released from rest and moves to the left; after it has moved 6.00 cm, its kinetic energy is found to be $+1.50 \times 10^{-6}$ J. (a) What work was done by the electric force? (b) What is the potential of the starting point with respect to the end point? (c) What is the magnitude of $\vec{E}$?

23.15 • A charge of 28.0 nC is placed in a uniform electric field that is directed vertically upward and has a magnitude of 4.00×10^4 V/m. What work is done by the electric force when the charge moves (a) 0.450 m to the right; (b) 0.670 m upward; (c) 2.60 m at an angle of $45.0°$ downward from the horizontal?

23.16 • Two stationary point charges $+3.00$ nC and $+2.00$ nC are separated by a distance of 50.0 cm. An electron is released from rest at a point midway between the two charges and moves along the line connecting the two charges. What is the speed of the electron when it is 10.0 cm from the $+3.00$-nC charge?

23.17 •• Point charges $q_1 = +2.00 \ \mu C$ and $q_2 = -2.00 \ \mu C$ are placed at adjacent corners of a square for which the length of each side is 3.00 cm. Point a is at the center of the square, and point b is at the empty corner closest to q_2. Take the electric potential to be zero at a distance far from both charges. (a) What is the electric potential at point a due to q_1 and q_2? (b) What is the electric potential at point b? (c) A point charge $q_3 = -5.00 \ \mu C$ moves from point a to point b. How much work is done on q_3 by the electric forces exerted by q_1 and q_2? Is this work positive or negative?

23.18 • Two charges of equal magnitude Q are held a distance d apart. Consider only points on the line passing through both charges. (a) If the two charges have the same sign, find the location of all points (if there are any) at which (i) the potential (relative to infinity) is zero (is the electric field zero at these points?), and (ii) the electric field is zero (is the potential zero at these points?). (b) Repeat part (a) for two charges having opposite signs.

23.19 • Two point charges $q_1 = +2.40$ nC and $q_2 = -6.50$ nC are 0.100 m apart. Point A is midway between them; point B is 0.080 m from q_1 and 0.060 m from q_2 (Fig. E23.19). Take the electric potential to be zero at infinity. Find (a) the potential at point A;

Figure **E23.19**

(b) the potential at point B; (c) the work done by the electric field on a charge of 2.50 nC that travels from point B to point A.

23.20 • A positive charge $+q$ is located at the point $x = 0$, $y = -a$, and a negative charge $-q$ is located at the point $x = 0$, $y = +a$. (a) Derive an expression for the potential V at points on the y-axis as a function of the coordinate y. Take V to be zero at an infinite distance from the charges. (b) Graph V at points on the y-axis as a function of y over the range from $y = -4a$ to $y = +4a$. (c) Show that for $y > a$, the potential at a point on the positive y-axis is given by $V = -(1/4\pi\epsilon_0)2qa/y^2$. (d) What are the answers to parts (a) and (c) if the two charges are interchanged so that $+q$ is at $y = +a$ and $-q$ is at $y = -a$?

23.21 •• A positive charge q is fixed at the point $x = 0$, $y = 0$, and a negative charge $-2q$ is fixed at the point $x = a$, $y = 0$. (a) Show the positions of the charges in a diagram. (b) Derive an expression for the potential V at points on the x-axis as a function of the coordinate x. Take V to be zero at an infinite distance from the charges. (c) At which positions on the x-axis is $V = 0$? (d) Graph V at points on the x-axis as a function of x in the range from $x = -2a$ to $x = +2a$. (e) What does the answer to part (b) become when $x \gg a$? Explain why this result is obtained.

23.22 •• Consider the arrangement of point charges described in Exercise 23.21. (a) Derive an expression for the potential V at points on the y-axis as a function of the coordinate y. Take V to be zero at an infinite distance from the charges. (b) At which positions on the y-axis is $V = 0$? (c) Graph V at points on the y-axis as a function of y in the range from $y = -2a$ to $y = +2a$. (d) What does the answer to part (a) become when $y > a$? Explain why this result is obtained.

23.23 •• (a) An electron is to be accelerated from 3.00×10^6 m/s to 8.00×10^6 m/s. Through what potential difference must the electron pass to accomplish this? (b) Through what potential difference must the electron pass if it is to be slowed from 8.00×10^6 m/s to a halt?

23.24 • At a certain distance from a point charge, the potential and electric-field magnitude due to that charge are 4.98 V and 12.0 V/m, respectively. (Take the potential to be zero at infinity.) (a) What is the distance to the point charge? (b) What is the magnitude of the charge? (c) Is the electric field directed toward or away from the point charge?

23.25 • A uniform electric field has magnitude E and is directed in the negative x-direction. The potential difference between point a (at $x = 0.60$ m) and point b (at $x = 0.90$ m) is 240 V. (a) Which point, a or b, is at the higher potential? (b) Calculate the value of E. (c) A negative point charge $q = -0.200 \ \mu C$ is moved from b to a. Calculate the work done on the point charge by the electric field.

23.26 • For each of the following arrangements of two point charges, find all the points along the line passing through both charges for which the electric potential V is zero (take $V = 0$ infinitely far from the charges) and for which the electric field E is zero: (a) charges $+Q$ and $+2Q$ separated by a distance d, and (b) charges $-Q$ and $+2Q$ separated by a distance d. (c) Are both V and E zero at the same places? Explain.

Section 23.3 Calculating Electric Potential

23.27 •• A thin spherical shell with radius $R_1 = 3.00$ cm is concentric with a larger thin spherical shell with radius $R_2 = 5.00$ cm. Both shells are made of insulating material. The smaller shell has charge $q_1 = +6.00$ nC distributed uniformly over its surface, and the larger shell has charge $q_2 = -9.00$ nC distributed uniformly over its surface. Take the electric potential to be zero at an infinite distance from both shells. (a) What is the electric potential due to the two shells at the following distance from their common center: (i) $r = 0$; (ii) $r = 4.00$ cm; (iii) $r = 6.00$ cm? (b) What is the magnitude of the potential difference between the surfaces of the two shells? Which shell is at higher potential: the inner shell or the outer shell?

23.28 • A total electric charge of 3.50 nC is distributed uniformly over the surface of a metal sphere with a radius of 24.0 cm. If the potential is zero at a point at infinity, find the value of the potential at the following distances from the center of the sphere: (a) 48.0 cm; (b) 24.0 cm; (c) 12.0 cm.

23.29 •• A uniformly charged, thin ring has radius 15.0 cm and total charge $+24.0$ nC. An electron is placed on the ring's axis a distance 30.0 cm from the center of the ring and is constrained to stay on the axis of the ring. The electron is then released from rest. (a) Describe the subsequent motion of the electron. (b) Find the speed of the electron when it reaches the center of the ring.

23.30 •• An infinitely long line of charge has linear charge density 5.00×10^{-12} C/m. A proton (mass 1.67×10^{-27} kg, charge $+1.60 \times 10^{-19}$ C) is 18.0 cm from the line and moving directly toward the line at 1.50×10^3 m/s. (a) Calculate the proton's initial kinetic energy. (b) How close does the proton get to the line of charge?

23.31 • A very long wire carries a uniform linear charge density λ. Using a voltmeter to measure potential difference, you find that when one probe of the meter is placed 2.50 cm from the wire and the other probe is 1.00 cm farther from the wire, the meter reads 575 V. (a) What is λ? (b) If you now place one probe at 3.50 cm from the wire and the other probe 1.00 cm farther away, will the voltmeter read 575 V? If not, will it read more or less than 575 V? Why? (c) If you place both probes 3.50 cm from the wire but 17.0 cm from each other, what will the voltmeter read?

23.32 •• A very long insulating cylinder of charge of radius 2.50 cm carries a uniform linear density of 15.0 nC/m. If you put one probe of a voltmeter at the surface, how far from the surface must the other probe be placed so that the voltmeter reads 175 V?

23.33 •• A very long insulating cylindrical shell of radius 6.00 cm carries charge of linear density 8.50 μC/m spread uniformly over its outer surface. What would a voltmeter read if it were connected between (a) the surface of the cylinder and a point 4.00 cm above the surface, and (b) the surface and a point 1.00 cm from the central axis of the cylinder?

23.34 • A ring of diameter 8.00 cm is fixed in place and carries a charge of +5.00 μC uniformly spread over its circumference. (a) How much work does it take to move a tiny +3.00-μC charged ball of mass 1.50 g from very far away to the center of the ring? (b) Is it necessary to take a path along the axis of the ring? Why? (c) If the ball is slightly displaced from the center of the ring, what will it do and what is the maximum speed it will reach?

23.35 •• A very small sphere with positive charge $q = +8.00 \ \mu$C is released from rest at a point 1.50 cm from a very long line of uniform linear charge density $\lambda = +3.00 \ \mu$C/m. What is the kinetic energy of the sphere when it is 4.50 cm from the line of charge if the only force on it is the force exerted by the line of charge?

23.36 • Charge $Q = 5.00 \ \mu$C is distributed uniformly over the volume of an insulating sphere that has radius $R = 12.0$ cm. A small sphere with charge $q = +3.00 \ \mu$C and mass 6.00×10^{-5} kg is projected toward the center of the large sphere from an initial large distance. The large sphere is held at a fixed position and the small sphere can be treated as a point charge. What minimum speed must the small sphere have in order to come within 8.00 cm of the surface of the large sphere?

23.37 • BIO **Axons.** Neurons are the basic units of the nervous system. They contain long tubular structures called *axons* that propagate electrical signals away from the ends of the neurons. The axon contains a solution of potassium (K^+) ions and large negative organic ions. The axon membrane prevents the large ions from leaking out, but the smaller K^+ ions are able to penetrate the membrane to some degree (Fig. E23.37). This leaves an excess negative charge on the inner surface of the axon membrane and an excess positive charge on the outer surface, resulting in a potential difference across the membrane that prevents further K^+ ions from leaking out. Measurements show that this potential difference is typically about 70 mV. The thickness of the axon membrane itself varies from about 5 to 10 nm, so we'll use an average of 7.5 nm. We can model the membrane as a large sheet having equal and opposite charge densities on its faces. (a) Find the electric field inside the axon membrane, assuming (not too realistically) that it is filled with air. Which way does it point: into or out of the axon?

Figure **E23.37**

(b) Which is at a higher potential: the inside surface or the outside surface of the axon membrane?

23.38 • CP Two large, parallel conducting plates carrying opposite charges of equal magnitude are separated by 2.20 cm. (a) If the surface charge density for each plate has magnitude 47.0 nC/m^2, what is the magnitude of $\vec{E}$ in the region between the plates? (b) What is the potential difference between the two plates? (c) If the separation between the plates is doubled while the surface charge density is kept constant at the value in part (a), what happens to the magnitude of the electric field and to the potential difference?

23.39 • Two large, parallel, metal plates carry opposite charges of equal magnitude. They are separated by 45.0 mm, and the potential difference between them is 360 V. (a) What is the magnitude of the electric field (assumed to be uniform) in the region between the plates? (b) What is the magnitude of the force this field exerts on a particle with charge +2.40 nC? (c) Use the results of part (b) to compute the work done by the field on the particle as it moves from the higher-potential plate to the lower. (d) Compare the result of part (c) to the change of potential energy of the same charge, computed from the electric potential.

23.40 • BIO **Electrical Sensitivity of Sharks.** Certain sharks can detect an electric field as weak as 1.0 μV/m. To grasp how weak this field is, if you wanted to produce it between two parallel metal plates by connecting an ordinary 1.5-V AA battery across these plates, how far apart would the plates have to be?

23.41 •• (a) Show that V for a spherical shell of radius R, that has charge q distributed uniformly over its surface, is the same as V for a solid conductor with radius R and charge q. (b) You rub an inflated balloon on the carpet and it acquires a potential that is 1560 V lower than its potential before it became charged. If the charge is uniformly distributed over the surface of the balloon and if the radius of the balloon is 15 cm, what is the net charge on the balloon? (c) In light of its 1200-V potential difference relative to you, do you think this balloon is dangerous? Explain.

23.42 •• (a) How much excess charge must be placed on a copper sphere 25.0 cm in diameter so that the potential of its center, relative to infinity, is 1.50 kV? (b) What is the potential of the sphere's surface relative to infinity?

23.43 • The electric field at the surface of a charged, solid, copper sphere with radius 0.200 m is 3800 N/C, directed toward the center of the sphere. What is the potential at the center of the sphere, if we take the potential to be zero infinitely far from the sphere?

Section 23.4 Equipotential Surfaces and Section 23.5 Potential Gradient

23.44 • A very large plastic sheet carries a uniform charge density of -6.00 nC/m^2 on one face. (a) As you move away from the sheet along a line perpendicular to it, does the potential increase or decrease? How do you know, without doing any calculations? Does your answer depend on where you choose the reference point for potential? (b) Find the spacing between equipotential surfaces that differ from each other by 1.00 V. What type of surfaces are these?

23.45 • CALC In a certain region of space, the electric potential is $V(x, y, z) = Axy - Bx^2 + Cy$, where A, B, and C are positive constants. (a) Calculate the x-, y-, and z-components of the electric field. (b) At which points is the electric field equal to zero?

23.46 • CALC In a certain region of space the electric potential is given by $V = +Ax^2y - Bxy^2$, where $A = 5.00$ V/m^3 and $B = 8.00$ V/m^3. Calculate the magnitude and direction of the electric field at the point in the region that has coordinates $x = 2.00$ m, $y = 0.400$ m, and $z = 0$.

23.47 •• **CALC** A metal sphere with radius r_a is supported on an insulating stand at the center of a hollow, metal, spherical shell with radius r_b. There is charge $+q$ on the inner sphere and charge $-q$ on the outer spherical shell. (a) Calculate the potential $V(r)$ for (i) $r < r_a$; (ii) $r_a < r < r_b$; (iii) $r > r_b$. (*Hint:* The net potential is the sum of the potentials due to the individual spheres.) Take V to be zero when r is infinite. (b) Show that the potential of the inner sphere with respect to the outer is

$$V_{ab} = \frac{q}{4\pi\epsilon_0}\left(\frac{1}{r_a} - \frac{1}{r_b}\right)$$

(c) Use Eq. (23.23) and the result from part (a) to show that the electric field at any point between the spheres has magnitude

$$E(r) = \frac{V_{ab}}{(1/r_a - 1/r_b)}\frac{1}{r^2}$$

(d) Use Eq. (23.23) and the result from part (a) to find the electric field at a point outside the larger sphere at a distance r from the center, where $r > r_b$. (e) Suppose the charge on the outer sphere is not $-q$ but a negative charge of different magnitude, say $-Q$. Show that the answers for parts (b) and (c) are the same as before but the answer for part (d) is different.

23.48 • A metal sphere with radius $r_a = 1.20$ cm is supported on an insulating stand at the center of a hollow, metal, spherical shell with radius $r_b = 9.60$ cm. Charge $+q$ is put on the inner sphere and charge $-q$ on the outer spherical shell. The magnitude of q is chosen to make the potential difference between the spheres 500 V, with the inner sphere at higher potential. (a) Use the result of Exercise 23.47(b) to calculate q. (b) With the help of the result of Exercise 23.47(a), sketch the equipotential surfaces that correspond to 500, 400, 300, 200, 100, and 0 V. (c) In your sketch, show the electric field lines. Are the electric field lines and equipotential surfaces mutually perpendicular? Are the equipotential surfaces closer together when the magnitude of $\vec{E}$ is largest?

23.49 • A very long cylinder of radius 2.00 cm carries a uniform charge density of 1.50 nC/m. (a) Describe the shape of the equipotential surfaces for this cylinder. (b) Taking the reference level for the zero of potential to be the surface of the cylinder, find the radius of equipotential surfaces having potentials of 10.0 V, 20.0 V, and 30.0 V. (c) Are the equipotential surfaces equally spaced? If not, do they get closer together or farther apart as r increases?

PROBLEMS

23.50 • **CP** A point charge $q_1 = +5.00$ μC is held fixed in space. From a horizontal distance of 6.00 cm, a small sphere with mass 4.00×10^{-3} kg and charge $q_2 = +2.00$ μC is fired toward the fixed charge with an initial speed of 40.0 m/s. Gravity can be neglected. What is the acceleration of the sphere at the instant when its speed is 25.0 m/s?

23.51 ••• A point charge $q_1 = 4.00$ nC is placed at the origin, and a second point charge $q_2 = -3.00$ nC is placed on the x-axis at $x = +20.0$ cm. A third point charge $q_3 = 2.00$ nC is to be placed on the x-axis between q_1 and q_2. (Take as zero the potential energy of the three charges when they are infinitely far apart.) (a) What is the potential energy of the system of the three charges if q_3 is placed at $x = +10.0$ cm? (b) Where should q_3 be placed to make the potential energy of the system equal to zero?

23.52 ••• A small sphere with mass 5.00×10^{-7} kg and charge $+3.00$ μC is released from rest a distance of 0.400 m above a large horizontal insulating sheet of charge that has uniform surface charge density $\sigma = +8.00$ pC/m². Using energy methods, calculate the speed of the sphere when it is 0.100 m above the sheet of charge?

23.53 •• **Determining the Size of the Nucleus.** When radium-226 decays radioactively, it emits an alpha particle (the nucleus of helium), and the end product is radon-222. We can model this decay by thinking of the radium-226 as consisting of an alpha particle emitted from the surface of the spherically symmetric radon-222 nucleus, and we can treat the alpha particle as a point charge. The energy of the alpha particle has been measured in the laboratory and has been found to be 4.79 MeV when the alpha particle is essentially infinitely far from the nucleus. Since radon is much heavier than the alpha particle, we can assume that there is no appreciable recoil of the radon after the decay. The radon nucleus contains 86 protons, while the alpha particle has 2 protons and the radium nucleus has 88 protons. (a) What was the electric potential energy of the alpha–radon combination just before the decay, in MeV and in joules? (b) Use your result from part (a) to calculate the radius of the radon nucleus.

23.54 •• **CP** A proton and an alpha particle are released from rest when they are 0.225 nm apart. The alpha particle (a helium nucleus) has essentially four times the mass and two times the charge of a proton. Find the maximum *speed* and maximum *acceleration* of each of these particles. When do these maxima occur: just following the release of the particles or after a very long time?

23.55 • A particle with charge $+7.60$ nC is in a uniform electric field directed to the left. Another force, in addition to the electric force, acts on the particle so that when it is released from rest, it moves to the right. After it has moved 8.00 cm, the additional force has done 6.50×10^{-5} J of work and the particle has 4.35×10^{-5} J of kinetic energy. (a) What work was done by the electric force? (b) What is the potential of the starting point with respect to the end point? (c) What is the magnitude of the electric field?

23.56 • **CP** In the *Bohr model* of the hydrogen atom, a single electron revolves around a single proton in a circle of radius r. Assume that the proton remains at rest. (a) By equating the electric force to the electron mass times its acceleration, derive an expression for the electron's speed. (b) Obtain an expression for the electron's kinetic energy, and show that its magnitude is just half that of the electric potential energy. (c) Obtain an expression for the total energy, and evaluate it using $r = 5.29 \times 10^{-11}$ m. Give your numerical result in joules and in electron volts.

23.57 •• **CALC** A vacuum tube diode consists of concentric cylindrical electrodes, the negative cathode and the positive anode. Because of the accumulation of charge near the cathode, the electric potential between the electrodes is not a linear function of the position, even with planar geometry, but is given by

$$V(x) = Cx^{4/3}$$

where x is the distance from the cathode and C is a constant, characteristic of a particular diode and operating conditions. Assume that the distance between the cathode and anode is 13.0 mm and the potential difference between electrodes is 240 V. (a) Determine the value of C. (b) Obtain a formula for the electric field between the electrodes as a function of x. (c) Determine the force on an electron when the electron is halfway between the electrodes.

23.58 •• Two oppositely charged, identical insulating spheres, each 50.0 cm in diameter and carrying a uniform charge of magnitude 250 μC, are placed 1.00 m apart center to center (Fig. P23.58). (a) If a voltmeter is connected between the nearest points (a and b) on their surfaces, what will it read? (b) Which point, a or b, is at the higher potential? How can you know this without any calculations?

Figure **P23.58**

23.59 •• **An Ionic Crystal.** Figure P23.59 shows eight point charges arranged at the corners of a cube with sides of length d. The values of the charges are $+q$ and $-q$, as shown. This is a model of one cell of a cubic ionic crystal. In sodium chloride (NaCl), for instance, the positive ions are Na$^+$ and the negative ions are Cl$^-$. (a) Calculate the potential energy U of this arrangement. (Take as zero the potential energy of the eight charges when they are infinitely far apart.) (b) In part (a), you should have found that $U < 0$. Explain the relationship between this result and the observation that such ionic crystals exist in nature.

Figure **P23.59**

23.60 • (a) Calculate the potential energy of a system of two small spheres, one carrying a charge of 2.00 μC and the other a charge of -3.50 μC, with their centers separated by a distance of 0.250 m. Assume zero potential energy when the charges are infinitely separated. (b) Suppose that one of the spheres is held in place and the other sphere, which has a mass of 1.50 g, is shot away from it. What minimum initial speed would the moving sphere need in order to escape completely from the attraction of the fixed sphere? (To escape, the moving sphere would have to reach a velocity of zero when it was infinitely distant from the fixed sphere.)

23.61 •• **The H$_2^+$ Ion.** The H$_2^+$ ion is composed of two protons, each of charge $+e = 1.60 \times 10^{-19}$ C, and an electron of charge $-e$ and mass 9.11×10^{-31} kg. The separation between the protons is 1.07×10^{-10} m. The protons and the electron may be treated as point charges. (a) Suppose the electron is located at the point midway between the two protons. What is the potential energy of the interaction between the electron and the two protons? (Do not include the potential energy due to the interaction between the two protons.) (b) Suppose the electron in part (a) has a velocity of magnitude 1.50×10^6 m/s in a direction along the perpendicular bisector of the line connecting the two protons. How far from the point midway between the two protons can the electron move? Because the masses of the protons are much greater than the electron mass, the motions of the protons are very slow and can be ignored. (*Note:* A realistic description of the electron motion requires the use of quantum mechanics, not Newtonian mechanics.)

23.62 •• **CP** A small sphere with mass 1.50 g hangs by a thread between two parallel vertical plates 5.00 cm apart (Fig. P23.62). The plates are insulating and have uniform

Figure **P23.62**

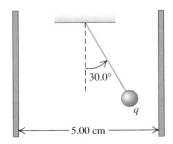

surface charge densities $+\sigma$ and $-\sigma$. The charge on the sphere is $q = 8.90 \times 10^{-6}$ C. What potential difference between the plates will cause the thread to assume an angle of 30.0° with the vertical?

23.63 • **CALC Coaxial Cylinders.** A long metal cylinder with radius a is supported on an insulating stand on the axis of a long, hollow, metal tube with radius b. The positive charge per unit length on the inner cylinder is λ, and there is an equal negative charge per unit length on the outer cylinder. (a) Calculate the potential $V(r)$ for (i) $r < a$; (ii) $a < r < b$; (iii) $r > b$. (*Hint:* The net potential is the sum of the potentials due to the individual conductors.) Take $V = 0$ at $r = b$. (b) Show that the potential of the inner cylinder with respect to the outer is

$$V_{ab} = \frac{\lambda}{2\pi\epsilon_0} \ln\frac{b}{a}$$

(c) Use Eq. (23.23) and the result from part (a) to show that the electric field at any point between the cylinders has magnitude

$$E(r) = \frac{V_{ab}}{\ln(b/a)}\frac{1}{r}$$

(d) What is the potential difference between the two cylinders if the outer cylinder has no net charge?

23.64 •• A *Geiger counter* detects radiation such as alpha particles by using the fact that the radiation ionizes the air along its path. A thin wire lies on the axis of a hollow metal cylinder and is insulated from it (Fig. P23.64). A large potential difference is established between the wire and the outer cylinder, with the wire at higher potential; this sets up a strong electric field directed radially outward. When ionizing radiation enters the device, it ionizes a few air molecules. The free electrons produced are accelerated by the electric field toward the wire and, on the way there, ionize many more air molecules. Thus a current pulse is produced that can be detected by appropriate electronic circuitry and converted to an audible "click." Suppose the radius of the central wire is 145 μm and the radius of the hollow cylinder is 1.80 cm. What potential difference between the wire and the cylinder produces an electric field of 2.00×10^4 V/m at a distance of 1.20 cm from the axis of the wire? (The wire and cylinder are both very long in comparison to their radii, so the results of Problem 23.63 apply.)

Figure **P23.64**

23.65 • **CP Deflection in a CRT.** Cathode-ray tubes (CRTs) are often found in oscilloscopes and computer monitors. In Fig. P23.65 an electron with an initial speed of 6.50×10^6 m/s is projected along the axis midway between the deflection plates of a cathode-ray tube. The potential difference between the two plates is 22.0 V and the lower plate is the one at higher potential. (a) What is the force (magnitude and direction) on the electron when it is between the plates? (b) What is the acceleration of the electron (magnitude and direction) when acted on by the force in part (a)? (c) How far below the axis has the electron moved when it reaches the end of the plates? (d) At what angle with the axis is it moving as it leaves the plates? (e) How far below the axis will it strike the fluorescent screen S?

Figure **P23.65**

23.66 •• **CP Deflecting Plates of an Oscilloscope.** The vertical deflecting plates of a typical classroom oscilloscope are a pair of parallel square metal plates carrying equal but opposite charges. Typical dimensions are about 3.0 cm on a side, with a separation of about 5.0 mm. The potential difference between the plates is 25.0 V. The plates are close enough that we can ignore fringing at the ends. Under these conditions: (a) how much charge is on each plate, and (b) how strong is the electric field between the plates? (c) If an electron is ejected at rest from the negative plate, how fast is it moving when it reaches the positive plate?

23.67 •• *Electrostatic precipitators* use electric forces to remove pollutant particles from smoke, in particular in the smokestacks of coal-burning power plants. One form of precipitator consists of a vertical, hollow, metal cylinder with a thin wire, insulated from the cylinder, running along its axis (Fig. P23.67). A large potential difference is established between the wire and the outer cylinder, with the wire at lower potential. This sets up a strong radial electric field directed inward.

Figure **P23.67**

The field produces a region of ionized air near the wire. Smoke enters the precipitator at the bottom, ash and dust in it pick up electrons, and the charged pollutants are accelerated toward the outer cylinder wall by the electric field. Suppose the radius of the central wire is 90.0 μm, the radius of the cylinder is 14.0 cm, and a potential difference of 50.0 kV is established between the wire and the cylinder. Also assume that the wire and cylinder are both very long in comparison to the cylinder radius, so the results of Problem 23.63 apply. (a) What is the magnitude of the electric field midway between the wire and the cylinder wall? (b) What magnitude of charge must a 30.0-μg ash particle have if the electric field computed in part (a) is to exert a force ten times the weight of the particle?

23.68 •• **CALC** A disk with radius R has uniform surface charge density σ. (a) By regarding the disk as a series of thin concentric rings, calculate the electric potential V at a point on the disk's axis a distance x from the center of the disk. Assume that the potential is zero at infinity. (*Hint:* Use the result of Example 23.11 in Section 23.3.) (b) Calculate $-\partial V/\partial x$. Show that the result agrees with the expression for E_x calculated in Example 21.11 (Section 21.5).

23.69 •• **CALC** (a) From the expression for E obtained in Problem 22.42, find the expressions for the electric potential V as a function of r, both inside and outside the cylinder. Let $V = 0$ at the surface of the cylinder. In each case, express your result in terms of the charge per unit length λ of the charge distribution. (b) Graph V and E as functions of r from $r = 0$ to $r = 3R$.

23.70 • **CALC** A thin insulating rod is bent into a semicircular arc of radius a, and a total electric charge Q is distributed uniformly along the rod. Calculate the potential at the center of curvature of the arc if the potential is assumed to be zero at infinity.

23.71 ••• **CALC Self-Energy of a Sphere of Charge.** A solid sphere of radius R contains a total charge Q distributed uniformly throughout its volume. Find the energy needed to assemble this charge by bringing infinitesimal charges from far away. This energy is called the "self-energy" of the charge distribution. (*Hint:* After you have assembled a charge q in a sphere of radius r, how much energy would it take to add a spherical shell of thickness dr having charge dq? Then integrate to get the total energy.)

23.72 •• **CALC** (a) From the expression for E obtained in Example 22.9 (Section 22.4), find the expression for the electric potential V as a function of r both inside and outside the uniformly charged sphere. Assume that $V = 0$ at infinity. (b) Graph V and E as functions of r from $r = 0$ to $r = 3R$.

23.73 •• Charge $Q = +4.00 \mu$C is distributed uniformly over the volume of an insulating sphere that has radius $R = 5.00$ cm. What is the potential difference between the center of the sphere and the surface of the sphere?

23.74 • An insulating spherical shell with inner radius 25.0 cm and outer radius 60.0 cm carries a charge of $+150.0 \mu$C uniformly distributed over its outer surface (see Exercise 23.41). Point a is at the center of the shell, point b is on the inner surface, and point c is on the outer surface. (a) What will a voltmeter read if it is connected between the following points: (i) a and b; (ii) b and c; (iii) c and infinity; (iv) a and c? (b) Which is at higher potential: (i) a or b; (ii) b or c; (iii) a or c? (c) Which, if any, of the answers would change sign if the charge were -150μC?

23.75 •• Exercise 23.41 shows that, outside a spherical shell with uniform surface charge, the potential is the same as if all the charge were concentrated into a point charge at the center of the sphere. (a) Use this result to show that for two uniformly charged insulating shells, the force they exert on each other and their mutual electrical energy are the same as if all the charge were concentrated at their centers. (*Hint:* See Section 13.6.) (b) Does this same result hold for solid insulating spheres, with charge distributed uniformly throughout their volume? (c) Does this same result hold for the force between two charged conducting shells? Between two charged solid conductors? Explain.

23.76 •• **CP** Two plastic spheres, each carrying charge uniformly distributed throughout its interior, are initially placed in contact and then released. One sphere is 60.0 cm in diameter, has mass 50.0 g, and contains -10.0μC of charge. The other sphere is 40.0 cm in diameter, has mass 150.0 g, and contains -30.0μC of charge. Find the maximum acceleration and the maximum speed achieved by each sphere (relative to the fixed point of their initial location in space), assuming that no other forces are acting on them. (*Hint:* The uniformly distributed charges behave as though they were concentrated at the centers of the two spheres.)

23.77 • **CALC** Use the electric field calculated in Problem 22.45 to calculate the potential difference between the solid conducting sphere and the thin insulating shell.

23.78 • **CALC** Consider a solid conducting sphere inside a hollow conducting sphere, with radii and charges specified in Problem 22.44. Take $V = 0$ as $r \to \infty$. Use the electric field calculated in Problem 22.44 to calculate the potential V at the following values of r: (a) $r = c$ (at the outer surface of the hollow sphere); (b) $r = b$ (at the inner surface of the hollow sphere); (c) $r = a$ (at the surface of the solid sphere); (d) $r = 0$ (at the center of the solid sphere).

23.79 • **CALC** Electric charge is distributed uniformly along a thin rod of length a, with total charge Q. Take the potential to be zero at infinity. Find the potential at the following points (Fig. P23.79): (a) point P, a distance x to the right of the rod, and (b) point R, a distance y above the right-hand end of the rod. (c) In parts (a) and (b), what does your result reduce to as x or y becomes much larger than a?

Figure **P23.79**

23.80 • (a) If a spherical raindrop of radius 0.650 mm carries a charge of -3.60 pC uniformly distributed over its volume, what is the potential at its surface? (Take the potential to be zero at an infinite distance from the raindrop.) (b) Two identical raindrops, each with radius and charge specified in part (a), collide and merge into one larger raindrop. What is the radius of this larger drop, and what is the potential at its surface, if its charge is uniformly distributed over its volume?

23.81 •• Two metal spheres of different sizes are charged such that the electric potential is the same at the surface of each. Sphere A has a radius three times that of sphere B. Let Q_A and Q_B be the charges on the two spheres, and let E_A and E_B be the electric-field magnitudes at the surfaces of the two spheres. What are (a) the ratio Q_B/Q_A and (b) the ratio E_B/E_A?

23.82 • An alpha particle with kinetic energy 11.0 MeV makes a head-on collision with a lead nucleus at rest. What is the distance of closest approach of the two particles? (Assume that the lead nucleus remains stationary and that it may be treated as a point charge. The atomic number of lead is 82. The alpha particle is a helium nucleus, with atomic number 2.)

23.83 • A metal sphere with radius R_1 has a charge Q_1. Take the electric potential to be zero at an infinite distance from the sphere. (a) What are the electric field and electric potential at the surface of the sphere? This sphere is now connected by a long, thin conducting wire to another sphere of radius R_2 that is several meters from the first sphere. Before the connection is made, this second sphere is uncharged. After electrostatic equilibrium has been reached, what are (b) the total charge on each sphere; (c) the electric potential at the surface of each sphere; (d) the electric field at the surface of each sphere? Assume that the amount of charge on the wire is much less than the charge on each sphere.

23.84 ••• CALC Use the charge distribution and electric field calculated in Problem 22.65. (a) Show that for $r \geq R$ the potential is identical to that produced by a point charge Q. (Take the potential to be zero at infinity.) (b) Obtain an expression for the electric potential valid in the region $r \leq R$.

23.85 •• CP **Nuclear Fusion in the Sun.** The source of the sun's energy is a sequence of nuclear reactions that occur in its core. The first of these reactions involves the collision of two protons, which fuse together to form a heavier nucleus and release energy. For this process, called *nuclear fusion,* to occur, the two protons must first approach until their surfaces are essentially in contact. (a) Assume both protons are moving with the same speed and they collide head-on. If the radius of the proton is 1.2×10^{-15} m, what is the minimum speed that will allow fusion to occur? The charge distribution within a proton is spherically symmetric, so the electric field and potential outside a proton are the same as if it were a point charge. The mass of the proton is 1.67×10^{-27} kg. (b) Another nuclear fusion reaction that occurs in the sun's core involves a collision between two helium nuclei, each of which has 2.99 times the mass of the proton, charge $+2e$, and radius 1.7×10^{-15} m. Assuming the same collision geometry as in part (a), what minimum speed is required for this fusion reaction to take place if the nuclei must approach a center-to-center

distance of about 3.5×10^{-15} m? As for the proton, the charge of the helium nucleus is uniformly distributed throughout its volume. (c) In Section 18.3 it was shown that the average translational kinetic energy of a particle with mass m in a gas at absolute temperature T is $\frac{3}{2}kT$, where k is the Boltzmann constant (given in Appendix F). For two protons with kinetic energy equal to this average value to be able to undergo the process described in part (a), what absolute temperature is required? What absolute temperature is required for two average helium nuclei to be able to undergo the process described in part (b)? (At these temperatures, atoms are completely ionized, so nuclei and electrons move separately.) (d) The temperature in the sun's core is about 1.5×10^7 K. How does this compare to the temperatures calculated in part (c)? How can the reactions described in parts (a) and (b) occur at all in the interior of the sun? (*Hint:* See the discussion of the distribution of molecular speeds in Section 18.5.)

23.86 • CALC The electric potential V in a region of space is given by

$$V(x, y, z) = A(x^2 - 3y^2 + z^2)$$

where A is a constant. (a) Derive an expression for the electric field $\vec{E}$ at any point in this region. (b) The work done by the field when a 1.50-μC test charge moves from the point $(x, y, z) = (0, 0, 0.250$ m) to the origin is measured to be 6.00×10^{-5} J. Determine A. (c) Determine the electric field at the point $(0, 0, 0.250$ m). (d) Show that in every plane parallel to the xz-plane the equipotential contours are circles. (e) What is the radius of the equipotential contour corresponding to $V = 1280$ V and $y = 2.00$ m?

23.87 •• **Nuclear Fission.** The unstable nucleus of uranium-236 can be regarded as a uniformly charged sphere of charge $Q = +92e$ and radius $R = 7.4 \times 10^{-15}$ m. In nuclear fission, this can divide into two smaller nuclei, each with half the charge and half the volume of the original uranium-236 nucleus. This is one of the reactions that occurred in the nuclear weapon that exploded over Hiroshima, Japan, in August 1945. (a) Find the radii of the two "daughter" nuclei of charge $+46e$. (b) In a simple model for the fission process, immediately after the uranium-236 nucleus has undergone fission, the "daughter" nuclei are at rest and just touching, as shown in Fig. P23.87. Calculate the kinetic energy that each of the "daughter" nuclei will have when they are very far apart. (c) In this model the sum of the kinetic energies of the two "daughter" nuclei, calculated in part (b), is the energy released by the fission of one uranium-236 nucleus. Calculate the energy released by the fission of 10.0 kg of uranium-236. The atomic mass of uranium-236 is 236 u, where 1 u = 1 atomic mass unit = 1.66×10^{-24} kg. Express your answer both in joules and in kilotons of TNT (1 kiloton of TNT releases 4.18×10^{12} J when it explodes). (d) In terms of this model, discuss why an atomic bomb could just as well be called an "electric bomb."

Figure **P23.87**

CHALLENGE PROBLEMS

23.88 ••• CP CALC In a certain region, a charge distribution exists that is spherically symmetric but nonuniform. That is, the volume charge density $\rho(r)$ depends on the distance r from the center of the distribution but not on the spherical polar angles θ and ϕ. The electric potential $V(r)$ due to this charge distribution is

$$V(r) = \begin{cases} \dfrac{\rho_0 a^2}{18\epsilon_0}\left[1 - 3\left(\dfrac{r}{a}\right)^2 + 2\left(\dfrac{r}{a}\right)^3\right] & \text{for } r \le a \\ 0 & \text{for } r \ge a \end{cases}$$

where ρ_0 is a constant having units of C/m^3 and a is a constant having units of meters. (a) Derive expressions for $\vec{E}$ for the regions $r \le a$ and $r \ge a$. [*Hint:* Use Eq. (23.23).] Explain why $\vec{E}$ has only a radial component. (b) Derive an expression for $\rho(r)$ in each of the two regions $r \le a$ and $r \ge a$. [*Hint:* Use Gauss's law for two spherical shells, one of radius r and the other of radius $r + dr$. The charge contained in the infinitesimal spherical shell of radius dr is $dq = 4\pi r^2 \rho(r)\, dr$.] (c) Show that the net charge contained in the volume of a sphere of radius greater than or equal to a is zero. [*Hint:* Integrate the expressions derived in part (b) for $\rho(r)$ over a spherical volume of radius greater than or equal to a.] Is this result consistent with the electric field for $r > a$ that you calculated in part (a)?

23.89 ••• CP In experiments in which atomic nuclei collide, head-on collisions like that described in Problem 23.82 do happen, but "near misses" are more common. Suppose the alpha particle in Problem 23.82 was not "aimed" at the center of the lead nucleus, but had an initial nonzero angular momentum (with respect to the stationary lead nucleus) of magnitude $L = p_0 b$, where p_0 is the magnitude of the initial momentum of the alpha particle and $b = 1.00 \times 10^{-12}$ m. What is the distance of closest approach? Repeat for $b = 1.00 \times 10^{-13}$ m and $b = 1.00 \times 10^{-14}$ m.

23.90 ••• CALC A hollow, thin-walled insulating cylinder of radius R and length L (like the cardboard tube in a roll of toilet paper) has charge Q uniformly distributed over its surface. (a) Calculate the electric potential at all points along the axis of the tube. Take the origin to be at the center of the tube, and take the potential to be zero at infinity. (b) Show that if $L \ll R$, the result of part (a) reduces to the potential on the axis of a ring of charge of radius R. (See Example 23.11 in Section 23.3.) (c) Use the result of part (a) to find the electric field at all points along the axis of the tube.

23.91 ••• **The Millikan Oil-Drop Experiment.** The charge of an electron was first measured by the American physicist Robert Millikan during 1909–1913. In his experiment, oil is sprayed in very fine drops (around 10^{-4} mm in diameter) into the space between two parallel horizontal plates separated by a distance d. A potential difference V_{AB} is maintained between the parallel plates, causing a downward electric field between them. Some of the oil drops acquire a negative charge because of frictional effects or because of ionization of the surrounding air by x rays or radioactivity. The drops are observed through a microscope. (a) Show that an oil drop of radius r at rest between the plates will remain at rest if the magnitude of its charge is

$$q = \frac{4\pi}{3}\frac{\rho r^3 g d}{V_{AB}}$$

where ρ is the density of the oil. (Ignore the buoyant force of the air.) By adjusting V_{AB} to keep a given drop at rest, the charge on that drop can be determined, provided its radius is known. (b) Millikan's oil drops were much too small to measure their radii directly. Instead, Millikan determined r by cutting off the electric field and measuring the *terminal speed* v_t of the drop as it fell. (We discussed the concept of terminal speed in Section 5.3.) The viscous force F on a sphere of radius r moving with speed v through a fluid with viscosity η is given by Stokes's law: $F = 6\pi\eta r v$. When the drop is falling at v_t, the viscous force just balances the weight $w = mg$ of the drop. Show that the magnitude of the charge on the drop is

$$q = 18\pi \frac{d}{V_{AB}}\sqrt{\frac{\eta^3 v_t^3}{2\rho g}}$$

Within the limits of their experimental error, every one of the thousands of drops that Millikan and his coworkers measured had a charge equal to some small integer multiple of a basic charge e. That is, they found drops with charges of $\pm 2e$, $\pm 5e$, and so on, but none with values such as $0.76e$ or $2.49e$. A drop with charge $-e$ has acquired one extra electron; if its charge is $-2e$, it has acquired two extra electrons, and so on. (c) A charged oil drop in a Millikan oil-drop apparatus is observed to fall 1.00 mm at constant speed in 39.3 s if $V_{AB} = 0$. The same drop can be held at rest between two plates separated by 1.00 mm if $V_{AB} = 9.16$ V. How many excess electrons has the drop acquired, and what is the radius of the drop? The viscosity of air is 1.81×10^{-5} N·s/m², and the density of the oil is 824 kg/m³.

23.92 •• CP Two point charges are moving to the right along the x-axis. Point charge 1 has charge $q_1 = 2.00\ \mu C$, mass $m_1 = 6.00 \times 10^{-5}$ kg, and speed v_1. Point charge 2 is to the right of q_1 and has charge $q_2 = -5.00\ \mu C$, mass $m_2 = 3.00 \times 10^{-5}$ kg, and speed v_2. At a particular instant, the charges are separated by a distance of 9.00 mm and have speeds $v_1 = 400$ m/s and $v_2 = 1300$ m/s. The only forces on the particles are the forces they exert on each other. (a) Determine the speed v_{cm} of the center of mass of the system. (b) The *relative energy* E_{rel} of the system is defined as the total energy minus the kinetic energy contributed by the motion of the center of mass:

$$E_{rel} = E - \tfrac{1}{2}(m_1 + m_2)v_{cm}^2$$

where $E = \tfrac{1}{2}m_1 v_1^2 + \tfrac{1}{2}m_2 v_2^2 + q_1 q_2/4\pi\epsilon_0 r$ is the total energy of the system and r is the distance between the charges. Show that $E_{rel} = \tfrac{1}{2}\mu v^2 + q_1 q_2/4\pi\epsilon_0 r$, where $\mu = m_1 m_2/(m_1 + m_2)$ is called the *reduced mass* of the system and $v = v_2 - v_1$ is the relative speed of the moving particles. (c) For the numerical values given above, calculate the numerical value of E_{rel}. (d) Based on the result of part (c), for the conditions given above, will the particles escape from one another? Explain. (e) If the particles do escape, what will be their final relative speed when $r \to \infty$? If the particles do not escape, what will be their distance of maximum separation? That is, what will be the value of r when $v = 0$? (f) Repeat parts (c)–(e) for $v_1 = 400$ m/s and $v_2 = 1800$ m/s when the separation is 9.00 mm.

Answers

Chapter Opening Question ?

A large, constant potential difference V_{ab} is maintained between the welding tool (a) and the metal pieces to be welded (b). From Example 23.9 (Section 23.3) the electric field between two conductors separated by a distance d has magnitude $E = V_{ab}/d$. Hence d must be small in order for the field magnitude E to be large enough to ionize the gas between the conductors a and b (see Section 23.3) and produce an arc through this gas.

Test Your Understanding Questions

23.1 Answers: (a) (i), (b) (ii) The three charges q_1, q_2, and q_3 are all positive, so all three of the terms in the sum in Eq. (23.11)— q_1q_2/r_{12}, q_1q_3/r_{13}, and q_2q_3/r_{23}—are positive. Hence the total electric potential energy U is positive. This means that it would take positive work to bring the three charges from infinity to the positions shown in Fig. 21.14, and hence *negative* work to move the three charges from these positions back to infinity.

23.2 Answer: no If $V = 0$ at a certain point, $\vec{E}$ does *not* have to be zero at that point. An example is point c in Figs. 21.23 and 23.13, for which there is an electric field in the $+x$-direction (see Example 21.9 in Section 21.5) even though $V = 0$ (see Example 23.4). This isn't a surprising result because V and $\vec{E}$ are quite different quantities: V is the net amount of work required to bring a unit charge from infinity to the point in question, whereas $\vec{E}$ is the electric force that acts on a unit charge when it arrives at that point.

23.3 Answer: no If $\vec{E} = 0$ at a certain point, V does *not* have to be zero at that point. An example is point O at the center of the charged ring in Figs. 21.23 and 23.21. From Example 21.9 (Section 21.5), the electric field is zero at O because the electric-field contributions from different parts of the ring completely cancel. From Example 23.11, however, the potential at O is *not* zero: This point corresponds to $x = 0$, so $V = (1/4\pi\epsilon_0)(Q/a)$. This value of V corresponds to the work that would have to be done to move a unit positive test charge along a path from infinity to point O; it is nonzero because the charged ring repels the test charge, so positive work must be done to move the test charge toward the ring.

23.4 Answer: no If the positive charges in Fig. 23.23 were replaced by negative charges, and vice versa, the equipotential surfaces would be the same but the sign of the potential would be reversed. For example, the surfaces in Fig. 23.23b with potential $V = +30$ V and $V = -50$ V would have potential $V = -30$ V and $V = +50$ V, respectively.

23.5 Answer: (iii) From Eqs. (23.19), the components of the electric field are $E_x = -\partial V/\partial x = B + Dy$, $E_y = -\partial V/\partial y = 3Cy^2 + Dx$, and $E_z = -\partial V/\partial z = 0$. The value of A has no effect, which means that we can add a constant to the electric potential at all points without changing $\vec{E}$ or the potential difference between two points. The potential does not depend on z, so the z-component of $\vec{E}$ is zero. Note that at the origin the electric field is not zero because it has a nonzero x-component: $E_x = B$, $E_y = 0$, $E_z = 0$.

Bridging Problem

Answer: $\dfrac{qQ}{8\pi\epsilon_0 a} \ln\left(\dfrac{L + a}{L - a}\right)$

24 CAPACITANCE AND DIELECTRICS

LEARNING GOALS

By studying this chapter, you will learn:

- The nature of capacitors, and how to calculate a quantity that measures their ability to store charge.
- How to analyze capacitors connected in a network.
- How to calculate the amount of energy stored in a capacitor.
- What dielectrics are, and how they make capacitors more effective.

? The energy used in a camera's flash unit is stored in a capacitor, which consists of two closely spaced conductors that carry opposite charges. If the amount of charge on the conductors is doubled, by what factor does the stored energy increase?

When you set an old-fashioned spring mousetrap or pull back the string of an archer's bow, you are storing mechanical energy as elastic potential energy. A capacitor is a device that stores *electric* potential energy and electric charge. To make a capacitor, just insulate two conductors from each other. To store energy in this device, transfer charge from one conductor to the other so that one has a negative charge and the other has an equal amount of positive charge. Work must be done to move the charges through the resulting potential difference between the conductors, and the work done is stored as electric potential energy.

Capacitors have a tremendous number of practical applications in devices such as electronic flash units for photography, pulsed lasers, air bag sensors for cars, and radio and television receivers. We'll encounter many of these applications in later chapters (particularly Chapter 31, in which we'll see the crucial role played by capacitors in the alternating-current circuits that pervade our technological society). In this chapter, however, our emphasis is on the fundamental properties of capacitors. For a particular capacitor, the ratio of the charge on each conductor to the potential difference between the conductors is a constant, called the *capacitance*. The capacitance depends on the sizes and shapes of the conductors and on the insulating material (if any) between them. Compared to the case in which there is only vacuum between the conductors, the capacitance increases when an insulating material (a *dielectric*) is present. This happens because a redistribution of charge, called *polarization,* takes place within the insulating material. Studying polarization will give us added insight into the electrical properties of matter.

Capacitors also give us a new way to think about electric potential energy. The energy stored in a charged capacitor is related to the electric field in the space between the conductors. We will see that electric potential energy can be regarded as being stored *in the field itself.* The idea that the electric field is itself a storehouse of energy is at the heart of the theory of electromagnetic waves and our modern understanding of the nature of light, to be discussed in Chapter 32.

24.1 Capacitors and Capacitance

Any two conductors separated by an insulator (or a vacuum) form a **capacitor** (Fig. 24.1). In most practical applications, each conductor initially has zero net charge and electrons are transferred from one conductor to the other; this is called *charging* the capacitor. Then the two conductors have charges with equal magnitude and opposite sign, and the *net* charge on the capacitor as a whole remains zero. We will assume throughout this chapter that this is the case. When we say that a capacitor has charge Q, or that a charge Q is *stored* on the capacitor, we mean that the conductor at higher potential has charge $+Q$ and the conductor at lower potential has charge $-Q$ (assuming that Q is positive). Keep this in mind in the following discussion and examples.

In circuit diagrams a capacitor is represented by either of these symbols:

In either symbol the vertical lines (straight or curved) represent the conductors and the horizontal lines represent wires connected to either conductor. One common way to charge a capacitor is to connect these two wires to opposite terminals of a battery. Once the charges Q and $-Q$ are established on the conductors, the battery is disconnected. This gives a fixed *potential difference* V_{ab} between the conductors (that is, the potential of the positively charged conductor a with respect to the negatively charged conductor b) that is just equal to the voltage of the battery.

The electric field at any point in the region between the conductors is proportional to the magnitude Q of charge on each conductor. It follows that the potential difference V_{ab} between the conductors is also proportional to Q. If we double the magnitude of charge on each conductor, the charge density at each point doubles, the electric field at each point doubles, and the potential difference between conductors doubles; however, the *ratio* of charge to potential difference does not change. This ratio is called the **capacitance** C of the capacitor:

$$C = \frac{Q}{V_{ab}} \qquad \text{(definition of capacitance)} \qquad (24.1)$$

The SI unit of capacitance is called one **farad** (1 F), in honor of the 19th-century English physicist Michael Faraday. From Eq. (24.1), one farad is equal to one *coulomb per volt* (1 C/V):

$$1\ \text{F} = 1\ \text{farad} = 1\ \text{C/V} = 1\ \text{coulomb/volt}$$

CAUTION **Capacitance vs. coulombs** Don't confuse the symbol C for capacitance (which is always in italics) with the abbreviation C for coulombs (which is never italicized). ▮

The greater the capacitance C of a capacitor, the greater the magnitude Q of charge on either conductor for a given potential difference V_{ab} and hence the greater the amount of stored energy. (Remember that potential is potential energy per unit charge.) Thus *capacitance is a measure of the ability of a capacitor to store energy*. We will see that the value of the capacitance depends only on the shapes and sizes of the conductors and on the nature of the insulating material between them. (The above remarks about capacitance being independent of Q and V_{ab} do not apply to certain special types of insulating materials. We won't discuss these materials in this book, however.)

Calculating Capacitance: Capacitors in Vacuum

We can calculate the capacitance C of a given capacitor by finding the potential difference V_{ab} between the conductors for a given magnitude of charge Q and

24.1 Any two conductors a and b insulated from each other form a capacitor.

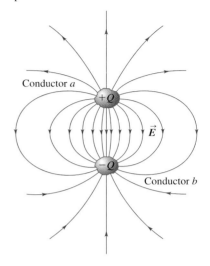

Conductor a

$+Q$

$\vec{E}$

$-Q$

Conductor b

Mastering**PHYSICS**

ActivPhysics 11.11.6: Electric Potential: Qualitative Introduction
ActivPhysics 11.12.1 and 11.12.3: Electric Potential, Field, and Force

24.2 A charged parallel-plate capacitor.

(a) Arrangement of the capacitor plates

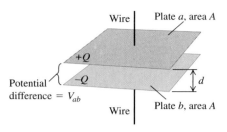

(b) Side view of the electric field $\vec{E}$

When the separation of the plates is small compared to their size, the fringing of the field is slight.

24.3 Inside a condenser microphone is a capacitor with one rigid plate and one flexible plate. The two plates are kept at a constant potential difference V_{ab}. Sound waves cause the flexible plate to move back and forth, varying the capacitance C and causing charge to flow to and from the capacitor in accordance with the relationship $C = Q/V_{ab}$. Thus a sound wave is converted to a charge flow that can be amplified and recorded digitally.

then using Eq. (24.1). For now we'll consider only *capacitors in vacuum;* that is, we'll assume that the conductors that make up the capacitor are separated by empty space.

The simplest form of capacitor consists of two parallel conducting plates, each with area A, separated by a distance d that is small in comparison with their dimensions (Fig. 24.2a). When the plates are charged, the electric field is almost completely localized in the region between the plates (Fig. 24.2b). As we discussed in Example 22.8 (Section 22.4), the field between such plates is essentially *uniform,* and the charges on the plates are uniformly distributed over their opposing surfaces. We call this arrangement a **parallel-plate capacitor.**

We worked out the electric-field magnitude E for this arrangement in Example 21.12 (Section 21.5) using the principle of superposition of electric fields and again in Example 22.8 (Section 22.4) using Gauss's law. It would be a good idea to review those examples. We found that $E = \sigma/\epsilon_0$, where σ is the magnitude (absolute value) of the surface charge density on each plate. This is equal to the magnitude of the total charge Q on each plate divided by the area A of the plate, or $\sigma = Q/A$, so the field magnitude E can be expressed as

$$E = \frac{\sigma}{\epsilon_0} = \frac{Q}{\epsilon_0 A}$$

The field is uniform and the distance between the plates is d, so the potential difference (voltage) between the two plates is

$$V_{ab} = Ed = \frac{1}{\epsilon_0}\frac{Qd}{A}$$

From this we see that the capacitance C of a parallel-plate capacitor in vacuum is

$$C = \frac{Q}{V_{ab}} = \epsilon_0 \frac{A}{d} \qquad \begin{array}{l}\text{(capacitance of a parallel-plate} \\ \text{capacitor in vacuum)}\end{array} \qquad (24.2)$$

The capacitance depends only on the geometry of the capacitor; it is directly proportional to the area A of each plate and inversely proportional to their separation d. The quantities A and d are constants for a given capacitor, and ϵ_0 is a universal constant. Thus in vacuum the capacitance C is a constant independent of the charge on the capacitor or the potential difference between the plates. If one of the capacitor plates is flexible, the capacitance C changes as the plate separation d changes. This is the operating principle of a condenser microphone (Fig. 24.3).

When matter is present between the plates, its properties affect the capacitance. We will return to this topic in Section 24.4. Meanwhile, we remark that if the space contains air at atmospheric pressure instead of vacuum, the capacitance differs from the prediction of Eq. (24.2) by less than 0.06%.

In Eq. (24.2), if A is in square meters and d in meters, C is in farads. The units of ϵ_0 are $C^2/N \cdot m^2$, so we see that

$$1\text{ F} = 1\text{ }C^2/N \cdot m = 1\text{ }C^2/J$$

Because $1\text{ V} = 1\text{ J/C}$ (energy per unit charge), this is consistent with our definition $1\text{ F} = 1\text{ C/V}$. Finally, the units of ϵ_0 can be expressed as $1\text{ }C^2/N \cdot m^2 = 1\text{ F/m}$, so

$$\epsilon_0 = 8.85 \times 10^{-12}\text{ F/m}$$

This relationship is useful in capacitance calculations, and it also helps us to verify that Eq. (24.2) is dimensionally consistent.

One farad is a very large capacitance, as the following example shows. In many applications the most convenient units of capacitance are the *microfarad*

($1 \mu F = 10^{-6}$ F) and the *picofarad* (1 pF $= 10^{-12}$ F). For example, the flash unit in a point-and-shoot camera uses a capacitor of a few hundred microfarads (Fig. 24.4), while capacitances in a radio tuning circuit are typically from 10 to 100 picofarads.

For *any* capacitor in vacuum, the capacitance C depends only on the shapes, dimensions, and separation of the conductors that make up the capacitor. If the conductor shapes are more complex than those of the parallel-plate capacitor, the expression for capacitance is more complicated than in Eq. (24.2). In the following examples we show how to calculate C for two other conductor geometries.

24.4 A commercial capacitor is labeled with the value of its capacitance. For these capacitors, $C = 2200 \mu F$, $1000 \mu F$, and $470 \mu F$.

Example 24.1   Size of a 1-F capacitor

The parallel plates of a 1.0-F capacitor are 1.0 mm apart. What is their area?

SOLUTION

IDENTIFY and SET UP: This problem uses the relationship among the capacitance C, plate separation d, and plate area A (our target variable) for a parallel-plate capacitor. We solve Eq. (24.2) for A.

EXECUTE: From Eq. (24.2),

$$A = \frac{Cd}{\epsilon_0} = \frac{(1.0 \text{ F})(1.0 \times 10^{-3} \text{ m})}{8.85 \times 10^{-12} \text{ F/m}} = 1.1 \times 10^{8} \text{ m}^2$$

EVALUATE: This corresponds to a square about 10 km (about 6 miles) on a side! The volume of such a capacitor would be at least $Ad = 1.1 \times 10^5$ m^3, equivalent to that of a cube about 50 m on a side. In fact, it's possible to make 1-F capacitors a few *centimeters* on a side. The trick is to have an appropriate substance between the plates rather than a vacuum, so that (among other things) the plate separation d can greatly reduced. We'll explore this further in Section 24.4.

Example 24.2   Properties of a parallel-plate capacitor

The plates of a parallel-plate capacitor in vacuum are 5.00 mm apart and 2.00 m^2 in area. A 10.0-kV potential difference is applied across the capacitor. Compute (a) the capacitance; (b) the charge on each plate; and (c) the magnitude of the electric field between the plates.

SOLUTION

IDENTIFY and SET UP: We are given the plate area A, the plate spacing d, and the potential difference $V_{ab} = 1.00 \times 10^4$ V for this parallel-plate capacitor. Our target variables are the capacitance C, the charge Q on each plate, and the electric-field magnitude E. We use Eq. (24.2) to calculate C and then use Eq. (24.1) and V_{ab} to find Q. We use $E = Q/\epsilon_0 A$ to find E.

EXECUTE: (a) From Eq. (24.2),

$$C = \epsilon_0 \frac{A}{d} = (8.85 \times 10^{-12} \text{ F/m}) \frac{(2.00 \text{ m}^2)}{5.00 \times 10^{-3} \text{ m}}$$

$$= 3.54 \times 10^{-9} \text{ F} = 0.00354 \mu F$$

(b) The charge on the capacitor is

$$Q = CV_{ab} = (3.54 \times 10^{-9} \text{ C/V})(1.00 \times 10^4 \text{ V})$$

$$= 3.54 \times 10^{-5} \text{ C} = 35.4 \mu C$$

The plate at higher potential has charge $+35.4 \mu C$, and the other plate has charge $-35.4 \mu C$.

(c) The electric-field magnitude is

$$E = \frac{\sigma}{\epsilon_0} = \frac{Q}{\epsilon_0 A} = \frac{3.54 \times 10^{-5} \text{ C}}{(8.85 \times 10^{-12} \text{ C}^2/\text{N} \cdot \text{m}^2)(2.00 \text{ m}^2)}$$

$$= 2.00 \times 10^6 \text{ N/C}$$

EVALUATE: We can also find E by recalling that the electric field is equal in magnitude to the potential gradient [Eq. (23.22)]. The field between the plates is uniform, so

$$E = \frac{V_{ab}}{d} = \frac{1.00 \times 10^4 \text{ V}}{5.00 \times 10^{-3} \text{ m}} = 2.00 \times 10^6 \text{ V/m}$$

(Remember that 1 N/C $=$ 1 V/m.)

Example 24.3 **A spherical capacitor**

Two concentric spherical conducting shells are separated by vacuum (Fig. 24.5). The inner shell has total charge $+Q$ and outer radius r_a, and the outer shell has charge $-Q$ and inner radius r_b. Find the capacitance of this spherical capacitor.

SOLUTION

IDENTIFY and SET UP: By definition, the capacitance C is the magnitude Q of the charge on either sphere divided by the potential difference V_{ab} between the spheres. We first find V_{ab}, and then use Eq. (24.1) to find the capacitance $C = Q/V_{ab}$.

EXECUTE: Using a Gaussian surface such as that shown in Fig. 24.5, we found in Example 22.5 (Section 22.4) that the charge on a conducting sphere produces zero field *inside* the sphere, so the outer sphere makes no contribution to the field between the spheres. Therefore the electric field *and* the electric potential

24.5 A spherical capacitor.

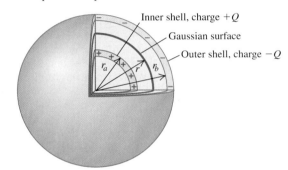

between the shells are the same as those outside a charged conducting sphere with charge $+Q$. We considered that problem in Example 23.8 (Section 23.3), so the same result applies here: The potential at any point between the spheres is $V = Q/4\pi\epsilon_0 r$. Hence the potential of the inner (positive) conductor at $r = r_a$ with respect to that of the outer (negative) conductor at $r = r_b$ is

$$V_{ab} = V_a - V_b = \frac{Q}{4\pi\epsilon_0 r_a} - \frac{Q}{4\pi\epsilon_0 r_b}$$

$$= \frac{Q}{4\pi\epsilon_0}\left(\frac{1}{r_a} - \frac{1}{r_b}\right) = \frac{Q}{4\pi\epsilon_0}\frac{r_b - r_a}{r_a r_b}$$

The capacitance is then

$$C = \frac{Q}{V_{ab}} = 4\pi\epsilon_0 \frac{r_a r_b}{r_b - r_a}$$

As an example, if $r_a = 9.5$ cm and $r_b = 10.5$ cm,

$$C = 4\pi(8.85 \times 10^{-12}\ \text{F/m})\frac{(0.095\ \text{m})(0.105\ \text{m})}{0.010\ \text{m}}$$

$$= 1.1 \times 10^{-10}\ \text{F} = 110\ \text{pF}$$

EVALUATE: We can relate our expression for C to that for a parallel-plate capacitor. The quantity $4\pi r_a r_b$ is intermediate between the areas $4\pi r_a^2$ and $4\pi r_b^2$ of the two spheres; in fact, it's the *geometric mean* of these two areas, which we can denote by A_gm. The distance between spheres is $d = r_b - r_a$, so we can write $C = 4\pi\epsilon_0 r_a r_b/(r_b - r_a) = \epsilon_0 A_\text{gm}/d$. This has the same form as for parallel plates: $C = \epsilon_0 A/d$. If the distance between spheres is very small in comparison to their radii, their capacitance is the same as that of parallel plates with the same area and spacing.

Example 24.4 **A cylindrical capacitor**

Two long, coaxial cylindrical conductors are separated by vacuum (Fig. 24.6). The inner cylinder has radius r_a and linear charge density $+\lambda$. The outer cylinder has inner radius r_b and linear charge density $-\lambda$. Find the capacitance per unit length for this capacitor.

SOLUTION

IDENTIFY and SET UP: As in Example 24.3, we use the definition of capacitance, $C = Q/V_{ab}$. We use the result of Example 23.10

24.6 A long cylindrical capacitor. The linear charge density λ is assumed to be positive in this figure. The magnitude of charge in a length L of either cylinder is λL.

(Section 23.3) to find the potential difference V_{ab} between the cylinders, and find the charge Q on a length L of the cylinders from the linear charge density. We then find the corresponding capacitance C using Eq. (24.1). Our target variable is this capacitance divided by L.

EXECUTE: As in Example 24.3, the potential V between the cylinders is not affected by the presence of the charged outer cylinder. Hence our result in Example 23.10 for the potential outside a charged conducting cylinder also holds in this example for potential in the space between the cylinders:

$$V = \frac{\lambda}{2\pi\epsilon_0}\ln\frac{r_0}{r}$$

Here r_0 is the arbitrary, *finite* radius at which $V = 0$. We take $r_0 = r_b$, the radius of the inner surface of the outer cylinder. Then the potential at the outer surface of the inner cylinder (at which $r = r_a$) is just the potential V_{ab} of the inner (positive) cylinder a with respect to the outer (negative) cylinder b:

$$V_{ab} = \frac{\lambda}{2\pi\epsilon_0}\ln\frac{r_b}{r_a}$$

If λ is positive as in Fig. 24.6, then V_{ab} is positive as well: The inner cylinder is at higher potential than the outer.

The total charge Q in a length L is $Q = \lambda L$, so from Eq. (24.1) the capacitance C of a length L is

$$C = \frac{Q}{V_{ab}} = \frac{\lambda L}{\dfrac{\lambda}{2\pi\epsilon_0}\ln\dfrac{r_b}{r_a}} = \frac{2\pi\epsilon_0 L}{\ln(r_b/r_a)}$$

The capacitance per unit length is

$$\frac{C}{L} = \frac{2\pi\epsilon_0}{\ln(r_b/r_a)}$$

Substituting $\epsilon_0 = 8.85 \times 10^{-12}$ F/m $= 8.85$ pF/m, we get

$$\frac{C}{L} = \frac{55.6 \text{ pF/m}}{\ln(r_b/r_a)}$$

EVALUATE: The capacitance of coaxial cylinders is determined entirely by their dimensions, just as for parallel-plate and spherical capacitors. Ordinary coaxial cables are made like this but with an insulating material instead of vacuum between the conductors. A typical cable used for connecting a television to a cable TV feed has a capacitance per unit length of 69 pF/m.

Test Your Understanding of Section 24.1 A capacitor has vacuum in the space between the conductors. If you double the amount of charge on each conductor, what happens to the capacitance? (i) It increases; (ii) it decreases; (iii) it remains the same; (iv) the answer depends on the size or shape of the conductors.

24.2 Capacitors in Series and Parallel

Capacitors are manufactured with certain standard capacitances and working voltages (Fig. 24.7). However, these standard values may not be the ones you actually need in a particular application. You can obtain the values you need by combining capacitors; many combinations are possible, but the simplest combinations are a series connection and a parallel connection.

Capacitors in Series

Figure 24.8a is a schematic diagram of a **series connection.** Two capacitors are connected in series (one after the other) by conducting wires between points a and b. Both capacitors are initially uncharged. When a constant positive potential difference V_{ab} is applied between points a and b, the capacitors become charged; the figure shows that the charge on *all* conducting plates has the same magnitude. To see why, note first that the top plate of C_1 acquires a positive charge Q. The electric field of this positive charge pulls negative charge up to the bottom plate of C_1 until all of the field lines that begin on the top plate end on the bottom plate. This requires that the bottom plate have charge $-Q$. These negative charges had to come from the top plate of C_2, which becomes positively charged with charge $+Q$. This positive charge then pulls negative charge $-Q$ from the connection at point b onto the bottom plate of C_2. The total charge on the lower plate of C_1 and the upper plate of C_2 together must always be zero because these plates aren't connected to anything except each other. Thus *in a series connection the magnitude of charge on all plates is the same.*

Referring to Fig. 24.8a, we can write the potential differences between points a and c, c and b, and a and b as

$$V_{ac} = V_1 = \frac{Q}{C_1} \qquad V_{cb} = V_2 = \frac{Q}{C_2}$$

$$V_{ab} = V = V_1 + V_2 = Q\left(\frac{1}{C_1} + \frac{1}{C_2}\right)$$

and so

$$\frac{V}{Q} = \frac{1}{C_1} + \frac{1}{C_2} \qquad (24.3)$$

Following a common convention, we use the symbols V_1, V_2, and V to denote the potential *differences* V_{ac} (across the first capacitor), V_{cb} (across the second capacitor), and V_{ab} (across the entire combination of capacitors), respectively.

24.7 An assortment of commercially available capacitors.

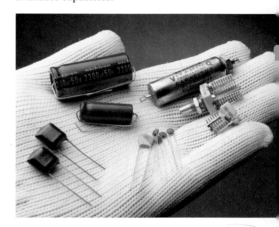

24.8 A series connection of two capacitors.

(a) Two capacitors in series

Capacitors in series:
• The capacitors have the same charge Q.
• Their potential differences add:
 $V_{ac} + V_{cb} = V_{ab}$.

(b) The equivalent single capacitor

Equivalent capacitance is less than the individual capacitances:

$$C_{eq} = \frac{Q}{V}$$

$$\frac{1}{C_{eq}} = \frac{1}{C_1} + \frac{1}{C_2}$$

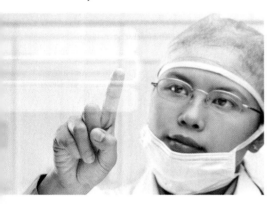

The **equivalent capacitance** C_{eq} of the series combination is defined as the capacitance of a *single* capacitor for which the charge Q is the same as for the combination, when the potential difference V is the same. In other words, the combination can be replaced by an *equivalent capacitor* of capacitance C_{eq}. For such a capacitor, shown in Fig. 24.8b,

$$C_{eq} = \frac{Q}{V} \quad \text{or} \quad \frac{1}{C_{eq}} = \frac{V}{Q} \tag{24.4}$$

Combining Eqs. (24.3) and (24.4), we find

$$\frac{1}{C_{eq}} = \frac{1}{C_1} + \frac{1}{C_2}$$

We can extend this analysis to any number of capacitors in series. We find the following result for the *reciprocal* of the equivalent capacitance:

$$\frac{1}{C_{eq}} = \frac{1}{C_1} + \frac{1}{C_2} + \frac{1}{C_3} + \cdots \quad \text{(capacitors in series)} \tag{24.5}$$

The reciprocal of the equivalent capacitance of a series combination equals the sum of the reciprocals of the individual capacitances. In a series connection the equivalent capacitance is always *less than* any individual capacitance.

CAUTION **Capacitors in series** The magnitude of charge is the same on all plates of all the capacitors in a series combination; however, the potential differences of the individual capacitors are *not* the same unless their individual capacitances are the same. The potential differences of the individual capacitors add to give the total potential difference across the series combination: $V_{total} = V_1 + V_2 + V_3 + \cdots$.

Capacitors in Parallel

24.9 A parallel connection of two capacitors.

(a) Two capacitors in parallel

Capacitors in parallel:
• The capacitors have the same potential V.
• The charge on each capacitor depends on its capacitance: $Q_1 = C_1 V$, $Q_2 = C_2 V$.

(b) The equivalent single capacitor

The arrangement shown in Fig. 24.9a is called a **parallel connection.** Two capacitors are connected in parallel between points a and b. In this case the upper plates of the two capacitors are connected by conducting wires to form an equipotential surface, and the lower plates form another. Hence *in a parallel connection the potential difference for all individual capacitors is the same* and is equal to $V_{ab} = V$. The charges Q_1 and Q_2 are not necessarily equal, however, since charges can reach each capacitor independently from the source (such as a battery) of the voltage V_{ab}. The charges are

$$Q_1 = C_1 V \quad \text{and} \quad Q_2 = C_2 V$$

The *total* charge Q of the combination, and thus the total charge on the equivalent capacitor, is

$$Q = Q_1 + Q_2 = (C_1 + C_2)V$$

so

$$\frac{Q}{V} = C_1 + C_2 \tag{24.6}$$

The parallel combination is equivalent to a single capacitor with the same total charge $Q = Q_1 + Q_2$ and potential difference V as the combination (Fig. 24.9b). The equivalent capacitance of the combination, C_{eq}, is the same as the capacitance Q/V of this single equivalent capacitor. So from Eq. (24.6),

$$C_{eq} = C_1 + C_2$$

In the same way we can show that for any number of capacitors in parallel,

$$C_{eq} = C_1 + C_2 + C_3 + \cdots \qquad \text{(capacitors in parallel)} \qquad (24.7)$$

The equivalent capacitance of a parallel combination equals the *sum* of the individual capacitances. In a parallel connection the equivalent capacitance is always *greater than* any individual capacitance.

CAUTION **Capacitors in parallel** The potential differences are the same for all the capacitors in a parallel combination; however, the charges on individual capacitors are *not* the same unless their individual capacitances are the same. The charges on the individual capacitors add to give the total charge on the parallel combination: $Q_{total} = Q_1 + Q_2 + Q_3 + \cdots$. [Compare these statements to those in the "Caution" paragraph following Eq. (24.5).]

Problem-Solving Strategy 24.1   **Equivalent Capacitance**

IDENTIFY *the relevant concepts:* The concept of equivalent capacitance is useful whenever two or more capacitors are connected.

SET UP *the problem* using the following steps:
1. Make a drawing of the capacitor arrangement.
2. Identify all groups of capacitors that are connected in series or in parallel.
3. Keep in mind that when we say a capacitor "has charge Q," we mean that the plate at higher potential has charge $+Q$ and the other plate has charge $-Q$.

EXECUTE *the solution* as follows:
1. Use Eq. (24.5) to find the equivalent capacitance of capacitors connected in series, as in Fig. 24.8. Such capacitors each have the *same charge* if they were uncharged before they were connected; that charge is the same as that on the equivalent capacitor. The potential difference across the combination is the sum of the potential differences across the individual capacitors.

2. Use Eq. (24.7) to find the equivalent capacitance of capacitors connected in parallel, as in Fig. 24.9. Such capacitors all have the *same potential difference* across them; that potential difference is the same as that across the equivalent capacitor. The total charge on the combination is the sum of the charges on the individual capacitors.
3. After replacing all the series or parallel groups you initially identified, you may find that more such groups reveal themselves. Replace those groups using the same procedure as above until no more replacements are possible. If you then need to find the charge or potential difference for an individual original capacitor, you may have to retrace your steps.

EVALUATE *your answer:* Check whether your result makes sense. If the capacitors are connected in series, the equivalent capacitance C_{eq} must be *smaller* than any of the individual capacitances. If the capacitors are connected in parallel, C_{eq} must be *greater* than any of the individual capacitances.

Example 24.5   **Capacitors in series and in parallel**

In Figs. 24.8 and 24.9, let $C_1 = 6.0 \ \mu\text{F}$, $C_2 = 3.0 \ \mu\text{F}$, and $V_{ab} = 18 \text{ V}$. Find the equivalent capacitance and the charge and potential difference for each capacitor when the capacitors are connected (a) in series (see Fig. 24.8) and (b) in parallel (see Fig. 24.9).

SOLUTION

IDENTIFY and SET UP: In both parts of this example a target variable is the equivalent capacitance C_{eq}, which is given by Eq. (24.5) for the series combination in part (a) and by Eq. (24.7) for the parallel combination in part (b). In each part we find the charge and potential difference using the definition of capacitance, Eq. (24.1), and the rules outlined in Problem-Solving Strategy 24.1.

EXECUTE: (a) From Eq. (24.5) for a series combination,

$$\frac{1}{C_{eq}} = \frac{1}{C_1} + \frac{1}{C_2} = \frac{1}{6.0 \ \mu\text{F}} + \frac{1}{3.0 \ \mu\text{F}} \qquad C_{eq} = 2.0 \ \mu\text{F}$$

The charge Q on each capacitor in series is the same as that on the equivalent capacitor:

$$Q = C_{eq}V = (2.0 \ \mu\text{F})(18 \text{ V}) = 36 \ \mu\text{C}$$

The potential difference across each capacitor is inversely proportional to its capacitance:

$$V_{ac} = V_1 = \frac{Q}{C_1} = \frac{36 \ \mu\text{C}}{6.0 \ \mu\text{F}} = 6.0 \text{ V}$$

$$V_{cb} = V_2 = \frac{Q}{C_2} = \frac{36 \ \mu\text{C}}{3.0 \ \mu\text{F}} = 12.0 \text{ V}$$

(b) From Eq. (24.7) for a parallel combination,

$$C_{eq} = C_1 + C_2 = 6.0 \ \mu\text{F} + 3.0 \ \mu\text{F} = 9.0 \ \mu\text{F}$$

The potential difference across each of the capacitors is the same as that across the equivalent capacitor, 18 V. The charge on each capacitor is directly proportional to its capacitance:

$$Q_1 = C_1V = (6.0 \ \mu\text{F})(18 \text{ V}) = 108 \ \mu\text{C}$$
$$Q_2 = C_2V = (3.0 \ \mu\text{F})(18 \text{ V}) = 54 \ \mu\text{C}$$

EVALUATE: As expected, the equivalent capacitance C_{eq} for the series combination in part (a) is less than either C_1 or C_2, while

Continued

that for the parallel combination in part (b) is greater than either C_1 or C_2. For two capacitors in series, as in part (a), the charge is the same on either capacitor and the *larger* potential difference appears across the capacitor with the *smaller* capacitance. Furthermore, the sum of the potential differences across the individual capacitors in series equals the potential difference across the equivalent capacitor: $V_{ac} + V_{cb} = V_{ab} = 18$ V. By contrast, for two capacitors in parallel, as in part (b), each capacitor has the same potential difference and the *larger* charge appears on the capacitor with the *larger* capacitance. Can you show that the total charge $Q_1 + Q_2$ on the parallel combination is equal to the charge $Q = C_{eq}V$ on the equivalent capacitor?

Example 24.6 **A capacitor network**

Find the equivalent capacitance of the five-capacitor network shown in Fig. 24.10a.

SOLUTION

IDENTIFY and SET UP: These capacitors are neither all in series nor all in parallel. We can, however, identify portions of the arrangement that *are* either in series or parallel. We combine these as described in Problem-Solving Strategy 24.1 to find the net equivalent capacitance, using Eq. (24.5) for series connections and Eq. (24.7) for parallel connections.

EXECUTE: The caption of Fig. 24.10 outlines our procedure. We first use Eq. (24.5) to replace the 12-μF and 6-μF series combination by its equivalent capacitance C':

$$\frac{1}{C'} = \frac{1}{12\ \mu\text{F}} + \frac{1}{6\ \mu\text{F}} \qquad C' = 4\ \mu\text{F}$$

This gives us the equivalent combination of Fig. 24.10b. Now we see three capacitors in parallel, and we use Eq. (24.7) to replace them with their equivalent capacitance C'':

$$C'' = 3\ \mu\text{F} + 11\ \mu\text{F} + 4\ \mu\text{F} = 18\ \mu\text{F}$$

This gives us the equivalent combination of Fig. 24.10c, which has two capacitors in series. We use Eq. (24.5) to replace them with their equivalent capacitance C_{eq}, which is our target variable (Fig. 24.10d):

$$\frac{1}{C_{eq}} = \frac{1}{18\ \mu\text{F}} + \frac{1}{9\ \mu\text{F}} \qquad C_{eq} = 6\ \mu\text{F}$$

EVALUATE: If the potential difference across the entire network in Fig. 24.10a is $V_{ab} = 9.0$ V, the net charge on the network is $Q = C_{eq}V_{ab} = (6\ \mu\text{F})(9.0\ \text{V}) = 54\ \mu\text{C}$. Can you find the charge on, and the voltage across, each of the five individual capacitors?

24.10 (a) A capacitor network between points a and b. (b) The 12-μF and 6-μF capacitors in series in (a) are replaced by an equivalent 4-μF capacitor. (c) The 3-μF, 11-μF, and 4-μF capacitors in parallel in (b) are replaced by an equivalent 18-μF capacitor. (d) Finally, the 18-μF and 9-μF capacitors in series in (c) are replaced by an equivalent 6-μF capacitor.

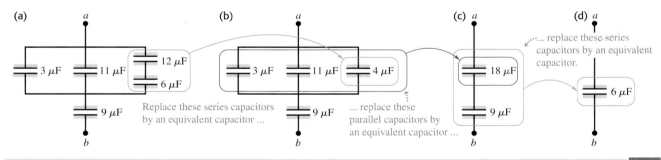

Test Your Understanding of Section 24.2 You want to connect a 4-μF capacitor and an 8-μF capacitor. (a) With which type of connection will the 4-μF capacitor have a greater potential difference across it than the 8-μF capacitor? (i) series; (ii) parallel; (iii) either series or parallel; (iv) neither series nor parallel. (b) With which type of connection will the 4-μF capacitor have a greater charge than the 8-μF capacitor? (i) series; (ii) parallel; (iii) either series or parallel; (iv) neither series nor parallel.

24.3 Energy Storage in Capacitors and Electric-Field Energy

Many of the most important applications of capacitors depend on their ability to store energy. The electric potential energy stored in a charged capacitor is just equal to the amount of work required to charge it—that is, to separate opposite charges and place them on different conductors. When the capacitor is discharged, this stored energy is recovered as work done by electrical forces.

We can calculate the potential energy U of a charged capacitor by calculating the work W required to charge it. Suppose that when we are done charging the capacitor, the final charge is Q and the final potential difference is V. From Eq. (24.1) these quantities are related by

$$V = \frac{Q}{C}$$

Let q and v be the charge and potential difference, respectively, at an intermediate stage during the charging process; then $v = q/C$. At this stage the work dW required to transfer an additional element of charge dq is

$$dW = v \, dq = \frac{q \, dq}{C}$$

The total work W needed to increase the capacitor charge q from zero to a final value Q is

$$W = \int_0^W dW = \frac{1}{C} \int_0^Q q \, dq = \frac{Q^2}{2C} \quad \text{(work to charge a capacitor)} \quad (24.8)$$

This is also equal to the total work done by the electric field on the charge when the capacitor discharges. Then q *decreases* from an initial value Q to zero as the elements of charge dq "fall" through potential differences v that vary from V down to zero.

If we define the potential energy of an *uncharged* capacitor to be zero, then W in Eq. (24.8) is equal to the potential energy U of the charged capacitor. The final stored charge is $Q = CV$, so we can express U (which is equal to W) as

$$U = \frac{Q^2}{2C} = \tfrac{1}{2}CV^2 = \tfrac{1}{2}QV \quad \begin{array}{l}\text{(potential energy stored}\\ \text{in a capacitor)}\end{array} \quad (24.9)$$

When Q is in coulombs, C in farads (coulombs per volt), and V in volts (joules per coulomb), U is in joules.

The last form of Eq. (24.9), $U = \tfrac{1}{2}QV$, shows that the total work W required to charge the capacitor is equal to the total charge Q multiplied by the *average* potential difference $\tfrac{1}{2}V$ during the charging process.

The expression $U = \tfrac{1}{2}(Q^2/C)$ in Eq. (24.9) shows that a charged capacitor is the electrical analog of a stretched spring with elastic potential energy $U = \tfrac{1}{2}kx^2$. The charge Q is analogous to the elongation x, and the *reciprocal* of the capacitance, $1/C$, is analogous to the force constant k. The energy supplied to a capacitor in the charging process is analogous to the work we do on a spring when we stretch it.

Equations (24.8) and (24.9) tell us that capacitance measures the ability of a capacitor to store both energy and charge. If a capacitor is charged by connecting it to a battery or other source that provides a fixed potential difference V, then increasing the value of C gives a greater charge $Q = CV$ and a greater amount of stored energy $U = \tfrac{1}{2}CV^2$. If instead the goal is to transfer a given quantity of charge Q from one conductor to another, Eq. (24.8) shows that the work W required is inversely proportional to C; the greater the capacitance, the easier it is to give a capacitor a fixed amount of charge.

Applications of Capacitors: Energy Storage

Most practical applications of capacitors take advantage of their ability to store and release energy. In electronic flash units used by photographers, the energy stored in a capacitor (see Fig. 24.4) is released by depressing the camera's shutter button. This provides a conducting path from one capacitor plate to the other through the flash tube. Once this path is established, the stored energy is rapidly converted into a brief but intense flash of light. An extreme example of the same principle is the Z machine at Sandia National Laboratories in New Mexico,

24.11 The Z machine uses a large number of capacitors in parallel to give a tremendous equivalent capacitance C (see Section 24.2). Hence a large amount of energy $U = \frac{1}{2}CV^2$ can be stored with even a modest potential difference V. The arcs shown here are produced when the capacitors discharge their energy into a target, which is no larger than a spool of thread. This heats the target to a temperature higher than 2×10^9 K.

which is used in experiments in controlled nuclear fusion (Fig. 24.11). A bank of charged capacitors releases more than a million joules of energy in just a few billionths of a second. For that brief space of time, the power output of the Z machine is 2.9×10^{14} W, or about 80 times the power output of all the electric power plants on earth combined!

In other applications, the energy is released more slowly. Springs in the suspension of an automobile help smooth out the ride by absorbing the energy from sudden jolts and releasing that energy gradually; in an analogous way, a capacitor in an electronic circuit can smooth out unwanted variations in voltage due to power surges. We'll discuss these circuits in detail in Chapter 26.

Electric-Field Energy

We can charge a capacitor by moving electrons directly from one plate to another. This requires doing work against the electric field between the plates. Thus we can think of the energy as being stored *in the field* in the region between the plates. To develop this relationship, let's find the energy *per unit volume* in the space between the plates of a parallel-plate capacitor with plate area A and separation d. We call this the **energy density,** denoted by u. From Eq. (24.9) the total stored potential energy is $\frac{1}{2}CV^2$ and the volume between the plates is just Ad; hence the energy density is

$$u = \text{Energy density} = \frac{\frac{1}{2}CV^2}{Ad} \qquad (24.10)$$

From Eq. (24.2) the capacitance C is given by $C = \epsilon_0 A/d$. The potential difference V is related to the electric-field magnitude E by $V = Ed$. If we use these expressions in Eq. (24.10), the geometric factors A and d cancel, and we find

$$u = \frac{1}{2}\epsilon_0 E^2 \qquad \text{(electric energy density in a vacuum)} \qquad (24.11)$$

Although we have derived this relationship only for a parallel-plate capacitor, it turns out to be valid for any capacitor in vacuum and indeed *for any electric field configuration in vacuum.* This result has an interesting implication. We think of vacuum as space with no matter in it, but vacuum can nevertheless have electric fields and therefore energy. Thus "empty" space need not be truly empty after all. We will use this idea and Eq. (24.11) in Chapter 32 in connection with the energy transported by electromagnetic waves.

CAUTION **Electric-field energy is electric potential energy** It's a common misconception that electric-field energy is a new kind of energy, different from the electric potential energy described before. This is *not* the case; it is simply a different way of interpreting electric potential energy. We can regard the energy of a given system of charges as being a shared property of all the charges, or we can think of the energy as being a property of the electric field that the charges create. Either interpretation leads to the same value of the potential energy.

Example 24.7 **Transferring charge and energy between capacitors**

We connect a capacitor $C_1 = 8.0\ \mu\text{F}$ to a power supply, charge it to a potential difference $V_0 = 120$ V, and disconnect the power supply (Fig. 24.12). Switch S is open. (a) What is the charge Q_0 on C_1? (b) What is the energy stored in C_1? (c) Capacitor $C_2 = 4.0\ \mu\text{F}$ is initially uncharged. We close switch S. After charge no longer flows, what is the potential difference across each capacitor, and what is the charge on each capacitor? (d) What is the final energy of the system?

24.12 When the switch S is closed, the charged capacitor C_1 is connected to an uncharged capacitor C_2. The center part of the switch is an insulating handle; charge can flow only between the two upper terminals and between the two lower terminals.

IDENTIFY and SET UP: In parts (a) and (b) we find the charge Q_0 and stored energy $U_{initial}$ for the single charged capacitor C_1 using Eqs. (24.1) and (24.9), respectively. After we close switch S, one wire connects the upper plates of the two capacitors and another wire connects the lower plates; the capacitors are now connected in parallel. In part (c) we use the character of the parallel connection to determine how Q_0 is shared between the two capacitors. In part (d) we again use Eq. (24.9) to find the energy stored in capacitors C_1 and C_2; the energy of the system is the sum of these values.

EXECUTE: (a) The initial charge Q_0 on C_1 is

$$Q_0 = C_1 V_0 = (8.0 \ \mu\text{F})(120 \ \text{V}) = 960 \ \mu\text{C}$$

(b) The energy initially stored in C_1 is

$$U_{initial} = \tfrac{1}{2} Q_0 V_0 = \tfrac{1}{2}(960 \times 10^{-6} \ \text{C})(120 \ \text{V}) = 0.058 \ \text{J}$$

(c) When we close the switch, the positive charge Q_0 is distributed over the upper plates of both capacitors and the negative charge $-Q_0$ is distributed over the lower plates. Let Q_1 and Q_2 be the magnitudes of the final charges on the capacitors. Conservation of charge requires that $Q_1 + Q_2 = Q_0$. The potential difference V between the plates is the same for both capacitors because they are connected in parallel, so the charges are $Q_1 = C_1 V$ and $Q_2 = C_2 V$. We now have three independent equations relating the three unknowns Q_1, Q_2, and V. Solving these, we find

$$V = \frac{Q_0}{C_1 + C_2} = \frac{960 \ \mu\text{C}}{8.0 \ \mu\text{F} + 4.0 \ \mu\text{F}} = 80 \ \text{V}$$

$$Q_1 = 640 \ \mu\text{C} \qquad Q_2 = 320 \ \mu\text{C}$$

(d) The final energy of the system is

$$U_{final} = \tfrac{1}{2} Q_1 V + \tfrac{1}{2} Q_2 V = \tfrac{1}{2} Q_0 V$$

$$= \tfrac{1}{2}(960 \times 10^{-6} \ \text{C})(80 \ \text{V}) = 0.038 \ \text{J}$$

EVALUATE: The final energy is less than the initial energy; the difference was converted to energy of some other form. The conductors become a little warmer because of their resistance, and some energy is radiated as electromagnetic waves. We'll study the behavior of capacitors in more detail in Chapters 26 and 31.

Example 24.8 **Electric-field energy**

(a) What is the magnitude of the electric field required to store 1.00 J of electric potential energy in a volume of 1.00 m^3 in vacuum? (b) If the field magnitude is 10 times larger than that, how much energy is stored per cubic meter?

IDENTIFY and SET UP: We use the relationship between the electric-field magnitude E and the energy density u. In part (a) we use the given information to find u; then we use Eq. (24.11) to find the corresponding value of E. In part (b), Eq. (24.11) tells us how u varies with E.

EXECUTE: (a) The desired energy density is $u = 1.00 \ \text{J/m}^3$. Then from Eq. (24.11),

$$E = \sqrt{\frac{2u}{\epsilon_0}} = \sqrt{\frac{2(1.00 \ \text{J/m}^3)}{8.85 \times 10^{-12} \ \text{C}^2/\text{N}\cdot\text{m}^2}}$$

$$= 4.75 \times 10^5 \ \text{N/C} = 4.75 \times 10^5 \ \text{V/m}$$

(b) Equation (24.11) shows that u is proportional to E^2. If E increases by a factor of 10, u increases by a factor of $10^2 = 100$, so the energy density becomes $u = 100 \ \text{J/m}^3$.

EVALUATE: Dry air can sustain an electric field of about 3×10^6 V/m without experiencing *dielectric breakdown*, which we will discuss in Section 24.4. There we will see that field magnitudes in practical insulators can be as great as this or even larger.

Example 24.9 **Two ways to calculate energy stored in a capacitor**

The spherical capacitor described in Example 24.3 (Section 24.1) has charges $+Q$ and $-Q$ on its inner and outer conductors. Find the electric potential energy stored in the capacitor (a) by using the capacitance C found in Example 24.3 and (b) by integrating the electric-field energy density u.

IDENTIFY and SET UP: We can determine the energy U stored in a capacitor in two ways: in terms of the work done to put the charges on the two conductors, and in terms of the energy in the electric field between the conductors. The descriptions are equivalent, so they must give us the same result. In Example 24.3 we found the capacitance C and the field magnitude E in the space between the conductors. (The electric field is zero inside the inner sphere and is also zero outside the inner surface of the outer sphere, because a Gaussian surface with radius $r < r_a$ or $r > r_b$ encloses zero net charge. Hence the energy density is nonzero only in the space between the spheres, $r_a < r < r_b$.) In part (a) we use Eq. (24.9) to find U. In part (b) we use Eq. (24.11) to find u, which we integrate over the volume between the spheres to find U.

EXECUTE: (a) From Example 24.3, the spherical capacitor has capacitance

$$C = 4\pi\epsilon_0 \frac{r_a r_b}{r_b - r_a}$$

where r_a and r_b are the radii of the inner and outer conducting spheres, respectively. From Eq. (24.9) the energy stored in this capacitor is

$$U = \frac{Q^2}{2C} = \frac{Q^2}{8\pi\epsilon_0} \frac{r_b - r_a}{r_a r_b}$$

Continued

(b) The electric field in the region $r_a < r < r_b$ between the two conducting spheres has magnitude $E = Q/4\pi\epsilon_0 r^2$. The energy density in this region is

$$u = \tfrac{1}{2}\epsilon_0 E^2 = \tfrac{1}{2}\epsilon_0\left(\frac{Q}{4\pi\epsilon_0 r^2}\right)^2 = \frac{Q^2}{32\pi^2\epsilon_0 r^4}$$

The energy density is *not* uniform; it decreases rapidly with increasing distance from the center of the capacitor. To find the total electric-field energy, we integrate u (the energy per unit volume) over the region $r_a < r < r_b$. We divide this region into spherical shells of radius r, surface area $4\pi r^2$, thickness dr, and volume $dV = 4\pi r^2\, dr$. Then

$$
\begin{aligned}
U = \int u\, dV &= \int_{r_a}^{r_b}\left(\frac{Q^2}{32\pi^2\epsilon_0 r^4}\right)4\pi r^2\, dr \\
&= \frac{Q^2}{8\pi\epsilon_0}\int_{r_a}^{r_b}\frac{dr}{r^2} = \frac{Q^2}{8\pi\epsilon_0}\left(-\frac{1}{r_b}+\frac{1}{r_a}\right) \\
&= \frac{Q^2}{8\pi\epsilon_0}\,\frac{r_b - r_a}{r_a r_b}
\end{aligned}
$$

EVALUATE: Electric potential energy can be regarded as being associated with either the *charges*, as in part (a), or the *field*, as in part (b); the calculated amount of stored energy is the same in either case.

Test Your Understanding of Section 24.3 You want to connect a 4-μF capacitor and an 8-μF capacitor. With which type of connection will the 4-μF capacitor have a greater amount of *stored energy* than the 8-μF capacitor? (i) series; (ii) parallel; (iii) either series or parallel; (iv) neither series nor parallel.

24.4 Dielectrics

24.13 A common type of capacitor uses dielectric sheets to separate the conductors.

Conductor
(metal foil)

Conductor
(metal foil)

Dielectric
(plastic sheets)

Most capacitors have a nonconducting material, or **dielectric,** between their conducting plates. A common type of capacitor uses long strips of metal foil for the plates, separated by strips of plastic sheet such as Mylar. A sandwich of these materials is rolled up, forming a unit that can provide a capacitance of several microfarads in a compact package (Fig. 24.13).

Placing a solid dielectric between the plates of a capacitor serves three functions. First, it solves the mechanical problem of maintaining two large metal sheets at a very small separation without actual contact.

Second, using a dielectric increases the maximum possible potential difference between the capacitor plates. As we described in Section 23.3, any insulating material, when subjected to a sufficiently large electric field, experiences a partial ionization that permits conduction through it. This is called **dielectric breakdown.** Many dielectric materials can tolerate stronger electric fields without breakdown than can air. Thus using a dielectric allows a capacitor to sustain a higher potential difference V and so store greater amounts of charge and energy.

Third, the capacitance of a capacitor of given dimensions is *greater* when there is a dielectric material between the plates than when there is vacuum. We can demonstrate this effect with the aid of a sensitive *electrometer,* a device that measures the potential difference between two conductors without letting any appreciable charge flow from one to the other. Figure 24.14a shows an electrometer connected across a charged capacitor, with magnitude of charge Q on each plate and potential difference V_0. When we insert an uncharged sheet of dielectric, such as glass, paraffin, or polystyrene, between the plates, experiment shows that the potential difference *decreases* to a smaller value V (Fig. 24.14b). When we remove the dielectric, the potential difference returns to its original value V_0, showing that the original charges on the plates have not changed.

The original capacitance C_0 is given by $C_0 = Q/V_0$, and the capacitance C with the dielectric present is $C = Q/V$. The charge Q is the same in both cases, and V is less than V_0, so we conclude that the capacitance C with the dielectric present is *greater* than C_0. When the space between plates is completely filled by the dielectric, the ratio of C to C_0 (equal to the ratio of V_0 to V) is called the **dielectric constant** of the material, K:

$$K = \frac{C}{C_0} \qquad \text{(definition of dielectric constant)} \qquad (24.12)$$

When the charge is constant, $Q = C_0V_0 = CV$ and $C/C_0 = V_0/V$. In this case, Eq. (24.12) can be rewritten as

$$V = \frac{V_0}{K} \quad \text{(when } Q \text{ is constant)} \tag{24.13}$$

With the dielectric present, the potential difference for a given charge Q is *reduced* by a factor K.

The dielectric constant K is a pure number. Because C is always greater than C_0, K is always greater than unity. Some representative values of K are given in Table 24.1. For vacuum, $K = 1$ by definition. For air at ordinary temperatures and pressures, K is about 1.0006; this is so nearly equal to 1 that for most purposes an air capacitor is equivalent to one in vacuum. Note that while water has a very large value of K, it is usually not a very practical dielectric for use in capacitors. The reason is that while pure water is a very poor conductor, it is also an excellent ionic solvent. Any ions that are dissolved in the water will cause charge to flow between the capacitor plates, so the capacitor discharges.

Table 24.1 Values of Dielectric Constant K at 20°C

Material	K	Material	K
Vacuum	1	Polyvinyl chloride	3.18
Air (1 atm)	1.00059	Plexiglas®	3.40
Air (100 atm)	1.0548	Glass	5–10
Teflon	2.1	Neoprene	6.70
Polyethylene	2.25	Germanium	16
Benzene	2.28	Glycerin	42.5
Mica	3–6	Water	80.4
Mylar	3.1	Strontium titanate	310

No real dielectric is a perfect insulator. Hence there is always some *leakage current* between the charged plates of a capacitor with a dielectric. We tacitly ignored this effect in Section 24.2 when we derived expressions for the equivalent capacitances of capacitors in series, Eq. (24.5), and in parallel, Eq. (24.7). But if a leakage current flows for a long enough time to substantially change the charges from the values we used to derive Eqs. (24.5) and (24.7), those equations may no longer be accurate.

Induced Charge and Polarization

When a dielectric material is inserted between the plates while the charge is kept constant, the potential difference between the plates decreases by a factor K. Therefore the electric field between the plates must decrease by the same factor. If E_0 is the vacuum value and E is the value with the dielectric, then

$$E = \frac{E_0}{K} \quad \text{(when } Q \text{ is constant)} \tag{24.14}$$

Since the electric-field magnitude is smaller when the dielectric is present, the surface charge density (which causes the field) must be smaller as well. The surface charge on the conducting plates does not change, but an *induced* charge of the opposite sign appears on each surface of the dielectric (Fig. 24.15). The dielectric was originally electrically neutral and is still neutral; the induced surface charges arise as a result of *redistribution* of positive and negative charge within the dielectric material, a phenomenon called **polarization.** We first encountered polarization in Section 21.2, and we suggest that you reread the discussion of Fig. 21.8. We will assume that the induced surface charge is *directly proportional* to the electric-field magnitude E in the material; this is indeed the case for many common dielectrics. (This direct proportionality is analogous to

24.14 Effect of a dielectric between the plates of a parallel-plate capacitor. **(a)** With a given charge, the potential difference is V_0. **(b)** With the same charge but with a dielectric between the plates, the potential difference V is smaller than V_0.

(a)

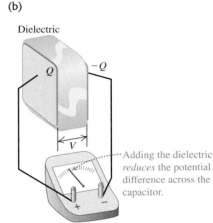

(b)

Adding the dielectric *reduces* the potential difference across the capacitor.

24.15 Electric field lines with **(a)** vacuum between the plates and **(b)** dielectric between the plates.

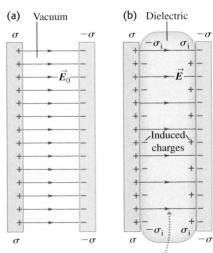

For a given charge density σ, the induced charges on the dielectric's surfaces reduce the electric field between the plates.

Hooke's law for a spring.) In that case, K is a constant for any particular material. When the electric field is very strong or if the dielectric is made of certain crystalline materials, the relationship between induced charge and the electric field can be more complex; we won't consider such cases here.

We can derive a relationship between this induced surface charge and the charge on the plates. Let's denote the magnitude of the charge per unit area induced on the surfaces of the dielectric (the induced surface charge density) by σ_i. The magnitude of the surface charge density on the capacitor plates is σ, as usual. Then the *net* surface charge on each side of the capacitor has magnitude $(\sigma - \sigma_i)$, as shown in Fig. 24.15b. As we found in Example 21.12 (Section 21.5) and in Example 22.8 (Section 22.4), the field between the plates is related to the net surface charge density by $E = \sigma_{net}/\epsilon_0$. Without and with the dielectric, respectively, we have

$$E_0 = \frac{\sigma}{\epsilon_0} \qquad E = \frac{\sigma - \sigma_i}{\epsilon_0} \tag{24.15}$$

Using these expressions in Eq. (24.14) and rearranging the result, we find

$$\sigma_i = \sigma\left(1 - \frac{1}{K}\right) \qquad \text{(induced surface charge density)} \tag{24.16}$$

This equation shows that when K is very large, σ_i is nearly as large as σ. In this case, σ_i nearly cancels σ, and the field and potential difference are much smaller than their values in vacuum.

The product $K\epsilon_0$ is called the **permittivity** of the dielectric, denoted by ϵ:

$$\epsilon = K\epsilon_0 \qquad \text{(definition of permittivity)} \tag{24.17}$$

In terms of ϵ we can express the electric field within the dielectric as

$$E = \frac{\sigma}{\epsilon} \tag{24.18}$$

The capacitance when the dielectric is present is given by

$$C = KC_0 = K\epsilon_0\frac{A}{d} = \epsilon\frac{A}{d} \qquad \begin{array}{l}\text{(parallel-plate capacitor,}\\ \text{dielectric between plates)}\end{array} \tag{24.19}$$

We can repeat the derivation of Eq. (24.11) for the energy density u in an electric field for the case in which a dielectric is present. The result is

$$u = \tfrac{1}{2}K\epsilon_0E^2 = \tfrac{1}{2}\epsilon E^2 \qquad \text{(electric energy density in a dielectric)} \tag{24.20}$$

In empty space, where $K = 1$, $\epsilon = \epsilon_0$ and Eqs. (24.19) and (24.20) reduce to Eqs. (24.2) and (24.11), respectively, for a parallel-plate capacitor in vacuum. For this reason, ϵ_0 is sometimes called the "permittivity of free space" or the "permittivity of vacuum." Because K is a pure number, ϵ and ϵ_0 have the same units, $C^2/N \cdot m^2$ or F/m.

Equation (24.19) shows that extremely high capacitances can be obtained with plates that have a large surface area A and are separated by a small distance d by a dielectric with a large value of K. In an *electrolytic double-layer capacitor,* tiny carbon granules adhere to each plate: The value of A is the combined surface area of the granules, which can be tremendous. The plates with granules attached are separated by a very thin dielectric sheet. A capacitor of this kind can have a capacitance of 5000 farads yet fit in the palm of your hand (compare Example 24.1 in Section 24.1).

Several practical devices make use of the way in which a capacitor responds to a change in dielectric constant. One example is an electric stud finder, used by home repair workers to locate metal studs hidden behind a wall's surface. It consists of a metal plate with associated circuitry. The plate acts as one half of a capacitor, with the wall acting as the other half. If the stud finder moves over a metal stud, the effective dielectric constant for the capacitor changes, changing the capacitance and triggering a signal.

Problem-Solving Strategy 24.2 Dielectrics

IDENTIFY *the relevant concepts:* The relationships in this section are useful whenever there is an electric field in a dielectric, such as a dielectric between charged capacitor plates. Typically you must relate the potential difference V_{ab} between the plates, the electric field magnitude E in the capacitor, the charge density σ on the capacitor plates, and the induced charge density σ_i on the surfaces of the capacitor.

SET UP *the problem* using the following steps:
1. Make a drawing of the situation.
2. Identify the target variables, and choose which equations from this section will help you solve for those variables.

EXECUTE *the solution* as follows:
1. In problems such as the next example, it is easy to get lost in a blizzard of formulas. Ask yourself at each step what kind of

quantity each symbol represents. For example, distinguish clearly between charges and charge densities, and between electric fields and electric potential differences.
2. Check for consistency of units. Distances must be in meters. A microfarad is 10^{-6} farad, and so on. Don't confuse the numerical value of ϵ_0 with the value of $1/4\pi\epsilon_0$. Electric-field magnitude can be expressed in both N/C and V/m. The units of ϵ_0 are $C^2/N \cdot m^2$ or F/m.

EVALUATE *your answer:* With a dielectric present, (a) the capacitance is greater than without a dielectric; (b) for a given charge on the capacitor, the electric field and potential difference are less than without a dielectric; and (c) the magnitude of the induced surface charge density σ_i on the dielectric is less than that of the charge density σ on the capacitor plates.

Example 24.10 A capacitor with and without a dielectric

Suppose the parallel plates in Fig. 24.15 each have an area of 2000 cm^2 (2.00×10^{-1} m^2) and are 1.00 cm (1.00×10^{-2} m) apart. We connect the capacitor to a power supply, charge it to a potential difference $V_0 = 3.00$ kV, and disconnect the power supply. We then insert a sheet of insulating plastic material between the plates, completely filling the space between them. We find that the potential difference decreases to 1.00 kV while the charge on each capacitor plate remains constant. Find (a) the original capacitance C_0; (b) the magnitude of charge Q on each plate; (c) the capacitance C after the dielectric is inserted; (d) the dielectric constant K of the dielectric; (e) the permittivity ϵ of the dielectric; (f) the magnitude of the induced charge Q_i on each face of the dielectric; (g) the original electric field E_0 between the plates; and (h) the electric field E after the dielectric is inserted.

SOLUTION

IDENTIFY and SET UP: This problem uses most of the relationships we have discussed for capacitors and dielectrics. (Energy relationships are treated in Example 24.11.) Most of the target variables can be obtained in several ways. The methods used below are a sample; we encourage you to think of others and compare your results.

EXECUTE: (a) With vacuum between the plates, we use Eq. (24.19) with $K = 1$:

$$C_0 = \epsilon_0 \frac{A}{d} = (8.85 \times 10^{-12} \text{ F/m})\frac{2.00 \times 10^{-1} \text{ m}^2}{1.00 \times 10^{-2} \text{ m}}$$

$$= 1.77 \times 10^{-10} \text{ F} = 177 \text{ pF}$$

(b) From the definition of capacitance, Eq. (24.1),

$$Q = C_0 V_0 = (1.77 \times 10^{-10} \text{ F})(3.00 \times 10^3 \text{ V})$$

$$= 5.31 \times 10^{-7} \text{ C} = 0.531 \text{ } \mu\text{C}$$

(c) When the dielectric is inserted, Q is unchanged but the potential difference decreases to $V = 1.00$ kV. Hence from Eq. (24.1), the new capacitance is

$$C = \frac{Q}{V} = \frac{5.31 \times 10^{-7} \text{ C}}{1.00 \times 10^3 \text{ V}} = 5.31 \times 10^{-10} \text{ F} = 531 \text{ pF}$$

(d) From Eq. (24.12), the dielectric constant is

$$K = \frac{C}{C_0} = \frac{5.31 \times 10^{-10} \text{ F}}{1.77 \times 10^{-10} \text{ F}} = \frac{531 \text{ pF}}{177 \text{ pF}} = 3.00$$

Alternatively, from Eq. (24.13),

$$K = \frac{V_0}{V} = \frac{3000 \text{ V}}{1000 \text{ V}} = 3.00$$

(e) Using K from part (d) in Eq. (24.17), the permittivity is

$$\epsilon = K\epsilon_0 = (3.00)(8.85 \times 10^{-12} \text{ C}^2/\text{N} \cdot \text{m}^2)$$

$$= 2.66 \times 10^{-11} \text{ C}^2/\text{N} \cdot \text{m}^2$$

(f) Multiplying both sides of Eq. (24.16) by the plate area A gives the induced charge $Q_i = \sigma_i A$ in terms of the charge $Q = \sigma A$ on each plate:

$$Q_i = Q\left(1 - \frac{1}{K}\right) = (5.31 \times 10^{-7} \text{ C})\left(1 - \frac{1}{3.00}\right)$$

$$= 3.54 \times 10^{-7} \text{ C}$$

Continued

(g) Since the electric field between the plates is uniform, its magnitude is the potential difference divided by the plate separation:

$$E_0 = \frac{V_0}{d} = \frac{3000 \text{ V}}{1.00 \times 10^{-2} \text{ m}} = 3.00 \times 10^5 \text{ V/m}$$

(h) After the dielectric is inserted,

$$E = \frac{V}{d} = \frac{1000 \text{ V}}{1.00 \times 10^{-2} \text{ m}} = 1.00 \times 10^5 \text{ V/m}$$

or, from Eq. (24.18),

$$E = \frac{\sigma}{\epsilon} = \frac{Q}{\epsilon A} = \frac{5.31 \times 10^{-7} \text{ C}}{(2.66 \times 10^{-11} \text{ C}^2/\text{N} \cdot \text{m}^2)(2.00 \times 10^{-1} \text{ m}^2)}$$

$$= 1.00 \times 10^5 \text{ V/m}$$

or, from Eq. (24.15),

$$E = \frac{\sigma - \sigma_i}{\epsilon_0} = \frac{Q - Q_i}{\epsilon_0 A}$$

$$= \frac{(5.31 - 3.54) \times 10^{-7} \text{ C}}{(8.85 \times 10^{-12} \text{ C}^2/\text{N} \cdot \text{m}^2)(2.00 \times 10^{-1} \text{ m}^2)}$$

$$= 1.00 \times 10^5 \text{ V/m}$$

or, from Eq. (24.14),

$$E = \frac{E_0}{K} = \frac{3.00 \times 10^5 \text{ V/m}}{3.00} = 1.00 \times 10^5 \text{ V/m}$$

EVALUATE: Inserting the dielectric increased the capacitance by a factor of $K = 3.00$ and reduced the electric field between the plates by a factor of $1/K = 1/3.00$. It did so by developing induced charges on the faces of the dielectric of magnitude $Q(1 - 1/K) = Q(1 - 1/3.00) = 0.667Q$.

Example 24.11 Energy storage with and without a dielectric

Find the energy stored in the electric field of the capacitor in Example 24.10 and the energy density, both before and after the dielectric sheet is inserted.

SOLUTION

IDENTIFY and SET UP: We now consider the ideas of energy stored in a capacitor and of electric-field energy density. We use Eq. (24.9) to find the stored energy and Eq. (24.20) to find the energy density.

EXECUTE: From Eq. (24.9), the stored energies U_0 and U without and with the dielectric in place are

$$U_0 = \tfrac{1}{2}C_0 V_0^2 = \tfrac{1}{2}(1.77 \times 10^{-10} \text{ F})(3000 \text{ V})^2 = 7.97 \times 10^{-4} \text{ J}$$

$$U = \tfrac{1}{2}C V^2 = \tfrac{1}{2}(5.31 \times 10^{-10} \text{ F})(1000 \text{ V})^2 = 2.66 \times 10^{-4} \text{ J}$$

The final energy is one-third of the original energy.

Equation (24.20) gives the energy densities without and with the dielectric:

$$u_0 = \tfrac{1}{2}\epsilon_0 E_0^2 = \tfrac{1}{2}(8.85 \times 10^{-12} \text{ C}^2/\text{N} \cdot \text{m}^2)(3.00 \times 10^5 \text{ N/C})^2$$

$$= 0.398 \text{ J/m}^3$$

$$u = \tfrac{1}{2}\epsilon E^2 = \tfrac{1}{2}(2.66 \times 10^{-11} \text{ C}^2/\text{N} \cdot \text{m}^2)(1.00 \times 10^5 \text{ N/C})^2$$

$$= 0.133 \text{ J/m}^3$$

The energy density with the dielectric is one-third of the original energy density.

EVALUATE: We can check our answer for u_0 by noting that the volume between the plates is $V = (0.200 \text{ m}^2)(0.0100 \text{ m}) =$

0.00200 m³. Since the electric field between the plates is uniform, u_0 is uniform as well and the energy density is just the stored energy divided by the volume:

$$u_0 = \frac{U_0}{V} = \frac{7.97 \times 10^{-4} \text{ J}}{0.00200 \text{ m}^3} = 0.398 \text{ J/m}^3$$

This agrees with our earlier answer. You can use the same approach to check our result for u.

In general, when a dielectric is inserted into a capacitor while the charge on each plate remains the same, the permittivity ϵ increases by a factor of K (the dielectric constant), and the electric field E and the energy density $u = \tfrac{1}{2}\epsilon E^2$ decrease by a factor of $1/K$. Where does the energy go? The answer lies in the fringing field at the edges of a real parallel-plate capacitor. As Fig. 24.16 shows, that field tends to pull the dielectric into the space between the plates, doing work on it as it does so. We could attach a spring to the left end of the dielectric in Fig. 24.16 and use this force to stretch the spring. Because work is done by the field, the field energy density decreases.

24.16 The fringing field at the edges of the capacitor exerts forces $\vec{F}_{-i}$ and $\vec{F}_{+i}$ on the negative and positive induced surface charges of a dielectric, pulling the dielectric into the capacitor.

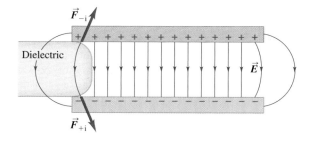

Dielectric Breakdown

We mentioned earlier that when a dielectric is subjected to a sufficiently strong electric field, *dielectric breakdown* takes place and the dielectric becomes a conductor. This occurs when the electric field is so strong that electrons are ripped loose from their molecules and crash into other molecules, liberating even more electrons. This avalanche of moving charge forms a spark or arc discharge. Lightning is a dramatic example of dielectric breakdown in air.

Because of dielectric breakdown, capacitors always have maximum voltage ratings. When a capacitor is subjected to excessive voltage, an arc may form through a layer of dielectric, burning or melting a hole in it. This arc creates a conducting path (a short circuit) between the conductors. If a conducting path remains after the arc is extinguished, the device is rendered permanently useless as a capacitor.

The maximum electric-field magnitude that a material can withstand without the occurrence of breakdown is called its **dielectric strength.** This quantity is affected significantly by temperature, trace impurities, small irregularities in the metal electrodes, and other factors that are difficult to control. For this reason we can give only approximate figures for dielectric strengths. The dielectric strength of dry air is about 3×10^6 V/m. Table 24.2 lists the dielectric strengths of a few common insulating materials. Note that the values are all substantially greater than the value for air. For example, a layer of polycarbonate 0.01 mm thick (about the smallest practical thickness) has 10 times the dielectric strength of air and can withstand a maximum voltage of about $(3 \times 10^7 \text{ V/m})(1 \times 10^{-5} \text{ m}) = 300$ V.

Table 24.2 Dielectric Constant and Dielectric Strength of Some Insulating Materials

Material	Dielectric Constant, K	Dielectric Strength, E_m (V/m)
Polycarbonate	2.8	3×10^7
Polyester	3.3	6×10^7
Polypropylene	2.2	7×10^7
Polystyrene	2.6	2×10^7
Pyrex glass	4.7	1×10^7

Test Your Understanding of Section 24.4 The space between the plates of an isolated parallel-plate capacitor is filled by a slab of dielectric with dielectric constant K. The two plates of the capacitor have charges Q and $-Q$. You pull out the dielectric slab. If the charges do not change, how does the energy in the capacitor change when you remove the slab? (i) It increases; (ii) it decreases; (iii) it remains the same.

24.5 Molecular Model of Induced Charge

In Section 24.4 we discussed induced surface charges on a dielectric in an electric field. Now let's look at how these surface charges can arise. If the material were a *conductor*, the answer would be simple. Conductors contain charge that is free to move, and when an electric field is present, some of the charge redistributes itself on the surface so that there is no electric field inside the conductor. But an ideal dielectric has *no* charges that are free to move, so how can a surface charge occur?

To understand this, we have to look again at rearrangement of charge at the *molecular* level. Some molecules, such as H_2O and N_2O, have equal amounts of positive and negative charges but a lopsided distribution, with excess positive charge concentrated on one side of the molecule and negative charge on the other. As we described in Section 21.7, such an arrangement is called an *electric dipole,* and the molecule is called a *polar molecule.* When no electric field is present in a gas or liquid with polar molecules, the molecules are oriented randomly (Fig. 24.17a). When they are placed in an electric field, however, they tend to orient themselves as in Fig. 24.17b, as a result of the electric-field torques described in Section 21.7. Because of thermal agitation, the alignment of the molecules with $\vec{E}$ is not perfect.

Application **Dielectric Cell Membrane**

Application **Dielectric Cell Membrane**
The membrane of a living cell behaves like a dielectric between the plates of a capacitor. The membrane is made of two sheets of lipid molecules, with their water-insoluble ends in the middle and their water-soluble ends (shown in red) on the surfaces of the membrane. The conductive fluids on either side of the membrane (water with negative ions inside the cell, water with positive ions outside) act as charged capacitor plates, and the nonconducting membrane acts as a dielectric with K of about 10. The potential difference V across the membrane is about 0.07 V and the membrane thickness d is about 7×10^{-9} m, so the electric field $E = V/d$ in the membrane is about 10^7 V/m—close to the dielectric strength of the membrane. If the membrane were made of air, V and E would be larger by a factor of $K \approx 10$ and dielectric breakdown would occur.

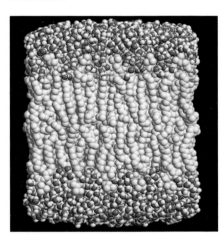

24.17 Polar molecules (a) without and (b) with an applied electric field $\vec{E}$.

(a)

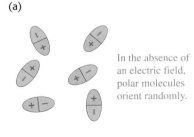

In the absence of an electric field, polar molecules orient randomly.

(b)

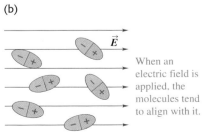

When an electric field is applied, the molecules tend to align with it.

24.18 Nonpolar molecules (a) without and (b) with an applied electric field $\vec{E}$.

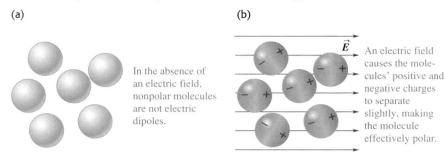

(a)

In the absence of an electric field, nonpolar molecules are not electric dipoles.

(b)

$\vec{E}$ An electric field causes the molecules' positive and negative charges to separate slightly, making the molecule effectively polar.

Even a molecule that is *not* ordinarily polar *becomes* a dipole when it is placed in an electric field because the field pushes the positive charges in the molecules in the direction of the field and pushes the negative charges in the opposite direction. This causes a redistribution of charge within the molecule (Fig. 24.18). Such dipoles are called *induced* dipoles.

With either polar or nonpolar molecules, the redistribution of charge caused by the field leads to the formation of a layer of charge on each surface of the dielectric material (Fig. 24.19). These layers are the surface charges described in Section 24.4; their surface charge density is denoted by σ_i. The charges are *not* free to move indefinitely, as they would be in a conductor, because each charge is bound to a molecule. They are in fact called **bound charges** to distinguish them from the **free charges** that are added to and removed from the conducting capacitor plates. In the interior of the material the net charge per unit volume remains zero. As we have seen, this redistribution of charge is called *polarization,* and we say that the material is *polarized.*

The four parts of Fig. 24.20 show the behavior of a slab of dielectric when it is inserted in the field between a pair of oppositely charged capacitor plates. Figure 24.20a shows the original field. Figure 24.20b is the situation after the dielectric has been inserted but before any rearrangement of charges has occurred. Figure 24.20c shows by thinner arrows the additional field set up in the dielectric by its induced surface charges. This field is *opposite* to the original field, but it is not great enough to cancel the original field completely because the charges in the dielectric are not free to move indefinitely. The resultant field

24.19 Polarization of a dielectric in an electric field $\vec{E}$ gives rise to thin layers of bound charges on the surfaces, creating surface charge densities σ_i and $-\sigma_i$. The sizes of the molecules are greatly exaggerated for clarity.

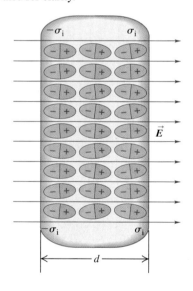

24.20 (a) Electric field of magnitude E_0 between two charged plates. (b) Introduction of a dielectric of dielectric constant K. (c) The induced surface charges and their field. (d) Resultant field of magnitude E_0/K.

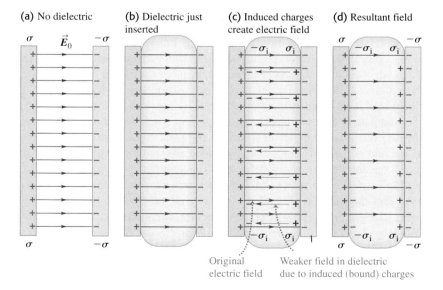

(a) No dielectric

(b) Dielectric just inserted

(c) Induced charges create electric field

(d) Resultant field

Original electric field

Weaker field in dielectric due to induced (bound) charges

in the dielectric, shown in Fig. 24.20d, is therefore decreased in magnitude. In the field-line representation, some of the field lines leaving the positive plate go through the dielectric, while others terminate on the induced charges on the faces of the dielectric.

As we discussed in Section 21.2, polarization is also the reason a charged body, such as an electrified plastic rod, can exert a force on an *uncharged* body such as a bit of paper or a pith ball. Figure 24.21 shows an uncharged dielectric sphere B in the radial field of a positively charged body A. The induced positive charges on B experience a force toward the right, while the force on the induced negative charges is toward the left. The negative charges are closer to A, and thus are in a stronger field, than are the positive charges. The force toward the left is stronger than that toward the right, and B is attracted toward A, even though its net charge is zero. The attraction occurs whether the sign of A's charge is positive or negative (see Fig. 21.8). Furthermore, the effect is not limited to dielectrics; an uncharged conducting body would be attracted in the same way.

Test Your Understanding of Section 24.5 A parallel-plate capacitor has charges Q and −Q on its two plates. A dielectric slab with K = 3 is then inserted into the space between the plates as shown in Fig. 24.20. Rank the following electric-field magnitudes in order from largest to smallest. (i) the field before the slab is inserted; (ii) the resultant field after the slab is inserted; (iii) the field due to the bound charges. ▮

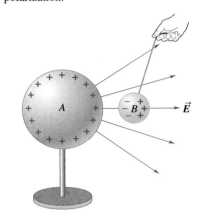

24.21 A neutral sphere B in the radial electric field of a positively charged sphere A is attracted to the charge because of polarization.

24.6 Gauss's Law in Dielectrics

We can extend the analysis of Section 24.4 to reformulate Gauss's law in a form that is particularly useful for dielectrics. Figure 24.22 is a close-up view of the left capacitor plate and left surface of the dielectric in Fig. 24.15b. Let's apply Gauss's law to the rectangular box shown in cross section by the purple line; the surface area of the left and right sides is A. The left side is embedded in the conductor that forms the left capacitor plate, and so the electric field everywhere on that surface is zero. The right side is embedded in the dielectric, where the electric field has magnitude E, and $E_\perp = 0$ everywhere on the other four sides. The total charge enclosed, including both the charge on the capacitor plate and the induced charge on the dielectric surface, is $Q_{encl} = (\sigma - \sigma_i)A$, so Gauss's law gives

$$EA = \frac{(\sigma - \sigma_i)A}{\epsilon_0} \qquad (24.21)$$

This equation is not very illuminating as it stands because it relates two unknown quantities: E inside the dielectric and the induced surface charge density σ_i. But now we can use Eq. (24.16), developed for this same situation, to simplify this equation by eliminating σ_i. Equation (24.16) is

$$\sigma_i = \sigma\left(1 - \frac{1}{K}\right) \quad \text{or} \quad \sigma - \sigma_i = \frac{\sigma}{K}$$

Combining this with Eq. (24.21), we get

$$EA = \frac{\sigma A}{K\epsilon_0} \quad \text{or} \quad KEA = \frac{\sigma A}{\epsilon_0} \qquad (24.22)$$

Equation (24.22) says that the flux of $K\vec{E}$, not $\vec{E}$, through the Gaussian surface in Fig. 24.22 is equal to the enclosed *free* charge σA divided by ϵ_0. It turns out that for *any* Gaussian surface, whenever the induced charge is proportional to the electric field in the material, we can rewrite Gauss's law as

$$\oint K\vec{E} \cdot d\vec{A} = \frac{Q_{encl\text{-free}}}{\epsilon_0} \qquad \text{(Gauss's law in a dielectric)} \qquad (24.23)$$

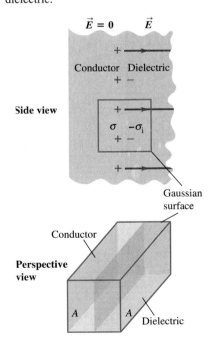

24.22 Gauss's law with a dielectric. This figure shows a close-up of the left-hand capacitor plate in Fig. 24.15b. The Gaussian surface is a rectangular box that lies half in the conductor and half in the dielectric.

where $Q_{encl\text{-}free}$ is the total *free* charge (not bound charge) enclosed by the Gaussian surface. The significance of these results is that the right sides contain only the *free* charge on the conductor, not the bound (induced) charge. In fact, although we have not proved it, Eq. (24.23) remains valid even when different parts of the Gaussian surface are embedded in dielectrics having different values of K, provided that the value of K in each dielectric is independent of the electric field (usually the case for electric fields that are not too strong) and that we use the appropriate value of K for each point on the Gaussian surface.

Example 24.12   **A spherical capacitor with dielectric**

Use Gauss's law to find the capacitance of the spherical capacitor of Example 24.3 (Section 24.1) if the volume between the shells is filled with an insulating oil with dielectric constant K.

SOLUTION

IDENTIFY and SET UP: The spherical symmetry of the problem is not changed by the presence of the dielectric, so as in Example 24.3, we use a concentric spherical Gaussian surface of radius r between the shells. Since a dielectric is present, we use Gauss's law in the form of Eq. (24.23).

EXECUTE: From Eq. (24.23),

$$\oint K\vec{E} \cdot d\vec{A} = \oint KE\, dA = KE \oint dA = (KE)(4\pi r^2) = \frac{Q}{\epsilon_0}$$

$$E = \frac{Q}{4\pi K\epsilon_0 r^2} = \frac{Q}{4\pi \epsilon r^2}$$

where $\epsilon = K\epsilon_0$. Compared to the case in which there is vacuum between the shells, the electric field is reduced by a factor of $1/K$. The potential difference V_{ab} between the shells is reduced by the same factor, and so the capacitance $C = Q/V_{ab}$ is *increased* by a factor of K, just as for a parallel-plate capacitor when a dielectric is inserted. Using the result of Example 24.3, we find that the capacitance with the dielectric is

$$C = \frac{4\pi K\epsilon_0 r_a r_b}{r_b - r_a} = \frac{4\pi \epsilon r_a r_b}{r_b - r_a}$$

EVALUATE: If the dielectric fills the volume between the two conductors, the capacitance is just K times the value with no dielectric. The result is more complicated if the dielectric only partially fills this volume (see Challenge Problem 24.78).

Test Your Understanding of Section 24.6   A single point charge q is imbedded in a dielectric of dielectric constant K. At a point inside the dielectric a distance r from the point charge, what is the magnitude of the electric field? (i) $q/4\pi\epsilon_0 r^2$; (ii) $Kq/4\pi\epsilon_0 r^2$; (iii) $q/4\pi K\epsilon_0 r^2$; (iv) none of these.

Capacitors and capacitance: A capacitor is any pair of conductors separated by an insulating material. When the capacitor is charged, there are charges of equal magnitude Q and opposite sign on the two conductors, and the potential V_{ab} of the positively charged conductor with respect to the negatively charged conductor is proportional to Q. The capacitance C is defined as the ratio of Q to V_{ab}. The SI unit of capacitance is the farad (F): $1\text{ F} = 1\text{ C/V}$.

A parallel-plate capacitor consists of two parallel conducting plates, each with area A, separated by a distance d. If they are separated by vacuum, the capacitance depends only on A and d. For other geometries, the capacitance can be found by using the definition $C = Q/V_{ab}$. (See Examples 24.1–24.4.)

$$C = \frac{Q}{V_{ab}} \quad (24.1)$$

$$C = \frac{Q}{V_{ab}} = \epsilon_0 \frac{A}{d} \quad (24.2)$$

Capacitors in series and parallel: When capacitors with capacitances $C_1, C_2, C_3, \ldots$ are connected in series, the reciprocal of the equivalent capacitance C_{eq} equals the sum of the reciprocals of the individual capacitances. When capacitors are connected in parallel, the equivalent capacitance C_{eq} equals the sum of the individual capacitances. (See Examples 24.5 and 24.6.)

$$\frac{1}{C_{eq}} = \frac{1}{C_1} + \frac{1}{C_2} + \frac{1}{C_3} + \cdots$$
(capacitors in series) $\quad (24.5)$

$$C_{eq} = C_1 + C_2 + C_3 + \cdots$$
(capacitors in parallel) $\quad (24.7)$

Energy in a capacitor: The energy U required to charge a capacitor C to a potential difference V and a charge Q is equal to the energy stored in the capacitor. This energy can be thought of as residing in the electric field between the conductors; the energy density u (energy per unit volume) is proportional to the square of the electric-field magnitude. (See Examples 24.7–24.9.)

$$U = \frac{Q^2}{2C} = \tfrac{1}{2}CV^2 = \tfrac{1}{2}QV \quad (24.9)$$

$$u = \tfrac{1}{2}\epsilon_0 E^2 \quad (24.11)$$

Dielectrics: When the space between the conductors is filled with a dielectric material, the capacitance increases by a factor K, called the dielectric constant of the material. The quantity $\epsilon = K\epsilon_0$ is called the permittivity of the dielectric. For a fixed amount of charge on the capacitor plates, induced charges on the surface of the dielectric decrease the electric field and potential difference between the plates by the same factor K. The surface charge results from polarization, a microscopic rearrangement of charge in the dielectric. (See Example 24.10.)

Under sufficiently strong fields, dielectrics become conductors, a situation called dielectric breakdown. The maximum field that a material can withstand without breakdown is called its dielectric strength.

In a dielectric, the expression for the energy density is the same as in vacuum but with ϵ_0 replaced by $\epsilon = K\epsilon$. (See Example 24.11.)

Gauss's law in a dielectric has almost the same form as in vacuum, with two key differences: $\vec{E}$ is replaced by $K\vec{E}$ and Q_{encl} is replaced by $Q_{encl\text{-free}}$, which includes only the free charge (not bound charge) enclosed by the Gaussian surface. (See Example 24.12.)

$$C = KC_0 = K\epsilon_0 \frac{A}{d} = \epsilon \frac{A}{d}$$
(parallel-plate capacitor filled with dielectric) $\quad (24.19)$

$$u = \tfrac{1}{2}K\epsilon_0 E^2 = \tfrac{1}{2}\epsilon E^2 \quad (24.20)$$

$$\oint K\vec{E} \cdot d\vec{A} = \frac{Q_{encl\text{-free}}}{\epsilon_0} \quad (24.23)$$

Dielectric between plates

BRIDGING PROBLEM Electric-Field Energy and Capacitance of a Conducting Sphere

A solid conducting sphere of radius R carries a charge Q. Calculate the electric-field energy density at a point a distance r from the center of the sphere for (a) $r < R$ and (b) $r > R$. (c) Calculate the total electric-field energy associated with the charged sphere. (d) How much work is required to assemble the charge Q on the sphere? (e) Use the result of part (c) to find the capacitance of the sphere. (You can think of the second conductor as a hollow conducting shell of infinite radius.)

SOLUTION GUIDE

See MasteringPhysics® study area for a Video Tutor solution

IDENTIFY and SET UP

1. You know the electric field for this situation at all values of r from Example 22.5 (Section 22.4). You'll use this to find the electric-field energy density u and the *total* electric-field energy U. You can then find the capacitance from the relationship $U = Q^2/2C$.
2. To find U, consider a spherical shell of radius r and thickness dr that has volume $dV = 4\pi r^2 dr$. The energy stored in this volume

is $u \, dV$, and the total energy is the integral of $u \, dV$ from $r = 0$ to $r \to \infty$. Set up this integral.

EXECUTE

3. Find u for $r < R$ and for $r > R$.
4. Substitute your results from step 3 into the expression from step 2. Then calculate the integral to find the total electric-field energy U.
5. Use your understanding of the energy stored in a charge distribution to find the work required to assemble the charge Q.
6. Find the capacitance of the sphere.

EVALUATE

7. Where is the electric-field energy density greatest? Where is it least?
8. How would the results be affected if the solid sphere were replaced by a hollow conducting sphere of the same radius R?
9. You can find the potential difference between the sphere and infinity from $C = Q/V$. Does this agree with the result of Example 23.8 (Section 23.3)?

Problems

For instructor-assigned homework, go to www.masteringphysics.com

•, ••, •••: Problems of increasing difficulty. **CP**: Cumulative problems incorporating material from earlier chapters. **CALC**: Problems requiring calculus. **BIO**: Biosciences problems.

DISCUSSION QUESTIONS

Q24.1 Equation (24.2) shows that the capacitance of a parallel-plate capacitor becomes larger as the plate separation d decreases. However, there is a practical limit to how small d can be made, which places limits on how large C can be. Explain what sets the limit on d. (*Hint:* What happens to the magnitude of the electric field as $d \to 0$?)

Q24.2 Suppose several different parallel-plate capacitors are charged up by a constant-voltage source. Thinking of the actual movement and position of the charges on an atomic level, why does it make sense that the capacitances are proportional to the surface areas of the plates? Why does it make sense that the capacitances are *inversely* proportional to the distance between the plates?

Q24.3 Suppose the two plates of a capacitor have different areas. When the capacitor is charged by connecting it to a battery, do the charges on the two plates have equal magnitude, or may they be different? Explain your reasoning.

Q24.4 At the Fermi National Accelerator Laboratory (Fermilab) in Illinois, protons are accelerated around a ring 2 km in radius to speeds that approach that of light. The energy for this is stored in capacitors the size of a house. When these capacitors are being charged, they make a very loud creaking sound. What is the origin of this sound?

Q24.5 In the parallel-plate capacitor of Fig. 24.2, suppose the plates are pulled apart so that the separation d is much larger than the size of the plates. (a) Is it still accurate to say that the electric field between the plates is uniform? Why or why not? (b) In the sit-

uation shown in Fig. 24.2, the potential difference between the plates is $V_{ab} = Qd/\epsilon_0 A$. If the plates are pulled apart as described above, is V_{ab} more or less than this formula would indicate? Explain your reasoning. (c) With the plates pulled apart as described above, is the capacitance more than, less than, or the same as that given by Eq. (24.2)? Explain your reasoning.

Q24.6 A parallel-plate capacitor is charged by being connected to a battery and is kept connected to the battery. The separation between the plates is then doubled. How does the electric field change? The charge on the plates? The total energy? Explain your reasoning.

Q24.7 A parallel-plate capacitor is charged by being connected to a battery and is then disconnected from the battery. The separation between the plates is then doubled. How does the electric field change? The potential difference? The total energy? Explain your reasoning.

Q24.8 Two parallel-plate capacitors, identical except that one has twice the plate separation of the other, are charged by the same voltage source. Which capacitor has a stronger electric field between the plates? Which capacitor has a greater charge? Which has greater energy density? Explain your reasoning.

Q24.9 The charged plates of a capacitor attract each other, so to pull the plates farther apart requires work by some external force. What becomes of the energy added by this work? Explain your reasoning.

Q24.10 The two plates of a capacitor are given charges $\pm Q$. The capacitor is then disconnected from the charging device so that the charges on the plates can't change, and the capacitor is immersed in a tank of oil. Does the electric field between the plates increase, decrease, or stay the same? Explain your reasoning. How can this field be measured?

Q24.11 As shown in Table 24.1, water has a very large dielectric constant $K = 80.4$. Why do you think water is not commonly used as a dielectric in capacitors?

Q24.12 Is dielectric strength the same thing as dielectric constant? Explain any differences between the two quantities. Is there a simple relationship between dielectric strength and dielectric constant (see Table 24.2)?

Q24.13 A capacitor made of aluminum foil strips separated by Mylar film was subjected to excessive voltage, and the resulting dielectric breakdown melted holes in the Mylar. After this, the capacitance was found to be about the same as before, but the breakdown voltage was much less. Why?

Q24.14 Suppose you bring a slab of dielectric close to the gap between the plates of a charged capacitor, preparing to slide it between the plates. What force will you feel? What does this force tell you about the energy stored between the plates once the dielectric is in place, compared to before the dielectric is in place?

Q24.15 The freshness of fish can be measured by placing a fish between the plates of a capacitor and measuring the capacitance. How does this work? (*Hint:* As time passes, the fish dries out. See Table 24.1.)

Q24.16 *Electrolytic* capacitors use as their dielectric an extremely thin layer of nonconducting oxide between a metal plate and a conducting solution. Discuss the advantage of such a capacitor over one constructed using a solid dielectric between the metal plates.

Q24.17 In terms of the dielectric constant K, what happens to the electric flux through the Gaussian surface shown in Fig. 24.22 when the dielectric is inserted into the previously empty space between the plates? Explain.

Q24.18 A parallel-plate capacitor is connected to a power supply that maintains a fixed potential difference between the plates. (a) If a sheet of dielectric is then slid between the plates, what happens to (i) the electric field between the plates, (ii) the magnitude of charge on each plate, and (iii) the energy stored in the capacitor? (b) Now suppose that before the dielectric is inserted, the charged capacitor is disconnected from the power supply. In this case, what happens to (i) the electric field between the plates, (ii) the magnitude of charge on each plate, and (iii) the energy stored in the capacitor? Explain any differences between the two situations.

Q24.19 Liquid dielectrics that have polar molecules (such as water) always have dielectric constants that decrease with increasing temperature. Why?

Q24.20 A conductor is an extreme case of a dielectric, since if an electric field is applied to a conductor, charges are free to move within the conductor to set up "induced charges." What is the dielectric constant of a perfect conductor? Is it $K = 0$, $K \rightarrow \infty$, or something in between? Explain your reasoning.

EXERCISES

Section 24.1 Capacitors and Capacitance

24.1 • The plates of a parallel-plate capacitor are 2.50 mm apart, and each carries a charge of magnitude 80.0 nC. The plates are in vacuum. The electric field between the plates has a magnitude of 4.00×10^6 V/m. (a) What is the potential difference between the plates? (b) What is the area of each plate? (c) What is the capacitance?

24.2 • The plates of a parallel-plate capacitor are 3.28 mm apart, and each has an area of 12.2 cm^2. Each plate carries a charge of magnitude 4.35×10^{-8} C. The plates are in vacuum. (a) What is the capacitance? (b) What is the potential difference between the plates? (c) What is the magnitude of the electric field between the plates?

24.3 • A parallel-plate air capacitor of capacitance 245 pF has a charge of magnitude 0.148 μC on each plate. The plates are 0.328 mm apart. (a) What is the potential difference between the plates? (b) What is the area of each plate? (c) What is the electric-field magnitude between the plates? (d) What is the surface charge density on each plate?

24.4 •• **Capacitance of an Oscilloscope.** Oscilloscopes have parallel metal plates inside them to deflect the electron beam. These plates are called the *deflecting plates*. Typically, they are squares 3.0 cm on a side and separated by 5.0 mm, with vacuum in between. What is the capacitance of these deflecting plates and hence of the oscilloscope? (*Note:* This capacitance can sometimes have an effect on the circuit you are trying to study and must be taken into consideration in your calculations.)

24.5 • A 10.0-μF parallel-plate capacitor with circular plates is connected to a 12.0-V battery. (a) What is the charge on each plate? (b) How much charge would be on the plates if their separation were doubled while the capacitor remained connected to the battery? (c) How much charge would be on the plates if the capacitor were connected to the 12.0-V battery after the radius of each plate was doubled without changing their separation?

24.6 • A 10.0-μF parallel-plate capacitor is connected to a 12.0-V battery. After the capacitor is fully charged, the battery is disconnected without loss of any of the charge on the plates. (a) A voltmeter is connected across the two plates without discharging them. What does it read? (b) What would the voltmeter read if (i) the plate separation were doubled; (ii) the radius of each plate were doubled but their separation was unchanged?

24.7 •• How far apart would parallel pennies have to be to make a 1.00-pF capacitor? Does your answer suggest that you are justified in treating these pennies as infinite sheets? Explain.

24.8 • A 5.00-pF, parallel-plate, air-filled capacitor with circular plates is to be used in a circuit in which it will be subjected to potentials of up to 1.00×10^2 V. The electric field between the plates is to be no greater than 1.00×10^4 N/C. As a budding electrical engineer for Live-Wire Electronics, your tasks are to (a) design the capacitor by finding what its physical dimensions and separation must be; (b) find the maximum charge these plates can hold.

24.9 • A parallel-plate air capacitor is to store charge of magnitude 240.0 pC on each plate when the potential difference between the plates is 42.0 V. (a) If the area of each plate is 6.80 cm^2, what is the separation between the plates? (b) If the separation between the two plates is double the value calculated in part (a), what potential difference is required for the capacitor to store charge of magnitude 240.0 pC on each plate?

24.10 • A cylindrical capacitor consists of a solid inner conducting core with radius 0.250 cm, surrounded by an outer hollow conducting tube. The two conductors are separated by air, and the length of the cylinder is 12.0 cm. The capacitance is 36.7 pF. (a) Calculate the inner radius of the hollow tube. (b) When the capacitor is charged to 125 V, what is the charge per unit length λ on the capacitor?

24.11 • A capacitor is made from two hollow, coaxial, iron cylinders, one inside the other. The inner cylinder is negatively charged and the outer is positively charged; the magnitude of the charge on each is 10.0 pC. The inner cylinder has radius 0.50 mm, the outer one has radius 5.00 mm, and the length of each cylinder is 18.0 cm. (a) What is the capacitance? (b) What applied potential difference is necessary to produce these charges on the cylinders?

24.12 •• A cylindrical capacitor has an inner conductor of radius 1.5 mm and an outer conductor of radius 3.5 mm. The two conductors are separated by vacuum, and the entire capacitor is 2.8 m long. (a) What is the capacitance per unit length? (b) The potential of the inner conductor is 350 mV higher than that of the outer conductor. Find the charge (magnitude and sign) on both conductors.

24.13 •• A spherical capacitor contains a charge of 3.30 nC when connected to a potential difference of 220 V. If its plates are separated by vacuum and the inner radius of the outer shell is 4.00 cm, calculate: (a) the capacitance; (b) the radius of the inner sphere; (c) the electric field just outside the surface of the inner sphere.

24.14 • A spherical capacitor is formed from two concentric, spherical, conducting shells separated by vacuum. The inner sphere has radius 15.0 cm and the capacitance is 116 pF. (a) What is the radius of the outer sphere? (b) If the potential difference between the two spheres is 220 V, what is the magnitude of charge on each sphere?

Section 24.2 Capacitors in Series and Parallel

24.15 • **BIO Electric Eels.** Electric eels and electric fish generate large potential differences that are used to stun enemies and prey. These potentials are produced by cells that each can generate 0.10 V. We can plausibly model such cells as charged capacitors. (a) How should these cells be connected (in series or in parallel) to produce a total potential of more than 0.10 V? (b) Using the connection in part (a), how many cells must be connected together to produce the 500-V surge of the electric eel?

24.16 • For the system of capacitors shown in Fig. E24.16, find the equivalent capacitance (a) between b and c, and (b) between a and c.

24.17 • In Fig. E24.17, each capacitor has $C = 4.00 \ \mu F$ and $V_{ab} = +28.0$ V. Calculate (a) the charge on each capacitor; (b) the potential difference across each capacitor; (c) the potential difference between points a and d.

24.18 • In Fig. 24.8a, let $C_1 = 3.00 \ \mu F$, $C_2 = 5.00 \ \mu F$, and $V_{ab} = +52.0$ V. Calculate (a) the charge on each capacitor and (b) the potential difference across each capacitor.

24.19 • In Fig. 24.9a, let $C_1 = 3.00 \ \mu F$, $C_2 = 5.00 \ \mu F$, and $V_{ab} = +52.0$ V. Calculate (a) the charge on each capacitor and (b) the potential difference across each capacitor.

24.20 • In Fig. E24.20, $C_1 = 6.00 \ \mu F$, $C_2 = 3.00 \ \mu F$, and $C_3 = 5.00 \ \mu F$. The capacitor network is connected to an applied potential V_{ab}. After the charges on the capacitors have reached their final values, the charge on C_2 is 40.0 μC. (a) What are the charges on capacitors C_1 and C_3? (b) What is the applied voltage V_{ab}?

24.21 •• For the system of capacitors shown in Fig. E24.21, a potential difference of 25 V is maintained across ab. (a) What is the equivalent capacitance of this system between a and b? (b) How much charge is stored by this system? (c) How much charge does the 6.5-nF capacitor store? (d) What is the potential difference across the 7.5-nF capacitor?

24.22 • Figure E24.22 shows a system of four capacitors, where the potential difference across ab is 50.0 V. (a) Find the equivalent capacitance of this system between a and b. (b) How much charge is stored by this combination of capacitors? (c) How much charge is stored in each of the 10.0-μF and the 9.0-μF capacitors?

24.23 •• Suppose the 3-μF capacitor in Fig. 24.10a were removed and replaced by a different one, and that this changed the equivalent capacitance between points a and b to 8 μF. What would be the capacitance of the replacement capacitor?

Figure **E24.16**

Figure **E24.17**

Figure **E24.20**

Figure **E24.21**

Figure **E24.22**

Section 24.3 Energy Storage in Capacitors and Electric-Field Energy

24.24 • A parallel-plate air capacitor has a capacitance of 920 pF. The charge on each plate is 2.55 μC. (a) What is the potential difference between the plates? (b) If the charge is kept constant, what will be the potential difference between the plates if the separation is doubled? (c) How much work is required to double the separation?

24.25 • A 5.80-μF, parallel-plate, air capacitor has a plate separation of 5.00 mm and is charged to a potential difference of 400 V. Calculate the energy density in the region between the plates, in units of J/m^3.

24.26 • An air capacitor is made from two flat parallel plates 1.50 mm apart. The magnitude of charge on each plate is 0.0180 μC when the potential difference is 200 V. (a) What is the capacitance? (b) What is the area of each plate? (c) What maximum voltage can be applied without dielectric breakdown? (Dielectric breakdown for air occurs at an electric-field strength of 3.0×10^6 V/m.) (d) When the charge is 0.0180 μC, what total energy is stored?

24.27 • A parallel-plate vacuum capacitor with plate area A and separation x has charges $+Q$ and $-Q$ on its plates. The capacitor is disconnected from the source of charge, so the charge on each plate remains fixed. (a) What is the total energy stored in the capacitor? (b) The plates are pulled apart an additional distance dx. What is the change in the stored energy? (c) If F is the force with which the plates attract each other, then the change in the stored energy must equal the work $dW = F\,dx$ done in pulling the plates apart. Find an expression for F. (d) Explain why F is *not* equal to QE, where E is the electric field between the plates.

24.28 •• A parallel-plate vacuum capacitor has 8.38 J of energy stored in it. The separation between the plates is 2.30 mm. If the separation is decreased to 1.15 mm, what is the energy stored (a) if the capacitor is disconnected from the potential source so the charge on the plates remains constant, and (b) if the capacitor remains connected to the potential source so the potential difference between the plates remains constant?

24.29 • You have two identical capacitors and an external potential source. (a) Compare the total energy stored in the capacitors when they are connected to the applied potential in series and in parallel. (b) Compare the maximum amount of charge stored in each case. (c) Energy storage in a capacitor can be limited by the maximum electric field between the plates. What is the ratio of the electric field for the series and parallel combinations?

24.30 • For the capacitor network shown in Fig. E24.30, the potential difference across ab is 36 V. Find (a) the total charge stored in this network; (b) the charge on each capacitor; (c) the total energy stored in the network; (d) the energy stored in each capacitor; (e) the potential differences across each capacitor.

Figure **E24.30**

24.31 • For the capacitor network shown in Fig. E24.31, the potential difference across ab is 220 V. Find (a) the total charge stored in this network; (b) the charge on each capacitor; (c) the total energy stored in the network; (d) the energy stored in each capacitor; (e) the potential differences across each capacitor.

Figure **E24.31**

24.32 • A 0.350-m-long cylindrical capacitor consists of a solid conducting core with a radius of 1.20 mm and an outer hollow conducting tube with an inner radius of 2.00 mm. The two conductors are separated by air and charged to a potential difference of 6.00 V. Calculate (a) the charge per length for the capacitor; (b) the total charge on the capacitor; (c) the capacitance; (d) the energy stored in the capacitor when fully charged.

24.33 • A cylindrical air capacitor of length 15.0 m stores 3.20×10^{-9} J of energy when the potential difference between the two conductors is 4.00 V. (a) Calculate the magnitude of the charge on each conductor. (b) Calculate the ratio of the radii of the inner and outer conductors.

24.34 •• A capacitor is formed from two concentric spherical conducting shells separated by vacuum. The inner sphere has radius 12.5 cm, and the outer sphere has radius 14.8 cm. A potential difference of 120 V is applied to the capacitor. (a) What is the energy density at $r = 12.6$ cm, just outside the inner sphere? (b) What is the energy density at $r = 14.7$ cm, just inside the outer sphere? (c) For a parallel-plate capacitor the energy density is uniform in the region between the plates, except near the edges of the plates. Is this also true for a spherical capacitor?

Section 24.4 Dielectrics

24.35 • A 12.5-μF capacitor is connected to a power supply that keeps a constant potential difference of 24.0 V across the plates. A piece of material having a dielectric constant of 3.75 is placed between the plates, completely filling the space between them. (a) How much energy is stored in the capacitor before and after the dielectric is inserted? (b) By how much did the energy change during the insertion? Did it increase or decrease?

24.36 • A parallel-plate capacitor has capacitance $C_0 = 5.00$ pF when there is air between the plates. The separation between the plates is 1.50 mm. (a) What is the maximum magnitude of charge Q that can be placed on each plate if the electric field in the region between the plates is not to exceed 3.00×10^4 V/m? (b) A dielectric with $K = 2.70$ is inserted between the plates of the capacitor, completely filling the volume between them. Now what is the maximum magnitude of charge on each plate if the electric field between the plates is not to exceed 3.00×10^4 V/m?

24.37 • Two parallel plates have equal and opposite charges. When the space between the plates is evacuated, the electric field is $E = 3.20 \times 10^5$ V/m. When the space is filled with dielectric, the electric field is $E = 2.50 \times 10^5$ V/m. (a) What is the charge density on each surface of the dielectric? (b) What is the dielectric constant?

24.38 • A budding electronics hobbyist wants to make a simple 1.0-nF capacitor for tuning her crystal radio, using two sheets of aluminum foil as plates, with a few sheets of paper between them as a dielectric. The paper has a dielectric constant of 3.0, and the thickness of one sheet of it is 0.20 mm. (a) If the sheets of paper measure 22 × 28 cm and she cuts the aluminum foil to the same dimensions, how many sheets of paper should she use between her plates to get the proper capacitance? (b) Suppose for convenience she wants to use a single sheet of posterboard, with the same dielectric constant but a thickness of 12.0 mm, instead of the paper. What area of aluminum foil will she need for her plates to get her 1.0 nF of capacitance? (c) Suppose she goes high-tech and finds a sheet of Teflon of the same thickness as the posterboard to use as a dielectric. Will she need a larger or smaller area of Teflon than of posterboard? Explain.

24.39 • The dielectric to be used in a parallel-plate capacitor has a dielectric constant of 3.60 and a dielectric strength of 1.60×10^7 V/m. The capacitor is to have a capacitance of 1.25×10^{-9} F and must be able to withstand a maximum potential difference of 5500 V. What is the minimum area the plates of the capacitor may have?

24.40 •• **BIO** **Potential in Human Cells.** Some cell walls in the human body have a layer of negative charge on the inside surface and a layer of positive charge of equal magnitude on the outside surface. Suppose that the charge density on either surface is $\pm 0.50 \times 10^{-3}$ C/m², the cell wall is 5.0 nm thick, and the cell-wall material is air. (a) Find the magnitude of $\vec{E}$ in the wall between the two layers of charge. (b) Find the potential difference between the inside and the outside of the cell. Which is at the higher potential? (c) A typical cell in the human body has a volume of 10^{-16} m³. Estimate the total electric-field energy stored in the wall of a cell of this size. (*Hint:* Assume that the cell is spherical, and calculate the volume of the cell wall.) (d) In reality, the cell wall is made up, not of air, but of tissue with a dielectric constant of 5.4. Repeat parts (a) and (b) in this case.

24.41 • A capacitor has parallel plates of area 12 cm² separated by 2.0 mm. The space between the plates is filled with polystyrene (see Table 24.2). (a) Find the permittivity of polystyrene. (b) Find the maximum permissible voltage across the capacitor to avoid dielectric breakdown. (c) When the voltage equals the value found in part (b), find the surface charge density on each plate and the induced surface charge density on the surface of the dielectric.

24.42 • A constant potential difference of 12 V is maintained between the terminals of a 0.25-μF, parallel-plate, air capacitor. (a) A sheet of Mylar is inserted between the plates of the capacitor, completely filling the space between the plates. When this is done, how much additional charge flows onto the positive plate of the capacitor (see Table 24.1)? (b) What is the total induced charge on either face of the Mylar sheet? (c) What effect does the Mylar sheet have on the electric field between the plates? Explain how you can reconcile this with the increase in charge on the plates, which acts to *increase* the electric field.

24.43 • When a 360-nF air capacitor (1 nF = 10^{-9} F) is connected to a power supply, the energy stored in the capacitor is 1.85×10^{-5} J. While the capacitor is kept connected to the power supply, a slab of dielectric is inserted that completely fills the space between the plates. This increases the stored energy by 2.32×10^{-5} J. (a) What is the potential difference between the capacitor plates? (b) What is the dielectric constant of the slab?

24.44 • A parallel-plate capacitor has capacitance $C = 12.5$ pF when the volume between the plates is filled with air. The plates are circular, with radius 3.00 cm. The capacitor is connected to a battery, and a charge of magnitude 25.0 pC goes onto each plate. With the capacitor still connected to the battery, a slab of dielectric is inserted between the plates, completely filling the space between the plates. After the dielectric has been inserted, the charge on each plate has magnitude 45.0 pC. (a) What is the dielectric constant K of the dielectric? (b) What is the potential difference between the plates before and after the dielectric has been inserted? (c) What is the electric field at a point midway between the plates before and after the dielectric has been inserted?

Section 24.6 Gauss's Law in Dielectrics

24.45 • A parallel-plate capacitor has the volume between its plates filled with plastic with dielectric constant K. The magnitude of the charge on each plate is Q. Each plate has area A, and the distance between the plates is d. (a) Use Gauss's law as stated in Eq. (24.23) to calculate the magnitude of the electric field in the dielectric. (b) Use the electric field determined in part (a) to calculate the potential difference between the two plates. (c) Use the result of part (b) to determine the capacitance of the capacitor. Compare your result to Eq. (24.12).

24.46 • A parallel-plate capacitor has plates with area 0.0225 m^2 separated by 1.00 mm of Teflon. (a) Calculate the charge on the plates when they are charged to a potential difference of 12.0 V. (b) Use Gauss's law (Eq. 24.23) to calculate the electric field inside the Teflon. (c) Use Gauss's law to calculate the electric field if the voltage source is disconnected and the Teflon is removed.

PROBLEMS

24.47 • Electronic flash units for cameras contain a capacitor for storing the energy used to produce the flash. In one such unit, the flash lasts for $\frac{1}{675}$ s with an average light power output of 2.70×10^5 W. (a) If the conversion of electrical energy to light is 95% efficient (the rest of the energy goes to thermal energy), how much energy must be stored in the capacitor for one flash? (b) The capacitor has a potential difference between its plates of 125 V when the stored energy equals the value calculated in part (a). What is the capacitance?

24.48 • A parallel-plate air capacitor is made by using two plates 16 cm square, spaced 3.7 mm apart. It is connected to a 12-V battery. (a) What is the capacitance? (b) What is the charge on each

plate? (c) What is the electric field between the plates? (d) What is the energy stored in the capacitor? (e) If the battery is disconnected and then the plates are pulled apart to a separation of 7.4 mm, what are the answers to parts (a)–(d)?

24.49 •• Suppose the battery in Problem 24.48 remains connected while the plates are pulled apart. What are the answers then to parts (a)–(d) after the plates have been pulled apart?

24.50 ••• BIO **Cell Membranes.** Cell membranes (the walled enclosure around a cell) are typically about 7.5 nm thick. They are partially permeable to allow charged material to pass in and out, as needed. Equal but opposite charge densities build up on the inside and

Figure **P24.50**

outside faces of such a membrane, and these charges prevent additional charges from passing through the cell wall. We can model a cell membrane as a parallel-plate capacitor, with the membrane itself containing proteins embedded in an organic material to give the membrane a dielectric constant of about 10. (See Fig. P24.50.) (a) What is the capacitance per square centimeter of such a cell wall? (b) In its normal resting state, a cell has a potential difference of 85 mV across its membrane. What is the electric field inside this membrane?

24.51 • A capacitor is made from two hollow, coaxial copper cylinders, one inside the other. There is air in the space between the cylinders. The inner cylinder has net positive charge and the outer cylinder has net negative charge. The inner cylinder has radius 2.50 mm, the outer cylinder has radius 3.10 mm, and the length of each cylinder is 36.0 cm. If the potential difference between the surfaces of the two cylinders is 80.0 V, what is the magnitude of the electric field at a point between the two cylinders that is a distance of 2.80 mm from their common axis and midway between the ends of the cylinders?

24.52 ••• In one type of computer keyboard, each key holds a small metal plate that serves as one plate of a parallel-plate, air-filled capacitor. When the key is depressed, the plate separation decreases and the capacitance increases. Electronic circuitry detects the change in capacitance and thus detects that the key has been pressed. In one particular keyboard, the area of each metal plate is 42.0 mm^2, and the separation between the plates is 0.700 mm before the key is depressed. (a) Calculate the capacitance before the key is depressed. (b) If the circuitry can detect a change in capacitance of 0.250 pF, how far must the key be depressed before the circuitry detects its depression?

24.53 •• A 20.0-μF capacitor is charged to a potential difference of 800 V. The terminals of the charged capacitor are then connected to those of an uncharged 10.0-μF capacitor. Compute (a) the original charge of the system, (b) the final potential difference across each capacitor, (c) the final energy of the system, and (d) the decrease in energy when the capacitors are connected.

24.54 •• In Fig. 24.9a, let $C_1 = 9.0\ \mu$F, $C_2 = 4.0\ \mu$F, and $V_{ab} = 36$ V. Suppose the charged capacitors are disconnected from the source and from each other, and then reconnected to each other with plates of *opposite* sign together. By how much does the energy of the system decrease?

24.55 • For the capacitor network shown in Fig. P24.55, the potential difference across ab is 12.0 V. Find (a) the total energy stored in this network and (b) the energy stored in the 4.80-μF capacitor.

Figure **P24.55**

24.56 •• Several 0.25-μF capacitors are available. The voltage across each is not to exceed 600 V. You need to make a capacitor with capacitance 0.25 μF to be connected across a potential difference of 960 V. (a) Show in a diagram how an equivalent capacitor with the desired properties can be obtained. (b) No dielectric is a perfect insulator that would not permit the flow of any charge through its volume. Suppose that the dielectric in one of the capacitors in your diagram is a moderately good conductor. What will happen in this case when your combination of capacitors is connected across the 960-V potential difference?

24.57 • In Fig. P24.57, $C_1 = C_5 = 8.4$ μF and $C_2 = C_3 = C_4 = 4.2$ μF. The applied potential is $V_{ab} = 220$ V. (a) What is the equivalent capacitance of the network between points a and b? (b) Calculate the charge on each capacitor and the potential difference across each capacitor.

Figure **P24.57**

24.58 •• You are working on an electronics project requiring a variety of capacitors, but you have only a large supply of 100-nF capacitors available. Show how you can connect these capacitors to produce each of the following equivalent capacitances: (a) 50 nF; (b) 450 nF; (c) 25 nF; (d) 75 nF.

24.59 •• In Fig. E24.20, $C_1 = 3.00$ μF and $V_{ab} = 150$ V. The charge on capacitor C_1 is 150 μC and the charge on C_3 is 450 μC. What are the values of the capacitances of C_2 and C_3?

24.60 • The capacitors in Fig. P24.60 are initially uncharged and are connected, as in the diagram, with switch S open. The applied potential difference is $V_{ab} = +210$ V. (a) What is the potential difference V_{cd}? (b) What is the potential difference across each capacitor after switch S is closed? (c) How much charge flowed through the switch when it was closed?

Figure **P24.60**

24.61 •• Three capacitors having capacitances of 8.4, 8.4, and 4.2 μF are connected in series across a 36-V potential difference. (a) What is the charge on the 4.2-μF capacitor? (b) What is the total energy stored in all three capacitors? (c) The capacitors are disconnected from the potential difference without allowing them to discharge. They are then reconnected in parallel with each other, with the positively charged plates connected together. What is the voltage across each capacitor in the parallel combination? (d) What is the total energy now stored in the capacitors?

24.62 • **Capacitance of a Thundercloud.** The charge center of a thundercloud, drifting 3.0 km above the earth's surface, contains 20 C of negative charge. Assuming the charge center has a radius of 1.0 km, and modeling the charge center and the earth's surface as parallel plates, calculate: (a) the capacitance of the system; (b)

the potential difference between charge center and ground; (c) the average strength of the electric field between cloud and ground; (d) the electrical energy stored in the system.

24.63 •• In Fig. P24.63, each capacitance C_1 is 6.9 μF, and each capacitance C_2 is 4.6 μF. (a) Compute the equivalent capacitance of the network between points a and b. (b) Compute the charge on each of the three capacitors nearest a and b when $V_{ab} = 420$ V. (c) With 420 V across a and b, compute V_{cd}.

Figure **P24.63**

24.64 • Each combination of capacitors between points a and b in Fig. P24.64 is first connected across a 120-V battery, charging the combination to 120 V. These combinations are then connected to make the circuits shown. When the switch S is thrown, a surge of charge for the discharging capacitors flows to trigger the signal device. How much charge flows through the signal device in each case?

Figure **P24.64**

(a)

(b)

24.65 • A parallel-plate capacitor with only air between the plates is charged by connecting it to a battery. The capacitor is then disconnected from the battery, without any of the charge leaving the plates. (a) A voltmeter reads 45.0 V when placed across the capacitor. When a dielectric is inserted between the plates, completely filling the space, the voltmeter reads 11.5 V. What is the dielectric constant of this material? (b) What will the voltmeter read if the dielectric is now pulled partway out so it fills only one-third of the space between the plates?

24.66 •• An air capacitor is made by using two flat plates, each with area A, separated by a distance d. Then a metal slab having thickness a (less than d) and the same shape and size as the plates is inserted between them, parallel to the plates and not touching either plate (Fig. P24.66). (a) What is the capacitance of this arrangement? (b) Express the capacitance as a multiple of the capacitance C_0 when the metal slab is not present. (c) Discuss what happens to the capacitance in the limits $a \to 0$ and $a \to d$.

Figure **P24.66**

24.67 •• **Capacitance of the Earth.** Consider a spherical capacitor with one conductor being a solid conducting sphere of radius R and the other conductor being at infinity. (a) Use Eq. (24.1) and what you know about the potential at the surface of a conducting sphere with charge Q to derive an expression for the capacitance of the charged sphere. (b) Use your result in part (a) to calculate the capacitance of the earth. The earth is a good conductor and has a radius of 6380 km. Compare your results to the capacitance of typical capacitors used in electronic circuits, which ranges from 10 pF to 100 pF.

24.68 •• A potential difference $V_{ab} = 48.0$ V is applied across the capacitor network of Fig. E24.17. If $C_1 = C_2 = 4.00$ μF and

$C_4 = 8.00 \ \mu F$, what must the capacitance C_3 be if the network is to store 2.90×10^{-3} J of electrical energy?

24.69 • **Earth-Ionosphere Capacitance.** The earth can be considered as a single-conductor capacitor (see Problem 24.67). It can also be considered in combination with a charged layer of the atmosphere, the ionosphere, as a spherical capacitor with two plates, the surface of the earth being the negative plate. The ionosphere is at a level of about 70 km, and the potential difference between earth and ionosphere is about 350,000 V. Calculate: (a) the capacitance of this system; (b) the total charge on the capacitor; (c) the energy stored in the system.

24.70 • **CALC** The inner cylinder of a long, cylindrical capacitor has radius r_a and linear charge density $+\lambda$. It is surrounded by a coaxial cylindrical conducting shell with inner radius r_b and linear charge density $-\lambda$ (see Fig. 24.6). (a) What is the energy density in the region between the conductors at a distance r from the axis? (b) Integrate the energy density calculated in part (a) over the volume between the conductors in a length L of the capacitor to obtain the total electric-field energy per unit length. (c) Use Eq. (24.9) and the capacitance per unit length calculated in Example 24.4 (Section 24.1) to calculate U/L. Does your result agree with that obtained in part (b)?

24.71 •• **CP** A capacitor has a potential difference of 2.25×10^3 V between its plates. A short aluminum wire with initial temperature $23.0°C$ is connected between the plates of the capacitor and all the energy stored in the capacitor goes into heating the wire. The wire has mass 12.0 g. If no heat is lost to the surroundings and the final temperature of the wire is $34.2°C$, what is the capacitance of the capacitor?

24.72 •• A parallel-plate capacitor is made from two plates 12.0 cm on each side and 4.50 mm apart. Half of the space between these plates contains only air, but the other half is filled with Plexiglas® of dielectric constant 3.40 (Fig. P24.72). An 18.0-V battery is connected across the plates. (a) What is the capacitance of this combination? (*Hint:* Can you think of this capacitor as equivalent to two capacitors in parallel?) (b) How much energy is stored in the capacitor? (c) If we remove the Plexiglas® but change nothing else, how much energy will be stored in the capacitor?

Figure **P24.72**

24.73 •• A parallel-plate capacitor has square plates that are 8.00 cm on each side and 3.80 mm apart. The space between the plates is completely filled with two square slabs of dielectric, each 8.00 cm on a side and 1.90 mm thick. One slab is pyrex glass and the other is polystyrene. If the potential difference between the plates is 86.0 V, how much electrical energy is stored in the capacitor?

24.74 •• A fuel gauge uses a capacitor to determine the height of the fuel in a tank. The effective dielectric constant K_{eff} changes from a value of 1 when the tank is empty to a value of K, the dielectric constant of the fuel, when the tank is full. The appropriate electronic circuitry can determine the effective dielectric constant of the combined air and fuel between the capacitor plates. Each of the two rectangular plates has a width

Figure **P24.74**

w and a length L (Fig. P24.74). The height of the fuel between the plates is h. You can ignore any fringing effects. (a) Derive an expression for K_{eff} as a function of h. (b) What is the effective dielectric constant for a tank $\frac{1}{4}$ full, $\frac{1}{2}$ full, and $\frac{3}{4}$ full if the fuel is gasoline ($K = 1.95$)? (c) Repeat part (b) for methanol ($K = 33.0$). (d) For which fuel is this fuel gauge more practical?

24.75 •• Three square metal plates A, B, and C, each 12.0 cm on a side and 1.50 mm thick, are arranged as in Fig. P24.75. The plates are separated by sheets of paper 0.45 mm thick and with dielectric constant 4.2. The outer plates are connected together and connected to point b. The inner plate is connected to point a. (a) Copy the diagram and show by plus and minus signs the charge distribution on the plates when point a is maintained at a positive potential relative to point b. (b) What is the capacitance between points a and b?

Figure **P24.75**

CHALLENGE PROBLEMS

24.76 ••• **CP** The parallel-plate air capacitor in Fig. P24.76 consists of two horizontal conducting plates of equal area A. The bottom plate rests on a fixed support, and the top plate is suspended by four springs with spring constant k, positioned at each of the four corners of the top plate as shown in the figure. When uncharged, the plates are separated by a distance z_0. A battery is connected to the plates and produces a potential difference V between them. This causes the plate separation to decrease to z. Neglect any fringing effects. (a) Show that the electrostatic force between the charged plates has a magnitude $\epsilon_0 AV^2/2z^2$. (*Hint:* See Exercise 24.27.) (b) Obtain an expression that relates the plate separation z to the potential difference V. The resulting equation will be cubic in z. (c) Given the values $A = 0.300 \ \text{m}^2$, $z_0 = 1.20$ mm, $k = 25.0$ N/m, and $V = 120$ V, find the two values of z for which the top plate will be in equilibrium. (*Hint:* You can solve the cubic equation by plugging a trial value of z into the equation and then adjusting your guess until the equation is satisfied to three significant figures. Locating the roots of the cubic equation graphically can help you pick starting values of z for this trial-and-error procedure. One root of the cubic equation has a nonphysical negative value.) (d) For each of the two values of z found in part (c), is the equilibrium stable or unstable? For stable equilibrium a small displacement of the object will give rise to a net force tending to return the object to the equilibrium position. For unstable equilibrium a small displacement gives rise to a net force that takes the object farther away from equilibrium.

Figure **P24.76**

24.77 ••• Two square conducting plates with sides of length L are separated by a distance D. A dielectric slab with constant K with dimensions $L \times L \times D$ is inserted a distance x into the space between the plates, as shown in Fig. P24.77. (a) Find the capacitance

C of this system. (b) Suppose that the capacitor is connected to a battery that maintains a constant potential difference *V* between the plates. If the dielectric slab is inserted an additional distance *dx* into the space between the plates, show that the change in stored energy is

$$dU = +\frac{(K-1)\epsilon_0 V^2 L}{2D}dx$$

(c) Suppose that before the slab is moved by *dx*, the plates are disconnected from the battery, so that the charges on the plates remain constant. Determine the magnitude of the charge on each plate, and then show that when the slab is moved *dx* farther into the space between the plates, the stored energy changes by an amount that is the *negative* of the expression for *dU* given in part (b). (d) If *F* is the force exerted on the slab by the charges on the plates, then *dU* should equal the work done *against* this force to move the slab a distance *dx*. Thus *dU* = −*F dx*. Show that applying this expression to the result of part (b) suggests that the electric force on the slab pushes it *out* of the capacitor, while the result of part (c) suggests that the force

Figure **P24.77**

Dielectric slab, constant *K*

pulls the slab *into* the capacitor. (e) Figure 24.16 shows that the force in fact pulls the slab into the capacitor. Explain why the result of part (b) gives an incorrect answer for the direction of this force, and calculate the magnitude of the force. (This method does not require knowledge of the nature of the fringing field.)

24.78 ••• An isolated spherical capacitor has charge +*Q* on its inner conductor (radius r_a) and charge −*Q* on its outer conductor (radius r_b). Half of the volume between the two conductors is then filled with a liquid dielectric of constant *K*, as shown in cross section in Fig. P24.78. (a) Find the capacitance of the half-filled capacitor. (b) Find the magnitude of $\vec{E}$ in the volume between the two conductors as a function of the distance *r* from the center of the capacitor. Give answers for both the upper and lower halves of this volume. (c) Find the surface density of free charge on the upper and lower halves of the inner and outer conductors. (d) Find the surface density of bound charge on the inner ($r = r_a$) and outer ($r = r_b$) surfaces of the dielectric. (e) What is the surface density of bound charge on the flat surface of the dielectric? Explain.

Figure **P24.78**

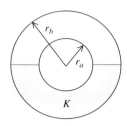

Answers

Chapter Opening Question ?

Equation (24.9) shows that the energy stored in a capacitor with capacitance *C* and charge *Q* is $U = Q^2/2C$. If the charge *Q* is doubled, the stored energy increases by a factor of $2^2 = 4$. Note that if the value of *Q* is too great, the electric-field magnitude inside the capacitor will exceed the dielectric strength of the material between the plates and dielectric breakdown will occur (see Section 24.4). This puts a practical limit on the amount of energy that can be stored.

Test Your Understanding Questions

24.1 Answer: (iii) The capacitance does not depend on the value of the charge *Q*. Doubling the value of *Q* causes the potential difference V_{ab} to double, so the capacitance $C = Q/V_{ab}$ remains the same. These statements are true no matter what the geometry of the capacitor.

24.2 Answers: (a) (i), (b) (iv) In a series connection the two capacitors carry the same charge *Q* but have different potential differences $V_{ab} = Q/C$; the capacitor with the smaller capacitance *C* has the greater potential difference. In a parallel connection the two capacitors have the same potential difference V_{ab} but carry different charges $Q = CV_{ab}$; the capacitor with the larger capacitance *C* has the greater charge. Hence a 4-μF capacitor will have a greater potential difference than an 8-μF capacitor if the two are connected in series. The 4-μF capacitor cannot carry more charge than the 8-μF capacitor no matter how they are connected: In a series connection they will carry the same charge, and in a parallel connection the 8-μF capacitor will carry more charge.

24.3 Answer: (i) Capacitors connected in series carry the same charge *Q*. To compare the amount of energy stored, we use the expression $U = Q^2/2C$ from Eq. (24.9); it shows that the capacitor with the *smaller* capacitance ($C = 4$ μF) has more stored

energy in a series combination. By contrast, capacitors in parallel have the same potential difference *V*, so to compare them we use $U = \frac{1}{2}CV^2$ from Eq. (24.9). It shows that in a parallel combination, the capacitor with the *larger* capacitance ($C = 8$ μF) has more stored energy. (If we had instead used $U = \frac{1}{2}CV^2$ to analyze the series combination, we would have to account for the different potential differences across the two capacitors. Likewise, using $U = Q^2/2C$ to study the parallel combination would require us to account for the different charges on the capacitors.)

24.4 Answer: (i) Here *Q* remains the same, so we use $U = Q^2/2C$ from Eq. (24.9) for the stored energy. Removing the dielectric lowers the capacitance by a factor of $1/K$; since *U* is inversely proportional to *C*, the stored energy *increases* by a factor of *K*. It takes work to pull the dielectric slab out of the capacitor because the fringing field tries to pull the slab back in (Fig. 24.16). The work that you do goes into the energy stored in the capacitor.

24.5 Answer: (i), (iii), (ii) Equation (24.14) says that if E_0 is the initial electric-field magnitude (before the dielectric slab is inserted), then the resultant field magnitude after the slab is inserted is $E_0/K = E_0/3$. The magnitude of the resultant field equals the difference between the initial field magnitude and the magnitude E_i of the field due to the bound charges (see Fig. 24.20). Hence $E_0 - E_i = E_0/3$ and $E_i = 2E_0/3$.

24.6 Answer: (iii) Equation (24.23) shows that this situation is the same as an isolated point charge in vacuum but with $\vec{E}$ replaced by $K\vec{E}$. Hence KE at the point of interest is equal to $q/4\pi\epsilon_0 r^2$, and so $E = q/4\pi K\epsilon_0 r^2$. As in Example 24.12, filling the space with a dielectric reduces the electric field by a factor of $1/K$.

Bridging Problem

Answers: (a) 0   **(b)** $Q^2/32\pi^2\epsilon_0 r^4$ **(c)** $Q^2/8\pi\epsilon_0 R$
   (d) $Q^2/8\pi\epsilon_0 R$ **(e)** $C = 4\pi\epsilon_0 R$

25 CURRENT, RESISTANCE, AND ELECTROMOTIVE FORCE

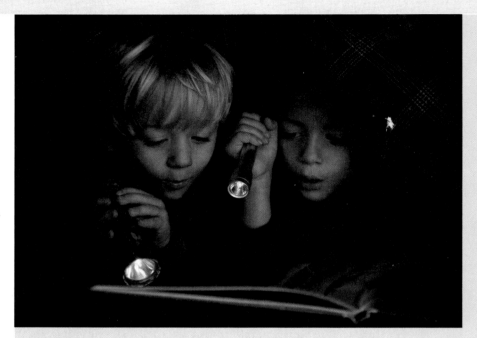

? In a flashlight, is the amount of current that flows out of the bulb less than, greater than, or equal to the amount of current that flows into the bulb?

In the past four chapters we studied the interactions of electric charges *at rest;* now we're ready to study charges *in motion.* An *electric current* consists of charges in motion from one region to another. If the charges follow a conducting path that forms a closed loop, the path is called an *electric circuit.*

Fundamentally, electric circuits are a means for conveying *energy* from one place to another. As charged particles move within a circuit, electric potential energy is transferred from a source (such as a battery or generator) to a device in which that energy is either stored or converted to another form: into sound in a stereo system or into heat and light in a toaster or light bulb. Electric circuits are useful because they allow energy to be transported without any moving parts (other than the moving charged particles themselves). They are at the heart of flashlights, computers, radio and television transmitters and receivers, and household and industrial power distribution systems. Your nervous system is a specialized electric circuit that carries vital signals from one part of your body to another.

In Chapter 26 we will see how to analyze electric circuits and will examine some practical applications of circuits. Before we can do so, however, you must understand the basic properties of electric currents. These properties are the subject of this chapter. We'll begin by describing the nature of electric conductors and considering how they are affected by temperature. We'll learn why a short, fat, cold copper wire is a better conductor than a long, skinny, hot steel wire. We'll study the properties of batteries and see how they cause current and energy transfer in a circuit. In this analysis we will use the concepts of current, potential difference (or voltage), resistance, and electromotive force. Finally, we'll look at electric current in a material from a microscopic viewpoint.

25.1 Current

A **current** is any motion of charge from one region to another. In this section we'll discuss currents in conducting materials. The vast majority of technological applications of charges in motion involve currents of this kind.

In electrostatic situations (discussed in Chapters 21 through 24) the electric field is zero everywhere within the conductor, and there is *no* current. However, this does not mean that all charges within the conductor are at rest. In an ordinary metal such as copper or alumium, some of the electrons are free to move within the conducting material. These free electrons move randomly in all directions, somewhat like the molecules of a gas but with much greater speeds, of the order of 10^6 m/s. The electrons nonetheless do not escape from the conducting material, because they are attracted to the positive ions of the material. The motion of the electrons is random, so there is no *net* flow of charge in any direction and hence no current.

Now consider what happens if a constant, steady electric field $\vec{E}$ is established inside a conductor. (We'll see later how this can be done.) A charged particle (such as a free electron) inside the conducting material is then subjected to a steady force $\vec{F} = q\vec{E}$. If the charged particle were moving in *vacuum,* this steady force would cause a steady acceleration in the direction of $\vec{F}$, and after a time the charged particle would be moving in that direction at high speed. But a charged particle moving in a *conductor* undergoes frequent collisions with the massive, nearly stationary ions of the material. In each such collision the particle's direction of motion undergoes a random change. The net effect of the electric field $\vec{E}$ is that in addition to the random motion of the charged particles within the conductor, there is also a very slow net motion or *drift* of the moving charged particles as a group in the direction of the electric force $\vec{F} = q\vec{E}$ (Fig. 25.1). This motion is described in terms of the **drift velocity** $\vec{v}_d$ of the particles. As a result, there is a net current in the conductor.

While the random motion of the electrons has a very fast average speed of about 10^6 m/s, the drift speed is very slow, often on the order of 10^{-4} m/s. Given that the electrons move so slowly, you may wonder why the light comes on immediately when you turn on the switch of a flashlight. The reason is that the electric field is set up in the wire with a speed approaching the speed of light, and electrons start to move all along the wire at very nearly the same time. The time that it takes any individual electron to get from the switch to the light bulb isn't really relevant. A good analogy is a group of soldiers standing at attention when the sergeant orders them to start marching; the order reaches the soldiers' ears at the speed of sound, which is much faster than their marching speed, so all the soldiers start to march essentially in unison.

The Direction of Current Flow

The drift of moving charges through a conductor can be interpreted in terms of work and energy. The electric field $\vec{E}$ does work on the moving charges. The resulting kinetic energy is transferred to the material of the conductor by means of collisions with the ions, which vibrate about their equilibrium positions in the crystalline structure of the conductor. This energy transfer increases the average vibrational energy of the ions and therefore the temperature of the material. Thus much of the work done by the electric field goes into heating the conductor, *not* into making the moving charges move ever faster and faster. This heating is sometimes useful, as in an electric toaster, but in many situations is simply an unavoidable by-product of current flow.

In different current-carrying materials, the charges of the moving particles may be positive or negative. In metals the moving charges are always (negative) electrons, while in an ionized gas (plasma) or an ionic solution the moving charges may include both electrons and positively charged ions. In a semiconductor

25.1 If there is no electric field inside a conductor, an electron moves randomly from point P_1 to point P_2 in a time Δt. If an electric field $\vec{E}$ is present, the electric force $\vec{F} = q\vec{E}$ imposes a small drift (greatly exaggerated here) that takes the electron to point P'_2, a distance $v_d \Delta t$ from P_2 in the direction of the force.

Conductor without internal $\vec{E}$ field

Path of electron without $\vec{E}$ field. Electron moves randomly.

Path of electron with $\vec{E}$ field. The motion is mostly random, but ...

P_1

P_2

$v_d\Delta t$ P'_2

...the $\vec{E}$ field results in a net displacement along the wire.

Conductor with internal $\vec{E}$ field

$\vec{E}$ $\vec{F} = q\vec{E}$ $\vec{E}$

An electron has a negative charge q, so the force on it due to the $\vec{E}$ field is in the direction opposite to $\vec{E}$.

25.2 The same current can be produced by (a) positive charges moving in the direction of the electric field $\vec{E}$ or (b) the same number of negative charges moving at the same speed in the direction opposite to $\vec{E}$.

(a)

A **conventional current** is treated as a flow of positive charges, regardless of whether the free charges in the conductor are positive, negative, or both.

(b)

In a metallic conductor, the moving charges are electrons — but the *current* still points in the direction positive charges would flow.

25.3 The current I is the time rate of charge transfer through the cross-sectional area A. The random component of each moving charged particle's motion averages to zero, and the current is in the same direction as $\vec{E}$ whether the moving charges are positive (as shown here) or negative (see Fig. 25.2b).

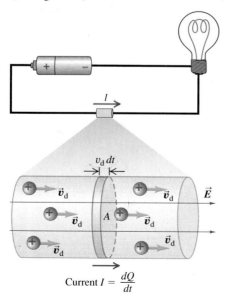

Current $I = \dfrac{dQ}{dt}$

material such as germanium or silicon, conduction is partly by electrons and partly by motion of *vacancies,* also known as *holes;* these are sites of missing electrons and act like positive charges.

Figure 25.2 shows segments of two different current-carrying materials. In Fig. 25.2a the moving charges are positive, the electric force is in the same direction as $\vec{E}$, and the drift velocity $\vec{v}_d$ is from left to right. In Fig. 25.2b the charges are negative, the electric force is opposite to $\vec{E}$, and the drift velocity $\vec{v}_d$ is from right to left. In both cases there is a net flow of positive charge from left to right, and positive charges end up to the right of negative ones. We *define* the current, denoted by I, to be in the direction in which there is a flow of *positive* charge. Thus we describe currents as though they consisted entirely of positive charge flow, even in cases in which we know that the actual current is due to electrons. Hence the current is to the right in both Figs. 25.2a and 25.2b. This choice or convention for the direction of current flow is called **conventional current.** While the direction of the conventional current is *not* necessarily the same as the direction in which charged particles are actually moving, we'll find that the sign of the moving charges is of little importance in analyzing electric circuits.

Figure 25.3 shows a segment of a conductor in which a current is flowing. We consider the moving charges to be *positive,* so they are moving in the same direction as the current. We define the current through the cross-sectional area A to be *the net charge flowing through the area per unit time.* Thus, if a net charge dQ flows through an area in a time dt, the current I through the area is

$$I = \frac{dQ}{dt} \qquad \text{(definition of current)} \qquad (25.1)$$

CAUTION **Current is not a vector** Although we refer to the *direction* of a current, current as defined by Eq. (25.1) is *not* a vector quantity. In a current-carrying wire, the current is always along the length of the wire, regardless of whether the wire is straight or curved. No single vector could describe motion along a curved path, which is why current is not a vector. We'll usually describe the direction of current either in words (as in "the current flows clockwise around the circuit") or by choosing a current to be positive if it flows in one direction along a conductor and negative if it flows in the other direction.

The SI unit of current is the **ampere;** one ampere is defined to be *one coulomb per second* (1 A = 1 C/s). This unit is named in honor of the French scientist André Marie Ampère (1775–1836). When an ordinary flashlight (D-cell size) is turned on, the current in the flashlight is about 0.5 to 1 A; the current in the wires of a car engine's starter motor is around 200 A. Currents in radio and television circuits are usually expressed in *milliamperes* (1 mA = 10^{-3} A) or *micro-amperes* (1 μA = 10^{-6} A), and currents in computer circuits are expressed in *nanoamperes* (1 nA = 10^{-9} A) or *picoamperes* (1 pA = 10^{-12} A).

Current, Drift Velocity, and Current Density

We can express current in terms of the drift velocity of the moving charges. Let's consider again the situation of Fig. 25.3 of a conductor with cross-sectional area A and an electric field $\vec{E}$ directed from left to right. To begin with, we'll assume that the free charges in the conductor are positive; then the drift velocity is in the same direction as the field.

Suppose there are n moving charged particles per unit volume. We call n the **concentration** of particles; its SI unit is m^{-3}. Assume that all the particles move with the same drift velocity with magnitude v_d. In a time interval dt, each particle moves a distance $v_d\, dt$. The particles that flow out of the right end of the shaded cylinder with length $v_d\, dt$ during dt are the particles that were within this cylinder at the beginning of the interval dt. The volume of the cylinder is $A v_d\, dt$, and the number of particles within it is $n A v_d\, dt$. If each particle has a charge q, the charge dQ that flows out of the end of the cylinder during time dt is

$$dQ = q(nAv_d\, dt) = nqv_d A\, dt$$

and the current is

$$I = \frac{dQ}{dt} = nqv_d A$$

The current *per unit cross-sectional area* is called the **current density** J:

$$J = \frac{I}{A} = nqv_d$$

The units of current density are amperes per square meter (A/m^2).

If the moving charges are negative rather than positive, as in Fig. 25.2b, the drift velocity is opposite to $\vec{E}$. But the *current* is still in the same direction as $\vec{E}$ at each point in the conductor. Hence the current I and current density J don't depend on the sign of the charge, and so in the above expressions for I and J we replace the charge q by its absolute value $|q|$:

$$I = \frac{dQ}{dt} = n|q|v_d A \quad \text{(general expression for current)} \quad \text{(25.2)}$$

$$J = \frac{I}{A} = n|q|v_d \quad \text{(general expression for current density)} \quad \text{(25.3)}$$

The current in a conductor is the product of the concentration of moving charged particles, the magnitude of charge of each such particle, the magnitude of the drift velocity, and the cross-sectional area of the conductor.

We can also define a *vector* current density $\vec{J}$ that includes the direction of the drift velocity:

$$\vec{J} = nq\vec{v}_d \quad \text{(vector current density)} \quad \text{(25.4)}$$

There are *no* absolute value signs in Eq. (25.4). If q is positive, $\vec{v}_d$ is in the same direction as $\vec{E}$; if q is negative, $\vec{v}_d$ is opposite to $\vec{E}$. In either case, $\vec{J}$ is in the same direction as $\vec{E}$. Equation (25.3) gives the *magnitude J* of the vector current density $\vec{J}$.

CAUTION **Current density vs. current** Note that current density $\vec{J}$ is a vector, but current I is not. The difference is that the current density $\vec{J}$ describes how charges flow at a certain point, and the vector's direction tells you about the direction of the flow at that point. By contrast, the current I describes how charges flow through an extended object such as a wire. For example, I has the same value at all points in the circuit of Fig. 25.3, but $\vec{J}$ does not: The current density is directed downward in the left-hand side of the loop and upward in the right-hand side. The magnitude of $\vec{J}$ can also vary around a circuit. In Fig. 25.3 the current density magnitude $J = I/A$ is less in the battery (which has a large cross-sectional area A) than in the wires (which have a small cross-sectional area).

In general, a conductor may contain several different kinds of moving charged particles having charges $q_1, q_2, \ldots$, concentrations $n_1, n_2, \ldots$, and drift velocities with magnitudes $v_{d1}, v_{d2}, \ldots$. An example is current flow in an ionic solution (Fig. 25.4). In a sodium chloride solution, current can be carried by both positive sodium ions and negative chlorine ions; the total current I is found by adding up the currents due to each kind of charged particle, using Eq. (25.2). Likewise, the total vector current density $\vec{J}$ is found by using Eq. (25.4) for each kind of charged particle and adding the results.

We will see in Section 25.4 that it is possible to have a current that is *steady* (that is, one that is constant in time) only if the conducting material forms a

25.4 Part of the electric circuit that includes this light bulb passes through a beaker with a solution of sodium chloride. The current in the solution is carried by both positive charges (Na^+ ions) and negative charges (Cl^- ions).

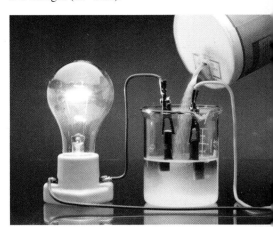

closed loop, called a *complete circuit*. In such a steady situation, the total charge in every segment of the conductor is constant. Hence the rate of flow of charge *out* at one end of a segment at any instant equals the rate of flow of charge *in* at the other end of the segment, and *the current is the same at all cross sections of the circuit*. We'll make use of this observation when we analyze electric circuits later in this chapter.

In many simple circuits, such as flashlights or cordless electric drills, the direction of the current is always the same; this is called *direct current*. But home appliances such as toasters, refrigerators, and televisions use *alternating current,* in which the current continuously changes direction. In this chapter we'll consider direct current only. Alternating current has many special features worthy of detailed study, which we'll examine in Chapter 31.

Example 25.1 | **Current density and drift velocity in a wire**

An 18-gauge copper wire (the size usually used for lamp cords), with a diameter of 1.02 mm, carries a constant current of 1.67 A to a 200-W lamp. The free-electron density in the wire is 8.5×10^{28} per cubic meter. Find (a) the current density and (b) the drift speed.

SOLUTION

IDENTIFY and SET UP: This problem uses the relationships among current I, current density J, and drift speed v_d. We are given I and the wire diameter d, so we use Eq. (25.3) to find J. We use Eq. (25.3) again to find v_d from J and the known electron density n.

EXECUTE: (a) The cross-sectional area is

$$A = \frac{\pi d^2}{4} = \frac{\pi (1.02 \times 10^{-3} \text{ m})^2}{4} = 8.17 \times 10^{-7} \text{ m}^2$$

The magnitude of the current density is then

$$J = \frac{I}{A} = \frac{1.67 \text{ A}}{8.17 \times 10^{-7} \text{ m}^2} = 2.04 \times 10^6 \text{ A/m}^2$$

(b) From Eq. (25.3) for the drift velocity magnitude v_d, we find

$$v_d = \frac{J}{n|q|} = \frac{2.04 \times 10^6 \text{ A/m}^2}{(8.5 \times 10^{28} \text{ m}^{-3})|-1.60 \times 10^{-19} \text{ C}|}$$
$$= 1.5 \times 10^{-4} \text{ m/s} = 0.15 \text{ mm/s}$$

EVALUATE: At this speed an electron would require 6700 s (almost 2 h) to travel 1 m along this wire. The speeds of random motion of the electrons are roughly 10^6 m/s, around 10^{10} times the drift speed. Picture the electrons as bouncing around frantically, with a very slow drift!

Test Your Understanding of Section 25.1 Suppose we replaced the wire in Example 25.1 with 12-gauge copper wire, which has twice the diameter of 18-gauge wire. If the current remains the same, what effect would this have on the magnitude of the drift velocity v_d? (i) none—v_d would be unchanged; (ii) v_d would be twice as great; (iii) v_d would be four times greater; (iv) v_d would be half as great; (v) v_d would be one-fourth as great.

25.2 Resistivity

The current density $\vec{J}$ in a conductor depends on the electric field $\vec{E}$ and on the properties of the material. In general, this dependence can be quite complex. But for some materials, especially metals, at a given temperature, $\vec{J}$ is nearly *directly proportional* to $\vec{E}$, and the ratio of the magnitudes of E and J is constant. This relationship, called Ohm's law, was discovered in 1826 by the German physicist Georg Simon Ohm (1787–1854). The word "law" should actually be in quotation marks, since **Ohm's law,** like the ideal-gas equation and Hooke's law, is an *idealized model* that describes the behavior of some materials quite well but is not a general description of *all* matter. In the following discussion we'll assume that Ohm's law is valid, even though there are many situations in which it is not. The situation is comparable to our representation of the behavior of the static and kinetic friction forces; we treated these friction forces as being directly proportional to the normal force, even though we knew that this was at best an approximate description.

Table 25.1 Resistivities at Room Temperature (20°C)

Substance		ρ ($\Omega \cdot$ m)	Substance		ρ ($\Omega \cdot$ m)
Conductors			**Semiconductors**		
Metals	Silver	1.47×10^{-8}		Pure carbon (graphite)	3.5×10^{-5}
	Copper	1.72×10^{-8}		Pure germanium	0.60
	Gold	2.44×10^{-8}		Pure silicon	2300
	Aluminum	2.75×10^{-8}	**Insulators**		
	Tungsten	5.25×10^{-8}		Amber	5×10^{14}
	Steel	20×10^{-8}		Glass	$10^{10}-10^{14}$
	Lead	22×10^{-8}		Lucite	$>10^{13}$
	Mercury	95×10^{-8}		Mica	$10^{11}-10^{15}$
Alloys	Manganin (Cu 84%, Mn 12%, Ni 4%)	44×10^{-8}		Quartz (fused)	75×10^{16}
	Constantan (Cu 60%, Ni 40%)	49×10^{-8}		Sulfur	10^{15}
	Nichrome	100×10^{-8}		Teflon	$>10^{13}$
				Wood	$10^{8}-10^{11}$

We define the **resistivity** ρ of a material as the ratio of the magnitudes of electric field and current density:

$$\rho = \frac{E}{J} \qquad \text{(definition of resistivity)} \qquad (25.5)$$

The greater the resistivity, the greater the field needed to cause a given current density, or the smaller the current density caused by a given field. From Eq. (25.5) the units of ρ are $(\text{V/m})/(\text{A/m}^2) = \text{V} \cdot \text{m/A}$. As we will discuss in the next section, 1 V/A is called one *ohm* (1 Ω; we use the Greek letter Ω, or omega, which is alliterative with "ohm"). So the SI units for ρ are $\Omega \cdot$ m (ohm-meters). Table 25.1 lists some representative values of resistivity. A perfect conductor would have zero resistivity, and a perfect insulator would have an infinite resistivity. Metals and alloys have the smallest resistivities and are the best conductors. The resistivities of insulators are greater than those of the metals by an enormous factor, on the order of 10^{22}.

The reciprocal of resistivity is **conductivity.** Its units are $(\Omega \cdot \text{m})^{-1}$. Good conductors of electricity have larger conductivity than insulators. Conductivity is the direct electrical analog of thermal conductivity. Comparing Table 25.1 with Table 17.5 (Thermal Conductivities), we note that good electrical conductors, such as metals, are usually also good conductors of heat. Poor electrical conductors, such as ceramic and plastic materials, are also poor thermal conductors. In a metal the free electrons that carry charge in electrical conduction also provide the principal mechanism for heat conduction, so we should expect a correlation between electrical and thermal conductivity. Because of the enormous difference in conductivity between electrical conductors and insulators, it is easy to confine electric currents to well-defined paths or circuits (Fig. 25.5). The variation in *thermal* conductivity is much less, only a factor of 10^3 or so, and it is usually impossible to confine heat currents to that extent.

Semiconductors have resistivities intermediate between those of metals and those of insulators. These materials are important because of the way their resistivities are affected by temperature and by small amounts of impurities.

A material that obeys Ohm's law reasonably well is called an *ohmic* conductor or a *linear* conductor. For such materials, at a given temperature, ρ is a *constant* that does not depend on the value of E. Many materials show substantial departures from Ohm's-law behavior; they are *nonohmic,* or *nonlinear.* In these materials, J depends on E in a more complicated manner.

Analogies with fluid flow can be a big help in developing intuition about electric current and circuits. For example, in the making of wine or maple syrup, the product is sometimes filtered to remove sediments. A pump forces the fluid through the filter under pressure; if the flow rate (analogous to J) is proportional to the pressure difference between the upstream and downstream sides (analogous to E), the behavior is analogous to Ohm's law.

25.5 The copper "wires," or traces, on this circuit board are printed directly onto the surface of the dark-colored insulating board. Even though the traces are very close to each other (only about a millimeter apart), the board has such a high resistivity (and low conductivity) that no current can flow between the traces.

Conducting paths
(traces)

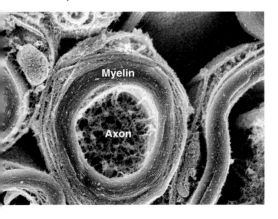

25.6 Variation of resistivity ρ with absolute temperature T for **(a)** a normal metal, **(b)** a semiconductor, and **(c)** a superconductor. In **(a)** the linear approximation to ρ as a function of T is shown as a green line; the approximation agrees exactly at $T = T_0$, where $\rho = \rho_0$.

(a)

(b)

(c)

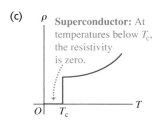

Resistivity and Temperature

The resistivity of a *metallic* conductor nearly always increases with increasing temperature, as shown in Fig. 25.6a. As temperature increases, the ions of the conductor vibrate with greater amplitude, making it more likely that a moving electron will collide with an ion as in Fig. 25.1; this impedes the drift of electrons through the conductor and hence reduces the current. Over a small temperature range (up to 100 C° or so), the resistivity of a metal can be represented approximately by the equation

$$\rho(T) = \rho_0[1 + \alpha(T - T_0)] \qquad \text{(temperature dependence of resistivity)} \qquad (25.6)$$

where ρ_0 is the resistivity at a reference temperature T_0 (often taken as 0°C or 20°C) and $\rho(T)$ is the resistivity at temperature T, which may be higher or lower than T_0. The factor α is called the **temperature coefficient of resistivity.** Some representative values are given in Table 25.2. The resistivity of the alloy manganin is practically independent of temperature.

Table 25.2 Temperature Coefficients of Resistivity (Approximate Values Near Room Temperature)

Material	$\alpha\,[(°C)^{-1}]$	Material	$\alpha\,[(°C)^{-1}]$
Aluminum	0.0039	Lead	0.0043
Brass	0.0020	Manganin	0.00000
Carbon (graphite)	−0.0005	Mercury	0.00088
Constantan	0.00001	Nichrome	0.0004
Copper	0.00393	Silver	0.0038
Iron	0.0050	Tungsten	0.0045

The resistivity of graphite (a nonmetal) *decreases* with increasing temperature, since at higher temperatures, more electrons are "shaken loose" from the atoms and become mobile; hence the temperature coefficient of resistivity of graphite is negative. This same behavior occurs for semiconductors (Fig. 25.6b). Measuring the resistivity of a small semiconductor crystal is therefore a sensitive measure of temperature; this is the principle of a type of thermometer called a *thermistor.*

Some materials, including several metallic alloys and oxides, show a phenomenon called *superconductivity.* As the temperature decreases, the resistivity at first decreases smoothly, like that of any metal. But then at a certain critical temperature T_c a phase transition occurs and the resistivity suddenly drops to zero, as shown in Fig. 25.6c. Once a current has been established in a superconducting ring, it continues indefinitely without the presence of any driving field.

Superconductivity was discovered in 1911 by the Dutch physicist Heike Kamerlingh Onnes (1853–1926). He discovered that at very low temperatures, below 4.2 K, the resistivity of mercury suddenly dropped to zero. For the next 75 years, the highest T_c attained was about 20 K. This meant that superconductivity occurred only when the material was cooled using expensive liquid helium, with a boiling-point temperature of 4.2 K, or explosive liquid hydrogen, with a boiling point of 20.3 K. But in 1986 Karl Müller and Johannes Bednorz discovered an oxide of barium, lanthanum, and copper with a T_c of nearly 40 K, and the race was on to develop "high-temperature" superconducting materials.

By 1987 a complex oxide of yttrium, copper, and barium had been found that has a value of T_c well above the 77 K boiling temperature of liquid nitrogen, a refrigerant that is both inexpensive and safe. The current (2010) record for T_c at atmospheric pressure is 138 K, and materials that are superconductors at room temperature may become a reality. The implications of these discoveries for power-distribution systems, computer design, and transportation are enormous. Meanwhile, superconducting electromagnets cooled by liquid helium are used in particle accelerators and some experimental magnetic-levitation railroads.

Superconductors have other exotic properties that require an understanding of magnetism to explore; we will discuss these further in Chapter 29.

Test Your Understanding of Section 25.2 You maintain a constant electric field inside a piece of semiconductor while lowering the semiconductor's temperature. What happens to the current density in the semiconductor? (i) It increases; (ii) it decreases; (iii) it remains the same.

25.3 Resistance

For a conductor with resistivity ρ, the current density $\vec{J}$ at a point where the electric field is $\vec{E}$ is given by Eq. (25.5), which we can write as

$$\vec{E} = \rho\vec{J} \qquad (25.7)$$

When Ohm's law is obeyed, ρ is constant and independent of the magnitude of the electric field, so $\vec{E}$ is directly proportional to $\vec{J}$. Often, however, we are more interested in the total current in a conductor than in $\vec{J}$ and more interested in the potential difference between the ends of the conductor than in $\vec{E}$. This is so largely because current and potential difference are much easier to measure than are $\vec{J}$ and $\vec{E}$.

Suppose our conductor is a wire with uniform cross-sectional area A and length L, as shown in Fig. 25.7. Let V be the potential difference between the higher-potential and lower-potential ends of the conductor, so that V is positive. The *direction* of the current is always from the higher-potential end to the lower-potential end. That's because current in a conductor flows in the direction of $\vec{E}$, no matter what the sign of the moving charges (Fig. 25.2), and because $\vec{E}$ points in the direction of *decreasing* electric potential (see Section 23.2). As the current flows through the potential difference, electric potential energy is lost; this energy is transferred to the ions of the conducting material during collisions.

We can also relate the *value* of the current I to the potential difference between the ends of the conductor. If the magnitudes of the current density $\vec{J}$ and the electric field $\vec{E}$ are uniform throughout the conductor, the total current I is given by $I = JA$, and the potential difference V between the ends is $V = EL$. When we solve these equations for J and E, respectively, and substitute the results in Eq. (25.7), we obtain

$$\frac{V}{L} = \frac{\rho I}{A} \quad \text{or} \quad V = \frac{\rho L}{A}I \qquad (25.8)$$

This shows that when ρ is constant, the total current I is proportional to the potential difference V.

The ratio of V to I for a particular conductor is called its **resistance** R:

$$R = \frac{V}{I} \qquad (25.9)$$

Comparing this definition of R to Eq. (25.8), we see that the resistance R of a particular conductor is related to the resistivity ρ of its material by

$$R = \frac{\rho L}{A} \qquad \text{(relationship between resistance and resistivity)} \qquad (25.10)$$

If ρ is constant, as is the case for ohmic materials, then so is R.

The equation

$$V = IR \qquad \text{(relationship among voltage, current, and resistance)} \qquad (25.11)$$

is often called Ohm's law, but it is important to understand that the real content of Ohm's law is the direct proportionality (for some materials) of V to I or of J to E.

PhET: Resistance in a Wire

25.7 A conductor with uniform cross section. The current density is uniform over any cross section, and the electric field is constant along the length.

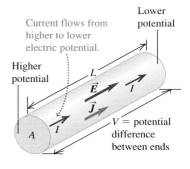

Current flows from higher to lower electric potential.

Higher potential

Lower potential

L

$\vec{E}$

I

$\vec{J}$

A

I

V = potential difference between ends

Equation (25.9) or (25.11) *defines* resistance R for *any* conductor, whether or not it obeys Ohm's law, but only when R is constant can we correctly call this relationship Ohm's law.

Interpreting Resistance

Equation (25.10) shows that the resistance of a wire or other conductor of uniform cross section is directly proportional to its length and inversely proportional to its cross-sectional area. It is also proportional to the resistivity of the material of which the conductor is made.

The flowing-fluid analogy is again useful. In analogy to Eq. (25.10), a narrow water hose offers more resistance to flow than a fat one, and a long hose has more resistance than a short one (Fig. 25.8). We can increase the resistance to flow by stuffing the hose with cotton or sand; this corresponds to increasing the resistivity. The flow rate is approximately proportional to the pressure difference between the ends. Flow rate is analogous to current, and pressure difference is analogous to potential difference ("voltage"). Let's not stretch this analogy too far, though; the water flow rate in a pipe is usually *not* proportional to its cross-sectional area (see Section 14.6).

The SI unit of resistance is the **ohm,** equal to one volt per ampere ($1\ \Omega = 1\ \text{V/A}$). The *kilohm* ($1\ \text{k}\Omega = 10^3\ \Omega$) and the *megohm* ($1\ \text{M}\Omega = 10^6\ \Omega$) are also in common use. A 100-m length of 12-gauge copper wire, the size usually used in household wiring, has a resistance at room temperature of about $0.5\ \Omega$. A 100-W, 120-V light bulb has a resistance (at operating temperature) of $140\ \Omega$. If the same current I flows in both the copper wire and the light bulb, the potential difference $V = IR$ is much greater across the light bulb, and much more potential energy is lost per charge in the light bulb. This lost energy is converted by the light bulb filament into light and heat. You don't want your household wiring to glow white-hot, so its resistance is kept low by using wire of low resistivity and large cross-sectional area.

Because the resistivity of a material varies with temperature, the resistance of a specific conductor also varies with temperature. For temperature ranges that are not too great, this variation is approximately a linear relationship, analogous to Eq. (25.6):

$$R(T) = R_0[1 + \alpha(T - T_0)] \tag{25.12}$$

In this equation, $R(T)$ is the resistance at temperature T and R_0 is the resistance at temperature T_0, often taken to be 0°C or 20°C. The *temperature coefficient of resistance* α is the same constant that appears in Eq. (25.6) if the dimensions L and A in Eq. (25.10) do not change appreciably with temperature; this is indeed the case for most conducting materials (see Problem 25.67). Within the limits of validity of Eq. (25.12), the *change* in resistance resulting from a temperature change $T - T_0$ is given by $R_0\alpha(T - T_0)$.

A circuit device made to have a specific value of resistance between its ends is called a **resistor.** Resistors in the range 0.01 to $10^7\ \Omega$ can be bought off the shelf. Individual resistors used in electronic circuitry are often cylindrical, a few millimeters in diameter and length, with wires coming out of the ends. The resistance may be marked with a standard code using three or four color bands near one end (Fig. 25.9), according to the scheme shown in Table 25.3. The first two bands (starting with the band nearest an end) are digits, and the third is a power-of-10 multiplier, as shown in Fig. 25.9. For example, green–violet–red means $57 \times 10^2\ \Omega$, or $5.7\ \text{k}\Omega$. The fourth band, if present, indicates the precision (tolerance) of the value; no band means $\pm 20\%$, a silver band $\pm 10\%$, and a gold band $\pm 5\%$. Another important characteristic of a resistor is the maximum *power* it can dissipate without damage. We'll return to this point in Section 25.5.

25.8 A long fire hose offers substantial resistance to water flow. To make water pass through the hose rapidly, the upstream end of the hose must be at much higher pressure than the end where the water emerges. In an analogous way, there must be a large potential difference between the ends of a long wire in order to cause a substantial electric current through the wire.

25.9 This resistor has a resistance of $5.7\ \text{k}\Omega$ with a precision (tolerance) of $\pm 10\%$.

Second digit Multiplier
First digit Tolerance

Table 25.3 Color Codes for Resistors

Color	Value as Digit	Value as Multiplier
Black	0	1
Brown	1	10
Red	2	10^2
Orange	3	10^3
Yellow	4	10^4
Green	5	10^5
Blue	6	10^6
Violet	7	10^7
Gray	8	10^8
White	9	10^9

25.10 Current–voltage relationships for two devices. Only for a resistor that obeys Ohm's law as in **(a)** is current I proportional to voltage V.

(a)

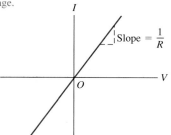

Ohmic resistor (e.g., typical metal wire): At a given temperature, current is proportional to voltage.

Slope $= \dfrac{1}{R}$

(b)

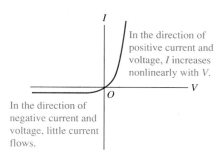

Semiconductor diode: a nonohmic resistor

In the direction of positive current and voltage, I increases nonlinearly with V.

In the direction of negative current and voltage, little current flows.

For a resistor that obeys Ohm's law, a graph of current as a function of potential difference (voltage) is a straight line (Fig. 25.10a). The slope of the line is $1/R$. If the sign of the potential difference changes, so does the sign of the current produced; in Fig. 25.7 this corresponds to interchanging the higher- and lower-potential ends of the conductor, so the electric field, current density, and current all reverse direction. In devices that do not obey Ohm's law, the relationship of voltage to current may not be a direct proportion, and it may be different for the two directions of current. Figure 25.10b shows the behavior of a semiconductor *diode*, a device used to convert alternating current to direct current and to perform a wide variety of logic functions in computer circuitry. For positive potentials V of the anode (one of two terminals of the diode) with respect to the cathode (the other terminal), I increases exponentially with increasing V; for negative potentials the current is extremely small. Thus a positive V causes a current to flow in the positive direction, but a potential difference of the other sign causes little or no current. Hence a diode acts like a one-way valve in a circuit.

Example 25.2 **Electric field, potential difference, and resistance in a wire**

The 18-gauge copper wire of Example 25.1 has a cross-sectional area of $8.20 \times 10^{-7}\,\text{m}^2$. It carries a current of 1.67 A. Find (a) the electric-field magnitude in the wire; (b) the potential difference between two points in the wire 50.0 m apart; (c) the resistance of a 50.0-m length of this wire.

SOLUTION

IDENTIFY and SET UP: We are given the cross-sectional area A and current I. Our target variables are the electric-field magnitude E, potential difference V, and resistance R. The current density is $J = I/A$. We find E from Eq. (25.5), $E = \rho J$ (Table 25.1 gives the resistivity ρ for copper). The potential difference is then the product of E and the length of the wire. We can use either Eq. (25.10) or Eq. (25.11) to find R.

EXECUTE: (a) From Table 25.1, $\rho = 1.72 \times 10^{-8}\,\Omega\cdot\text{m}$. Hence, using Eq. (25.5),

$$E = \rho J = \frac{\rho I}{A} = \frac{(1.72 \times 10^{-8}\,\Omega\cdot\text{m})(1.67\,\text{A})}{8.20 \times 10^{-7}\,\text{m}^2}$$

$$= 0.0350\,\text{V/m}$$

(b) The potential difference is

$$V = EL = (0.0350\,\text{V/m})(50.0\,\text{m}) = 1.75\,\text{V}$$

(c) From Eq. (25.10) the resistance of 50.0 m of this wire is

$$R = \frac{\rho L}{A} = \frac{(1.72 \times 10^{-8}\,\Omega\cdot\text{m})(50.0\,\text{m})}{8.20 \times 10^{-7}\,\text{m}^2} = 1.05\,\Omega$$

Alternatively, we can find R using Eq. (25.11):

$$R = \frac{V}{I} = \frac{1.75\,\text{V}}{1.67\,\text{A}} = 1.05\,\Omega$$

EVALUATE: We emphasize that the resistance of the wire is *defined* to be the ratio of voltage to current. If the wire is made of nonohmic material, then R is different for different values of V but is always given by $R = V/I$. Resistance is also always given by $R = \rho L/A$; if the material is nonohmic, ρ is not constant but depends on E (or, equivalently, on $V = EL$).

Example 25.3 **Temperature dependence of resistance**

Suppose the resistance of a copper wire is 1.05 Ω at 20°C. Find the resistance at 0°C and 100°C.

SOLUTION

IDENTIFY and SET UP: We are given the resistance $R_0 = 1.05\ \Omega$ at a reference temperature $T_0 = 20°C$. We use Eq. (25.12) to find the resistances at $T = 0°C$ and $T = 100°C$ (our target variables). taking the temperature coefficient of resistivity from Table 25.2.

EXECUTE: From Table 25.2, $\alpha = 0.00393\ (C°)^{-1}$ for copper. Then from Eq. (25.12),

$$R = R_0[1 + \alpha(T - T_0)]$$
$$= (1.05\ \Omega)\{1 + [0.00393\ (C°)^{-1}][0°C - 20°C]\}$$
$$= 0.97\ \Omega \text{ at } T = 0°C$$

$$R = (1.05\ \Omega)\{1 + [0.00393\ (C°)^{-1}][100°C - 20°C]\}$$
$$= 1.38\ \Omega \text{ at } T = 100°C$$

EVALUATE: The resistance at 100°C is greater than that at 0°C by a factor of $(1.38\ \Omega)/(0.97\ \Omega) = 1.42$: Raising the temperature of copper wire from 0°C to 100°C increases its resistance by 42%. From Eq. (25.11), $V = IR$, this means that 42% more voltage is required to produce the same current at 100°C than at 0°C. Designers of electric circuits that must operate over a wide temperature range must take this substantial effect into account.

Test Your Understanding of Section 25.3 Suppose you increase the voltage across the copper wire in Examples 25.2 and 25.3. The increased voltage causes more current to flow, which makes the temperature of the wire increase. (The same thing happens to the coils of an electric oven or a toaster when a voltage is applied to them. We'll explore this issue in more depth in Section 25.5.) If you double the voltage across the wire, the current in the wire increases. By what factor does it increase? (i) 2; (ii) greater than 2; (iii) less than 2.

25.4 Electromotive Force and Circuits

25.11 If an electric field is produced inside a conductor that is *not* part of a complete circuit, current flows for only a very short time.

(a) An electric field E_1 produced inside an isolated conductor causes a current.

(b) The current causes charge to build up at the ends.

The charge buildup produces an opposing field $\vec{E}_2$, thus reducing the current.

(c) After a very short time $\vec{E}_2$ has the same magnitude as $\vec{E}_1$; then the total field is $E_{total} = 0$ and the current stops completely.

For a conductor to have a steady current, it must be part of a path that forms a closed loop or **complete circuit.** Here's why. If you establish an electric field $\vec{E}_1$ inside an isolated conductor with resistivity ρ that is *not* part of a complete circuit, a current begins to flow with current density $\vec{J} = \vec{E}_1/\rho$ (Fig. 25.11a). As a result a net positive charge quickly accumulates at one end of the conductor and a net negative charge accumulates at the other end (Fig. 25.11b). These charges themselves produce an electric field $\vec{E}_2$ in the direction opposite to $\vec{E}_1$, causing the total electric field and hence the current to decrease. Within a very small fraction of a second, enough charge builds up on the conductor ends that the total electric field $\vec{E} = \vec{E}_1 + \vec{E}_2 = 0$ inside the conductor. Then $\vec{J} = 0$ as well, and the current stops altogether (Fig. 25.11c). So there can be no steady motion of charge in such an *incomplete* circuit.

To see how to maintain a steady current in a *complete* circuit, we recall a basic fact about electric potential energy: If a charge q goes around a complete circuit and returns to its starting point, the potential energy must be the same at the end of the round trip as at the beginning. As described in Section 25.3, there is always a *decrease* in potential energy when charges move through an ordinary conducting material with resistance. So there must be some part of the circuit in which the potential energy *increases*.

The problem is analogous to an ornamental water fountain that recycles its water. The water pours out of openings at the top, cascades down over the terraces and spouts (moving in the direction of decreasing gravitational potential energy), and collects in a basin in the bottom. A pump then lifts it back to the top (increasing the potential energy) for another trip. Without the pump, the water would just fall to the bottom and stay there.

Electromotive Force

In an electric circuit there must be a device somewhere in the loop that acts like the water pump in a water fountain (Fig. 25.12). In this device a charge travels

Pikachu, go,
Fantasy Myst (unreleased)

"uphill," from lower to higher potential energy, even though the electrostatic force is trying to push it from higher to lower potential energy. The direction of current in such a device is from lower to higher potential, just the opposite of what happens in an ordinary conductor. The influence that makes current flow from lower to higher potential is called **electromotive force** (abbreviated **emf** and pronounced "ee-em-eff"). This is a poor term because emf is *not* a force but an energy-per-unit-charge quantity, like potential. The SI unit of emf is the same as that for potential, the volt (1 V = 1 J/C). A typical flashlight battery has an emf of 1.5 V; this means that the battery does 1.5 J of work on every coulomb of charge that passes through it. We'll use the symbol $\mathcal{E}$ (a script capital E) for emf.

Every complete circuit with a steady current must include some device that provides emf. Such a device is called a **source of emf.** Batteries, electric generators, solar cells, thermocouples, and fuel cells are all examples of sources of emf. All such devices convert energy of some form (mechanical, chemical, thermal, and so on) into electric potential energy and transfer it into the circuit to which the device is connected. An *ideal* source of emf maintains a constant potential difference between its terminals, independent of the current through it. We define electromotive force quantitatively as the magnitude of this potential difference. As we will see, such an ideal source is a mythical beast, like the frictionless plane and the massless rope. We will discuss later how real-life sources of emf differ in their behavior from this idealized model.

Figure 25.13 is a schematic diagram of an ideal source of emf that maintains a potential difference between conductors *a* and *b*, called the *terminals* of the device. Terminal *a*, marked +, is maintained at *higher* potential than terminal *b*, marked −. Associated with this potential difference is an electric field $\vec{E}$ in the region around the terminals, both inside and outside the source. The electric field inside the device is directed from *a* to *b*, as shown. A charge *q* within the source experiences an electric force $\vec{F}_e = q\vec{E}$. But the source also provides an additional influence, which we represent as a nonelectrostatic force $\vec{F}_n$. This force, operating inside the device, pushes charge from *b* to *a* in an "uphill" direction against the electric force $\vec{F}_e$. Thus $\vec{F}_n$ maintains the potential difference between the terminals. If $\vec{F}_n$ were not present, charge would flow between the terminals until the potential difference was zero. The origin of the additional influence $\vec{F}_n$ depends on the kind of source. In a generator it results from magnetic-field forces on moving charges. In a battery or fuel cell it is associated with diffusion processes and varying electrolyte concentrations resulting from chemical reactions. In an electrostatic machine such as a Van de Graaff generator (see Fig. 22.26), an actual mechanical force is applied by a moving belt or wheel.

If a positive charge *q* is moved from *b* to *a* inside the source, the nonelectrostatic force $\vec{F}_n$ does a positive amount of work $W_n = q\mathcal{E}$ on the charge. This displacement is *opposite* to the electrostatic force $\vec{F}_e$, so the potential energy associated with the charge *increases* by an amount equal to qV_{ab}, where $V_{ab} = V_a - V_b$ is the (positive) potential of point *a* with respect to point *b*. For the ideal source of emf that we've described, $\vec{F}_e$ and $\vec{F}_n$ are equal in magnitude but opposite in direction, so the total work done on the charge *q* is zero; there is an increase in potential energy but *no* change in the kinetic energy of the charge. It's like lifting a book from the floor to a high shelf at constant speed. The increase in potential energy is just equal to the nonelectrostatic work W_n, so $q\mathcal{E} = qV_{ab}$, or

$$V_{ab} = \mathcal{E} \qquad \text{(ideal source of emf)} \qquad (25.13)$$

Now let's make a complete circuit by connecting a wire with resistance *R* to the terminals of a source (Fig. 25.14). The potential difference between terminals *a* and *b* sets up an electric field within the wire; this causes current to flow around the loop from *a* toward *b*, from higher to lower potential. Where the wire bends, equal amounts of positive and negative charge persist on the "inside" and "outside"

25.12 Just as a water fountain requires a pump, an electric circuit requires a source of electromotive force to sustain a steady current.

25.13 Schematic diagram of a source of emf in an "open-circuit" situation. The electric-field force $\vec{F}_e = q\vec{E}$ and the nonelectrostatic force $\vec{F}_n$ are shown for a positive charge *q*.

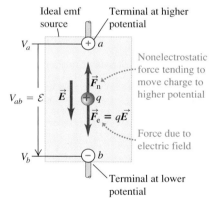

When the emf source is not part of a closed circuit, $F_n = F_e$ and there is no net motion of charge between the terminals.

Mastering**PHYSICS**

PhET: Battery Voltage
PhET: Signal Circuit
ActivPhysics 12.1: DC Series Circuits (Qualitative)

25.14 Schematic diagram of an ideal source of emf in a complete circuit. The electric-field force $\vec{F}_e = q\vec{E}$ and the non-electrostatic force $\vec{F}_n$ are shown for a positive charge q. The current is in the direction from a to b in the external circuit and from b to a within the source.

Potential across terminals creates electric field in circuit, causing charges to move.

Ideal emf source

V_a

$\vec{E}$

$(+)\, a$

$\vec{F}_n$

$V_{ab} = \mathcal{E}$ $\vec{E}$ $\vec{E}$ I

$\vec{F}_e$

V_b $(-)\, b$

$\vec{E}$

I

When a real (as opposed to ideal) emf source is connected to a circuit, V_{ab} and thus F_e fall, so that $F_n > F_e$ and $\vec{F}_n$ does work on the charges.

Application **Danger: Electric Ray!**
Electric rays deliver electric shocks to stun their prey and to discourage predators. (In ancient Rome, physicians practiced a primitive form of electroconvulsive therapy by placing electric rays on their patients to cure headaches and gout.) The shocks are produced by specialized flattened cells called electroplaques. Such a cell moves ions across membranes to produce an emf of about 0.05 V. Thousands of electroplaques are stacked on top of each other, so their emfs add to a total of as much as 200 V. These stacks make up more than half of an electric ray's body mass. A ray can use these to deliver an impressive current of up to 30 A for a few milliseconds.

of the bend. These charges exert the forces that cause the current to follow the bends in the wire.

From Eq. (25.11) the potential difference between the ends of the wire in Fig. 25.14 is given by $V_{ab} = IR$. Combining with Eq. (25.13), we have

$$\mathcal{E} = V_{ab} = IR \qquad \text{(ideal source of emf)} \qquad (25.14)$$

That is, when a positive charge q flows around the circuit, the potential *rise* $\mathcal{E}$ as it passes through the ideal source is numerically equal to the potential *drop* $V_{ab} = IR$ as it passes through the remainder of the circuit. Once $\mathcal{E}$ and R are known, this relationship determines the current in the circuit.

CAUTION **Current is not "used up" in a circuit** It's a common misconception that in a closed circuit, current is something that squirts out of the positive terminal of a battery and is consumed or "used up" by the time it reaches the negative terminal. In fact the current is the *same* at every point in a simple loop circuit like that in Fig. 25.14, even if the thickness of the wires is different at different points in the circuit. This happens because charge is conserved (that is, it can be neither created nor destroyed) and because charge cannot accumulate in the circuit devices we have described. If charge did accumulate, the potential differences would change with time. It's like the flow of water in an ornamental fountain; water flows out of the top of the fountain at the same rate at which it reaches the bottom, no matter what the dimensions of the fountain. None of the water is "used up" along the way!

Internal Resistance

Real sources of emf in a circuit don't behave in exactly the way we have described; the potential difference across a real source in a circuit is *not* equal to the emf as in Eq. (25.14). The reason is that charge moving through the material of any real source encounters *resistance*. We call this the **internal resistance** of the source, denoted by r. If this resistance behaves according to Ohm's law, r is constant and independent of the current I. As the current moves through r, it experiences an associated drop in potential equal to Ir. Thus, when a current is flowing through a source from the negative terminal b to the positive terminal a, the potential difference V_{ab} between the terminals is

$$V_{ab} = \mathcal{E} - Ir \qquad \begin{array}{l}\text{(terminal voltage, source}\\ \text{with internal resistance)}\end{array} \qquad (25.15)$$

The potential V_{ab}, called the **terminal voltage,** is less than the emf $\mathcal{E}$ because of the term Ir representing the potential drop across the internal resistance r. Expressed another way, the increase in potential energy qV_{ab} as a charge q moves from b to a within the source is now less than the work $q\mathcal{E}$ done by the nonelectrostatic force $\vec{F}_n$, since some potential energy is lost in traversing the internal resistance.

A 1.5-V battery has an emf of 1.5 V, but the terminal voltage V_{ab} of the battery is equal to 1.5 V only if no current is flowing through it so that $I = 0$ in Eq. (25.15). If the battery is part of a complete circuit through which current is flowing, the terminal voltage will be less than 1.5 V. *For a real source of emf, the terminal voltage equals the emf only if no current is flowing through the source* (Fig. 25.15). Thus we can describe the behavior of a source in terms of two properties: an emf $\mathcal{E}$, which supplies a constant potential difference independent of current, in series with an internal resistance r.

The current in the external circuit connected to the source terminals a and b is still determined by $V_{ab} = IR$. Combining this with Eq. (25.15), we find

$$\mathcal{E} - Ir = IR \quad \text{or} \quad I = \frac{\mathcal{E}}{R + r} \qquad \begin{array}{l}\text{(current, source with}\\ \text{internal resistance)}\end{array} \qquad (25.16)$$

That is, the current equals the source emf divided by the *total* circuit resistance $(R + r)$.

> **CAUTION** **A battery is not a "current source"** You might have thought that a battery or other source of emf always produces the same current, no matter what circuit it's used in. Equation (25.16) shows that this isn't so! The greater the resistance R of the external circuit, the less current the source will produce. It's analogous to pushing an object through a thick, viscous liquid such as oil or molasses; if you exert a certain steady push (emf), you can move a small object at high speed (small R, large I) or a large object at low speed (large R, small I).

Symbols for Circuit Diagrams

An important part of analyzing any electric circuit is drawing a schematic *circuit diagram.* Table 25.4 shows the usual symbols used in circuit diagrams. We will use these symbols extensively in this chapter and the next. We usually assume that the wires that connect the various elements of the circuit have negligible resistance; from Eq. (25.11), $V = IR$, the potential difference between the ends of such a wire is zero.

Table 25.4 includes two *meters* that are used to measure the properties of circuits. Idealized meters do not disturb the circuit in which they are connected. A **voltmeter,** introduced in Section 23.2, measures the potential difference between its terminals; an idealized voltmeter has infinitely large resistance and measures potential difference without having any current diverted through it. An ammeter measures the current passing through it; an idealized **ammeter** has zero resistance and has no potential difference between its terminals. Because meters act as part of the circuit in which they are connected, these properties are important to remember.

25.15 The emf of this battery—that is, the terminal voltage when it's not connected to anything—is 12 V. But because the battery has internal resistance, the terminal voltage of the battery is less than 12 V when it is supplying current to a light bulb.

Table 25.4 Symbols for Circuit Diagrams

	Conductor with negligible resistance
R resistor symbol	Resistor
$+ \varepsilon$ source symbol	Source of emf (longer vertical line always represents the positive terminal, usually the terminal with higher potential)
$\varepsilon +$ / $+ \varepsilon$ source with internal resistance	Source of emf with internal resistance r (r can be placed on either side)
V	Voltmeter (measures potential difference between its terminals)
A	Ammeter (measures current through it)

Conceptual Example 25.4 **A source in an open circuit**

Figure 25.16 shows a source (a battery) with emf $\mathcal{E} = 12$ V and internal resistance $r = 2\ \Omega$. (For comparison, the internal resistance of a commercial 12-V lead storage battery is only a few thousandths of an ohm.) The wires to the left of a and to the right of the ammeter A are not connected to anything. Determine the respective readings V_{ab} and I of the idealized voltmeter V and the idealized ammeter A.

25.16 A source of emf in an open circuit.

$$r = 2\ \Omega, \mathcal{E} = 12\text{ V}$$

Continued

SOLUTION

There is *zero* current because there is no complete circuit. (Our idealized voltmeter has an infinitely large resistance, so no current flows through it.) Hence the ammeter reads $I = 0$. Because there is no current through the battery, there is no potential difference across its internal resistance. From Eq. (25.15) with $I = 0$, the potential difference V_{ab} across the battery terminals is equal to the emf. So the voltmeter reads $V_{ab} = \mathcal{E} = 12$ V. The terminal voltage of a real, nonideal source equals the emf *only* if there is no current flowing through the source, as in this example.

Example 25.5 **A source in a complete circuit**

We add a 4-Ω resistor to the battery in Conceptual Example 25.4, forming a complete circuit (Fig. 25.17). What are the voltmeter and ammeter readings V_{ab} and I now?

SOLUTION

IDENTIFY and SET UP: Our target variables are the current I through the circuit $aa'b'b$ and the potential difference V_{ab}. We first find I using Eq. (25.16). To find V_{ab}, we can use either Eq. (25.11) or Eq. (25.15).

25.17 A source of emf in a complete circuit.

EXECUTE: The ideal ammeter has zero resistance, so the total resistance external to the source is $R = 4 \Omega$. From Eq. (25.16), the current through the circuit $aa'b'b$ is then

$$I = \frac{\mathcal{E}}{R + r} = \frac{12 \text{ V}}{4 \Omega + 2 \Omega} = 2 \text{ A}$$

Our idealized conducting wires and the idealized ammeter have zero resistance, so there is no potential difference between points a and a' or between points b and b'; that is, $V_{ab} = V_{a'b'}$. We find V_{ab} by considering a and b as the terminals of the resistor: From Ohm's law, Eq. (25.11), we then have

$$V_{a'b'} = IR = (2 \text{ A})(4 \ \Omega) = 8 \text{ V}$$

Alternatively, we can consider a and b as the terminals of the source. Then, from Eq. (25.15),

$$V_{ab} = \mathcal{E} - Ir = 12 \text{ V} - (2 \text{ A})(2 \ \Omega) = 8 \text{ V}$$

Either way, we see that the voltmeter reading is 8 V.

EVALUATE: With current flowing through the source, the terminal voltage V_{ab} is less than the emf $\mathcal{E}$. The smaller the internal resistance r, the less the difference between V_{ab} and $\mathcal{E}$.

Conceptual Example 25.6 **Using voltmeters and ammeters**

We move the voltmeter and ammeter in Example 25.5 to different positions in the circuit. What are the readings of the ideal voltmeter and ammeter in the situations shown in (a) Fig. 25.18a and (b) Fig. 25.18b?

SOLUTION

(a) The voltmeter now measures the potential difference between points a' and b'. As in Example 25.5, $V_{ab} = V_{a'b'}$, so the voltmeter reads the same as in Example 25.5: $V_{a'b'} = 8$ V.

25.18 Different placements of a voltmeter and an ammeter in a complete circuit.

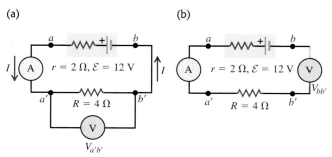

CAUTION **Current in a simple loop** As charges move through a resistor, there is a decrease in electric potential energy, but there is *no* change in the current. *The current in a simple loop is the same at every point;* it is not "used up" as it moves through a resistor. Hence the ammeter in Fig. 25.17 ("downstream" of the 4-Ω resistor) and the ammeter in Fig. 25.18b ("upstream" of the resistor) both read $I = 2$ A.

(b) There is no current through the ideal voltmeter because it has infinitely large resistance. Since the voltmeter is now part of the circuit, there is no current at all in the circuit, and the ammeter reads $I = 0$.

The voltmeter measures the potential difference $V_{bb'}$ between points b and b'. Since $I = 0$, the potential difference across the resistor is $V_{a'b'} = IR = 0$, and the potential difference between the ends a and a' of the idealized ammeter is also zero. So $V_{bb'}$ is equal to V_{ab}, the terminal voltage of the source. As in Conceptual Example 25.4, there is no current, so the terminal voltage equals the emf, and the voltmeter reading is $V_{ab} = \mathcal{E} = 12$ V.

This example shows that ammeters and voltmeters are circuit elements, too. Moving the voltmeter from the position in Fig. 25.18a to that in Fig. 25.18b makes large changes in the current and potential differences in the circuit. If you want to measure the potential difference between two points in a circuit without disturbing the circuit, use a voltmeter as in Fig. 25.17 or 25.18a, *not* as in Fig. 25.18b.

Example 25.7 A source with a short circuit

In the circuit of Example 25.5 we replace the 4-Ω resistor with a zero-resistance conductor. What are the meter readings now?

SOLUTION

IDENTIFY and SET UP: Figure 25.19 shows the new circuit. Our target variables are again I and V_{ab}. There is now a zero-resistance path between points a and b, through the lower loop, so the potential difference between these points must be zero.

25.19 Our sketch for this problem.

EXECUTE: We must have $V_{ab} = IR = I(0) = 0$, no matter what the current. We can therefore find the current I from Eq. (25.15):

$$V_{ab} = \mathcal{E} - Ir = 0$$

$$I = \frac{\mathcal{E}}{r} = \frac{12\ \mathrm{V}}{2\ \Omega} = 6\ \mathrm{A}$$

EVALUATE: The current has a different value than in Example 25.5, even though the same battery is used; the current depends on both the internal resistance r and the resistance of the external circuit.

The situation here is called a *short circuit*. The external-circuit resistance is zero, because terminals of the battery are connected directly to each other. The short-circuit current is equal to the emf $\mathcal{E}$ divided by the internal resistance r. *Warning:* Short circuits can be dangerous! An automobile battery or a household power line has very small internal resistance (much less than in these examples), and the short-circuit current can be great enough to melt a small wire or cause a storage battery to explode.

Potential Changes Around a Circuit

The net change in potential energy for a charge q making a round trip around a complete circuit must be zero. Hence the net change in *potential* around the circuit must also be zero; in other words, the algebraic sum of the potential differences and emfs around the loop is zero. We can see this by rewriting Eq. (25.16) in the form

$$\mathcal{E} - Ir - IR = 0$$

A potential gain of $\mathcal{E}$ is associated with the emf, and potential drops of Ir and IR are associated with the internal resistance of the source and the external circuit, respectively. Figure 25.20 is a graph showing how the potential varies as we go around the complete circuit of Fig. 25.17. The horizontal axis doesn't necessarily represent actual distances, but rather various points in the loop. If we take the potential to be zero at the negative terminal of the battery, then we have a rise $\mathcal{E}$ and a drop Ir in the battery and an additional drop IR in the external resistor, and as we finish our trip around the loop, the potential is back where it started.

In this section we have considered only situations in which the resistances are ohmic. If the circuit includes a nonlinear device such as a diode (see Fig. 25.10b), Eq. (25.16) is still valid but cannot be solved algebraically because R is not a constant. In such a situation, the current I can be found by using numerical techniques.

Finally, we remark that Eq. (25.15) is not always an adequate representation of the behavior of a source. The emf may not be constant, and what we have described as an internal resistance may actually be a more complex voltage–current relationship that doesn't obey Ohm's law. Nevertheless, the concept of internal resistance frequently provides an adequate description of batteries, generators, and other energy converters. The principal difference between a fresh flashlight battery and an old one is not in the emf, which decreases only slightly with use, but in the internal resistance, which may increase from less than an ohm when the battery is fresh to as much as 1000 Ω or more after long use. Similarly, a car battery can deliver less current to the starter motor on a cold morning than when the battery is warm, not because the emf is appreciably less but because the internal resistance increases with decreasing temperature.

25.20 Potential rises and drops in a circuit.

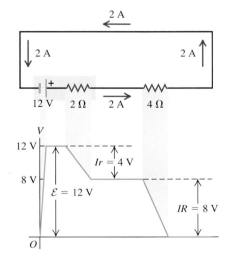

Test Your Understanding of Section 25.4 Rank the following circuits in order from highest to lowest current. (i) a 1.4-Ω resistor connected to a 1.5-V battery that has an internal resistance of 0.10 Ω; (ii) a 1.8-Ω resistor connected to a 4.0-V battery that has a terminal voltage of 3.6 V but an unknown internal resistance; (iii) an unknown resistor connected to a 12.0-V battery that has an internal resistance of 0.20 Ω and a terminal voltage of 11.0 V. ❙

25.5 Energy and Power in Electric Circuits

25.21 The power input to the circuit element between a and b is $P = (V_a - V_b)I = V_{ab}I$.

MasteringPHYSICS

PhET: Battery-Resistor Circuit
PhET: Circuit Construction Kit (AC+DC)
PhET: Circuit Construction Kit (DC Only)
PhET: Ohm's Law

Let's now look at some energy and power relationships in electric circuits. The box in Fig. 25.21 represents a circuit element with potential difference $V_a - V_b = V_{ab}$ between its terminals and current I passing through it in the direction from a toward b. This element might be a resistor, a battery, or something else; the details don't matter. As charge passes through the circuit element, the electric field does work on the charge. In a source of emf, additional work is done by the force $\vec{F}_n$ that we mentioned in Section 25.4.

As an amount of charge q passes through the circuit element, there is a change in potential energy equal to qV_{ab}. For example, if $q > 0$ and $V_{ab} = V_a - V_b$ is positive, potential energy decreases as the charge "falls" from potential V_a to lower potential V_b. The moving charges don't gain *kinetic* energy, because the current (the rate of charge flow) out of the circuit element must be the same as the current into the element. Instead, the quantity qV_{ab} represents energy transferred into the circuit element. This situation occurs in the coils of a toaster or electric oven, in which electrical energy is converted to thermal energy.

If the potential at a is lower than at b, then V_{ab} is negative and there is a net transfer of energy *out* of the circuit element. The element then acts as a source, delivering electrical energy into the circuit to which it is attached. This is the usual situation for a battery, which converts chemical energy into electrical energy and delivers it to the external circuit. Thus qV_{ab} can denote either a quantity of energy delivered to a circuit element or a quantity of energy extracted from that element.

In electric circuits we are most often interested in the *rate* at which energy is either delivered to or extracted from a circuit element. If the current through the element is I, then in a time interval dt an amount of charge $dQ = I\,dt$ passes through the element. The potential energy change for this amount of charge is $V_{ab}\,dQ = V_{ab}I\,dt$. Dividing this expression by dt, we obtain the *rate* at which energy is transferred either into or out of the circuit element. The time rate of energy transfer is *power*, denoted by P, so we write

$$P = V_{ab}I \qquad \text{(rate at which energy is delivered to or extracted from a circuit element)} \qquad (25.17)$$

The unit of V_{ab} is one volt, or one joule per coulomb, and the unit of I is one ampere, or one coulomb per second. Hence the unit of $P = V_{ab}I$ is one watt, as it should be:

$$(1\ \text{J/C})(1\ \text{C/s}) = 1\ \text{J/s} = 1\ \text{W}$$

Let's consider a few special cases.

Power Input to a Pure Resistance

If the circuit element in Fig. 25.21 is a resistor, the potential difference is $V_{ab} = IR$. From Eq. (25.17) the electrical power delivered to the resistor by the circuit is

$$P = V_{ab}I = I^2R = \frac{V_{ab}^2}{R} \qquad \text{(power delivered to a resistor)} \qquad (25.18)$$

In this case the potential at *a* (where the current enters the resistor) is always higher than that at *b* (where the current exits). Current enters the higher-potential terminal of the device, and Eq. (25.18) represents the rate of transfer of electric potential energy *into* the circuit element.

What becomes of this energy? The moving charges collide with atoms in the resistor and transfer some of their energy to these atoms, increasing the internal energy of the material. Either the temperature of the resistor increases or there is a flow of heat out of it, or both. In any of these cases we say that energy is *dissipated* in the resistor at a rate I^2R. Every resistor has a *power rating,* the maximum power the device can dissipate without becoming overheated and damaged. Some devices, such as electric heaters, are designed to get hot and transfer heat to their surroundings. But if the power rating is exceeded, even such a device may melt or even explode.

Power Output of a Source

The upper rectangle in Fig. 25.22a represents a source with emf $\mathcal{E}$ and internal resistance r, connected by ideal (resistanceless) conductors to an external circuit represented by the lower box. This could describe a car battery connected to one of the car's headlights (Fig. 25.22b). Point *a* is at higher potential than point *b*, so $V_a > V_b$ and V_{ab} is positive. Note that the current I is *leaving* the source at the higher-potential terminal (rather than entering there). Energy is being delivered to the external circuit, at a rate given by Eq. (25.17):

$$P = V_{ab}I$$

For a source that can be described by an emf $\mathcal{E}$ and an internal resistance r, we may use Eq. (25.15):

$$V_{ab} = \mathcal{E} - Ir$$

Multiplying this equation by I, we find

$$P = V_{ab}I = \mathcal{E}I - I^2r \qquad (25.19)$$

What do the terms $\mathcal{E}I$ and I^2r mean? In Section 25.4 we defined the emf $\mathcal{E}$ as the work per unit charge performed on the charges by the nonelectrostatic force as the charges are pushed "uphill" from *b* to *a* in the source. In a time dt, a charge $dQ = I\,dt$ flows through the source; the work done on it by this nonelectrostatic force is $\mathcal{E}\,dQ = \mathcal{E}I\,dt$. Thus $\mathcal{E}I$ is the *rate* at which work is done on the circulating charges by whatever agency causes the nonelectrostatic force in the source. This term represents the rate of conversion of nonelectrical energy to electrical energy within the source. The term I^2r is the rate at which electrical energy is *dissipated* in the internal resistance of the source. The difference $\mathcal{E}I - I^2r$ is the *net* electrical power output of the source—that is, the rate at which the source delivers electrical energy to the remainder of the circuit.

Power Input to a Source

Suppose that the lower rectangle in Fig. 25.22a is itself a source, with an emf *larger* than that of the upper source and with its emf opposite to that of the upper source. Figure 25.23 shows a practical example, an automobile battery (the upper circuit element) being charged by the car's alternator (the lower element). The current I in the circuit is then *opposite* to that shown in Fig. 25.22; the lower source is pushing current backward through the upper source. Because of this reversal of current, instead of Eq. (25.15) we have for the upper source

$$V_{ab} = \mathcal{E} + Ir$$

and instead of Eq. (25.19), we have

$$P = V_{ab}I = \mathcal{E}I + I^2r \qquad (25.20)$$

25.22 Energy conversion in a simple circuit.

(a) Diagrammatic circuit

- The emf source converts nonelectrical to electrical energy at a rate $\mathcal{E}I$.
- Its internal resistance *dissipates* energy at a rate I^2r.
- The difference $\mathcal{E}I - I^2r$ is its power output.

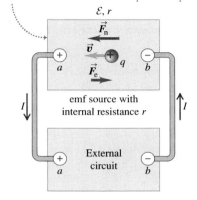

(b) A real circuit of the type shown in (a)

25.23 When two sources are connected in a simple loop circuit, the source with the larger emf delivers energy to the other source.

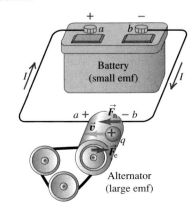

Work is being done *on,* rather than *by,* the agent that causes the nonelectrostatic force in the upper source. There is a conversion of electrical energy into nonelectrical energy in the upper source at a rate $\mathcal{E}I$. The term I^2r in Eq. (25.20) is again the rate of dissipation of energy in the internal resistance of the upper source, and the sum $\mathcal{E}I + I^2r$ is the total electrical power *input* to the upper source. This is what happens when a rechargeable battery (a storage battery) is connected to a charger. The charger supplies electrical energy to the battery; part of it is converted to chemical energy, to be reconverted later, and the remainder is dissipated (wasted) in the battery's internal resistance, warming the battery and causing a heat flow out of it. If you have a power tool or laptop computer with a rechargeable battery, you may have noticed that it gets warm while it is charging.

Problem-Solving Strategy 25.1   Power and Energy in Circuits

IDENTIFY *the relevant concepts:* The ideas of electric power input and output can be applied to any electric circuit. Many problems will ask you to explicitly consider power or energy.

SET UP *the problem* using the following steps:
1. Make a drawing of the circuit.
2. Identify the circuit elements, including sources of emf and resistors. We will introduce other circuit elements later, including capacitors (Chapter 26) and inductors (Chapter 30).
3. Identify the target variables. Typically they will be the power input or output for each circuit element, or the total amount of energy put into or taken out of a circuit element in a given time.

EXECUTE *the solution* as follows:
1. A source of emf $\mathcal{E}$ delivers power $\mathcal{E}I$ into a circuit when current I flows through the source in the direction from $-$ to $+$. (For example, energy is converted from chemical energy in a battery, or from mechanical energy in a generator.) In this case there is a *positive* power output to the circuit or, equivalently, a *negative* power input to the source.
2. A source of emf takes power $\mathcal{E}I$ from a circuit when current passes through the source from $+$ to $-$. (This occurs in charging a storage battery, when electrical energy is converted to chemical energy.) In this case there is a *negative* power output

to the circuit or, equivalently, a *positive* power input to the source.
3. There is always a *positive* power input to a resistor through which current flows, irrespective of the direction of current flow. This process removes energy from the circuit, converting it to heat at the rate $VI = I^2R = V^2/R$, where V is the potential difference across the resistor.
4. Just as in item 3, there always is a positive power input to the internal resistance r of a source through which current flows, irrespective of the direction of current flow. This process likewise removes energy from the circuit, converting it into heat at the rate I^2r.
5. If the power into or out of a circuit element is constant, the energy delivered to or extracted from that element is the product of power and elapsed time. (In Chapter 26 we will encounter situations in which the power is not constant. In such cases, calculating the total energy requires an integral over the relevant time interval.)

EVALUATE *your answer:* Check your results; in particular, check that energy is conserved. This conservation can be expressed in either of two forms: "net power input = net power output" or "the algebraic sum of the power inputs to the circuit elements is zero."

Example 25.8   Power input and output in a complete circuit

For the circuit that we analyzed in Example 25.5, find the rates of energy conversion (chemical to electrical) and energy dissipation in the battery, the rate of energy dissipation in the 4-Ω resistor, and the battery's net power output.

SOLUTION

IDENTIFY and SET UP: Figure 25.24 shows the circuit, gives values of quantities known from Example 25.5, and indicates how we find the target variables. We use Eq. (25.19) to find the battery's net power output, the rate of chemical-to-electrical energy conversion, and the rate of energy dissipation in the battery's internal resistance. We use Eq. (25.18) to find the power delivered to (and dissipated in) the 4-Ω resistor.

EXECUTE: From the first term in Eq. (25.19), the rate of energy conversion in the battery is

$$\mathcal{E}I = (12 \text{ V})(2 \text{ A}) = 24 \text{ W}$$

25.24 Our sketch for this problem.

From the second term in Eq. (25.19), the rate of dissipation of energy in the battery is

$$I^2r = (2 \text{ A})^2(2 \text{ }\Omega) = 8 \text{ W}$$

The *net* electrical power output of the battery is the difference between these: $\mathcal{E}I - I^2r = 16$ W. From Eq. (25.18), the electrical power input to, and the equal rate of dissipation of electrical energy in, the 4-Ω resistor are

$$V_{a'b'}I = (8\text{ V})(2\text{ A}) = 16\text{ W} \quad \text{and}$$
$$I^2R = (2\text{ A})^2(4\text{ }\Omega) = 16\text{ W}$$

EVALUATE: The rate $V_{a'b'}I$ at which energy is supplied to the 4-Ω resistor equals the rate I^2R at which energy is dissipated there. This is also equal to the battery's net power output: $P = V_{ab}I = (8\text{ V})(2\text{ A}) = 16$ W. In summary, the rate at which the source of emf supplies energy is $\mathcal{E}I = 24$ W, of which $I^2r = 8$ W is dissipated in the battery's internal resistor and $I^2R = 16$ W is dissipated in the external resistor.

Example 25.9   Increasing the resistance

Suppose we replace the external 4-Ω resistor in Fig. 25.24 with an 8-Ω resistor. How does this affect the electrical power dissipated in this resistor?

SOLUTION

IDENTIFY and SET UP: Our target variable is the power dissipated in the resistor to which the battery is connected. The situation is the same as in Example 25.8, but with a higher external resistance R.

EXECUTE: According to Eq. (25.18), the power dissipated in the resistor is $P = I^2R$. You might conclude that making the resistance R twice as great as in Example 25.8 should also make the power twice as great, or $2(16\text{ W}) = 32$ W. If instead you used the formula $P = V_{ab}^2/R$, you might conclude that the power should be one-half as great as in the preceding example, or $(16\text{ W})/2 = 8$ W. Which answer is correct?

In fact, *both* of these answers are *incorrect*. The first is wrong because changing the resistance R also changes the current in the circuit (remember, a source of emf does *not* generate the same current in all situations). The second answer is wrong because the potential difference V_{ab} across the resistor changes when the current changes. To get the correct answer, we first find the current just as we did in Example 25.5:

$$I = \frac{\mathcal{E}}{R+r} = \frac{12\text{ V}}{8\text{ }\Omega + 2\text{ }\Omega} = 1.2\text{ A}$$

The greater resistance causes the current to decrease. The potential difference across the resistor is

$$V_{ab} = IR = (1.2\text{ A})(8\text{ }\Omega) = 9.6\text{ V}$$

which is greater than that with the 4-Ω resistor. We can then find the power dissipated in the resistor in either of two ways:

$$P = I^2R = (1.2\text{ A})^2(8\text{ }\Omega) = 12\text{ W} \quad \text{or}$$
$$P = \frac{V_{ab}^2}{R} = \frac{(9.6\text{ V})^2}{8\text{ }\Omega} = 12\text{ W}$$

EVALUATE: Increasing the resistance R causes a *reduction* in the power input to the resistor. In the expression $P = I^2R$ the decrease in current is more important than the increase in resistance; in the expression $P = V_{ab}^2/R$ the increase in resistance is more important than the increase in V_{ab}. This same principle applies to ordinary light bulbs; a 50-W light bulb has a greater resistance than does a 100-W light bulb.

Can you show that replacing the 4-Ω resistor with an 8-Ω resistor decreases both the rate of energy conversion (chemical to electrical) in the battery and the rate of energy dissipation in the battery?

Example 25.10   Power in a short circuit

For the short-circuit situation of Example 25.7, find the rates of energy conversion and energy dissipation in the battery and the net power output of the battery.

SOLUTION

IDENTIFY and SET UP: Our target variables are again the power inputs and outputs associated with the battery. Figure 25.25 shows

25.25 Our sketch for this problem.

the circuit. This is the same situation as in Example 25.8, but now the external resistance R is zero.

EXECUTE: We found in Example 25.7 that the current in this situation is $I = 6$ A. From Eq. (25.19), the rate of energy conversion (chemical to electrical) in the battery is then

$$\mathcal{E}I = (12\text{ V})(6\text{ A}) = 72\text{ W}$$

and the rate of dissipation of energy in the battery is

$$I^2r = (6\text{ A})^2(2\text{ }\Omega) = 72\text{ W}$$

The net power output of the source is $\mathcal{E}I - I^2r = 0$. We get this same result from the expression $P = V_{ab}I$, because the terminal voltage V_{ab} of the source is zero.

EVALUATE: With ideal wires and an ideal ammeter, so that $R = 0$, *all* of the converted energy from the source is dissipated within the source. This is why a short-circuited battery is quickly ruined and may explode.

25.6 Theory of Metallic Conduction

25.26 Random motions of an electron in a metallic crystal **(a)** with zero electric field and **(b)** with an electric field that causes drift. The curvatures of the paths are greatly exaggerated.

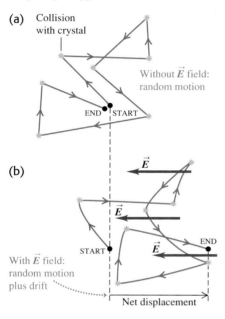

(a) Collision with crystal

Without $\vec{E}$ field: random motion

END START

(b)

$\vec{E}$

$\vec{E}$

START $\vec{E}$ END

With $\vec{E}$ field: random motion plus drift

Net displacement

Mastering**PHYSICS**

PhET: Conductivity

25.27 The motion of a ball rolling down an inclined plane and bouncing off pegs in its path is analogous to the motion of an electron in a metallic conductor with an electric field present.

We can gain additional insight into electrical conduction by looking at the microscopic origin of conductivity. We'll consider a very simple model that treats the electrons as classical particles and ignores their quantum-mechanical behavior in solids. Using this model, we'll derive an expression for the resistivity of a metal. Even though this model is not entirely correct, it will still help you to develop an intuitive idea of the microscopic basis of conduction.

In the simplest microscopic model of conduction in a metal, each atom in the metallic crystal gives up one or more of its outer electrons. These electrons are then free to move through the crystal, colliding at intervals with the stationary positive ions. The motion of the electrons is analogous to the motion of molecules of a gas moving through a porous bed of sand.

If there is no electric field, the electrons move in straight lines between collisions, the directions of their velocities are random, and on average they never get anywhere (Fig. 25.26a). But if an electric field is present, the paths curve slightly because of the acceleration caused by electric-field forces. Figure 25.26b shows a few paths of an electron in an electric field directed from right to left. As we mentioned in Section 25.1, the average speed of random motion is of the order of 10^6 m/s, while the average drift speed is *much* slower, of the order of 10^{-4} m/s. The average time between collisions is called the **mean free time,** denoted by τ. Figure 25.27 shows a mechanical analog of this electron motion.

We would like to derive from this model an expression for the resistivity ρ of a material, defined by Eq. (25.5):

$$\rho = \frac{E}{J} \qquad (25.21)$$

where E and J are the magnitudes of electric field and current density, respectively. The current density $\vec{J}$ is in turn given by Eq. (25.4):

$$\vec{J} = nq\vec{v}_d \qquad (25.22)$$

where n is the number of free electrons per unit volume, $q = -e$ is the charge of each, and $\vec{v}_d$ is their average drift velocity.

We need to relate the drift velocity $\vec{v}_d$ to the electric field $\vec{E}$. The value of $\vec{v}_d$ is determined by a steady-state condition in which, on average, the velocity *gains* of the charges due to the force of the $\vec{E}$ field are just balanced by the velocity *losses* due to collisions. To clarify this process, let's imagine turning on the two effects one at a time. Suppose that before time $t = 0$ there is no field. The electron motion is then completely random. A typical electron has velocity $\vec{v}_0$ at time $t = 0$, and the value of $\vec{v}_0$ averaged over many electrons (that is, the initial velocity of an average electron) is zero: $(\vec{v}_0)_{av} = 0$. Then at time $t = 0$ we turn on a constant electric field $\vec{E}$. The field exerts a force $\vec{F} = q\vec{E}$ on each charge, and this causes an acceleration $\vec{a}$ in the direction of the force, given by

$$\vec{a} = \frac{\vec{F}}{m} = \frac{q\vec{E}}{m}$$

where m is the electron mass. *Every* electron has this acceleration.

We wait for a time τ, the average time between collisions, and then "turn on" the collisions. An electron that has velocity $\vec{v}_0$ at time $t = 0$ has a velocity at time $t = \tau$ equal to

$$\vec{v} = \vec{v}_0 + \vec{a}\tau$$

The velocity $\vec{v}_{av}$ of an *average* electron at this time is the sum of the averages of the two terms on the right. As we have pointed out, the initial velocity $\vec{v}_0$ is zero for an average electron, so

$$\vec{v}_{av} = \vec{a}\tau = \frac{q\tau}{m}\vec{E} \qquad (25.23)$$

After time $t = \tau$, the tendency of the collisions to decrease the velocity of an average electron (by means of randomizing collisions) just balances the tendency of the $\vec{E}$ field to increase this velocity. Thus the velocity of an average electron, given by Eq. (25.23), is maintained over time and is equal to the drift velocity $\vec{v}_d$:

$$\vec{v}_d = \frac{q\tau}{m}\vec{E}$$

Now we substitute this equation for the drift velocity $\vec{v}_d$ into Eq. (25.22):

$$\vec{J} = nq\vec{v}_d = \frac{nq^2\tau}{m}\vec{E}$$

Comparing this with Eq. (25.21), which we can rewrite as $\vec{J} = \vec{E}/\rho$, and substituting $q = -e$ for an electron, we see that the resistivity ρ is given by

$$\rho = \frac{m}{ne^2\tau} \qquad (25.24)$$

If n and τ are independent of $\vec{E}$, then the resistivity is independent of $\vec{E}$ and the conducting material obeys Ohm's law.

Turning the interactions on one at a time may seem artificial. But the derivation would come out the same if each electron had its own clock and the $t = 0$ times were different for different electrons. If τ is the average time between collisions, then $\vec{v}_d$ is still the average electron drift velocity, even though the motions of the various electrons aren't actually correlated in the way we postulated.

What about the temperature dependence of resistivity? In a perfect crystal with no atoms out of place, a correct quantum-mechanical analysis would let the free electrons move through the crystal with no collisions at all. But the atoms vibrate about their equilibrium positions. As the temperature increases, the amplitudes of these vibrations increase, collisions become more frequent, and the mean free time τ decreases. So this theory predicts that the resistivity of a metal increases with temperature. In a superconductor, roughly speaking, there are no inelastic collisions, τ is infinite, and the resistivity ρ is zero.

In a pure semiconductor such as silicon or germanium, the number of charge carriers per unit volume, n, is not constant but increases very rapidly with increasing temperature. This increase in n far outweighs the decrease in the mean free time, and in a semiconductor the resistivity always decreases rapidly with increasing temperature. At low temperatures, n is very small, and the resistivity becomes so large that the material can be considered an insulator.

Electrons gain energy between collisions through the work done on them by the electric field. During collisions they transfer some of this energy to the atoms of the material of the conductor. This leads to an increase in the material's internal energy and temperature; that's why wires carrying current get warm. If the electric field in the material is large enough, an electron can gain enough energy between collisions to knock off electrons that are normally bound to atoms in the material. These can then knock off more electrons, and so on, leading to an avalanche of current. This is the basis of dielectric breakdown in insulators (see Section 24.4).

Example 25.11 Mean free time in copper

Calculate the mean free time between collisions in copper at room temperature.

SOLUTION

IDENTIFY and SET UP: We can obtain an expression for mean free time τ in terms of n, ρ, e, and m by rearranging Eq. (25.24). From Example 25.1 and Table 25.1, for copper $n = 8.5 \times 10^{28}$ m^{-3} and $\rho = 1.72 \times 10^{-8}$ $\Omega \cdot$m. In addition, $e = 1.60 \times 10^{-19}$ C and $m = 9.11 \times 10^{-31}$ kg for electrons.

EXECUTE: From Eq. (25.24), we get

$$\tau = \frac{m}{ne^2\rho}$$

$$= \frac{9.11 \times 10^{-31}\text{ kg}}{(8.5 \times 10^{28}\text{ m}^{-3})(1.60 \times 10^{-19}\text{ C})^2(1.72 \times 10^{-8}\ \Omega \cdot \text{m})}$$

$$= 2.4 \times 10^{-14}\text{ s}$$

EVALUATE: The mean free time is the average time between collisions for a given electron. Taking the reciprocal of this time, we find that each electron averages $1/\tau = 4.2 \times 10^{13}$ collisions per second!

Test Your Understanding of Section 25.6 Which of the following factors will, if increased, make it more difficult to produce a certain amount of current in a conductor? (There may be more than one correct answer.) (i) the mass of the moving charged particles in the conductor; (ii) the number of moving charged particles per cubic meter; (iii) the amount of charge on each moving particle; (iv) the average time between collisions for a typical moving charged particle. ❙

Current and current density: Current is the amount of charge flowing through a specified area, per unit time. The SI unit of current is the ampere (1 A = 1 C/s). The current I through an area A depends on the concentration n and charge q of the charge carriers, as well as on the magnitude of their drift velocity $\vec{v}_d$. The current density is current per unit cross-sectional area. Current is usually described in terms of a flow of positive charge, even when the charges are actually negative or of both signs. (See Example 25.1.)

$$I = \frac{dQ}{dt} = n|q|v_d A \quad (25.2)$$

$$\vec{J} = nq\vec{v}_d \quad (25.4)$$

Resistivity: The resistivity ρ of a material is the ratio of the magnitudes of electric field and current density. Good conductors have small resistivity; good insulators have large resistivity. Ohm's law, obeyed approximately by many materials, states that ρ is a constant independent of the value of E. Resistivity usually increases with temperature; for small temperature changes this variation is represented approximately by Eq. (25.6), where α is the temperature coefficient of resistivity.

$$\rho = \frac{E}{J} \quad (25.5)$$

$$\rho(T) = \rho_0[1 + \alpha(T - T_0)] \quad (25.6)$$

Metal: ρ increases with increasing T.

Resistors: The potential difference V across a sample of material that obeys Ohm's law is proportional to the current I through the sample. The ratio $V/I = R$ is the resistance of the sample. The SI unit of resistance is the ohm (1 Ω = 1 V/A). The resistance of a cylindrical conductor is related to its resistivity ρ, length L, and cross-sectional area A. (See Examples 25.2 and 25.3.)

$$V = IR \quad (25.11)$$

$$R = \frac{\rho L}{A} \quad (25.10)$$

Circuits and emf: A complete circuit has a continuous current-carrying path. A complete circuit carrying a steady current must contain a source of electromotive force (emf) $\mathcal{E}$. The SI unit of electromotive force is the volt (1 V). Every real source of emf has some internal resistance r, so its terminal potential difference V_{ab} depends on current. (See Examples 25.4–25.7.)

$$V_{ab} = \mathcal{E} - Ir \quad (25.15)$$
(source with internal resistance)

Energy and power in circuits: A circuit element with a potential difference $V_a - V_b = V_{ab}$ and a current I puts energy into a circuit if the current direction is from lower to higher potential in the device, and it takes energy out of the circuit if the current is opposite. The power P equals the product of the potential difference and the current. A resistor always takes electrical energy out of a circuit. (See Examples 25.8–25.10.)

$$P = V_{ab}I \quad (25.17)$$
(general circuit element)

$$P = V_{ab}I = I^2 R = \frac{V_{ab}^2}{R} \quad (25.18)$$
(power into a resistor)

Conduction in metals: The microscopic basis of conduction in metals is the motion of electrons that move freely through the metallic crystal, bumping into ion cores in the crystal. In a crude classical model of this motion, the resistivity of the material can be related to the electron mass, charge, speed of random motion, density, and mean free time between collisions. (See Example 25.11.)

BRIDGING PROBLEM **Resistivity, Temperature, and Power**

A toaster using a Nichrome heating element operates on 120 V. When it is switched on at 20°C, the heating element carries an initial current of 1.35 A. A few seconds later the current reaches the steady value of 1.23 A. (a) What is the final temperature of the element? The average value of the temperature coefficient of resistivity for Nichrome over the relevant temperature range is 4.5×10^{-4} $(C°)^{-1}$. (b) What is the power dissipated in the heating element initially and when the current reaches 1.23 A?

SOLUTION GUIDE

See MasteringPhysics® study area for a Video Tutor solution.

IDENTIFY and SET UP

1. A heating element acts as a resistor that converts electrical energy into thermal energy. The resistivity ρ of Nichrome depends on temperature, and hence so does the resistance $R = \rho L/A$ of the heating element and the current $I = V/R$ that it carries.

2. We are given $V = 120$ V and the initial and final values of I. Select an equation that will allow you to find the initial and

final values of resistance, and an equation that relates resistance to temperature [the target variable in part (a)].

3. The power P dissipated in the heating element depends on I and V. Select an equation that will allow you to calculate the initial and final values of P.

EXECUTE

4. Combine your equations from step 2 to give a relationship between the initial and final values of I and the initial and final temperatures (20°C and T_{final}).

5. Solve your expression from step 4 for T_{final}.

6. Use your equation from step 3 to find the initial and final powers.

EVALUATE

7. Is the final temperature greater than or less than 20°C? Does this make sense?

8. Is the final resistance greater than or less than the initial resistance? Again, does this make sense?

9. Is the final power greater than or less than the initial power? Does this agree with your observations in step 8?

Problems

For instructor-assigned homework, go to www.masteringphysics.com

•, ••, •••: Problems of increasing difficulty. **CP**: Cumulative problems incorporating material from earlier chapters. **CALC**: Problems requiring calculus. **BIO**: Biosciences problems.

DISCUSSION QUESTIONS

Q25.1 The definition of resistivity ($\rho = E/J$) implies that an electric field exists inside a conductor. Yet we saw in Chapter 21 that there can be no electric field inside a conductor. Is there a contradiction here? Explain.

Q25.2 A cylindrical rod has resistance R. If we triple its length and diameter, what is its resistance, in terms of R?

Q25.3 A cylindrical rod has resistivity ρ. If we triple its length and diameter, what is its resistivity, in terms of ρ?

Q25.4 Two copper wires with different diameters are joined end to end. If a current flows in the wire combination, what happens to electrons when they move from the larger-diameter wire into the smaller-diameter wire? Does their drift speed increase, decrease, or stay the same? If the drift speed changes, what is the force that causes the change? Explain your reasoning.

Q25.5 When is a 1.5-V AAA battery *not* actually a 1.5-V battery? That is, when do its terminals provide a potential difference of less than 1.5 V?

Q25.6 Can the potential difference between the terminals of a battery ever be opposite in direction to the emf? If it can, give an example. If it cannot, explain why not.

Q25.7 A rule of thumb used to determine the internal resistance of a source is that it is the open-circuit voltage divided by the short-circuit current. Is this correct? Why or why not?

Q25.8 Batteries are always labeled with their emf; for instance, an AA flashlight battery is labeled "1.5 volts." Would it also be appropriate to put a label on batteries stating how much current they provide? Why or why not?

Q25.9 We have seen that a coulomb is an enormous amount of charge; it is virtually impossible to place a charge of 1 C on an object. Yet, a current of 10 A, 10 C/s, is quite reasonable. Explain this apparent discrepancy.

Q25.10 Electrons in an electric circuit pass through a resistor. The wire on either side of the resistor has the same diameter. (a) How does the drift speed of the electrons before entering the resistor compare to the speed after leaving the resistor? Explain your reasoning. (b) How does the potential energy for an electron before entering the resistor compare to the potential energy after leaving the resistor? Explain your reasoning.

Q25.11 Current causes the temperature of a real resistor to increase. Why? What effect does this heating have on the resistance? Explain.

Q25.12 Which of the graphs in Fig. Q25.12 best illustrates the current I in a real resistor as a function of the potential difference V across it? Explain. (*Hint*: See Discussion Question Q25.11.)

Figure **Q25.12**

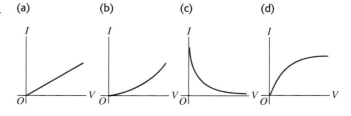

Q25.13 Why does an electric light bulb nearly always burn out just as you turn on the light, almost never while the light is shining?

Q25.14 A light bulb glows because it has resistance. The brightness of a light bulb increases with the electrical power dissipated in the bulb. (a) In the circuit shown in Fig. Q25.14a, the two bulbs A and B are identical. Compared to bulb A, does bulb B glow more brightly, just as brightly, or less brightly? Explain your reasoning. (b) Bulb B is removed from the circuit and the circuit is completed as shown in Fig. Q25.14b. Compared to the brightness of bulb A in Fig. Q25.14a, does bulb A now glow more brightly, just as brightly, or less brightly? Explain your reasoning.

Figure **Q25.14**

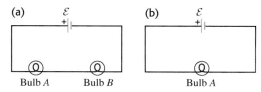

Q25.15 (See Discussion Question Q25.14.) An ideal ammeter A is placed in a circuit with a battery and a light bulb as shown in Fig. Q25.15a, and the ammeter reading is noted. The circuit is then reconnected as in Fig. Q25.15b, so that the positions of the ammeter and light bulb are reversed. (a) How does the ammeter reading in the situation shown in Fig. Q25.15a compare to the reading in the situation shown in Fig. Q25.15b? Explain your reasoning. (b) In which situation does the light bulb glow more brightly? Explain your reasoning.

Figure **Q25.15**

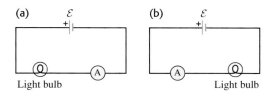

Q25.16 (See Discussion Question Q25.14.) Will a light bulb glow more brightly when it is connected to a battery as shown in Fig. Q25.16a, in which an ideal ammeter A is placed in the circuit, or when it is connected as shown in Fig. 25.16b, in which an ideal voltmeter V is placed in the circuit? Explain your reasoning.

Figure **Q25.16**

Q25.17 The energy that can be extracted from a storage battery is always less than the energy that goes into it while it is being charged. Why?

Q25.18 Eight flashlight batteries in series have an emf of about 12 V, similar to that of a car battery. Could they be used to start a car with a dead battery? Why or why not?

Q25.19 Small aircraft often have 24-V electrical systems rather than the 12-V systems in automobiles, even though the electrical power requirements are roughly the same in both applications. The explanation given by aircraft designers is that a 24-V system weighs less than a 12-V system because thinner wires can be used. Explain why this is so.

Q25.20 Long-distance, electric-power, transmission lines always operate at very high voltage, sometimes as much as 750 kV. What are the advantages of such high voltages? What are the disadvantages?

Q25.21 Ordinary household electric lines in North America usually operate at 120 V. Why is this a desirable voltage, rather than a value considerably larger or smaller? On the other hand, automobiles usually have 12-V electrical systems. Why is this a desirable voltage?

Q25.22 A fuse is a device designed to break a circuit, usually by melting when the current exceeds a certain value. What characteristics should the material of the fuse have?

Q25.23 High-voltage power supplies are sometimes designed intentionally to have rather large internal resistance as a safety precaution. Why is such a power supply with a large internal resistance safer than a supply with the same voltage but lower internal resistance?

Q25.24 The text states that good thermal conductors are also good electrical conductors. If so, why don't the cords used to connect toasters, irons, and similar heat-producing appliances get hot by conduction of heat from the heating element?

EXERCISES

Section 25.1 Current

25.1 • **Lightning Strikes.** During lightning strikes from a cloud to the ground, currents as high as 25,000 A can occur and last for about 40 μs. How much charge is transferred from the cloud to the earth during such a strike?

25.2 • A silver wire 2.6 mm in diameter transfers a charge of 420 C in 80 min. Silver contains 5.8×10^{28} free electrons per cubic meter. (a) What is the current in the wire? (b) What is the magnitude of the drift velocity of the electrons in the wire?

25.3 • A 5.00-A current runs through a 12-gauge copper wire (diameter 2.05 mm) and through a light bulb. Copper has 8.5×10^{28} free electrons per cubic meter. (a) How many electrons pass through the light bulb each second? (b) What is the current density in the wire? (c) At what speed does a typical electron pass by any given point in the wire? (d) If you were to use wire of twice the diameter, which of the above answers would change? Would they increase or decrease?

25.4 • An 18-gauge copper wire (diameter 1.02 mm) carries a current with a current density of 1.50×10^6 A/m². The density of free electrons for copper is 8.5×10^{28} electrons per cubic meter. Calculate (a) the current in the wire and (b) the drift velocity of electrons in the wire.

25.5 •• Copper has 8.5×10^{28} free electrons per cubic meter. A 71.0-cm length of 12-gauge copper wire that is 2.05 mm in diameter carries 4.85 A of current. (a) How much time does it take for an electron to travel the length of the wire? (b) Repeat part (a) for 6-gauge copper wire (diameter 4.12 mm) of the same length that carries the same current. (c) Generally speaking, how does changing the diameter of a wire that carries a given amount of current affect the drift velocity of the electrons in the wire?

25.6 • Consider the 18-gauge wire in Example 25.1. How many atoms are in 1.00 m³ of copper? With the density of free electrons given in the example, how many free electrons are there per copper atom?

25.7 • **CALC** The current in a wire varies with time according to the relationship $I = 55\ \text{A} - (0.65\ \text{A/s}^2)t^2$. (a) How many coulombs of charge pass a cross section of the wire in the time interval between $t = 0$ and $t = 8.0$ s? (b) What constant current would transport the same charge in the same time interval?

25.8 • Current passes through a solution of sodium chloride. In 1.00 s, 2.68×10^{16} Na$^+$ ions arrive at the negative electrode and 3.92×10^{16} Cl$^-$ ions arrive at the positive electrode. (a) What is the current passing between the electrodes? (b) What is the direction of the current?

25.9 • **BIO** **Transmission of Nerve Impulses.** Nerve cells transmit electric signals through their long tubular axons. These signals propagate due to a sudden rush of Na$^+$ ions, each with charge $+e$, into the axon. Measurements have revealed that typically about 5.6×10^{11} Na$^+$ ions enter each meter of the axon during a time of 10 ms. What is the current during this inflow of charge in a meter of axon?

Section 25.2 Resistivity and Section 25.3 Resistance

25.10 • (a) At room temperature what is the strength of the electric field in a 12-gauge copper wire (diameter 2.05 mm) that is needed to cause a 2.75-A current to flow? (b) What field would be needed if the wire were made of silver instead?

25.11 •• A 1.50-m cylindrical rod of diameter 0.500 cm is connected to a power supply that maintains a constant potential difference of 15.0 V across its ends, while an ammeter measures the current through it. You observe that at room temperature $(20.0°\text{C})$ the ammeter reads 18.5 A, while at 92.0°C it reads 17.2 A. You can ignore any thermal expansion of the rod. Find (a) the resistivity at 20.0°C and (b) the temperature coefficient of resistivity at 20°C for the material of the rod.

25.12 • A copper wire has a square cross section 2.3 mm on a side. The wire is 4.0 m long and carries a current of 3.6 A. The density of free electrons is $8.5 \times 10^{28}/\text{m}^3$. Find the magnitudes of (a) the current density in the wire and (b) the electric field in the wire. (c) How much time is required for an electron to travel the length of the wire?

25.13 • A 14-gauge copper wire of diameter 1.628 mm carries a current of 12.5 mA. (a) What is the potential difference across a 2.00-m length of the wire? (b) What would the potential difference in part (a) be if the wire were silver instead of copper, but all else were the same?

25.14 •• A wire 6.50 m long with diameter of 2.05 mm has a resistance of 0.0290 Ω. What material is the wire most likely made of?

25.15 •• A cylindrical tungsten filament 15.0 cm long with a diameter of 1.00 mm is to be used in a machine for which the temperature will range from room temperature $(20°\text{C})$ up to 120°C. It will carry a current of 12.5 A at all temperatures (consult Tables 25.1 and 25.2). (a) What will be the maximum electric field in this filament, and (b) what will be its resistance with that field? (c) What will be the maximum potential drop over the full length of the filament?

25.16 •• A ductile metal wire has resistance R. What will be the resistance of this wire in terms of R if it is stretched to three times its original length, assuming that the density and resistivity of the material do not change when the wire is stretched? (*Hint:* The amount of metal does not change, so stretching out the wire will affect its cross-sectional area.)

25.17 • In household wiring, copper wire 2.05 mm in diameter is often used. Find the resistance of a 24.0-m length of this wire.

25.18 •• What diameter must a copper wire have if its resistance is to be the same as that of an equal length of aluminum wire with diameter 3.26 mm?

25.19 • You need to produce a set of cylindrical copper wires 3.50 m long that will have a resistance of 0.125 Ω each. What will be the mass of each of these wires?

25.20 • A tightly coiled spring having 75 coils, each 3.50 cm in diameter, is made of insulated metal wire 3.25 mm in diameter. An ohmmeter connected across its opposite ends reads 1.74 Ω. What is the resistivity of the metal?

25.21 • An aluminum cube has sides of length 1.80 m. What is the resistance between two opposite faces of the cube?

25.22 • You apply a potential difference of 4.50 V between the ends of a wire that is 2.50 m in length and 0.654 mm in radius. The resulting current through the wire is 17.6 A. What is the resistivity of the wire?

25.23 • A current-carrying gold wire has diameter 0.84 mm. The electric field in the wire is 0.49 V/m. What are (a) the current carried by the wire; (b) the potential difference between two points in the wire 6.4 m apart; (c) the resistance of a 6.4-m length of this wire?

25.24 • A hollow aluminum cylinder is 2.50 m long and has an inner radius of 3.20 cm and an outer radius of 4.60 cm. Treat each surface (inner, outer, and the two end faces) as an equipotential surface. At room temperature, what will an ohmmeter read if it is connected between (a) the opposite faces and (b) the inner and outer surfaces?

25.25 • (a) What is the resistance of a Nichrome wire at 0.0°C if its resistance is 100.00 Ω at 11.5°C? (b) What is the resistance of a carbon rod at 25.8°C if its resistance is 0.0160 Ω at 0.0°C?

25.26 • A carbon resistor is to be used as a thermometer. On a winter day when the temperature is 4.0°C, the resistance of the carbon resistor is 217.3 Ω. What is the temperature on a spring day when the resistance is 215.8 Ω? (Take the reference temperature T_0 to be 4.0°C.)

25.27 • A strand of wire has resistance 5.60 $\mu\Omega$. Find the net resistance of 120 such strands if they are (a) placed side by side to form a cable of the same length as a single strand, and (b) connected end to end to form a wire 120 times as long as a single strand.

Section 25.4 Electromotive Force and Circuits

25.28 • Consider the circuit shown in Fig. E25.28. The terminal voltage of the 24.0-V battery is 21.2 V. What are (a) the internal resistance r of the battery and (b) the resistance R of the circuit resistor?

Figure **E25.28**

25.29 • A copper transmission cable 100 km long and 10.0 cm in diameter carries a current of 125 A. (a) What is the potential drop across the cable? (b) How much electrical energy is dissipated as thermal energy every hour?

25.30 • An idealized ammeter is connected to a battery as shown in Fig. E25.30. Find (a) the reading of the ammeter, (b) the current through the 4.00-Ω resistor, (c) the terminal voltage of the battery.

Figure **E25.30**

25.31 • An ideal voltmeter V is connected to a 2.0-Ω resistor and a battery with emf 5.0 V and internal resistance 0.5 Ω as shown in Fig. E25.31. (a) What is the current in the 2.0-Ω resistor? (b) What is the terminal voltage of the battery? (c) What is the reading on the voltmeter? Explain your answers.

Figure **E25.31**

0.5 Ω 5.0 V

2.0 Ω

25.32 • The circuit shown in Fig. E25.32 contains two batteries, each with an emf and an internal resistance, and two resistors. Find (a) the current in the circuit (magnitude *and* direction); (b) the terminal voltage V_{ab} of the 16.0-V battery; (c) the potential difference V_{ac} of point *a* with respect to point *c*. (d) Using Fig. 25.20 as a model, graph the potential rises and drops in this circuit.

Figure **E25.32**

1.6 Ω 16.0 V
a   *b*
5.0 Ω   9.0 Ω
1.4 Ω 8.0 V
c

25.33 • When switch S in Fig. E25.33 is open, the voltmeter V of the battery reads 3.08 V. When the switch is closed, the voltmeter reading drops to 2.97 V, and the ammeter A reads 1.65 A. Find the emf, the internal resistance of the battery, and the circuit resistance *R*. Assume that the two meters are ideal, so they don't affect the circuit.

Figure **E25.33**

V

r   ℰ

R
S   A

25.34 • In the circuit of Fig. E25.32, the 5.0-Ω resistor is removed and replaced by a resistor of unknown resistance *R*. When this is done, an ideal voltmeter connected across the points *b* and *c* reads 1.9 V. Find (a) the current in the circuit and (b) the resistance *R*. (c) Graph the potential rises and drops in this circuit (see Fig. 25.20).

25.35 • In the circuit shown in Fig. E25.32, the 16.0-V battery is removed and reinserted with the opposite polarity, so that its negative terminal is now next to point *a*. Find (a) the current in the circuit (magnitude *and* direction); (b) the terminal voltage V_{ba} of the 16.0-V battery; (c) the potential difference V_{ac} of point *a* with respect to point *c*. (d) Graph the potential rises and drops in this circuit (see Fig. 25.20).

25.36 • The following measurements were made on a Thyrite resistor:

I (A)	0.50	1.00	2.00	4.00
V_{ab} (V)	2.55	3.11	3.77	4.58

(a) Graph V_{ab} as a function of *I*. (b) Does Thyrite obey Ohm's law? How can you tell? (c) Graph the resistance $R = V_{ab}/I$ as a function of *I*.

25.37 • The following measurements of current and potential difference were made on a resistor constructed of Nichrome wire:

I (A)	0.50	1.00	2.00	4.00
V_{ab} (V)	1.94	3.88	7.76	15.52

(a) Graph V_{ab} as a function of *I*. (b) Does Nichrome obey Ohm's law? How can you tell? (c) What is the resistance of the resistor in ohms?

25.38 •• The circuit shown in Fig. E25.38 contains two batteries, each with an emf and an internal resistance, and two resistors. Find

(a) the current in the circuit (magnitude and direction) and (b) the terminal voltage V_{ab} of the 16.0-V battery.

Figure **E25.38**

1.6 Ω 16.0 V
a   *b*
5.0 Ω   9.0 Ω
1.4 Ω 8.0 V

Section 25.5 Energy and Power in Electric Circuits

25.39 • **Light Bulbs.** The power rating of a light bulb (such as a 100-W bulb) is the power it dissipates when connected across a 120-V potential difference. What is the resistance of (a) a 100-W bulb and (b) a 60-W bulb? (c) How much current does each bulb draw in normal use?

25.40 • If a "75-W" bulb (see Problem 25.39) is connected across a 220-V potential difference (as is used in Europe), how much power does it dissipate?

25.41 • **European Light Bulb.** In Europe the standard voltage in homes is 220 V instead of the 120 V used in the United States. Therefore a "100-W" European bulb would be intended for use with a 220-V potential difference (see Problem 25.40). (a) If you bring a "100-W" European bulb home to the United States, what should be its U.S. power rating? (b) How much current will the 100-W European bulb draw in normal use in the United States?

25.42 • A battery-powered global positioning system (GPS) receiver operating on 9.0 V draws a current of 0.13 A. How much electrical energy does it consume during 1.5 h?

25.43 • Consider a resistor with length *L*, uniform cross-sectional area *A*, and uniform resistivity ρ that is carrying a current with uniform current density *J*. Use Eq. (25.18) to find the electrical power dissipated per unit volume, *p*. Express your result in terms of (a) *E* and *J*; (b) *J* and ρ; (c) *E* and ρ.

25.44 • **BIO** **Electric Eels.** Electric eels generate electric pulses along their skin that can be used to stun an enemy when they come into contact with it. Tests have shown that these pulses can be up to 500 V and produce currents of 80 mA (or even larger). A typical pulse lasts for 10 ms. What power and how much energy are delivered to the unfortunate enemy with a single pulse, assuming a steady current?

25.45 • **BIO** **Treatment of Heart Failure.** A heart defibrillator is used to enable the heart to start beating if it has stopped. This is done by passing a large current of 12 A through the body at 25 V for a very short time, usually about 3.0 ms. (a) What power does the defibrillator deliver to the body, and (b) how much energy is transferred?

25.46 • Consider the circuit of Fig. E25.32. (a) What is the total rate at which electrical energy is dissipated in the 5.0-Ω and 9.0-Ω resistors? (b) What is the power output of the 16.0-V battery? (c) At what rate is electrical energy being converted to other forms in the 8.0-V battery? (d) Show that the power output of the 16.0-V battery equals the overall rate of dissipation of electrical energy in the rest of the circuit.

25.47 •• The capacity of a storage battery, such as those used in automobile electrical systems, is rated in ampere-hours (A · h). A 50-A · h battery can supply a current of 50 A for 1.0 h, or 25 A for 2.0 h, and so on. (a) What total energy can be supplied by a 12-V, 60-A · h battery if its internal resistance is negligible? (b) What volume (in liters) of gasoline has a total heat of combustion equal to the energy obtained in part (a)? (See Section 17.6; the density of gasoline is 900 kg/m^3.) (c) If a generator with an average electrical power output of 0.45 kW is connected to the battery, how much time will be required for it to charge the battery fully?

25.48 • In the circuit analyzed in Example 25.8 the 4.0-Ω resistor is replaced by a 8.0-Ω resistor, as in Example 25.9. (a) Calculate the rate of conversion of chemical energy to electrical energy in the battery. How does your answer compare to the result calculated in Example 25.8? (b) Calculate the rate of electrical energy dissipation in the internal resistance of the battery. How does your answer compare to the result calculated in Example 25.8? (c) Use the results of parts (a) and (b) to calculate the net power output of the battery. How does your result compare to the electrical power dissipated in the 8.0-Ω resistor as calculated for this circuit in Example 25.9?

25.49 •• A 25.0-Ω bulb is connected across the terminals of a 12.0-V battery having 3.50 Ω of internal resistance. What percentage of the power of the battery is dissipated across the internal resistance and hence is not available to the bulb?

25.50 • An idealized voltmeter is connected across the terminals of a 15.0-V battery, and a 75.0-Ω appliance is also connected across its terminals. If the voltmeter reads 11.3 V: (a) how much power is being dissipated by the appliance, and (b) what is the internal resistance of the battery?

25.51 • In the circuit in Fig. E25.51, find (a) the rate of conversion of internal (chemical) energy to electrical energy within the battery; (b) the rate of dissipation of electrical energy in the battery; (c) the rate of dissipation of electrical energy in the external resistor.

Figure **E25.51**

25.52 •• A typical small flashlight contains two batteries, each having an emf of 1.5 V, connected in series with a bulb having resistance 17 Ω. (a) If the internal resistance of the batteries is negligible, what power is delivered to the bulb? (b) If the batteries last for 5.0 h, what is the total energy delivered to the bulb? (c) The resistance of real batteries increases as they run down. If the initial internal resistance is negligible, what is the combined internal resistance of both batteries when the power to the bulb has decreased to half its initial value? (Assume that the resistance of the bulb is constant. Actually, it will change somewhat when the current through the filament changes, because this changes the temperature of the filament and hence the resistivity of the filament wire.)

25.53 • A "540-W" electric heater is designed to operate from 120-V lines. (a) What is its resistance? (b) What current does it draw? (c) If the line voltage drops to 110 V, what power does the heater take? (Assume that the resistance is constant. Actually, it will change because of the change in temperature.) (d) The heater coils are metallic, so that the resistance of the heater decreases with decreasing temperature. If the change of resistance with temperature is taken into account, will the electrical power consumed by the heater be larger or smaller than what you calculated in part (c)? Explain.

Section 25.6 Theory of Metallic Conduction

25.54 •• Pure silicon contains approximately 1.0×10^{16} free electrons per cubic meter. (a) Referring to Table 25.1, calculate the mean free time τ for silicon at room temperature. (b) Your answer in part (a) is much greater than the mean free time for copper given in Example 25.11. Why, then, does pure silicon have such a high resistivity compared to copper?

PROBLEMS

25.55 • An electrical conductor designed to carry large currents has a circular cross section 2.50 mm in diameter and is 14.0 m long. The resistance between its ends is 0.104 Ω. (a) What is the resistivity of the material? (b) If the electric-field magnitude in the conductor is 1.28 V/m, what is the total current? (c) If the material has 8.5×10^{28} free electrons per cubic meter, find the average drift speed under the conditions of part (b).

25.56 •• A plastic tube 25.0 m long and 3.00 cm in diameter is dipped into a silver solution, depositing a layer of silver 0.100 mm thick uniformly over the outer surface of the tube. If this coated tube is then connected across a 12.0-V battery, what will be the current?

25.57 •• On your first day at work as an electrical technician, you are asked to determine the resistance per meter of a long piece of wire. The company you work for is poorly equipped. You find a battery, a voltmeter, and an ammeter, but no meter for directly measuring resistance (an ohmmeter). You put the leads from the voltmeter across the terminals of the battery, and the meter reads 12.6 V. You cut off a 20.0-m length of wire and connect it to the battery, with an ammeter in series with it to measure the current in the wire. The ammeter reads 7.00 A. You then cut off a 40.0-m length of wire and connect it to the battery, again with the ammeter in series to measure the current. The ammeter reads 4.20 A. Even though the equipment you have available to you is limited, your boss assures you of its high quality: The ammeter has very small resistance, and the voltmeter has very large resistance. What is the resistance of 1 meter of wire?

25.58 • A 2.0-mm length of wire is made by welding the end of a 120-cm-long silver wire to the end of an 80-cm-long copper wire. Each piece of wire is 0.60 mm in diameter. The wire is at room temperature, so the resistivities are as given in Table 25.1. A potential difference of 5.0 V is maintained between the ends of the 2.0-m composite wire. (a) What is the current in the copper section? (b) What is the current in the silver section? (c) What is the magnitude of $\vec{E}$ in the copper? (d) What is the magnitude of $\vec{E}$ in the silver? (e) What is the potential difference between the ends of the silver section of wire?

25.59 • A 3.00-m length of copper wire at 20°C has a 1.20-m-long section with diameter 1.60 mm and a 1.80-m-long section with diameter 0.80 mm. There is a current of 2.5 mA in the 1.60-mm-diameter section. (a) What is the current in the 0.80-mm-diameter section? (b) What is the magnitude of $\vec{E}$ in the 1.60-mm-diameter section? (c) What is the magnitude of $\vec{E}$ in the 0.80-mm-diameter section? (d) What is the potential difference between the ends of the 3.00-m length of wire?

25.60 • **Critical Current Density in Superconductors.** One problem with some of the newer high-temperature superconductors is getting a large enough current density for practical use without causing the resistance to reappear. The maximum current density for which the material will remain a superconductor is called the critical current density of the material. In 1987, IBM research labs had produced thin films with critical current densities of 1.0×10^5 A/cm^2. (a) How much current could an 18-gauge wire (see Example 25.1 in Section 25.1) of this material carry and still remain superconducting? (b) Researchers are trying to develop superconductors with critical current densities of 1.0×10^6 A/cm^2. What diameter cylindrical wire of such a material would be needed to carry 1000 A without losing its superconductivity?

25.61 •• **CP** A Nichrome heating element that has resistance 28.0 Ω is connected to a battery that has emf 96.0 V and internal resistance 1.2 Ω. An aluminum cup with mass 0.130 kg contains 0.200 kg of water. The heating element is placed in the water and the electrical energy dissipated in the resistance of the heating element all goes into the cup and water. The element itself has very small mass. How much time does it take for the temperature of the cup and water to rise from 21.2°C to 34.5°C? (The change of the resistance of the Nichrome due to its temperature change can be neglected.)

25.62 •• A resistor with resistance R is connected to a battery that has emf 12.0 V and internal resistance $r = 0.40\ \Omega$. For what two values of R will the power dissipated in the resistor be 80.0 W?

25.63 •• CP BIO **Struck by Lightning.** Lightning strikes can involve currents as high as 25,000 A that last for about 40 μs. If a person is struck by a bolt of lightning with these properties, the current will pass through his body. We shall assume that his mass is 75 kg, that he is wet (after all, he is in a rainstorm) and therefore has a resistance of 1.0 kΩ, and that his body is all water (which is reasonable for a rough, but plausible, approximation). (a) By how many degrees Celsius would this lightning bolt increase the temperature of 75 kg of water? (b) Given that the internal body temperature is about 37°C, would the person's temperature actually increase that much? Why not? What would happen first?

25.64 •• In the Bohr model of the hydrogen atom, the electron makes 6.0×10^{15} rev/s around the nucleus. What is the average current at a point on the orbit of the electron?

25.65 • CALC A material of resistivity ρ is formed into a solid, truncated cone of height h and radii r_1 and r_2 at either end (Fig. P25.65). (a) Calculate the resistance of the cone between the two flat end faces. (*Hint:* Imagine slicing the cone into very many thin disks, and calculate the resistance of one such disk.) (b) Show that your result agrees with Eq. (25.10) when $r_1 = r_2$.

Figure **P25.65**

25.66 • CALC The region between two concentric conducting spheres with radii a and b is filled with a conducting material with resistivity ρ. (a) Show that the resistance between the spheres is given by

$$R = \frac{\rho}{4\pi}\left(\frac{1}{a} - \frac{1}{b}\right)$$

(b) Derive an expression for the current density as a function of radius, in terms of the potential difference V_{ab} between the spheres. (c) Show that the result in part (a) reduces to Eq. (25.10) when the separation $L = b - a$ between the spheres is small.

25.67 ••• The temperature coefficient of resistance α in Eq. (25.12) equals the temperature coefficient of resistivity α in Eq. (25.6) only if the coefficient of thermal expansion is small. A cylindrical column of mercury is in a vertical glass tube. At 20°C, the length of the mercury column is 12.0 cm. The diameter of the mercury column is 1.6 mm and doesn't change with temperature because glass has a small coefficient of thermal expansion. The coefficient of volume expansion of the mercury is given in Table 17.2, its resistivity at 20°C is given in Table 25.1, and its temperature coefficient of resistivity is given in Table 25.2. (a) At 20°C, what is the resistance between the ends of the mercury column? (b) The mercury column is heated to 60°C. What is the change in its resistivity? (c) What is the change in its length? Explain why the coefficient of volume expansion, rather than the coefficient of linear expansion, determines the change in length. (d) What is the change in its resistance? (*Hint:* Since the percentage changes in ρ and L are small, you may find it helpful to derive from Eq. (25.10) an equation for ΔR in terms of $\Delta\rho$ and ΔL.) (e) What is the temperature coefficient of resistance α for the mercury column, as defined in Eq. (25.12)? How does this value compare with the temperature coefficient of resistivity? Is the effect of the change in length important?

25.68 • (a) What is the potential difference V_{ad} in the circuit of Fig. P25.68? (b) What is the terminal voltage of the 4.00-V battery? (c) A battery with emf 10.30 V and internal resistance 0.50 Ω is inserted in the circuit at d, with its negative terminal connected to the negative terminal of the 8.00-V battery. What is the difference of potential V_{bc} between the terminals of the 4.00-V battery now?

Figure **P25.68**

25.69 • The potential difference across the terminals of a battery is 8.40 V when there is a current of 1.50 A in the battery from the negative to the positive terminal. When the current is 3.50 A in the reverse direction, the potential difference becomes 10.20 V. (a) What is the internal resistance of the battery? (b) What is the emf of the battery?

25.70 •• BIO A person with body resistance between his hands of 10 kΩ accidentally grasps the terminals of a 14-kV power supply. (a) If the internal resistance of the power supply is 2000 Ω, what is the current through the person's body? (b) What is the power dissipated in his body? (c) If the power supply is to be made safe by increasing its internal resistance, what should the internal resistance be for the maximum current in the above situation to be 1.00 mA or less?

25.71 • BIO The average bulk resistivity of the human body (apart from surface resistance of the skin) is about 5.0 $\Omega \cdot$ m. The conducting path between the hands can be represented approximately as a cylinder 1.6 m long and 0.10 m in diameter. The skin resistance can be made negligible by soaking the hands in salt water. (a) What is the resistance between the hands if the skin resistance is negligible? (b) What potential difference between the hands is needed for a lethal shock current of 100 mA? (Note that your result shows that small potential differences produce dangerous currents when the skin is damp.) (c) With the current in part (b), what power is dissipated in the body?

25.72 • A typical cost for electric power is $0.120 per kilowatt-hour. (a) Some people leave their porch light on all the time. What is the yearly cost to keep a 75-W bulb burning day and night? (b) Suppose your refrigerator uses 400 W of power when it's running, and it runs 8 hours a day. What is the yearly cost of operating your refrigerator?

25.73 •• A 12.6-V car battery with negligible internal resistance is connected to a series combination of a 3.2-Ω resistor that obeys Ohm's law and a thermistor that does not obey Ohm's law but instead has a current–voltage relationship $V = \alpha I + \beta I^2$, with $\alpha = 3.8\ \Omega$ and $\beta = 1.3\ \Omega/$A. What is the current through the 3.2-Ω resistor?

25.74 •• A cylindrical copper cable 1.50 km long is connected across a 220.0-V potential difference. (a) What should be its diameter so that it produces heat at a rate of 75.0 W? (b) What is the electric field inside the cable under these conditions?

25.75 •• **A Nonideal Ammeter.** Unlike the idealized ammeter described in Section 25.4, any real ammeter has a nonzero resistance. (a) An ammeter with resistance R_A is connected in series with a resistor R and a battery of emf $\mathcal{E}$ and internal resistance r. The current measured by the ammeter is I_A. Find the current through the circuit if the ammeter is removed so that the battery and the resistor form a complete circuit. Express your answer in terms of I_A, r, R_A, and R. The more "ideal" the ammeter, the smaller the difference between this current and the current I_A. (b) If $R = 3.80\ \Omega$, $\mathcal{E} = 7.50\ V$, and $r = 0.45\ \Omega$, find the maximum value of the ammeter resistance R_A so that I_A is within 1.0% of the current in the circuit when the ammeter is absent. (c) Explain why your answer in part (b) represents a *maximum* value.

25.76 • **CALC** A 1.50-m cylinder of radius 1.10 cm is made of a complicated mixture of materials. Its resistivity depends on the distance x from the left end and obeys the formula $\rho(x) = a + bx^2$, where a and b are constants. At the left end, the resistivity is $2.25 \times 10^{-8}\ \Omega \cdot m$, while at the right end it is $8.50 \times 10^{-8}\ \Omega \cdot m$. (a) What is the resistance of this rod? (b) What is the electric field at its midpoint if it carries a 1.75-A current? (c) If we cut the rod into two 75.0-cm halves, what is the resistance of each half?

25.77 •• According to the U.S. National Electrical Code, copper wire used for interior wiring of houses, hotels, office buildings, and industrial plants is permitted to carry no more than a specified maximum amount of current. The table below shows the maximum current I_{max} for several common sizes of wire with varnished cambric insulation. The "wire gauge" is a standard used to describe the diameter of wires. Note that the larger the diameter of the wire, the *smaller* the wire gauge.

Wire gauge	Diameter (cm)	I_{max} (A)
14	0.163	18
12	0.205	25
10	0.259	30
8	0.326	40
6	0.412	60
5	0.462	65
4	0.519	85

(a) What considerations determine the maximum current-carrying capacity of household wiring? (b) A total of 4200 W of power is to be supplied through the wires of a house to the household electrical appliances. If the potential difference across the group of appliances is 120 V, determine the gauge of the thinnest permissible wire that can be used. (c) Suppose the wire used in this house is of the gauge found in part (b) and has total length 42.0 m. At what rate is energy dissipated in the wires? (d) The house is built in a community where the consumer cost of electric energy is $0.11 per kilowatt-hour. If the house were built with wire of the next larger diameter than that found in part (b), what would be the savings in electricity costs in one year? Assume that the appliances are kept on for an average of 12 hours a day.

25.78 •• **Compact Fluorescent Bulbs.** Compact fluorescent bulbs are much more efficient at producing light than are ordinary incandescent bulbs. They initially cost much more, but they last far longer and use much less electricity. According to one study of these bulbs, a compact bulb that produces as much light as a 100-W incandescent bulb uses only 23 W of power. The compact bulb lasts 10,000 hours, on the average, and costs $11.00, whereas the incandescent bulb costs only $0.75, but lasts just 750 hours. The study assumed that electricity costs $0.080 per kilowatt-hour and that the bulbs are on for 4.0 h per day. (a) What is the total cost (including the price of the bulbs) to run each bulb for 3.0 years? (b) How much do you save over 3.0 years if you use a compact fluorescent bulb instead of an incandescent bulb? (c) What is the resistance of a "100-W" fluorescent bulb? (Remember, it actually uses only 23 W of power and operates across 120 V.)

25.79 • In the circuit of Fig. P25.79, find (a) the current through the 8.0-Ω resistor and (b) the total rate of dissipation of electrical energy in the 8.0-Ω resistor and in the internal resistance of the batteries. (c) In one of the batteries, chemical energy is being converted into electrical energy. In which one is this happening, and at what rate? (d) In one of the batteries, electrical energy is being converted into chemical energy. In which one is this happening, and at what rate? (e) Show that the overall rate of production of electrical energy equals the overall rate of consumption of electrical energy in the circuit.

Figure **P25.79**

25.80 • A lightning bolt strikes one end of a steel lightning rod, producing a 15,000-A current burst that lasts for 65 μs. The rod is 2.0 m long and 1.8 cm in diameter, and its other end is connected to the ground by 35 m of 8.0-mm-diameter copper wire. (a) Find the potential difference between the top of the steel rod and the lower end of the copper wire during the current burst. (b) Find the total energy deposited in the rod and wire by the current burst.

25.81 • A 12.0-V battery has an internal resistance of 0.24 Ω and a capacity of 50.0 A·h (see Exercise 25.47). The battery is charged by passing a 10-A current through it for 5.0 h. (a) What is the terminal voltage during charging? (b) What total electrical energy is supplied to the battery during charging? (c) What electrical energy is dissipated in the internal resistance during charging? (d) The battery is now completely discharged through a resistor, again with a constant current of 10 A. What is the external circuit resistance? (e) What total electrical energy is supplied to the external resistor? (f) What total electrical energy is dissipated in the internal resistance? (g) Why are the answers to parts (b) and (e) not the same?

25.82 • Repeat Problem 25.81 with charge and discharge currents of 30 A. The charging and discharging times will now be 1.7 h rather than 5.0 h. What differences in performance do you see?

25.83 •• **CP** Consider the circuit shown in Fig. P25.83. The emf source has negligible internal resistance. The resistors have resistances $R_1 = 6.00\ \Omega$ and $R_2 = 4.00\ \Omega$. The capacitor has capacitance $C = 9.00\ \mu F$. When the capacitor is fully charged, the magnitude of the charge on its plates is $Q = 36.0\ \mu C$. Calculate the emf $\mathcal{E}$.

Figure **P25.83**

25.84 •• **CP** Consider the circuit shown in Fig. P25.84. The battery has emf 60.0 V and negligible internal resistance. $R_2 = 2.00\ \Omega$, $C_1 = 3.00\ \mu F$, and $C_2 = 6.00\ \mu F$. After the capacitors have attained their final charges, the charge on C_1 is $Q_1 = 18.0\ \mu C$. (a) What is the final charge on C_2? (b) What is the resistance R_1?

Figure **P25.84**

CHALLENGE PROBLEMS

25.85 ••• The *Tolman-Stewart experiment* in 1916 demonstrated that the free charges in a metal have negative charge and provided a quantitative measurement of their charge-to-mass ratio,

Figure **P25.85**

$|q|/m$. The experiment consisted of abruptly stopping a rapidly rotating spool of wire and measuring the potential difference that this produced between the ends of the wire. In a simplified model of this experiment, consider a metal rod of length L that is given a uniform acceleration $\vec{a}$ to the right. Initially the free charges in the metal lag behind the rod's motion, thus setting up an electric field $\vec{E}$ in the rod. In the steady state this field exerts a force on the free charges that makes them accelerate along with the rod. (a) Apply $\sum \vec{F} = m\vec{a}$ to the free charges to obtain an expression for $|q|/m$ in terms of the magnitudes of the induced electric field $\vec{E}$ and the acceleration $\vec{a}$. (b) If all the free charges in the metal rod have the same acceleration, the electric field $\vec{E}$ is the same at all points in the rod. Use this fact to rewrite the expression for $|q|/m$ in terms of the potential V_{bc} between the ends of the rod (Fig. P25.85). (c) If the free charges have negative charge, which end of the rod, b or c, is at higher potential? (d) If the rod is 0.50 m long and the free

charges are electrons (charge $q = -1.60 \times 10^{-19}$ C, mass 9.11×10^{-31} kg), what magnitude of acceleration is required to produce a potential difference of 1.0 mV between the ends of the rod? (e) Discuss why the actual experiment used a rotating spool of thin wire rather than a moving bar as in our simplified analysis.

25.86 ••• CALC A source with emf $\mathcal{E}$ and internal resistance r is connected to an external circuit. (a) Show that the power output of the source is maximum when the current in the circuit is one-half the short-circuit current of the source. (b) If the external circuit consists of a resistance R, show that the power output is maximum when $R = r$ and that the maximum power is $\mathcal{E}^2/4r$.

25.87 ••• CALC The resistivity of a semiconductor can be modified by adding different amounts of impurities. A rod of semiconducting material of length L and cross-sectional area A lies along the x-axis between $x = 0$ and $x = L$. The material obeys Ohm's law, and its resistivity varies along the rod according to $\rho(x) = \rho_0 \exp(-x/L)$. The end of the rod at $x = 0$ is at a potential V_0 greater than the end at $x = L$. (a) Find the total resistance of the rod and the current in the rod. (b) Find the electric-field magnitude $E(x)$ in the rod as a function of x. (c) Find the electric potential $V(x)$ in the rod as a function of x. (d) Graph the functions $\rho(x)$, $E(x)$, and $V(x)$ for values of x between $x = 0$ and $x = L$.

Answers

Chapter Opening Question

The current out equals the current in. In other words, charge must enter the bulb at the same rate as it exits the bulb. It is not "used up" or consumed as it flows through the bulb.

Test Your Understanding Questions

25.1 Answer: (v) Doubling the diameter increases the cross-sectional area A by a factor of 4. Hence the current-density magnitude $J = I/A$ is reduced to $\frac{1}{4}$ of the value in Example 25.1, and the magnitude of the drift velocity $v_d = J/n|q|$ is reduced by the same factor. The new magnitude is $v_d = (0.15 \text{ mm/s})/4 = 0.038 \text{ mm/s}$. This behavior is the same as that of an incompressible fluid, which slows down when it moves from a narrow pipe to a broader one (see Section 14.4).

25.2 Answer: (ii) Figure 25.6b shows that the resistivity ρ of a semiconductor increases as the temperature decreases. From Eq. (25.5), the magnitude of the current density is $J = E/\rho$, so the current density decreases as the temperature drops and the resistivity increases.

25.3 Answer: (iii) Solving Eq. (25.11) for the current shows that $I = V/R$. If the resistance R of the wire remained the same, doubling the voltage V would make the current I double as well. However, we saw in Example 25.3 that the resistance is *not* constant: As the current increases and the temperature increases, R increases as well. Thus doubling the voltage produces a current that is *less* than double the original current. An ohmic conductor is one for which $R = V/I$ has the same value no matter what the voltage, so the wire is *nonohmic*. (In many practical problems the temperature

change of the wire is so small that it can be ignored, so we can safely regard the wire as being ohmic. We do so in almost all examples in this book.)

25.4 Answer: (iii), (ii), (i) For circuit (i), we find the current from Eq. (25.16): $I = \mathcal{E}/(R + r) = (1.5 \text{ V})/(1.4 \ \Omega + 0.10 \ \Omega) = 1.0 \text{ A}$. For circuit (ii), we note that the terminal voltage $v_{ab} = 3.6$ V equals the voltage IR across the 1.8-Ω resistor: $V_{ab} = IR$, so $I = V_{ab}/R = (3.6 \text{ V})/(1.8 \ \Omega) = 2.0 \text{ A}$. For circuit (iii), we use Eq. (25.15) for the terminal voltage: $V_{ab} = \mathcal{E} - Ir$, so $I = (\mathcal{E} - V_{ab})/r = (12.0 \text{ V} - 11.0 \text{ V})/(0.20 \ \Omega) = 5.0 \text{ A}$.

25.5 Answer: (iii), (ii), (i) These are the same circuits that we analyzed in Test Your Understanding of Section 25.4. In each case the net power output of the battery is $P = V_{ab}I$, where V_{ab} is the battery terminal voltage. For circuit (i), we found that $I = 1.0$ A, so $V_{ab} = \mathcal{E} - Ir = 1.5 \text{ V} - (1.0 \text{ A})(0.10 \ \Omega) = 1.4 \text{ V}$, so $P = (1.4 \text{ V})(1.0 \text{ A}) = 1.4 \text{ W}$. For circuit (ii), we have $V_{ab} = 3.6$ V and found that $I = 2.0$ A, so $P = (3.6 \text{ V})(2.0 \text{ A}) = 7.2 \text{ W}$. For circuit (iii), we have $V_{ab} = 11.0$ V and found that $I = 5.0$ A, so $P = (11.0 \text{ V})(5.0 \text{ A}) = 55 \text{ A}$.

25.6 Answer: (i) The difficulty of producing a certain amount of current increases as the resistivity ρ increases. From Eq. (25.24), $\rho = m/ne^2\tau$, so increasing the mass m will increase the resistivity. That's because a more massive charged particle will respond more sluggishly to an applied electric field and hence drift more slowly. To produce the same current, a greater electric field would be needed. (Increasing n, e, or τ would decrease the resistivity and make it easier to produce a given current.)

Bridging Problem

Answers: (a) 237°C **(b)** 162 W initially, 148 W at 1.23 A

26 DIRECT-CURRENT CIRCUITS

? In a complex circuit like the one on this circuit board, is it possible to connect several resistors with different resistances so that they all have the same potential difference? If so, will the current be the same through all of the resistors?

If you look inside your TV, your computer, or under the hood of a car, you will find circuits of much greater complexity than the simple circuits we studied in Chapter 25. Whether connected by wires or integrated in a semiconductor chip, these circuits often include several sources, resistors, and other circuit elements interconnected in a *network*.

In this chapter we study general methods for analyzing such networks, including how to find voltages and currents of circuit elements. We'll learn how to determine the equivalent resistance for several resistors connected in series or in parallel. For more general networks we need two rules called *Kirchhoff's rules*. One is based on the principle of conservation of charge applied to a junction; the other is derived from energy conservation for a charge moving around a closed loop. We'll discuss instruments for measuring various electrical quantities. We'll also look at a circuit containing resistance and capacitance, in which the current varies with time.

Our principal concern in this chapter is with **direct-current** (dc) circuits, in which the direction of the current does not change with time. Flashlights and automobile wiring systems are examples of direct-current circuits. Household electrical power is supplied in the form of **alternating current** (ac), in which the current oscillates back and forth. The same principles for analyzing networks apply to both kinds of circuits, and we conclude this chapter with a look at household wiring systems. We'll discuss alternating-current circuits in detail in Chapter 31.

ActivPhysics 12.1: DC Series Circuits (Qualitative)

26.1 Resistors in Series and Parallel

Resistors turn up in all kinds of circuits, ranging from hair dryers and space heaters to circuits that limit or divide current or reduce or divide a voltage. Such circuits often contain several resistors, so it's appropriate to consider *combinations* of resistors. A simple example is a string of light bulbs used for holiday decorations;

each bulb acts as a resistor, and from a circuit-analysis perspective the string of bulbs is simply a combination of resistors.

Suppose we have three resistors with resistances R_1, R_2, and R_3. Figure 26.1 shows four different ways in which they might be connected between points a and b. When several circuit elements such as resistors, batteries, and motors are connected in sequence as in Fig. 26.1a, with only a single current path between the points, we say that they are connected in **series.** We studied *capacitors* in series in Section 24.2; we found that, because of conservation of charge, capacitors in series all have the same charge if they are initially uncharged. In circuits we're often more interested in the *current,* which is charge flow per unit time.

The resistors in Fig. 26.1b are said to be connected in **parallel** between points a and b. Each resistor provides an alternative path between the points. For circuit elements that are connected in parallel, the *potential difference* is the same across each element. We studied capacitors in parallel in Section 24.2.

In Fig. 26.1c, resistors R_2 and R_3 are in parallel, and this combination is in series with R_1. In Fig. 26.1d, R_2 and R_3 are in series, and this combination is in parallel with R_1.

For any combination of resistors we can always find a *single* resistor that could replace the combination and result in the same total current and potential difference. For example, a string of holiday light bulbs could be replaced by a single, appropriately chosen light bulb that would draw the same current and have the same potential difference between its terminals as the original string of bulbs. The resistance of this single resistor is called the **equivalent resistance** of the combination. If any one of the networks in Fig. 26.1 were replaced by its equivalent resistance R_{eq}, we could write

$$V_{ab} = IR_{eq} \quad \text{or} \quad R_{eq} = \frac{V_{ab}}{I}$$

where V_{ab} is the potential difference between terminals a and b of the network and I is the current at point a or b. To compute an equivalent resistance, we assume a potential difference V_{ab} across the actual network, compute the corresponding current I, and take the ratio V_{ab}/I.

Resistors in Series

We can derive general equations for the equivalent resistance of a series or parallel combination of resistors. If the resistors are in *series,* as in Fig. 26.1a, the current I must be the same in all of them. (As we discussed in Section 25.4, current is *not* "used up" as it passes through a circuit.) Applying $V = IR$ to each resistor, we have

$$V_{ax} = IR_1 \qquad V_{xy} = IR_2 \qquad V_{yb} = IR_3$$

The potential differences across each resistor need not be the same (except for the special case in which all three resistances are equal). The potential difference V_{ab} across the entire combination is the sum of these individual potential differences:

$$V_{ab} = V_{ax} + V_{xy} + V_{yb} = I(R_1 + R_2 + R_3)$$

and so

$$\frac{V_{ab}}{I} = R_1 + R_2 + R_3$$

The ratio V_{ab}/I is, by definition, the equivalent resistance R_{eq}. Therefore

$$R_{eq} = R_1 + R_2 + R_3$$

It is easy to generalize this to any number of resistors:

$$R_{eq} = R_1 + R_2 + R_3 + \cdots \quad \text{(resistors in series)} \quad (26.1)$$

26.1 Four different ways of connecting three resistors.

(a) R_1, R_2, and R_3 in series

(b) R_1, R_2, and R_3 in parallel

(c) R_1 in series with parallel combination of R_2 and R_3

(d) R_1 in parallel with series combination of R_2 and R_3

The equivalent resistance of *any number* of resistors in series equals the sum of their individual resistances.

The equivalent resistance is *greater than* any individual resistance.

Let's compare this result with Eq. (24.5) for *capacitors* in series. Resistors in series add directly because the voltage across each is directly proportional to its resistance and to the common current. Capacitors in series add reciprocally because the voltage across each is directly proportional to the common charge but *inversely* proportional to the individual capacitance.

Resistors in Parallel

If the resistors are in *parallel,* as in Fig. 26.1b, the current through each resistor need not be the same. But the potential difference between the terminals of each resistor must be the same and equal to V_{ab} (Fig. 26.2). (Remember that the potential difference between any two points does not depend on the path taken between the points.) Let's call the currents in the three resistors I_1, I_2, and I_3. Then from $I = V/R$,

$$I_1 = \frac{V_{ab}}{R_1} \qquad I_2 = \frac{V_{ab}}{R_2} \qquad I_3 = \frac{V_{ab}}{R_3}$$

In general, the current is different through each resistor. Because charge is not accumulating or draining out of point a, the total current I must equal the sum of the three currents in the resistors:

$$I = I_1 + I_2 + I_3 = V_{ab}\left(\frac{1}{R_1} + \frac{1}{R_2} + \frac{1}{R_3}\right) \quad \text{or}$$

$$\frac{I}{V_{ab}} = \frac{1}{R_1} + \frac{1}{R_2} + \frac{1}{R_3}$$

But by the definition of the equivalent resistance R_{eq}, $I/V_{ab} = 1/R_{eq}$, so

$$\frac{1}{R_{eq}} = \frac{1}{R_1} + \frac{1}{R_2} + \frac{1}{R_3}$$

Again it is easy to generalize to *any number* of resistors in parallel:

$$\frac{1}{R_{eq}} = \frac{1}{R_1} + \frac{1}{R_2} + \frac{1}{R_3} + \cdots \qquad \text{(resistors in parallel)} \qquad (26.2)$$

For *any number* of resistors in parallel, the *reciprocal* of the equivalent resistance equals the *sum of the reciprocals* of their individual resistances.

The equivalent resistance is always *less than* any individual resistance.

Compare this with Eq. (24.7) for *capacitors* in parallel. Resistors in parallel add reciprocally because the current in each is proportional to the common voltage across them and *inversely* proportional to the resistance of each. Capacitors in parallel add directly because the charge on each is proportional to the common voltage across them and *directly* proportional to the capacitance of each.

For the special case of *two* resistors in parallel,

$$\frac{1}{R_{eq}} = \frac{1}{R_1} + \frac{1}{R_2} = \frac{R_1 + R_2}{R_1 R_2} \quad \text{and}$$

$$R_{eq} = \frac{R_1 R_2}{R_1 + R_2} \qquad \text{(two resistors in parallel)} \qquad (26.3)$$

26.2 A car's headlights and taillights are connected in parallel. Hence each light is exposed to the full potential difference supplied by the car's electrical system, giving maximum brightness. Another advantage is that if one headlight or taillight burns out, the other one keeps shining (see Example 26.2).

Mastering**PHYSICS**

ActivPhysics 12.2: DC Parallel Circuits

Because $V_{ab} = I_1R_1 = I_2R_2$, it follows that

$$\frac{I_1}{I_2} = \frac{R_2}{R_1} \quad \text{(two resistors in parallel)} \quad (26.4)$$

This shows that the currents carried by two resistors in parallel are *inversely proportional* to their resistances. More current goes through the path of least resistance.

Problem-Solving Strategy 26.1   **Resistors in Series and Parallel**

IDENTIFY *the relevant concepts:* As in Fig. 26.1, many resistor networks are made up of resistors in series, in parallel, or a combination thereof. Such networks can be replaced by a single equivalent resistor. The logic is similar to that of Problem-Solving Strategy 24.1 for networks of capacitors.

SET UP *the problem* using the following steps:
1. Make a drawing of the resistor network.
2. Identify groups of resistors connected in series or parallel.
3. Identify the target variables. They could include the equivalent resistance of the network, the potential difference across each resistor, or the current through each resistor.

EXECUTE *the solution* as follows:
1. Use Eq. (26.1) or (26.2), respectively, to find the equivalent resistance for series or parallel combinations.
2. If the network is more complex, try reducing it to series and parallel combinations. For example, in Fig. 26.1c we first replace the parallel combination of R_2 and R_3 with its equivalent resistance;

this then forms a series combination with R_1. In Fig. 26.1d, the combination of R_2 and R_3 in series forms a parallel combination with R_1.
3. Keep in mind that the total potential difference across resistors connected in series is the sum of the individual potential differences. The potential difference across resistors connected in parallel is the same for every resistor and equals the potential difference across the combination.
4. The current through resistors connected in series is the same through every resistor and equals the current through the combination. The total current through resistors connected in parallel is the sum of the currents through the individual resistors.

EVALUATE *your answer:* Check whether your results are consistent. The equivalent resistance of resistors connected in series should be greater than that of any individual resistor; that of resistors in parallel should be less than that of any individual resistor.

Example 26.1   **Equivalent resistance**

Find the equivalent resistance of the network in Fig. 26.3a and the current in each resistor. The source of emf has negligible internal resistance.

SOLUTION

IDENTIFY and SET UP: This network of three resistors is a *combination* of series and parallel resistances, as in Fig. 26.1c. We determine

26.3 Steps in reducing a combination of resistors to a single equivalent resistor and finding the current in each resistor.

(a)

(b) ⟹ (c) ⟹ (d) ⟹ (e) ⟹ (f)

Continued

the equivalent resistance of the parallel 6-Ω and 3-Ω resistors, and then that of their series combination with the 4-Ω resistor: This is the equivalent resistance R_{eq} of the network as a whole. We then find the current in the emf, which is the same as that in the 4-Ω resistor. The potential difference is the same across each of the parallel 6-Ω and 3-Ω resistors; we use this to determine how the current is divided between these.

EXECUTE: Figures 26.3b and 26.3c show successive steps in reducing the network to a single equivalent resistance R_{eq}. From Eq. (26.2), the 6-Ω and 3-Ω resistors in parallel in Fig. 26.3a are equivalent to the single 2-Ω resistor in Fig. 26.3b:

$$\frac{1}{R_{6\,\Omega+3\,\Omega}} = \frac{1}{6\ \Omega} + \frac{1}{3\ \Omega} = \frac{1}{2\ \Omega}$$

[Equation (26.3) gives the same result.] From Eq. (26.1) the series combination of this 2-Ω resistor with the 4-Ω resistor is equivalent to the single 6-Ω resistor in Fig. 26.3c.

We reverse these steps to find the current in each resistor of the original network. In the circuit shown in Fig. 26.3d (identical to Fig. 26.3c), the current is $I = V_{ab}/R = (18\ \text{V})/(6\ \Omega) = 3\ \text{A}$. So the current in the 4-Ω and 2-Ω resistors in Fig. 26.3e (identical to Fig. 26.3b) is also 3 A. The potential difference V_{cb} across the 2-Ω resistor is therefore $V_{cb} = IR = (3\ \text{A})(2\ \Omega) = 6\ \text{V}$. This potential difference must also be 6 V in Fig. 26.3f (identical to Fig. 26.3a). From $I = V_{cb}/R$, the currents in the 6-Ω and 3-Ω resistors in Fig. 26.3f are respectively $(6\ \text{V})/(6\ \Omega) = 1\ \text{A}$ and $(6\ \text{V})/(3\ \Omega) = 2\ \text{A}$.

EVALUATE: Note that for the two resistors in parallel between points c and b in Fig. 26.3f, there is twice as much current through the 3-Ω resistor as through the 6-Ω resistor; more current goes through the path of least resistance, in accordance with Eq. (26.4). Note also that the total current through these two resistors is 3 A, the same as it is through the 4-Ω resistor between points a and c.

Example 26.2 **Series versus parallel combinations**

Two identical light bulbs, each with resistance $R = 2\ \Omega$, are connected to a source with $\mathcal{E} = 8\ \text{V}$ and negligible internal resistance. Find the current through each bulb, the potential difference across each bulb, and the power delivered to each bulb and to the entire network if the bulbs are connected (a) in series and (b) in parallel. (c) Suppose one of the bulbs burns out; that is, its filament breaks and current can no longer flow through it. What happens to the other bulb in the series case? In the parallel case?

SOLUTION

IDENTIFY and SET UP: The light bulbs are just resistors in simple series and parallel connections (Figs. 26.4a and 26.4b). Once we find the current I through each bulb, we can find the power delivered to each bulb using Eq. (25.18), $P = I^2R = V^2/R$.

EXECUTE: (a) From Eq. (26.1) the equivalent resistance of the two bulbs between points a and c in Fig. 26.4a is $R_{eq} = 2R = 2(2\ \Omega) = 4\ \Omega$. In series, the current is the same through each bulb:

$$I = \frac{V_{ac}}{R_{eq}} = \frac{8\ \text{V}}{4\ \Omega} = 2\ \text{A}$$

Since the bulbs have the same resistance, the potential difference is the same across each bulb:

$$V_{ab} = V_{bc} = IR = (2\ \text{A})(2\ \Omega) = 4\ \text{V}$$

From Eq. (25.18), the power delivered to each bulb is

$$P = I^2R = (2\ \text{A})^2(2\ \Omega) = 8\ \text{W} \qquad \text{or}$$

$$P = \frac{V_{ab}^2}{R} = \frac{V_{bc}^2}{R} = \frac{(4\ \text{V})^2}{2\ \Omega} = 8\ \text{W}$$

The total power delivered to both bulbs is $P_{tot} = 2P = 16\ \text{W}$.

(b) If the bulbs are in parallel, as in Fig. 26.4b, the potential difference V_{de} across each bulb is the same and equal to 8 V, the terminal voltage of the source. Hence the current through each light bulb is

$$I = \frac{V_{de}}{R} = \frac{8\ \text{V}}{2\ \Omega} = 4\ \text{A}$$

and the power delivered to each bulb is

$$P = I^2R = (4\ \text{A})^2(2\ \Omega) = 32\ \text{W} \qquad \text{or}$$

$$P = \frac{V_{de}^2}{R} = \frac{(8\ \text{V})^2}{2\ \Omega} = 32\ \text{W}$$

Both the potential difference across each bulb and the current through each bulb are twice as great as in the series case. Hence the power delivered to each bulb is *four* times greater, and each bulb is brighter.

The total power delivered to the parallel network is $P_{total} = 2P = 64\ \text{W}$, four times greater than in the series case. The

26.4 Our sketches for this problem.

(a) Light bulbs in series

(b) Light bulbs in parallel

26.5 When connected to the same source, two light bulbs in series (shown at top) draw less power and glow less brightly than when they are in parallel (shown at bottom).

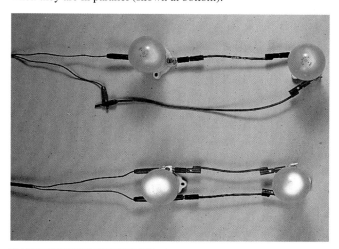

increased power compared to the series case isn't obtained "for free"; energy is extracted from the source four times more rapidly in the parallel case than in the series case. If the source is a battery, it will be used up four times as fast.

(c) In the series case the same current flows through both bulbs. If one bulb burns out, there will be no current in the circuit, and neither bulb will glow.

In the parallel case the potential difference across either bulb is unchanged if a bulb burns out. The current through the functional bulb and the power delivered to it are unchanged.

EVALUATE: Our calculation isn't completely accurate, because the resistance $R = V/I$ of real light bulbs depends on the potential difference V across the bulb. That's because the filament resistance increases with increasing operating temperature and therefore with increasing V. But bulbs connected in series across a source do in fact glow less brightly than when connected in parallel across the same source (Fig. 26.5).

Test Your Understanding of Section 26.1 Suppose all three of the resistors shown in Fig. 26.1 have the same resistance, so $R_1 = R_2 = R_3 = R$. Rank the four arrangements shown in parts (a)–(d) of Fig. 26.1 in order of their equivalent resistance, from highest to lowest.

26.2 Kirchhoff's Rules

Many practical resistor networks cannot be reduced to simple series-parallel combinations. Figure 26.6a shows a dc power supply with emf $\mathcal{E}_1$ charging a battery with a smaller emf $\mathcal{E}_2$ and feeding current to a light bulb with resistance R. Figure 26.6b is a "bridge" circuit, used in many different types of measurement and control systems. (Problem 26.81 describes one important application of a "bridge" circuit.) To compute the currents in these networks, we'll use the techniques developed by the German physicist Gustav Robert Kirchhoff (1824–1887).

First, here are two terms that we will use often. A **junction** in a circuit is a point where three or more conductors meet. A **loop** is any closed conducting path. In Fig. 26.6a points a and b are junctions, but points c and d are not; in Fig. 26.6b the points a, b, c, and d are junctions, but points e and f are not. The blue lines in Figs. 26.6a and 26.6b show some possible loops in these circuits.

Kirchhoff's rules are the following two statements:
Kirchhoff's junction rule: *The algebraic sum of the currents into any junction is zero.* That is,

$$\sum I = 0 \quad \text{(junction rule, valid at any junction)} \quad (26.5)$$

Kirchhoff's loop rule: *The algebraic sum of the potential differences in any loop, including those associated with emfs and those of resistive elements, must equal zero.* That is,

$$\sum V = 0 \quad \text{(loop rule, valid for any closed loop)} \quad (26.6)$$

26.6 Two networks that cannot be reduced to simple series-parallel combinations of resistors.

(a)

(b)

26.7 Kirchhoff's junction rule states that as much current flows into a junction as flows out of it.

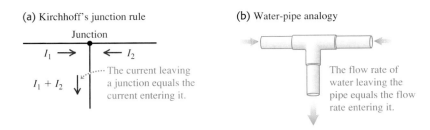

(a) Kirchhoff's junction rule

(b) Water-pipe analogy

The junction rule is based on *conservation of electric charge*. No charge can accumulate at a junction, so the total charge entering the junction per unit time must equal the total charge leaving per unit time (Fig. 26.7a). Charge per unit time is current, so if we consider the currents entering a junction to be positive and those leaving to be negative, the algebraic sum of currents into a junction must be zero. It's like a T branch in a water pipe (Fig. 26.7b); if you have a total of 1 liter per minute coming in the two pipes, you can't have 3 liters per minute going out the third pipe. We may as well confess that we used the junction rule (without saying so) in Section 26.1 in the derivation of Eq. (26.2) for resistors in parallel.

The loop rule is a statement that the electrostatic force is *conservative*. Suppose we go around a loop, measuring potential differences across successive circuit elements as we go. When we return to the starting point, we must find that the *algebraic sum* of these differences is zero; otherwise, we could not say that the potential at this point has a definite value.

Sign Conventions for the Loop Rule

In applying the loop rule, we need some sign conventions. Problem-Solving Strategy 26.2 describes in detail how to use these, but here's a quick overview. We first assume a direction for the current in each branch of the circuit and mark it on a diagram of the circuit. Then, starting at any point in the circuit, we imagine traveling around a loop, adding emfs and *IR* terms as we come to them. When we travel through a source in the direction from − to +, the emf is considered to be *positive;* when we travel from + to −, the emf is considered to be *negative* (Fig. 26.8a). When we travel through a resistor in the *same* direction as the assumed current, the *IR* term is *negative* because the current goes in the direction of decreasing potential. When we travel through a resistor in the direction *opposite* to the assumed current, the *IR* term is *positive* because this represents a rise of potential (Fig. 26.8b).

Kirchhoff's two rules are all we need to solve a wide variety of network problems. Usually, some of the emfs, currents, and resistances are known, and others are unknown. We must always obtain from Kirchhoff's rules a number of independent equations equal to the number of unknowns so that we can solve the equations simultaneously. Often the hardest part of the solution is not understanding the basic principles but keeping track of algebraic signs!

26.8 Use these sign conventions when you apply Kirchhoff's loop rule. In each part of the figure "Travel" is the direction that we imagine going around the loop, which is not necessarily the direction of the current.

(a) Sign conventions for emfs

(b) Sign conventions for resistors

Problem-Solving Strategy 26.2 Kirchhoff's Rules

IDENTIFY *the relevant concepts:* Kirchhoff's rules are useful for analyzing any electric circuit.

SET UP *the problem* using the following steps:

1. Draw a circuit diagram, leaving room to label all quantities, known and unknown. Indicate an assumed direction for each unknown current and emf. (Kirchhoff's rules will yield the magnitudes *and directions* of unknown currents and emfs. If the actual direction of a quantity is opposite to your assumption, the resulting quantity will have a negative sign.)
2. As you label currents, it helpful to use Kirchhoff's junction rule, as in Fig. 26.9, so as to express the currents in terms of as few quantities as possible.
3. Identify the target variables.

EXECUTE *the solution* as follows:

1. Choose any loop in the network and choose a direction (clockwise or counterclockwise) to travel around the loop as you apply Kirchhoff's loop rule. The direction need not be the same as any assumed current direction.

2. Travel around the loop in the chosen direction, adding potential differences algebraically as you cross them. Use the sign conventions of Fig. 26.8.
3. Equate the sum obtained in step 2 to zero in accordance with the loop rule.
4. If you need more independent equations, choose another loop and repeat steps 1–3; continue until you have as many independent equations as unknowns or until every circuit element has been included in at least one loop.
5. Solve the equations simultaneously to determine the unknowns.
6. You can use the loop-rule bookkeeping system to find the potential V_{ab} of any point a with respect to any other point b. Start at b and add the potential changes you encounter in going from b to a, using the same sign rules as in step 2. The algebraic sum of these changes is $V_{ab} = V_a - V_b$.

EVALUATE *your answer:* Check all the steps in your algebra. Apply steps 1 and 2 to a loop you have not yet considered; if the sum of potential drops isn't zero, you've made an error somewhere.

26.9 Applying the junction rule to point a reduces the number of unknown currents from three to two.

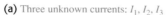

(a) Three unknown currents: I_1, I_2, I_3

(b) Applying the junction rule to point a eliminates I_3.

Example 26.3 A single-loop circuit

The circuit shown in Fig. 26.10a contains two batteries, each with an emf and an internal resistance, and two resistors. Find (a) the current in the circuit, (b) the potential difference V_{ab}, and (c) the power output of the emf of each battery.

SOLUTION

IDENTIFY and SET UP: There are no junctions in this single-loop circuit, so we don't need Kirchhoff's junction rule. To apply Kirchhoff's loop rule, we first assume a direction for the current; let's assume a counterclockwise direction as shown in Fig. 26.10a.

EXECUTE: (a) Starting at a and traveling counterclockwise with the current, we add potential increases and decreases and equate the sum to zero as in Eq. (26.6):

$$-I(4\ \Omega) - 4\ \text{V} - I(7\ \Omega) + 12\ \text{V} - I(2\ \Omega) - I(3\ \Omega) = 0$$

Collecting like terms and solving for I, we find

$$8\ \text{V} = I(16\ \Omega) \quad \text{and} \quad I = 0.5\ \text{A}$$

The positive result for I shows that our assumed current direction is correct.

(b) To find V_{ab}, the potential at a with respect to b, we start at b and add potential changes as we go toward a. There are two paths from b to a; taking the lower one, we find

$$V_{ab} = (0.5\ \text{A})(7\ \Omega) + 4\ \text{V} + (0.5\ \text{A})(4\ \Omega)$$
$$= 9.5\ \text{V}$$

Point a is at 9.5 V higher potential than b. All the terms in this sum, including the IR terms, are positive because each represents an *increase* in potential as we go from b to a. Taking the upper path, we find

$$V_{ab} = 12\ \text{V} - (0.5\ \text{A})(2\ \Omega) - (0.5\ \text{A})(3\ \Omega)$$
$$= 9.5\ \text{V}$$

Here the IR terms are negative because our path goes in the direction of the current, with potential decreases through the resistors. The results for V_{ab} are the same for both paths, as they must be in order for the total potential change around the loop to be zero.

Continued

(c) The power outputs of the emf of the 12-V and 4-V batteries are

$$P_{12V} = \mathcal{E}I = (12 \text{ V})(0.5 \text{ A}) = 6 \text{ W}$$
$$P_{4V} = \mathcal{E}I = (-4 \text{ V})(0.5 \text{ A}) = -2 \text{ W}$$

The negative sign in $\mathcal{E}$ for the 4-V battery appears because the current actually runs from the higher-potential side of the battery to the lower-potential side. The negative value of P means that we are *storing* energy in that battery; the 12-V battery is *recharging* it (if it is in fact rechargeable; otherwise, we're destroying it).

EVALUATE: By applying the expression $P = I^2R$ to each of the four resistors in Fig. 26.10a, you can show that the total power

dissipated in all four resistors is 4 W. Of the 6 W provided by the emf of the 12-V battery, 2 W goes into storing energy in the 4-V battery and 4 W is dissipated in the resistances.

The circuit shown in Fig. 26.10a is much like that used when a fully charged 12-V storage battery (in a car with its engine running) is used to "jump-start" a car with a run-down battery (Fig. 26.10b). The run-down battery is slightly recharged in the process. The 3-Ω and 7-Ω resistors in Fig. 26.10a represent the resistances of the jumper cables and of the conducting path through the automobile with the run-down battery. (The values of the resistances in actual automobiles and jumper cables are considerably lower.)

26.10 (a) In this example we travel around the loop in the same direction as the assumed current, so all the *IR* terms are negative. The potential decreases as we travel from + to − through the bottom emf but increases as we travel from − to + through the top emf. (b) A real-life example of a circuit of this kind.

Example 26.4 | **Charging a battery**

In the circuit shown in Fig. 26.11, a 12-V power supply with unknown internal resistance r is connected to a run-down rechargeable battery with unknown emf $\mathcal{E}$ and internal resistance 1 Ω and to an indicator light bulb of resistance 3 Ω carrying a current of 2 A. The current through the run-down battery is 1 A in the direction shown. Find r, $\mathcal{E}$, and the current I through the power supply.

SOLUTION

IDENTIFY and SET UP: This circuit has more than one loop, so we must apply both the junction and loop rules. We assume the direction of the current through the 12-V power supply, and the polarity of the run-down battery, to be as shown in Fig. 26.11. There are three target variables, so we need three equations.

26.11 In this circuit a power supply charges a run-down battery and lights a bulb. An assumption has been made about the polarity of the emf $\mathcal{E}$ of the run-down battery. Is this assumption correct?

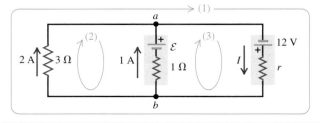

EXECUTE: We apply the junction rule, Eq. (26.5), to point *a*:

$$-I + 1 \text{ A} + 2 \text{ A} = 0 \qquad \text{so} \qquad I = 3 \text{ A}$$

To determine r, we apply the loop rule, Eq. (26.6), to the large, outer loop (1):

$$12 \text{ V} - (3 \text{ A})r - (2 \text{ A})(3 \text{ } \Omega) = 0 \qquad \text{so} \qquad r = 2 \text{ } \Omega$$

To determine $\mathcal{E}$, we apply the loop rule to the left-hand loop (2):

$$-\mathcal{E} + (1 \text{ A})(1 \text{ } \Omega) - (2 \text{ A})(3 \text{ } \Omega) = 0 \qquad \text{so} \qquad \mathcal{E} = -5 \text{ V}$$

The negative value for $\mathcal{E}$ shows that the actual polarity of this emf is opposite to that shown in Fig. 26.11. As in Example 26.3, the battery is being recharged.

EVALUATE: Try applying the junction rule at point *b* instead of point *a*, and try applying the loop rule by traveling counterclockwise rather than clockwise around loop (1). You'll get the same results for I and r. We can check our result for $\mathcal{E}$ by using the right-hand loop (3):

$$12 \text{ V} - (3 \text{ A})(2 \text{ } \Omega) - (1 \text{ A})(1 \text{ } \Omega) + \mathcal{E} = 0$$

which again gives us $\mathcal{E} = -5 \text{ V}$.

As an additional check, we note that $V_{ba} = V_b - V_a$ equals the voltage across the 3-Ω resistance, which is $(2 \text{ A})(3 \text{ } \Omega) = 6 \text{ V}$. Going from *a* to *b* by the top branch, we encounter potential differences $+12 \text{ V} - (3 \text{ A})(2 \text{ } \Omega) = +6 \text{ V}$, and going by the middle branch, we find $-(-5 \text{ V}) + (1 \text{ A})(1 \text{ } \Omega) = +6 \text{ V}$. The three ways of getting V_{ba} give the same results.

Example 26.5 **Power in a battery-charging circuit**

In the circuit of Example 26.4 (shown in Fig. 26.11), find the power delivered by the 12-V power supply and by the battery being recharged, and find the power dissipated in each resistor.

SOLUTION

IDENTIFY and SET UP: We use the results of Section 25.5, in which we found that the power delivered *from* an emf to a circuit is $\mathcal{E}I$ and the power delivered *to* a resistor from a circuit is $V_{ab}I = I^2R$. We know the values of all relevant quantities from Example 26.4.

EXECUTE: The power output P_{s} from the emf of the power supply is

$$P_{\text{supply}} = \mathcal{E}_{\text{supply}}I_{\text{supply}} = (12 \text{ V})(3 \text{ A}) = 36 \text{ W}$$

The power dissipated in the power supply's internal resistance r is

$$P_{r-\text{supply}} = I_{\text{supply}}^2 r_{\text{supply}} = (3 \text{ A})^2(2 \text{ } \Omega) = 18 \text{ W}$$

so the power supply's *net* power output is $P_{\text{net}} = 36 \text{ W} - 18 \text{ W} = 18 \text{ W}$. Alternatively, from Example 26.4 the terminal voltage of the battery is $V_{ba} = 6 \text{ V}$, so the net power output is

$$P_{\text{net}} = V_{ba}I_{\text{supply}} = (6 \text{ V})(3 \text{ A}) = 18 \text{ W}$$

The power output of the emf $\mathcal{E}$ of the battery being charged is

$$P_{\text{emf}} = \mathcal{E}I_{\text{battery}} = (-5 \text{ V})(1 \text{ A}) = -5 \text{ W}$$

This is negative because the 1-A current runs through the battery from the higher-potential side to the lower-potential side. (As we mentioned in Example 26.4, the polarity assumed for this battery in Fig. 26.11 was wrong.) We are storing energy in the battery as we charge it. Additional power is dissipated in the battery's internal resistance; this power is

$$P_{r-\text{battery}} = I_{\text{battery}}^2 r_{\text{battery}} = (1 \text{ A})^2(1 \text{ } \Omega) = 1 \text{ W}$$

The total power input to the battery is thus $1 \text{ W} + |-5 \text{ W}| = 6 \text{ W}$. Of this, 5 W represents useful energy stored in the battery; the remainder is wasted in its internal resistance.

The power dissipated in the light bulb is

$$P_{\text{bulb}} = I_{\text{bulb}}^2 R_{\text{bulb}} = (2 \text{ A})^2(3 \text{ } \Omega) = 12 \text{ W}$$

EVALUATE: As a check, note that all of the power from the supply is accounted for. Of the 18 W of net power from the power supply, 5 W goes to recharge the battery, 1 W is dissipated in the battery's internal resistance, and 12 W is dissipated in the light bulb.

Example 26.6 **A complex network**

Figure 26.12 shows a "bridge" circuit of the type described at the beginning of this section (see Fig. 26.6b). Find the current in each resistor and the equivalent resistance of the network of five resistors.

SOLUTION

IDENTIFY and SET UP: This network is neither a series combination nor a parallel combination. Hence we must use Kirchhoff's rules to find the values of the target variables. There are five unknown currents, but by applying the junction rule to junctions a and b, we can represent them in terms of three unknown currents I_1, I_2, and I_3, as shown in Fig. 26.12.

26.12 A network circuit with several resistors.

EXECUTE: We apply the loop rule to the three loops shown:

$$13 \text{ V} - I_1(1 \text{ } \Omega) - (I_1 - I_3)(1 \text{ } \Omega) = 0 \qquad (1)$$
$$-I_2(1 \text{ } \Omega) - (I_2 + I_3)(2 \text{ } \Omega) + 13 \text{ V} = 0 \qquad (2)$$
$$-I_1(1 \text{ } \Omega) - I_3(1 \text{ } \Omega) + I_2(1 \text{ } \Omega) = 0 \qquad (3)$$

One way to solve these simultaneous equations is to solve Eq. (3) for I_2, obtaining $I_2 = I_1 + I_3$, and then substitute this expression into Eq. (2) to eliminate I_2. We then have

$$13 \text{ V} = I_1(2 \text{ } \Omega) - I_3(1 \text{ } \Omega) \qquad (1')$$
$$13 \text{ V} = I_1(3 \text{ } \Omega) + I_3(5 \text{ } \Omega) \qquad (2')$$

Now we can eliminate I_3 by multiplying Eq. (1′) by 5 and adding the two equations. We obtain

$$78 \text{ V} = I_1(13 \text{ } \Omega) \qquad I_1 = 6 \text{ A}$$

We substitute this result into Eq. (1′) to obtain $I_3 = -1 \text{ A}$, and from Eq. (3) we find $I_2 = 5 \text{ A}$. The negative value of I_3 tells us that its direction is opposite to the direction we assumed.

The total current through the network is $I_1 + I_2 = 11 \text{ A}$, and the potential drop across it is equal to the battery emf, 13 V. The equivalent resistance of the network is therefore

$$R_{\text{eq}} = \frac{13 \text{ V}}{11 \text{ A}} = 1.2 \text{ } \Omega$$

EVALUATE: You can check our results for I_1, I_2, and I_3 by substituting them back into Eqs. (1)–(3). What do you find?

Example 26.7 **A potential difference in a complex network**

In the circuit of Example 26.6 (Fig. 26.12), find the potential difference V_{ab}.

SOLUTION

IDENTIFY and SET UP: Our target variable $V_{ab} = V_a - V_b$ is the potential at point a with respect to point b. To find it, we start at point b and follow a path to point a, adding potential rises and drops as we go. We can follow any of several paths from b to a; the result must be the same for all such paths, which gives us a way to check our result.

EXECUTE: The simplest path is through the center 1-Ω resistor. In Example 26.6 we found $I_3 = -1$ A, showing that the actual

current direction through this resistor is from right to left. Thus, as we go from b to a, there is a *drop* of potential with magnitude $|I_3|R = (1 \text{ A})(1 \ \Omega) = 1$ V. Hence $V_{ab} = -1$ V, and the potential at a is 1 V less than at point b.

EVALUATE: To check our result, let's try a path from b to a that goes through the lower two resistors. The currents through these are

$$I_2 + I_3 = 5 \text{ A} + (-1 \text{ A}) = 4 \text{ A} \quad \text{and}$$
$$I_1 - I_3 = 6 \text{ A} - (-1 \text{ A}) = 7 \text{ A}$$

and so

$$V_{ab} = -(4 \text{ A})(2 \ \Omega) + (7 \text{ A})(1 \ \Omega) = -1 \text{ V}$$

You can confirm this result using some other paths from b to a.

26.13 This ammeter (top) and voltmeter (bottom) are both d'Arsonval galvanometers. The difference has to do with their internal connections (see Fig. 26.15).

Test Your Understanding of Section 26.2 Subtract Eq. (1) from Eq. (2) in Example 26.6. To which loop in Fig. 26.12 does this equation correspond? Would this equation have simplified the solution of Example 26.6?

26.3 Electrical Measuring Instruments

We've been talking about potential difference, current, and resistance for two chapters, so it's about time we said something about how to *measure* these quantities. Many common devices, including car instrument panels, battery chargers, and inexpensive electrical instruments, measure potential difference (voltage), current, or resistance using a **d'Arsonval galvanometer** (Fig. 26.13). In the following discussion we'll often call it just a *meter*. A pivoted coil of fine wire is placed in the magnetic field of a permanent magnet (Fig. 26.14). Attached to the coil is a spring, similar to the hairspring on the balance wheel of a watch. In the equilibrium position, with no current in the coil, the pointer is at zero. When there is a current in the coil, the magnetic field exerts a torque on the coil that is proportional to the current. (We'll discuss this magnetic interaction in detail in Chapter 27.) As the coil turns, the spring exerts a restoring torque that is proportional to the angular displacement.

Thus the angular deflection of the coil and pointer is directly proportional to the coil current, and the device can be calibrated to measure current. The maximum deflection, typically 90° or so, is called *full-scale deflection*. The essential electrical characteristics of the meter are the current I_{fs} required for full-scale deflection (typically on the order of 10 μA to 10 mA) and the resistance R_c of the coil (typically on the order of 10 to 1000 Ω).

The meter deflection is proportional to the *current* in the coil. If the coil obeys Ohm's law, the current is proportional to the *potential difference* between the terminals of the coil, and the deflection is also proportional to this potential difference. For example, consider a meter whose coil has a resistance $R_c = 20.0 \ \Omega$ and that deflects full scale when the current in its coil is $I_{fs} = 1.00$ mA. The corresponding potential difference for full-scale deflection is

$$V = I_{fs}R_c = (1.00 \times 10^{-3} \text{ A})(20.0 \ \Omega) = 0.0200 \text{ V}$$

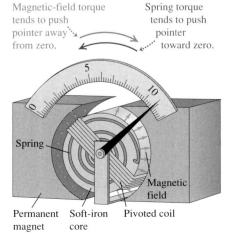

26.14 A d'Arsonval galvanometer, showing a pivoted coil with attached pointer, a permanent magnet supplying a magnetic field that is uniform in magnitude, and a spring to provide restoring torque, which opposes magnetic-field torque.

Magnetic-field torque tends to push pointer away from zero.

Spring torque tends to push pointer toward zero.

Spring

Magnetic field

Permanent magnet   Soft-iron core   Pivoted coil

Ammeters

A current-measuring instrument is usually called an **ammeter** (or milliammeter, microammeter, and so forth, depending on the range). *An ammeter always measures the current passing through it.* An *ideal* ammeter, discussed in Section 25.4, would have *zero* resistance, so including it in a branch of a circuit would not affect the current in that branch. Real ammeters always have some finite resistance, but it is always desirable for an ammeter to have as little resistance as possible.

We can adapt any meter to measure currents that are larger than its full-scale reading by connecting a resistor in parallel with it (Fig. 26.15a) so that some of the current bypasses the meter coil. The parallel resistor is called a **shunt resistor** or simply a *shunt,* denoted as R_{sh}.

Suppose we want to make a meter with full-scale current I_{fs} and coil resistance R_c into an ammeter with full-scale reading I_a. To determine the shunt resistance R_{sh} needed, note that at full-scale deflection the total current through the parallel combination is I_a, the current through the coil of the meter is I_{fs}, and the current through the shunt is the difference $I_a - I_{fs}$. The potential difference V_{ab} is the same for both paths, so

$$I_{fs}R_c = (I_a - I_{fs})R_{sh} \qquad \text{(for an ammeter)} \qquad (26.7)$$

26.15 Using the same meter to measure (a) current and (b) voltage.

Example 26.8   Designing an ammeter

What shunt resistance is required to make the 1.00-mA, 20.0-Ω meter described above into an ammeter with a range of 0 to 50.0 mA?

SOLUTION

IDENTIFY and SET UP: Since the meter is being used as an ammeter, its internal connections are as shown in Fig. 26.15a. Our target variable is the shunt resistance R_{sh}, which we will find using Eq. (26.7). The ammeter must handle a maximum current $I_a = 50.0 \times 10^{-3}$ A. The coil resistance is $R_c = 20.0$ Ω, and the meter shows full-scale deflection when the current through the coil is $I_{fs} = 1.00 \times 10^{-3}$ A.

EXECUTE: Solving Eq. (26.7) for R_{sh}, we find

$$R_{sh} = \frac{I_{fs}R_c}{I_a - I_{fs}} = \frac{(1.00 \times 10^{-3}\text{ A})(20.0\ \Omega)}{50.0 \times 10^{-3}\text{ A} - 1.00 \times 10^{-3}\text{ A}}$$

$$= 0.408\ \Omega$$

EVALUATE: It's useful to consider the equivalent resistance R_{eq} of the ammeter as a whole. From Eq. (26.2),

$$R_{eq} = \left(\frac{1}{R_c} + \frac{1}{R_{sh}}\right)^{-1} = \left(\frac{1}{20.0\ \Omega} + \frac{1}{0.408\ \Omega}\right)^{-1}$$

$$= 0.400\ \Omega$$

The shunt resistance is so small in comparison to the coil resistance that the equivalent resistance is very nearly equal to the shunt resistance. The result is an ammeter with a low equivalent resistance and the desired 0–50.0-mA range. At full-scale deflection, $I = I_a = 50.0$ mA, the current through the galvanometer is 1.00 mA, the current through the shunt resistor is 49.0 mA, and $V_{ab} = 0.0200$ V. If the current I is *less* than 50.0 mA, the coil current and the deflection are proportionally less.

Voltmeters

This same basic meter may also be used to measure potential difference or *voltage.* A voltage-measuring device is called a **voltmeter**. A voltmeter always measures the potential difference between two points, and its terminals must be connected to these points. (Example 25.6 in Section 25.4 described what can happen if a voltmeter is connected incorrectly.) As we discussed in Section 25.4, an ideal voltmeter would have *infinite* resistance, so connecting it between two points in a circuit would not alter any of the currents. Real voltmeters always have finite resistance, but a voltmeter should have large enough resistance that connecting it in a circuit does not change the other currents appreciably.

For the meter described in Example 26.8 the voltage across the meter coil at full-scale deflection is only $I_{fs}R_c = (1.00 \times 10^{-3}$ A$)(20.0\ \Omega) = 0.0200$ V. We can extend this range by connecting a resistor R_s in *series* with the coil (Fig. 26.15b). Then only a fraction of the total potential difference appears across the coil itself, and the remainder appears across R_s. For a voltmeter with full-scale reading V_V, we need a series resistor R_s in Fig. 26.15b such that

$$V_V = I_{fs}(R_c + R_s) \qquad \text{(for a voltmeter)} \qquad (26.8)$$

Application **Electromyography**
A fine needle containing two electrodes is being inserted into a muscle in this patient's hand. By using a sensitive voltmeter to measure the potential difference between these electrodes, a physician can probe the muscle's electrical activity. This is an important technique for diagnosing neurological and neuromuscular diseases.

Example 26.9 Designing a voltmeter

What series resistance is required to make the 1.00-mA, 20.0-Ω meter described above into a voltmeter with a range of 0 to 10.0 V?

SOLUTION

IDENTIFY and SET UP: Since this meter is being used as a voltmeter, its internal connections are as shown in Fig. 26.15b. Our target variable is the series resistance R_s. The maximum allowable voltage across the voltmeter is $V_V = 10.0$ V. We want this to occur when the current through the coil is $I_{fs} = 1.00 \times 10^{-3}$ A. Our target variable is the series resistance R_s, which we find using Eq. (26.8).

EXECUTE: From Eq. (26.8),

$$R_s = \frac{V_V}{I_{fs}} - R_c = \frac{10.0 \text{ V}}{0.00100 \text{ A}} - 20.0 \ \Omega = 9980 \ \Omega$$

EVALUATE: At full-scale deflection, $V_{ab} = 10.0$ V, the voltage across the meter is 0.0200 V, the voltage across R_s is 9.98 V, and the current through the voltmeter is 0.00100 A. Most of the voltage appears across the series resistor. The meter's equivalent resistance is a desirably high $R_{eq} = 20.0 \ \Omega + 9980 \ \Omega = 10{,}000 \ \Omega$. Such a meter is called a "1000 ohms-per-volt" meter, referring to the ratio of resistance to full-scale deflection. In normal operation the current through the circuit element being measured (I in Fig. 26.15b) is much greater than 0.00100 A, and the resistance between points a and b in the circuit is much less than 10,000 Ω. The voltmeter draws off only a small fraction of the current and thus disturbs the circuit being measured only slightly.

Mastering PHYSICS

ActivPhysics 12.4: Using Ammeters and Voltmeters

Ammeters and Voltmeters in Combination

A voltmeter and an ammeter can be used together to measure *resistance* and *power.* The resistance R of a resistor equals the potential difference V_{ab} between its terminals divided by the current I; that is, $R = V_{ab}/I$. The power input P to any circuit element is the product of the potential difference across it and the current through it: $P = V_{ab}I$. In principle, the most straightforward way to measure R or P is to measure V_{ab} and I simultaneously.

With practical ammeters and voltmeters this isn't quite as simple as it seems. In Fig. 26.16a, ammeter A reads the current I in the resistor R. Voltmeter V, however, reads the *sum* of the potential difference V_{ab} across the resistor and the potential difference V_{bc} across the ammeter. If we transfer the voltmeter terminal from c to b, as in Fig. 26.16b, then the voltmeter reads the potential difference V_{ab} correctly, but the ammeter now reads the *sum* of the current I in the resistor and the current I_V in the voltmeter. Either way, we have to correct the reading of one instrument or the other unless the corrections are small enough to be negligible.

26.16 Ammeter–voltmeter method for measuring resistance.

Example 26.10 Measuring resistance I

The voltmeter in the circuit of Fig. 26.16a reads 12.0 V and the ammeter reads 0.100 A. The meter resistances are $R_V = 10{,}000 \ \Omega$ (for the voltmeter) and $R_A = 2.00 \ \Omega$ (for the ammeter). What are the resistance R and the power dissipated in the resistor?

SOLUTION

IDENTIFY and SET UP: The ammeter reads the current $I = 0.100$ A through the resistor, and the voltmeter reads the potential difference

between a and c. If the ammeter were *ideal* (that is, if $R_A = 0$), there would be zero potential difference between b and c, the voltmeter reading $V = 12.0$ V would be equal to the potential difference V_{ab} across the resistor, and the resistance would simply be equal to $R = V/I = (12.0 \text{ V})/(0.100 \text{ A}) = 120 \ \Omega$. The ammeter is *not* ideal, however (its resistance is $R_A = 2.00 \ \Omega$), so the voltmeter reading V is actually the sum of the potential differences V_{bc} (across the ammeter) and V_{ab} (across the resistor). We use Ohm's law to find the voltage V_{bc} from the known current and ammeter resistance. Then we solve for V_{ab} and the resistance R. Given these, we are able to calculate the power P into the resistor.

EXECUTE: From Ohm's law, $V_{bc} = IR_A = (0.100 \text{ A})(2.00 \text{ }\Omega) = 0.200 \text{ V}$ and $V_{ab} = IR$. The sum of these is $V = 12.0 \text{ V}$, so the potential difference across the resistor is $V_{ab} = V - V_{bc} = (12.0 \text{ V}) - (0.200 \text{ V}) = 11.8 \text{ V}$. Hence the resistance is

$$R = \frac{V_{ab}}{I} = \frac{11.8 \text{ V}}{0.100 \text{ A}} = 118 \text{ }\Omega$$

The power dissipated in this resistor is

$$P = V_{ab}I = (11.8 \text{ V})(0.100 \text{ A}) = 1.18 \text{ W}$$

EVALUATE: You can confirm this result for the power by using the alternative formula $P = I^2R$. Do you get the same answer?

Example 26.11 **Measuring resistance II**

Suppose the meters of Example 26.10 are connected to a different resistor as shown in Fig. 26.16b, and the readings obtained on the meters are the same as in Example 26.10. What is the value of this new resistance R, and what is the power dissipated in the resistor?

SOLUTION

IDENTIFY and SET UP: In Example 26.10 the ammeter read the actual current through the resistor, but the voltmeter reading was not the same as the potential difference across the resistor. Now the situation is reversed: The voltmeter reading $V = 12.0 \text{ V}$ shows the actual potential difference V_{ab} across the resistor, but the ammeter reading $I_A = 0.100 \text{ A}$ is *not* equal to the current I through the resistor. Applying the junction rule at b in Fig. 26.16b shows that $I_A = I + I_V$, where I_V is the current through the voltmeter. We find I_V from the given values of V and the voltmeter resistance R_V, and we use this value to find the resistor current I. We then determine the resistance R from I and the voltmeter reading, and calculate the power as in Example 26.10.

EXECUTE: We have $I_V = V/R_V = (12.0 \text{ V})/(10,000 \text{ }\Omega) = 1.20 \text{ mA}$. The actual current I in the resistor is $I = I_A - I_V = 0.100 \text{ A} - 0.0012 \text{ A} = 0.0988 \text{ A}$, and the resistance is

$$R = \frac{V_{ab}}{I} = \frac{12.0 \text{ V}}{0.0988 \text{ A}} = 121 \text{ }\Omega$$

The power dissipated in the resistor is

$$P = V_{ab}I = (12.0 \text{ V})(0.0988 \text{ A}) = 1.19 \text{ W}$$

EVALUATE: Had the meters been ideal, our results would have been $R = 12.0 \text{ V}/0.100 \text{ A} = 120 \text{ }\Omega$ and $P = VI = (12.0 \text{ V}) \times (0.100 \text{ A}) = 1.2 \text{ W}$ both here and in Example 26.10. The actual (correct) results are not too different in either case. That's because the ammeter and voltmeter are nearly ideal: Compared with the resistance R under test, the ammeter resistance R_A is very small and the voltmeter resistance R_V is very large. Under these conditions, treating the meters as ideal yields pretty good results; accurate work requires calculations as in these two examples.

Ohmmeters

An alternative method for measuring resistance is to use a d'Arsonval meter in an arrangement called an **ohmmeter.** It consists of a meter, a resistor, and a source (often a flashlight battery) connected in series (Fig. 26.17). The resistance R to be measured is connected between terminals x and y.

The series resistance R_s is variable; it is adjusted so that when terminals x and y are short-circuited (that is, when $R = 0$), the meter deflects full scale. When nothing is connected to terminals x and y, so that the circuit between x and y is *open* (that is, when $R \to \infty$), there is no current and hence no deflection. For any intermediate value of R the meter deflection depends on the value of R, and the meter scale can be calibrated to read the resistance R directly. Larger currents correspond to smaller resistances, so this scale reads backward compared to the scale showing the current.

In situations in which high precision is required, instruments containing d'Arsonval meters have been supplanted by electronic instruments with direct digital readouts. Digital voltmeters can be made with extremely high internal resistance, of the order of 100 MΩ. Figure 26.18 shows a digital *multimeter,* an instrument that can measure voltage, current, or resistance over a wide range.

26.17 Ohmmeter circuit. The resistor R_s has a variable resistance, as is indicated by the arrow through the resistor symbol. To use the ohmmeter, first connect x directly to y and adjust R_s until the meter reads zero. Then connect x and y across the resistor R and read the scale.

The Potentiometer

The *potentiometer* is an instrument that can be used to measure the emf of a source without drawing any current from the source; it also has a number of other useful applications. Essentially, it balances an unknown potential difference against an adjustable, measurable potential difference.

26.18 This digital multimeter can be used as a voltmeter (red arc), ammeter (yellow arc), or ohmmeter (green arc).

26.19 A potentiometer.

(a) Potentiometer circuit

(b) Circuit symbol for potentiometer (variable resistor)

The principle of the potentiometer is shown schematically in Fig. 26.19a. A resistance wire ab of total resistance R_{ab} is permanently connected to the terminals of a source of known emf $\mathcal{E}_1$. A sliding contact c is connected through the galvanometer G to a second source whose emf $\mathcal{E}_2$ is to be measured. As contact c is moved along the resistance wire, the resistance R_{cb} between points c and b varies; if the resistance wire is uniform, R_{cb} is proportional to the length of wire between c and b. To determine the value of $\mathcal{E}_2$, contact c is moved until a position is found at which the galvanometer shows no deflection; this corresponds to zero current passing through $\mathcal{E}_2$. With $I_2 = 0$, Kirchhoff's loop rule gives

$$\mathcal{E}_2 = IR_{cb}$$

With $I_2 = 0$, the current I produced by the emf $\mathcal{E}_1$ has the same value no matter what the value of the emf $\mathcal{E}_2$. We calibrate the device by replacing $\mathcal{E}_2$ by a source of known emf; then any unknown emf $\mathcal{E}_2$ can be found by measuring the length of wire cb for which $I_2 = 0$. Note that for this to work, V_{ab} must be greater than $\mathcal{E}_2$.

The term *potentiometer* is also used for any variable resistor, usually having a circular resistance element and a sliding contact controlled by a rotating shaft and knob. The circuit symbol for a potentiometer is shown in Fig. 26.19b.

Test Your Understanding of Section 26.3 You want to measure the current through and the potential difference across the 2-Ω resistor shown in Fig. 26.12 (Example 26.6 in Section 26.2). (a) How should you connect an ammeter and a voltmeter to do this? (i) ammeter and voltmeter both in series with the 2-Ω resistor; (ii) ammeter in series with the 2-Ω resistor and voltmeter connected between points b and d; (iii) ammeter connected between points b and d and voltmeter in series with the 2-Ω resistor; (iv) ammeter and voltmeter both connected between points b and d. (b) What resistances should these meters have? (i) Ammeter and voltmeter resistances should both be much greater than 2 Ω; (ii) ammeter resistance should be much greater than 2 Ω and voltmeter resistance should be much less than 2 Ω; (iii) ammeter resistance should be much less than 2 Ω and voltmeter resistance should be much greater than 2 Ω; (iv) ammeter and voltmeter resistances should both be much less than 2 Ω.

26.4 *R-C* Circuits

In the circuits we have analyzed up to this point, we have assumed that all the emfs and resistances are *constant* (time independent) so that all the potentials, currents, and powers are also independent of time. But in the simple act of charging or discharging a capacitor we find a situation in which the currents, voltages, and powers *do* change with time.

Many devices incorporate circuits in which a capacitor is alternately charged and discharged. These include flashing traffic lights, automobile turn signals, and electronic flash units. Understanding what happens in such circuits is thus of great practical importance.

Charging a Capacitor

Figure 26.20 shows a simple circuit for charging a capacitor. A circuit such as this that has a resistor and a capacitor in series is called an ***R-C* circuit.** We idealize the battery (or power supply) to have a constant emf $\mathcal{E}$ and zero internal resistance ($r = 0$), and we neglect the resistance of all the connecting conductors.

We begin with the capacitor initially uncharged (Fig. 26.20a); then at some initial time $t = 0$ we close the switch, completing the circuit and permitting current around the loop to begin charging the capacitor (Fig. 26.20b). For all practical purposes, the current begins at the same instant in every conducting part of the circuit, and at each instant the current is the same in every part.

CAUTION **Lowercase means time-varying** Up to this point we have been working with constant potential differences (voltages), currents, and charges, and we have used *capital* letters *V*, *I*, and *Q*, respectively, to denote these quantities. To distinguish between quantities that vary with time and those that are constant, we will use *lowercase* letters *v*, *i*, and *q* for time-varying voltages, currents, and charges, respectively. We suggest that you follow this same convention in your own work.

Because the capacitor in Fig. 26.20 is initially uncharged, the potential difference v_{bc} across it is zero at $t = 0$. At this time, from Kirchhoff's loop law, the voltage v_{ab} across the resistor R is equal to the battery emf $\mathcal{E}$. The initial ($t = 0$) current through the resistor, which we will call I_0, is given by Ohm's law: $I_0 = v_{ab}/R = \mathcal{E}/R$.

As the capacitor charges, its voltage v_{bc} increases and the potential difference v_{ab} across the resistor decreases, corresponding to a decrease in current. The sum of these two voltages is constant and equal to $\mathcal{E}$. After a long time the capacitor becomes fully charged, the current decreases to zero, and the potential difference v_{ab} across the resistor becomes zero. Then the entire battery emf $\mathcal{E}$ appears across the capacitor and $v_{bc} = \mathcal{E}$.

Let q represent the charge on the capacitor and i the current in the circuit at some time t after the switch has been closed. We choose the positive direction for the current to correspond to positive charge flowing onto the left-hand capacitor plate, as in Fig. 26.20b. The instantaneous potential differences v_{ab} and v_{bc} are

$$v_{ab} = iR \qquad v_{bc} = \frac{q}{C}$$

Using these in Kirchhoff's loop rule, we find

$$\mathcal{E} - iR - \frac{q}{C} = 0 \qquad (26.9)$$

The potential drops by an amount iR as we travel from a to b and by q/C as we travel from b to c. Solving Eq. (26.9) for i, we find

$$i = \frac{\mathcal{E}}{R} - \frac{q}{RC} \qquad (26.10)$$

At time $t = 0$, when the switch is first closed, the capacitor is uncharged, and so $q = 0$. Substituting $q = 0$ into Eq. (26.10), we find that the *initial* current I_0 is given by $I_0 = \mathcal{E}/R$, as we have already noted. If the capacitor were not in the circuit, the last term in Eq. (26.10) would not be present; then the current would be *constant* and equal to $\mathcal{E}/R$.

As the charge q increases, the term q/RC becomes larger and the capacitor charge approaches its final value, which we will call Q_f. The current decreases and eventually becomes zero. When $i = 0$, Eq. (26.10) gives

$$\frac{\mathcal{E}}{R} = \frac{Q_f}{RC} \qquad Q_f = C\mathcal{E} \qquad (26.11)$$

Note that the final charge Q_f does not depend on R.

Figure 26.21 shows the current and capacitor charge as functions of time. At the instant the switch is closed ($t = 0$), the current jumps from zero to its initial value $I_0 = \mathcal{E}/R$; after that, it gradually approaches zero. The capacitor charge starts at zero and gradually approaches the final value given by Eq. (26.11), $Q_f = C\mathcal{E}$.

We can derive general expressions for the charge q and current i as functions of time. With our choice of the positive direction for current (Fig. 26.20b), i equals the rate at which positive charge arrives at the left-hand (positive)

26.20 Charging a capacitor. (a) Just before the switch is closed, the charge q is zero. (b) When the switch closes (at $t = 0$), the current jumps from zero to $\mathcal{E}/R$. As time passes, q approaches Q_f and the current i approaches zero.

(a) Capacitor initially uncharged

(b) Charging the capacitor

When the switch is closed, the charge on the capacitor increases over time while the current decreases.

26.21 Current i and capacitor charge q as functions of time for the circuit of Fig. 26.20. The initial current is I_0 and the initial capacitor charge is zero. The current asymptotically approaches zero, and the capacitor charge asymptotically approaches a final value of Q_f.

(a) Graph of current versus time for a charging capacitor

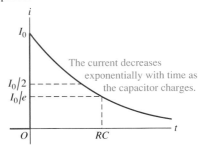

The current decreases exponentially with time as the capacitor charges.

(b) Graph of capacitor charge versus time for a charging capacitor

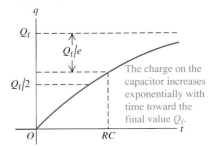

The charge on the capacitor increases exponentially with time toward the final value Q_f.

plate of the capacitor, so $i = dq/dt$. Making this substitution in Eq. (26.10), we have

$$\frac{dq}{dt} = \frac{\mathcal{E}}{R} - \frac{q}{RC} = -\frac{1}{RC}(q - C\mathcal{E})$$

We can rearrange this to

$$\frac{dq}{q - C\mathcal{E}} = -\frac{dt}{RC}$$

and then integrate both sides. We change the integration variables to q' and t' so that we can use q and t for the upper limits. The lower limits are $q' = 0$ and $t' = 0$:

$$\int_0^q \frac{dq'}{q' - C\mathcal{E}} = -\int_0^t \frac{dt'}{RC}$$

When we carry out the integration, we get

$$\ln\left(\frac{q - C\mathcal{E}}{-C\mathcal{E}}\right) = -\frac{t}{RC}$$

Exponentiating both sides (that is, taking the inverse logarithm) and solving for q, we find

$$\frac{q - C\mathcal{E}}{-C\mathcal{E}} = e^{-t/RC}$$

$$q = C\mathcal{E}(1 - e^{-t/RC}) = Q_f(1 - e^{-t/RC}) \quad \begin{array}{l}\text{(R-C circuit, charging} \\ \text{capacitor)}\end{array} \quad (26.12)$$

The instantaneous current i is just the time derivative of Eq. (26.12):

$$i = \frac{dq}{dt} = \frac{\mathcal{E}}{R}e^{-t/RC} = I_0 e^{-t/RC} \quad \begin{array}{l}\text{(R-C circuit, charging} \\ \text{capacitor)}\end{array} \quad (26.13)$$

The charge and current are both *exponential* functions of time. Figure 26.21a is a graph of Eq. (26.13) and Fig. 26.21b is a graph of Eq. (26.12).

Time Constant

After a time equal to RC, the current in the R-C circuit has decreased to $1/e$ (about 0.368) of its initial value. At this time, the capacitor charge has reached $(1 - 1/e) = 0.632$ of its final value $Q_f = C\mathcal{E}$. The product RC is therefore a measure of how quickly the capacitor charges. We call RC the **time constant,** or the **relaxation time,** of the circuit, denoted by τ:

$$\tau = RC \quad \text{(time constant for R-C circuit)} \quad (26.14)$$

When τ is small, the capacitor charges quickly; when it is larger, the charging takes more time. If the resistance is small, it's easier for current to flow, and the capacitor charges more quickly. If R is in ohms and C in farads, τ is in seconds.

In Fig. 26.21a the horizontal axis is an *asymptote* for the curve. Strictly speaking, i never becomes exactly zero. But the longer we wait, the closer it gets. After a time equal to $10RC$, the current has decreased to 0.000045 of its initial value. Similarly, the curve in Fig. 26.21b approaches the horizontal dashed line labeled Q_f as an asymptote. The charge q never attains exactly this value, but after a time equal to $10RC$, the difference between q and Q_f is only 0.000045 of Q_f. We invite you to verify that the product RC has units of time.

PhET: Circuit Construction Kit (AC+DC)
PhET: Circuit Construction Kit (DC Only)
ActivPhysics 12.6: Capacitance
ActivPhysics 12.7: Series and Parallel Capacitors
ActivPhysics 12.8: Circuit Time Constants

Application Pacemakers and Capacitors
This x-ray image shows a pacemaker implanted in a patient with a malfunctioning sinoatrial node, the part of the heart that generates the electrical signal to trigger heartbeats. The pacemaker circuit contains a battery, a capacitor, and a computer-controlled switch. To maintain regular beating, once per second the switch discharges the capacitor and sends an electrical pulse along the lead to the heart. The switch then flips to allow the capacitor to recharge for the next pulse.

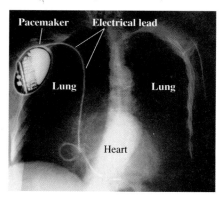

Discharging a Capacitor

Now suppose that after the capacitor in Fig. 26.21b has acquired a charge Q_0, we remove the battery from our *R-C* circuit and connect points *a* and *c* to an open switch (Fig. 26.22a). We then close the switch and at the same instant reset our stopwatch to $t = 0$; at that time, $q = Q_0$. The capacitor then *discharges* through the resistor, and its charge eventually decreases to zero.

Again let *i* and *q* represent the time-varying current and charge at some instant after the connection is made. In Fig. 26.22b we make the same choice of the positive direction for current as in Fig. 26.20b. Then Kirchhoff's loop rule gives Eq. (26.10) but with $\mathcal{E} = 0$; that is,

$$i = \frac{dq}{dt} = -\frac{q}{RC} \tag{26.15}$$

The current *i* is now negative; this is because positive charge *q* is leaving the left-hand capacitor plate in Fig. 26.22b, so the current is in the direction opposite to that shown in the figure. At time $t = 0$, when $q = Q_0$, the initial current is $I_0 = -Q_0/RC$.

To find *q* as a function of time, we rearrange Eq. (26.15), again change the names of the variables to q' and t', and integrate. This time the limits for q' are Q_0 to *q*. We get

$$\int_{Q_0}^{q} \frac{dq'}{q'} = -\frac{1}{RC} \int_{0}^{t} dt'$$

$$\ln \frac{q}{Q_0} = -\frac{t}{RC}$$

$$q = Q_0 e^{-t/RC} \qquad \text{(R-C circuit, discharging capacitor)} \tag{26.16}$$

The instantaneous current *i* is the derivative of this with respect to time:

$$i = \frac{dq}{dt} = -\frac{Q_0}{RC} e^{-t/RC} = I_0 e^{-t/RC} \qquad \begin{array}{l}\text{(R-C circuit,}\\ \text{discharging capacitor)}\end{array} \tag{26.17}$$

We graph the current and the charge in Fig. 26.23; both quantities approach zero exponentially with time. Comparing these results with Eqs. (26.12) and (26.13), we note that the expressions for the current are identical, apart from the sign of I_0. The capacitor charge approaches zero asymptotically in Eq. (26.16), while the *difference* between *q* and *Q* approaches zero asymptotically in Eq. (26.12).

Energy considerations give us additional insight into the behavior of an *R-C* circuit. While the capacitor is charging, the instantaneous rate at which the battery delivers energy to the circuit is $P = \mathcal{E}i$. The instantaneous rate at which electrical energy is dissipated in the resistor is i^2R, and the rate at which energy is stored in the capacitor is $iv_{bc} = iq/C$. Multiplying Eq. (26.9) by *i*, we find

$$\mathcal{E}i = i^2R + \frac{iq}{C} \tag{26.18}$$

This means that of the power $\mathcal{E}i$ supplied by the battery, part (i^2R) is dissipated in the resistor and part (iq/C) is stored in the capacitor.

The *total* energy supplied by the battery during charging of the capacitor equals the battery emf $\mathcal{E}$ multiplied by the total charge Q_f, or $\mathcal{E}Q_f$. The total energy stored in the capacitor, from Eq. (24.9), is $Q_f\mathcal{E}/2$. Thus, of the energy supplied by the battery, *exactly half* is stored in the capacitor, and the other half is dissipated in the resistor. This half-and-half division of energy doesn't depend on *C*, *R*, or $\mathcal{E}$. You can verify this result by taking the integral over time of each of the power quantities in Eq. (26.18) (see Problem 26.88).

26.22 Discharging a capacitor. (a) Before the switch is closed at time $t = 0$, the capacitor charge is Q_0 and the current is zero. (b) At time *t* after the switch is closed, the capacitor charge is *q* and the current is *i*. The actual current direction is opposite to the direction shown; *i* is negative. After a long time, *q* and *i* both approach zero.

(a) Capacitor initially charged

(b) Discharging the capacitor

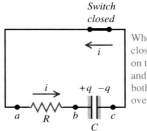

When the switch is closed, the charge on the capacitor and the current both decrease over time.

26.23 Current *i* and capacitor charge *q* as functions of time for the circuit of Fig. 26.22. The initial current is I_0 and the initial capacitor charge is Q_0. Both *i* and *q* asymptotically approach zero.

(a) Graph of current versus time for a discharging capacitor

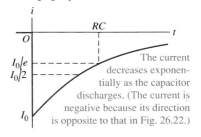

The current decreases exponentially as the capacitor discharges. (The current is negative because its direction is opposite to that in Fig. 26.22.)

(b) Graph of capacitor charge versus time for a discharging capacitor

The charge on the capacitor decreases exponentially as the capacitor discharges.

Example 26.12 Charging a capacitor

A 10-MΩ resistor is connected in series with a 1.0-μF capacitor and a battery with emf 12.0 V. Before the switch is closed at time $t = 0$, the capacitor is uncharged. (a) What is the time constant? (b) What fraction of the final charge Q_f is on the capacitor at $t = 46$ s? (c) What fraction of the initial current I_0 is still flowing at $t = 46$ s?

SOLUTION

IDENTIFY and SET UP: This is the same situation as shown in Fig. 26.20, with $R = 10$ MΩ, $C = 1.0$ μF, and $\mathcal{E} = 12.0$ V. The charge q and current i vary with time as shown in Fig. 26.21. Our target variables are (a) the time constant τ, (b) the ratio q/Q_f at $t = 46$ s, and (c) the ratio i/I_0 at $t = 46$ s. Equation (26.14) gives τ. For a capacitor being charged, Eq. (26.12) gives q and Eq. (26.13) gives i.

EXECUTE: (a) From Eq. (26.14),
$$\tau = RC = (10 \times 10^6 \ \Omega)(1.0 \times 10^{-6} \ \text{F}) = 10 \ \text{s}$$

(b) From Eq. (26.12),
$$\frac{q}{Q_f} = 1 - e^{-t/RC} = 1 - e^{-(46 \ \text{s})/(10 \ \text{s})} = 0.99$$

(c) From Eq. (26.13),
$$\frac{i}{I_0} = e^{-t/RC} = e^{-(46 \ \text{s})/(10 \ \text{s})} = 0.010$$

EVALUATE: After 4.6 time constants the capacitor is 99% charged and the charging current has decreased to 1.0% of its initial value. The circuit would charge more rapidly if we reduced the time constant by using a smaller resistance.

Example 26.13 Discharging a capacitor

The resistor and capacitor of Example 26.12 are reconnected as shown in Fig. 26.22. The capacitor has an initial charge of 5.0 μC and is discharged by closing the switch at $t = 0$. (a) At what time will the charge be equal to 0.50 μC? (b) What is the current at this time?

SOLUTION

IDENTIFY and SET UP: Now the capacitor is being discharged, so q and i vary with time as in Fig. 26.23, with $Q_0 = 5.0 \times 10^{-6}$ C. Again we have $RC = \tau = 10$ s. Our target variables are (a) the value of t at which $q = 0.50$ μC and (b) the value of i at this time. We first solve Eq. (26.16) for t, and then solve Eq. (26.17) for i.

EXECUTE: (a) Solving Eq. (26.16) for the time t gives
$$t = -RC \ln \frac{q}{Q_0} = -(10 \ \text{s}) \ln \frac{0.50 \ \mu\text{C}}{5.0 \ \mu\text{C}} = 23 \ \text{s} = 2.3\tau$$

(b) From Eq. (26.17), with $Q_0 = 5.0$ μC $= 5.0 \times 10^{-6}$ C,
$$i = -\frac{Q_0}{RC} e^{-t/RC} = -\frac{5.0 \times 10^{-6} \ \text{C}}{10 \ \text{s}} e^{-2.3} = -5.0 \times 10^{-8} \ \text{A}$$

EVALUATE: The current in part (b) is negative because i has the opposite sign when the capacitor is discharging than when it is charging. Note that we could have avoided evaluating $e^{-t/RC}$ by noticing that at the time in question, $q = 0.10Q_0$; from Eq. (26.16) this means that $e^{-t/RC} = 0.10$.

Test Your Understanding of Section 26.4 The energy stored in a capacitor is equal to $q^2/2C$. When a capacitor is discharged, what fraction of the initial energy remains after an elapsed time of one time constant? (i) $1/e$; (ii) $1/e^2$; (iii) $1 - 1/e$; (iv) $(1 - 1/e)^2$; (v) answer depends on how much energy was stored initially.

26.5 Power Distribution Systems

We conclude this chapter with a brief discussion of practical household and automotive electric-power distribution systems. Automobiles use direct-current (dc) systems, while nearly all household, commercial, and industrial systems use alternating current (ac) because of the ease of stepping voltage up and down with transformers. Most of the same basic wiring concepts apply to both. We'll talk about alternating-current circuits in greater detail in Chapter 31.

The various lamps, motors, and other appliances to be operated are always connected in *parallel* to the power source (the wires from the power company for houses, or from the battery and alternator for a car). If appliances were connected in series, shutting one appliance off would shut them all off (see Example 26.2 in Section 26.1). Figure 26.24 shows the basic idea of house wiring. One side of the "line," as the pair of conductors is called, is called the *neutral* side; it is always connected to

26.24 Schematic diagram of part of a house wiring system. Only two branch circuits are shown; an actual system might have four to thirty branch circuits. Lamps and appliances may be plugged into the outlets. The grounding wires, which normally carry no current, are not shown.

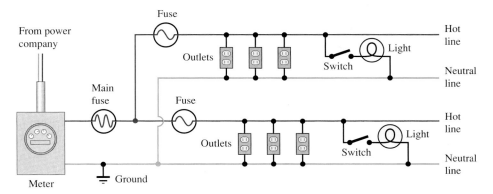

"ground" at the entrance panel. For houses, *ground* is an actual electrode driven into the earth (which is usually a good conductor) or sometimes connected to the household water pipes. Electricians speak of the "hot" side and the "neutral" side of the line. Most modern house wiring systems have *two* hot lines with opposite polarity with respect to the neutral. We'll return to this detail later.

Household voltage is nominally 120 V in the United States and Canada, and often 240 V in Europe. (For alternating current, which varies sinusoidally with time, these numbers represent the *root-mean-square* voltage, which is $1/\sqrt{2}$ times the peak voltage. We'll discuss this further in Section 31.1.) The amount of current I drawn by a given device is determined by its power input P, given by Eq. (25.17): $P = VI$. Hence $I = P/V$. For example, the current in a 100-W light bulb is

$$I = \frac{P}{V} = \frac{100 \text{ W}}{120 \text{ V}} = 0.83 \text{ A}$$

The power input to this bulb is actually determined by its resistance R. Using Eq. (25.18), which states that $P = VI = I^2R = V^2/R$ for a resistor, the resistance of this bulb at operating temperature is

$$R = \frac{V}{I} = \frac{120 \text{ V}}{0.83 \text{ A}} = 144 \text{ } \Omega \qquad \text{or} \qquad R = \frac{V^2}{P} = \frac{(120 \text{ V})^2}{100 \text{ W}} = 144 \text{ } \Omega$$

Similarly, a 1500-W waffle iron draws a current of $(1500 \text{ W})/(120 \text{ V}) = 12.5 \text{ A}$ and has a resistance, at operating temperature, of 9.6 Ω. Because of the temperature dependence of resistivity, the resistances of these devices are considerably less when they are cold. If you measure the resistance of a 100-W light bulb with an ohmmeter (whose small current causes very little temperature rise), you will probably get a value of about 10 Ω. When a light bulb is turned on, this low resistance causes an initial surge of current until the filament heats up. That's why a light bulb that's ready to burn out nearly always does so just when you turn it on.

Circuit Overloads and Short Circuits

The maximum current available from an individual circuit is limited by the resistance of the wires. As we discussed in Section 25.5, the I^2R power loss in the wires causes them to become hot, and in extreme cases this can cause a fire or melt the wires. Ordinary lighting and outlet wiring in houses usually uses 12-gauge wire. This has a diameter of 2.05 mm and can carry a maximum current of 20 A safely (without overheating). Larger-diameter wires of the same length have lower resistance [see Eq. (25.10)]. Hence 8-gauge (3.26 mm) or 6-gauge (4.11 mm) are used for high-current appliances such as clothes dryers, and 2-gauge (6.54 mm) or larger is used for the main power lines entering a house.

26.25 (a) Excess current will melt the thin wire of lead–tin alloy that runs along the length of a fuse, inside the transparent housing. (b) The switch on this circuit breaker will flip if the maximum allowable current is exceeded.

(a)

(b)

Protection against overloading and overheating of circuits is provided by fuses or circuit breakers. A *fuse* contains a link of lead–tin alloy with a very low melting temperature; the link melts and breaks the circuit when its rated current is exceeded (Fig. 26.25a). A *circuit breaker* is an electromechanical device that performs the same function, using an electromagnet or a bimetallic strip to "trip" the breaker and interrupt the circuit when the current exceeds a specified value (Fig. 26.25b). Circuit breakers have the advantage that they can be reset after they are tripped, while a blown fuse must be replaced.

If your system has fuses and you plug too many high-current appliances into the same outlet, the fuse blows. *Do not* replace the fuse with one of larger rating; if you do, you risk overheating the wires and starting a fire. The only safe solution is to distribute the appliances among several circuits. Modern kitchens often have three or four separate 20-A circuits.

Contact between the hot and neutral sides of the line causes a *short circuit.* Such a situation, which can be caused by faulty insulation or by any of a variety of mechanical malfunctions, provides a very low-resistance current path, permitting a very large current that would quickly melt the wires and ignite their insulation if the current were not interrupted by a fuse or circuit breaker (see Example 25.10 in Section 25.5). An equally dangerous situation is a broken wire that interrupts the current path, creating an *open circuit.* This is hazardous because of the sparking that can occur at the point of intermittent contact.

In approved wiring practice, a fuse or breaker is placed *only* in the hot side of the line, never in the neutral side. Otherwise, if a short circuit should develop because of faulty insulation or other malfunction, the ground-side fuse could blow. The hot side would still be live and would pose a shock hazard if you touched the live conductor and a grounded object such as a water pipe. For similar reasons the wall switch for a light fixture is always in the hot side of the line, never the neutral side.

Further protection against shock hazard is provided by a third conductor called the *grounding wire,* included in all present-day wiring. This conductor corresponds to the long round or U-shaped prong of the three-prong connector plug on an appliance or power tool. It is connected to the neutral side of the line at the entrance panel. The grounding wire normally carries no current, but it connects the metal case or frame of the device to ground. If a conductor on the hot side of the line accidentally contacts the frame or case, the grounding conductor provides a current path, and the fuse blows. Without the ground wire, the frame could become "live"—that is, at a potential 120 V above ground. Then if you touched it and a water pipe (or even a damp basement floor) at the same time, you could get a dangerous shock (Fig. 26.26). In some situations, especially outlets located outdoors or near a sink or other water pipes, a special kind of circuit breaker called a *ground-fault interrupter* (GFI or GFCI) is used. This device senses the difference in current between the hot and neutral conductors (which is normally zero) and trips when this difference exceeds some very small value, typically 5 mA.

Household and Automotive Wiring

Most modern household wiring systems actually use a slight elaboration of the system described above. The power company provides *three* conductors. One is neutral; the other two are both at 120 V with respect to the neutral but with opposite polarity, giving a voltage between them of 240 V. The power company calls this a *three-wire line,* in contrast to the 120-V two-wire (plus ground wire) line described above. With a three-wire line, 120-V lamps and appliances can be connected between neutral and either hot conductor, and high-power devices requiring 240 V, such as electric ranges and clothes dryers, are connected between the two hot lines.

All of the above discussion can be applied directly to automobile wiring. The voltage is about 13 V (direct current); the power is supplied by the battery and by

(a) Two-prong plug   (b) Three-prong plug

26.26 (a) If a malfunctioning electric drill is connected to a wall socket via a two-prong plug, a person may receive a shock. (b) When the drill malfunctions when connected via a three-prong plug, a person touching it receives no shock, because electric charge flows through the ground wire (shown in green) to the third prong and into the ground rather than into the person's body. If the ground current is appreciable, the fuse blows.

the alternator, which charges the battery when the engine is running. The neutral side of each circuit is connected to the body and frame of the vehicle. For this low voltage a separate grounding conductor is not required for safety. The fuse or circuit breaker arrangement is the same in principle as in household wiring. Because of the lower voltage (less energy per charge), more current (a greater number of charges per second) is required for the same power; a 100-W headlight bulb requires a current of about $(100\ \text{W})/(13\ \text{V}) = 8\ \text{A}$.

Although we spoke of *power* in the above discussion, what we buy from the power company is *energy*. Power is energy transferred per unit time, so energy is average power multiplied by time. The usual unit of energy sold by the power company is the kilowatt-hour $(1\ \text{kW} \cdot \text{h})$:

$$1\ \text{kW} \cdot \text{h} = (10^3\ \text{W})(3600\ \text{s}) = 3.6 \times 10^6\ \text{W} \cdot \text{s} = 3.6 \times 10^6\ \text{J}$$

In the United States, one kilowatt-hour typically costs 8 to 27 cents, depending on the location and quantity of energy purchased. To operate a 1500-W (1.5-kW) waffle iron continuously for 1 hour requires 1.5 kW · h of energy; at 10 cents per kilowatt-hour, the energy cost is 15 cents. The cost of operating any lamp or appliance for a specified time can be calculated in the same way if the power rating is known. However, many electric cooking utensils (including waffle irons) cycle on and off to maintain a constant temperature, so the average power may be less than the power rating marked on the device.

Example 26.14   A kitchen circuit

An 1800-W toaster, a 1.3-kW electric frying pan, and a 100-W lamp are plugged into the same 20-A, 120-V circuit. (a) What current is drawn by each device, and what is the resistance of each device? (b) Will this combination trip the circuit breaker?

SOLUTION

IDENTIFY and SET UP: When plugged into the same circuit, the three devices are connected in parallel, so the voltage across each appliance is $V = 120$ V. We find the current I drawn by each device using the relationship $P = VI$, where P is the power input of the device. To find the resistance R of each device we use the relationship $P = V^2/R$.

EXECUTE: (a) To simplify the calculation of current and resistance, we note that $I = P/V$ and $R = V^2/P$. Hence

$$I_{\text{toaster}} = \frac{1800\ \text{W}}{120\ \text{V}} = 15\ \text{A} \qquad R_{\text{toaster}} = \frac{(120\ \text{V})^2}{1800\ \text{W}} = 8\ \Omega$$

$$I_{\text{frying pan}} = \frac{1300\ \text{W}}{120\ \text{V}} = 11\ \text{A} \qquad R_{\text{frying pan}} = \frac{(120\ \text{V})^2}{1300\ \text{W}} = 11\ \Omega$$

$$I_{\text{lamp}} = \frac{100\ \text{W}}{120\ \text{V}} = 0.83\ \text{A} \qquad R_{\text{lamp}} = \frac{(120\ \text{V})^2}{100\ \text{W}} = 144\ \Omega$$

For constant voltage the device with the *least* resistance (in this case the toaster) draws the most current and receives the most power.

Continued

(b) The total current through the line is the sum of the currents drawn by the three devices:

$$I = I_{\text{toaster}} + I_{\text{frying pan}} + I_{\text{lamp}}$$
$$= 15 \text{ A} + 11 \text{ A} + 0.83 \text{ A} = 27 \text{ A}$$

This exceeds the 20-A rating of the line, and the circuit breaker will indeed trip.

EVALUATE: We could also find the total current by using $I = P/V$ and dividing the total power P delivered to all three devices by the voltage:

$$I = \frac{P_{\text{toaster}} + P_{\text{frying pan}} + P_{\text{lamp}}}{V}$$
$$= \frac{1800 \text{ W} + 1300 \text{ W} + 100 \text{ W}}{120 \text{ V}} = 27 \text{ A}$$

A third way to determine I is to use $I = V/R_{\text{eq}}$, where R_{eq} is the equivalent resistance of the three devices in parallel:

$$I = \frac{V}{R_{\text{eq}}} = (120 \text{ V})\left(\frac{1}{8 \text{ } \Omega} + \frac{1}{11 \text{ } \Omega} + \frac{1}{144 \text{ } \Omega}\right) = 27 \text{ A}$$

Appliances with such current demands are common, so modern kitchens have more than one 20-A circuit. To keep currents safely below 20 A, the toaster and frying pan should be plugged into different circuits.

Test Your Understanding of Section 26.5 To prevent the circuit breaker in Example 26.14 from blowing, a home electrician replaces the circuit breaker with one rated at 40 A. Is this a reasonable thing to do?

Resistors in series and parallel: When several resistors $R_1, R_2, R_3, \ldots$ are connected in series, the equivalent resistance R_{eq} is the sum of the individual resistances. The same *current* flows through all the resistors in a series connection. When several resistors are connected in parallel, the reciprocal of the equivalent resistance R_{eq} is the sum of the reciprocals of the individual resistances. All resistors in a parallel connection have the same *potential difference* between their terminals. (See Examples 26.1 and 26.2.)

$$R_{eq} = R_1 + R_2 + R_3 + \cdots \quad (26.1)$$
(resistors in series)

$$\frac{1}{R_{eq}} = \frac{1}{R_1} + \frac{1}{R_2} + \frac{1}{R_3} + \cdots \quad (26.2)$$
(resistors in parallel)

Kirchhoff's rules: Kirchhoff's junction rule is based on conservation of charge. It states that the algebraic sum of the currents into any junction must be zero. Kirchhoff's loop rule is based on conservation of energy and the conservative nature of electrostatic fields. It states that the algebraic sum of potential differences around any loop must be zero. Careful use of consistent sign rules is essential in applying Kirchhoff's rules. (See Examples 26.3–26.7.)

$$\sum I = 0 \quad \text{(junction rule)} \quad (26.5)$$
$$\sum V = 0 \quad \text{(loop rule)} \quad (26.6)$$

Electrical measuring instruments: In a d'Arsonval galvanometer, the deflection is proportional to the current in the coil. For a larger current range, a shunt resistor is added, so some of the current bypasses the meter coil. Such an instrument is called an ammeter. If the coil and any additional series resistance included obey Ohm's law, the meter can also be calibrated to read potential difference or voltage. The instrument is then called a voltmeter. A good ammeter has very low resistance; a good voltmeter has very high resistance. (See Examples 26.8–26.11.)

R-C circuits: When a capacitor is charged by a battery in series with a resistor, the current and capacitor charge are not constant. The charge approaches its final value asymptotically and the current approaches zero asymptotically. The charge and current in the circuit are given by Eqs. (26.12) and (26.13). After a time $\tau = RC$, the charge has approached within $1/e$ of its final value. This time is called the time constant or relaxation time of the circuit. When the capacitor discharges, the charge and current are given as functions of time by Eqs. (26.16) and (26.17). The time constant is the same for charging and discharging. (See Examples 26.12 and 26.13.)

Capacitor charging:
$$q = C\mathcal{E}\left(1 - e^{-t/RC}\right)$$
$$= Q_f\left(1 - e^{-t/RC}\right) \quad (26.12)$$
$$i = \frac{dq}{dt} = \frac{\mathcal{E}}{R}e^{-t/RC}$$
$$= I_0 e^{-t/RC} \quad (26.13)$$

Capacitor discharging:
$$q = Q_0 e^{-t/RC} \quad (26.16)$$
$$i = \frac{dq}{dt} = -\frac{Q_0}{RC}e^{-t/RC}$$
$$= I_0 e^{-t/RC} \quad (26.17)$$

Household wiring: In household wiring systems, the various electrical devices are connected in parallel across the power line, which consists of a pair of conductors, one "hot" and the other "neutral." An additional "ground" wire is included for safety. The maximum permissible current in a circuit is determined by the size of the wires and the maximum temperature they can tolerate. Protection against excessive current and the resulting fire hazard is provided by fuses or circuit breakers. (See Example 26.14.)

BRIDGING PROBLEM | Two Capacitors and Two Resistors

A 2.40-μF capacitor and a 3.60-μF capacitor are connected in series. (a) A charge of 5.20 mC is placed on each capacitor. What is the energy stored in the capacitors? (b) A 655-Ω resistor is connected to the terminals of the capacitor combination, and a voltmeter with resistance $4.58 \times 10^4 \ \Omega$ is connected across the resistor. What is the rate of change of the energy stored in the capacitors just after the connection is made? (c) How long after the connection is made has the energy stored in the capacitors decreased to $1/e$ of its initial value? (d) At the instant calculated in part (c), what is the rate of change of the energy stored in the capacitors?

SOLUTION GUIDE

See MasteringPhysics® study area for a Video Tutor solution.

IDENTIFY and SET UP

1. The two capacitors act as a single equivalent capacitor (see Section 24.2), and the resistor and voltmeter act as a single equivalent resistor. Select equations that will allow you to calculate the values of these equivalent circuit elements.

2. Equation (24.9) gives the energy stored in a capacitor. Equations (26.16) and (26.17) give the capacitor charge and current as functions of time. Use these to set up the solutions to the various parts of this problem. (*Hint:* The rate at which energy is lost by the capacitors equals the rate at which energy is dissipated in the resistances.)

EXECUTE

3. Find the stored energy at $t = 0$.
4. Find the rate of change of the stored energy at $t = 0$.
5. Find the value of t at which the stored energy has $1/e$ of the value you found in step 3.
6. Find the rate of change of the stored energy at the time you found in step 5.

EVALUATE

7. Check your results from steps 4 and 6 by calculating the rate of change in a different way. (*Hint:* The rate of change of the stored energy U is dU/dt.)

Problems

For instructor-assigned homework, go to www.masteringphysics.com

•, ••, •••: Problems of increasing difficulty. **CP**: Cumulative problems incorporating material from earlier chapters. **CALC**: Problems requiring calculus. **BIO**: Biosciences problems.

DISCUSSION QUESTIONS

Q26.1 In which 120-V light bulb does the filament have greater resistance: a 60-W bulb or a 120-W bulb? If the two bulbs are connected to a 120-V line in series, through which bulb will there be the greater voltage drop? What if they are connected in parallel? Explain your reasoning.

Q26.2 Two 120-V light bulbs, one 25-W and one 200-W, were connected in series across a 240-V line. It seemed like a good idea at the time, but one bulb burned out almost immediately. Which one burned out, and why?

Q26.3 You connect a number of identical light bulbs to a flashlight battery. (a) What happens to the brightness of each bulb as more and more bulbs are added to the circuit if you connect them (i) in series and (ii) in parallel? (b) Will the battery last longer if the bulbs are in series or in parallel? Explain your reasoning.

Q26.4 In the circuit shown in Fig. Q26.4, three identical light bulbs are connected to a flashlight battery. How do the brightnesses of the bulbs compare? Which light bulb has the greatest current passing through it? Which light bulb has the greatest potential difference between its terminals? What happens if bulb A is unscrewed? Bulb B? Bulb C? Explain your reasoning.

Figure **Q26.4**

Q26.5 If two resistors R_1 and R_2 ($R_2 > R_1$) are connected in series as shown in Fig. Q26.5, which of the following must be true? In each case justify your answer. (a) $I_1 = I_2 = I_3$. (b) The current is greater in R_1 than in R_2. (c) The electrical power consumption is the same for both resistors. (d) The electrical power consumption is greater in R_2 than in R_1.

Figure **Q26.5**

$\xrightarrow{I_1} a \ R_1 \ \xrightarrow{I_2} b \ R_2 \ \xrightarrow{I_3} c$

(e) The potential drop is the same across both resistors. (f) The potential at point a is the same as at point c. (g) The potential at point b is lower than at point c. (h) The potential at point c is lower than at point b.

Q26.6 If two resistors R_1 and R_2 ($R_2 > R_1$) are connected in parallel as shown in Fig. Q26.6, which of the following must be true? In each case justify your answer. (a) $I_1 = I_2$. (b) $I_3 = I_4$. (c) The current is greater in R_1 than in R_2. (d) The rate of electrical energy consumption is the same for both resistors. (e) The rate of electrical energy consumption is greater in R_2 than in R_1. (f) $V_{cd} = V_{ef} = V_{ab}$. (g) Point c is at higher potential than point d. (h) Point f is at higher potential than point e. (i) Point c is at higher potential than point e.

Figure **Q26.6**

Q26.7 Why do the lights on a car become dimmer when the starter is operated?

Q26.8 A resistor consists of three identical metal strips connected as shown in Fig. Q26.8. If one of the strips is cut out, does the ammeter reading increase, decrease, or stay the same? Why?

Figure **Q26.8**

Q26.9 A light bulb is connected in the circuit shown in Fig. Q26.9. If we close the switch S, does the bulb's brightness increase, decrease, or remain the same? Explain why.

Figure **Q26.9**

Q26.10 A real battery, having nonnegligible internal resistance, is connected across a light bulb as shown in Fig. Q26.10. When the switch S is closed, what happens to the brightness of the bulb? Why?

Figure **Q26.10**

Q26.11 If the battery in Discussion Question Q26.10 is ideal with no internal resistance, what will happen to the brightness of the bulb when S is closed? Why?

Q26.12 For the circuit shown in Fig. Q26.12 what happens to the brightness of the bulbs when the switch S is closed if the battery (a) has no internal resistance and (b) has nonnegligible internal resistance? Explain why.

Figure **Q26.12**

Q26.13 Is it possible to connect resistors together in a way that cannot be reduced to some combination of series and parallel combinations? If so, give examples. If not, state why not.

Q26.14 The direction of current in a battery can be reversed by connecting it to a second battery of greater emf with the positive terminals of the two batteries together. When the direction of current is reversed in a battery, does its emf also reverse? Why or why not?

Q26.15 In a two-cell flashlight, the batteries are usually connected in series. Why not connect them in parallel? What possible advantage could there be in connecting several identical batteries in parallel?

Q26.16 The greater the diameter of the wire used in household wiring, the greater the maximum current that can safely be carried by the wire. Why is this? Does the maximum permissible current depend on the length of the wire? Does it depend on what the wire is made of? Explain your reasoning.

Q26.17 The emf of a flashlight battery is roughly constant with time, but its internal resistance increases with age and use. What sort of meter should be used to test the freshness of a battery?

Q26.18 Is it possible to have a circuit in which the potential difference across the terminals of a battery in the circuit is zero? If so, give an example. If not, explain why not.

Q26.19 Verify that the time constant RC has units of time.

Q26.20 For very large resistances it is easy to construct R-C circuits that have time constants of several seconds or minutes. How might this fact be used to measure very large resistances, those that are too large to measure by more conventional means?

Q26.21 Whan a capacitor, battery, and resistor are connected in series, does the resistor affect the maximum charge stored on the capacitor? Why or why not? What purpose does the resistor serve?

EXERCISES

Section 26.1 Resistors in Series and Parallel

26.1 •• A uniform wire of resistance R is cut into three equal lengths. One of these is formed into a circle and connected between the other two (Fig. E26.1). What is the resistance between the opposite ends a and b?

Figure **E26.1**

26.2 •• A machine part has a resistor X protruding from an opening in the side. This resistor is connected to three other resistors, as shown in Fig. E26.2. An ohmmeter connected across a and b reads 2.00 Ω. What is the resistance of X?

Figure **E26.2**

| | 15.0 Ω | 5.0 Ω | 10.0 Ω |

26.3 • A resistor with $R_1 = 25.0$ Ω is connected to a battery that has negligible internal resistance and electrical energy is dissipated by R_1 at a rate of 36.0 W. If a second resistor with $R_2 = 15.0$ Ω is connected in series with R_1, what is the total rate at which electrical energy is dissipated by the two resistors?

26.4 • A 32-Ω resistor and a 20-Ω resistor are connected in parallel, and the combination is connected across a 240-V dc line. (a) What is the resistance of the parallel combination? (b) What is the total current through the parallel combination? (c) What is the current through each resistor?

26.5 • A triangular array of resistors is shown in Fig. E26.5. What current will this array draw from a 35.0-V battery having negligible internal resistance if we connect it across (a) ab; (b) bc; (c) ac? (d) If the battery has an internal resistance of 3.00 Ω, what current will the array draw if the battery is connected across bc?

Figure **E26.5**

26.6 •• For the circuit shown in Fig. E26.6 both meters are idealized, the battery has no appreciable internal resistance, and the ammeter reads 1.25 A. (a) What does the voltmeter read? (b) What is the emf $\mathcal{E}$ of the battery?

Figure **E26.6**

26.7 •• For the circuit shown in Fig. E26.7 find the reading of the idealized ammeter if the battery has an internal resistance of 3.26 Ω.

Figure **E26.7**

26.8 • Three resistors having resistances of 1.60 Ω, 2.40 Ω, and 4.80 Ω are connected in parallel to a 28.0-V battery that has negligible internal resistance. Find (a) the equivalent resistance of the combination; (b) the current in each resistor; (c) the total current through the battery; (d) the voltage across each resistor; (e) the power dissipated in each resistor. (f) Which resistor dissipates the most power: the one with the greatest resistance or the least resistance? Explain why this should be.

26.9 • Now the three resistors of Exercise 26.8 are connected in series to the same battery. Answer the same questions for this situation.

26.10 •• **Power Rating of a Resistor.** The *power rating* of a resistor is the maximum power the resistor can safely dissipate without too great a rise in temperature and hence damage to the resistor. (a) If the power rating of a 15-kΩ resistor is 5.0 W, what is the maximum allowable potential difference across the terminals of the resistor? (b) A 9.0-kΩ resistor is to be connected across a 120-V potential difference. What power rating is required? (c) A 100.0-Ω and a 150.0-Ω resistor, both rated at 2.00 W, are connected in series across a variable potential difference. What is the greatest this potential difference can be without overheating either resistor, and what is the rate of heat generated in each resistor under these conditions?

26.11 • In Fig. E26.11, $R_1 = 3.00$ Ω, $R_2 = 6.00$ Ω, and $R_3 = 5.00$ Ω. The battery has negligible internal resistance. The current I_2 through R_2 is 4.00 A. (a) What are the currents I_1 and I_3? (b) What is the emf of the battery?

Figure **E26.11**

26.12 •• In Fig. E26.11 the battery has emf 25.0 V and negligible internal resistance. $R_1 = 5.00\ \Omega$. The current through R_1 is 1.50 A and the current through $R_3 = 4.50$ A. What are the resistances R_2 and R_3?

26.13 • Compute the equivalent resistance of the network in Fig. E26.13, and find the current in each resistor. The battery has negligible internal resistance.

26.14 • Compute the equivalent resistance of the network in Fig. E26.14, and find the current in each resistor. The battery has negligible internal resistance.

26.15 • In the circuit of Fig. E26.15, each resistor represents a light bulb. Let $R_1 = R_2 = R_3 = R_4 = 4.50\ \Omega$ and $\mathcal{E} = 9.00$ V. (a) Find the current in each bulb. (b) Find the power dissipated in each bulb. Which bulb or bulbs glow the brightest? (c) Bulb R_4 is now removed from the circuit, leaving a break in the wire at its position. Now what is the current in each of the remaining bulbs R_1, R_2, and R_3? (d) With bulb R_4 removed, what is the power dissipated in each of the remaining bulbs? (e) Which light bulb(s) glow brighter as a result of removing R_4? Which bulb(s) glow less brightly? Discuss why there are different effects on different bulbs.

26.16 • Consider the circuit shown in Fig. E26.16. The current through the 6.00-Ω resistor is 4.00 A, in the direction shown. What are the currents through the 25.0-Ω and 20.0-Ω resistors?

26.17 • In the circuit shown in Fig. E26.17, the voltage across the 2.00-Ω resistor is 12.0 V. What are the emf of the battery and the current through the 6.00-Ω resistor?

26.18 • **A Three-Way Light Bulb.** A three-way light bulb has three brightness settings (low, medium, and high) but only two filaments. (a) A particular three-way light bulb connected across a 120-V line can dissipate 60 W, 120 W, or 180 W. Describe how the two filaments are arranged in the bulb, and calculate the resistance of each filament. (b) Suppose the filament with the higher resistance burns out. How much power will the bulb dissipate on each of the three brightness settings? What will be the brightness (low, medium, or high) on each setting? (c) Repeat part (b) for the situation in which the filament with the lower resistance burns out.

26.19 •• **Working Late!** You are working late in your electronics shop and find that you need various resistors for a project. But alas, all you have is a big box of 10.0-Ω resistors. Show how you can make each of the following equivalent resistances by a combination of your 10.0-Ω resistors: (a) 35 Ω, (b) 1.0 Ω, (c) 3.33 Ω, (d) 7.5 Ω.

26.20 • In the circuit shown in Fig. E26.20, the rate at which R_1 is dissipating electrical energy is 20.0 W. (a) Find R_1 and R_2. (b) What is the emf of the battery? (c) Find the current through both R_2 and the 10.0-Ω resistor. (d) Calculate the total electrical power consumption in all the resistors and the electrical power delivered by the battery. Show that your results are consistent with conservation of energy.

26.21 • **Light Bulbs in Series and in Parallel.** Two light bulbs have resistances of 400 Ω and 800 Ω. If the two light bulbs are connected in series across a 120-V line, find (a) the current through each bulb; (b) the power dissipated in each bulb; (c) the total power dissipated in both bulbs. The two light bulbs are now connected in parallel across the 120-V line. Find (d) the current through each bulb; (e) the power dissipated in each bulb; (f) the total power dissipated in both bulbs. (g) In each situation, which of the two bulbs glows the brightest? (h) In which situation is there a greater total light output from both bulbs combined?

26.22 • **Light Bulbs in Series.** A 60-W, 120-V light bulb and a 200-W, 120-V light bulb are connected in series across a 240-V line. Assume that the resistance of each bulb does not vary with current. (*Note:* This description of a light bulb gives the power it dissipates when connected to the stated potential difference; that is, a 25-W, 120-V light bulb dissipates 25 W when connected to a 120-V line.) (a) Find the current through the bulbs. (b) Find the power dissipated in each bulb. (c) One bulb burns out very quickly. Which one? Why?

26.23 •• **CP** In the circuit in Fig. E26.23, a 20.0-Ω resistor is inside 100 g of pure water that is surrounded by insulating styrofoam. If the water is initially at 10.0°C, how long will it take for its temperature to rise to 58.0°C?

Section 26.2 Kirchhoff's Rules

26.24 •• The batteries shown in the circuit in Fig. E26.24 have negligibly small internal resistances. Find the current through (a) the 30.0-Ω resistor; (b) the 20.0-Ω resistor; (c) the 10.0-V battery.

26.25 • In the circuit shown in Fig. E26.25 find (a) the current in resistor R; (b) the resistance R; (c) the unknown emf $\mathcal{E}$. (d) If the circuit is broken at point x, what is the current in resistor R?

26.26 • Find the emfs $\mathcal{E}_1$ and $\mathcal{E}_2$ in the circuit of Fig. E26.26, and find the potential difference of point b relative to point a.

26.27 • In the circuit shown in Fig. E26.27, find (a) the current in the 3.00-Ω resistor; (b) the unknown emfs $\mathcal{E}_1$ and $\mathcal{E}_2$; (c) the resistance R. Note that three currents are given.

Figure **E26.13**

$\mathcal{E} = 60.0$ V, $r = 0$

Figure **E26.14**

$\mathcal{E} = 48.0$ V, $r = 0$

Figure **E26.15**

Figure **E26.16**

Figure **E26.17**

Figure **E26.20**

Figure **E26.23**

Figure **E26.24**

Figure **E26.25**

Figure **E26.26**

Figure **E26.27**

26.28 ·· In the circuit shown in Fig. E26.28, find (a) the current in each branch and (b) the potential difference V_{ab} of point a relative to point b.

Figure **E26.28**

26.29 · The 10.00-V battery in Fig. E26.28 is removed from the circuit and reinserted with the opposite polarity, so that its positive terminal is now next to point a. The rest of the circuit is as shown in the figure. Find (a) the current in each branch and (b) the potential difference V_{ab} of point a relative to point b.

26.30 · The 5.00-V battery in Fig. E26.28 is removed from the circuit and replaced by a 20.00-V battery, with its negative terminal next to point b. The rest of the circuit is as shown in the figure. Find (a) the current in each branch and (b) the potential difference V_{ab} of point a relative to point b.

26.31 ·· In the circuit shown in Fig. E26.31 the batteries have negligible internal resistance and the meters are both idealized. With the switch S open, the voltmeter reads 15.0 V. (a) Find the emf $\mathcal{E}$ of the battery. (b) What will the ammeter read when the switch is closed?

Figure **E26.31**

26.32 ·· In the circuit shown in Fig. E26.32 both batteries have insignificant internal resistance and the idealized ammeter reads 1.50 A in the direction shown. Find the emf $\mathcal{E}$ of the battery. Is the polarity shown correct?

Figure **E26.32**

26.33 · In the circuit shown in Fig. E26.33 all meters are idealized and the batteries have no appreciable internal resistance. (a) Find the reading of the voltmeter with the switch S open. Which point is at a higher potential: a or b?

Figure **E26.33**

(b) With the switch closed, find the reading of the voltmeter and the ammeter. Which way (up or down) does the current flow through the switch?

26.34 ·· In the circuit shown in Fig. E26.34, the 6.0-Ω resistor is consuming energy at a rate of 24 J/s when the current through it flows as shown. (a) Find the current through the ammeter A. (b) What are the polarity and emf $\mathcal{E}$ of the battery, assuming it has negligible internal resistance?

Figure **E26.34**

Section 26.3 Electrical Measuring Instruments

26.35 · The resistance of a galvanometer coil is 25.0 Ω, and the current required for full-scale deflection is 500 μA. (a) Show in a diagram how to convert the galvanometer to an ammeter reading 20.0 mA full scale, and compute the shunt resistance. (b) Show how to convert the galvanometer to a voltmeter reading 500 mV full scale, and compute the series resistance.

26.36 · The resistance of the coil of a pivoted-coil galvanometer is 9.36 Ω, and a current of 0.0224 A causes it to deflect full scale. We want to convert this galvanometer to an ammeter reading 20.0 A full scale. The only shunt available has a resistance of 0.0250 Ω. What resistance R must be connected in series with the coil (Fig. E26.36)?

Figure **E26.36**

26.37 · A circuit consists of a series combination of 6.00-kΩ and 5.00-kΩ resistors connected across a 50.0-V battery having negligible internal resistance. You want to measure the true potential difference (that is, the potential difference without the meter present) across the 5.00-kΩ resistor using a voltmeter having an internal resistance of 10.0 kΩ. (a) What potential difference does the voltmeter measure across the 5.00-kΩ resistor? (b) What is the *true* potential difference across this resistor when the meter is not present? (c) By what percentage is the voltmeter reading in error from the true potential difference?

26.38 · A galvanometer having a resistance of 25.0 Ω has a 1.00-Ω shunt resistance installed to convert it to an ammeter. It is then used to measure the current in a circuit consisting of a 15.0-Ω resistor connected across the terminals of a 25.0-V battery having no appreciable internal resistance. (a) What current does the ammeter measure? (b) What should be the *true* current in the circuit (that is, the current without the ammeter present)? (c) By what percentage is the ammeter reading in error from the *true* current?

26.39 · In the ohmmeter in Fig. E26.39 M is a 2.50-mA meter of resistance 65.0 Ω. (A 2.50-mA meter deflects full scale when the current through it is 2.50 mA.) The battery B has an emf of 1.52 V and negligible internal resistance. R is chosen so that when the terminals a and b are shorted ($R_x = 0$), the meter reads full scale. When a and b are open ($R_x = \infty$), the meter reads zero. (a) What is the resistance of the resistor R? (b) What current indicates a resistance R_x of 200 Ω? (c) What values of R_x correspond to meter deflections of $\frac{1}{4}$, $\frac{1}{2}$, and $\frac{3}{4}$ of full scale if the deflection is proportional to the current through the galvanometer?

Figure **E26.39**

Section 26.4 *R-C* Circuits

26.40 · A 4.60-μF capacitor that is initially uncharged is connected in series with a 7.50-kΩ resistor and an emf source with $\mathcal{E}$ = 245 V and negligible internal resistance. Just after the circuit is completed, what are (a) the voltage drop across the capacitor;

(b) the voltage drop across the resistor; (c) the charge on the capacitor; (d) the current through the resistor? (e) A long time after the circuit is completed (after many time constants) what are the values of the quantities in parts (a)–(d)?

26.41 • A capacitor is charged to a potential of 12.0 V and is then connected to a voltmeter having an internal resistance of 3.40 MΩ. After a time of 4.00 s the voltmeter reads 3.0 V. What are (a) the capacitance and (b) the time constant of the circuit?

26.42 • A 12.4-μF capacitor is connected through a 0.895-MΩ resistor to a constant potential difference of 60.0 V. (a) Compute the charge on the capacitor at the following times after the connections are made: 0, 5.0 s, 10.0 s, 20.0 s, and 100.0 s. (b) Compute the charging currents at the same instants. (c) Graph the results of parts (a) and (b) for t between 0 and 20 s.

26.43 •• **CP** In the circuit shown in Fig. E26.43 both capacitors are initially charged to 45.0 V. (a) How long after closing the switch S will the potential across each capacitor be reduced to 10.0 V, and (b) what will be the current at that time?

Figure **E26.43**

26.44 • A resistor and a capacitor are connected in series to an emf source. The time constant for the circuit is 0.870 s. (a) A second capacitor, identical to the first, is added in series. What is the time constant for this new circuit? (b) In the original circuit a second capacitor, identical to the first, is connected in parallel with the first capacitor. What is the time constant for this new circuit?

26.45 • An emf source with $\mathcal{E} = 120$ V, a resistor with $R = 80.0$ Ω, and a capacitor with $C = 4.00$ μF are connected in series. As the capacitor charges, when the current in the resistor is 0.900 A, what is the magnitude of the charge on each plate of the capacitor?

26.46 • A 1.50-μF capacitor is charging through a 12.0-Ω resistor using a 10.0-V battery. What will be the current when the capacitor has acquired $\frac{1}{4}$ of its maximum charge? Will it be $\frac{1}{4}$ of the maximum current?

26.47 •• **CP** In the circuit shown in Fig. E26.47 each capacitor initially has a charge of magnitude 3.50 nC on its plates. After the switch S is closed, what will be the current in the circuit at the instant that the capacitors have lost 80.0% of their initial stored energy?

Figure **E26.47**

26.48 • A 12.0-μF capacitor is charged to a potential of 50.0 V and then discharged through a 175-Ω resistor. How long does it take the capacitor to lose (a) half of its charge and (b) half of its stored energy?

26.49 • In the circuit in Fig. E26.49 the capacitors are all initially uncharged, the battery has no internal resistance, and the ammeter is idealized. Find the reading of the ammeter (a) just after the switch S is closed and (b) after the switch has been closed for a very long time.

Figure **E26.49**

26.50 • In the circuit shown in Fig. E26.50, $C = 5.90$ μF, $\mathcal{E} = 28.0$ V, and the emf has negligible resistance. Initially the capacitor is uncharged and the switch S is in position 1. The switch is then moved to position 2, so that the capacitor begins to charge. (a) What will be the charge on the capacitor a long time after the switch is moved to position 2? (b) After the switch has been in position 2 for 3.00 ms, the charge on the capacitor is measured to be 110 μC. What is the value of the resistance R? (c) How long after the switch is moved to position 2 will the charge on the capacitor be equal to 99.0% of the final value found in part (a)?

Figure **E26.50**

26.51 • A capacitor with $C = 1.50 \times 10^{-5}$ F is connected as shown in Fig. E26.50 with a resistor with $R = 980$ Ω and an emf source with $\mathcal{E} = 18.0$ V and negligible internal resistance. Initially the capacitor is uncharged and the switch S is in position 1. The switch is then moved to position 2, so that the capacitor begins to charge. After the switch has been in position 2 for 10.0 ms, the switch is moved back to position 1 so that the capacitor begins to discharge. (a) Compute the charge on the capacitor just *before* the switch is thrown from position 2 back to position 1. (b) Compute the voltage drops across the resistor and across the capacitor at the instant described in part (a). (c) Compute the voltage drops across the resistor and across the capacitor just *after* the switch is thrown from position 2 back to position 1. (d) Compute the charge on the capacitor 10.0 ms after the switch is thrown from position 2 back to position 1.

Section 26.5 Power Distribution Systems

26.52 • The heating element of an electric dryer is rated at 4.1 kW when connected to a 240-V line. (a) What is the current in the heating element? Is 12-gauge wire large enough to supply this current? (b) What is the resistance of the dryer's heating element at its operating temperature? (c) At 11 cents per kWh, how much does it cost per hour to operate the dryer?

26.53 • A 1500-W electric heater is plugged into the outlet of a 120-V circuit that has a 20-A circuit breaker. You plug an electric hair dryer into the same outlet. The hair dryer has power settings of 600 W, 900 W, 1200 W, and 1500 W. You start with the hair dryer on the 600-W setting and increase the power setting until the circuit breaker trips. What power setting caused the breaker to trip?

26.54 • **CP** The heating element of an electric stove consists of a heater wire embedded within an electrically insulating material, which in turn is inside a metal casing. The heater wire has a resistance of 20 Ω at room temperature (23.0°C) and a temperature coefficient of resistivity $\alpha = 2.8 \times 10^{-3} (\text{C}°)^{-1}$. The heating element operates from a 120-V line. (a) When the heating element is first turned on, what current does it draw and what electrical power does it dissipate? (b) When the heating element has reached an operating temperature of 280°C (536°F), what current does it draw and what electrical power does it dissipate?

PROBLEMS

26.55 •• In Fig. P26.55, the battery has negligible internal resistance and $\mathcal{E} = 48.0$ V. $R_1 = R_2 = 4.00$ Ω and $R_4 = 3.00$ Ω. What must the resistance R_3 be for the resistor network to dissipate electrical energy at a rate of 295 W?

Figure **P26.55**

26.56 • A 400-Ω, 2.4-W resistor is needed, but only several 400-Ω, 1.2-W resistors are available (see Exercise 26.10). (a) What two different combinations of the available units give the required resistance and power rating? (b) For each of the resistor networks from part (a), what power is dissipated in each resistor when 2.4 W is dissipated by the combination?

26.57 • CP A 20.0-m-long cable consists of a solid-inner, cylindrical, nickel core 10.0 cm in diameter surrounded by a solid-outer cylindrical shell of copper 10.0 cm in inside diameter and 20.0 cm in outside diameter. The resistivity of nickel is 7.8×10^{-8} Ω·m. (a) What is the resistance of this cable? (b) If we think of this cable as a single material, what is its equivalent resistivity?

26.58 • Two identical 3.00-Ω wires are laid side by side and soldered together so they touch each other for half of their lengths. What is the equivalent resistance of this combination?

26.59 • The two identical light bulbs in Example 26.2 (Section 26.1) are connected in parallel to a different source, one with $\mathcal{E} = 8.0$ V and internal resistance 0.8 Ω. Each light bulb has a resistance $R = 2.0$ Ω (assumed independent of the current through the bulb). (a) Find the current through each bulb, the potential difference across each bulb, and the power delivered to each bulb. (b) Suppose one of the bulbs burns out, so that its filament breaks and current no longer flows through it. Find the power delivered to the remaining bulb. Does the remaining bulb glow more or less brightly after the other bulb burns out than before?

26.60 •• Each of the three resistors in Fig. P26.60 has a resistance of 2.4 Ω and can dissipate a maximum of 48 W without becoming excessively heated. What is the maximum power the circuit can dissipate?

Figure **P26.60**

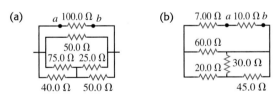

26.61 • If an ohmmeter is connected between points a and b in each of the circuits shown in Fig. P26.61, what will it read?

Figure **P26.61**

(a)
a 100.0 Ω b
50.0 Ω
75.0 Ω 25.0 Ω
40.0 Ω 50.0 Ω

(b)
7.00 Ω a 10.0 Ω b
60.0 Ω
20.0 Ω 30.0 Ω
45.0 Ω

26.62 •• CP For the circuit shown in Fig. P26.62 a 20.0-Ω resistor is embedded in a large block of ice at 0.00°C, and the battery has negligible internal resistance. At what rate (in g/s) is this circuit melting the ice? (The latent heat of fusion for ice is 3.34×10^{5} J/kg.)

Figure **P26.62**

20.0 Ω — Ice
15.0 Ω 10.0 Ω 45.0 V
20.0 Ω
10.0 Ω
5.00 Ω

Figure **P26.63**

5.00 Ω   8.00 Ω
I_2 I_1
12.00 1.00 1.00 9.00
V   Ω I_3 Ω   V
10.00 Ω

26.63 • Calculate the three currents I_1, I_2, and I_3 indicated in the circuit diagram shown in Fig. P26.63.

26.64 ••• What must the emf $\mathcal{E}$ in Fig. P26.64 be in order for the current through the 7.00-Ω resistor to be 1.80 A? Each emf source has negligible internal resistance.

Figure **P26.64**

Figure **P26.65**

26.65 • Find the current through each of the three resistors of the circuit shown in Fig. P26.65. The emf sources have negligible internal resistance.

26.66 • (a) Find the current through the battery and each resistor in the circuit shown in Fig. P26.66. (b) What is the equivalent resistance of the resistor network?

Figure **P26.66**

$R_1 = 1.00$ Ω $R_2 = 2.00$ Ω
$R_3 = 1.00$ Ω
14.0 V
$R_4 = 2.00$ Ω $R_5 = 1.00$ Ω

26.67 •• (a) Find the potential of point a with respect to point b in Fig. P26.67. (b) If points a and b are connected by a wire with negligible resistance, find the current in the 12.0-V battery.

Figure **P26.67**

1.00 Ω 12.0 V
2.00 Ω a b 1.00 Ω 10.0 V 1.00 Ω
2.00 Ω 1.00 Ω 8.0 V 3.00 Ω 2.00 Ω

26.68 •• Consider the circuit shown in Fig. P26.68. (a) What must the emf $\mathcal{E}$ of the battery be in order for a current of 2.00 A to flow through the 5.00-V battery as shown? Is the polarity of the battery correct as shown? (b) How long does it take for 60.0 J of thermal energy to be produced in the 10.0-Ω resistor?

Figure **P26.68**

10.0 Ω 20.0 Ω
60.0 Ω
2.00 A   60.0 Ω
30.0 Ω   5.0 Ω
5.0 V
5.0 Ω   15.0 Ω $\mathcal{E}$ 10.0 V
20.0 Ω

26.69 •• CP A 1.00-km cable having a cross-sectional area of 0.500 cm² is to be constructed out of equal lengths of copper and aluminum. This could be accomplished either by making a 0.50-km cable of each one and welding them together end to end or by making two parallel 1.00-km cables, one of each metal (Fig. P26.69). Calculate the resistance of the 1.00-km cable for both designs to see which one provides the least resistance.

Figure **P26.69**

26.70 ••• In the circuit shown in Fig. P26.70 all the resistors are rated at a maximum power of 2.00 W. What is the maximum emf $\mathcal{E}$ that the battery can have without burning up any of the resistors?

Figure **P26.70**

26.71 • In the circuit shown in Fig. P26.71, the current in the 20.0-V battery is 5.00 A in the direction shown and the voltage across the 8.00-Ω resistor is 16.0 V, with the lower end of the resistor at higher potential. Find (a) the emf (including its polarity) of the battery X; (b) the current I through the 200.0-V battery (including its direction); (c) the resistance R.

Figure **P26.71**

26.72 •• Three identical resistors are connected in series. When a certain potential difference is applied across the combination, the total power dissipated is 36 W. What power would be dissipated if the three resistors were connected in parallel across the same potential difference?

26.73 • A resistor R_1 consumes electrical power P_1 when connected to an emf $\mathcal{E}$. When resistor R_2 is connected to the same emf, it consumes electrical power P_2. In terms of P_1 and P_2, what is the total electrical power consumed when they are both connected to this emf source (a) in parallel and (b) in series?

26.74 • The capacitor in Fig. P26.74 is initially uncharged. The switch is closed at $t = 0$. (a) Immediately after the switch is closed, what is the current through each resistor? (b) What is the final charge on the capacitor?

Figure **P26.74**

$R_1 = 8.00\ \Omega$

$+ |\mathcal{E} = 42.0\ \text{V}$
$R_2 =$
$6.00\ \Omega$

$R_3 = 3.00\ \Omega$

$C = 4.00\ \mu\text{F}$

26.75 •• A 2.00-μF capacitor that is initially uncharged is connected in series with a 6.00-kΩ resistor and an emf source with $\mathcal{E} = 90.0$ V and negligible internal resistance. The circuit is completed at $t = 0$. (a) Just after the circuit is completed, what is the rate at which electrical energy is being dissipated in the resistor? (b) At what value of t is the rate at which electrical energy is being dissipated in the resistor equal to the rate at which electrical energy is being stored in the capacitor? (c) At the time calculated in part (b), what is the rate at which electrical energy is being dissipated in the resistor?

26.76 •• A 6.00-μF capacitor that is initially uncharged is connected in series with a 5.00-Ω resistor and an emf source with $\mathcal{E} = 50.0$ V and negligible internal resistance. At the instant when the resistor is dissipating electrical energy at a rate of 250 W, how much energy has been stored in the capacitor?

26.77 • Figure P26.77 employs a convention often used in circuit diagrams. The battery (or other power supply) is not shown explicitly. It is understood that the point at the top, labeled "36.0 V," is connected to the positive terminal of a 36.0-V battery having negligible internal resistance, and that the "ground" symbol at the bottom is connected to the negative terminal of the battery. The circuit is completed through the battery, even though it is not shown on the diagram. (a) What is the potential difference V_{ab}, the potential of point a relative to point b, when the switch S is open? (b) What is the current through switch S when it is closed? (c) What is the equivalent resistance when switch S is closed?

Figure **P26.77**

26.78 • (See Problem 26.77.) (a) What is the potential of point a with respect to point b in Fig. P26.78 when switch S is open? (b) Which point, a or b, is at the higher potential? (c) What is the final potential of point b with respect to ground when switch S is closed? (d) How much does the charge on each capacitor change when S is closed?

Figure **P26.78**

26.79 • Point a in Fig. P26.79 is maintained at a constant potential of 400 V above ground. (See Problem 26.77.) (a) What is the reading of a voltmeter with the proper range and with resistance $5.00 \times 10^4\ \Omega$ when connected between point b and ground? (b) What is the reading of a voltmeter with resistance $5.00 \times 10^6\ \Omega$? (c) What is the reading of a voltmeter with infinite resistance?

Figure **P26.79**

26.80 •• A 150-V voltmeter has a resistance of 30,000 Ω. When connected in series with a large resistance R across a 110-V line, the meter reads 74 V. Find the resistance R.

26.81 •• **The Wheatstone Bridge.** The circuit shown in Fig. P26.81, called a *Wheatstone bridge,* is used to determine the value of an unknown resistor X by comparison with three resistors M, N, and P whose resistances can be varied. For each setting, the resistance of each resistor is precisely known. With switches K_1 and K_2 closed,

Figure **P26.81**

these resistors are varied until the current in the galvanometer G is zero; the bridge is then said to be *balanced*. (a) Show that under this condition the unknown resistance is given by $X = MP/N$. (This method permits very high precision in comparing resistors.) (b) If the galvanometer G shows zero deflection when $M = 850.0 \ \Omega$, $N = 15.00 \ \Omega$, and $P = 33.48 \ \Omega$, what is the unknown resistance X?

26.82 • A 2.36-μF capacitor that is initially uncharged is connected in series with a 5.86-Ω resistor and an emf source with $\mathcal{E} = 120$ V and negligible internal resistance. (a) Just after the connection is made, what are (i) the rate at which electrical energy is being dissipated in the resistor; (ii) the rate at which the electrical energy stored in the capacitor is increasing; (iii) the electrical power output of the source? How do the answers to parts (i), (ii), and (iii) compare? (b) Answer the same questions as in part (a) at a long time after the connection is made. (c) Answer the same questions as in part (a) at the instant when the charge on the capacitor is one-half its final value.

26.83 • A 224-Ω resistor and a 589-Ω resistor are connected in series across a 90.0-V line. (a) What is the voltage across each resistor? (b) A voltmeter connected across the 224-Ω resistor reads 23.8 V. Find the voltmeter resistance. (c) Find the reading of the same voltmeter if it is connected across the 589-Ω resistor. (d) The readings on this voltmeter are lower than the "true" voltages (that is, without the voltmeter present). Would it be possible to design a voltmeter that gave readings *higher* than the "true" voltages? Explain.

26.84 • A resistor with $R = 850 \ \Omega$ is connected to the plates of a charged capacitor with capacitance $C = 4.62 \ \mu$F. Just before the connection is made, the charge on the capacitor is 6.90 mC. (a) What is the energy initially stored in the capacitor? (b) What is the electrical power dissipated in the resistor just after the connection is made? (c) What is the electrical power dissipated in the resistor at the instant when the energy stored in the capacitor has decreased to half the value calculated in part (a)?

26.85 • A capacitor that is initially uncharged is connected in series with a resistor and an emf source with $\mathcal{E} = 110$ V and negligible internal resistance. Just after the circuit is completed, the current through the resistor is 6.5×10^{-5} A. The time constant for the circuit is 5.2 s. What are the resistance of the resistor and the capacitance of the capacitor?

26.86 ••• An R-C circuit has a time constant RC. (a) If the circuit is discharging, how long will it take for its stored energy to be reduced to $1/e$ of its initial value? (b) If it is charging, how long will it take for the stored energy to reach $1/e$ of its maximum value?

26.87 • Strictly speaking, Eq. (26.16) implies that an *infinite* amount of time is required to discharge a capacitor completely. Yet for practical purposes, a capacitor may be considered to be fully discharged after a finite length of time. To be specific, consider a capacitor with capacitance C connected to a resistor R to be fully discharged if its charge q differs from zero by no more than the charge of one electron. (a) Calculate the time required to reach this state if $C = 0.920 \ \mu$F, $R = 670$ kΩ, and $Q_0 = 7.00 \ \mu$C. How many time constants is this? (b) For a given Q_0, is the time required to reach this state always the same number of time constants, independent of the values of C and R? Why or why not?

26.88 • **CALC** The current in a charging capacitor is given by Eq. (26.13). (a) The instantaneous power supplied by the battery is $\mathcal{E}i$. Integrate this to find the total energy supplied by the battery. (b) The instantaneous power dissipated in the resistor is i^2R. Integrate this to find the total energy dissipated in the resistor. (c) Find the final energy stored in the capacitor, and show that this equals the total energy supplied by the battery less the energy dissipated in

the resistor, as obtained in parts (a) and (b). (d) What fraction of the energy supplied by the battery is stored in the capacitor? How does this fraction depend on R?

26.89 ••• **CALC** (a) Using Eq. (26.17) for the current in a discharging capacitor, derive an expression for the instantaneous power $P = i^2R$ dissipated in the resistor. (b) Integrate the expression for P to find the total energy dissipated in the resistor, and show that this is equal to the total energy initially stored in the capacitor.

CHALLENGE PROBLEMS

26.90 ••• **A Capacitor Burglar Alarm.** The capacitance of a capacitor can be affected by dielectric material that, although not inside the capacitor, is near enough to the capacitor to be polarized by the fringing electric field that exists near a charged capacitor. This effect is usually of

Figure **P26.90**

the order of picofarads (pF), but it can be used with appropriate electronic circuitry to detect a change in the dielectric material surrounding the capacitor. Such a dielectric material might be the human body, and the effect described above might be used in the design of a burglar alarm. Consider the simplified circuit shown in Fig. P26.90. The voltage source has emf $\mathcal{E} = 1000$ V, and the capacitor has capacitance $C = 10.0$ pF. The electronic circuitry for detecting the current, represented as an ammeter in the diagram, has negligible resistance and is capable of detecting a current that persists at a level of at least 1.00 μA for at least 200 μs after the capacitance has changed abruptly from C to C'. The burglar alarm is designed to be activated if the capacitance changes by 10%. (a) Determine the charge on the 10.0-pF capacitor when it is fully charged. (b) If the capacitor is fully charged before the intruder is detected, assuming that the time taken for the capacitance to change by 10% is short enough to be ignored, derive an equation that expresses the current through the resistor R as a function of the time t since the capacitance has changed. (c) Determine the range of values of the resistance R that will meet the design specifications of the burglar alarm. What happens if R is too small? Too large? (*Hint:* You will not be able to solve this part analytically but must use numerical methods. Express R as a logarithmic function of R plus known quantities. Use a trial value of R and calculate from the expression a new value. Continue to do this until the input and output values of R agree to within three significant figures.)

26.91 ••• **An Infinite Network.** As shown in Fig. P26.91, a network of resistors of resistances R_1 and R_2 extends to infinity toward the right. Prove that the total resistance R_T of the infinite network is equal to

Figure **P26.91**

$$R_T = R_1 + \sqrt{R_1^2 + 2R_1R_2}$$

(*Hint:* Since the network is infinite, the resistance of the network to the right of points c and d is also equal to R_T.)

26.92 ••• Suppose a resistor R lies along each edge of a cube (12 resistors in all) with connections at the corners. Find the equivalent resistance between two diagonally opposite corners of the cube (points a and b in Fig. P26.92).

Figure **P26.92**

26.93 ••• **BIO Attenuator Chains and Axons.** The infinite network of resistors shown in Fig. P26.91 is known as an *attenuator chain,* since this chain of resistors causes the potential difference between the upper and lower wires to decrease, or attenuate, along the length of the chain. (a) Show that if the potential difference between the points a and b in Fig. 26.91 is V_{ab}, then the potential difference between points c and d is $V_{cd} = V_{ab}/(1 + \beta)$, where $\beta = 2R_1(R_T + R_2)/R_T R_2$ and R_T, the total resistance of the network, is given in Challenge Problem 26.91. (See the hint given in that problem.) (b) If the potential difference between terminals a and b at the left end of the infinite network is V_0, show that the potential difference between the upper and lower wires n segments from the left end is $V_n = V_0/(1 + \beta)^n$. If $R_1 = R_2$, how many segments are needed to decrease the potential difference V_n to less than 1.0% of V_0? (c) An infinite attenuator chain provides a model of the propagation of a voltage pulse along a nerve fiber, or axon. Each segment of the network in Fig. P26.91 represents a short segment of the axon of length Δx. The resistors R_1 represent the resistance of the fluid inside and outside the membrane wall of the axon. The resistance of the membrane to current flowing through the wall is represented by R_2. For an axon segment of length $\Delta x = 1.0\ \mu\text{m}$, $R_1 = 6.4 \times 10^3\ \Omega$ and $R_2 = 8.0 \times 10^8\ \Omega$ (the membrane wall is a good insulator). Calculate the total resistance R_T and β for an infinitely long axon. (This is a good approximation, since the length of an axon is much greater than its width; the largest axons in the human nervous system are longer than 1 m but only about 10^{-7} m in radius.) (d) By what fraction does the potential difference between the inside and outside of the axon decrease over a distance of 2.0 mm? (e) The attenuation of the potential difference calculated in part (d) shows that the axon cannot simply be a passive, current-carrying electrical cable; the potential difference must periodically be reinforced along the axon's length. This reinforcement mechanism is slow, so a signal propagates along the axon at only about 30 m/s. In situations where faster response is required, axons are covered with a segmented sheath of fatty myelin. The segments are about 2 mm long, separated by gaps called the *nodes of Ranvier.* The myelin increases the resistance of a 1.0-μm-long segment of the membrane to $R_2 = 3.3 \times 10^{12}\ \Omega$. For such a myelinated axon, by what fraction does the potential difference between the inside and outside of the axon decrease over the distance from one node of Ranvier to the next? This smaller attenuation means the propagation speed is increased.

Answers

Chapter Opening Question

The potential difference V is the same across resistors connected in parallel. However, there is a different current I through each resistor if the resistances R are different: $I = V/R$.

Test Your Understanding Questions

26.1 Answer: (a), (c), (d), (b) Here's why: The three resistors in Fig. 26.1a are in series, so $R_{eq} = R + R + R = 3R$. In Fig. 26.1b the three resistors are in parallel, so $1/R_{eq} = 1/R + 1/R + 1/R = 3/R$ and $R_{eq} = R/3$. In Fig. 26.1c the second and third resistors are in parallel, so their equivalent resistance R_{23} is given by $1/R_{23} = 1/R + 1/R = 2/R$; hence $R_{23} = R/2$. This combination is in series with the first resistor, so the three resistors together have equivalent resistance $R_{eq} = R + R/2 = 3R/2$. In Fig. 26.1d the second and third resistors are in series, so their equivalent resistance is $R_{23} = R + R = 2R$. This combination is in parallel with the first resistor, so the equivalent resistance of the three-resistor combination is given by $1/R_{eq} = 1/R + 1/2R = 3/2R$. Hence $R_{eq} = 2R/3$.

26.2 Answer: loop *cbdac* Equation (2) minus Eq. (1) gives $-I_2(1\ \Omega) - (I_2 + I_3)(2\ \Omega) + (I_1 - I_3)(1\ \Omega) + I_1(1\ \Omega) = 0$. We can obtain this equation by applying the loop rule around the path from c to b to d to a to c in Fig. 26.12. This isn't a new equation, so it would not have helped with the solution of Example 26.6.

26.3 Answers: (a) (ii), (b) (iii) An ammeter must always be placed in series with the circuit element of interest, and a voltmeter must always be placed in parallel. Ideally the ammeter would have zero resistance and the voltmeter would have infinite resistance so that their presence would have no effect on either the resistor current or the voltage. Neither of these idealizations is possible, but the ammeter resistance should be much less than 2 Ω and the voltmeter resistance should be much greater than 2 Ω.

26.4 Answer: (ii) After one time constant, $t = RC$ and the initial charge Q_0 has decreased to $Q_0 e^{-t/RC} = Q_0 e^{-RC/RC} = Q_0 e^{-1} = Q_0/e$. Hence the stored energy has decreased from $Q_0^2/2C$ to $(Q_0/e)^2/2C = Q_0^2/2Ce^2$, a fraction $1/e^2 = 0.135$ of its initial value. This result doesn't depend on the initial value of the energy.

26.5 Answer: no This is a very dangerous thing to do. The circuit breaker will allow currents up to 40 A, double the rated value of the wiring. The amount of power $P = I^2R$ dissipated in a section of wire can therefore be up to four times the rated value, so the wires could get very warm and start a fire.

Bridging Problem

Answers: (a) 9.39 J **(b)** 2.02×10^4 W **(c)** 4.65×10^{-4} s **(d)** 7.43×10^3 W

MAGNETIC FIELD AND MAGNETIC FORCES

27

? Magnetic resonance imaging (MRI) makes it possible to see details of soft tissue (such as in the foot shown here) that aren't visible in x-ray images. Yet soft tissue isn't a magnetic material (it's not attracted to a magnet). How does MRI work?

Everybody uses magnetic forces. They are at the heart of electric motors, microwave ovens, loudspeakers, computer printers, and disk drives. The most familiar examples of magnetism are permanent magnets, which attract unmagnetized iron objects and can also attract or repel other magnets. A compass needle aligning itself with the earth's magnetism is an example of this interaction. But the *fundamental* nature of magnetism is the interaction of moving electric charges. Unlike electric forces, which act on electric charges whether they are moving or not, magnetic forces act only on *moving* charges.

We saw in Chapter 21 that the electric force arises in two stages: (1) a charge produces an electric field in the space around it, and (2) a second charge responds to this field. Magnetic forces also arise in two stages. First, a *moving* charge or a collection of moving charges (that is, an electric current) produces a *magnetic* field. Next, a second current or moving charge responds to this magnetic field, and so experiences a magnetic force.

In this chapter we study the second stage in the magnetic interaction—that is, how moving charges and currents *respond* to magnetic fields. In particular, we will see how to calculate magnetic forces and torques, and we will discover why magnets can pick up iron objects like paper clips. In Chapter 28 we will complete our picture of the magnetic interaction by examining how moving charges and currents *produce* magnetic fields.

27.1 Magnetism

Magnetic phenomena were first observed at least 2500 years ago in fragments of magnetized iron ore found near the ancient city of Magnesia (now Manisa, in western Turkey). These fragments were examples of what are now called **permanent magnets;** you probably have several permanent magnets on your refrigerator

27.1 (a) Two bar magnets attract when opposite poles (N and S, or S and N) are next to each other. (b) The bar magnets repel when like poles (N and N, or S and S) are next to each other.

(a) Opposite poles attract.

(b) Like poles repel.

27.2 (a) Either pole of a bar magnet attracts an unmagnetized object that contains iron, such as a nail. (b) A real-life example of this effect.

(a)

(b)

door at home. Permanent magnets were found to exert forces on each other as well as on pieces of iron that were not magnetized. It was discovered that when an iron rod is brought in contact with a natural magnet, the rod also becomes magnetized. When such a rod is floated on water or suspended by a string from its center, it tends to line itself up in a north-south direction. The needle of an ordinary compass is just such a piece of magnetized iron.

Before the relationship of magnetic interactions to moving charges was understood, the interactions of permanent magnets and compass needles were described in terms of *magnetic poles.* If a bar-shaped permanent magnet, or *bar magnet,* is free to rotate, one end points north. This end is called a *north pole* or *N pole;* the other end is a *south pole* or *S pole.* Opposite poles attract each other, and like poles repel each other (Fig. 27.1). An object that contains iron but is not itself magnetized (that is, it shows no tendency to point north or south) is attracted by *either* pole of a permanent magnet (Fig. 27.2). This is the attraction that acts between a magnet and the unmagnetized steel door of a refrigerator. By analogy to electric interactions, we describe the interactions in Figs. 27.1 and 27.2 by saying that a bar magnet sets up a *magnetic field* in the space around it and a second body responds to that field. A compass needle tends to align with the magnetic field at the needle's position.

The earth itself is a magnet. Its north geographic pole is close to a magnetic *south* pole, which is why the north pole of a compass needle points north. The earth's magnetic axis is not quite parallel to its geographic axis (the axis of rotation), so a compass reading deviates somewhat from geographic north. This deviation, which varies with location, is called *magnetic declination* or *magnetic variation.* Also, the magnetic field is not horizontal at most points on the earth's surface; its angle up or down is called *magnetic inclination.* At the magnetic poles the magnetic field is vertical.

Figure 27.3 is a sketch of the earth's magnetic field. The lines, called *magnetic field lines,* show the direction that a compass would point at each location; they are discussed in detail in Section 27.3. The direction of the field at any point can be defined as the direction of the force that the field would exert on a magnetic

27.3 A sketch of the earth's magnetic field. The field, which is caused by currents in the earth's molten core, changes with time; geologic evidence shows that it reverses direction entirely at irregular intervals of 10^4 to 10^6 years.

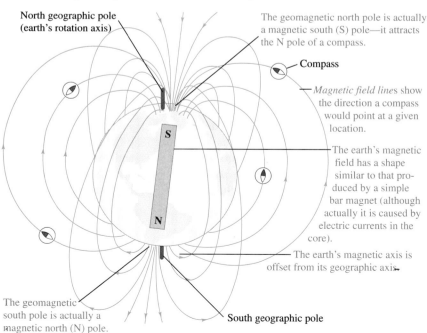

North geographic pole (earth's rotation axis)

The geomagnetic north pole is actually a magnetic south (S) pole—it attracts the N pole of a compass.

Compass

Magnetic field lines show the direction a compass would point at a given location.

The earth's magnetic field has a shape similar to that produced by a simple bar magnet (although actually it is caused by electric currents in the core).

The earth's magnetic axis is offset from its geographic axis.

The geomagnetic south pole is actually a magnetic north (N) pole.

South geographic pole

north pole. In Section 27.2 we'll describe a more fundamental way to define the direction and magnitude of a magnetic field.

Magnetic Poles Versus Electric Charge

The concept of magnetic poles may appear similar to that of electric charge, and north and south poles may seem analogous to positive and negative charge. But the analogy can be misleading. While isolated positive and negative charges exist, there is *no* experimental evidence that a single isolated magnetic pole exists; poles always appear in pairs. If a bar magnet is broken in two, each broken end becomes a pole (Fig. 27.4). The existence of an isolated magnetic pole, or **magnetic monopole,** would have sweeping implications for theoretical physics. Extensive searches for magnetic monopoles have been carried out, but so far without success.

The first evidence of the relationship of magnetism to moving charges was discovered in 1820 by the Danish scientist Hans Christian Oersted. He found that a compass needle was deflected by a current-carrying wire, as shown in Fig. 27.5 Similar investigations were carried out in France by André Ampère. A few years later, Michael Faraday in England and Joseph Henry in the United States discovered that moving a magnet near a conducting loop can cause a current in the loop. We now know that the magnetic forces between two bodies shown in Figs. 27.1 and 27.2 are fundamentally due to interactions between moving electrons in the atoms of the bodies. (There are also *electric* interactions between the two bodies, but these are far weaker than the magnetic interactions because the two bodies are electrically neutral.) Inside a magnetized body such as a permanent magnet, there is a *coordinated* motion of certain of the atomic electrons; in an unmagnetized body these motions are not coordinated. (We'll describe these motions further in Section 27.7, and see how the interactions shown in Figs. 27.1 and 27.2 come about.)

Electric and magnetic interactions prove to be intimately connected. Over the next several chapters we will develop the unifying principles of electromagnetism, culminating in the expression of these principles in *Maxwell's equations.* These equations represent the synthesis of electromagnetism, just as Newton's laws of motion are the synthesis of mechanics, and like Newton's laws they represent a towering achievement of the human intellect.

Test Your Understanding of Section 27.1   Suppose you cut off the part of the compass needle shown in Fig. 27.5a that is painted gray. You discard this part, drill a hole in the remaining red part, and place the red part on the pivot at the center of the compass. Will the red part still swing east and west when a current is applied as in Fig. 27.5b?   ❙

27.2 Magnetic Field

To introduce the concept of magnetic field properly, let's review our formulation of *electric* interactions in Chapter 21, where we introduced the concept of *electric* field. We represented electric interactions in two steps:

1. A distribution of electric charge at rest creates an electric field $\vec{E}$ in the surrounding space.
2. The electric field exerts a force $\vec{F} = q\vec{E}$ on any other charge q that is present in the field.

We can describe magnetic interactions in a similar way:

1. A moving charge or a current creates a **magnetic field** in the surrounding space (in addition to its *electric* field).
2. The magnetic field exerts a force $\vec{F}$ on any other moving charge or current that is present in the field.

27.4 Breaking a bar magnet. Each piece has a north and south pole, even if the pieces are different sizes. (The smaller the piece, the weaker its magnetism.)

In contrast to electric charges, magnetic poles always come in pairs and can't be isolated.

Breaking a magnet in two ...

... yields two magnets, not two isolated poles.

27.5 In Oersted's experiment, a compass is placed directly over a horizontal wire (here viewed from above). When the compass is placed directly under the wire, the compass deflection is reversed.

(a)

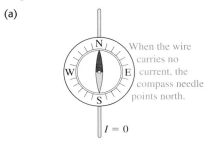

When the wire carries no current, the compass needle points north.

$I = 0$

(b)

When the wire carries a current, the compass needle deflects. The direction of deflection depends on the direction of the current.

27.6 The magnetic force $\vec{F}$ acting on a positive charge q moving with velocity $\vec{v}$ is perpendicular to both $\vec{v}$ and the magnetic field $\vec{B}$. For given values of the speed v and magnetic field strength B, the force is greatest when $\vec{v}$ and $\vec{B}$ are perpendicular.

(a)

A charge moving **parallel** to a magnetic field experiences **zero magnetic force.**

(b)

A charge moving at an angle ϕ to a magnetic field experiences a magnetic force with magnitude $F = |q|v_\perp B = |q|vB \sin \phi$.

$\vec{F}$ is perpendicular to the plane containing $\vec{v}$ and $\vec{B}$.

(c)

A charge moving **perpendicular** to a magnetic field experiences a maximal magnetic force with magnitude $F_{\text{max}} = qvB.$

In this chapter we'll concentrate on the *second* aspect of the interaction: Given the presence of a magnetic field, what force does it exert on a moving charge or a current? In Chapter 28 we will come back to the problem of how magnetic fields are *created* by moving charges and currents.

Like electric field, magnetic field is a *vector field*—that is, a vector quantity associated with each point in space. We will use the symbol $\vec{B}$ for magnetic field. At any position the direction of $\vec{B}$ is defined as the direction in which the north pole of a compass needle tends to point. The arrows in Fig. 27.3 suggest the direction of the earth's magnetic field; for any magnet, $\vec{B}$ points out of its north pole and into its south pole.

Magnetic Forces on Moving Charges

There are four key characteristics of the magnetic force on a moving charge. First, its magnitude is proportional to the magnitude of the charge. If a $1\text{-}\mu\text{C}$ charge and a $2\text{-}\mu\text{C}$ charge move through a given magnetic field with the same velocity, experiments show that the force on the $2\text{-}\mu\text{C}$ charge is twice as great as the force on the $1\text{-}\mu\text{C}$ charge. Second, the magnitude of the force is also proportional to the magnitude, or "strength," of the field; if we double the magnitude of the field (for example, by using two identical bar magnets instead of one) without changing the charge or its velocity, the force doubles.

A third characteristic is that the magnetic force depends on the particle's velocity. This is quite different from the electric-field force, which is the same whether the charge is moving or not. A charged particle at rest experiences *no* magnetic force. And fourth, we find by experiment that the magnetic force $\vec{F}$ *does not* have the same direction as the magnetic field $\vec{B}$ but instead is always *perpendicular* to both $\vec{B}$ and the velocity $\vec{v}$. The magnitude F of the force is found to be proportional to the component of $\vec{v}$ perpendicular to the field; when that component is zero (that is, when $\vec{v}$ and $\vec{B}$ are parallel or antiparallel), the force is zero.

Figure 27.6 shows these relationships. The direction of $\vec{F}$ is always perpendicular to the plane containing $\vec{v}$ and $\vec{B}$. Its magnitude is given by

$$F = |q|v_\perp B = |q|vB \sin \phi \qquad (27.1)$$

where $|q|$ is the magnitude of the charge and ϕ is the angle measured from the direction of $\vec{v}$ to the direction of $\vec{B}$, as shown in the figure.

This description does not specify the direction of $\vec{F}$ completely; there are always two directions, opposite to each other, that are both perpendicular to the plane of $\vec{v}$ and $\vec{B}$. To complete the description, we use the same right-hand rule that we used to define the vector product in Section 1.10. (It would be a good idea to review that section before you go on.) Draw the vectors $\vec{v}$ and $\vec{B}$ with their tails together, as in Fig. 27.7a. Imagine turning $\vec{v}$ until it points in the direction of $\vec{B}$ (turning through the smaller of the two possible angles). Wrap the fingers of your right hand around the line perpendicular to the plane of $\vec{v}$ and $\vec{B}$ so that they curl around with the sense of rotation from $\vec{v}$ to $\vec{B}$. Your thumb then points in the direction of the force $\vec{F}$ on a *positive* charge. (Alternatively, the direction of the force $\vec{F}$ on a positive charge is the direction in which a right-hand-thread screw would advance if turned the same way.)

This discussion shows that the force on a charge q moving with velocity $\vec{v}$ in a magnetic field $\vec{B}$ is given, both in magnitude and in direction, by

$$\vec{F} = q\vec{v} \times \vec{B} \qquad \text{(magnetic force on a moving charged particle)} \qquad (27.2)$$

This is the first of several vector products we will encounter in our study of magnetic-field relationships. It's important to note that Eq. (27.2) was *not* deduced theoretically; it is an observation based on *experiment*.

27.7 Finding the direction of the magnetic force on a moving charged particle.

(a)

Right-hand rule for the direction of magnetic force on a **positive** charge moving in a magnetic field:

① Place the $\vec{v}$ and $\vec{B}$ vectors tail to tail.

② Imagine turning $\vec{v}$ toward $\vec{B}$ in the $\vec{v}$-$\vec{B}$ plane (through the smaller angle).

③ The force acts along a line perpendicular to the $\vec{v}$-$\vec{B}$ plane. Curl the fingers of your *right hand* around this line in the same direction you rotated $\vec{v}$. Your thumb now points in the direction the force acts.

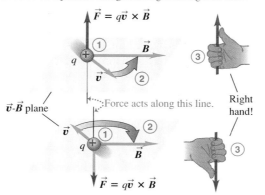

(b)

If the charge is negative, the direction of the force is *opposite* to that given by the right-hand rule.

Equation (27.2) is valid for both positive and negative charges. When q is negative, the direction of the force $\vec{F}$ is opposite to that of $\vec{v} \times \vec{B}$ (Fig. 27.7b). If two charges with equal magnitude and opposite sign move in the same $\vec{B}$ field with the same velocity (Fig. 27.8), the forces have equal magnitude and opposite direction. Figures 27.6, 27.7, and 27.8 show several examples of the relationships of the directions of $\vec{F}$, $\vec{v}$, and $\vec{B}$ for both positive and negative charges. Be sure you understand the relationships shown in these figures.

Equation (27.1) gives the magnitude of the magnetic force $\vec{F}$ in Eq. (27.2). We can express this magnitude in a different but equivalent way. Since ϕ is the angle between the directions of vectors $\vec{v}$ and $\vec{B}$, we may interpret $B\sin\phi$ as the component of $\vec{B}$ perpendicular to $\vec{v}$—that is, $B_\perp$. With this notation the force magnitude is

$$F = |q|vB_\perp \tag{27.3}$$

This form is sometimes more convenient, especially in problems involving *currents* rather than individual particles. We will discuss forces on currents later in this chapter.

From Eq. (27.1) the *units* of B must be the same as the units of F/qv. Therefore the SI unit of B is equivalent to $1 \text{ N} \cdot \text{s}/\text{C} \cdot \text{m}$, or, since one ampere is one coulomb per second ($1 \text{ A} = 1 \text{ C/s}$), $1 \text{ N}/\text{A} \cdot \text{m}$. This unit is called the **tesla** (abbreviated T), in honor of Nikola Tesla (1856–1943), the prominent Serbian-American scientist and inventor:

$$1 \text{ tesla} = 1 \text{ T} = 1 \text{ N}/\text{A} \cdot \text{m}$$

Another unit of B, the **gauss** ($1 \text{ G} = 10^{-4} \text{ T}$), is also in common use.

The magnetic field of the earth is of the order of 10^{-4} T or 1 G. Magnetic fields of the order of 10 T occur in the interior of atoms and are important in the analysis of atomic spectra. The largest steady magnetic field that can be produced at present in the laboratory is about 45 T. Some pulsed-current electromagnets can produce fields of the order of 120 T for millisecond time intervals.

Measuring Magnetic Fields with Test Charges

To explore an unknown magnetic field, we can measure the magnitude and direction of the force on a *moving* test charge and then use Eq. (27.2) to determine $\vec{B}$. The electron beam in a cathode-ray tube, such as that in an older television set (not a flat screen), is a convenient device for this. The electron gun shoots out a narrow beam of electrons at a known speed. If there is no force to deflect the beam, it strikes the center of the screen.

27.8 Two charges of the same magnitude but opposite sign moving with the same velocity in the same magnetic field. The magnetic forces on the charges are equal in magnitude but opposite in direction.

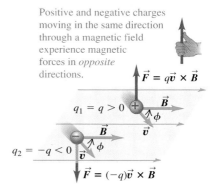

Positive and negative charges moving in the same direction through a magnetic field experience magnetic forces in *opposite* directions.

Application Magnetic Fields of the Body
All living cells are electrically active, and the feeble electric currents within the body produce weak but measurable magnetic fields. The fields produced by skeletal muscles have magnitudes less than 10^{-10} T, about one-millionth as strong as the earth's magnetic field. The brain produces magnetic fields that are far weaker, only about 10^{-12} T.

If a magnetic field is present, in general the electron beam is deflected. But if the beam is parallel or antiparallel to the field, then $\phi = 0$ or π in Eq. (27.1) and $F = 0$; there is no force and hence no deflection. If we find that the electron beam is not deflected when its direction is parallel to a certain axis as in Fig. 27.9a, the $\vec{B}$ vector must point either up or down along that axis.

If we then turn the tube 90° (Fig. 27.9b), $\phi = \pi/2$ in Eq. (27.1) and the magnetic force is maximum; the beam is deflected in a direction perpendicular to the plane of $\vec{B}$ and $\vec{v}$. The direction and magnitude of the deflection determine the direction and magnitude of $\vec{B}$. We can perform additional experiments in which the angle between $\vec{B}$ and $\vec{v}$ is between zero and 90° to confirm Eq. (27.1). We note that the electron has a negative charge; the force in Fig. 27.9b is opposite in direction to the force on a positive charge.

When a charged particle moves through a region of space where *both* electric and magnetic fields are present, both fields exert forces on the particle. The total force $\vec{F}$ is the vector sum of the electric and magnetic forces:

$$\vec{F} = q(\vec{E} + \vec{v} \times \vec{B}) \qquad (27.4)$$

MasteringPHYSICS

ActivPhysics 13.4: Magnetic Force on a Particle

27.9 Determining the direction of a magnetic field using a cathode-ray tube. Because electrons have a negative charge, the magnetic force $\vec{F} = q\vec{v} \times \vec{B}$ in part (b) points opposite to the direction given by the right-hand rule (see Fig. 27.7b).

(a) If the tube axis is parallel to the *y*-axis, the beam is undeflected, so $\vec{B}$ is in either the $+y$- or the $-y$-direction.

Electron beam

(b) If the tube axis is parallel to the *x*-axis, the beam is deflected in the $-z$-direction, so $\vec{B}$ is in the $+y$-direction.

Problem-Solving Strategy 27.1 **Magnetic Forces**

IDENTIFY *the relevant concepts:* The equation $\vec{F} = q\vec{v} \times \vec{B}$ allows you to determine the magnetic force on a moving charged particle.

SET UP *the problem* using the following steps:
1. Draw the velocity $\vec{v}$ and magnetic field $\vec{B}$ with their tails together so that you can visualize the plane that contains them.
2. Determine the angle ϕ between $\vec{v}$ and $\vec{B}$.
3. Identify the target variables.

EXECUTE *the solution* as follows:
1. Express the magnetic force using Eq. (27.2), $\vec{F} = q\vec{v} \times \vec{B}$. Equation (27.1) gives the magnitude of the force, $F = qvB\sin\phi$.

2. Remember that $\vec{F}$ is perpendicular to the plane containing $\vec{v}$ and $\vec{B}$. The right-hand rule (see Fig. 27.7) gives the direction of $\vec{v} \times \vec{B}$. If q is negative, $\vec{F}$ is *opposite* to $\vec{v} \times \vec{B}$.

EVALUATE *your answer:* Whenever possible, solve the problem in two ways to confirm that the results agree. Do it directly from the geometric definition of the vector product. Then find the components of the vectors in some convenient coordinate system and calculate the vector product from the components. Verify that the results agree.

Example 27.1 **Magnetic force on a proton**

A beam of protons ($q = 1.6 \times 10^{-19}$ C) moves at 3.0×10^5 m/s through a uniform 2.0-T magnetic field directed along the positive *z*-axis, as in Fig. 27.10. The velocity of each proton lies in the *xz*-plane and is directed at 30° to the $+z$-axis. Find the force on a proton.

SOLUTION

IDENTIFY and SET UP: This problem uses the expression $\vec{F} = q\vec{v} \times \vec{B}$ for the magnetic force $\vec{F}$ on a moving charged particle. The target variable is $\vec{F}$.

EXECUTE: The charge is positive, so the force is in the same direction as the vector product $\vec{v} \times \vec{B}$. From the right-hand rule, this direction is along the negative y-axis. The magnitude of the force, from Eq. (27.1), is

27.10 Directions of $\vec{v}$ and $\vec{B}$ for a proton in a magnetic field.

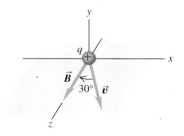

$$F = qvB \sin \phi$$
$$= (1.6 \times 10^{-19}\ \text{C})(3.0 \times 10^5\ \text{m/s})(2.0\ \text{T})(\sin 30°)$$
$$= 4.8 \times 10^{-14}\ \text{N}$$

EVALUATE: We check our result by evaluating the force using vector language and Eq. (27.2). We have

$$\vec{v} = (3.0 \times 10^5\ \text{m/s})(\sin 30°)\hat{\imath} + (3.0 \times 10^5\ \text{m/s})(\cos 30°)\hat{k}$$
$$\vec{B} = (2.0\ \text{T})\hat{k}$$
$$\vec{F} = q\vec{v} \times \vec{B}$$
$$= (1.6 \times 10^{-19}\ \text{C})(3.0 \times 10^5\ \text{m/s})(2.0\ \text{T})$$
$$\times (\sin 30°\hat{\imath} + \cos 30°\hat{k}) \times \hat{k}$$
$$= (-4.8 \times 10^{-14}\ \text{N})\hat{\jmath}$$

(Recall that $\hat{\imath} \times \hat{k} = -\hat{\jmath}$ and $\hat{k} \times \hat{k} = \mathbf{0}$.) We again find that the force is in the negative y-direction with magnitude 4.8×10^{-14} N.

If the beam consists of *electrons* rather than protons, the charge is negative ($q = -1.6 \times 10^{-19}$ C) and the direction of the force is reversed. The force is now directed along the *positive* y-axis, but the magnitude is the same as before, $F = 4.8 \times 10^{-14}$ N.

Test Your Understanding of Section 27.2 The figure at right shows a uniform magnetic field $\vec{B}$ directed into the plane of the paper (shown by the blue ×'s). A particle with a negative charge moves in the plane. Which of the three paths—1, 2, or 3—does the particle follow?

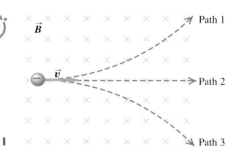

27.3 Magnetic Field Lines and Magnetic Flux

We can represent any magnetic field by **magnetic field lines,** just as we did for the earth's magnetic field in Fig. 27.3. The idea is the same as for the electric field lines we introduced in Section 21.6. We draw the lines so that the line through any point is tangent to the magnetic field vector $\vec{B}$ at that point (Fig. 27.11). Just as with electric field lines, we draw only a few representative lines; otherwise, the lines would fill up all of space. Where adjacent field lines are close together, the field magnitude is large; where these field lines are far apart, the field magnitude is small. Also, because the direction of $\vec{B}$ at each point is unique, field lines never intersect.

CAUTION **Magnetic field lines are not "lines of force"** Magnetic field lines are sometimes called "magnetic lines of force," but that's not a good name for them; unlike electric field lines, they *do not* point in the direction of the force on a charge (Fig. 27.12). Equation (27.2) shows that the force on a moving charged particle is always perpendicular to the magnetic field, and hence to the magnetic field line that passes through the particle's position. The direction of the force depends on the particle's velocity and the sign of its charge, so just looking at magnetic field lines cannot in itself tell you the direction of the force on an arbitrary moving charged particle. Magnetic field lines *do* have the direction that a compass needle would point at each location; this may help you to visualize them.

Figures 27.11 and 27.13 show magnetic field lines produced by several common sources of magnetic field. In the gap between the poles of the magnet shown in Fig. 27.13a, the field lines are approximately straight, parallel, and equally spaced, showing that the magnetic field in this region is approximately *uniform* (that is, constant in magnitude and direction).

27.11 The magnetic field lines of a permanent magnet. Note that the field lines pass through the interior of the magnet.

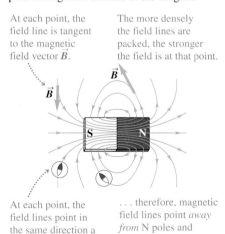

At each point, the field line is tangent to the magnetic field vector $\vec{B}$.

The more densely the field lines are packed, the stronger the field is at that point.

At each point, the field lines point in the same direction a compass would . . .

. . . therefore, magnetic field lines point *away from* N poles and *toward* S poles.

27.12 Magnetic field lines are *not* "lines of force."

Magnetic field lines are *not* "lines of force." The force on a charged particle is not along the direction of a field line.

The direction of the magnetic force depends on the velocity $\vec{v}$, as expressed by the magnetic force law $\vec{F} = q\vec{v} \times \vec{B}$.

Because magnetic-field patterns are three-dimensional, it's often necessary to draw magnetic field lines that point into or out of the plane of a drawing. To do this we use a dot (·) to represent a vector directed out of the plane and a cross (×) to represent a vector directed into the plane (Fig. 27.13b). To remember these, think of a dot as the head of an arrow coming directly toward you, and think of a cross as the feathers of an arrow flying directly away from you.

Iron filings, like compass needles, tend to align with magnetic field lines. Hence they provide an easy way to visualize field lines (Fig. 27.14).

Magnetic Flux and Gauss's Law for Magnetism

We define the **magnetic flux** Φ_B through a surface just as we defined electric flux in connection with Gauss's law in Section 22.2. We can divide any surface into elements of area dA (Fig. 27.15). For each element we determine $B_\perp$, the component of $\vec{B}$ normal to the surface at the position of that element, as shown. From the figure, $B_\perp = B\cos\phi$, where ϕ is the angle between the direction of $\vec{B}$ and a line perpendicular to the surface. (Be careful not to confuse ϕ with Φ_B.) In general,

27.13 Magnetic field lines produced by some common sources of magnetic field.

(a) Magnetic field of a C-shaped magnet

Between flat, parallel magnetic poles, the magnetic field is nearly uniform.

(b) Magnetic field of a straight current-carrying wire

To represent a field coming out of or going into the plane of the paper, we use dots and crosses, respectively.

$\vec{B}$ directed out of plane

$\vec{B}$ directed into plane

Perspective view   *Wire in plane of paper*

(c) Magnetic fields of a current-carrying loop and a current-carrying coil (solenoid)

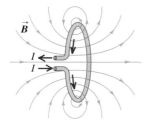

Notice that the field of the loop and, especially, that of the coil look like the field of a bar magnet (see Fig. 27.11).

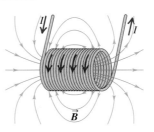

27.14 (a) Like little compass needles, iron filings line up tangent to magnetic field lines. (b) Drawing of the field lines for the situation shown in (a).

(a)

(b)

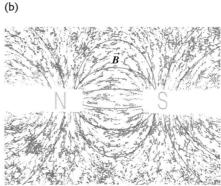

this component varies from point to point on the surface. We define the magnetic flux $d\Phi_B$ through this area as

$$d\Phi_B = B_\perp \, dA = B\cos\phi \, dA = \vec{B} \cdot d\vec{A} \qquad (27.5)$$

The *total* magnetic flux through the surface is the sum of the contributions from the individual area elements:

$$\Phi_B = \int B_\perp \, dA = \int B\cos\phi \, dA = \int \vec{B} \cdot d\vec{A} \quad \begin{array}{l}\text{(magnetic flux}\\ \text{through a surface)}\end{array} \quad (27.6)$$

(This equation uses the concepts of vector area and surface integral that we introduced in Section 22.2; you may want to review that discussion.)

Magnetic flux is a *scalar* quantity. If $\vec{B}$ is uniform over a plane surface with total area A, then $B_\perp$ and ϕ are the same at all points on the surface, and

$$\Phi_B = B_\perp A = BA\cos\phi \qquad (27.7)$$

If $\vec{B}$ happens to be perpendicular to the surface, then $\cos\phi = 1$ and Eq. (27.7) reduces to $\Phi_B = BA$. We will use the concept of magnetic flux extensively during our study of electromagnetic induction in Chapter 29.

The SI unit of magnetic flux is equal to the unit of magnetic field (1 T) times the unit of area (1 m^2). This unit is called the **weber** (1 Wb), in honor of the German physicist Wilhelm Weber (1804–1891):

$$1 \text{ Wb} = 1 \text{ T} \cdot \text{m}^2$$

Also, $1 \text{ T} = 1 \text{ N/A} \cdot \text{m}$, so

$$1 \text{ Wb} = 1 \text{ T} \cdot \text{m}^2 = 1 \text{ N} \cdot \text{m/A}$$

In Gauss's law the total *electric* flux through a closed surface is proportional to the total electric charge enclosed by the surface. For example, if the closed surface encloses an electric dipole, the total electric flux is zero because the total charge is zero. (You may want to review Section 22.3 on Gauss's law.) By analogy, if there were such a thing as a single magnetic charge (magnetic monopole), the total *magnetic* flux through a closed surface would be proportional to the total magnetic charge enclosed. But we have mentioned that no magnetic monopole has ever been observed, despite intensive searches. We conclude:

The total magnetic flux through a closed surface is always zero.

Symbolically,

$$\oint \vec{B} \cdot d\vec{A} = 0 \qquad \text{(magnetic flux through any closed surface)} \quad (27.8)$$

This equation is sometimes called *Gauss's law for magnetism*. You can verify it by examining Figs. 27.11 and 27.13; if you draw a closed surface anywhere in any of the field maps shown in those figures, you will see that every field line that enters the surface also exits from it; the net flux through the surface is zero. It also follows from Eq. (27.8) that magnetic field lines always form closed loops.

CAUTION **Magnetic field lines have no ends** Unlike electric field lines that begin and end on electric charges, magnetic field lines *never* have end points; such a point would indicate the presence of a monopole. You might be tempted to draw magnetic field lines that begin at the north pole of a magnet and end at a south pole. But as Fig. 27.11 shows, the field lines of a magnet actually continue through the interior of the magnet. Like all other magnetic field lines, they form closed loops.

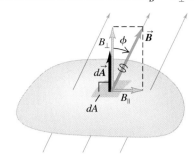

27.15 The magnetic flux through an area element dA is defined to be $d\Phi_B = B_\perp \, dA$.

For Gauss's law, which always deals with *closed* surfaces, the vector area element $d\vec{A}$ in Eq. (27.6) always points *out of* the surface. However, some applications of *magnetic* flux involve an *open* surface with a boundary line; there is then an ambiguity of sign in Eq. (27.6) because of the two possible choices of direction for $d\vec{A}$. In these cases we choose one of the two sides of the surface to be the "positive" side and use that choice consistently.

If the element of area dA in Eq. (27.5) is at right angles to the field lines, then $B_\perp = B$; calling the area $dA_\perp$, we have

$$B = \frac{d\Phi_B}{dA_\perp} \qquad (27.9)$$

That is, the magnitude of magnetic field is equal to *flux per unit area* across an area at right angles to the magnetic field. For this reason, magnetic field $\vec{B}$ is sometimes called **magnetic flux density.**

Example 27.2 Magnetic flux calculations

Figure 27.16a is a perspective view of a flat surface with area 3.0 cm^2 in a uniform magnetic field $\vec{B}$. The magnetic flux through this surface is $+0.90 \text{ mWb}$. Find the magnitude of the magnetic field and the direction of the area vector $\vec{A}$.

27.16 (a) A flat area A in a uniform magnetic field $\vec{B}$. (b) The area vector $\vec{A}$ makes a $60°$ angle with $\vec{B}$. (If we had chosen $\vec{A}$ to point in the opposite direction, ϕ would have been $120°$ and the magnetic flux Φ_B would have been negative.)

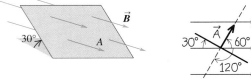

(a) Perspective view

(b) Our sketch of the problem (edge-on view)

SOLUTION

IDENTIFY and SET UP: Our target variables are the field magnitude B and the direction of the area vector. Because $\vec{B}$ is uniform, B and ϕ are the same at all points on the surface. Hence we can use Eq. (27.7), $\Phi_B = BA \cos \phi$.

EXECUTE: The area A is $3.0 \times 10^{-4} \text{ m}^2$; the direction of $\vec{A}$ is perpendicular to the surface, so ϕ could be either $60°$ or $120°$. But Φ_B, B, and A are all positive, so $\cos \phi$ must also be positive. This rules out $120°$, so $\phi = 60°$ (Fig. 27.16b). Hence we find

$$B = \frac{\Phi_B}{A \cos \phi} = \frac{0.90 \times 10^{-3} \text{ Wb}}{(3.0 \times 10^{-4} \text{ m}^2)(\cos 60°)} = 6.0 \text{ T}$$

EVALUATE: In many problems we are asked to calculate the flux of a given magnetic field through a given area. This example is somewhat different: It tests your understanding of the definition of magnetic flux.

Test Your Understanding of Section 27.3 Imagine moving along the axis of the current-carrying loop in Fig. 27.13c, starting at a point well to the left of the loop and ending at a point well to the right of the loop. (a) How would the magnetic field strength vary as you moved along this path? (i) It would be the same at all points along the path; (ii) it would increase and then decrease; (iii) it would decrease and then increase. (b) Would the magnetic field direction vary as you moved along the path?

27.4 Motion of Charged Particles in a Magnetic Field

When a charged particle moves in a magnetic field, it is acted on by the magnetic force given by Eq. (27.2), and the motion is determined by Newton's laws. Figure 27.17a shows a simple example. A particle with positive charge q is at point O, moving with velocity $\vec{v}$ in a uniform magnetic field $\vec{B}$ directed into the plane of the figure. The vectors $\vec{v}$ and $\vec{B}$ are perpendicular, so the magnetic force $\vec{F} = q\vec{v} \times \vec{B}$ has magnitude $F = qvB$ and a direction as shown in the figure. The force is *always* perpendicular to $\vec{v}$, so it cannot change the *magnitude* of the velocity, only its direction. To put it differently, the magnetic force never has a component parallel to the particle's motion, so the magnetic force can never do *work* on the particle. This is true even if the magnetic field is not uniform.

> **Motion of a charged particle under the action of a magnetic field alone is always motion with constant speed.**

Using this principle, we see that in the situation shown in Fig. 27.17a the magnitudes of both $\vec{F}$ and $\vec{v}$ are constant. At points such as P and S the directions of force and velocity have changed as shown, but their magnitudes are the same. The particle therefore moves under the influence of a constant-magnitude force that is always at right angles to the velocity of the particle. Comparing the discussion of circular motion in Sections 3.4 and 5.4, we see that the particle's path is a *circle,* traced out with constant speed v. The centripetal acceleration is v^2/R and only the magnetic force acts, so from Newton's second law,

$$F = |q|vB = m\frac{v^2}{R} \qquad (27.10)$$

where m is the mass of the particle. Solving Eq. (27.10) for the radius R of the circular path, we find

$$R = \frac{mv}{|q|B} \qquad \text{(radius of a circular orbit in a magnetic field)} \qquad (27.11)$$

We can also write this as $R = p/|q|B$, where $p = mv$ is the magnitude of the particle's momentum. If the charge q is negative, the particle moves *clockwise* around the orbit in Fig. 27.17a.

The angular speed ω of the particle can be found from Eq. (9.13), $v = R\omega$. Combining this with Eq. (27.11), we get

$$\omega = \frac{v}{R} = v\frac{|q|B}{mv} = \frac{|q|B}{m} \qquad (27.12)$$

The number of revolutions per unit time is $f = \omega/2\pi$. This frequency f is independent of the radius R of the path. It is called the **cyclotron frequency;** in a particle accelerator called a *cyclotron,* particles moving in nearly circular paths are given a boost twice each revolution, increasing their energy and their orbital radii but not their angular speed or frequency. Similarly, one type of *magnetron,* a common source of microwave radiation for microwave ovens and radar systems, emits radiation with a frequency equal to the frequency of circular motion of electrons in a vacuum chamber between the poles of a magnet.

If the direction of the initial velocity is *not* perpendicular to the field, the velocity *component* parallel to the field is constant because there is no force parallel to the field. Then the particle moves in a helix (Fig. 27.18). The radius of the helix is given by Eq. (27.11), where v is now the component of velocity perpendicular to the $\vec{B}$ field.

Motion of a charged particle in a nonuniform magnetic field is more complex. Figure 27.19 shows a field produced by two circular coils separated by some distance. Particles near either coil experience a magnetic force toward the center of the region; particles with appropriate speeds spiral repeatedly from one end of the region to the other and back. Because charged particles can be trapped in such a magnetic field, it is called a *magnetic bottle.* This technique is used to confine very hot plasmas with temperatures of the order of 10^6 K. In a similar way the earth's nonuniform magnetic field traps charged particles coming from the sun in doughnut-shaped regions around the earth, as shown in Fig. 27.20. These regions, called the *Van Allen radiation belts,* were discovered in 1958 using data obtained by instruments aboard the Explorer I satellite.

27.17 A charged particle moves in a plane perpendicular to a uniform magnetic field $\vec{B}$.

(a) The orbit of a charged particle in a uniform magnetic field

A charge moving at right angles to a uniform $\vec{B}$ field moves in a circle at constant speed because $\vec{F}$ and $\vec{v}$ are always perpendicular to each other.

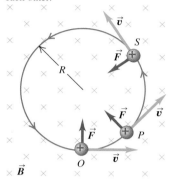

(b) An electron beam (seen as a white arc) curving in a magnetic field

27.18 The general case of a charged particle moving in a uniform magnetic field $\vec{B}$. The magnetic field does no work on the particle, so its speed and kinetic energy remain constant.

This particle's motion has components both parallel ($v_{\parallel}$) and perpendicular ($v_{\perp}$) to the magnetic field, so it moves in a helical path.

27.19 A magnetic bottle. Particles near either end of the region experience a magnetic force toward the center of the region. This is one way of containing an ionized gas that has a temperature of the order of 10^6 K, which would vaporize any material container.

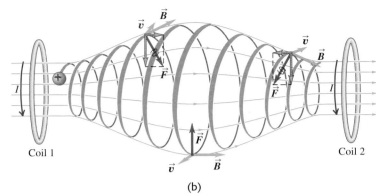

Coil 1   Coil 2

27.20 (a) The Van Allen radiation belts around the earth. Near the poles, charged particles from these belts can enter the atmosphere, producing the aurora borealis ("northern lights") and aurora australis ("southern lights"). (b) A photograph of the aurora borealis.

(a)   (b)

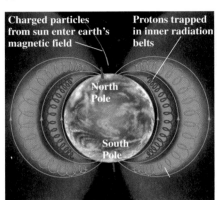

Charged particles from sun enter earth's magnetic field

Protons trapped in inner radiation belts

North Pole

South Pole

27.21 This bubble chamber image shows the result of a high-energy gamma ray (which does not leave a track) that collides with an electron in a hydrogen atom. This electron flies off to the right at high speed. Some of the energy in the collision is transformed into a second electron and a positron (a positively charged electron). A magnetic field is directed into the plane of the image, which makes the positive and negative particles curve off in different directions.

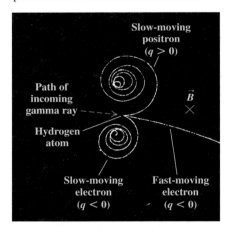

Slow-moving positron ($q > 0$)

Path of incoming gamma ray

Hydrogen atom

$\vec{B}$

Slow-moving electron ($q < 0$)

Fast-moving electron ($q < 0$)

Magnetic forces on charged particles play an important role in studies of elementary particles. Figure 27.21 shows a chamber filled with liquid hydrogen and with a magnetic field directed into the plane of the photograph. A high-energy gamma ray dislodges an electron from a hydrogen atom, sending it off at high speed and creating a visible track in the liquid hydrogen. The track shows the electron curving downward due to the magnetic force. The energy of the collision also produces another electron and a *positron* (a positively charged electron). Because of their opposite charges, the trajectories of the electron and the positron curve in opposite directions. As these particles plow through the liquid hydrogen, they collide with other charged particles, losing energy and speed. As a result, the radius of curvature decreases as suggested by Eq. (27.11). (The electron's speed is comparable to the speed of light, so Eq. (27.11) isn't directly applicable here.) Similar experiments allow physicists to determine the mass and charge of newly discovered particles.

Problem-Solving Strategy 27.2   **Motion in Magnetic Fields**

(MP)

IDENTIFY *the relevant concepts:* In analyzing the motion of a charged particle in electric and magnetic fields, you will apply Newton's second law of motion, $\sum \vec{F} = m\vec{a}$, with the net force given by $\sum \vec{F} = q(\vec{E} + \vec{v} \times \vec{B})$. Often other forces such as gravity can be neglected. Many of the problems are similar to the trajectory and circular-motion problems in Sections 3.3, 3.4, and 5.4; it would be a good idea to review those sections.

SET UP *the problem* using the following steps:
1. Determine the target variable(s).
2. Often the use of components is the most efficient approach. Choose a coordinate system and then express all vector quanti-

ties (including , and) in terms of their components in this system.

EXECUTE *the solution* as follows:
1. If the particle moves perpendicular to a uniform magnetic field, the trajectory is a circle with a radius and angular speed given by Eqs. (27.11) and (27.12), respectively.
2. If your calculation involves a more complex trajectory, use $\sum \vec{F} = m\vec{a}$ in component form: $\sum F_x = ma_x$, and so forth. This approach is particularly useful when both electric and magnetic fields are present.

EVALUATE *your answer:* Check whether your results are reasonable.

Example 27.3 **Electron motion in a magnetron**

A magnetron in a microwave oven emits electromagnetic waves with frequency $f = 2450$ MHz. What magnetic field strength is required for electrons to move in circular paths with this frequency?

SOLUTION

IDENTIFY and SET UP: The problem refers to circular motion as shown in Fig. 27.17a. We use Eq. (27.12) to solve for the field magnitude B.

EXECUTE: The angular speed that corresponds to the frequency f is $\omega = 2\pi f = (2\pi)(2450 \times 10^6 \text{ s}^{-1}) = 1.54 \times 10^{10} \text{ s}^{-1}$. Then from Eq. (27.12),

$$B = \frac{m\omega}{|q|} = \frac{(9.11 \times 10^{-31} \text{ kg})(1.54 \times 10^{10} \text{ s}^{-1})}{1.60 \times 10^{-19} \text{ C}} = 0.0877 \text{ T}$$

EVALUATE: This is a moderate field strength, easily produced with a permanent magnet. Incidentally, 2450-MHz electromagnetic waves are useful for heating and cooking food because they are strongly absorbed by water molecules.

Example 27.4 **Helical particle motion in a magnetic field**

In a situation like that shown in Fig. 27.18, the charged particle is a proton ($q = 1.60 \times 10^{-19}$ C, $m = 1.67 \times 10^{-27}$ kg) and the uniform, 0.500-T magnetic field is directed along the x-axis. At $t = 0$ the proton has velocity components $v_x = 1.50 \times 10^5$ m/s, $v_y = 0$, and $v_z = 2.00 \times 10^5$ m/s. Only the magnetic force acts on the proton. (a) At $t = 0$, find the force on the proton and its acceleration. (b) Find the radius of the resulting helical path, the angular speed of the proton, and the *pitch* of the helix (the distance traveled along the helix axis per revolution).

SOLUTION

IDENTIFY and SET UP: The magnetic force is $\vec{F} = q\vec{v} \times \vec{B}$; Newton's second law gives the resulting acceleration. Because $\vec{F}$ is perpendicular to $\vec{v}$, the proton's speed does not change. Hence Eq. (27.11) gives the radius of the helical trajectory if we replace v with the velocity component perpendicular to $\vec{B}$. Equation (27.12) gives the angular speed ω, which yields the time T for one revolution (the *period*). Given the velocity component parallel to the magnetic field, we can then determine the pitch.

EXECUTE: (a) With $\vec{B} = B\hat{\imath}$ and $\vec{v} = v_x\hat{\imath} + v_z\hat{k}$, Eq. (27.2) yields

$$\vec{F} = q\vec{v} \times \vec{B} = q(v_x\hat{\imath} + v_z\hat{k}) \times B\hat{\imath} = qv_zB\hat{\jmath}$$
$$= (1.60 \times 10^{-19} \text{ C})(2.00 \times 10^5 \text{ m/s})(0.500 \text{ T})\hat{\jmath}$$
$$= (1.60 \times 10^{-14} \text{ N})\hat{\jmath}$$

(Recall that that $\hat{\imath} \times \hat{\imath} = 0$ and $\hat{k} \times \hat{\imath} = \hat{\jmath}$.) The resulting acceleration is

$$\vec{a} = \frac{\vec{F}}{m} = \frac{1.60 \times 10^{-14} \text{ N}}{1.67 \times 10^{-27} \text{ kg}}\hat{\jmath} = (9.58 \times 10^{12} \text{ m/s}^2)\hat{\jmath}$$

(b) Since $v_y = 0$, the component of velocity perpendicular to $\vec{B}$ is v_z; then from Eq. (27.11),

$$R = \frac{mv_z}{|q|B} = \frac{(1.67 \times 10^{-27} \text{ kg})(2.00 \times 10^5 \text{ m/s})}{(1.60 \times 10^{-19} \text{ C})(0.500 \text{ T})}$$
$$= 4.18 \times 10^{-3} \text{ m} = 4.18 \text{ mm}$$

From Eq. (27.12) the angular speed is

$$\omega = \frac{|q|B}{m} = \frac{(1.60 \times 10^{-19} \text{ C})(0.500 \text{ T})}{1.67 \times 10^{-27} \text{ kg}} = 4.79 \times 10^7 \text{ rad/s}$$

The period is $T = 2\pi/\omega = 2\pi/(4.79 \times 10^7 \text{ s}^{-1}) = 1.31 \times 10^{-7}$ s. The pitch is the distance traveled along the x-axis in this time, or

$$v_xT = (1.50 \times 10^5 \text{ m/s})(1.31 \times 10^{-7} \text{ s})$$
$$= 0.0197 \text{ m} = 19.7 \text{ mm}$$

EVALUATE: Although the magnetic force has a tiny magnitude, it produces an immense acceleration because the proton mass is so small. Note that the pitch of the helix is almost five times greater than the radius R, so this helix is much more "stretched out" than that shown in Fig. 27.18.

Test Your Understanding of Section 27.4 (a) If you double the speed of the charged particle in Fig. 27.17a while keeping the magnetic field the same (as well as the charge and the mass), how does this affect the radius of the trajectory? (i) The radius is unchanged; (ii) the radius is twice as large; (iii) the radius is four times as large; (iv) the radius is $\frac{1}{2}$ as large; (v) the radius is $\frac{1}{4}$ as large. (b) How does this affect the time required for one complete circular orbit? (i) The time is unchanged; (ii) the time is twice as long; (iii) the time is four times as long; (iv) the time is $\frac{1}{2}$ as long; (v) the time is $\frac{1}{4}$ as long.

27.5 Applications of Motion of Charged Particles

This section describes several applications of the principles introduced in this chapter. Study them carefully, watching for applications of Problem-Solving Strategy 27.2 (Section 27.4).

Velocity Selector

27.22 (a) A velocity selector for charged particles uses perpendicular $\vec{E}$ and $\vec{B}$ fields. Only charged particles with $v = E/B$ move through undeflected. (b) The electric and magnetic forces on a positive charge. The forces are reversed if the charge is negative.

(a) Schematic diagram of velocity selector

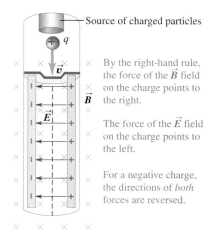

Source of charged particles

By the right-hand rule, the force of the $\vec{B}$ field on the charge points to the right.

The force of the $\vec{E}$ field on the charge points to the left.

For a negative charge, the directions of *both* forces are reversed.

(b) Free-body diagram for a positive particle

$F_E = qE$ $F_B = qvB$

Only if a charged particle has $v = E/B$ do the electric and magnetic forces cancel. All other particles are deflected.

In a beam of charged particles produced by a heated cathode or a radioactive material, not all particles move with the same speed. Many applications, however, require a beam in which all the particle speeds are the same. Particles of a specific speed can be selected from the beam using an arrangement of electric and magnetic fields called a *velocity selector*. In Fig. 27.22a a charged particle with mass m, charge q, and speed v enters a region of space where the electric and magnetic fields are perpendicular to the particle's velocity and to each other. The electric field $\vec{E}$ is to the left, and the magnetic field $\vec{B}$ is into the plane of the figure. If q is positive, the electric force is to the left, with magnitude qE, and the magnetic force is to the right, with magnitude qvB. For given field magnitudes E and B, for a particular value of v the electric and magnetic forces will be equal in magnitude; the total force is then zero, and the particle travels in a straight line with constant velocity. For zero total force, $\sum F_y = 0$, we need $-qE + qvB = 0$; solving for the speed v for which there is no deflection, we find

$$v = \frac{E}{B} \qquad (27.13)$$

Only particles with speeds equal to E/B can pass through without being deflected by the fields (Fig. 27.22b). By adjusting E and B appropriately, we can select particles having a particular speed for use in other experiments. Because q divides out in Eq. (27.13), a velocity selector for positively charged particles also works for electrons or other negatively charged particles.

Thomson's e/m Experiment

In one of the landmark experiments in physics at the end of the 19th century, J. J. Thomson (1856–1940) used the idea just described to measure the ratio of charge to mass for the electron. For this experiment, carried out in 1897 at the Cavendish Laboratory in Cambridge, England, Thomson used the apparatus shown in Fig. 27.23. In a highly evacuated glass container, electrons from the hot cathode are accelerated and formed into a beam by a potential difference V between the two anodes A and A'. The speed v of the electrons is determined by the accelerating

27.23 Thomson's apparatus for measuring the ratio e/m for the electron.

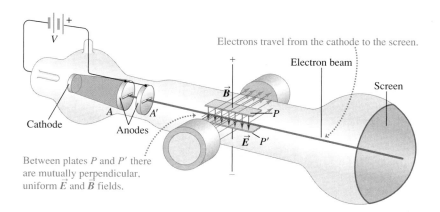

Electrons travel from the cathode to the screen.

Electron beam

Screen

Cathode

Anodes

Between plates P and P' there are mutually perpendicular, uniform $\vec{E}$ and $\vec{B}$ fields.

potential V. The gained kinetic energy $\frac{1}{2}mv^2$ equals the lost electric potential energy eV, where e is the magnitude of the electron charge:

$$\tfrac{1}{2}mv^2 = eV \quad \text{or} \quad v = \sqrt{\frac{2eV}{m}} \quad (27.14)$$

The electrons pass between the plates P and P' and strike the screen at the end of the tube, which is coated with a material that fluoresces (glows) at the point of impact. The electrons pass straight through the plates when Eq. (27.13) is satisfied; combining this with Eq. (27.14), we get

$$\frac{E}{B} = \sqrt{\frac{2eV}{m}} \quad \text{so} \quad \frac{e}{m} = \frac{E^2}{2VB^2} \quad (27.15)$$

All the quantities on the right side can be measured, so the ratio e/m of charge to mass can be determined. It is *not* possible to measure e or m separately by this method, only their ratio.

The most significant aspect of Thomson's e/m measurements was that he found a *single value* for this quantity. It did not depend on the cathode material, the residual gas in the tube, or anything else about the experiment. This independence showed that the particles in the beam, which we now call electrons, are a common constituent of all matter. Thus Thomson is credited with the first discovery of a subatomic particle, the electron.

The most precise value of e/m available as of this writing is

$$e/m = 1.758820150(44) \times 10^{11}\,\text{C/kg}$$

In this expression, (44) indicates the likely uncertainty in the last two digits, 50.

Fifteen years after Thomson's experiments, the American physicist Robert Millikan succeeded in measuring the charge of the electron precisely (see Challenge Problem 23.91). This value, together with the value of e/m, enables us to determine the *mass* of the electron. The most precise value available at present is

$$m = 9.10938215(45) \times 10^{-31}\,\text{kg}$$

Mass Spectrometers

Techniques similar to Thomson's e/m experiment can be used to measure masses of ions and thus measure atomic and molecular masses. In 1919, Francis Aston (1877–1945), a student of Thomson's, built the first of a family of instruments called **mass spectrometers.** A variation built by Bainbridge is shown in Fig. 27.24. Positive ions from a source pass through the slits S_1 and S_2, forming a narrow beam. Then the ions pass through a velocity selector with crossed $\vec{E}$ and $\vec{B}$ fields, as we have described, to block all ions except those with speeds v equal to E/B. Finally, the ions pass into a region with a magnetic field $\vec{B}'$ perpendicular to the figure, where they move in circular arcs with radius R determined by Eq. (27.11): $R = mv/qB'$. Ions with different masses strike the detector (in Bainbridge's design, a photographic plate) at different points, and the values of R can be measured. We assume that each ion has lost one electron, so the net charge of each ion is just $+e$. With everything known in this equation except m, we can compute the mass m of the ion.

One of the earliest results from this work was the discovery that neon has two species of atoms, with atomic masses 20 and 22 g/mol. We now call these species **isotopes** of the element. Later experiments have shown that many elements have several isotopes, atoms that are identical in their chemical behavior but different in mass owing to differing numbers of neutrons in their nuclei. This is just one of the many applications of mass spectrometers in chemistry and physics.

MasteringPHYSICS

ActivPhysics 13.8: Velocity Selector

27.24 Bainbridge's mass spectrometer utilizes a velocity selector to produce particles with uniform speed v. In the region of magnetic field B', particles with greater mass ($m_2 > m_1$) travel in paths with larger radius ($R_2 > R_1$).

Velocity selector selects particles with speed v.

Particle detector

Magnetic field separates particles by mass; the greater a particle's mass, the larger is the radius of its path.

Example 27.5 An e/m demonstration experiment

You set out to reproduce Thomson's e/m experiment with an accelerating potential of 150 V and a deflecting electric field of magnitude 6.0×10^6 N/C. (a) At what fraction of the speed of light do the electrons move? (b) What magnetic-field magnitude will yield zero beam deflection? (c) With this magnetic field, how will the electron beam behave if you increase the accelerating potential above 150 V?

SOLUTION

IDENTIFY and SET UP: This is the situation shown in Fig. 27.23. We use Eq. (27.14) to determine the electron speed and Eq. (27.13) to determine the required magnetic field B.

EXECUTE: (a) From Eq. (27.14), the electron speed v is

$$v = \sqrt{2(e/m)V} = \sqrt{2(1.76 \times 10^{11} \text{ C/kg})(150 \text{ V})}$$
$$= 7.27 \times 10^6 \text{ m/s} = 0.024c$$

(b) From Eq. (27.13), the required field strength is

$$B = \frac{E}{v} = \frac{6.00 \times 10^6 \text{ N/C}}{7.27 \times 10^6 \text{ m/s}} = 0.83 \text{ T}$$

(c) Increasing the accelerating potential V increases the electron speed v. In Fig. 27.23 this doesn't change the upward electric force eE, but it increases the downward magnetic force evB. Therefore the electron beam will turn *downward* and will hit the end of the tube below the undeflected position.

EVALUATE: The required magnetic field is relatively large because the electrons are moving fairly rapidly (2.4% of the speed of light). If the maximum available magnetic field is less than 0.83 T, the electric field strength E would have to be reduced to maintain the desired ratio E/B in Eq. (27.15).

Example 27.6 Finding leaks in a vacuum system

There is almost no helium in ordinary air, so helium sprayed near a leak in a vacuum system will quickly show up in the output of a vacuum pump connected to such a system. You are designing a leak detector that uses a mass spectrometer to detect He^+ ions (charge $+e = +1.60 \times 10^{-19}$ C, mass 6.65×10^{-27} kg). The ions emerge from the velocity selector with a speed of 1.00×10^5 m/s. They are curved in a semicircular path by a magnetic field B' and are detected at a distance of 10.16 cm from the slit S_3 in Fig. 27.24. Calculate the magnitude of the magnetic field B'.

SOLUTION

IDENTIFY and SET UP: After it passes through the slit, the ion follows a circular path as described in Section 27.4 (see Fig. 27.17). We solve Eq. (27.11) for B'.

EXECUTE: The distance given is the *diameter* of the semicircular path shown in Fig. 27.24, so the radius is $R = \frac{1}{2}(10.16 \times 10^{-2}$ m$)$. From Eq. (27.11), $R = mv/qB'$, we get

$$B' = \frac{mv}{qR} = \frac{(6.65 \times 10^{-27} \text{ kg})(1.00 \times 10^5 \text{ m/s})}{(1.60 \times 10^{-19} \text{ C})(5.08 \times 10^{-2} \text{ m})}$$
$$= 0.0818 \text{ T}$$

EVALUATE: Helium leak detectors are widely used with high-vacuum systems. Our result shows that only a small magnetic field is required, so leak detectors can be relatively compact.

Mastering**PHYSICS**

ActivPhysics 13.7: Mass Spectrometer

27.25 Forces on a moving positive charge in a current-carrying conductor.

Test Your Understanding of Section 27.5 In Example 27.6 He^+ ions with charge $+e$ move at 1.00×10^5 m/s in a straight line through a velocity selector. Suppose the He^+ ions were replaced with He^{2+} ions, in which both electrons have been removed from the helium atom and the ion charge is $+2e$. At what speed must the He^{2+} ions travel through the same velocity selector in order to move in a straight line? (i) about 4.00×10^5 m/s; (ii) about 2.00×10^5 m/s; (iii) 1.00×10^5 m/s; (iv) about 0.50×10^5 m/s; (v) about 0.25×10^5 m/s.

27.6 Magnetic Force on a Current-Carrying Conductor

What makes an electric motor work? Within the motor are conductors that carry currents (that is, whose charges are in motion), as well as magnets that exert forces on the moving charges. Hence there is a magnetic force along the length of each current-carrying conductor, and these forces make the motor turn. The moving-coil galvanometer that we described in Section 26.3 also uses magnetic forces on conductors.

We can compute the force on a current-carrying conductor starting with the magnetic force $\vec{F} = q\vec{v} \times \vec{B}$ on a single moving charge. Figure 27.25 shows a straight segment of a conducting wire, with length l and cross-sectional area A; the current is from bottom to top. The wire is in a uniform magnetic field $\vec{B}$, perpendicular to the plane of the diagram and directed *into* the plane. Let's assume first that the moving charges are positive. Later we'll see what happens when they are negative.

The drift velocity $\vec{v}_d$ is upward, perpendicular to $\vec{B}$. The average force on each charge is $\vec{F} = q\vec{v}_d \times \vec{B}$, directed to the left as shown in the figure; since $\vec{v}_d$ and $\vec{B}$ are perpendicular, the magnitude of the force is $F = qv_dB$.

We can derive an expression for the *total* force on all the moving charges in a length l of conductor with cross-sectional area A using the same language we used in Eqs. (25.2) and (25.3) of Section 25.1. The number of charges per unit volume is n; a segment of conductor with length l has volume Al and contains a number of charges equal to nAl. The total force $\vec{F}$ on *all* the moving charges in this segment has magnitude

$$F = (nAl)(qv_dB) = (nqv_dA)(lB) \qquad (27.16)$$

From Eq. (25.3) the current density is $J = nqv_d$. The product JA is the total current I, so we can rewrite Eq. (27.16) as

$$F = IlB \qquad (27.17)$$

If the $\vec{B}$ field is not perpendicular to the wire but makes an angle ϕ with it, we handle the situation the same way we did in Section 27.2 for a single charge. Only the component of $\vec{B}$ perpendicular to the wire (and to the drift velocities of the charges) exerts a force; this component is $B_\perp = B\sin\phi$. The magnetic force on the wire segment is then

$$F = IlB_\perp = IlB\sin\phi \qquad (27.18)$$

The force is always perpendicular to both the conductor and the field, with the direction determined by the same right-hand rule we used for a moving positive charge (Fig. 27.26). Hence this force can be expressed as a vector product, just like the force on a single moving charge. We represent the segment of wire with a vector $\vec{l}$ along the wire in the direction of the current; then the force $\vec{F}$ on this segment is

$$\vec{F} = I\vec{l} \times \vec{B} \qquad \text{(magnetic force on a straight wire segment)} \qquad (27.19)$$

Figure 27.27 illustrates the directions of $\vec{B}$, $\vec{l}$, and $\vec{F}$ for several cases.

If the conductor is not straight, we can divide it into infinitesimal segments $d\vec{l}$. The force $d\vec{F}$ on each segment is

$$d\vec{F} = I\,d\vec{l} \times \vec{B} \qquad \text{(magnetic force on an infinitesimal wire section)} \qquad (27.20)$$

Then we can integrate this expression along the wire to find the total force on a conductor of any shape. The integral is a *line integral,* the same mathematical operation we have used to define work (Section 6.3) and electric potential (Section 23.2).

CAUTION **Current is not a vector** Recall from Section 25.1 that the current I is not a vector. The direction of current flow is described by $d\vec{l}$, not I. If the conductor is curved, the current I is the same at all points along its length, but $d\vec{l}$ changes direction so that it is always tangent to the conductor.

Finally, what happens when the moving charges are negative, such as electrons in a metal? Then in Fig. 27.25 an upward current corresponds to a downward drift velocity. But because q is now negative, the direction of the force $\vec{F}$ is the same as before. Thus Eqs. (27.17) through (27.20) are valid for *both* positive and negative charges and even when *both* signs of charge are present at once. This happens in some semiconductor materials and in ionic solutions.

A common application of the magnetic forces on a current-carrying wire is found in loudspeakers (Fig. 27.28). The radial magnetic field created by the permanent

27.26 A straight wire segment of length $\vec{l}$ carries a current I in the direction of $\vec{l}$. The magnetic force on this segment is perpendicular to both $\vec{l}$ and the magnetic field $\vec{B}$.

Force $\vec{F}$ on a straight wire carrying a positive current and oriented at an angle ϕ to a magnetic field $\vec{B}$:

• Magnitude is $F = IlB_\perp = IlB\sin\phi$.
• Direction of $\vec{F}$ is given by the right-hand rule.

27.27 Magnetic field $\vec{B}$, length $\vec{l}$, and force $\vec{F}$ vectors for a straight wire carrying a current I.

(a)

(b)

Reversing $\vec{B}$ reverses the force direction.

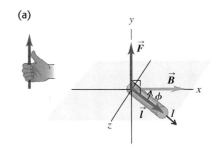

(c)

Reversing the current [relative to (b)] reverses the force direction.

27.28 (a) Components of a loudspeaker. (b) The permanent magnet creates a magnetic field that exerts forces on the current in the voice coil; for a current *I* in the direction shown, the force is to the right. If the electric current in the voice coil oscillates, the speaker cone attached to the voice coil oscillates at the same frequency.

(a)

(b)

ActivPhysics 13.5: Magnetic Force on Wire

magnet exerts a force on the voice coil that is proportional to the current in the coil; the direction of the force is either to the left or to the right, depending on the direction of the current. The signal from the amplifier causes the current to oscillate in direction and magnitude. The coil and the speaker cone to which it is attached respond by oscillating with an amplitude proportional to the amplitude of the current in the coil. Turning up the volume knob on the amplifier increases the current amplitude and hence the amplitudes of the cone's oscillation and of the sound wave produced by the moving cone.

Example 27.7   **Magnetic force on a straight conductor**

A straight horizontal copper rod carries a current of 50.0 A from west to east in a region between the poles of a large electromagnet. In this region there is a horizontal magnetic field toward the northeast (that is, 45° north of east) with magnitude 1.20 T. (a) Find the magnitude and direction of the force on a 1.00-m section of rod. (b) While keeping the rod horizontal, how should it be oriented to maximize the magnitude of the force? What is the force magnitude in this case?

SOLUTION

IDENTIFY and SET UP: Figure 27.29 shows the situation. This is a straight wire segment in a uniform magnetic field, as in Fig. 27.26. Our target variables are the force $\vec{F}$ on the segment and the angle ϕ for which the force magnitude F is greatest. We find the magnitude of the magnetic force using Eq. (27.18) and the direction from the right-hand rule.

EXECUTE: (a) The angle ϕ between the directions of current and field is 45°. From Eq. (27.18) we obtain

27.29 Our sketch of the copper rod as seen from overhead.

$F = IlB\sin\phi = (50.0\ \text{A})(1.00\ \text{m})(1.20\ \text{T})(\sin 45°) = 42.4\ \text{N}$

The direction of the force is perpendicular to the plane of the current and the field, both of which lie in the horizontal plane. Thus the force must be vertical; the right-hand rule shows that it is vertically *upward* (out of the plane of the figure).

(b) From $F = IlB\sin\phi$, F is maximum for $\phi = 90°$, so that $\vec{l}$ and $\vec{B}$ are perpendicular. To keep $\vec{F} = I\vec{l} \times \vec{B}$ upward, we rotate the rod *clockwise* by 45° from its orientation in Fig. 27.29, so that the current runs toward the southeast. Then $F = IlB = (50.0\ \text{A})(1.00\ \text{m})(1.20\ \text{T}) = 60.0\ \text{N}$.

EVALUATE: You can check the result in part (a) by using Eq. (27.19) to calculate the force vector. If we use a coordinate system with the *x*-axis pointing east, the *y*-axis north, and the *z*-axis upward, we have $\vec{l} = (1.00\ \text{m})\hat{\imath}$, $\vec{B} = (1.20\ \text{T})[(\cos 45°)\hat{\imath} + (\sin 45°)\hat{\jmath}]$, and

$$\vec{F} = I\vec{l} \times \vec{B}$$
$$= (50\ \text{A})(1.00\ \text{m})\hat{\imath} \times (1.20\ \text{T})[(\cos 45°)\hat{\imath} + (\sin 45°)\hat{\jmath}]$$
$$= (42.4\ \text{N})\hat{k}$$

Note that the maximum upward force of 60.0 N can hold the conductor in midair against the force of gravity—that is, *magnetically levitate* the conductor—if its weight is 60.0 N and its mass is $m = w/g = (60.0\ \text{N})/(9.8\ \text{m/s}^2) = 6.12\ \text{kg}$. Magnetic levitation is used in some high-speed trains to suspend the train over the tracks. Eliminating rolling friction in this way allows the train to achieve speeds of over 400 km/h.

Example 27.8 **Magnetic force on a curved conductor**

In Fig. 27.30 the magnetic field $\vec{B}$ is uniform and perpendicular to the plane of the figure, pointing out of the page. The conductor, carrying current I to the left, has three segments: (1) a straight segment with length L perpendicular to the plane of the figure, (2) a semicircle with radius R, and (3) another straight segment with length L parallel to the x-axis. Find the total magnetic force on this conductor.

SOLUTION

IDENTIFY and SET UP: The magnetic field $\vec{B} = B\hat{k}$ is uniform, so we find the forces $\vec{F}_1$ and $\vec{F}_3$ on the straight segments (1) and (3) using Eq. (27.19). We divide the curved segment (2) into infinitesimal straight segments and find the corresponding force $d\vec{F}_2$ on each straight segment using Eq. (27.20). We then integrate to find $\vec{F}_2$. The total magnetic force on the conductor is then $\vec{F} = \vec{F}_1 + \vec{F}_2 + \vec{F}_3$.

27.30 What is the total magnetic force on the conductor?

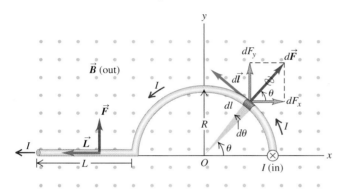

EXECUTE: For segment (1), $\vec{L} = -L\hat{k}$. Hence from Eq. (27.19), $\vec{F}_1 = I\vec{L} \times \vec{B} = 0$. For segment (3), $\vec{L} = -L\hat{i}$, so $\vec{F}_3 = I\vec{L} \times \vec{B} = I(-L\hat{i}) \times (B\hat{k}) = ILB\hat{j}$.

For the curved segment (2), Fig. 27.20 shows a segment $d\vec{l}$ with length $dl = R\,d\theta$, at angle θ. The right-hand rule shows that the direction of $d\vec{l} \times \vec{B}$ is radially outward from the center; make sure you can verify this. Because $d\vec{l}$ and $\vec{B}$ are perpendicular, the magnitude dF_2 of the force on the segment $d\vec{l}$ is just $dF_2 = I\,dl\,B = I(R\,d\theta)B$. The components of the force on this segment are

$$dF_{2x} = IR\,d\theta\,B\cos\theta \qquad dF_{2y} = IR\,d\theta\,B\sin\theta$$

To find the components of the total force, we integrate these expressions with respect to θ from $\theta = 0$ to $\theta = \pi$ to take in the whole semicircle. The results are

$$F_{2x} = IRB\int_0^\pi \cos\theta\,d\theta = 0$$

$$F_{2y} = IRB\int_0^\pi \sin\theta\,d\theta = 2IRB$$

Hence $\vec{F}_2 = 2IRB\hat{j}$. Finally, adding the forces on all three segments, we find that the total force is in the positive y-direction:

$$\vec{F} = \vec{F}_1 + \vec{F}_2 + \vec{F}_3 = 0 + 2IRB\hat{j} + ILB\hat{j} = IB(2R + L)\hat{j}$$

EVALUATE: We could have predicted from symmetry that the x-component of $\vec{F}_2$ would be zero: On the right half of the semicircle the x-component of the force is positive (to the right) and on the left half it is negative (to the left); the positive and negative contributions to the integral cancel. The result is that $\vec{F}_2$ is the force that would be exerted if we replaced the semicircle with a *straight* segment of length $2R$ along the x-axis. Do you see why?

Test Your Understanding of Section 27.6 The figure at right shows a top view of two conducting rails on which a conducting bar can slide. A uniform magnetic field is directed perpendicular to the plane of the figure as shown. A battery is to be connected to the two rails so that when the switch is closed, current will flow through the bar and cause a magnetic force to push the bar to the right. In which orientation, A or B, should the battery be placed in the circuit?

27.7 Force and Torque on a Current Loop

Current-carrying conductors usually form closed loops, so it is worthwhile to use the results of Section 27.6 to find the *total* magnetic force and torque on a conductor in the form of a loop. Many practical devices make use of the magnetic force or torque on a conducting loop, including loudspeakers (see Fig. 27.28) and galvanometers (see Section 26.3). Hence the results of this section are of substantial practical importance. These results will also help us understand the behavior of bar magnets described in Section 27.1.

As an example, let's look at a rectangular current loop in a uniform magnetic field. We can represent the loop as a series of straight line segments. We will find

Mastering PHYSICS

ActivPhysics 13.6: Magnetic Torque on a Loop

27.31 Finding the torque on a current-carrying loop in a uniform magnetic field.

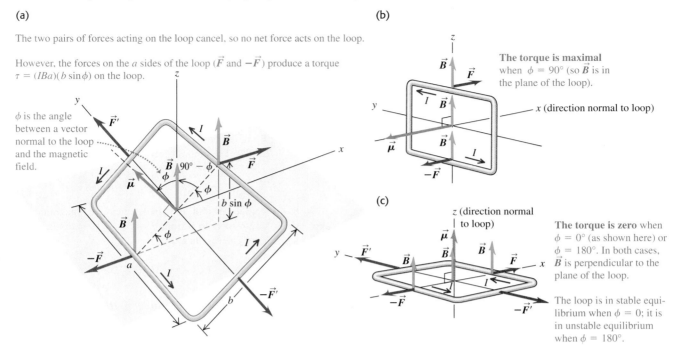

(a)

The two pairs of forces acting on the loop cancel, so no net force acts on the loop.

However, the forces on the a sides of the loop ($\vec{F}$ and $-\vec{F}$) produce a torque $\tau = (IBa)(b\sin\phi)$ on the loop.

ϕ is the angle between a vector normal to the loop and the magnetic field.

(b)

The torque is maximal when $\phi = 90°$ (so $\vec{B}$ is in the plane of the loop).

x (direction normal to loop)

(c)

z (direction normal to loop)

The torque is zero when $\phi = 0°$ (as shown here) or $\phi = 180°$. In both cases, $\vec{B}$ is perpendicular to the plane of the loop.

The loop is in stable equilibrium when $\phi = 0$; it is in unstable equilibrium when $\phi = 180°$.

that the total *force* on the loop is zero but that there can be a net *torque* acting on the loop, with some interesting properties.

Figure 27.31a shows a rectangular loop of wire with side lengths a and b. A line perpendicular to the plane of the loop (i.e., a *normal* to the plane) makes an angle ϕ with the direction of the magnetic field $\vec{B}$, and the loop carries a current I. The wires leading the current into and out of the loop and the source of emf are omitted to keep the diagram simple.

The force $\vec{F}$ on the right side of the loop (length a) is to the right, in the $+x$-direction as shown. On this side, $\vec{B}$ is perpendicular to the current direction, and the force on this side has magnitude

$$F = IaB \qquad (27.21)$$

A force $-\vec{F}$ with the same magnitude but opposite direction acts on the opposite side of the loop, as shown in the figure.

The sides with length b make an angle $(90° - \phi)$ with the direction of $\vec{B}$. The forces on these sides are the vectors $\vec{F}'$ and $-\vec{F}'$; their magnitude F' is given by

$$F' = IbB\sin(90° - \phi) = IbB\cos\phi$$

The lines of action of both forces lie along the y-axis.

The *total* force on the loop is zero because the forces on opposite sides cancel out in pairs.

The net force on a current loop in a uniform magnetic field is zero. However, the net torque is not in general equal to zero.

(You may find it helpful at this point to review the discussion of torque in Section 10.1.) The two forces $\vec{F}'$ and $-\vec{F}'$ in Fig. 27.31a lie along the same line and so give rise to zero net torque with respect to any point. The two forces $\vec{F}$ and $-\vec{F}$ lie along different lines, and each gives rise to a torque about the y-axis. According to the right-hand rule for determining the direction of torques, the vector torques due to $\vec{F}$ and $-\vec{F}$ are both in the $+y$-direction; hence the net vector torque $\vec{\tau}$ is in the $+y$-direction as well. The moment arm for each of these forces (equal to the perpendicular distance from the rotation axis to the line of action of the force) is $(b/2)\sin\phi$, so the torque due to each force has magnitude $F(b/2)\sin\phi$. If we use Eq. (27.21) for F, the magnitude of the net torque is

$$\tau = 2F(b/2)\sin\phi = (IBa)(b\sin\phi) \qquad (27.22)$$

The torque is greatest when $\phi = 90°$, $\vec{B}$ is in the plane of the loop, and the normal to this plane is perpendicular to $\vec{B}$ (Fig. 27.31b). The torque is zero when ϕ is $0°$ or $180°$ and the normal to the loop is parallel or antiparallel to the field (Fig. 27.31c). The value $\phi = 0°$ is a stable equilibrium position because the torque is zero there, and when the loop is rotated slightly from this position, the resulting torque tends to rotate it back toward $\phi = 0°$. The position $\phi = 180°$ is an *unstable* equilibrium position; if displaced slightly from this position, the loop tends to move farther away from $\phi = 180°$. Figure 27.31 shows rotation about the y-axis, but because the net force on the loop is zero, Eq. (27.22) for the torque is valid for *any* choice of axis.

The area A of the loop is equal to ab, so we can rewrite Eq. (27.22) as

$$\tau = IBA\sin\phi \qquad \text{(magnitude of torque on a current loop)} \qquad (27.23)$$

The product IA is called the **magnetic dipole moment** or **magnetic moment** of the loop, for which we use the symbol μ (the Greek letter mu):

$$\mu = IA \qquad (27.24)$$

It is analogous to the electric dipole moment introduced in Section 21.7. In terms of μ, the magnitude of the torque on a current loop is

$$\tau = \mu B\sin\phi \qquad (27.25)$$

where ϕ is the angle between the normal to the loop (the direction of the vector area $\vec{A}$) and $\vec{B}$. The torque tends to rotate the loop in the direction of *decreasing* ϕ—that is, toward its stable equilibrium position in which the loop lies in the xy-plane perpendicular to the direction of the field $\vec{B}$ (Fig. 27.31c). A current loop, or any other body that experiences a magnetic torque given by Eq. (27.25), is also called a **magnetic dipole.**

Magnetic Torque: Vector Form

We can also define a vector magnetic moment $\vec{\mu}$ with magnitude IA: This is shown in Fig. 27.31. The direction of $\vec{\mu}$ is defined to be perpendicular to the plane of the loop, with a sense determined by a right-hand rule, as shown in Fig. 27.32. Wrap the fingers of your right hand around the perimeter of the loop in the direction of the current. Then extend your thumb so that it is perpendicular to the plane of the loop; its direction is the direction of $\vec{\mu}$ (and of the vector area $\vec{A}$ of the loop). The torque is greatest when $\vec{\mu}$ and $\vec{B}$ are perpendicular and is zero when they are parallel or antiparallel. In the stable equilibrium position, $\vec{\mu}$ and $\vec{B}$ are parallel.

Finally, we can express this interaction in terms of the torque vector $\vec{\tau}$, which we used for *electric*-dipole interactions in Section 21.7. From Eq. (27.25) the magnitude of $\vec{\tau}$ is equal to the magnitude of $\vec{\mu} \times \vec{B}$, and reference to Fig. 27.31 shows that the directions are also the same. So we have

$$\vec{\tau} = \vec{\mu} \times \vec{B} \qquad \text{(vector torque on a current loop)} \qquad (27.26)$$

This result is directly analogous to the result we found in Section 21.7 for the torque exerted by an *electric* field $\vec{E}$ on an *electric* dipole with dipole moment $\vec{p}$.

Potential Energy for a Magnetic Dipole

When a magnetic dipole changes orientation in a magnetic field, the field does work on it. In an infinitesimal angular displacement $d\phi$, the work dW is given by

27.32 The right-hand rule determines the direction of the magnetic moment of a current-carrying loop. This is also the direction of the loop's area vector $\vec{A}$; $\vec{\mu} = I\vec{A}$ is a vector equation.

$\tau\,d\phi$, and there is a corresponding change in potential energy. As the above discussion suggests, the potential energy is least when $\vec{\mu}$ and $\vec{B}$ are parallel and greatest when they are antiparallel. To find an expression for the potential energy U as a function of orientation, we can make use of the beautiful symmetry between the electric and magnetic dipole interactions. The torque on an *electric* dipole in an *electric* field is $\vec{\tau} = \vec{p} \times \vec{E}$; we found in Section 21.7 that the corresponding potential energy is $U = -\vec{p} \cdot \vec{E}$. The torque on a *magnetic* dipole in a *magnetic* field is $\vec{\tau} = \vec{\mu} \times \vec{B}$, so we can conclude immediately that the corresponding potential energy is

$$U = -\vec{\mu} \cdot \vec{B} = -\mu B \cos\phi \quad \text{(potential energy for a magnetic dipole)} \quad (27.27)$$

With this definition, U is zero when the magnetic dipole moment is perpendicular to the magnetic field.

Magnetic Torque: Loops and Coils

Although we have derived Eqs. (27.21) through (27.27) for a rectangular current loop, all these relationships are valid for a plane loop of any shape at all. Any planar loop may be approximated as closely as we wish by a very large number of rectangular loops, as shown in Fig. 27.33. If these loops all carry equal currents in the same clockwise sense, then the forces and torques on the sides of two loops adjacent to each other cancel, and the only forces and torques that do not cancel are due to currents around the boundary. Thus all the above relationships are valid for a plane current loop of any shape, with the magnetic moment $\vec{\mu}$ given by $\vec{\mu} = I\vec{A}$.

We can also generalize this whole formulation to a coil consisting of N planar loops close together; the effect is simply to multiply each force, the magnetic moment, the torque, and the potential energy by a factor of N.

An arrangement of particular interest is the **solenoid,** a helical winding of wire, such as a coil wound on a circular cylinder (Fig. 27.34). If the windings are closely spaced, the solenoid can be approximated by a number of circular loops lying in planes at right angles to its long axis. The total torque on a solenoid in a magnetic field is simply the sum of the torques on the individual turns. For a solenoid with N turns in a uniform field B, the magnetic moment is $\mu = NIA$ and

$$\tau = NIAB \sin\phi \quad (27.28)$$

where ϕ is the angle between the axis of the solenoid and the direction of the field. The magnetic moment vector $\vec{\mu}$ is along the solenoid axis. The torque is greatest when the solenoid axis is perpendicular to the magnetic field and zero when they are parallel. The effect of this torque is to tend to rotate the solenoid into a position where its axis is parallel to the field. Solenoids are also useful as *sources* of magnetic field, as we'll discuss in Chapter 28.

The d'Arsonval galvanometer, described in Section 26.3, makes use of a magnetic torque on a coil carrying a current. As Fig. 26.14 shows, the magnetic field is not uniform but is *radial,* so the side thrusts on the coil are always perpendicular to its plane. Thus the angle ϕ in Eq. (27.28) is always 90°, and the magnetic torque is directly proportional to the current, no matter what the orientation of the coil. A restoring torque proportional to the angular displacement of the coil is provided by two hairsprings, which also serve as current leads to the coil. When current is supplied to the coil, it rotates along with its attached pointer until the restoring spring torque just balances the magnetic torque. Thus the pointer deflection is proportional to the current.

An important medical application of the torque on a magnetic dipole is *magnetic resonance imaging* (MRI). A patient is placed in a magnetic field of about 1.5 T, more than 10^4 times stronger than the earth's field. The nucleus of each hydrogen atom in the tissue to be imaged has a magnetic dipole moment,

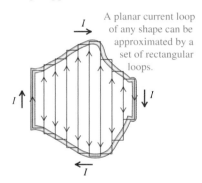

27.33 The collection of rectangles exactly matches the irregular plane loop in the limit as the number of rectangles approaches infinity and the width of each rectangle approaches zero.

A planar current loop of any shape can be approximated by a set of rectangular loops.

27.34 The torque $\vec{\tau} = \vec{\mu} \times \vec{B}$ on this solenoid in a uniform magnetic field is directed straight into the page. An actual solenoid has many more turns, wrapped closely together.

The torque tends to make the solenoid rotate clockwise in the plane of the page, aligning magnetic moment $\vec{\mu}$ with field $\vec{B}$.

which experiences a torque that aligns it with the applied field. The tissue is then illuminated with radio waves of just the right frequency to flip these magnetic moments out of alignment. The extent to which these radio waves are absorbed in the tissue is proportional to the amount of hydrogen present. Hence hydrogen-rich soft tissue looks quite different from hydrogen-deficient bone, which makes MRI ideal for analyzing details in soft tissue that cannot be seen in x-ray images (see the image that opens this chapter).

Example 27.9   Magnetic torque on a circular coil

A circular coil 0.0500 m in radius, with 30 turns of wire, lies in a horizontal plane. It carries a counterclockwise (as viewed from above) current of 5.00 A. The coil is in a uniform 1.20-T magnetic field directed toward the right. Find the magnitudes of the magnetic moment and the torque on the coil.

SOLUTION

IDENTIFY and SET UP: This problem uses the definition of magnetic moment and the expression for the torque on a magnetic dipole in a magnetic field. Figure 27.35 shows the situation. Equation (27.24) gives the magnitude μ of the magnetic moment of a single turn of wire; for N turns, the magnetic moment is N times greater. Equation (27.25) gives the magnitude τ of the torque.

EXECUTE: The area of the coil is $A = \pi r^2$. From Eq. (27.24), the total magnetic moment of all 30 turns is

$$\mu_{\text{total}} = NIA = 30(5.00 \text{ A})\pi(0.0500 \text{ m})^2 = 1.18 \text{ A} \cdot \text{m}^2$$

The angle ϕ between the direction of $\vec{B}$ and the direction of $\vec{\mu}$ (which is along the normal to the plane of the coil) is 90°. From Eq. (27.25), the torque on the coil is

$$\tau = \mu_{\text{total}}B \sin \phi = (1.18 \text{ A} \cdot \text{m}^2)(1.20 \text{ T})(\sin 90°)$$
$$= 1.41 \text{ N} \cdot \text{m}$$

EVALUATE: The torque tends to rotate the right side of the coil down and the left side up, into a position where the normal to its plane is parallel to $\vec{B}$.

27.35 Our sketch for this problem.

Example 27.10   Potential energy for a coil in a magnetic field

If the coil in Example 27.9 rotates from its initial orientation to one in which its magnetic moment $\vec{\mu}$ is parallel to $\vec{B}$, what is the change in potential energy?

SOLUTION

IDENTIFY and SET UP: Equation (27.27) gives the potential energy for each orientation. The initial position is as shown in Fig. 27.35, with $\phi_1 = 90°$. In the final orientation, the coil has been rotated 90° clockwise so that $\vec{\mu}$ and $\vec{B}$ are parallel, so the angle between these vectors is $\phi_2 = 0$.

EXECUTE: From Eq. (27.27), the potential energy change is

$$\Delta U = U_2 - U_1 = -\mu B \cos \phi_2 - (-\mu B \cos \phi_1)$$
$$= -\mu B(\cos \phi_2 - \cos \phi_1)$$
$$= -(1.18 \text{ A} \cdot \text{m}^2)(1.20 \text{ T})(\cos 0° - \cos 90°) = -1.41 \text{ J}$$

EVALUATE: The potential energy decreases because the rotation is in the direction of the magnetic torque that we found in Example 27.9.

Magnetic Dipole in a Nonuniform Magnetic Field

We have seen that a current loop (that is, a magnetic dipole) experiences zero net force in a uniform magnetic field. Figure 27.36 shows two current loops in the *nonuniform* $\vec{B}$ field of a bar magnet; in both cases the net force on the loop is *not* zero. In Fig. 27.36a the magnetic moment $\vec{\mu}$ is in the direction opposite to the field, and the force $d\vec{F} = I\,d\vec{l} \times \vec{B}$ on a segment of the loop has both a radial component and a component to the right. When these forces are summed to find the net force $\vec{F}$ on the loop, the radial components cancel so that the net force is to the right, away from the magnet. Note that in this case the force is toward the region where the field lines are farther apart and the field magnitude B is less. The polarity of the bar magnet is reversed in Fig. 27.36b, so $\vec{\mu}$ and $\vec{B}$ are parallel;

27.36 Forces on current loops in a nonuniform $\vec{B}$ field. In each case the axis of the bar magnet is perpendicular to the plane of the loop and passes through the center of the loop.

(a) Net force on this coil is away from north pole of magnet.

(b) Net force on same coil is toward south pole of magnet.

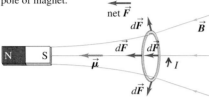

27.37 (a) An unmagnetized piece of iron. (Only a few representative atomic moments are shown.) (b) A magnetized piece of iron (bar magnet). The net magnetic moment of the bar magnet points from its south pole to its north pole. (c) A bar magnet in a magnetic field.

(a) Unmagnetized iron: magnetic moments are oriented randomly.

(b) In a bar magnet, the magnetic moments are aligned.

(c) A magnetic field creates a torque on the bar magnet that tends to align its dipole moment with the $\vec{B}$ field.

now the net force on the loop is to the left, toward the region of greater field magnitude near the magnet. Later in this section we'll use these observations to explain why bar magnets can pick up unmagnetized iron objects.

Magnetic Dipoles and How Magnets Work

The behavior of a solenoid in a magnetic field (see Fig. 27.34) resembles that of a bar magnet or compass needle; if free to turn, both the solenoid and the magnet orient themselves with their axes parallel to the $\vec{B}$ field. In both cases this is due to the interaction of moving electric charges with a magnetic field; the difference is that in a bar magnet the motion of charge occurs on the microscopic scale of the atom.

Think of an electron as being like a spinning ball of charge. In this analogy the circulation of charge around the spin axis is like a current loop, and so the electron has a net magnetic moment. (This analogy, while helpful, is inexact; an electron isn't really a spinning sphere. A full explanation of the origin of an electron's magnetic moment involves quantum mechanics, which is beyond our scope here.) In an iron atom a substantial fraction of the electron magnetic moments align with each other, and the atom has a nonzero magnetic moment. (By contrast, the atoms of most elements have little or no net magnetic moment.) In an unmagnetized piece of iron there is no overall alignment of the magnetic moments of the atoms; their vector sum is zero, and the net magnetic moment is zero (Fig. 27.37a). But in an iron bar magnet the magnetic moments of many of the atoms are parallel, and there is a substantial net magnetic moment $\vec{\mu}$ (Fig. 27.37b). If the magnet is placed in a magnetic field $\vec{B}$, the field exerts a torque given by Eq. (27.26) that tends to align $\vec{\mu}$ with $\vec{B}$ (Fig. 27.37c). A bar magnet tends to align with a $\vec{B}$ field so that a line from the south pole to the north pole of the magnet is in the direction of $\vec{B}$; hence the real significance of a magnet's north and south poles is that they represent the head and tail, respectively, of the magnet's dipole moment $\vec{\mu}$.

The torque experienced by a current loop in a magnetic field also explains how an unmagnetized iron object like that in Fig. 27.37a becomes magnetized. If an unmagnetized iron paper clip is placed next to a powerful magnet, the magnetic moments of the paper clip's atoms tend to align with the $\vec{B}$ field of the magnet. When the paper clip is removed, its atomic dipoles tend to remain aligned, and the paper clip has a net magnetic moment. The paper clip can be demagnetized by being dropped on the floor or heated; the added internal energy jostles and re-randomizes the atomic dipoles.

The magnetic-dipole picture of a bar magnet explains the attractive and repulsive forces between bar magnets shown in Fig. 27.1. The magnetic moment $\vec{\mu}$ of a bar magnet points from its south pole to its north pole, so the current loops in Figs. 27.36a and 27.36b are both equivalent to a magnet with its north pole on the left. Hence the situation in Fig. 27.36a is equivalent to two bar magnets with their north poles next to each other; the resultant force is repulsive, just as in Fig. 27.1b. In Fig. 27.36b we again have the equivalent of two bar magnets end to end, but with the south pole of the left-hand magnet next to the north pole of the right-hand magnet. The resultant force is attractive, as in Fig. 27.1a.

Finally, we can explain how a magnet can attract an unmagnetized iron object (see Fig. 27.2). It's a two-step process. First, the atomic magnetic moments of the iron tend to align with the $\vec{B}$ field of the magnet, so the iron acquires a net magnetic dipole moment $\vec{\mu}$ parallel to the field. Second, the nonuniform field of the magnet attracts the magnetic dipole. Figure 27.38a shows an example. The north pole of the magnet is closer to the nail (which contains iron), and the magnetic dipole produced in the nail is equivalent to a loop with a current that circulates in a direction opposite to that shown in Fig. 27.36a. Hence the net magnetic force on the nail is opposite to the force on the loop in Fig. 27.36a, and the nail is attracted toward the magnet. Changing the polarity of the magnet, as in Fig. 27.38b, reverses the directions of both $\vec{B}$ and $\vec{\mu}$. The situation is now equivalent to that shown in Fig. 27.36b; like the loop in that figure, the nail is attracted toward the magnet. Hence a previously unmagnetized object containing iron is attracted to *either* pole of a magnet. By contrast, objects made of brass, aluminum, or wood hardly respond at all to a magnet; the atomic magnetic dipoles of these materials, if present at all, have less tendency to align with an external field.

Our discussion of how magnets and pieces of iron interact has just scratched the surface of a diverse subject known as *magnetic properties of materials.* We'll discuss these properties in more depth in Section 28.8.

Test Your Understanding of Section 27.7 Figure 27.13c depicts the magnetic field lines due to a circular current-carrying loop. (a) What is the direction of the magnetic moment of this loop? (b) Which side of the loop is equivalent to the north pole of a magnet, and which side is equivalent to the south pole? ❙

27.8 The Direct-Current Motor

Electric motors play an important role in contemporary society. In a motor a magnetic torque acts on a current-carrying conductor, and electric energy is converted to mechanical energy. As an example, let's look at a simple type of direct-current (dc) motor, shown in Fig. 27.39.

The moving part of the motor is the *rotor,* a length of wire formed into an open-ended loop and free to rotate about an axis. The ends of the rotor wires are attached to circular conducting segments that form a *commutator.* In Fig. 27.39a, each of the two commutator segments makes contact with one of the terminals, or *brushes,* of an external circuit that includes a source of emf. This causes a current to flow into the rotor on one side, shown in red, and out of the rotor on the other side, shown in blue. Hence the rotor is a current loop with a magnetic moment $\vec{\mu}$. The rotor lies between opposing poles of a permanent magnet, so there is a magnetic field $\vec{B}$ that exerts a torque $\vec{\tau} = \vec{\mu} \times \vec{B}$ on the rotor. For the rotor orientation shown in Fig. 27.39a the torque causes the rotor to turn counterclockwise, in the direction that will align $\vec{\mu}$ with $\vec{B}$.

In Fig. 27.39b the rotor has rotated by 90° from its orientation in Fig. 27.39a. If the current through the rotor were constant, the rotor would now be in its equilibrium orientation; it would simply oscillate around this orientation. But here's where the commutator comes into play; each brush is now in contact with *both* segments of the commutator. There is no potential difference between the

27.38 A bar magnet attracts an unmagnetized iron nail in two steps. First, the $\vec{B}$ field of the bar magnet gives rise to a net magnetic moment in the nail. Second, because the field of the bar magnet is not uniform, this magnetic dipole is attracted toward the magnet. The attraction is the same whether the nail is closer to (a) the magnet's north pole or (b) the magnet's south pole.

(a)

(b)

27.39 Schematic diagram of a simple dc motor. The rotor is a wire loop that is free to rotate about an axis; the rotor ends are attached to the two curved conductors that form the commutator. (The rotor halves are colored red and blue for clarity.) The commutator segments are insulated from one another.

(a) Brushes are aligned with commutator segments.

• Current flows into the red side of the rotor and out of the blue side.
• Therefore the magnetic torque causes the rotor to spin counterclockwise.

(b) Rotor has turned 90°.

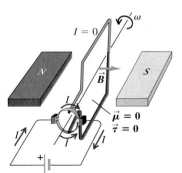

• Each brush is in contact with both commutator segments, so the current bypasses the rotor altogether.
• No magnetic torque acts on the rotor.

(c) Rotor has turned 180°.

• The brushes are again aligned with commutator segments. This time the current flows into the blue side of the rotor and out of the red side.
• Therefore the magnetic torque again causes the rotor to spin counterclockwise.

commutators, so at this instant no current flows through the rotor, and the magnetic moment is zero. The rotor continues to rotate counterclockwise because of its inertia, and current again flows through the rotor as in Fig. 27.39c. But now current enters on the *blue* side of the rotor and exits on the *red* side, just the opposite of the situation in Fig. 27.39a. While the direction of the current has reversed with respect to the rotor, the rotor itself has rotated 180° and the magnetic moment $\vec{\mu}$ is in the same direction with respect to the magnetic field. Hence the magnetic torque $\vec{\tau}$ is in the same direction in Fig. 27.39c as in Fig. 27.39a. Thanks to the commutator, the current reverses after every 180° of rotation, so the torque is always in the direction to rotate the rotor counterclockwise. When the motor has come "up to speed," the average magnetic torque is just balanced by an opposing torque due to air resistance, friction in the rotor bearings, and friction between the commutator and brushes.

The simple motor shown in Fig. 27.39 has only a single turn of wire in its rotor. In practical motors, the rotor has many turns; this increases the magnetic moment and the torque so that the motor can spin larger loads. The torque can also be increased by using a stronger magnetic field, which is why many motor designs use electromagnets instead of a permanent magnet. Another drawback of the simple design in Fig. 27.39 is that the magnitude of the torque rises and falls as the rotor spins. This can be remedied by having the rotor include several independent coils of wire oriented at different angles (Fig. 27.40).

Power for Electric Motors

Because a motor converts electric energy to mechanical energy or work, it requires electric energy input. If the potential difference between its terminals is V_{ab} and the current is I, then the power input is $P = V_{ab}I$. Even if the motor coils have negligible resistance, there must be a potential difference between the terminals if P is to be different from zero. This potential difference results principally from magnetic forces exerted on the currents in the conductors of the rotor as they rotate through the magnetic field. The associated electromotive force $\mathcal{E}$ is called an *induced* emf; it is also called a *back* emf because its sense is opposite to that of the current. In Chapter 29 we will study induced emfs resulting from motion of conductors in magnetic fields.

In a *series* motor the rotor is connected in series with the electromagnet that produces the magnetic field; in a *shunt* motor they are connected in parallel. In a series motor with internal resistance r, V_{ab} is greater than $\mathcal{E}$, and the difference is the potential drop Ir across the internal resistance. That is,

$$V_{ab} = \mathcal{E} + Ir \qquad (27.29)$$

Because the magnetic force is proportional to velocity, $\mathcal{E}$ is *not* constant but is proportional to the speed of rotation of the rotor.

27.40 This motor from a computer disk drive has 12 current-carrying coils. They interact with permanent magnets on the turntable (not shown) to make the turntable rotate. (This design is the reverse of the design in Fig. 27.39, in which the permanent magnets are stationary and the coil rotates.) Because there are multiple coils, the magnetic torque is very nearly constant and the turntable spins at a very constant rate.

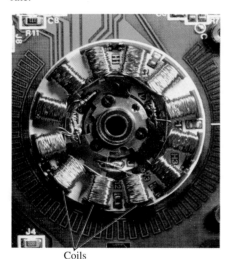

Coils

Example 27.11   A series dc motor

A dc motor with its rotor and field coils connected in series has an internal resistance of 2.00 Ω. When running at full load on a 120-V line, it draws a 4.00-A current. (a) What is the emf in the rotor? (b) What is the power delivered to the motor? (c) What is the rate of dissipation of energy in the internal resistance? (d) What is the mechanical power developed? (e) What is the motor's efficiency? (f) What happens if the machine being driven by the motor jams, so that the rotor suddenly stops turning?

SOLUTION

IDENTIFY and SET UP: This problem uses the ideas of power and potential drop in a series dc motor. We are given the internal

resistance $r = 2.00$ Ω, the voltage $V_{ab} = 120$ V across the motor, and the current $I = 4.00$ A through the motor. We use Eq. (27.29) to determine the emf $\mathcal{E}$ from these quantities. The power delivered to the motor is $V_{ab}I$, the rate of energy dissipation is I^2r, and the power output by the motor is the difference between the power input and the power dissipated. The efficiency e is the ratio of mechanical power output to electric power input.

EXECUTE: (a) From Eq. (27.29), $V_{ab} = \mathcal{E} + Ir$, we have

$$120 \text{ V} = \mathcal{E} + (4.00 \text{ A})(2.00 \text{ } \Omega) \quad \text{and so} \quad \mathcal{E} = 112 \text{ V}$$

(b) The power delivered to the motor from the source is

$$P_{input} = V_{ab}I = (120 \text{ V})(4.00 \text{ A}) = 480 \text{ W}$$

(c) The power dissipated in the resistance r is

$$P_{dissipated} = I^2r = (4.00 \text{ A})^2(2.00 \text{ } \Omega) = 32 \text{ W}$$

(d) The mechanical power output is the electric power input minus the rate of dissipation of energy in the motor's resistance (assuming that there are no other power losses):

$$P_{output} = P_{input} - P_{dissipated} = 480 \text{ W} - 32 \text{ W} = 448 \text{ W}$$

(e) The efficiency e is the ratio of mechanical power output to electric power input:

$$e = \frac{P_{output}}{P_{input}} = \frac{448 \text{ W}}{480 \text{ W}} = 0.93 = 93\%$$

(f) With the rotor stalled, the back emf $\mathcal{E}$ (which is proportional to rotor speed) goes to zero. From Eq. (27.29) the current becomes

$$I = \frac{V_{ab}}{r} = \frac{120 \text{ V}}{2.00 \text{ } \Omega} = 60 \text{ A}$$

and the power dissipated in the resistance r becomes

$$P_{dissipated} = I^2r = (60 \text{ A})^2(2.00 \text{ } \Omega) = 7200 \text{ W}$$

EVALUATE: If this massive overload doesn't blow a fuse or trip a circuit breaker, the coils will quickly melt. When the motor is first turned on, there's a momentary surge of current until the motor picks up speed. This surge causes greater-than-usual voltage drops ($V = IR$) in the power lines supplying the current. Similar effects are responsible for the momentary dimming of lights in a house when an air conditioner or dishwasher motor starts.

Test Your Understanding of Section 27.8 In the circuit shown in Fig. 27.39, you add a switch in series with the source of emf so that the current can be turned on and off. When you close the switch and allow current to flow, will the rotor begin to turn no matter what its original orientation? ❙

27.9 The Hall Effect

The reality of the forces acting on the moving charges in a conductor in a magnetic field is strikingly demonstrated by the *Hall effect,* an effect analogous to the transverse deflection of an electron beam in a magnetic field in vacuum. (The effect was discovered by the American physicist Edwin Hall in 1879 while he was still a graduate student.) To describe this effect, let's consider a conductor in the form of a flat strip, as shown in Fig. 27.41. The current is in the direction of the $+x$-axis and there is a uniform magnetic field $\vec{B}$ perpendicular to the plane of the strip, in the $+y$-direction. The drift velocity of the moving charges (charge magnitude $|q|$) has magnitude v_d. Figure 27.41a shows the case of negative charges, such as electrons in a metal, and Fig. 27.41b shows positive charges. In both cases the magnetic force is upward, just as the magnetic force on a conductor is the same whether the moving charges are positive or negative. In either case a moving charge is driven toward the *upper* edge of the strip by the magnetic force $F_z = |q|v_dB$.

If the charge carriers are electrons, as in Fig. 27.41a, an excess negative charge accumulates at the upper edge of the strip, leaving an excess positive charge at its lower edge. This accumulation continues until the resulting transverse electrostatic field $\vec{E}_e$ becomes large enough to cause a force (magnitude $|q|E_e$) that is equal and opposite to the magnetic force (magnitude $|q|v_dB$). After that, there is no longer any net transverse force to deflect the moving charges. This electric field causes a transverse potential difference between opposite edges of the strip, called the *Hall voltage* or the *Hall emf.* The polarity depends on whether the moving charges are positive or negative. Experiments show that for metals the upper edge of the strip in Fig. 27.41a *does* become negatively charged, showing that the charge carriers in a metal are indeed negative electrons.

However, if the charge carriers are *positive,* as in Fig. 27.41b, then *positive* charge accumulates at the upper edge, and the potential difference is *opposite* to the situation with negative charges. Soon after the discovery of the Hall effect in 1879, it was observed that some materials, particularly some *semiconductors,* show a Hall emf opposite to that of the metals, as if their charge carriers were positively charged. We now know that these materials conduct by a process known as *hole conduction.* Within such a material there are locations, called *holes,* that would normally be occupied by an electron but are actually empty. A missing negative charge is equivalent to a positive charge. When an electron moves in one direction to fill a hole, it leaves another hole behind it. The hole migrates in the direction opposite to that of the electron.

27.41 Forces on charge carriers in a conductor in a magnetic field.

(a) Negative charge carriers (electrons)

The charge carriers are pushed toward the top of the strip ...

... so point *a* is at a higher potential than point *b*.

(b) Positive charge carriers

The charge carriers are again pushed toward the top of the strip ...

... so the polarity of the potential difference is opposite to that for negative charge carriers.

In terms of the coordinate axes in Fig. 27.41b, the electrostatic field $\vec{E}_e$ for the positive-q case is in the $-z$-direction; its z-component E_z is negative. The magnetic field is in the $+y$-direction, and we write it as B_y. The magnetic force (in the $+z$-direction) is qv_dB_y. The current density J_x is in the $+x$-direction. In the steady state, when the forces qE_z and qv_dB_y are equal in magnitude and opposite in direction,

$$qE_z + qv_dB_y = 0 \quad \text{or} \quad E_z = -v_dB_y$$

This confirms that when q is positive, E_z is negative. The current density J_x is

$$J_x = nqv_d$$

Eliminating v_d between these equations, we find

$$nq = \frac{-J_xB_y}{E_z} \quad \text{(Hall effect)} \qquad (27.30)$$

Note that this result (as well as the entire derivation) is valid for both positive and negative q. When q is negative, E_z is positive, and conversely.

We can measure J_x, B_y, and E_z, so we can compute the product nq. In both metals and semiconductors, q is equal in magnitude to the electron charge, so the Hall effect permits a direct measurement of n, the concentration of current-carrying charges in the material. The *sign* of the charges is determined by the polarity of the Hall emf, as we have described.

The Hall effect can also be used for a direct measurement of electron drift speed v_d in metals. As we saw in Chapter 25, these speeds are very small, often of the order of 1 mm/s or less. If we move the entire conductor in the opposite direction to the current with a speed equal to the drift speed, then the electrons are at rest with respect to the magnetic field, and the Hall emf disappears. Thus the conductor speed needed to make the Hall emf vanish is equal to the drift speed.

Example 27.12 A Hall-effect measurement

You place a strip of copper, 2.0 mm thick and 1.50 cm wide, in a uniform 0.40-T magnetic field as shown in Fig. 27.41a. When you run a 75-A current in the $+x$-direction, you find that the potential at the bottom of the slab is $0.81\,\mu\text{V}$ higher than at the top. From this measurement, determine the concentration of mobile electrons in copper.

SOLUTION

IDENTIFY and SET UP: This problem describes a Hall-effect experiment. We use Eq. (27.30) to determine the mobile electron concentration n.

EXECUTE: First we find the current density J_x and the electric field E_z:

$$J_x = \frac{I}{A} = \frac{75\ \text{A}}{(2.0 \times 10^{-3}\ \text{m})(1.50 \times 10^{-2}\ \text{m})} = 2.5 \times 10^6\ \text{A/m}^2$$

$$E_z = \frac{V}{d} = \frac{0.81 \times 10^{-6}\ \text{V}}{1.5 \times 10^{-2}\ \text{m}} = 5.4 \times 10^{-5}\ \text{V/m}$$

Then, from Eq. (27.30),

$$n = \frac{-J_xB_y}{qE_z} = \frac{-(2.5 \times 10^6\ \text{A/m}^2)(0.40\ \text{T})}{(-1.60 \times 10^{-19}\ \text{C})(5.4 \times 10^{-5}\ \text{V/m})}$$

$$= 11.6 \times 10^{28}\ \text{m}^{-3}$$

EVALUATE: The actual value of n for copper is $8.5 \times 10^{28}\ \text{m}^{-3}$. The difference shows that our simple model of the Hall effect, which ignores quantum effects and electron interactions with the ions, must be used with caution. This example also shows that with good conductors, the Hall emf is very small even with large current densities. In practice, Hall-effect devices for magnetic-field measurements use semiconductor materials, for which moderate current densities give much larger Hall emfs.

Test Your Understanding of Section 27.9 A copper wire of square cross section is oriented vertically. The four sides of the wire face north, south, east, and west. There is a uniform magnetic field directed from east to west, and the wire carries current downward. Which side of the wire is at the highest electric potential? (i) north side; (ii) south side; (iii) east side; (iv) west side.

Magnetic forces: Magnetic interactions are fundamentally interactions between moving charged particles. These interactions are described by the vector magnetic field, denoted by $\vec{B}$. A particle with charge q moving with velocity $\vec{v}$ in a magnetic field $\vec{B}$ experiences a force $\vec{F}$ that is perpendicular to both $\vec{v}$ and $\vec{B}$. The SI unit of magnetic field is the tesla ($1\ \text{T} = 1\ \text{N/A} \cdot \text{m}$). (See Example 27.1.)

$$\vec{F} = q\vec{v} \times \vec{B} \qquad (27.2)$$

Magnetic field lines and flux: A magnetic field can be represented graphically by magnetic field lines. At each point a magnetic field line is tangent to the direction of $\vec{B}$ at that point. Where field lines are close together the field magnitude is large, and vice versa. Magnetic flux Φ_B through an area is defined in an analogous way to electric flux. The SI unit of magnetic flux is the weber ($1\ \text{Wb} = 1\ \text{T} \cdot \text{m}^2$). The net magnetic flux through any closed surface is zero (Gauss's law for magnetism). As a result, magnetic field lines always close on themselves. (See Example 27.2.)

$$\Phi_B = \int B_\perp \, dA$$

$$= \int B \cos\phi \, dA \qquad (27.6)$$

$$= \int \vec{B} \cdot d\vec{A}$$

$$\oint \vec{B} \cdot d\vec{A} = 0 \quad \text{(closed surface)} \quad (27.8)$$

Motion in a magnetic field: The magnetic force is always perpendicular to $\vec{v}$; a particle moving under the action of a magnetic field alone moves with constant speed. In a uniform field, a particle with initial velocity perpendicular to the field moves in a circle with radius R that depends on the magnetic field strength B and the particle mass m, speed v, and charge q. (See Examples 27.3 and 27.4.)

Crossed electric and magnetic fields can be used as a velocity selector. The electric and magnetic forces exactly cancel when $v = E/B$. (See Examples 27.5 and 27.6.)

$$R = \frac{mv}{|q|B} \qquad (27.11)$$

Magnetic force on a conductor: A straight segment of a conductor carrying current I in a uniform magnetic field $\vec{B}$ experiences a force $\vec{F}$ that is perpendicular to both $\vec{B}$ and the vector $\vec{l}$, which points in the direction of the current and has magnitude equal to the length of the segment. A similar relationship gives the force $d\vec{F}$ on an infinitesimal current-carrying segment $d\vec{l}$. (See Examples 27.7 and 27.8.)

$$\vec{F} = I\vec{l} \times \vec{B} \qquad (27.19)$$

$$d\vec{F} = I \, d\vec{l} \times \vec{B} \qquad (27.20)$$

Magnetic torque: A current loop with area A and current I in a uniform magnetic field $\vec{B}$ experiences no net magnetic force, but does experience a magnetic torque of magnitude τ. The vector torque $\vec{\tau}$ can be expressed in terms of the magnetic moment $\vec{\mu} = I\vec{A}$ of the loop, as can the potential energy U of a magnetic moment in a magnetic field $\vec{B}$. The magnetic moment of a loop depends only on the current and the area; it is independent of the shape of the loop. (See Examples 27.9 and 27.10.)

$$\tau = IBA \sin\phi \qquad (27.23)$$

$$\vec{\tau} = \vec{\mu} \times \vec{B} \qquad (27.26)$$

$$U = -\vec{\mu} \cdot \vec{B} = -\mu B \cos\phi \qquad (27.27)$$

Electric motors: In a dc motor a magnetic field exerts a torque on a current in the rotor. Motion of the rotor through the magnetic field causes an induced emf called a back emf. For a series motor, in which the rotor coil is in parallel with coils that produce the magnetic field, the terminal voltage is the sum of the back emf and the drop Ir across the internal resistance. (See Example 27.11.)

The Hall effect: The Hall effect is a potential difference perpendicular to the direction of current in a conductor, when the conductor is placed in a magnetic field. The Hall potential is determined by the requirement that the associated electric field must just balance the magnetic force on a moving charge. Hall-effect measurements can be used to determine the sign of charge carriers and their concentration n. (See Example 27.12.)

$$nq = \frac{-J_x B_y}{E_z} \qquad (27.30)$$

BRIDGING PROBLEM | **Magnetic Torque on a Current-Carrying Ring**

A circular ring with area 4.45 cm^2 is carrying a current of 12.5 A. The ring, initially at rest, is immersed in a region of uniform magnetic field given by $\vec{B} = (1.15 \times 10^{-2} \text{ T})(12\hat{i} + 3\hat{j} - 4\hat{k})$. The ring is positioned initially such that its magnetic moment is given by $\vec{\mu}_i = \mu(-0.800\hat{i} + 0.600\hat{j})$, where μ is the (positive) magnitude of the magnetic moment. (a) Find the initial magnetic torque on the ring. (b) The ring (which is free to rotate around one diameter) is released and turns through an angle of 90.0°, at which point its magnetic moment is given by $\vec{\mu}_f = -\mu\hat{k}$. Determine the decrease in potential energy. (c) If the moment of inertia of the ring about a diameter is 8.50×10^{-7} kg·m^2, determine the angular speed of the ring as it passes through the second position.

SOLUTION GUIDE

See MasteringPhysics® study area for a Video Tutor solution. (MP)

IDENTIFY and SET UP

1. The current-carrying ring acts as a magnetic dipole, so you can use the equations for a magnetic dipole·in a uniform magnetic field.

2. There are no nonconservative forces acting on the ring as it rotates, so the sum of its rotational kinetic energy (discussed in Section 9.4) and the potential energy is conserved.

EXECUTE

3. Use the vector expression for the torque on a magnetic dipole to find the answer to part (a). (*Hint:* You may want to review Section 1.10.)
4. Find the change in potential energy from the first orientation of the ring to the second orientation.
5. Use your result from step 4 to find the rotational kinetic energy of the ring when it is in the second orientation.
6. Use your result from step 5 to find the ring's angular speed when it is in the second orientation.

EVALUATE

7. If the ring were free to rotate around *any* diameter, in what direction would the magnetic moment point when the ring is in a state of stable equilibrium?

Problems | For instructor-assigned homework, go to www.masteringphysics.com (MP)

•, ••, •••: Problems of increasing difficulty. **CP**: Cumulative problems incorporating material from earlier chapters. **CALC**: Problems requiring calculus. **BIO**: Biosciences problems.

DISCUSSION QUESTIONS

Q27.1 Can a charged particle move through a magnetic field without experiencing any force? If so, how? If not, why not?
Q27.2 At any point in space, the electric field $\vec{E}$ is defined to be in the direction of the electric force on a positively charged particle at that point. Why don't we similarly define the magnetic field $\vec{B}$ to be in the direction of the magnetic force on a moving, positively charged particle?
Q27.3 Section 27.2 describes a procedure for finding the direction of the magnetic force using your right hand. If you use the same procedure, but with your left hand, will you get the correct direction for the force? Explain.

Q27.4 The magnetic force on a moving charged particle is always perpendicular to the magnetic field $\vec{B}$. Is the trajectory of a moving charged particle always perpendicular to the magnetic field lines? Explain your reasoning.

Q27.5 A charged particle is fired into a cubical region of space where there is a uniform magnetic field. Outside this region, there is no magnetic field. Is it possible that the particle will remain inside the cubical region? Why or why not?

Q27.6 If the magnetic force does no work on a charged particle, how can it have any effect on the particle's motion? Are there other examples of forces that do no work but have a significant effect on a particle's motion?

Q27.7 A charged particle moves through a region of space with constant velocity (magnitude and direction). If the external magnetic field is zero in this region, can you conclude that the external electric field in the region is also zero? Explain. (By "external" we mean fields other than those produced by the charged particle.) If the external electric field is zero in the region, can you conclude that the external magnetic field in the region is also zero?

Q27.8 How might a loop of wire carrying a current be used as a compass? Could such a compass distinguish between north and south? Why or why not?

Q27.9 How could the direction of a magnetic field be determined by making only *qualitative* observations of the magnetic force on a straight wire carrying a current?

Q27.10 A loose, floppy loop of wire is carrying current *I*. The loop of wire is placed on a horizontal table in a uniform magnetic field $\vec{B}$ perpendicular to the plane of the table. This causes the loop of wire to expand into a circular shape while still lying on the table. In a diagram, show all possible orientations of the current *I* and magnetic field $\vec{B}$ that could cause this to occur. Explain your reasoning.

Q27.11 Several charges enter a uniform magnetic field directed into the page. (a) What path would a positive charge *q* moving with a velocity of magnitude *v* follow through the field? (b) What path would a positive charge *q* moving with a velocity of magnitude *2v* follow through the field? (c) What path would a negative charge *−q* moving with a velocity of magnitude *v* follow through the field? (d) What path would a neutral particle follow through the field?

Q27.12 Each of the lettered points at the corners of the cube in Fig. Q27.12 represents a positive charge *q* moving with a velocity of magnitude *v* in the direction indicated. The region in the figure is in a uniform magnetic field $\vec{B}$, parallel to the *x*-axis and directed toward the right. Which charges experience a force due to $\vec{B}$? What is the direction of the force on each charge?

Figure **Q27.12**

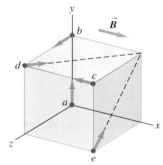

Q27.13 A student claims that if lightning strikes a metal flagpole, the force exerted by the earth's magnetic field on the current in the pole can be large enough to bend it. Typical lightning currents are of the order of 10^4 to 10^5 A. Is the student's opinion justified? Explain your reasoning.

Q27.14 Could an accelerator be built in which *all* the forces on the particles, for steering and for increasing speed, are magnetic forces? Why or why not?

Q27.15 An ordinary loudspeaker such as that shown in Fig. 27.28 should not be placed next to a computer monitor or TV screen. Why not?

Q27.16 The magnetic force acting on a charged particle can never do work because at every instant the force is perpendicular to the velocity. The torque exerted by a magnetic field can do work on a current loop when the loop rotates. Explain how these seemingly contradictory statements can be reconciled.

Q27.17 If an emf is produced in a dc motor, would it be possible to use the motor somehow as a generator or source, taking power out of it rather than putting power into it? How might this be done?

Q27.18 When the polarity of the voltage applied to a dc motor is reversed, the direction of motion does *not* reverse. Why not? How *could* the direction of motion be reversed?

Q27.19 In a Hall-effect experiment, is it possible that *no* transverse potential difference will be observed? Under what circumstances might this happen?

Q27.20 Hall-effect voltages are much greater for relatively poor conductors (such as germanium) than for good conductors (such as copper), for comparable currents, fields, and dimensions. Why?

EXERCISES

Section 27.2 Magnetic Field

27.1 • A particle with a charge of -1.24×10^{-8} C is moving with instantaneous velocity $\vec{v} = (4.19 \times 10^4 \text{ m/s})\hat{\imath} + (-3.85 \times 10^4 \text{ m/s})\hat{\jmath}$. What is the force exerted on this particle by a magnetic field (a) $\vec{B} = (1.40 \text{ T})\hat{\imath}$ and (b) $\vec{B} = (1.40 \text{ T})\hat{k}$?

27.2 • A particle of mass 0.195 g carries a charge of -2.50×10^{-8} C. The particle is given an initial horizontal velocity that is due north and has magnitude 4.00×10^4 m/s. What are the magnitude and direction of the minimum magnetic field that will keep the particle moving in the earth's gravitational field in the same horizontal, northward direction?

27.3 • In a 1.25-T magnetic field directed vertically upward, a particle having a charge of magnitude 8.50 μC and initially moving northward at 4.75 km/s is deflected toward the east. (a) What is the sign of the charge of this particle? Make a sketch to illustrate how you found your answer. (b) Find the magnetic force on the particle.

27.4 • A particle with mass 1.81×10^{-3} kg and a charge of 1.22×10^{-8} C has, at a given instant, a velocity $\vec{v} = (3.00 \times 10^4 \text{ m/s})\hat{\jmath}$. What are the magnitude and direction of the particle's acceleration produced by a uniform magnetic field $\vec{B} = (1.63 \text{ T})\hat{\imath} + (0.980 \text{ T})\hat{\jmath}$?

27.5 • An electron experiences a magnetic force of magnitude 4.60×10^{-15} N when moving at an angle of 60.0° with respect to a magnetic field of magnitude 3.50×10^{-3} T. Find the speed of the electron.

27.6 • An electron moves at 2.50×10^6 m/s through a region in which there is a magnetic field of unspecified direction and magnitude 7.40×10^{-2} T. (a) What are the largest and smallest possible magnitudes of the acceleration of the electron due to the magnetic field? (b) If the actual acceleration of the electron is one-fourth of the largest magnitude in part (a), what is the angle between the electron velocity and the magnetic field?

27.7 •• CP A particle with charge 7.80 μC is moving with velocity $\vec{v} = -(3.80 \times 10^3 \text{ m/s})\hat{\jmath}$. The magnetic force on the particle is measured to be $\vec{F} = +(7.60 \times 10^{-3} \text{ N})\hat{\imath} - (5.20 \times 10^{-3} \text{ N})\hat{k}$. (a) Calculate all the components of the magnetic field you can from this information. (b) Are there components of the magnetic field that are not determined by the measurement of the force? Explain. (c) Calculate the scalar product $\vec{B} \cdot \vec{F}$. What is the angle between $\vec{B}$ and $\vec{F}$?

27.8 •• CP A particle with charge -5.60 nC is moving in a uniform magnetic field $\vec{B} = -(1.25 \text{ T})\hat{k}$. The magnetic force on the particle is measured to be $\vec{F} = -(3.40 \times 10^{-7} \text{ N})\hat{\imath} + (7.40 \times 10^{-7} \text{ N})\hat{\jmath}$. (a) Calculate all the components of the velocity of the particle that you can from this information. (b) Are there components of the velocity that are not determined by the measurement of the force? Explain. (c) Calculate the scalar product $\vec{v} \cdot \vec{F}$. What is the angle between $\vec{v}$ and $\vec{F}$?

27.9 •• A group of particles is traveling in a magnetic field of unknown magnitude and direction. You observe that a proton moving at 1.50 km/s in the $+x$-direction experiences a force of 2.25×10^{-16} N in the $+y$-direction, and an electron moving at 4.75 km/s in the $-z$-direction experiences a force of 8.50×10^{-16} N in the $+y$-direction. (a) What are the magnitude and direction of the magnetic field? (b) What are the magnitude and direction of the magnetic force on an electron moving in the $-y$-direction at 3.20 km/s?

Section 27.3 Magnetic Field Lines and Magnetic Flux

27.10 • A flat, square surface with side length 3.40 cm is in the xy-plane at $z = 0$. Calculate the magnitude of the flux through this surface produced by a magnetic field $\vec{B} = (0.200 \text{ T})\hat{\imath} + (0.300 \text{ T})\hat{\jmath} - (0.500 \text{ T})\hat{k}$.

27.11 • A circular area with a radius of 6.50 cm lies in the xy-plane. What is the magnitude of the magnetic flux through this circle due to a uniform magnetic field $B = 0.230$ T (a) in the $+z$-direction; (b) at an angle of 53.1° from the $+z$-direction; (c) in the $+y$-direction?

27.12 • A horizontal rectangular surface has dimensions 2.80 cm by 3.20 cm and is in a uniform magnetic field that is directed at an angle of 30.0° above the horizontal. What must the magnitude of the magnetic field be in order to produce a flux of 4.20×10^{-4} Wb through the surface?

27.13 •• An open plastic soda bottle with an opening diameter of 2.5 cm is placed on a table. A uniform 1.75-T magnetic field directed upward and oriented 25° from vertical encompasses the bottle. What is the total magnetic flux through the plastic of the soda bottle?

27.14 •• The magnetic field $\vec{B}$ in a certain region is 0.128 T, and its direction is that of the $+z$-axis in Fig. E27.14. (a) What is the magnetic flux across the surface *abcd* in the figure? (b) What is the magnetic flux across the surface *befc*? (c) What is the magnetic flux across the surface *aefd*? (d) What is the net flux through all five surfaces that enclose the shaded volume?

Figure **E27.14**

Section 27.4 Motion of Charged Particles in a Magnetic Field

27.15 •• An electron at point A in Fig. E27.15 has a speed v_0 of 1.41×10^6 m/s. Find (a) the magnitude and direction of the magnetic field that will cause the electron to follow the semicircular path from A to B, and (b) the time required for the electron to move from A to B.

27.16 •• Repeat Exercise 27.15 for the case in which the particle is a proton rather than an electron.

Figure **E27.15**

27.17 • CP A 150-g ball containing 4.00×10^8 excess electrons is dropped into a 125-m vertical shaft. At the bottom of the shaft, the ball suddenly enters a uniform horizontal magnetic field that has magnitude 0.250 T and direction from east to west. If air resistance is negligibly small, find the magnitude and direction of the force that this magnetic field exerts on the ball just as it enters the field.

27.18 • An alpha particle (a He nucleus, containing two protons and two neutrons and having a mass of 6.64×10^{-27} kg) traveling horizontally at 35.6 km/s enters a uniform, vertical, 1.10-T magnetic field. (a) What is the diameter of the path followed by this alpha particle? (b) What effect does the magnetic field have on the speed of the particle? (c) What are the magnitude and direction of the acceleration of the alpha particle while it is in the magnetic field? (d) Explain why the speed of the particle does not change even though an unbalanced external force acts on it.

27.19 • CP A particle with charge 6.40×10^{-19} C travels in a circular orbit with radius 4.68 mm due to the force exerted on it by a magnetic field with magnitude 1.65 T and perpendicular to the orbit. (a) What is the magnitude of the linear momentum $\vec{p}$ of the particle? (b) What is the magnitude of the angular momentum $\vec{L}$ of the particle?

27.20 • (a) An ^{16}O nucleus (charge $+8e$) moving horizontally from west to east with a speed of 500 km/s experiences a magnetic force of 0.00320 nN vertically downward. Find the magnitude and direction of the weakest magnetic field required to produce this force. Explain how this same force could be caused by a larger magnetic field. (b) An electron moves in a uniform, horizontal, 2.10-T magnetic field that is toward the west. What must the magnitude and direction of the minimum velocity of the electron be so that the magnetic force on it will be 4.60 pN, vertically upward? Explain how the velocity could be greater than this minimum value and the force still have this same magnitude and direction.

27.21 • A deuteron (the nucleus of an isotope of hydrogen) has a mass of 3.34×10^{-27} kg and a charge of $+e$. The deuteron travels in a circular path with a radius of 6.96 mm in a magnetic field with magnitude 2.50 T. (a) Find the speed of the deuteron. (b) Find the time required for it to make half a revolution. (c) Through what potential difference would the deuteron have to be accelerated to acquire this speed?

27.22 • In an experiment with cosmic rays, a vertical beam of particles that have charge of magnitude $3e$ and mass 12 times the proton mass enters a uniform horizontal magnetic field of 0.250 T and is bent in a semicircle of diameter 95.0 cm, as shown in Fig. E27.22. (a) Find the speed of the particles and the sign of their charge. (b) Is it reasonable to ignore the gravity force on the particles? (c) How does the speed of the particles as they enter the field compare to their speed as they exit the field?

Figure **E27.22**

27.23 • A physicist wishes to produce electromagnetic waves of frequency 3.0 THz (1 THz = 1 terahertz = 10^{12} Hz) using a magnetron (see Example 27.3). (a) What magnetic field would be required? Compare this field with the strongest constant magnetic fields yet produced on earth, about 45 T. (b) Would there be any advantage to using protons instead of electrons in the magnetron? Why or why not?

27.24 ⋅⋅ A beam of protons traveling at 1.20 km/s enters a uniform magnetic field, traveling perpendicular to the field. The beam exits the magnetic field, leaving the field in a direction perpendicular to its original direction (Fig. E27.24). The beam travels a distance of 1.18 cm *while in the field*. What is the magnitude of the magnetic field?

Figure **E27.24**

27.25 ⋅ An electron in the beam of a TV picture tube is accelerated by a potential difference of 2.00 kV. Then it passes through a region of transverse magnetic field, where it moves in a circular arc with radius 0.180 m. What is the magnitude of the field?

27.26 ⋅ A singly charged ion of ^{7}Li (an isotope of lithium) has a mass of 1.16×10^{-26} kg. It is accelerated through a potential difference of 220 V and then enters a magnetic field with magnitude 0.723 T perpendicular to the path of the ion. What is the radius of the ion's path in the magnetic field?

27.27 ⋅⋅ A proton ($q = 1.60 \times 10^{-19}$ C, $m = 1.67 \times 10^{-27}$ kg) moves in a uniform magnetic field $\vec{B} = (0.500 \text{ T})\hat{\imath}$. At $t = 0$ the proton has velocity components $v_x = 1.50 \times 10^5$ m/s, $v_y = 0$, and $v_z = 2.00 \times 10^5$ m/s (see Example 27.4). (a) What are the magnitude and direction of the magnetic force acting on the proton? In addition to the magnetic field there is a uniform electric field in the +x-direction, $\vec{E} = (+2.00 \times 10^4 \text{ V/m})\hat{\imath}$. (b) Will the proton have a component of acceleration in the direction of the electric field? (c) Describe the path of the proton. Does the electric field affect the radius of the helix? Explain. (d) At $t = T/2$, where T is the period of the circular motion of the proton, what is the x-component of the displacement of the proton from its position at $t = 0$?

Section 27.5 Applications of Motion of Charged Particles

27.28 ⋅ (a) What is the speed of a beam of electrons when the simultaneous influence of an electric field of 1.56×10^4 V/m and a magnetic field of 4.62×10^{-3} T, with both fields normal to the beam and to each other, produces no deflection of the electrons? (b) In a diagram, show the relative orientation of the vectors $\vec{v}$, $\vec{E}$, and $\vec{B}$. (c) When the electric field is removed, what is the radius of the electron orbit? What is the period of the orbit?

27.29 ⋅ In designing a velocity selector that uses uniform perpendicular electric and magnetic fields, you want to select positive ions of charge $+5e$ that are traveling perpendicular to the fields at 8.75 km/s. The magnetic field available to you has a magnitude of 0.550 T. (a) What magnitude of electric field do you need? (b) Show how the two fields should be oriented relative to each other and to the velocity of the ions. (c) Will your velocity selector also allow the following ions (having the same velocity as the $+5e$ ions) to pass through undeflected: (i) negative ions of charge $-5e$, (ii) positive ions of charge different from $+5e$?

27.30 ⋅ **Crossed $\vec{E}$ and $\vec{B}$ Fields.** A particle with initial velocity $\vec{v}_0 = (5.85 \times 10^3 \text{ m/s})\hat{\jmath}$ enters a region of uniform electric and magnetic fields. The magnetic field in the region is $\vec{B} = -(1.35 \text{ T})\hat{k}$. Calculate the magnitude and direction of the electric field in the region if the particle is to pass through undeflected, for a particle of charge (a) $+0.640$ nC and (b) -0.320 nC. You can ignore the weight of the particle.

27.31 ⋅⋅ A 150-V battery is connected across two parallel metal plates of area 28.5 cm^2 and separation 8.20 mm. A beam of alpha particles (charge $+2e$, mass 6.64×10^{-27} kg) is accelerated from rest through a potential difference of 1.75 kV and enters the region between the plates perpendicular to the electric field, as shown in Fig. E27.31. What magnitude and direction of magnetic field are needed so that the alpha particles emerge undeflected from between the plates?

Figure **E27.31**

27.32 ⋅ A singly ionized (one electron removed) ^{40}K atom passes through a velocity selector consisting of uniform perpendicular electric and magnetic fields. The selector is adjusted to allow ions having a speed of 4.50 km/s to pass through undeflected when the magnetic field is 0.0250 T. The ions next enter a second uniform magnetic field (B') oriented at right angles to their velocity. ^{40}K contains 19 protons and 21 neutrons and has a mass of 6.64×10^{-26} kg. (a) What is the magnitude of the electric field in the velocity selector? (b) What must be the magnitude of B' so that the ions will be bent into a semicircle of radius 12.5 cm?

27.33 ⋅ Singly ionized (one electron removed) atoms are accelerated and then passed through a velocity selector consisting of perpendicular electric and magnetic fields. The electric field is 155 V/m and the magnetic field is 0.0315 T. The ions next enter a uniform magnetic field of magnitude 0.0175 T that is oriented perpendicular to their velocity. (a) How fast are the ions moving when they emerge from the velocity selector? (b) If the radius of the path of the ions in the second magnetic field is 17.5 cm, what is their mass?

27.34 ⋅ In the Bainbridge mass spectrometer (see Fig. 27.24), the magnetic-field magnitude in the velocity selector is 0.650 T, and ions having a speed of 1.82×10^6 m/s pass through undeflected. (a) What is the electric-field magnitude in the velocity selector? (b) If the separation of the plates is 5.20 mm, what is the potential difference between plates P and P'?

27.35 ⋅⋅ **BIO Ancient Meat Eating.** The amount of meat in prehistoric diets can be determined by measuring the ratio of the isotopes nitrogen-15 to nitrogen-14 in bone from human remains. Carnivores concentrate ^{15}N, so this ratio tells archaeologists how much meat was consumed by ancient people. Use the spectrometer of Exercise 27.34 to find the separation of the ^{14}N and ^{15}N isotopes at the detector. The measured masses of these isotopes are 2.32×10^{-26} kg (^{14}N) and 2.49×10^{-26} kg (^{15}N).

Section 27.6 Magnetic Force on a Current-Carrying Conductor

27.36 ⋅ A straight, 2.5-m wire carries a typical household current of 1.5 A (in one direction) at a location where the earth's magnetic field is 0.55 gauss from south to north. Find the magnitude and direction of the force that our planet's magnetic field exerts on this wire if is oriented so that the current in it is running (a) from west to east, (b) vertically upward, (c) from north to south. (d) Is the magnetic force ever large enough to cause significant effects under normal household conditions?

27.37 ⋅ A straight, 2.00-m, 150-g wire carries a current in a region where the earth's magnetic field is horizontal with a magnitude of 0.55 gauss. (a) What is the minimum value of the current in this wire so that its weight is completely supported by the magnetic force due to earth's field, assuming that no other forces except gravity act on it? Does it seem likely that such a wire could support this size of current? (b) Show how the wire would have to be oriented relative to the earth's magnetic field to be supported in this way.

27.38 •• An electromagnet produces a magnetic field of 0.550 T in a cylindrical region of radius 2.50 cm between its poles. A straight wire carrying a current of 10.8 A passes through the center of this region and is perpendicular to both the axis of the cylindrical region and the magnetic field. What magnitude of force is exerted on the wire?

27.39 •• A long wire carrying 4.50 A of current makes two 90° bends, as shown in Fig. E27.39. The bent part of the wire passes through a uniform 0.240-T magnetic field directed as shown in the figure and confined to a limited region of space. Find the magnitude and direction of the force that the magnetic field exerts on the wire.

Figure **E27.39**

27.40 • A straight, vertical wire carries a current of 1.20 A downward in a region between the poles of a large superconducting electromagnet, where the magnetic field has magnitude $B = 0.588$ T and is horizontal. What are the magnitude and direction of the magnetic force on a 1.00-cm section of the wire that is in this uniform magnetic field, if the magnetic field direction is (a) east; (b) south; (c) 30.0° south of west?

27.41 • A thin, 50.0-cm-long metal bar with mass 750 g rests on, but is not attached to, two metallic supports in a uniform 0.450-T magnetic field, as shown in Fig. E27.41. A battery and a 25.0-Ω resistor in series are connected to the supports. (a) What is the highest voltage the battery can have without breaking the circuit at the supports? (b) The battery voltage has the maximum value calculated in part (a). If the resistor suddenly gets partially short-circuited, decreasing its resistance to 2.0 Ω, find the initial acceleration of the bar.

Figure **E27.41**

27.42 • **Magnetic Balance.** The circuit shown in Fig. E27.42 is used to make a magnetic balance to weigh objects. The mass m to be measured is hung from the center of the bar that is in a uniform magnetic field of 1.50 T, directed into the plane of the figure. The battery voltage can be adjusted to vary the current in the circuit. The horizontal bar is 60.0 cm long and is made of extremely light-weight material. It is connected to the battery by thin vertical wires that can support no appreciable tension; all the weight of the suspended mass m is supported by the magnetic force on the bar. A resistor with $R = 5.00$ Ω is in series with the bar; the resistance of the rest of the circuit is much less than this. (a) Which point, a or b, should be the positive terminal of the battery? (b) If the maximum terminal voltage of the battery is 175 V, what is the greatest mass m that this instrument can measure?

27.43 • Consider the conductor and current in Example 27.8, but now let the magnetic field be parallel to the x-axis. (a) What are the magnitude and direction of the total magnetic force on the conductor? (b) In Example 27.8, the total force is the same as if we replaced the semicircle with a straight segment along the x-axis. Is

that still true when the magnetic field is in this different direction? Can you explain why, or why not?

Section 27.7 Force and Torque on a Current Loop

27.44 •• The plane of a 5.0 cm × 8.0 cm rectangular loop of wire is parallel to a 0.19-T magnetic field. The loop carries a current of 6.2 A. (a) What torque acts on the loop? (b) What is the magnetic moment of the loop? (c) What is the maximum torque that can be obtained with the same total length of wire carrying the same current in this magnetic field?

27.45 • The 20.0 cm × 35.0 cm rectangular circuit shown in Fig. E27.45 is hinged along side ab. It carries a clockwise 5.00-A current and is located in a uniform 1.20-T magnetic field oriented perpendicular to two of its sides, as shown. (a) Draw a clear diagram showing the direction of the force that the magnetic field exerts on each segment of the circuit (ab, bc, etc.). (b) Of the four forces you drew in part (a), decide which ones exert a torque about the hinge ab. Then calculate only those forces that exert this torque. (c) Use your results from part (b) to calculate the torque that the magnetic field exerts on the circuit about the hinge axis ab.

Figure **E27.45**

27.46 • A rectangular coil of wire, 22.0 cm by 35.0 cm and carrying a current of 1.40 A, is oriented with the plane of its loop perpendicular to a uniform 1.50-T magnetic field, as shown in Fig. E27.46. (a) Calculate the net force and torque that the magnetic field exerts on the coil. (b) The coil is rotated through a 30.0° angle about the axis shown, with the left side coming out of the plane of the figure and the right side going into the plane. Calculate the net force and torque that the magnetic field now exerts on the coil. (*Hint:* In order to help visualize this three-dimensional problem, make a careful drawing of the coil as viewed along the rotation axis.)

Figure **E27.46**

27.47 • CP A uniform rectangular coil of total mass 212 g and dimensions 0.500 m × 1.00 m is oriented with its plane parallel to a uniform 3.00-T magnetic field (Fig. E27.47). A current of 2.00 A is suddenly started in the coil. (a) About which axis (A_1 or A_2) will the coil begin to rotate? Why? (b) Find the initial angular acceleration of the coil just after the current is started.

Figure **E27.47**

Figure **E27.42**

27.48 • A circular coil with area A and N turns is free to rotate about a diameter that coincides with the x-axis. Current I is circulating in the coil. There is a uniform magnetic field $\vec{B}$ in the positive y-direction. Calculate the magnitude and direction of the torque $\vec{\tau}$

Figure **E27.48**

and the value of the potential energy U, as given in Eq. (27.27), when the coil is oriented as shown in parts (a) through (d) of Fig. E27.48.

27.49 •• A coil with magnetic moment 1.45 A · m² is oriented initially with its magnetic moment antiparallel to a uniform 0.835-T magnetic field. What is the change in potential energy of the coil when it is rotated 180° so that its magnetic moment is parallel to the field?

Section 27.8 The Direct-Current Motor

27.50 • A dc motor with its rotor and field coils connected in series has an internal resistance of 3.2 Ω. When the motor is running at full load on a 120-V line, the emf in the rotor is 105 V. (a) What is the current drawn by the motor from the line? (b) What is the power delivered to the motor? (c) What is the mechanical power developed by the motor?

27.51 •• In a shunt-wound dc motor with the field coils and rotor connected in parallel (Fig. E27.51), the resistance R_f of the field coils is 106 Ω, and the resistance R_r of the rotor is 5.9 Ω. When a potential difference of 120 V is applied to the brushes and the motor is running at full speed delivering mechanical power, the current supplied to it is 4.82 A. (a) What is the current in the field coils? (b) What is the current in the rotor? (c) What is the induced emf developed by the motor? (d) How much mechanical power is developed by this motor?

Figure **E27.51**

27.52 • A shunt-wound dc motor with the field coils and rotor connected in parallel (see Fig. E27.51) operates from a 120-V dc power line. The resistance of the field windings, R_f, is 218 Ω. The resistance of the rotor, R_r, is 5.9 Ω. When the motor is running, the rotor develops an emf $\mathcal{E}$. The motor draws a current of 4.82 A from the line. Friction losses amount to 45.0 W. Compute (a) the field current; (b) the rotor current; (c) the emf $\mathcal{E}$; (d) the rate of development of thermal energy in the field windings; (e) the rate of development of thermal energy in the rotor; (f) the power input to the motor; (g) the efficiency of the motor.

Section 27.9 The Hall Effect

27.53 • Figure E27.53 shows a portion of a silver ribbon with $z_1 = 11.8$ mm and $y_1 = 0.23$ mm, carrying a current of 120 A in the +x-direction. The ribbon lies in a uniform magnetic field, in the y-direction, with magnitude 0.95 T. Apply the simplified model of the Hall effect presented in Section 27.9. If there are 5.85×10^{28} free electrons per cubic meter, find (a) the magnitude of the drift velocity of the electrons in the x-direction; (b) the magnitude and direction of the electric field in the z-direction due to the Hall effect; (c) the Hall emf.

Figure **E27.53**

27.54 • Let Fig. E27.53 represent a strip of an unknown metal of the same dimensions as those of the silver ribbon in Exercise 27.53. When the magnetic field is 2.29 T and the current is 78.0 A, the Hall emf is found to be 131 μV. What does the simplified model of the Hall effect presented in Section 27.9 give for the density of free electrons in the unknown metal?

PROBLEMS

27.55 • When a particle of charge $q > 0$ moves with a velocity of $\vec{v}_1$ at 45.0° from the +x-axis in the xy-plane, a uniform magnetic field exerts a force $\vec{F}_1$ along the $-z$-axis (Fig. P27.55). When the same particle moves with a velocity $\vec{v}_2$ with the same magnitude as $\vec{v}_1$ but along the +z-axis, a force $\vec{F}_2$ of magnitude F_2 is exerted on it along the +x-axis. (a) What are the magnitude (in terms of q, v_1, and F_2) and direction of the magnetic field? (b) What is the magnitude of $\vec{F}_1$ in terms of F_2?

Figure **P27.55**

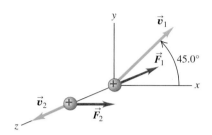

27.56 • A particle with charge 9.45×10^{-8} C is moving in a region where there is a uniform magnetic field of 0.650 T in the +x-direction. At a particular instant of time the velocity of the particle has components $v_x = -1.68 \times 10^4$ m/s, $v_y = -3.11 \times 10^4$ m/s, and $v_z = 5.85 \times 10^4$ m/s. What are the components of the force on the particle at this time?

27.57 ••• **CP** **Fusion Reactor.** If two deuterium nuclei (charge $+e$, mass 3.34×10^{-27} kg) get close enough together, the attraction of the strong nuclear force will fuse them to make an isotope of helium, releasing vast amounts of energy. The range of this force is about 10^{-15} m. This is the principle behind the fusion reactor. The deuterium nuclei are moving much too fast to be contained by physical walls, so they are confined magnetically. (a) How fast would two nuclei have to move so that in a head-on collision they would get close enough to fuse? (Assume their speeds are equal. Treat the nuclei as point charges, and assume that a separation of 1.0×10^{-15} is required for fusion.) (b) What strength magnetic field is needed to make deuterium nuclei with this speed travel in a circle of diameter 2.50 m?

27.58 •• **Magnetic Moment of the Hydrogen Atom.** In the Bohr model of the hydrogen atom (see Section 38.5), in the lowest energy state the electron orbits the proton at a speed of 2.2×10^6 m/s in a circular orbit of radius 5.3×10^{-11} m. (a) What is the orbital period of the electron? (b) If the orbiting electron is considered to be a current loop, what is the current I? (c) What is the magnetic moment of the atom due to the motion of the electron?

27.59 •• You wish to hit a target from several meters away with a charged coin having a mass of 4.25 g and a charge of +2500 μC. The coin is given an initial velocity of 12.8 m/s, and a downward, uniform electric field with field strength 27.5 N/C exists throughout the region. If you aim directly at the target and fire the coin horizontally, what magnitude and direction of uniform magnetic field are needed in the region for the coin to hit the target?

27.60 • A cyclotron is to accelerate protons to an energy of 5.4 MeV. The superconducting electromagnet of the cyclotron produces a 2.9-T magnetic field perpendicular to the proton orbits. (a) When the protons have achieved a kinetic energy of 2.7 MeV, what is the radius of their circular orbit and what is their angular speed? (b) Repeat part (a) when the protons have achieved their final kinetic energy of 5.4 MeV.

27.61 • The magnetic poles of a small cyclotron produce a magnetic field with magnitude 0.85 T. The poles have a radius of 0.40 m, which is the maximum radius of the orbits of the accelerated particles. (a) What is the maximum energy to which protons ($q = 1.60 \times 10^{-19}$ C, $m = 1.67 \times 10^{-27}$ kg) can be accelerated by this cyclotron? Give your answer in electron volts and in joules. (b) What is the time for one revolution of a proton orbiting at this maximum radius? (c) What would the magnetic-field magnitude have to be for the maximum energy to which a proton can be accelerated to be twice that calculated in part (a)? (d) For $B = 0.85$ T, what is the maximum energy to which alpha particles ($q = 3.20 \times 10^{-19}$ C, $m = 6.65 \times 10^{-27}$ kg) can be accelerated by this cyclotron? How does this compare to the maximum energy for protons?

27.62 •• A particle with charge q is moving with speed v in the $-y$-direction. It is moving in a uniform magnetic field $\vec{B} = B_x\hat{\imath} + B_y\hat{\jmath} + B_z\hat{k}$. (a) What are the components of the force $\vec{F}$ exerted on the particle by the magnetic field? (b) If $q > 0$, what must the signs of the components of $\vec{B}$ be if the components of $\vec{F}$ are all nonnegative? (c) If $q < 0$ and $B_x = B_y = B_z > 0$, find the direction of $\vec{F}$ and find the magnitude of $\vec{F}$ in terms of $|q|$, v, and B_x.

27.63 •• A particle with negative charge q and mass $m = 2.58 \times 10^{-15}$ kg is traveling through a region containing a uniform magnetic field $\vec{B} = -(0.120 \text{ T})\hat{k}$. At a particular instant of time the velocity of the particle is $\vec{v} = (1.05 \times 10^6 \text{ m/s})(-3\hat{\imath} + 4\hat{\jmath} + 12\hat{k})$ and the force $\vec{F}$ on the particle has a magnitude of 2.45 N. (a) Determine the charge q. (b) Determine the acceleration $\vec{a}$ of the particle. (c) Explain why the path of the particle is a helix, and determine the radius of curvature R of the circular component of the helical path. (d) Determine the cyclotron frequency of the particle. (e) Although helical motion is not periodic in the full sense of the word, the x- and y-coordinates do vary in a periodic way. If the coordinates of the particle at $t = 0$ are $(x, y, z) = (R, 0, 0)$, determine its coordinates at a time $t = 2T$, where T is the period of the motion in the xy-plane.

27.64 •• **BIO** **Medical Uses of Cyclotrons.** The largest cyclotron in the United States is the *Tevatron* at Fermilab, near Chicago, Illinois. It is called a Tevatron because it can accelerate particles to energies in the TeV range: 1 tera-eV $= 10^{12}$ eV. Its circumference is 6.4 km, and it currently can produce a maximum energy of 2.0 TeV. In a certain medical experiment, protons will be accelerated to energies of 1.25 MeV and aimed at a tumor to destroy its cells. (a) How fast are these protons moving when they hit the tumor? (b) How strong must the magnetic field be to bend the protons in the circle indicated?

27.65 • A magnetic field exerts a torque τ on a round current-carrying loop of wire. What will be the torque on this loop (in terms of τ) if its diameter is tripled?

27.66 •• A particle of charge $q > 0$ is moving at speed v in the $+z$-direction through a region of uniform magnetic field $\vec{B}$. The magnetic force on the particle is $\vec{F} = F_0(3\hat{\imath} + 4\hat{\jmath})$, where F_0 is a positive constant. (a) Determine the components B_x, B_y, and B_z, or at least as many of the three components as is possible from the information given. (b) If it is given in addition that the magnetic field has magnitude $6F_0/qv$, determine as much as you can about the remaining components of $\vec{B}$.

27.67 •• Suppose the electric field between the plates in Fig. 27.24 is 1.88×10^4 V/m and the magnetic field in both regions is 0.682 T. If the source contains the three isotopes of krypton, ^{82}Kr, ^{84}Kr, and ^{86}Kr, and the ions are singly charged, find the distance between the lines formed by the three isotopes on the particle

detector. Assume the atomic masses of the isotopes (in atomic mass units) are equal to their mass numbers, 82, 84, and 86. (One atomic mass unit = 1 u = 1.66×10^{-27} kg.)

27.68 •• **Mass Spectrograph.** A mass spectrograph is used to measure the masses of ions, or to separate ions of different masses (see Section 27.5). In one design for such an instrument, ions with mass m and charge q are accelerated through a potential difference V. They enter a uniform magnetic field that is perpendicular to their velocity, and they are deflected in a semicircular path of radius R. A detector measures where the ions complete the semicircle and from this it is easy to calculate R. (a) Derive the equation for calculating the mass of the ion from measurements of B, V, R, and q. (b) What potential difference V is needed so that singly ionized ^{12}C atoms will have $R = 50.0$ cm in a 0.150-T magnetic field? (c) Suppose the beam consists of a mixture of ^{12}C and ^{14}C ions. If v and B have the same values as in part (b), calculate the separation of these two isotopes at the detector. Do you think that this beam separation is sufficient for the two ions to be distinguished? (Make the assumption described in Problem 27.67 for the masses of the ions.)

27.69 •• A straight piece of conducting wire with mass M and length L is placed on a frictionless incline tilted at an angle θ from the horizontal (Fig. P27.69). There is a uniform, vertical magnetic field $\vec{B}$ at all points (produced by an arrangement of magnets not shown in the figure). To keep the wire from sliding down the incline, a voltage source is attached to the ends of the wire. When just the right amount of current flows through the wire, the wire remains at rest. Determine the magnitude and direction of the current in the wire that will cause the wire to remain at rest. Copy the figure and draw the direction of the current on your copy. In addition, show in a free-body diagram all the forces that act on the wire.

Figure **P27.69**

27.70 •• **CP** A 2.60-N metal bar, 1.50 m long and having a resistance of 10.0 Ω, rests horizontally on conducting wires connecting it to the circuit shown in Fig. P27.70. The bar is in a uniform, horizontal, 1.60-T magnetic field and is not attached to the wires in the circuit. What is the acceleration of the bar just after the switch S is closed?

Figure **P27.70**

27.71 •• **Using Gauss's Law for Magnetism.** In a certain region of space, the magnetic field $\vec{B}$ is not uniform. The magnetic field has both a z-component and a component that points radially away from or toward the z-axis. The z-component is given by $B_z(z) = \beta z$, where β is a positive constant. The radial component B_r depends only on r, the radial distance from the z-axis. (a) Use Gauss's law for magnetism, Eq. (27.8), to find the radial component B_r as a function of r. (*Hint:* Try a cylindrical Gaussian surface of radius r concentric with the z-axis, with one end at $z = 0$ and the other at $z = L$.) (b) Sketch the magnetic field lines.

27.72 •• **CP** A plastic circular loop has radius R, and a positive charge q is distributed uniformly around the circumference of the loop. The loop is then rotated around its central axis, perpendicular to the plane of the loop, with angular speed ω. If the loop is in a region where there is a uniform magnetic field $\vec{B}$ directed parallel to the plane of the loop, calculate the magnitude of the magnetic torque on the loop.

27.73 •• **BIO Determining Diet.** One method for determining the amount of corn in early Native American diets is the *stable isotope ratio analysis* (SIRA) technique. As corn photosynthesizes, it concentrates the isotope carbon-13, whereas most other plants concentrate carbon-12. Overreliance on corn consumption can then be correlated with certain diseases, because corn lacks the essential amino acid lysine. Archaeologists use a mass spectrometer to separate the ^{12}C and ^{13}C isotopes in samples of human remains. Suppose you use a velocity selector to obtain singly ionized (missing one electron) atoms of speed 8.50 km/s, and you want to bend them within a uniform magnetic field in a semicircle of diameter 25.0 cm for the ^{12}C. The measured masses of these isotopes are 1.99×10^{-26} kg (^{12}C) and 2.16×10^{-26} kg (^{13}C). (a) What strength of magnetic field is required? (b) What is the diameter of the ^{13}C semicircle? (c) What is the separation of the ^{12}C and ^{13}C ions at the detector at the end of the semicircle? Is this distance large enough to be easily observed?

27.74 •• **CP An Electromagnetic Rail Gun.** A conducting bar with mass m and length L slides over horizontal rails that are connected to a voltage source. The voltage source maintains a constant current I in the rails and bar, and a constant, uniform, vertical magnetic field $\vec{B}$ fills the region between the rails (Fig. P27.74). (a) Find the magnitude and direction of the net force on the conducting bar. Ignore friction, air resistance, and electrical resistance. (b) If the bar has mass m, find the distance d that the bar must move along the rails from rest to attain speed v. (c) It has been suggested that rail guns based on this principle could accelerate payloads into earth orbit or beyond. Find the distance the bar must travel along the rails if it is to reach the escape speed for the earth (11.2 km/s). Let $B = 0.80$ T, $I = 2.0 \times 10^3$ A, $m = 25$ kg, and $L = 50$ cm. For simplicity assume the net force on the object is equal to the magnetic force, as in parts (a) and (b), even though gravity plays an important role in an actual launch in space.

Figure **P27.74**

27.75 • A long wire carrying a 6.00-A current reverses direction by means of two right-angle bends, as shown in Fig. P27.75. The part of the wire where the bend occurs is in a magnetic field of 0.666 T confined to the circular region of diameter 75 cm, as shown. Find the magnitude and direction of the net force that the magnetic field exerts on this wire.

Figure **P27.75**

27.76 • A wire 25.0 cm long lies along the z-axis and carries a current of 7.40 A in the $+z$-direction. The magnetic field is uniform and has components $B_x = -0.242$ T, $B_y = -0.985$ T, and $B_z = -0.336$ T. (a) Find the components of the magnetic force on the wire. (b) What is the magnitude of the net magnetic force on the wire?

27.77 •• **CP** The rectangular loop of wire shown in Fig. P27.77 has a mass of 0.15 g per centimeter of length and is pivoted about side ab on a frictionless axis. The current in the wire is 8.2 A in the direction shown. Find the magnitude and direction of the magnetic field parallel to the y-axis that will cause the loop to swing up until its plane makes an angle of 30.0° with the yz-plane.

Figure **P27.77**

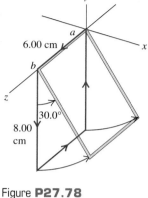

27.78 •• The rectangular loop shown in Fig. P27.78 is pivoted about the y-axis and carries a current of 15.0 A in the direction indicated. (a) If the loop is in a uniform magnetic field with magnitude 0.48 T in the $+x$-direction, find the magnitude and direction of the torque required to hold the loop in the position shown. (b) Repeat part (a) for the case in which the field is in the $-z$-direction. (c) For each of the above magnetic fields, what torque would be required if the loop were pivoted about an axis through its center, parallel to the y-axis?

Figure **P27.78**

27.79 •• **CP CALC** A thin, uniform rod with negligible mass and length 0.200 m is attached to the floor by a frictionless hinge at point P (Fig. P27.79). A horizontal spring with force constant $k = 4.80$ N/m connects the other end of the rod to a vertical wall. The rod is in a uniform magnetic field $B = 0.340$ T directed into the plane of the figure. There is current $I = 6.50$ A in the rod, in the direction shown. (a) Calculate the torque due to the magnetic force on the rod, for an axis at P. Is it correct to take the total magnetic force to act at the center of gravity of the rod when calculating the torque? Explain. (b) When the rod is in equilibrium and makes an angle of 53.0° with the floor, is the spring stretched or compressed? (c) How much energy is stored in the spring when the rod is in equilibrium?

Figure **P27.79**

27.80 •• The loop of wire shown in Fig. P27.80 forms a right triangle and carries a current $I = 5.00$ A in the direction shown. The loop is in a uniform magnetic field that has magnitude $B = 3.00$ T and the same direction as the current in side PQ of the loop. (a) Find the force exerted by the magnetic field on each side of the triangle. If the force is not zero, specify its direction. (b) What is the net force on the loop? (c) The loop is pivoted about an axis that lies along side *PR*. Use the forces calculated in part (a) to calculate the torque on each side of the loop (see Problem 27.79). (d) What is the magnitude of the net torque on the loop? Calculate the net torque from the torques calculated in part (c) and also from Eq. (27.28). Do these two results agree? (e) Is the net torque directed to rotate point *Q* into the plane of the figure or out of the plane of the figure?

Figure **P27.80**

27.81 •• **CP** A uniform, 458-g metal bar 75.0 cm long carries a current *I* in a uniform, horizontal 1.25-T magnetic field as shown in Fig. P27.81. The directions of *I* and $\vec{B}$ are shown in the figure. The bar is free to rotate about a frictionless hinge at point *b*. The other end of the bar rests on a conducting support at point *a* but is not attached there. The bar rests at an angle of 60.0° above the horizontal. What is the largest value the current *I* can have without breaking the electrical contact at *a*? (See Problem 27.77.)

Figure **P27.81**

27.82 •• **Paleoclimate.** Climatologists can determine the past temperature of the earth by comparing the ratio of the isotope oxygen-18 to the isotope oxygen-16 in air trapped in ancient ice sheets, such as those in Greenland. In one method for separating these isotopes, a sample containing both of them is first singly ionized (one electron is removed) and then accelerated from rest through a potential difference *V*. This beam then enters a magnetic field *B* at right angles to the field and is bent into a quarter-circle. A particle detector at the end of the path measures the amount of each isotope. (a) Show that the separation Δr of the two isotopes at the detector is given by

$$\Delta r = \frac{\sqrt{2eV}}{eB}\left(\sqrt{m_{18}} - \sqrt{m_{16}}\right)$$

where m_{16} and m_{18} are the masses of the two oxygen isotopes, (b) The measured masses of the two isotopes are 2.66×10^{-26} kg (^{16}O) and 2.99×10^{-26} kg (^{18}O). If the magnetic field is 0.050 T, what must be the accelerating potential *V* so that these two isotopes will be separated by 4.00 cm at the detector?

27.83 •• **CALC** A Voice Coil. It was shown in Section 27.7 that the net force on a current loop in a *uniform* magnetic field is zero. The magnetic force on the voice coil of a loudspeaker (see Fig. 27.28) is nonzero because the magnetic field at the coil is not uniform. A voice coil in a loudspeaker has 50 turns of wire and a diameter of 1.56 cm, and the current in the coil is 0.950 A. Assume that the magnetic field at each point of the coil has a constant magnitude of 0.220 T and is directed at an angle of 60.0° outward from the normal to the plane of the coil (Fig. P27.83). Let the axis of the coil be in the *y*-direction. The current in the coil is in the direction shown (counterclockwise as viewed from a point above the coil on the *y*-axis). Calculate the magnitude and direction of the net magnetic force on the coil.

Figure **P27.83**

27.84 •• **Quark Model of the Neutron.** The neutron is a particle with zero charge. Nonetheless, it has a nonzero magnetic moment with *z*-component 9.66×10^{-27} A·m². This can be explained by the internal structure of the neutron. A substantial body of evidence indicates that a neutron is composed of three fundamental particles called *quarks*: an "up" (*u*) quark, of charge $+2e/3$, and two "down" (*d*) quarks, each of charge $-e/3$. The combination of the three quarks produces a net charge of $2e/3 - e/3 - e/3 = 0$. If the quarks are in motion, they can produce a nonzero magnetic moment. As a very simple model, suppose the *u* quark moves in a counterclockwise circular path and the *d* quarks move in a clockwise circular path, all of radius *r* and all with the same speed *v* (Fig. P27.84). (a) Determine the current due to the circulation of the *u* quark. (b) Determine the magnitude of the magnetic moment due to the circulating *u* quark. (c) Determine the magnitude of the magnetic moment of the three-quark system. (Be careful to use the correct magnetic moment directions.) (d) With what speed *v* must the quarks move if this model is to reproduce the magnetic moment of the neutron? Use $r = 1.20 \times 10^{-15}$ m (the radius of the neutron) for the radius of the orbits.

Figure **P27.84**

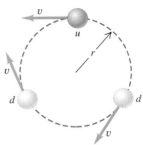

27.85 •• **CALC Force on a Current Loop in a Nonuniform Magnetic Field.** It was shown in Section 27.7 that the net force on a current loop in a *uniform* magnetic field is zero. But what if $\vec{B}$ is *not* uniform? Figure P27.85 shows a square loop of wire that lies in the *xy*-plane. The loop has corners at $(0, 0)$, $(0, L)$, $(L, 0)$, and (L, L) and carries a constant current *I* in the clockwise direction. The magnetic field has no *x*-component but has both *y*- and *z*-components: $\vec{B} = (B_0 z/L)\hat{\jmath} + (B_0 y/L)\hat{k}$, where B_0 is a positive constant. (a) Sketch the magnetic field lines in the *yz*-plane. (b) Find the magnitude and direction of the magnetic force exerted on each of the sides of the loop by integrating Eq. (27.20). (c) Find the magnitude and direction of the net magnetic force on the loop.

Figure **P27.85**

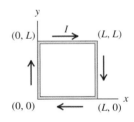

27.86 • **CALC Torque on a Current Loop in a Nonuniform Magnetic Field.** In Section 27.7 the expression for the torque on a current loop was derived assuming that the magnetic field $\vec{B}$ was uniform. But what if $\vec{B}$ is *not* uniform? Figure P27.85 shows a square loop of wire that lies in the *xy*-plane. The loop has corners at $(0, 0)$, $(0, L)$, $(L, 0)$, and (L, L) and carries a constant current *I* in the clockwise direction. The magnetic field has no *z*-component but has both *x*- and *y*-components: $\vec{B} = (B_0 y/L)\hat{\imath} + (B_0 x/L)\hat{\jmath}$, where B_0 is a positive constant. (a) Sketch the magnetic field lines in the *xy*-plane. (b) Find the magnitude and direction of the magnetic force exerted on each of the sides of the loop by integrating Eq. (27.20). (c) If the loop is free to rotate about the *x*-axis, find the magnitude and direction of the magnetic torque on the loop. (d) Repeat part (c) for the case in which the loop is free to rotate about the *y*-axis. (e) Is Eq. (27.26), $\vec{\tau} = \vec{\mu} \times \vec{B}$, an appropriate description of the torque on this loop? Why or why not?

27.87 •• **CP** An insulated wire with mass $m = 5.40 \times 10^{-5}$ kg is bent into the shape of an inverted U such that the horizontal part has a length $l = 15.0$ cm. The bent ends of the wire are partially immersed in two pools of mercury, with 2.5 cm of each end below the mercury's surface. The entire structure is in a region containing a uniform 0.00650-T magnetic field directed into the page (Fig. P27.87). An electrical connection from the mercury pools is made through the ends of the wires. The mercury pools are connected to a 1.50-V battery and a switch S. When switch S is closed, the wire jumps 35.0 cm into the air, measured from its initial position. (a) Determine the speed v of the wire as it leaves the mercury. (b) Assuming that the current I through the wire was constant from the time the switch was closed until the wire left the mercury, determine I. (c) Ignoring the resistance of the mercury and the circuit wires, determine the resistance of the moving wire.

Figure **P27.87**

27.88 •• A circular loop of wire with area A lies in the xy-plane. As viewed along the z-axis looking in the $-z$-direction toward the origin, a current I is circulating clockwise around the loop. The torque produced by an external magnetic field $\vec{B}$ is given by $\vec{\tau} = D(4\hat{i} - 3\hat{j})$, where D is a positive constant, and for this orientation of the loop the magnetic potential energy $U = -\vec{\mu} \cdot \vec{B}$ is negative. The magnitude of the magnetic field is $B_0 = 13D/IA$. (a) Determine the vector magnetic moment of the current loop. (b) Determine the components B_x, B_y, and B_z of $\vec{B}$.

CHALLENGE PROBLEMS

27.89 ••• A particle with charge 2.15 μC and mass 3.20 $\times$ 10^{-11} kg is initially traveling in the $+y$-direction with a speed $v_0 = 1.45 \times 10^5$ m/s. It then enters a region containing a uniform magnetic field that is directed into, and perpendicular to, the page in Fig. P27.89. The magnitude of the field is 0.420 T. The

Figure **P27.89**

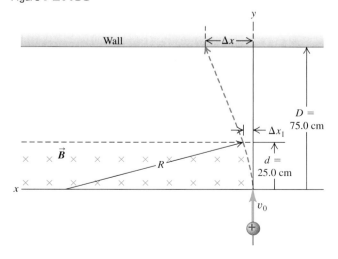

region extends a distance of 25.0 cm along the initial direction of travel; 75.0 cm from the point of entry into the magnetic field region is a wall. The length of the field-free region is thus 50.0 cm. When the charged particle enters the magnetic field, it follows a curved path whose radius of curvature is R. It then leaves the magnetic field after a time t_1, having been deflected a distance Δx_1. The particle then travels in the field-free region and strikes the wall after undergoing a total deflection Δx. (a) Determine the radius R of the curved part of the path. (b) Determine t_1, the time the particle spends in the magnetic field. (c) Determine Δx_1, the horizontal deflection at the point of exit from the field. (d) Determine Δx, the total horizontal deflection.

27.90 ••• **The Electromagnetic Pump.** Magnetic forces acting on conducting fluids provide a convenient means of pumping these fluids. For example, this method can be used to pump blood without the damage to the cells that can be caused by a mechanical pump. A horizontal tube with rectangular cross section (height h, width w) is placed at right angles to a uniform magnetic field with magnitude B so that a length l is in the field (Fig. P27.90). The tube is filled with a conducting liquid, and an electric current of density J is maintained in the third mutually perpendicular direction. (a) Show that the difference of pressure between a point in the liquid on a vertical plane through ab and a point in the liquid on another vertical plane through cd, under conditions in which the liquid is prevented from flowing, is $\Delta p = JlB$. (b) What current density is needed to provide a pressure difference of 1.00 atm between these two points if $B = 2.20$ T and $l = 35.0$ mm?

Figure **P27.90**

Liquid metal or blood

27.91 ••• **CP A Cycloidal Path.** A particle with mass m and positive charge q starts from rest at the origin shown in Fig. P27.91. There is a uniform electric field $\vec{E}$ in the $+y$-direction and a uniform magnetic field $\vec{B}$ directed out of the page. It is shown in more advanced books that the path is a *cycloid* whose radius of curvature at the top points is twice the y-coordinate at that level. (a) Explain why the path has this general shape and why it is repetitive. (b) Prove that the speed at any point is equal to $\sqrt{2qEy/m}$. (*Hint:* Use energy conservation.) (c) Applying Newton's second law at the top point and taking as given that the radius of curvature here equals $2y$, prove that the speed at this point is $2E/B$.

Figure **P27.91**

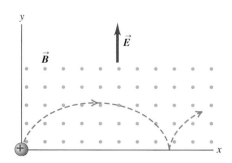

Answers

Chapter Opening Question

In MRI the nuclei of hydrogen atoms within soft tissue act like miniature current loops whose magnetic moments align with an applied field. See Section 27.7 for details.

Test Your Understanding Questions

27.1 Answer: yes When a magnet is cut apart, each part has a north and south pole (see Fig. 27.4). Hence the small red part behaves much like the original, full-sized compass needle.

27.2 Answer: path 3 Applying the right-hand rule to the vectors $\vec{v}$ (which points to the right) and $\vec{B}$ (which points into the plane of the figure) says that the force $\vec{F} = q\vec{v} \times \vec{B}$ on a *positive* charge would point *upward*. Since the charge is *negative,* the force points *downward* and the particle follows a trajectory that curves downward.

27.3 Answers: (a) (ii), (b) no The magnitude of $\vec{B}$ would increase as you moved to the right, reaching a maximum as you pass through the plane of the loop. As you moved beyond the plane of the loop, the field magnitude would decrease. You can tell this from the spacing of the field lines: The closer the field lines, the stronger the field. The direction of the field would be to the right at all points along the path, since the path is along a field line and the direction of $\vec{B}$ at any point is tangent to the field line through that point.

27.4 Answers: (a) (ii), (b) (i) The radius of the orbit as given by Eq. (27.11) is directly proportional to the speed, so doubling the particle speed causes the radius to double as well. The particle has twice as far to travel to complete one orbit but is traveling at double the speed, so the time for one orbit is unchanged. This result also follows from Eq. (27.12), which states that the angular speed ω is independent of the linear speed v. Hence the time per orbit, $T = 2\pi/\omega$, likewise does not depend on v.

27.5 Answer: (iii) From Eq. (27.13), the speed $v = E/B$ at which particles travel straight through the velocity selector does not depend on the magnitude or sign of the charge or the mass of the particle. All that is required is that the particles (in this case, ions) have a nonzero charge.

27.6 Answer: A This orientation will cause current to flow clockwise around the circuit and hence through the conducting bar in the direction from the top to the bottom of the figure. From the right-hand rule, the magnetic force $\vec{F} = I\vec{l} \times \vec{B}$ on the bar will then point to the right.

27.7 Answers: (a) to the right; (b) north pole on the right, south pole on the left If you wrap the fingers of your right hand around the coil in the direction of the current, your right thumb points to the right (perpendicular to the plane of the coil). This is the direction of the magnetic moment $\vec{\mu}$. The magnetic moment points from the south pole to the north pole, so the right side of the loop is equivalent to a north pole and the left side is equivalent to a south pole.

27.8 Answer: no The rotor will not begin to turn when the switch is closed if the rotor is initially oriented as shown in Fig. 27.39b. In this case there is no current through the rotor and hence no magnetic torque. This situation can be remedied by using multiple rotor coils oriented at different angles around the rotation axis. With this arrangement, there is always a magnetic torque no matter what the orientation.

27.9 Answer: (ii) The mobile charge carriers in copper are negatively charged electrons, which move upward through the wire to give a downward current. From the right-hand rule, the force on a positively charged particle moving upward in a westward-pointing magnetic field would be to the south; hence the force on a negatively charged particle is to the north. The result is an excess of negative charge on the north side of the wire, leaving an excess of positive charge—and hence a higher electric potential—on the south side.

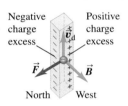

Bridging Problem

Answers: (a) $\tau_x = -1.54 \times 10^{-4}\,\text{N} \cdot \text{m}$,

$\tau_y = -2.05 \times 10^{-4}\,\text{N} \cdot \text{m}$,

$\tau_z = -6.14 \times 10^{-4}\,\text{N} \cdot \text{m}$

(b) $-7.55 \times 10^{-4}\,\text{J}$ (c) 42.1 rad/s

SOURCES OF MAGNETIC FIELD

? The immense cylinder in this photograph is actually a current-carrying coil, or solenoid, that generates a uniform magnetic field in its interior as part of an experiment at CERN, the European Organization for Nuclear Research. If two such solenoids were joined end to end, how much stronger would the magnetic field become?

In Chapter 27 we studied the forces exerted on moving charges and on current-carrying conductors in a magnetic field. We didn't worry about how the magnetic field got there; we simply took its existence as a given fact. But how are magnetic fields *created*? We know that both permanent magnets and electric currents in electromagnets create magnetic fields. In this chapter we will study these sources of magnetic field in detail.

We've learned that a charge creates an electric field and that an electric field exerts a force on a charge. But a *magnetic* field exerts a force only on a *moving* charge. Is it also true that a charge *creates* a magnetic field only when the charge is moving? In a word, yes.

Our analysis will begin with the magnetic field created by a single moving point charge. We can use this analysis to determine the field created by a small segment of a current-carrying conductor. Once we can do that, we can in principle find the magnetic field produced by *any* shape of conductor.

Then we will introduce Ampere's law, which plays a role in magnetism analogous to the role of Gauss's law in electrostatics. Ampere's law lets us exploit symmetry properties in relating magnetic fields to their sources.

Moving charged particles within atoms respond to magnetic fields and can also act as sources of magnetic field. We'll use these ideas to understand how certain magnetic materials can be used to intensify magnetic fields as well as why some materials such as iron act as permanent magnets.

28.1 Magnetic Field of a Moving Charge

Let's start with the basics, the magnetic field of a single point charge q moving with a constant velocity $\vec{v}$. In practical applications, such as the solenoid shown in the photo that opens this chapter, magnetic fields are produced by tremendous numbers of charged particles moving together in a current. But once we understand how to calculate the magnetic field due to a single point charge, it's a small leap to calculate the field due to a current-carrying wire or collection of wires.

As we did for electric fields, we call the location of the moving charge at a given instant the **source point** and the point P where we want to find the field the **field point.** In Section 21.4 we found that at a field point a distance r from a point charge q, the magnitude of the *electric* field $\vec{E}$ caused by the charge is proportional to the charge magnitude $|q|$ and to $1/r^2$, and the direction of $\vec{E}$ (for positive q) is along the line from source point to field point. The corresponding relationship for the *magnetic* field $\vec{B}$ of a point charge q moving with constant velocity has some similarities and some interesting differences.

Experiments show that the magnitude of $\vec{B}$ is also proportional to $|q|$ and to $1/r^2$. But the *direction* of $\vec{B}$ is *not* along the line from source point to field point. Instead, $\vec{B}$ is perpendicular to the plane containing this line and the particle's velocity vector $\vec{v}$, as shown in Fig. 28.1. Furthermore, the field *magnitude B* is also proportional to the particle's speed v and to the sine of the angle ϕ. Thus the magnetic field magnitude at point P is given by

$$B = \frac{\mu_0}{4\pi}\frac{|q|v\sin\phi}{r^2} \qquad (28.1)$$

where $\mu_0/4\pi$ is a proportionality constant (μ_0 is read as "mu-nought" or "mu-sub-zero"). The reason for writing the constant in this particular way will emerge shortly. We did something similar with Coulomb's law in Section 21.3.

Moving Charge: Vector Magnetic Field

We can incorporate both the magnitude and direction of $\vec{B}$ into a single vector equation using the vector product. To avoid having to say "the direction from the source q to the field point P" over and over, we introduce a *unit* vector $\hat{r}$ ("r-hat") that points from the source point to the field point. (We used $\hat{r}$ for the same purpose in Section 21.4.) This unit vector is equal to the vector $\vec{r}$ from the source to the field point divided by its magnitude: $\hat{r} = \vec{r}/r$. Then the $\vec{B}$ field of a moving point charge is

$$\vec{B} = \frac{\mu_0}{4\pi}\frac{q\vec{v}\times\hat{r}}{r^2} \qquad \text{(magnetic field of a point charge with constant velocity)} \qquad (28.2)$$

Figure 28.1 shows the relationship of $\hat{r}$ to P and also shows the magnetic field $\vec{B}$ at several points in the vicinity of the charge. At all points along a line through the charge parallel to the velocity $\vec{v}$, the field is zero because $\sin\phi = 0$ at all such points. At any distance r from q, $\vec{B}$ has its greatest magnitude at points lying in the plane perpendicular to $\vec{v}$, because there $\phi = 90°$ and $\sin\phi = 1$. If q is negative, the directions of $\vec{B}$ are opposite to those shown in Fig. 28.1.

Moving Charge: Magnetic Field Lines

A point charge in motion also produces an *electric* field, with field lines that radiate outward from a positive charge. The *magnetic* field lines are completely different. For a point charge moving with velocity $\vec{v}$, the magnetic field lines are *circles* centered on the line of $\vec{v}$ and lying in planes perpendicular to this line. The field-line directions for a positive charge are given by the following *right-hand rule,* one of several that we will encounter in this chapter: Grasp the velocity vector $\vec{v}$ with your right hand so that your right thumb points in the direction of $\vec{v}$; your fingers then curl around the line of $\vec{v}$ in the same sense as the magnetic field lines, assuming q is positive. Figure 28.1a shows parts of a few field lines; Fig. 28.1b shows some field lines in a plane through q, perpendicular to $\vec{v}$. If the point charge is negative, the directions of the field and field lines are the opposite of those shown in Fig. 28.1.

28.1 (a) Magnetic-field vectors due to a moving positive point charge q. At each point, $\vec{B}$ is perpendicular to the plane of $\vec{r}$ and $\vec{v}$, and its magnitude is proportional to the sine of the angle between them. (b) Magnetic field lines in a plane containing a moving positive charge.

(a) Perspective view

Right-hand rule for the magnetic field due to a positive charge moving at constant velocity: Point the thumb of your right hand in the direction of the velocity. Your fingers now curl around the charge in the direction of the magnetic field lines. (If the charge is negative, the field lines are in the opposite direction.)

For these field points, $\vec{r}$ and $\vec{v}$ both lie in the beige plane, and $\vec{B}$ is perpendicular to this plane.

For these field points, $\vec{r}$ and $\vec{v}$ both lie in the gold plane, and $\vec{B}$ is perpendicular to this plane.

(b) View from behind the charge

The $\times$ symbol indicates that the charge is moving into the plane of the page (away from you).

Equations (28.1) and (28.2) describe the $\vec{B}$ field of a point charge moving with *constant* velocity. If the charge *accelerates,* the field can be much more complicated. We won't need these more complicated results for our purposes. (The moving charged particles that make up a current in a wire accelerate at points where the wire bends and the direction of $\vec{v}$ changes. But because the magnitude v_d of the drift velocity in a conductor is typically very small, the centripetal acceleration v_d^2/r is so small that we can ignore its effects.)

As we discussed in Section 27.2, the unit of B is one tesla (1 T):

$$1\,T = 1\,N\cdot s/C\cdot m = 1\,N/A\cdot m$$

Using this with Eq. (28.1) or (28.2), we find that the units of the constant μ_0 are

$$1\,N\cdot s^2/C^2 = 1\,N/A^2 = 1\,Wb/A\cdot m = 1\,T\cdot m/A$$

In SI units the numerical value of μ_0 is exactly $4\pi \times 10^{-7}$. Thus

$$\mu_0 = 4\pi \times 10^{-7}\,N\cdot s^2/C^2 = 4\pi \times 10^{-7}\,Wb/A\cdot m$$
$$= 4\pi \times 10^{-7}\,T\cdot m/A \qquad (28.3)$$

It may seem incredible that μ_0 has *exactly* this numerical value! In fact this is a *defined* value that arises from the definition of the ampere, as we'll discuss in Section 28.4.

We mentioned in Section 21.3 that the constant $1/4\pi\epsilon_0$ in Coulomb's law is related to the speed of light c:

$$k = \frac{1}{4\pi\epsilon_0} = (10^{-7}\,N\cdot s^2/C^2)c^2$$

When we study electromagnetic waves in Chapter 32, we will find that their speed of propagation in vacuum, which is equal to the speed of light c, is given by

$$c^2 = \frac{1}{\epsilon_0\mu_0} \qquad (28.4)$$

If we solve the equation $k = 1/4\pi\epsilon_0$ for ϵ_0, substitute the resulting expression into Eq. (28.4), and solve for μ_0, we indeed get the value of μ_0 stated above. This discussion is a little premature, but it may give you a hint that electric and magnetic fields are intimately related to the nature of light.

Example 28.1 Forces between two moving protons

Two protons move parallel to the x-axis in opposite directions (Fig. 28.2) at the same speed v (small compared to the speed of light c). At the instant shown, find the electric and magnetic forces on the upper proton and compare their magnitudes.

SOLUTION

IDENTIFY and SET UP: Coulomb's law [Eq. (21.2)] gives the electric force F_E on the upper proton. The magnetic force law [Eq. (27.2)] gives the magnetic force on the upper proton; to use it, we must first use Eq. (28.2) to find the magnetic field that the lower proton produces at the position of the upper proton. The unit vector from the lower proton (the source) to the position of the upper proton is $\hat{r} = \hat{j}$.

EXECUTE: From Coulomb's law, the magnitude of the electric force on the upper proton is

$$F_E = \frac{1}{4\pi\epsilon_0}\frac{q^2}{r^2}$$

28.2 Electric and magnetic forces between two moving protons.

Continued

The forces are repulsive, and the force on the upper proton is vertically upward (in the $+y$-direction).

The velocity of the lower proton is $\vec{v} = v\hat{\imath}$. From the right-hand rule for the cross product $\vec{v} \times \hat{r}$ in Eq. (28.2), the $\vec{B}$ field due to the lower proton at the position of the upper proton is in the $+z$-direction (see Fig. 28.2). From Eq. (28.2), the field is

$$\vec{B} = \frac{\mu_0}{4\pi} \frac{q(v\hat{\imath}) \times \hat{\jmath}}{r^2} = \frac{\mu_0}{4\pi} \frac{qv}{r^2} \hat{k}$$

The velocity of the upper proton is $-\vec{v} = -v\hat{\imath}$, so the magnetic force on it is

$$\vec{F}_B = q(-\vec{v}) \times \vec{B} = q(-v\hat{\imath}) \times \frac{\mu_0}{4\pi} \frac{qv}{r^2} \hat{k} = \frac{\mu_0}{4\pi} \frac{q^2 v^2}{r^2} \hat{\jmath}$$

The magnetic interaction in this situation is also repulsive. The ratio of the force magnitudes is

$$\frac{F_B}{F_E} = \frac{\mu_0 q^2 v^2 / 4\pi r^2}{q^2 / 4\pi \epsilon_0 r^2} = \frac{\mu_0 v^2}{1/\epsilon_0} = \epsilon_0 \mu_0 v^2$$

With the relationship $\epsilon_0 \mu_0 = 1/c^2$, Eq. (28.4), this becomes

$$\frac{F_B}{F_E} = \frac{v^2}{c^2}$$

When v is small in comparison to the speed of light, the magnetic force is much smaller than the electric force.

EVALUATE: We have described the velocities, fields, and forces as they are measured by an observer who is stationary in the coordinate system of Fig. 28.2. In a coordinate system that moves with one of the charges, one of the velocities would be zero, so there would be *no* magnetic force. The explanation of this apparent paradox provided one of the paths that led to the special theory of relativity.

Test Your Understanding of Section 28.1 (a) If two protons are traveling parallel to each other in the *same* direction and at the same speed, is the magnetic force between them (i) attractive or (ii) repulsive? (b) Is the net force between them (i) attractive, (ii) repulsive, or (iii) zero? (Assume that the protons' speed is much slower than the speed of light.)

28.3 (a) Magnetic-field vectors due to a current element $d\vec{l}$. (b) Magnetic field lines in a plane containing the current element $d\vec{l}$. Compare this figure to Fig. 28.1 for the field of a moving point charge.

(a) Perspective view

Right-hand rule for the magnetic field due to a current element: Point the thumb of your right hand in the direction of the current. Your fingers now curl around the current element in the direction of the magnetic field lines.

For these field points, $\vec{r}$ and $d\vec{l}$ both lie in the beige plane, and $d\vec{B}$ is perpendicular to this plane.

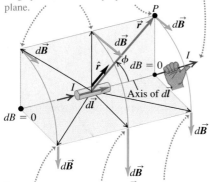

For these field points, $\vec{r}$ and $d\vec{l}$ both lie in the gold plane, and $d\vec{B}$ is perpendicular to this plane.

(b) View along the axis of the current element

Current directed into the plane of the page

28.2 Magnetic Field of a Current Element

Just as for the electric field, there is a **principle of superposition of magnetic fields:**

> **The total magnetic field caused by several moving charges is the vector sum of the fields caused by the individual charges.**

We can use this principle with the results of Section 28.1 to find the magnetic field produced by a current in a conductor.

We begin by calculating the magnetic field caused by a short segment $d\vec{l}$ of a current-carrying conductor, as shown in Fig. 28.3a. The volume of the segment is $A\,dl$, where A is the cross-sectional area of the conductor. If there are n moving charged particles per unit volume, each of charge q, the total moving charge dQ in the segment is

$$dQ = nqA\,dl$$

The moving charges in this segment are equivalent to a single charge dQ, traveling with a velocity equal to the *drift* velocity $\vec{v}_d$. (Magnetic fields due to the *random* motions of the charges will, on average, cancel out at every point.) From Eq. (28.1) the magnitude of the resulting field $d\vec{B}$ at any field point P is

$$dB = \frac{\mu_0}{4\pi} \frac{|dQ| v_d \sin\phi}{r^2} = \frac{\mu_0}{4\pi} \frac{n|q| v_d A\,dl \sin\phi}{r^2}$$

But from Eq. (25.2), $n|q| v_d A$ equals the current I in the element. So

$$dB = \frac{\mu_0}{4\pi} \frac{I\,dl \sin\phi}{r^2} \tag{28.5}$$

Current Element: Vector Magnetic Field

In vector form, using the unit vector $\hat{r}$ as in Section 28.1, we have

$$d\vec{B} = \frac{\mu_0}{4\pi} \frac{I\,d\vec{l} \times \hat{r}}{r^2} \qquad \text{(magnetic field of a current element)} \tag{28.6}$$

where $d\vec{l}$ is a vector with length dl, in the same direction as the current in the conductor.

Equations (28.5) and (28.6) are called the **law of Biot and Savart** (pronounced "Bee-oh" and "Suh-var"). We can use this law to find the total magnetic field $\vec{B}$ at any point in space due to the current in a complete circuit. To do this, we integrate Eq. (28.6) over all segments $d\vec{l}$ that carry current; symbolically,

$$\vec{B} = \frac{\mu_0}{4\pi} \int \frac{I\, d\vec{l} \times \hat{r}}{r^2} \qquad (28.7)$$

In the following sections we will carry out this vector integration for several examples.

Current Element: Magnetic Field Lines

As Fig. 28.3 shows, the field vectors $d\vec{B}$ and the magnetic field lines of a current element are exactly like those set up by a positive charge dQ moving in the direction of the drift velocity $\vec{v}_d$. The field lines are circles in planes perpendicular to $d\vec{l}$ and centered on the line of $d\vec{l}$. Their directions are given by the same right-hand rule that we introduced for point charges in Section 28.1.

We can't verify Eq. (28.5) or (28.6) directly because we can never experiment with an isolated segment of a current-carrying circuit. What we measure experimentally is the *total* $\vec{B}$ for a complete circuit. But we can still verify these equations indirectly by calculating $\vec{B}$ for various current configurations using Eq. (28.7) and comparing the results with experimental measurements.

If matter is present in the space around a current-carrying conductor, the field at a field point P in its vicinity will have an additional contribution resulting from the *magnetization* of the material. We'll return to this point in Section 28.8. However, unless the material is iron or some other ferromagnetic material, the additional field is small and is usually negligible. Additional complications arise if time-varying electric or magnetic fields are present or if the material is a superconductor; we'll return to these topics later.

Problem-Solving Strategy 28.1 **Magnetic-Field Calculations**

IDENTIFY *the relevant concepts:* The Biot–Savart law [Eqs. (28.5) and (28.6)] allows you to calculate the magnetic field at a field point P due to a current-carrying wire of any shape. The idea is to calculate the field element $d\vec{B}$ at P due to a representative current element in the wire and integrate all such field elements to find the field $\vec{B}$ at P.

SET UP *the problem* using the following steps:
1. Make a diagram showing a representative current element and the field point P.
2. Draw the current element $d\vec{l}$, being careful that it points in the direction of the current.
3. Draw the unit vector $\hat{r}$ directed *from* the current element (the source point) to P.
4. Identify the target variable (usually $\vec{B}$).

EXECUTE *the solution* as follows:
1. Use Eq. (28.5) or (28.6) to express the magnetic field $d\vec{B}$ at P from the representative current element.
2. Add up all the $d\vec{B}$'s to find the total field at point P. In some situations the $d\vec{B}$'s at point P have the same direction for all the current elements; then the magnitude of the total $\vec{B}$ field is the sum of the magnitudes of the $d\vec{B}$'s. But often the $d\vec{B}$'s have different directions for different current elements. Then you have to set up a coordinate system and represent each $d\vec{B}$ in terms of its components. The integral for the total $\vec{B}$ is then expressed in terms of an integral for each component.
3. Sometimes you can use the symmetry of the situation to prove that one component of $\vec{B}$ must vanish. Always be alert for ways to use symmetry to simplify the problem.
4. Look for ways to use the principle of superposition of magnetic fields. Later in this chapter we'll determine the fields produced by certain simple conductor shapes; if you encounter a conductor of a complex shape that can be represented as a combination of these simple shapes, you can use superposition to find the field of the complex shape. Examples include a rectangular loop and a semicircle with straight line segments on both sides.

EVALUATE *your answer:* Often your answer will be a mathematical expression for $\vec{B}$ as a function of the position of the field point. Check the answer by examining its behavior in as many limits as you can.

Example 28.2 **Magnetic field of a current segment**

A copper wire carries a steady 125-A current to an electroplating tank (Fig. 28.4). Find the magnetic field due to a 1.0-cm segment of this wire at a point 1.2 m away from it, if the point is (a) point P_1, straight out to the side of the segment, and (b) point P_2, in the xy-plane and on a line at 30° to the segment.

SOLUTION

IDENTIFY and SET UP: Although Eqs. (28.5) and (28.6) apply only to infinitesimal current elements, we may use either of them here because the segment length is much less than the distance to the field point. The current element is shown in red in Fig. 28.4 and points in the $-x$-direction (the direction of the current), so $d\vec{l} = dl(-\hat{\imath})$. The unit vector $\hat{r}$ for each field point is directed from the current element toward that point: $\hat{r}$ is in the $+y$-direction for point P_1 and at an angle of 30° above the $-x$-direction for point P_2.

28.4 Finding the magnetic field at two points due to a 1.0-cm segment of current-carrying wire (not shown to scale).

EXECUTE: (a) At point P_1, $\hat{r} = \hat{\jmath}$, so

$$\vec{B} = \frac{\mu_0}{4\pi} \frac{I\,d\vec{l} \times \hat{r}}{r^2} = \frac{\mu_0}{4\pi} \frac{I\,dl(-\hat{\imath}) \times \hat{\jmath}}{r^2} = -\frac{\mu_0}{4\pi} \frac{I\,dl}{r^2}\hat{k}$$

$$= -(10^{-7}\text{ T}\cdot\text{m/A})\frac{(125\text{ A})(1.0 \times 10^{-2}\text{ m})}{(1.2\text{ m})^2}\hat{k}$$

$$= -(8.7 \times 10^{-8}\text{ T})\hat{k}$$

The direction of $\vec{B}$ at P_1 is into the xy-plane of Fig. 28.4.

(b) At P_2, the unit vector is $\hat{r} = (-\cos 30°)\hat{\imath} + (\sin 30°)\hat{\jmath}$. From Eq. (28.6),

$$\vec{B} = \frac{\mu_0}{4\pi}\frac{I\,d\vec{l} \times \hat{r}}{r^2} = \frac{\mu_0}{4\pi}\frac{I\,dl(-\hat{\imath}) \times (-\cos 30°\hat{\imath} + \sin 30°\hat{\jmath})}{r^2}$$

$$= -\frac{\mu_0 I}{4\pi}\frac{dl\sin 30°}{r^2}\hat{k}$$

$$= -(10^{-7}\text{ T}\cdot\text{m/A})\frac{(125\text{ A})(1.0 \times 10^{-2}\text{ m})(\sin 30°)}{(1.2\text{ m})^2}\hat{k}$$

$$= -(4.3 \times 10^{-8}\text{ T})\hat{k}$$

The direction of $\vec{B}$ at P_2 is also into the xy-plane of Fig. 28.4.

EVALUATE: We can check our results for the direction of $\vec{B}$ by comparing them with Fig. 28.3. The xy-plane in Fig. 28.4 corresponds to the beige plane in Fig. 28.3, but here the direction of the current and hence of $d\vec{l}$ is the reverse of that shown in Fig. 28.3. Hence the direction of the magnetic field is reversed as well. Hence the field at points in the xy-plane in Fig. 28.4 must point *into,* not out of, that plane. This is just what we concluded above.

Test Your Understanding of Section 28.2 An infinitesimal current element located at the origin $(x = y = z = 0)$ carries current I in the positive y-direction. Rank the following locations in order of the strength of the magnetic field that the current element produces at that location, from largest to smallest value. (i) $x = L, y = 0, z = 0$; (ii) $x = 0, y = L, z = 0$; (iii) $x = 0, y = 0, z = L$; (iv) $x = L/\sqrt{2}, y = L/\sqrt{2}, z = 0$. 〔MP〕

28.5 Magnetic field produced by a straight current-carrying conductor of length $2a$.

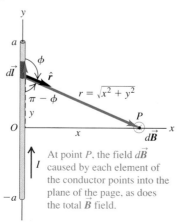

At point P, the field $d\vec{B}$ caused by each element of the conductor points into the plane of the page, as does the total $\vec{B}$ field.

28.3 Magnetic Field of a Straight Current-Carrying Conductor

Let's use the law of Biot and Savart to find the magnetic field produced by a straight current-carrying conductor. This result is useful because straight conducting wires are found in essentially all electric and electronic devices. Figure 28.5 shows such a conductor with length $2a$ carrying a current I. We will find $\vec{B}$ at a point a distance x from the conductor on its perpendicular bisector.

We first use the law of Biot and Savart, Eq. (28.5), to find the field $d\vec{B}$ caused by the element of conductor of length $dl = dy$ shown in Fig. 28.5. From the figure, $r = \sqrt{x^2 + y^2}$ and $\sin\phi = \sin(\pi - \phi) = x/\sqrt{x^2 + y^2}$. The right-hand rule for the vector product $d\vec{l} \times \hat{r}$ shows that the *direction* of $d\vec{B}$ is into the plane of the figure, perpendicular to the plane; furthermore, the directions of the $d\vec{B}$'s from *all* elements of the conductor are the same. Thus in integrating Eq. (28.7), we can just add the *magnitudes* of the $d\vec{B}$'s, a significant simplification.

Putting the pieces together, we find that the magnitude of the total $\vec{B}$ field is

$$B = \frac{\mu_0 I}{4\pi} \int_{-a}^{a} \frac{x\, dy}{(x^2 + y^2)^{3/2}}$$

We can integrate this by trigonometric substitution or by using an integral table:

$$B = \frac{\mu_0 I}{4\pi} \frac{2a}{x\sqrt{x^2 + a^2}} \qquad (28.8)$$

When the length $2a$ of the conductor is very great in comparison to its distance x from point P, we can consider it to be infinitely long. When a is much larger than x, $\sqrt{x^2 + a^2}$ is approximately equal to a; hence in the limit $a \to \infty$, Eq. (28.8) becomes

$$B = \frac{\mu_0 I}{2\pi x}$$

The physical situation has axial symmetry about the y-axis. Hence $\vec{B}$ must have the same *magnitude* at all points on a circle centered on the conductor and lying in a plane perpendicular to it, and the *direction* of $\vec{B}$ must be everywhere tangent to such a circle (Fig. 28.6). Thus, at all points on a circle of radius r around the conductor, the magnitude B is

$$B = \frac{\mu_0 I}{2\pi r} \qquad \text{(near a long, straight, current-carrying conductor)} \quad (28.9)$$

The geometry of this problem is similar to that of Example 21.10 (Section 21.5), in which we solved the problem of the *electric* field caused by an infinite line of charge. The same integral appears in both problems, and the field magnitudes in both problems are proportional to $1/r$. But the lines of $\vec{B}$ in the magnetic problem have completely different shapes than the lines of $\vec{E}$ in the analogous electrical problem. Electric field lines radiate outward from a positive line charge distribution (inward for negative charges). By contrast, magnetic field lines *encircle* the current that acts as their source. Electric field lines due to charges begin and end at those charges, but magnetic field lines always form closed loops and *never* have end points, irrespective of the shape of the current-carrying conductor that sets up the field. As we discussed in Section 27.3, this is a consequence of Gauss's law for magnetism, which states that the total magnetic flux through *any* closed surface is always zero:

$$\oint \vec{B} \cdot d\vec{A} = 0 \qquad \text{(magnetic flux through any closed surface)} \quad (28.10)$$

Any magnetic field line that enters a closed surface must also emerge from that surface.

28.6 Magnetic field around a long, straight, current-carrying conductor. The field lines are circles, with directions determined by the right-hand rule.

Right-hand rule for the magnetic field around a current-carrying wire: Point the thumb of your right hand in the direction of the current. Your fingers now curl around the wire in the direction of the magnetic field lines.

MasteringPHYSICS

ActivPhysics 13.1: Magnetic Field of a Wire

Example 28.3 **Magnetic field of a single wire**

A long, straight conductor carries a 1.0-A current. At what distance from the axis of the conductor does the resulting magnetic field have magnitude $B = 0.5 \times 10^{-4}$ T (about that of the earth's magnetic field in Pittsburgh)?

SOLUTION

IDENTIFY and SET UP: The length of a "long" conductor is much greater than the distance from the conductor to the field point. Hence we can use the ideas of this section. The geometry is the same as that of Fig. 28.6, so we use Eq. (28.9). All of the quantities in this equation are known except the target variable, the distance r.

EXECUTE: We solve Eq. (28.9) for r:

$$r = \frac{\mu_0 I}{2\pi B} = \frac{(4\pi \times 10^{-7}\,\text{T}\cdot\text{m/A})(1.0\,\text{A})}{(2\pi)(0.5 \times 10^{-4}\,\text{T})}$$

$$= 4 \times 10^{-3}\,\text{m} = 4\,\text{mm}$$

EVALUATE: As we saw in Example 26.14, currents of an ampere or more are typical of those found in the wiring of home appliances. This example shows that the magnetic fields produced by these appliances are very weak even very close to the wire; the fields are proportional to $1/r$, so they become even weaker at greater distances.

Example 28.4 Magnetic field of two wires

Figure 28.7a is an end-on view of two long, straight, parallel wires perpendicular to the xy-plane, each carrying a current I but in opposite directions. (a) Find $\vec{B}$ at points P_1, P_2, and P_3. (b) Find an expression for $\vec{B}$ at any point on the x-axis to the right of wire 2.

SOLUTION

IDENTIFY and SET UP: We can find the magnetic fields $\vec{B}_1$ and $\vec{B}_2$ due to wires 1 and 2 at each point using the ideas of this section. By the superposition principle, the magnetic field at each point is then $\vec{B} = \vec{B}_1 + \vec{B}_2$. We use Eq. (28.9) to find the magnitudes B_1 and B_2 of these fields and the right-hand rule to find the corresponding directions. Figure 28.7a shows $\vec{B}_1$, $\vec{B}_2$, and $\vec{B} = \vec{B}_{\text{total}}$ at each point; you should confirm that the directions and relative magnitudes shown are correct. Figure 28.7b shows some of the magnetic field lines due to this two-wire system.

EXECUTE: (a) Since point P_1 is a distance $2d$ from wire 1 and a distance $4d$ from wire 2, $B_1 = \mu_0 I / 2\pi(2d) = \mu_0 I / 4\pi d$ and $B_2 = \mu_0 I / 2\pi(4d) = \mu_0 I / 8\pi d$. The right-hand rule shows that $\vec{B}_1$ is in the negative y-direction and $\vec{B}_2$ is in the positive y-direction, so

$$\vec{B}_{\text{total}} = \vec{B}_1 + \vec{B}_2 = -\frac{\mu_0 I}{4\pi d}\hat{\jmath} + \frac{\mu_0 I}{8\pi d}\hat{\jmath} = -\frac{\mu_0 I}{8\pi d}\hat{\jmath} \quad \text{(point } P_1\text{)}$$

At point P_2, a distance d from both wires, $\vec{B}_1$ and $\vec{B}_2$ are both in the positive y-direction, and both have the same magnitude $B_1 = B_2 = \mu_0 I / 2\pi d$. Hence

$$\vec{B}_{\text{total}} = \vec{B}_1 + \vec{B}_2 = \frac{\mu_0 I}{2\pi d}\hat{\jmath} + \frac{\mu_0 I}{2\pi d}\hat{\jmath} = \frac{\mu_0 I}{\pi d}\hat{\jmath} \quad \text{(point } P_2\text{)}$$

Finally, at point P_3 the right-hand rule shows that $\vec{B}_1$ is in the positive y-direction and $\vec{B}_2$ is in the negative y-direction. This point is a distance $3d$ from wire 1 and a distance d from wire 2, so $B_1 = \mu_0 I / 2\pi(3d) = \mu_0 I / 6\pi d$ and $B_2 = \mu_0 I / 2\pi d$. The total field at P_3 is

$$\vec{B}_{\text{total}} = \vec{B}_1 + \vec{B}_2 = \frac{\mu_0 I}{6\pi d}\hat{\jmath} - \frac{\mu_0 I}{2\pi d}\hat{\jmath} = -\frac{\mu_0 I}{3\pi d}\hat{\jmath} \quad \text{(point } P_3\text{)}$$

The same technique can be used to find $\vec{B}_{\text{total}}$ at any point; for points off the x-axis, caution must be taken in vector addition, since $\vec{B}_1$ and $\vec{B}_2$ need no longer be simply parallel or antiparallel.

(b) At any point on the x-axis to the right of wire 2 (that is, for $x > d$), $\vec{B}_1$ and $\vec{B}_2$ are in the same directions as at P_3. Such a point is a distance $x + d$ from wire 1 and a distance $x - d$ from wire 2, so the total field is

$$\vec{B}_{\text{total}} = \vec{B}_1 + \vec{B}_2 = \frac{\mu_0 I}{2\pi(x + d)}\hat{\jmath} - \frac{\mu_0 I}{2\pi(x - d)}\hat{\jmath}$$

$$= -\frac{\mu_0 I d}{\pi(x^2 - d^2)}\hat{\jmath}$$

where we combined the two terms using a common denominator.

EVALUATE: Consider our result from part (b) at a point very far from the wires, so that x is much larger than d. Then the d^2 term in the denominator can be neglected, and the magnitude of the total field is approximately $B_{\text{total}} = \mu_0 I d / \pi x^2$. For a single wire, Eq. (28.9) shows that the magnetic field decreases with distance in proportion to $1/x$; for two wires carrying opposite currents, $\vec{B}_1$ and $\vec{B}_2$ partially cancel each other, and so B_{total} decreases more rapidly, in proportion to $1/x^2$. This effect is used in communication systems such as telephone or computer networks. The wiring is arranged so that a conductor carrying a signal in one direction and the conductor carrying the return signal are side by side, as in Fig. 28.7a, or twisted around each other (Fig. 28.8). As a result, the magnetic field due to these signals *outside* the conductors is very small, making it less likely to exert unwanted forces on other information-carrying currents.

28.8 Computer cables, or cables for audio-video equipment, create little or no magnetic field. This is because within each cable, closely spaced wires carry current in both directions along the length of the cable. The magnetic fields from these opposing currents cancel each other.

28.7 (a) Two long, straight conductors carrying equal currents in opposite directions. The conductors are seen end-on. (b) Map of the magnetic field produced by the two conductors. The field lines are closest together between the conductors, where the field is strongest.

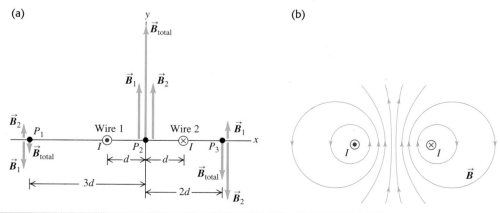

Test Your Understanding of Section 28.3 The figure at right shows a circuit that lies on a horizontal table. A compass is placed on top of the circuit as shown. A battery is to be connected to the circuit so that when the switch is closed, the compass needle deflects counterclockwise. In which orientation, A or B, should the battery be placed in the circuit?

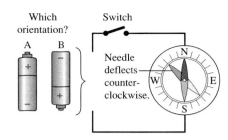

28.4 Force Between Parallel Conductors

In Example 28.4 (Section 28.3) we showed how to use the principle of superposition of magnetic fields to find the total field due to two long current-carrying conductors. Another important aspect of this configuration is the *interaction force* between the conductors. This force plays a role in many practical situations in which current-carrying wires are close to each other. Figure 28.9 shows segments of two long, straight, parallel conductors separated by a distance r and carrying currents I and I' in the same direction. Each conductor lies in the magnetic field set up by the other, so each experiences a force. The figure shows some of the field lines set up by the current in the lower conductor.

From Eq. (28.9) the lower conductor produces a $\vec{B}$ field that, at the position of the upper conductor, has magnitude

$$B = \frac{\mu_0 I}{2\pi r}$$

From Eq. (27.19) the force that this field exerts on a length L of the upper conductor is $\vec{F} = I'\vec{L} \times \vec{B}$, where the vector $\vec{L}$ is in the direction of the current I' and has magnitude L. Since $\vec{B}$ is perpendicular to the length of the conductor and hence to $\vec{L}$, the magnitude of this force is

$$F = I'LB = \frac{\mu_0 II'L}{2\pi r}$$

and the force *per unit length* F/L is

$$\frac{F}{L} = \frac{\mu_0 II'}{2\pi r} \quad \text{(two long, parallel, current-carrying conductors)} \quad (28.11)$$

Applying the right-hand rule to $\vec{F} = I'\vec{L} \times \vec{B}$ shows that the force on the upper conductor is directed *downward*.

The current in the *upper* conductor also sets up a field at the position of the *lower* one. Two successive applications of the right-hand rule for vector products (one to find the direction of the $\vec{B}$ field due to the upper conductor, as in Section 28.2, and one to find the direction of the force that this field exerts on the lower conductor, as in Section 27.6) show that the force on the lower conductor is *upward*. Thus *two parallel conductors carrying current in the same direction attract each other.* If the direction of either current is reversed, the forces also reverse. *Parallel conductors carrying currents in opposite directions repel each other.*

Magnetic Forces and Defining the Ampere

The attraction or repulsion between two straight, parallel, current-carrying conductors is the basis of the official SI definition of the **ampere:**

> **One ampere** is that unvarying current that, if present in each of two parallel conductors of infinite length and one meter apart in empty space, causes each conductor to experience a force of exactly 2×10^{-7} newtons per meter of length.

From Eq. (28.11) you can see that this definition of the ampere is what leads us to choose the value of $4\pi \times 10^{-7}$ T·m/A for μ_0. It also forms the basis of the SI

28.9 Parallel conductors carrying currents in the same direction attract each other. The diagrams show how the magnetic field $\vec{B}$ caused by the current in the lower conductor exerts a force $\vec{F}$ on the upper conductor.

The magnetic field of the lower wire exerts an attractive force on the upper wire. By the same token, the upper wire attracts the lower one.

If the wires had currents in *opposite* directions, they would *repel* each other.

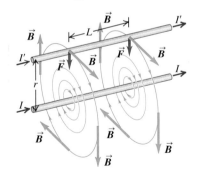

definition of the coulomb, which is the amount of charge transferred in one second by a current of one ampere.

This is an *operational definition;* it gives us an actual experimental procedure for measuring current and defining a unit of current. For high-precision standardization of the ampere, coils of wire are used instead of straight wires, and their separation is only a few centimeters. Even more precise measurements of the standardized ampere are possible using a version of the Hall effect (see Section 27.9).

Mutual forces of attraction exist not only between *wires* carrying currents in the same direction, but also between the longitudinal elements of a single current-carrying conductor. If the conductor is a liquid or an ionized gas (a plasma), these forces result in a constriction of the conductor. This is called the *pinch effect.* The high temperature produced by the pinch effect in a plasma has been used in one technique to bring about nuclear fusion.

Example 28.5 **Forces between parallel wires**

Two straight, parallel, superconducting wires 4.5 mm apart carry equal currents of 15,000 A in opposite directions. What force, per unit length, does each wire exert on the other?

SOLUTION

IDENTIFY and SET UP: Figure 28.10 shows the situation. We find F/L, the magnetic force per unit length of wire, using Eq. (28.11).

28.10 Our sketch for this problem.

$I = 15{,}000 \text{ A}$
L
$r = 4.5 \text{ mm}$
$I' = 15{,}000 \text{ A}$

EXECUTE: The conductors *repel* each other because the currents are in opposite directions. From Eq. (28.11) the force per unit length is

$$\frac{F}{L} = \frac{\mu_0 I I'}{2\pi r} = \frac{(4\pi \times 10^{-7} \text{ T} \cdot \text{m/A})(15{,}000 \text{ A})^2}{(2\pi)(4.5 \times 10^{-3} \text{ m})}$$

$$= 1.0 \times 10^4 \text{ N/m}$$

EVALUATE: This is a large force, more than one ton per meter. Currents and separations of this magnitude are used in superconducting electromagnets in particle accelerators, and mechanical stress analysis is a crucial part of the design process.

28.11 This electromagnet contains a current-carrying coil with numerous turns of wire. The resulting magnetic field can pick up large quantities of steel bars and other iron-bearing items.

Test Your Understanding of Section 28.4 A solenoid is a wire wound into a helical coil. The figure at left shows a solenoid that carries a current I. (a) Is the *magnetic* force that one turn of the coil exerts on an adjacent turn (i) attractive, (ii) repulsive, or (iii) zero? (b) Is the *electric* force that one turn of the coil exerts on an adjacent turn (i) attractive, (ii) repulsive, or (iii) zero? (c) Is the *magnetic* force between opposite sides of the same turn of the coil (i) attractive, (ii) repulsive, or (iii) zero? (d) Is the *electric* force between opposite sides of the same turn of the coil (i) attractive, (ii) repulsive, or (iii) zero?

28.5 Magnetic Field of a Circular Current Loop

If you look inside a doorbell, a transformer, an electric motor, or an electromagnet (Fig. 28.11), you will find coils of wire with a large number of turns, spaced so closely that each turn is very nearly a planar circular loop. A current in such a coil is used to establish a magnetic field. So it is worthwhile to derive an expression for the magnetic field produced by a single circular conducting loop carrying a current or by N closely spaced circular loops forming a coil. In Section 27.7 we considered the force and torque on such a current loop placed in an external magnetic field produced by other currents; we are now about to find the magnetic field produced by the loop itself.

Figure 28.12 shows a circular conductor with radius a. A current I is led into and out of the loop through two long, straight wires side by side; the currents in these straight wires are in opposite directions, and their magnetic fields very nearly cancel each other (see Example 28.4 in Section 28.3).

We can use the law of Biot and Savart, Eq. (28.5) or (28.6), to find the magnetic field at a point P on the axis of the loop, at a distance x from the center. As the figure shows, $d\vec{l}$ and $\hat{r}$ are perpendicular, and the direction of the field $d\vec{B}$ caused by this particular element $d\vec{l}$ lies in the xy-plane. Since $r^2 = x^2 + a^2$, the magnitude dB of the field due to element $d\vec{l}$ is

$$dB = \frac{\mu_0 I}{4\pi} \frac{dl}{(x^2 + a^2)} \qquad (28.12)$$

The components of the vector $d\vec{B}$ are

$$dB_x = dB \cos\theta = \frac{\mu_0 I}{4\pi} \frac{dl}{(x^2 + a^2)} \frac{a}{(x^2 + a^2)^{1/2}} \qquad (28.13)$$

$$dB_y = dB \sin\theta = \frac{\mu_0 I}{4\pi} \frac{dl}{(x^2 + a^2)} \frac{x}{(x^2 + a^2)^{1/2}} \qquad (28.14)$$

The *total* field $\vec{B}$ at P has only an x-component (it is perpendicular to the plane of the loop). Here's why: For every element $d\vec{l}$ there is a corresponding element on the opposite side of the loop, with opposite direction. These two elements give equal contributions to the x-component of $d\vec{B}$, given by Eq. (28.13), but *opposite* components perpendicular to the x-axis. Thus all the perpendicular components cancel and only the x-components survive.

To obtain the x-component of the total field $\vec{B}$, we integrate Eq. (28.13), including all the $d\vec{l}$'s around the loop. Everything in this expression except dl is constant and can be taken outside the integral, and we have

$$B_x = \int \frac{\mu_0 I}{4\pi} \frac{a \, dl}{(x^2 + a^2)^{3/2}} = \frac{\mu_0 I a}{4\pi (x^2 + a^2)^{3/2}} \int dl$$

The integral of dl is just the circumference of the circle, $\int dl = 2\pi a$, and we finally get

$$B_x = \frac{\mu_0 I a^2}{2(x^2 + a^2)^{3/2}} \qquad \text{(on the axis of a circular loop)} \qquad (28.15)$$

The *direction* of the magnetic field on the axis of a current-carrying loop is given by a right-hand rule. If you curl the fingers of your right hand around the loop in the direction of the current, your right thumb points in the direction of the field (Fig. 28.13).

Magnetic Field on the Axis of a Coil

Now suppose that instead of the single loop in Fig. 28.12 we have a coil consisting of N loops, all with the same radius. The loops are closely spaced so that the plane of each loop is essentially the same distance x from the field point P. Then the total field is N times the field of a single loop:

$$B_x = \frac{\mu_0 N I a^2}{2(x^2 + a^2)^{3/2}} \qquad \text{(on the axis of } N \text{ circular loops)} \qquad (28.16)$$

The factor N in Eq. (28.16) is the reason coils of wire, not single loops, are used to produce strong magnetic fields; for a desired field strength, using a single loop might require a current I so great as to exceed the rating of the loop's wire.

Figure 28.14 shows a graph of B_x as a function of x. The maximum value of the field is at $x = 0$, the center of the loop or coil:

$$B_x = \frac{\mu_0 N I}{2a} \qquad \text{(at the center of } N \text{ circular loops)} \qquad (28.17)$$

As we go out along the axis, the field decreases in magnitude.

28.12 Magnetic field on the axis of a circular loop. The current in the segment $d\vec{l}$ causes the field $d\vec{B}$, which lies in the xy-plane. The currents in other $d\vec{l}$'s cause $d\vec{B}$'s with different components perpendicular to the x-axis; these components add to zero. The x-components of the $d\vec{B}$'s combine to give the total $\vec{B}$ field at point P.

MasteringPHYSICS

PhET: Faraday's Electromagnetic Lab
PhET: Magnets and Electromagnets
ActivPhysics 13.2: Magnetic Field of a Loop

28.13 The right-hand rule for the direction of the magnetic field produced on the axis of a current-carrying coil.

Right-hand rule for the magnetic field produced by a current in a loop:

When the fingers of your right hand curl in the direction of I, your right thumb points in the direction of $\vec{B}$.

28.14 Graph of the magnetic field along the axis of a circular coil with N turns. When x is much larger than a, the field magnitude decreases approximately as $1/x^3$.

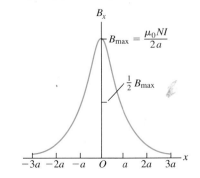

Application **Magnetic Fields for MRI**
The diagnostic technique called MRI, or magnetic resonance imaging (see Section 27.7), requires a magnetic field of about 1.5 T. In a typical MRI scan, the patient lies inside a coil that produces the intense field. The currents required are very high, so the coils are bathed in liquid helium at a temperature of 4.2 K to keep them from overheating.

28.15 Magnetic field lines produced by the current in a circular loop. At points on the axis the $\vec{B}$ field has the same direction as the magnetic moment of the loop.

In Section 27.7 we defined the *magnetic dipole moment* μ (or *magnetic moment*) of a current-carrying loop to be equal to IA, where A is the cross-sectional area of the loop. If there are N loops, the total magnetic moment is NIA. The circular loop in Fig. 28.12 has area $A = \pi a^2$, so the magnetic moment of a single loop is $\mu = I\pi a^2$; for N loops, $\mu = NI\pi a^2$. Substituting these results into Eqs. (28.15) and (28.16), we find that both of these expressions can be written as

$$B_x = \frac{\mu_0 \mu}{2\pi(x^2 + a^2)^{3/2}} \quad \begin{array}{l}\text{(on the axis of any number}\\ \text{of circular loops)}\end{array} \quad (28.18)$$

We described a magnetic dipole in Section 27.7 in terms of its response to a magnetic field produced by currents outside the dipole. But a magnetic dipole is also a *source* of magnetic field; Eq. (28.18) describes the magnetic field *produced* by a magnetic dipole for points along the dipole axis. This field is directly proportional to the magnetic dipole moment μ. Note that the field along the x-axis is in the same direction as the vector magnetic moment $\vec{\mu}$; this is true on both the positive and negative x-axis.

CAUTION **Magnetic field of a coil** Equations (28.15), (28.16), and (28.18) are valid only on the *axis* of a loop or coil. Don't attempt to apply these equations at other points! ▮

Figure 28.15 shows some of the magnetic field lines surrounding a circular current loop (magnetic dipole) in planes through the axis. The directions of the field lines are given by the same right-hand rule as for a long, straight conductor. Grab the conductor with your right hand, with your thumb in the direction of the current; your fingers curl around in the same direction as the field lines. The field lines for the circular current loop are closed curves that encircle the conductor; they are *not* circles, however.

Example 28.6 **Magnetic field of a coil**

A coil consisting of 100 circular loops with radius 0.60 m carries a 5.0-A current. (a) Find the magnetic field at a point along the axis of the coil, 0.80 m from the center. (b) Along the axis, at what distance from the center of the coil is the field magnitude $\frac{1}{8}$ as great as it is at the center?

SOLUTION

IDENTIFY and SET UP: This problem concerns the magnetic field magnitude B along the axis of a current-carrying coil, so we can use the ideas of this section, and in particular Eq. (28.16). We are given $N = 100$, $I = 5.0$ A, and $a = 0.60$ m. In part (a) our target variable is B_x at a given value of x. In part (b) the target variable is the value of x at which the field has $\frac{1}{8}$ of the magnitude that it has at the origin.

EXECUTE: (a) Using $x = 0.80$ m, from Eq. (28.16) we have

$$B_x = \frac{(4\pi \times 10^{-7}\,\text{T}\cdot\text{m/A})(100)(5.0\,\text{A})(0.60\,\text{m})^2}{2[(0.80\,\text{m})^2 + (0.60\,\text{m})^2]^{3/2}}$$

$$= 1.1 \times 10^{-4}\,\text{T}$$

(b) Considering Eq. (28.16), we want to find a value of x such that

$$\frac{1}{(x^2 + a^2)^{3/2}} = \frac{1}{8}\frac{1}{(0^2 + a^2)^{3/2}}$$

To solve this for x, we take the reciprocal of the whole thing and then take the $2/3$ power of both sides; the result is

$$x = \pm\sqrt{3}a = \pm 1.04\,\text{m}$$

EVALUATE: We check our answer in part (a) by finding the coil's magnetic moment and substituting the result into Eq. (28.18):

$$\mu = NI\pi a^2 = (100)(5.0\,\text{A})\pi(0.60\,\text{m})^2 = 5.7 \times 10^2\,\text{A}\cdot\text{m}^2$$

$$B_x = \frac{(4\pi \times 10^{-7}\,\text{T}\cdot\text{m/A})(5.7 \times 10^2\,\text{A}\cdot\text{m}^2)}{2\pi[(0.80\,\text{m})^2 + (0.60\,\text{m})^2]^{3/2}} = 1.1 \times 10^{-4}\,\text{T}$$

The magnetic moment μ is relatively large, yet it produces a rather small field, comparable to that of the earth. This illustrates how difficult it is to produce strong fields of 1 T or more.

Test Your Understanding of Section 28.5   Figure 28.12 shows the magnetic field $d\vec{B}$ produced at point P by a segment $d\vec{l}$ that lies on the positive y-axis (at the top of the loop). This field has components $dB_x > 0$, $dB_y > 0$, $dB_z = 0$. (a) What are the signs of the components of the field $d\vec{B}$ produced at P by a segment $d\vec{l}$ on the negative y-axis (at the bottom of the loop)? (i) $dB_x > 0$, $dB_y > 0$, $dB_z = 0$; (ii) $dB_x > 0$, $dB_y < 0$, $dB_z = 0$; (iii) $dB_x < 0$, $dB_y > 0$, $dB_z = 0$; (iv) $dB_x < 0$, $dB_y < 0$, $dB_z = 0$; (v) none of these. (b) What are the signs of the components of the field $d\vec{B}$ produced at P by a segment $d\vec{l}$ on the negative z-axis (at the right-hand side of the loop)? (i) $dB_x > 0$, $dB_y > 0$, $dB_z = 0$; (ii) $dB_x > 0$, $dB_y < 0$, $dB_z = 0$; (iii) $dB_x < 0$, $dB_y > 0$, $dB_z = 0$; (iv) $dB_x < 0$, $dB_y < 0$, $dB_z = 0$; (v) none of these.

28.6 Ampere's Law

So far our calculations of the magnetic field due to a current have involved finding the infinitesimal field $d\vec{B}$ due to a current element and then summing all the $d\vec{B}$'s to find the total field. This approach is directly analogous to our *electric-field* calculations in Chapter 21.

For the electric-field problem we found that in situations with a highly symmetric charge distribution, it was often easier to use Gauss's law to find $\vec{E}$. There is likewise a law that allows us to more easily find the *magnetic* fields caused by highly symmetric *current* distributions. But the law that allows us to do this, called *Ampere's law,* is rather different in character from Gauss's law.

Gauss's law for electric fields involves the flux of $\vec{E}$ through a closed surface; it states that this flux is equal to the total charge enclosed within the surface, divided by the constant ϵ_0. Thus this law relates electric fields and charge distributions. By contrast, Gauss's law for *magnetic* fields, Eq. (28.10), is *not* a relationship between magnetic fields and current distributions; it states that the flux of $\vec{B}$ through *any* closed surface is always zero, whether or not there are currents within the surface. So Gauss's law for $\vec{B}$ can't be used to determine the magnetic field produced by a particular current distribution.

Ampere's law is formulated not in terms of magnetic flux, but rather in terms of the *line integral* of $\vec{B}$ around a closed path, denoted by

$$\oint \vec{B} \cdot d\vec{l}$$

We used line integrals to define work in Chapter 6 and to calculate electric potential in Chapter 23. To evaluate this integral, we divide the path into infinitesimal segments $d\vec{l}$, calculate the scalar product of $\vec{B} \cdot d\vec{l}$ for each segment, and sum these products. In general, $\vec{B}$ varies from point to point, and we must use the value of $\vec{B}$ at the location of each $d\vec{l}$. An alternative notation is $\oint B_\parallel \, dl$, where $B_\parallel$ is the component of $\vec{B}$ parallel to $d\vec{l}$ at each point. The circle on the integral sign indicates that this integral is always computed for a *closed* path, one whose beginning and end points are the same.

Ampere's Law for a Long, Straight Conductor

To introduce the basic idea of Ampere's law, let's consider again the magnetic field caused by a long, straight conductor carrying a current I. We found in Section 28.3 that the field at a distance r from the conductor has magnitude

$$B = \frac{\mu_0 I}{2\pi r}$$

The magnetic field lines are circles centered on the conductor. Let's take the line integral of $\vec{B}$ around one such circle with radius r, as in Fig. 28.16a. At every point on the circle, $\vec{B}$ and $d\vec{l}$ are parallel, and so $\vec{B} \cdot d\vec{l} = B \, dl$; since r is constant around the circle, B is constant as well. Alternatively, we can say that $B_\parallel$ is constant and equal to B at every point on the circle. Hence we can take B

28.16 Three integration paths for the line integral of $\vec{B}$ in the vicinity of a long, straight conductor carrying current I *out* of the plane of the page (as indicated by the circle with a dot). The conductor is seen end-on.

(a) Integration path is a circle centered on the conductor; integration goes around the circle counterclockwise.

Result: $\oint \vec{B} \cdot d\vec{l} = \mu_0 I$

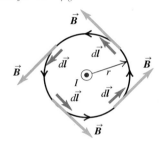

(b) Same integration path as in (a), but integration goes around the circle clockwise.

Result: $\oint \vec{B} \cdot d\vec{l} = -\mu_0 I$

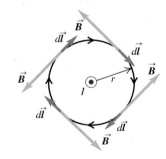

(c) An integration path that does not enclose the conductor

Result: $\oint \vec{B} \cdot dl = 0$

outside of the integral. The remaining integral is just the circumference of the circle, so

$$\oint \vec{B} \cdot d\vec{l} = \oint B_{\parallel} \, dl = B \oint dl = \frac{\mu_0 I}{2\pi r}(2\pi r) = \mu_0 I$$

The line integral is thus independent of the radius of the circle and is equal to μ_0 multiplied by the current passing through the area bounded by the circle.

In Fig. 28.16b the situation is the same, but the integration path now goes around the circle in the opposite direction. Now $\vec{B}$ and $d\vec{l}$ are antiparallel, so $\vec{B} \cdot d\vec{l} = -B \, dl$ and the line integral equals $-\mu_0 I$. We get the same result if the integration path is the same as in Fig. 28.16a, but the direction of the current is reversed. Thus $\oint \vec{B} \cdot d\vec{l}$ equals μ_0 multiplied by the current passing through the area bounded by the integration path, with a positive or negative sign depending on the direction of the current relative to the direction of integration.

There's a simple rule for the sign of the current; you won't be surprised to learn that it uses your right hand. Curl the fingers of your right hand around the integration path so that they curl in the direction of integration (that is, the direction that you use to evaluate $\oint \vec{B} \cdot d\vec{l}$). Then your right thumb indicates the positive current direction. Currents that pass through the integration path in this direction are positive; those in the opposite direction are negative. Using this rule, you should be able to convince yourself that the current is positive in Fig. 28.16a and negative in Fig. 28.16b. Here's another way to say the same thing: Looking at the surface bounded by the integration path, integrate counterclockwise around the path as in Fig. 28.16a. Currents moving toward you through the surface are positive, and those going away from you are negative.

An integration path that does *not* enclose the conductor is used in Fig. 28.16c. Along the circular arc ab of radius r_1, $\vec{B}$ and $d\vec{l}$ are parallel, and $B_{\parallel} = B_1 = \mu_0 I/2\pi r_1$; along the circular arc cd of radius r_2, $\vec{B}$ and $d\vec{l}$ are antiparallel and $B_{\parallel} = -B_2 = -\mu_0 I/2\pi r_2$. The $\vec{B}$ field is perpendicular to $d\vec{l}$ at each point on the straight sections bc and da, so $B_{\parallel} = 0$ and these sections contribute zero to the line integral. The total line integral is then

$$\oint \vec{B} \cdot d\vec{l} = \oint B_{\parallel} \, dl = B_1 \int_a^b dl + (0) \int_b^c dl + (-B_2) \int_c^d dl + (0) \int_d^a dl$$

$$= \frac{\mu_0 I}{2\pi r_1}(r_1 \theta) + 0 - \frac{\mu_0 I}{2\pi r_2}(r_2 \theta) + 0 = 0$$

The magnitude of $\vec{B}$ is greater on arc cd than on arc ab, but the arc length is less, so the contributions from the two arcs exactly cancel. Even though there is a magnetic field everywhere along the integration path, the line integral $\oint \vec{B} \cdot d\vec{l}$ is zero if there is no current passing through the area bounded by the path.

We can also derive these results for more general integration paths, such as the one in Fig. 28.17a. At the position of the line element $d\vec{l}$, the angle between $d\vec{l}$ and $\vec{B}$ is ϕ, and

$$\vec{B} \cdot d\vec{l} = B \, dl \cos \phi$$

From the figure, $dl \cos \phi = r \, d\theta$, where $d\theta$ is the angle subtended by $d\vec{l}$ at the position of the conductor and r is the distance of $d\vec{l}$ from the conductor. Thus

$$\oint \vec{B} \cdot d\vec{l} = \oint \frac{\mu_0 I}{2\pi r}(r \, d\theta) = \frac{\mu_0 I}{2\pi} \oint d\theta$$

But $\oint d\theta$ is just equal to 2π, the total angle swept out by the radial line from the conductor to $d\vec{l}$ during a complete trip around the path. So we get

28.17 (a) A more general integration path for the line integral of $\vec{B}$ around a long, straight conductor carrying current I *out* of the plane of the page. The conductor is seen end-on. (b) A more general integration path that does not enclose the conductor.

(a)

(b)

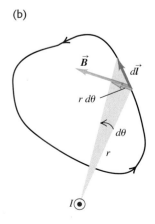

$$\oint \vec{B} \cdot d\vec{l} = \mu_0 I \qquad (28.19)$$

This result doesn't depend on the shape of the path or on the position of the wire inside it. If the current in the wire is opposite to that shown, the integral has the opposite sign. But if the path doesn't enclose the wire (Fig. 28.17b), then the net change in θ during the trip around the integration path is zero; $\oint d\theta$ is zero instead of 2π and the line integral is zero.

Ampere's Law: General Statement

Equation (28.19) is almost, but not quite, the general statement of Ampere's law. To generalize it even further, suppose *several* long, straight conductors pass through the surface bounded by the integration path. The total magnetic field $\vec{B}$ at any point on the path is the vector sum of the fields produced by the individual conductors. Thus the line integral of the total $\vec{B}$ equals μ_0 times the *algebraic sum* of the currents. In calculating this sum, we use the sign rule for currents described above. If the integration path does not enclose a particular wire, the line integral of the $\vec{B}$ field of that wire is zero, because the angle θ for that wire sweeps through a net change of zero rather than 2π during the integration. Any conductors present that are not enclosed by a particular path may still contribute to the value of $\vec{B}$ at every point, but the *line integrals* of their fields around the path are zero.

Thus we can replace I in Eq. (28.19) with I_{encl}, the algebraic sum of the currents *enclosed* or *linked* by the integration path, with the sum evaluated by using the sign rule just described (Fig. 28.18). Our statement of **Ampere's law** is then

$$\oint \vec{B} \cdot d\vec{l} = \mu_0 I_{encl} \qquad \text{(Ampere's law)} \qquad (28.20)$$

While we have derived Ampere's law only for the special case of the field of several long, straight, parallel conductors, Eq. (28.20) is in fact valid for conductors and paths of *any* shape. The general derivation is no different in principle from what we have presented, but the geometry is more complicated.

If $\oint \vec{B} \cdot d\vec{l} = 0$, it *does not* necessarily mean that $\vec{B} = \mathbf{0}$ everywhere along the path, only that the total current through an area bounded by the path is zero. In Figs. 28.16c and 28.17b, the integration paths enclose no current at all; in Fig. 28.19 there are positive and negative currents of equal magnitude through the area enclosed by the path. In both cases, $I_{encl} = 0$ and the line integral is zero.

> **CAUTION**   **Line integrals of electric and magnetic fields**   In Chapter 23 we saw that the line integral of the electrostatic field $\vec{E}$ around any closed path is equal to zero; this is a statement that the electrostatic force $\vec{F} = q\vec{E}$ on a point charge q is conservative, so this force does zero work on a charge that moves around a closed path that returns to the starting point. You might think that the value of the line integral $\oint \vec{B} \cdot d\vec{l}$ is similarly related to the question of whether the *magnetic* force is conservative. This isn't the case at all. Remember that the magnetic force $\vec{F} = q\vec{v} \times \vec{B}$ on a moving charged particle is always *perpendicular* to $\vec{B}$, so $\oint \vec{B} \cdot d\vec{l}$ is *not* related to the work done by the magnetic force; as stated in Ampere's law, this integral is related only to the total current through a surface bounded by the integration path. In fact, the magnetic force on a moving charged particle is *not* conservative. A conservative force depends only on the position of the body on which the force is exerted, but the magnetic force on a moving charged particle also depends on the *velocity* of the particle.

Equation (28.20) turns out to be valid only if the currents are steady and if no magnetic materials or time-varying electric fields are present. In Chapter 29 we will see how to generalize Ampere's law for time-varying fields.

28.18 Ampere's law.

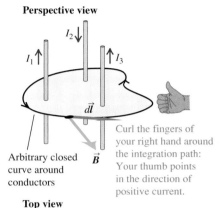

Perspective view

Arbitrary closed curve around conductors

Curl the fingers of your right hand around the integration path: Your thumb points in the direction of positive current.

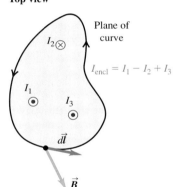

Top view

Plane of curve

$I_{encl} = I_1 - I_2 + I_3$

Ampere's law: If we calculate the line integral of the magnetic field around a closed curve, the result equals μ_0 times the total enclosed current: $\oint \vec{B} \cdot d\vec{l} = \mu_0 I_{encl}$.

28.19 Two long, straight conductors carrying equal currents in opposite directions. The conductors are seen end-on, and the integration path is counterclockwise. The line integral $\oint \vec{B} \cdot d\vec{l}$ gets zero contribution from the upper and lower segments, a positive contribution from the left segment, and a negative contribution from the right segment; the net integral is zero.

Test Your Understanding of Section 28.6 The figure at left shows magnetic field lines through the center of a permanent magnet. The magnet is not connected to a source of emf. One of the field lines is colored red. What can you conclude about the currents inside the permanent magnet within the region enclosed by this field line? (i) There are no currents inside the magnet; (ii) there are currents directed out of the plane of the page; (iii) there are currents directed into the plane of the page; (iv) not enough information is given to decide.

28.7 Applications of Ampere's Law

Ampere's law is useful when we can exploit the symmetry of a situation to evaluate the line integral of $\vec{B}$. Several examples are given below. Problem-Solving Strategy 28.2 is directly analogous to Problem-Solving Strategy 22.1 (Section 22.4) for applications of Gauss's law; we suggest you review that strategy now and compare the two methods.

Problem-Solving Strategy 28.2 | **Ampere's Law**

IDENTIFY *the relevant concepts:* Like Gauss's law, Ampere's law is most useful when the magnetic field is highly symmetric. In the form $\oint \vec{B} \cdot d\vec{l} = \mu_0 I_{encl}$, it can yield the magnitude of $\vec{B}$ as a function of position if we are given the magnitude and direction of the field-generating electric current.

SET UP *the problem* using the following steps:
1. Determine the target variable(s). Usually one will be the magnitude of the $\vec{B}$ field as a function of position.
2. Select the integration path you will use with Ampere's law. If you want to determine the magnetic field at a certain point, then the path must pass through that point. The integration path doesn't have to be any actual physical boundary. Usually it is a purely geometric curve; it may be in empty space, embedded in a solid body, or some of each. The integration path has to have enough *symmetry* to make evaluation of the integral possible. Ideally the path will be tangent to $\vec{B}$ in regions of interest; elsewhere the path should be perpendicular to $\vec{B}$ or should run through regions in which $\vec{B} = 0$.

EXECUTE *the solution* as follows:
1. Carry out the integral $\oint \vec{B} \cdot d\vec{l}$ along the chosen path. If $\vec{B}$ is tangent to all or some portion of the path and has the same magnitude B at every point, then its line integral is the product of B and the length of that portion of the path. If $\vec{B}$ is perpendicular to some portion of the path, or if $\vec{B} = 0$, that portion makes no contribution to the integral.
2. In the integral $\oint \vec{B} \cdot d\vec{l}$, $\vec{B}$ is the *total* magnetic field at each point on the path; it can be caused by currents enclosed *or not enclosed* by the path. If *no* net current is enclosed by the path, the field at points on the path need not be zero, but the integral $\oint \vec{B} \cdot d\vec{l}$ is always zero.
3. Determine the current I_{encl} enclosed by the integration path. A right-hand rule gives the sign of this current: If you curl the fingers of your right hand so that they follow the path in the direction of integration, then your right thumb points in the direction of positive current. If $\vec{B}$ is tangent to the path everywhere and I_{encl} is positive, the direction of $\vec{B}$ is the same as the direction of integration. If instead I_{encl} is negative, $\vec{B}$ is in the direction opposite to that of the integration.
4. Use Ampere's law $\oint \vec{B} \cdot d\vec{l} = \mu_0 I$ to solve for the target variable.

EVALUATE *your answer:* If your result is an expression for the field magnitude as a function of position, check it by examining how the expression behaves in different limits.

Example 28.7 | **Field of a long, straight, current-carrying conductor**

In Section 28.6 we derived Ampere's law using Eq. (28.9) for the field $\vec{B}$ of a long, straight, current-carrying conductor. Reverse this process, and use Ampere's law to find $\vec{B}$ for this situation.

SOLUTION

IDENTIFY and SET UP: The situation has cylindrical symmetry, so in Ampere's law we take our integration path to be a circle with radius r centered on the conductor and lying in a plane perpendicular to it, as in Fig. 28.16a. The field $\vec{B}$ is everywhere tangent to this circle and has the same magnitude B everywhere on the circle.

EXECUTE: With our choice of integration path, Ampere's law [Eq. (28.20)] becomes

$$\oint \vec{B} \cdot d\vec{l} = \oint B_{\parallel} \, dl = B(2\pi r) = \mu_0 I$$

Equation (28.9), $B = \mu_0 I / 2\pi r$, follows immediately.

Ampere's law determines the direction of $\vec{B}$ as well as its magnitude. Since we chose to go counterclockwise around the integration path, the positive direction for current is out of the plane of Fig. 28.16a; this is the same as the actual current direction in the figure, so I is positive and the integral $\oint \vec{B} \cdot d\vec{l}$ is also positive. Since the $d\vec{l}$'s run counterclockwise, the direction of $\vec{B}$ must be counterclockwise as well, as shown in Fig. 28.16a.

EVALUATE: Our results are consistent with those in Section 28.6.

Example 28.8   Field of a long cylindrical conductor

A cylindrical conductor with radius R carries a current I (Fig. 28.20). The current is uniformly distributed over the cross-sectional area of the conductor. Find the magnetic field as a function of the distance r from the conductor axis for points both inside $(r < R)$ and outside $(r > R)$ the conductor.

SOLUTION

IDENTIFY and SET UP: As in Example 28.7, the current distribution has cylindrical symmetry, and the magnetic field lines must be circles concentric with the conductor axis. To find the magnetic field inside and outside the conductor, we choose circular integration paths with radii $r < R$ and $r > R$, respectively (see Fig. 28.20).

EXECUTE: In either case the field $\vec{B}$ has the same magnitude at every point on the circular integration path and is tangent to the path. Thus the magnitude of the line integral is simply $B(2\pi r)$. To find the current I_{encl} enclosed by a circular integration path inside the conductor $(r < R,)$, note that the current density (current per unit area) is $J = I/\pi R^2$, so $I_{encl} = J(\pi r^2) = Ir^2/R^2$. Hence Ampere's law gives $B(2\pi r) = \mu_0 Ir^2/R^2$, or

28.20 To find the magnetic field at radius $r < R$, we apply Ampere's law to the circle enclosing the gray area. The current through the red area is $(r^2/R^2)I$. To find the magnetic field at radius $r > R$, we apply Ampere's law to the circle enclosing the entire conductor.

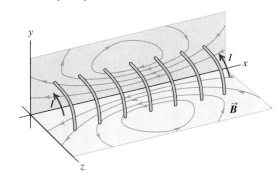

$$B = \frac{\mu_0 I}{2\pi}\frac{r}{R^2} \qquad \text{(inside the conductor, } r < R) \qquad (28.21)$$

A circular integration path outside the conductor encloses the total current in the conductor, so $I_{encl} = I$. Applying Ampere's law gives the same equation as in Example 28.7, with the same result for B:

$$B = \frac{\mu_0 I}{2\pi r} \qquad \text{(outside the conductor, } r > R) \qquad (28.22)$$

Outside the conductor, the magnetic field is the same as that of a long, straight conductor carrying current I, independent of the radius R over which the current is distributed. Indeed, the magnetic field outside *any* cylindrically symmetric current distribution is the same as if the entire current were concentrated along the axis of the distribution. This is analogous to the results of Examples 22.5 and 22.9 (Section 22.4), in which we found that the *electric* field outside a spherically symmetric *charged* body is the same as though the entire charge were concentrated at the center.

EVALUATE: Note that at the surface of the conductor $(r = R)$, Eqs. (28.21) and (28.22) agree, as they must. Figure 28.21 shows a graph of B as a function of r.

28.21 Magnitude of the magnetic field inside and outside a long, straight cylindrical conductor with radius R carrying a current I.

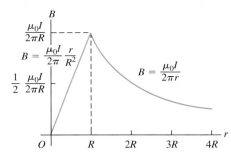

Example 28.9   Field of a solenoid

A solenoid consists of a helical winding of wire on a cylinder, usually circular in cross section. There can be thousands of closely spaced turns (often in several layers), each of which can be regarded as a circular loop. For simplicity, Fig. 28.22 shows a solenoid with only a few turns. All turns carry the same current I, and the total $\vec{B}$ field at every point is the vector sum of the fields caused by the individual turns. The figure shows field lines in the *xy*- and *xz*-planes. We draw field lines that are uniformly spaced at the center of the solenoid. Exact calculations show that for a long, closely wound solenoid, half of these field lines emerge from the ends and half "leak out" through the windings between the center and the end, as the figure suggests.

If the solenoid is long in comparison with its cross-sectional diameter and the coils are tightly wound, the field inside the solenoid near its midpoint is very nearly uniform over the cross section and parallel to the axis; the *external* field near the midpoint is very small.

28.22 Magnetic field lines produced by the current in a solenoid. For clarity, only a few turns are shown.

Continued

Use Ampere's law to find the field at or near the center of such a solenoid if it has n turns per unit length and carries current I.

SOLUTION

IDENTIFY and SET UP: We assume that $\vec{B}$ is uniform inside the solenoid and zero outside. Figure 28.23 shows the situation and our chosen integration path, rectangle $abcd$. Side ab, with length L, is parallel to the axis of the solenoid. Sides bc and da are taken to be very long so that side cd is far from the solenoid; then the field at side cd is negligibly small.

EXECUTE: Along side ab, $\vec{B}$ is parallel to the path and is constant. Our Ampere's-law integration takes us along side ab in the same direction as $\vec{B}$, so here $B_\parallel = +B$ and

$$\int_a^b \vec{B} \cdot d\vec{l} = BL$$

Along sides bc and da, $\vec{B}$ is perpendicular to the path and so $B_\parallel = 0$; along side cd, $\vec{B} = 0$ and so $B_\parallel = 0$. Around the entire closed path, then, we have $\oint \vec{B} \cdot d\vec{l} = BL$.

In a length L there are nL turns, each of which passes once through $abcd$ carrying current I. Hence the total current enclosed by the rectangle is $I_{encl} = nLI$. The integral $\oint \vec{B} \cdot d\vec{l}$ is

28.23 Our sketch for this problem.

positive, so from Ampere's law I_{encl} must be positive as well. This means that the current passing through the surface bounded by the integration path must be in the direction shown in Fig. 28.23. Ampere's law then gives $BL = \mu_0 nLI$, or

$$B = \mu_0 nI \quad \text{(solenoid)} \tag{28.23}$$

Side ab need not lie on the axis of the solenoid, so this result demonstrates that the field is uniform over the entire cross section at the center of the solenoid's length.

EVALUATE: Note that the *direction* of $\vec{B}$ inside the solenoid is in the same direction as the solenoid's vector magnetic moment $\vec{\mu}$, as we found in Section 28.5 for a single current-carrying loop.

For points along the axis, the field is strongest at the center of the solenoid and drops off near the ends. For a solenoid very long in comparison to its diameter, the field magnitude at each end is exactly half that at the center. This is approximately the case even for a relatively short solenoid, as Fig. 28.24 shows.

28.24 Magnitude of the magnetic field at points along the axis of a solenoid with length $4a$, equal to four times its radius a. The field magnitude at each end is about half its value at the center. (Compare with Fig. 28.14 for the field of N circular loops.)

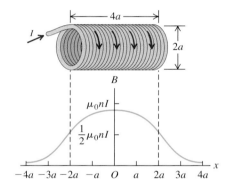

Example 28.10   Field of a toroidal solenoid

Figure 28.25a shows a doughnut-shaped **toroidal solenoid**, tightly wound with N turns of wire carrying a current I. (In a practical solenoid the turns would be much more closely spaced than they are in the figure.) Find the magnetic field at all points.

SOLUTION

IDENTIFY and SET UP: Ignoring the slight pitch of the helical windings, we can consider each turn of a tightly wound toroidal solenoid as a loop lying in a plane perpendicular to the large, circular axis of the toroid. The symmetry of the situation then tells us that the magnetic field lines must be circles concentric with the toroid axis. Therefore we choose circular integration paths (of which Fig. 28.25b shows three) for use with Ampere's law, so that the field $\vec{B}$ (if any) is tangent to each path at all points along the path.

EXECUTE: Along each path, $\oint \vec{B} \cdot d\vec{l}$ equals the product of B and the path circumference $l = 2\pi r$. The total current enclosed by path 1 is zero, so from Ampere's law the field $\vec{B} = 0$ everywhere on this path.

Each turn of the winding passes *twice* through the area bounded by path 3, carrying equal currents in opposite directions. The *net*

28.25 (a) A toroidal solenoid. For clarity, only a few turns of the winding are shown. (b) Integration paths (black circles) used to compute the magnetic field $\vec{B}$ set up by the current (shown as dots and crosses).

The magnetic field is confined almost entirely to the space enclosed by the windings (in blue).

current enclosed is therefore zero, and hence $\vec{B} = 0$ at all points on this path as well. We conclude that *the field of an ideal toroidal solenoid is confined to the space enclosed by the windings.* We can think of such a solenoid as a tightly wound, straight solenoid that has been bent into a circle.

For path 2, we have $\oint \vec{B} \cdot d\vec{l} = 2\pi r B$. Each turn of the winding passes *once* through the area bounded by this path, so $I_{encl} = NI$. We note that I_{encl} is positive for the clockwise direction of integration in Fig. 28.25b, so $\vec{B}$ is in the direction shown. Ampere's law then says that $2\pi r B = \mu_0 NI$, so

$$B = \frac{\mu_0 NI}{2\pi r} \quad \text{(toroidal solenoid)} \quad (28.24)$$

EVALUATE: Equation (28.24) indicates that B is *not* uniform over the interior of the core, because different points in the interior are difference distances r from the toroid axis. However, if the radial extent of the core is small in comparison to r, the variation is slight. In that case, considering that $2\pi r$ is the circumferential

length of the toroid and that $N/2\pi r$ is the number of turns per unit length n, the field may be written as $B = \mu_0 nI$, just as it is at the center of a long, *straight* solenoid.

In a real toroidal solenoid the turns are not precisely circular loops but rather segments of a bent helix. As a result, the external field is not exactly zero. To estimate its magnitude, we imagine Fig. 28.25a as being *very* roughly equivalent, for points outside the torus, to a *single-turn* circular loop with radius r. At the center of such a loop, Eq. (28.17) gives $B = \mu_0 I/2r$; this is smaller than the field inside the solenoid by the factor N/π.

The equations we have derived for the field in a closely wound straight or toroidal solenoid are strictly correct only for windings in *vacuum*. For most practical purposes, however, they can be used for windings in air or on a core of any nonmagnetic, nonsuperconducting material. In the next section we will show how these equations are modified if the core is a magnetic material.

Test Your Understanding of Section 28.7 Consider a conducting wire that runs along the central axis of a hollow conducting cylinder. Such an arrangement, called a *coaxial cable,* has many applications in telecommunications. (The cable that connects a television set to a local cable provider is an example of a coaxial cable.) In such a cable a current I runs in one direction along the hollow conducting cylinder and is spread uniformly over the cylinder's cross-sectional area. An equal current runs in the opposite direction along the central wire. How does the magnitude B of the magnetic field outside such a cable depend on the distance r from the central axis of the cable? (i) B is proportional to $1/r$; (ii) B is proportional to $1/r^2$; (iii) B is zero at all points outside the cable.

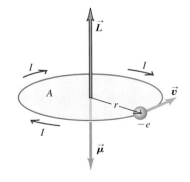

Hollow conducting cylinder   Insulator   Central wire

28.8 Magnetic Materials

In discussing how currents cause magnetic fields, we have assumed that the conductors are surrounded by vacuum. But the coils in transformers, motors, generators, and electromagnets nearly always have iron cores to increase the magnetic field and confine it to desired regions. Permanent magnets, magnetic recording tapes, and computer disks depend directly on the magnetic properties of materials; when you store information on a computer disk, you are actually setting up an array of microscopic permanent magnets on the disk. So it is worthwhile to examine some aspects of the magnetic properties of materials. After describing the atomic origins of magnetic properties, we will discuss three broad classes of magnetic behavior that occur in materials; these are called *paramagnetism, diamagnetism,* and *ferromagnetism.*

The Bohr Magneton

As we discussed briefly in Section 27.7, the atoms that make up all matter contain moving electrons, and these electrons form microscopic current loops that produce magnetic fields of their own. In many materials these currents are randomly oriented and cause no net magnetic field. But in some materials an external field (a field produced by currents outside the material) can cause these loops to become oriented preferentially with the field, so their magnetic fields *add* to the external field. We then say that the material is *magnetized.*

Let's look at how these microscopic currents come about. Figure 28.26 shows a primitive model of an electron in an atom. We picture the electron (mass m, charge $-e$) as moving in a circular orbit with radius r and speed v. This moving charge is equivalent to a current loop. In Section 27.7 we found that a current loop with area A and current I has a magnetic dipole moment μ given by $\mu = IA$; for the orbiting electron the area of the loop is $A = \pi r^2$. To find the current

28.26 An electron moving with speed v in a circular orbit of radius r has an angular momentum $\vec{L}$ and an oppositely directed orbital magnetic dipole moment $\vec{\mu}$. It also has a spin angular momentum and an oppositely directed spin magnetic dipole moment.

associated with the electron, we note that the orbital period T (the time for the electron to make one complete orbit) is the orbit circumference divided by the electron speed: $T = 2\pi r/v$. The equivalent current I is the total charge passing any point on the orbit per unit time, which is just the magnitude e of the electron charge divided by the orbital period T:

$$I = \frac{e}{T} = \frac{ev}{2\pi r}$$

The magnetic moment $\mu = IA$ is then

$$\mu = \frac{ev}{2\pi r}(\pi r^2) = \frac{evr}{2} \tag{28.25}$$

It is useful to express μ in terms of the *angular momentum L* of the electron. For a particle moving in a circular path, the magnitude of angular momentum equals the magnitude of momentum mv multiplied by the radius r—that is, $L = mvr$ (see Section 10.5). Comparing this with Eq. (28.25), we can write

$$\mu = \frac{e}{2m}L \tag{28.26}$$

Equation (28.26) is useful in this discussion because atomic angular momentum is *quantized;* its component in a particular direction is always an integer multiple of $h/2\pi$, where h is a fundamental physical constant called *Planck's constant.* The numerical value of h is

$$h = 6.626 \times 10^{-34} \text{ J} \cdot \text{s}$$

The quantity $h/2\pi$ thus represents a fundamental unit of angular momentum in atomic systems, just as e is a fundamental unit of charge. Associated with the quantization of $\vec{L}$ is a fundamental uncertainty in the *direction* of $\vec{L}$ and therefore of $\vec{\mu}$. In the following discussion, when we speak of the magnitude of a magnetic moment, a more precise statement would be "maximum component in a given direction." Thus, to say that a magnetic moment $\vec{\mu}$ is aligned with a magnetic field $\vec{B}$ really means that $\vec{\mu}$ has its maximum possible component in the direction of $\vec{B}$; such components are always quantized.

Equation (28.26) shows that associated with the fundamental unit of angular momentum is a corresponding fundamental unit of magnetic moment. If $L = h/2\pi$, then

$$\mu = \frac{e}{2m}\left(\frac{h}{2\pi}\right) = \frac{eh}{4\pi m} \tag{28.27}$$

This quantity is called the **Bohr magneton,** denoted by μ_B. Its numerical value is

$$\mu_B = 9.274 \times 10^{-24} \text{ A} \cdot \text{m}^2 = 9.274 \times 10^{-24} \text{ J/T}$$

You should verify that these two sets of units are consistent. The second set is useful when we compute the potential energy $U = -\vec{\mu} \cdot \vec{B}$ for a magnetic moment in a magnetic field.

Electrons also have an intrinsic angular momentum, called *spin,* that is not related to orbital motion but that can be pictured in a classical model as spinning on an axis. This angular momentum also has an associated magnetic moment, and its magnitude turns out to be almost exactly one Bohr magneton. (Effects having to do with quantization of the electromagnetic field cause the spin magnetic moment to be about $1.001 \mu_B$.)

Paramagnetism

In an atom, most of the various orbital and spin magnetic moments of the electrons add up to zero. However, in some cases the atom has a net magnetic moment that is of the order of μ_B. When such a material is placed in a magnetic field, the field exerts a torque on each magnetic moment, as given by Eq. (27.26): $\vec{\tau} = \vec{\mu} \times \vec{B}$. These torques tend to align the magnetic moments with the field, as we discussed in Section 27.7. In this position, the directions of the current loops are such as to *add* to the externally applied magnetic field.

We saw in Section 28.5 that the $\vec{B}$ field produced by a current loop is proportional to the loop's magnetic dipole moment. In the same way, the additional $\vec{B}$ field produced by microscopic electron current loops is proportional to the total magnetic moment $\vec{\mu}_{total}$ per unit volume V in the material. We call this vector quantity the **magnetization** of the material, denoted by $\vec{M}$:

$$\vec{M} = \frac{\vec{\mu}_{total}}{V} \qquad (28.28)$$

The additional magnetic field due to magnetization of the material turns out to be equal simply to $\mu_0 \vec{M}$, where μ_0 is the same constant that appears in the law of Biot and Savart and Ampere's law. When such a material completely surrounds a current-carrying conductor, the total magnetic field $\vec{B}$ in the material is

$$\vec{B} = \vec{B}_0 + \mu_0 \vec{M} \qquad (28.29)$$

where $\vec{B}_0$ is the field caused by the current in the conductor.

To check that the units in Eq. (28.29) are consistent, note that magnetization $\vec{M}$ is magnetic moment per unit volume. The units of magnetic moment are current times area $(A \cdot m^2)$, so the units of magnetization are $(A \cdot m^2)/m^3 = A/m$. From Section 28.1, the units of the constant μ_0 are $T \cdot m/A$. So the units of $\mu_0 \vec{M}$ are the same as the units of $\vec{B}$: $(T \cdot m/A)(A/m) = T$.

A material showing the behavior just described is said to be **paramagnetic.** The result is that the magnetic field at any point in such a material is greater by a dimensionless factor K_m, called the **relative permeability** of the material, than it would be if the material were replaced by vacuum. The value of K_m is different for different materials; for common paramagnetic solids and liquids at room temperature, K_m typically ranges from 1.00001 to 1.003.

All of the equations in this chapter that relate magnetic fields to their sources can be adapted to the situation in which the current-carrying conductor is embedded in a paramagnetic material. All that need be done is to replace μ_0 by $K_m \mu_0$. This product is usually denoted as μ and is called the **permeability** of the material:

$$\mu = K_m \mu_0 \qquad (28.30)$$

CAUTION **Two meanings of the symbol μ** Equation (28.30) involves some really dangerous notation because we have also used μ for magnetic dipole moment. It's customary to use μ for both quantities, but beware: From now on, every time you see a μ, make sure you know whether it is permeability or magnetic moment. You can usually tell from the context.

The amount by which the relative permeability differs from unity is called the **magnetic susceptibility,** denoted by χ_m:

$$\chi_m = K_m - 1 \qquad (28.31)$$

Both K_m and χ_m are dimensionless quantities. Table 28.1 lists values of magnetic susceptibility for several materials. For example, for aluminum, $\chi_m = 2.2 \times 10^{-5}$ and $K_m = 1.000022$. The first group of materials in the table are paramagnetic; we'll discuss the second group of materials, which are called *diamagnetic,* very shortly.

The tendency of atomic magnetic moments to align themselves parallel to the magnetic field (where the potential energy is minimum) is opposed by random thermal motion, which tends to randomize their orientations. For this reason, paramagnetic susceptibility always decreases with increasing temperature.

Table 28.1 Magnetic Susceptibilities of Paramagnetic and Diamagnetic Materials at $T = 20°C$

Material	$\chi_m = K_m - 1 \ (\times 10^{-5})$
Paramagnetic	
Iron ammonium alum	66
Uranium	40
Platinum	26
Aluminum	2.2
Sodium	0.72
Oxygen gas	0.19
Diamagnetic	
Bismuth	−16.6
Mercury	−2.9
Silver	−2.6
Carbon (diamond)	−2.1
Lead	−1.8
Sodium chloride	−1.4
Copper	−1.0

In many cases it is inversely proportional to the absolute temperature T, and the magnetization M can be expressed as

$$M = C\frac{B}{T} \qquad (28.32)$$

This relationship is called *Curie's law,* after its discoverer, Pierre Curie (1859–1906). The quantity C is a constant, different for different materials, called the *Curie constant.*

As we described in Section 27.7, a body with atomic magnetic dipoles is attracted to the poles of a magnet. In most paramagnetic substances this attraction is very weak due to thermal randomization of the atomic magnetic moments. But at very low temperatures the thermal effects are reduced, the magnetization increases in accordance with Curie's law, and the attractive forces are greater.

Example 28.11   Magnetic dipoles in a paramagnetic material

Nitric oxide (NO) is a paramagnetic compound. The magnetic moment of each NO molecule has a maximum component in any direction of about one Bohr magneton. Compare the interaction energy of such magnetic moments in a 1.5-T magnetic field with the average translational kinetic energy of molecules at 300 K.

SOLUTION

IDENTIFY and SET UP: This problem involves the energy of a magnetic moment in a magnetic field and the average thermal kinetic energy. We have Eq. (27.27), $U = -\vec{\mu} \cdot \vec{B}$, for the interaction energy of a magnetic moment $\vec{\mu}$ with a $\vec{B}$ field, and Eq. (18.16), $K = \frac{3}{2}kT$, for the average translational kinetic energy of a molecule at temperature T.

EXECUTE: We can write $U = -\mu_{\parallel}B$, where $\mu_{\parallel}$ is the component of the magnetic moment $\vec{\mu}$ in the direction of the $\vec{B}$ field. Here the maximum value of $\mu_{\parallel}$ is about μ_B, so

$$|U|_{\text{max}} \approx \mu_B B = (9.27 \times 10^{-24} \text{ J/T})(1.5 \text{ T})$$
$$= 1.4 \times 10^{-23} \text{ J} = 8.7 \times 10^{-5} \text{ eV}$$

The average translational kinetic energy K is

$$K = \frac{3}{2}kT = \frac{3}{2}(1.38 \times 10^{-23} \text{ J/K})(300 \text{ K})$$
$$= 6.2 \times 10^{-21} \text{ J} = 0.039 \text{ eV}$$

EVALUATE: At 300 K the magnetic interaction energy is only about 0.2% of the thermal kinetic energy, so we expect only a slight degree of alignment. This is why paramagnetic susceptibilities at ordinary temperature are usually very small.

Diamagnetism

In some materials the total magnetic moment of all the atomic current loops is zero when no magnetic field is present. But even these materials have magnetic effects because an external field alters electron motions within the atoms, causing additional current loops and induced magnetic dipoles comparable to the induced *electric* dipoles we studied in Section 28.5. In this case the additional field caused by these current loops is always *opposite* in direction to that of the external field. (This behavior is explained by Faraday's law of induction, which we will study in Chapter 29. An induced current always tends to cancel the field change that caused it.)

Such materials are said to be **diamagnetic.** They always have negative susceptibility, as shown in Table 28.1, and relative permeability K_m slightly *less* than unity, typically of the order of 0.99990 to 0.99999 for solids and liquids. Diamagnetic susceptibilities are very nearly temperature independent.

Ferromagnetism

There is a third class of materials, called **ferromagnetic** materials, that includes iron, nickel, cobalt, and many alloys containing these elements. In these materials, strong interactions between atomic magnetic moments cause them to line up parallel to each other in regions called **magnetic domains,** even when no external field is present. Figure 28.27 shows an example of magnetic domain structure. Within each domain, nearly all of the atomic magnetic moments are parallel.

When there is no externally applied field, the domain magnetizations are randomly oriented. But when a field $\vec{B}_0$ (caused by external currents) is present, the domains tend to orient themselves parallel to the field. The domain boundaries also shift; the domains that are magnetized in the field direction grow, and those that are magnetized in other directions shrink. Because the total magnetic moment of a domain may be many thousands of Bohr magnetons, the torques that tend to align the domains with an external field are much stronger than occur with paramagnetic materials. The relative permeability K_m is *much* larger than unity, typically of the order of 1000 to 100,000. As a result, an object made of a ferromagnetic material such as iron is strongly magnetized by the field from a permanent magnet and is attracted to the magnet (see Fig. 27.38). A paramagnetic material such as aluminum is also attracted to a permanent magnet, but K_m for paramagnetic materials is so much smaller for such a material than for ferromagnetic materials that the attraction is very weak. Thus a magnet can pick up iron nails, but not aluminum cans.

As the external field is increased, a point is eventually reached at which nearly *all* the magnetic moments in the ferromagnetic material are aligned parallel to the external field. This condition is called *saturation magnetization;* after it is reached, further increase in the external field causes no increase in magnetization or in the additional field caused by the magnetization.

Figure 28.28 shows a "magnetization curve," a graph of magnetization M as a function of external magnetic field B_0, for soft iron. An alternative description of this behavior is that K_m is not constant but decreases as B_0 increases. (Paramagnetic materials also show saturation at sufficiently strong fields. But the magnetic fields required are so large that departures from a linear relationship between M and B_0 in these materials can be observed only at very low temperatures, 1 K or so.)

For many ferromagnetic materials the relationship of magnetization to external magnetic field is different when the external field is increasing from when it is decreasing. Figure 28.29a shows this relationship for such a material. When the material is magnetized to saturation and then the external field is reduced to zero, some magnetization remains. This behavior is characteristic of permanent magnets, which retain most of their saturation magnetization when the magnetizing field is removed. To reduce the magnetization to zero requires a magnetic field in the reverse direction.

This behavior is called **hysteresis,** and the curves in Fig. 28.29 are called *hysteresis loops.* Magnetizing and demagnetizing a material that has hysteresis involve the dissipation of energy, and the temperature of the material increases during such a process.

28.27 In this drawing adapted from a magnified photo, the arrows show the directions of magnetization in the domains of a single crystal of nickel. Domains that are magnetized in the direction of an applied magnetic field grow larger.

(a) No field

(b) Weak field

(c) Stronger field

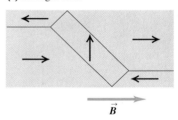

28.28 A magnetization curve for a ferromagnetic material. The magnetization M approaches its saturation value M_{sat} as the magnetic field B_0 (caused by external currents) becomes large.

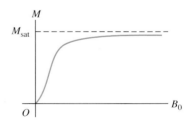

28.29 Hysteresis loops. The materials of both (a) and (b) remain strongly magnetized when B_0 is reduced to zero. Since (a) is also hard to demagnetize, it would be good for permanent magnets. Since (b) magnetizes and demagnetizes more easily, it could be used as a computer memory material. The material of (c) would be useful for transformers and other alternating-current devices where zero hysteresis would be optimal.

100 µm

Ferromagnetic materials are widely used in electromagnets, transformer cores, and motors and generators, in which it is desirable to have as large a magnetic field as possible for a given current. Because hysteresis dissipates energy, materials that are used in these applications should usually have as narrow a hysteresis loop as possible. Soft iron is often used; it has high permeability without appreciable hysteresis. For permanent magnets a broad hysteresis loop is usually desirable, with large zero-field magnetization and large reverse field needed to demagnetize. Many kinds of steel and many alloys, such as Alnico, are commonly used for permanent magnets. The remaining magnetic field in such a material, after it has been magnetized to near saturation, is typically of the order of 1 T, corresponding to a remaining magnetization $M = B/\mu_0$ of about 800,000 A/m.

Example 28.12 A ferromagnetic material

A cube-shaped permanent magnet is made of a ferromagnetic material with a magnetization M of about 8×10^5 A/m. The side length is 2 cm. (a) Find the magnetic dipole moment of the magnet. (b) Estimate the magnetic field due to the magnet at a point 10 cm from the magnet along its axis.

SOLUTION

IDENTIFY and SET UP: This problem uses the relationship between magnetization M and magnetic dipole moment μ_{total} and the idea that a magnetic dipole produces a magnetic field. We find μ_{total} using Eq. (28.28). To estimate the field, we approximate the magnet as a current loop with this same magnetic moment and use Eq. (28.18).

EXECUTE: (a) From Eq. (28.28),

$$\mu_{total} = MV = (8 \times 10^5 \text{ A/m})(2 \times 10^{-2} \text{ m})^3 = 6 \text{ A} \cdot \text{m}^2$$

(b) From Eq. (28.18), the magnetic field on the axis of a current loop with magnetic moment μ_{total} is

$$B = \frac{\mu_0 \mu_{total}}{2\pi(x^2 + a^2)^{3/2}}$$

where x is the distance from the loop and a is its radius. We can use this expression here if we take a to refer to the size of the permanent magnet. Strictly speaking, there are complications because our magnet does not have the same geometry as a circular current loop. But because $x = 10$ cm is fairly large in comparison to the 2-cm size of the magnet, the term a^2 is negligible in comparison to x^2 and can be ignored. So

$$B \approx \frac{\mu_0 \mu_{total}}{2\pi x^3} = \frac{(4\pi \times 10^{-7} \text{ T} \cdot \text{m/A})(6 \text{ A} \cdot \text{m}^2)}{2\pi(0.1 \text{ m})^3}$$
$$= 1 \times 10^{-3} \text{ T} = 10 \text{ G}$$

which is about ten times stronger than the earth's magnetic field.

EVALUATE: We calculated B at a point *outside* the magnetic material and therefore used μ_0, not the permeability μ of the magnetic material, in our calculation. You would substitute permeability μ for μ_0 if you were calculating B *inside* a material with relative permeability K_m, for which $\mu = K_m\mu_0$.

Test Your Understanding of Section 28.8 Which of the following materials are attracted to a magnet? (i) sodium; (ii) bismuth; (iii) lead; (iv) uranium.

Magnetic field of a moving charge: The magnetic field $\vec{B}$ created by a charge q moving with velocity $\vec{v}$ depends on the distance r from the source point (the location of q) to the field point (where $\vec{B}$ is measured). The $\vec{B}$ field is perpendicular to $\vec{v}$ and to $\hat{r}$, the unit vector directed from the source point to the field point. The principle of superposition of magnetic fields states that the total $\vec{B}$ field produced by several moving charges is the vector sum of the fields produced by the individual charges. (See Example 28.1.)

$$\vec{B} = \frac{\mu_0}{4\pi}\frac{q\vec{v}\times\hat{r}}{r^2}$$ (28.2)

Magnetic field of a current-carrying conductor: The law of Biot and Savart gives the magnetic field $d\vec{B}$ created by an element $d\vec{l}$ of a conductor carrying current I. The field $d\vec{B}$ is perpendicular to both $d\vec{l}$ and $\hat{r}$, the unit vector from the element to the field point. The $\vec{B}$ field created by a finite current-carrying conductor is the integral of $d\vec{B}$ over the length of the conductor. (See Example 28.2.)

$$d\vec{B} = \frac{\mu_0}{4\pi}\frac{I\,d\vec{l}\times\hat{r}}{r^2}$$ (28.6)

Magnetic field of a long, straight, current-carrying conductor: The magnetic field $\vec{B}$ at a distance r from a long, straight conductor carrying a current I has a magnitude that is inversely proportional to r. The magnetic field lines are circles coaxial with the wire, with directions given by the right-hand rule. (See Examples 28.3 and 28.4.)

$$B = \frac{\mu_0 I}{2\pi r}$$ (28.9)

Magnetic force between current-carrying conductors: Two long, parallel, current-carrying conductors attract if the currents are in the same direction and repel if the currents are in opposite directions. The magnetic force per unit length between the conductors depends on their currents I and I' and their separation r. The definition of the ampere is based on this relationship. (See Example 28.5.)

$$\frac{F}{L} = \frac{\mu_0 II'}{2\pi r}$$ (28.11)

Magnetic field of a current loop: The law of Biot and Savart allows us to calculate the magnetic field produced along the axis of a circular conducting loop of radius a carrying current I. The field depends on the distance x along the axis from the center of the loop to the field point. If there are N loops, the field is multiplied by N. At the center of the loop, $x = 0$. (See Example 28.6.)

$$B_x = \frac{\mu_0 I a^2}{2(x^2 + a^2)^{3/2}}$$ (28.15)
(circular loop)

$$B_x = \frac{\mu_0 NI}{2a}$$ (28.17)
(center of N circular loops)

Ampere's law: Ampere's law states that the line integral of $\vec{B}$ around any closed path equals μ_0 times the net current through the area enclosed by the path. The positive sense of current is determined by a right-hand rule. (See Examples 28.7–28.10.)

$$\oint \vec{B}\cdot d\vec{l} = \mu_0 I_{\text{encl}}$$ (28.20)

Magnetic fields due to current distributions: The table lists magnetic fields caused by several current distributions. In each case the conductor is carrying current I.

Current Distribution	Point in Magnetic Field	Magnetic-Field Magnitude
Long, straight conductor	Distance r from conductor	$B = \dfrac{\mu_0 I}{2\pi r}$
Circular loop of radius a	On axis of loop	$B = \dfrac{\mu_0 I a^2}{2(x^2 + a^2)^{3/2}}$
	At center of loop	$B = \dfrac{\mu_0 I}{2a}$ (for N loops, multiply these expressions by N)
Long cylindrical conductor of radius R	Inside conductor, $r < R$	$B = \dfrac{\mu_0 I}{2\pi} \dfrac{r}{R^2}$
	Outside conductor, $r > R$	$B = \dfrac{\mu_0 I}{2\pi r}$
Long, closely wound solenoid with n turns per unit length, near its midpoint	Inside solenoid, near center	$B = \mu_0 n I$
	Outside solenoid	$B \approx 0$
Tightly wound toroidal solenoid (toroid) with N turns	Within the space enclosed by the windings, distance r from symmetry axis	$B = \dfrac{\mu_0 N I}{2\pi r}$
	Outside the space enclosed by the windings	$B \approx 0$

Magnetic materials: When magnetic materials are present, the magnetization of the material causes an additional contribution to $\vec{B}$. For paramagnetic and diamagnetic materials, μ_0 is replaced in magnetic-field expressions by $\mu = K_m \mu_0$, where μ is the permeability of the material and K_m is its relative permeability. The magnetic susceptibility χ_m is defined as $\chi_m = K_m - 1$. Magnetic susceptibilities for paramagnetic materials are small positive quantities; those for diamagnetic materials are small negative quantities. For ferromagnetic materials, K_m is much larger than unity and is not constant. Some ferromagnetic materials are permanent magnets, retaining their magnetization even after the external magnetic field is removed. (See Examples 28.11 and 28.12.)

BRIDGING PROBLEM   Magnetic Field of a Charged, Rotating Dielectric Disk

A thin dielectric disk with radius a has a total charge $+Q$ distributed uniformly over its surface. It rotates n times per second about an axis perpendicular to the surface of the disk and passing through its center. Find the magnetic field at the center of the disk.

SOLUTION GUIDE

See MasteringPhysics® study area for a Video Tutor solution.

IDENTIFY and SET UP

1. Think of the rotating disk as a series of concentric rotating rings. Each ring acts as a circular current loop that produces a magnetic field at the center of the disk.
2. Use the results of Section 28.5 to find the magnetic field due to a single ring. Then integrate over all rings to find the total field.

EXECUTE

3. Find the charge on a ring with inner radius r and outer radius $r + dr$.

4. How long does it take the charge found in step 3 to make a complete trip around the rotating ring? Use this to find the current of the rotating ring.
5. Use a result from Section 28.5 to determine the magnetic field that this ring produces at the center of the disk.
6. Integrate your result from step 5 to find the total magnetic field from all rings with radii from $r = 0$ to $r = a$.

EVALUATE

7. Does your answer have the correct units?
8. Suppose all of the charge were concentrated at the rim of the disk (at $r = a$). Would this increase or decrease the field at the center of the disk?

•, ••, •••: Problems of increasing difficulty. **CP**: Cumulative problems incorporating material from earlier chapters. **CALC**: Problems requiring calculus. **BIO**: Biosciences problems.

DISCUSSION QUESTIONS

Q28.1 A topic of current interest in physics research is the search (thus far unsuccessful) for an isolated magnetic pole, or magnetic *monopole*. If such an entity were found, how could it be recognized? What would its properties be?

Q28.2 Streams of charged particles emitted from the sun during periods of solar activity create a disturbance in the earth's magnetic field. How does this happen?

Q28.3 The text discussed the magnetic field of an infinitely long, straight conductor carrying a current. Of course, there is no such thing as an infinitely long *anything*. How do you decide whether a particular wire is long enough to be considered infinite?

Q28.4 Two parallel conductors carrying current in the same direction attract each other. If they are permitted to move toward each other, the forces of attraction do work. From where does the energy come? Does this contradict the assertion in Chapter 27 that magnetic forces on moving charges do no work? Explain.

Q28.5 Pairs of conductors carrying current into or out of the power-supply components of electronic equipment are sometimes twisted together to reduce magnetic-field effects. Why does this help?

Q28.6 Suppose you have three long, parallel wires arranged so that in cross section they are at the corners of an equilateral triangle. Is there any way to arrange the currents so that all three wires attract each other? So that all three wires repel each other? Explain.

Q28.7 In deriving the force on one of the long, current-carrying conductors in Section 28.4, why did we use the magnetic field due to only one of the conductors? That is, why didn't we use the *total* magnetic field due to *both* conductors?

Q28.8 Two concentric, coplanar, circular loops of wire of different diameter carry currents in the same direction. Describe the nature of the force exerted on the inner loop by the outer loop and on the outer loop by the inner loop.

Q28.9 A current was sent through a helical coil spring. The spring contracted, as though it had been compressed. Why?

Q28.10 What are the relative advantages and disadvantages of Ampere's law and the law of Biot and Savart for practical calculations of magnetic fields?

Q28.11 Magnetic field lines never have a beginning or an end. Use this to explain why it is reasonable for the field of a toroidal solenoid to be confined entirely to its interior, while a straight solenoid *must* have some field outside.

Q28.12 If the magnitude of the magnetic field a distance R from a very long, straight, current-carrying wire is B, at what distance from the wire will the field have magnitude $3B$?

Q28.13 Two very long, parallel wires carry equal currents in opposite directions. (a) Is there any place that their magnetic fields completely cancel? If so, where? If not, why not? (b) How would the answer to part (a) change if the currents were in the same direction?

Figure **Q28.14**

Q28.14 In the circuit shown in Fig. Q28.14, when switch S is suddenly closed, the wire L is pulled toward the lower wire carrying current I. Which (a or b) is the positive terminal of the battery? How do you know?

Q28.15 A metal ring carries a current that causes a magnetic field B_0 at the center of the ring and a field B at point P a distance x from the center along the axis of the ring. If the radius of the ring is doubled, find the magnetic field at the center. Will the field at point P change by the same factor? Why?

Q28.16 Why should the permeability of a paramagnetic material be expected to decrease with increasing temperature?

Q28.17 If a magnet is suspended over a container of liquid air, it attracts droplets to its poles. The droplets contain only liquid oxygen; even though nitrogen is the primary constituent of air, it is not attracted to the magnet. Explain what this tells you about the magnetic susceptibilities of oxygen and nitrogen, and explain why a magnet in ordinary, room-temperature air doesn't attract molecules of oxygen *gas* to its poles.

Q28.18 What features of atomic structure determine whether an element is diamagnetic or paramagnetic? Explain.

Q28.19 The magnetic susceptibility of paramagnetic materials is quite strongly temperature dependent, but that of diamagnetic materials is nearly independent of temperature. Why the difference?

Q28.20 A cylinder of iron is placed so that it is free to rotate around its axis. Initially the cylinder is at rest, and a magnetic field is applied to the cylinder so that it is magnetized in a direction parallel to its axis. If the direction of the *external* field is suddenly reversed, the direction of magnetization will also reverse and the cylinder will begin rotating around its axis. (This is called the *Einstein–de Haas effect.*) Explain why the cylinder begins to rotate.

Q28.21 The discussion of magnetic forces on current loops in Section 27.7 commented that no net force is exerted on a complete loop in a uniform magnetic field, only a torque. Yet magnetized materials that contain atomic current loops certainly *do* experience net forces in magnetic fields. How is this discrepancy resolved?

Q28.22 Show that the units $A \cdot m^2$ and J/T for the Bohr magneton are equivalent.

EXERCISES

Section 26.1 Magnetic Field of a Moving Charge

28.1 •• A $+6.00\text{-}\mu C$ point charge is moving at a constant 8.00×10^6 m/s in the $+y$-direction, relative to a reference frame. At the instant when the point charge is at the origin of this reference frame, what is the magnetic-field vector $\vec{B}$ it produces at the following points: (a) $x = 0.500$ m, $y = 0$, $z = 0$; (b) $x = 0$, $y = -0.500$ m, $z = 0$; (c) $x = 0$, $y = 0$, $z = +0.500$ m; (d) $x = 0, y = -0.500$ m, $z = +0.500$ m?

28.2 • **Fields Within the Atom.** In the Bohr model of the hydrogen atom, the electron moves in a circular orbit of radius 5.3×10^{-11} m with a speed of 2.2×10^6 m/s. If we are viewing the atom in such a way that the electron's orbit is in the plane of the paper with the electron moving clockwise, find the magnitude and direction of the electric and magnetic fields that the electron produces at the location of the nucleus (treated as a point).

28.3 • An electron moves at $0.100c$ as shown in Fig. E28.3. Find the magnitude and direction of the magnetic field this electon produces at the following points, each 2.00 μm from the electron: (a) points A and B; (b) point C; (c) point D.

Figure **E28.3**

28.4 •• An alpha particle (charge $+2e$) and an electron move in opposite directions from the same point, each with the speed of 2.50×10^5 m/s (Fig. E28.4). Find the magnitude and direction of the total magnetic field these charges produce at point P, which is 1.75 nm from each of them.

Figure **E28.4**

28.5 • A -4.80-μC charge is moving at a constant speed of 6.80×10^5 m/s in the $+x$-direction relative to a reference frame. At the instant when the point charge is at the origin, what is the magnetic-field vector it produces at the following points: (a) $x = 0.500$ m, $y = 0$, $z = 0$; (b) $x = 0$, $y = 0.500$ m, $z = 0$; (c) $x = 0.500$ m, $y = 0.500$ m, $z = 0$; (d) $x = 0$, $y = 0$, $z = 0.500$ m?

28.6 • Positive point charges $q = +8.00$ μC and $q' = +3.00$ μC are moving relative to an observer at point P, as shown in Fig. E28.6. The distance d is 0.120 m, $v = 4.50 \times 10^6$ m/s, and $v' = 9.00 \times 10^6$ m/s. (a) When the two charges are at the locations shown in the figure, what are the magnitude and direction of the net magnetic field they produce at point P? (b) What are the magnitude and direction of the electric and magnetic forces that each charge exerts on the other, and what is the ratio of the magnitude of the electric force to the magnitude of the magnetic force? (c) If the direction of $\vec{v}'$ is reversed, so both charges are moving in the same direction, what are the magnitude and direction of the magnetic forces that the two charges exert on each other?

Figure **E28.6**

28.7 •• Figure E28.6 shows two point charges, q and q', moving relative to an observer at point P. Suppose that the lower charge is actually *negative*, with $q' = -q$. (a) Find the magnetic field (magnitude and direction) produced by the two charges at point P if (i) $v' = v/2$; (ii) $v' = v$; (iii) $v' = 2v$. (b) Find the direction of the magnetic force that q exerts on q', and find the direction of the magnetic force that q' exerts on q. (c) If $v = v' = 3.00 \times 10^5$ m/s, what is the ratio of the magnitude of the magnetic force acting on each charge to that of the Coulomb force acting on each charge?

28.8 •• An electron and a proton are each moving at 845 km/s in perpendicular paths as shown in Fig. E28.8. At the instant when they are at the positions shown in the figure, find the magnitude and direction of (a) the total magnetic field they produce at the origin; (b) the magnetic field the electron produces at the location of the proton; (c) the total electric force and the total magnetic force that the electron exerts on the proton.

Figure **E28.8**

28.9 • A negative charge $q = -3.60 \times 10^{-6}$ C is located at the origin and has velocity $\vec{v} = (7.50 \times 10^4 \text{ m/s})\hat{\imath} + (-4.90 \times 10^4 \text{ m/s})\hat{\jmath}$. At this instant what are the magnitude and direction of the magnetic field produced by this charge at the point $x = 0.200$ m, $y = -0.300$ m, $z = 0$?

Section 28.2 Magnetic Field of a Current Element

28.10 • A short current element $d\vec{l} = (0.500 \text{ mm})\hat{\jmath}$ carries a current of 8.20 A in the same direction as $d\vec{l}$. Point P is located at $\vec{r} = (-0.730 \text{ m})\hat{\imath} + (0.390 \text{ m})\hat{k}$. Use unit vectors to express the magnetic field at P produced by this current element.

28.11 • A straight wire carries a 10.0-A current (Fig. E28.11). $ABCD$ is a rectangle with point D in the middle of a 1.10-mm segment of the wire and point C in the wire. Find the magnitude and direction of the magnetic field due to this segment at (a) point A; (b) point B; (c) point C.

Figure **E28.11**

28.12 • A long, straight wire, carrying a current of 200 A, runs through a cubical wooden box, entering and leaving through holes in the centers of opposite faces (Fig. E28.12). The length of each side of the box is 20.0 cm. Consider an element dl of the wire 0.100 cm long at the center of the box. Compute the magnitude dB of the magnetic field produced by this element at the points a, b, c, d, and e in Fig. E28.12. Points a, c, and d are at the centers of the faces of the cube; point b is at the midpoint of one edge; and point e is at a corner. Copy the figure and show the directions and relative magnitudes of the field vectors. (*Note:* Assume that the length dl is small in comparison to the distances from the current element to the points where the magnetic field is to be calculated.)

Figure **E28.12**

28.13 •• A long, straight wire lies along the z-axis and carries a 4.00-A current in the $+z$-direction. Find the magnetic field (magnitude and direction) produced at the following points by a 0.500-mm segment of the wire centered at the origin: (a) $x = 2.00$ m, $y = 0$, $z = 0$; (b) $x = 0$, $y = 2.00$ m, $z = 0$; (c) $x = 2.00$ m, $y = 2.00$ m, $z = 0$; (d) $x = 0$, $y = 0$, $z = 2.00$ m.

28.14 •• Two parallel wires are 5.00 cm apart and carry currents in opposite directions, as shown in Fig. E28.14. Find the magnitude and direction of the magnetic field at point P due to two 1.50-mm segments of wire that are opposite each other and each 8.00 cm from P.

Figure **E28.14**

28.15 • A wire carrying a 28.0-A current bends through a right angle. Consider two 2.00-mm segments of wire, each 3.00 cm from the bend (Fig. E28.15). Find the magnitude and direction of the magnetic field these two segments produce at point P, which is midway between them.

Figure **E28.15**

28.16 •• A square wire loop 10.0 cm on each side carries a clockwise current of 15.0 A. Find the magnitude and direction of the magnetic field at its center due to the four 1.20-mm wire segments at the midpoint of each side.

Section 28.3 Magnetic Field of a Straight Current-Carrying Conductor

28.17 • **The Magnetic Field from a Lightning Bolt.** Lightning bolts can carry currents up to approximately 20 kA. We can model such a current as the equivalent of a very long, straight wire. (a) If you were unfortunate enough to be 5.0 m away from such a lightning bolt, how large a magnetic field would you experience? (b) How does this field compare to one you would experience by being 5.0 cm from a long, straight household current of 10 A?

28.18 • A very long, straight horizontal wire carries a current such that 3.50×10^{18} electrons per second pass any given point going from west to east. What are the magnitude and direction of the magnetic field this wire produces at a point 4.00 cm directly above it?

28.19 • **BIO Currents in the Heart.** The body contains many small currents caused by the motion of ions in the organs and cells. Measurements of the magnetic field around the chest due to currents in the heart give values of about 10 μG. Although the actual currents are rather complicated, we can gain a rough understanding of their magnitude if we model them as a long, straight wire. If the surface of the chest is 5.0 cm from this current, how large is the current in the heart?

28.20 • **BIO Bacteria Navigation.** Certain bacteria (such as *Aquaspirillum magnetotacticum*) tend to swim toward the earth's geographic north pole because they contain tiny particles, called magnetosomes, that are sensitive to a magnetic field. If a transmission line carrying 100 A is laid underwater, at what range of distances would the magnetic field from this line be great enough to interfere with the migration of these bacteria? (Assume that a field less than 5 percent of the earth's field would have little effect on the bacteria. Take the earth's field to be 5.0×10^{-5} T and ignore the effects of the seawater.)

28.21 • (a) How large a current would a very long, straight wire have to carry so that the magnetic field 2.00 cm from the wire is equal to 1.00 G (comparable to the earth's northward-pointing magnetic field)? (b) If the wire is horizontal with the current running from east to west, at what locations would the magnetic field of the wire point in the same direction as the horizontal component of the earth's magnetic field? (c) Repeat part (b) except the wire is vertical with the current going upward.

28.22 • Two long, straight wires, one above the other, are separated by a distance $2a$ and are parallel to the x-axis. Let the $+y$-axis be in the plane of the wires in the direction from the lower wire to the upper wire. Each wire carries current I in the $+x$-direction. What are the magnitude and direction of the net magnetic field of the two wires at a point in the plane of the wires (a) midway between them; (b) at a distance a above the upper wire; (c) at a distance a below the lower wire?

28.23 •• A long, straight wire lies along the y-axis and carries a current $I = 8.00$ A in the $-y$-direction (Fig. E28.23). In addition to the magnetic field due to the current in the wire, a uniform magnetic field $\vec{B}_0$ with magnitude 1.50×10^{-6} T is in the $+x$-direction What is the total field (magnitude and direction) at the following points in the xz-plane: (a) $x = 0$, $z = 1.00$ m; (b) $x = 1.00$ m, $z = 0$; (c) $x = 0$, $z = -0.25$ m?

Figure **E28.23**

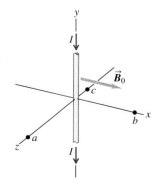

28.24 •• **BIO EMF.** Currents in dc transmission lines can be 100 A or more. Some people have expressed concern that the electromagnetic fields (EMFs) from such lines near their homes could cause health dangers. For a line with current 150 A and at a height of 8.0 m above the ground, what magnetic field does the line produce at ground level? Express your answer in teslas and as a percent of the earth's magnetic field, which is 0.50 gauss. Does this seem to be cause for worry?

28.25 • Two long, straight, parallel wires, 10.0 cm apart, carry equal 4.00-A currents in the same direction, as shown in Fig. E28.25. Find the magnitude and direction of the magnetic field at (a) point P_1, midway between the wires; (b) point P_2, 25.0 cm to the right of P_1; (c) point P_3, 20.0 cm directly above P_1.

Figure **E28.25**

28.26 •• A rectangular loop with dimensions 4.20 cm by 9.50 cm carries current I. The current in the loop produces a magnetic field at the center of the loop that has magnitude 5.50×10^{-5} T and direction away from you as you view the plane of the loop. What are the magnitude and direction (clockwise or counterclockwise) of the current in the loop?

28.27 • Four, long, parallel power lines each carry 100-A currents. A cross-sectional diagram of these lines is a square, 20.0 cm on each side. For each of the three cases shown in Fig. E28.27, calculate the magnetic field at the center of the square.

Figure **E28.27**

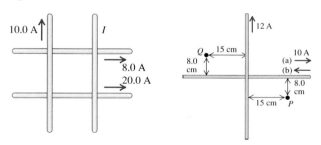

28.28 • Four very long, current-carrying wires in the same plane intersect to form a square 40.0 cm on each side, as shown in Fig. E28.28. Find the magnitude and direction of the current I so that the magnetic field at the center of the square is zero.

Figure **E28.28**   Figure **E28.29**

28.29 •• Two insulated wires perpendicular to each other in the same plane carry currents as shown in Fig. E28.29. Find the magnitude of the *net* magnetic field these wires produce at points P and Q if the 10.0 A-current is (a) to the right or (b) to the left.

Section 28.4 Force Between Parallel Conductors

28.30 • Three parallel wires each carry current I in the directions shown in Fig. E28.30. If the separation between adjacent wires is d, calculate the magnitude and direction of the net magnetic force per unit length on each wire.

Figure **E28.30**

28.31 • Two long, parallel wires are separated by a distance of 0.400 m (Fig. E28.31). The currents I_1 and I_2 have the directions shown. (a) Calculate the magnitude of the force exerted by each wire on a 1.20-m length of the other. Is the force attractive or repulsive? (b) Each current is doubled, so that I_1 becomes 10.0 A and I_2 becomes 4.00 A. Now what is the magnitude of the force that each wire exerts on a 1.20-m length of the other?

Figure **E28.31**

28.32 • Two long, parallel wires are separated by a distance of 2.50 cm. The force per unit length that each wire exerts on the other is 4.00×10^{-5} N/m, and the wires repel each other. The current in one wire is 0.600 A. (a) What is the current in the second wire? (b) Are the two currents in the same direction or in opposite directions?

28.33 • **Lamp Cord Wires.** The wires in a household lamp cord are typically 3.0 mm apart center to center and carry equal currents in opposite directions. If the cord carries current to a 100-W light bulb connected across a 120-V potential difference, what force per meter does each wire of the cord exert on the other? Is the force attractive or repulsive? Is this force large enough so it should be considered in the design of the lamp cord? (Model the lamp cord as a very long straight wire.)

28.34 • A long, horizontal wire AB rests on the surface of a table and carries a current I. Horizontal wire CD is vertically above wire AB and is free to slide up and down on the two vertical metal guides C and D (Fig. E28.34). Wire CD is connected through the sliding contacts to another wire that also carries a current I, opposite in direction to the current in wire AB. The mass per unit length of the wire CD is λ. To what equilibrium height h will the wire CD rise, assuming that the magnetic force on it is due entirely to the current in the wire AB?

Figure **E28.34**

Section 28.5 Magnetic Field of a Circular Current Loop

28.35 • **BIO** **Currents in the Brain.** The magnetic field around the head has been measured to be approximately 3.0×10^{-8} G. Although the currents that cause this field are quite complicated, we can get a rough estimate of their size by modeling them as a single circular current loop 16 cm (the width of a typical head) in diameter. What is the current needed to produce such a field at the center of the loop?

28.36 • Calculate the magnitude and direction of the magnetic field at point P due to the current in the semicircular section of wire shown in Fig. E28.36. (*Hint:* Does the current in the long, straight section of the wire produce any field at P?)

Figure **E28.36**

Figure **E28.37**

28.37 •• Calculate the magnitude of the magnetic field at point P of Fig. E28.37 in terms of R, I_1, and I_2. What does your expression give when $I_1 = I_2$?

28.38 •• A closely wound, circular coil with radius 2.40 cm has 800 turns. (a) What must the current in the coil be if the magnetic field at the center of the coil is 0.0580 T? (b) At what distance x from the center of the coil, on the axis of the coil, is the magnetic field half its value at the center?

28.39 •• A closely wound, circular coil with a diameter of 4.00 cm has 600 turns and carries a current of 0.500 A. What is the magnitude of the magnetic field (a) at the center of the coil and (b) at a point on the axis of the coil 8.00 cm from its center?

28.40 •• A closely wound coil has a radius of 6.00 cm and carries a current of 2.50 A. How many turns must it have if, at a point on the coil axis 6.00 cm from the center of the coil, the magnetic field is 6.39×10^{-4} T?

28.41 •• Two concentric circular loops of wire lie on a tabletop, one inside the other. The inner wire has a diameter of 20.0 cm and carries a clockwise current of 12.0 A, as viewed from above, and the outer wire has a diameter of 30.0 cm. What must be the magnitude and direction (as viewed from above) of the current in the outer wire so that the net magnetic field due to this combination of wires is zero at the common center of the wires?

Section 28.6 Ampere's Law

28.42 • Figure E28.42 shows, in cross section, several conductors that carry currents through the plane of the figure. The currents have the magnitudes $I_1 = 4.0$ A, $I_2 = 6.0$ A, and $I_3 = 2.0$ A, and the directions shown. Four paths, labeled a through d, are shown. What is the line integral $\oint \vec{B} \cdot d\vec{l}$ for each path? Each integral involves going around the path in the counterclockwise direction. Explain your answers.

Figure **E28.42**

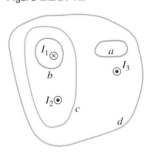

28.43 • A closed curve encircles several conductors. The line integral $\oint \vec{B} \cdot d\vec{l}$ around this curve is 3.83×10^{-4} T · m. (a) What is the net current in the conductors? (b) If you were to integrate around the curve in the opposite direction, what would be the value of the line integral? Explain.

Section 28.7 Applications of Ampere's Law

28.44 •• As a new electrical technician, you are designing a large solenoid to produce a uniform 0.150-T magnetic field near the center of the solenoid. You have enough wire for 4000 circular turns. This solenoid must be 1.40 m long and 2.80 cm in diameter. What current will you need to produce the necessary field?

28.45 • **Coaxial Cable.** A solid conductor with radius a is supported by insulating disks on the axis of a conducting tube with inner radius b and outer radius c (Fig. E28.45). The central conductor and tube carry equal currents I in opposite directions. The currents are distributed uniformly over the cross sections of each conductor. Derive an expression for the magnitude of the magnetic field (a) at points outside the central, solid conductor but inside the tube ($a < r < b$) and (b) at points outside the tube ($r > c$).

Figure **E28.45**

28.46 • Repeat Exercise 28.45 for the case in which the current in the central, solid conductor is I_1, the current in the tube is I_2, and these currents are in the same direction rather than in opposite directions.

28.47 • A long, straight, cylindrical wire of radius R carries a current uniformly distributed over its cross section. At what locations is the magnetic field produced by this current equal to half of its largest value? Consider points inside and outside the wire.

28.48 •• A 15.0-cm-long solenoid with radius 0.750 cm is closely wound with 600 turns of wire. The current in the windings is 8.00 A. Compute the magnetic field at a point near the center of the solenoid.

28.49 •• A solenoid is designed to produce a magnetic field of 0.0270 T at its center. It has radius 1.40 cm and length 40.0 cm, and the wire can carry a maximum current of 12.0 A. (a) What minimum number of turns per unit length must the solenoid have? (b) What total length of wire is required?

28.50 • A toroidal solenoid has an inner radius of 12.0 cm and an outer radius of 15.0 cm. It carries a current of 1.50 A. How many equally spaced turns must it have so that it will produce a magnetic field of 3.75 mT at points within the coils 14.0 cm from its center?

28.51 • A magnetic field of 37.2 T has been achieved at the MIT Francis Bitter National Magnetic Laboratory. Find the current needed to achieve such a field (a) 2.00 cm from a long, straight wire; (b) at the center of a circular coil of radius 42.0 cm that has 100 turns; (c) near the center of a solenoid with radius 2.40 cm, length 32.0 cm, and 40,000 turns.

28.52 • A toroidal solenoid (see Example 28.10) has inner radius $r_1 = 15.0$ cm and outer radius $r_2 = 18.0$ cm. The solenoid has 250 turns and carries a current of 8.50 A. What is the magnitude of the magnetic field at the following distances from the center of the torus: (a) 12.0 cm; (b) 16.0 cm; (c) 20.0 cm?

28.53 •• A wooden ring whose mean diameter is 14.0 cm is wound with a closely spaced toroidal winding of 600 turns. Compute the magnitude of the magnetic field at the center of the cross section of the windings when the current in the windings is 0.650 A.

Section 28.8 Magnetic Materials

28.54 •• A toroidal solenoid with 400 turns of wire and a mean radius of 6.0 cm carries a current of 0.25 A. The relative permeability of the core is 80. (a) What is the magnetic field in the core? (b) What part of the magnetic field is due to atomic currents?

28.55 • A toroidal solenoid with 500 turns is wound on a ring with a mean radius of 2.90 cm. Find the current in the winding that is required to set up a magnetic field of 0.350 T in the ring (a) if the ring is made of annealed iron ($K_m = 1400$) and (b) if the ring is made of silicon steel ($K_m = 5200$).

28.56 • The current in the windings of a toroidal solenoid is 2.400 A. There are 500 turns, and the mean radius is 25.00 cm. The toroidal solenoid is filled with a magnetic material. The magnetic field inside the windings is found to be 1.940 T. Calculate (a) the relative permeability and (b) the magnetic susceptibility of the material that fills the toroid.

28.57 • A long solenoid with 60 turns of wire per centimeter carries a current of 0.15 A. The wire that makes up the solenoid is wrapped around a solid core of silicon steel ($K_m = 5200$). (The wire of the solenoid is jacketed with an insulator so that none of the current flows into the core.) (a) For a point inside the core, find the magnitudes of (i) the magnetic field $\vec{B}_0$ due to the solenoid current; (ii) the magnetization $\vec{M}$; (iii) the total magnetic field $\vec{B}$. (b) In a sketch of the solenoid and core, show the directions of the vectors $\vec{B}$, $\vec{B}_0$, and $\vec{M}$ inside the core.

28.58 • When a certain paramagnetic material is placed in an external magnetic field of 1.5000 T, the field inside the material is measured to be 1.5023 T. Find (a) the relative permeability and (b) the magnetic permeability of this material.

PROBLEMS

28.59 •• A pair of point charges, $q = +8.00 \ \mu C$ and $q' = -5.00$ μC, are moving as shown in Fig. P28.59 with speeds $v = 9.00 \times 10^4$ m/s and $v' = 6.50 \times 10^4$ m/s. When the charges are at the locations shown in the figure, what are the magnitude and direction of (a) the magnetic field produced at the origin and (b) the magnetic force that q' exerts on q?

Figure **P28.59**

28.60 •• At a particular instant, charge $q_1 = +4.80 \times 10^{-6}$ C is at the point $(0, 0.250$ m, $0)$ and has velocity $\vec{v}_1 = (9.20 \times 10^5 \text{ m/s})\hat{\imath}$. Charge $q_2 = -2.90 \times 10^{-6}$ C is at the point $(0.150$ m, $0, 0)$ and has velocity $\vec{v}_2 = (-5.30 \times 10^5 \text{ m/s})\hat{\jmath}$. At this instant, what are the magnitude and direction of the magnetic force that q_1 exerts on q_2?

28.61 ••• Two long, parallel transmission lines, 40.0 cm apart, carry 25.0-A and 75.0-A currents. Find all locations where the net magnetic field of the two wires is zero if these currents are in (a) the same direction and (b) the opposite direction.

28.62 • A long, straight wire carries a current of 5.20 A. An electron is traveling in the vicinity of the wire. At the instant when the electron is 4.50 cm from the wire and traveling with a speed of 6.00×10^4 m/s directly toward the wire, what are the magnitude and direction (relative to the direction of the current) of the force that the magnetic field of the current exerts on the electron?

28.63 • CP A long, straight wire carries a 13.0-A current. An electron is fired parallel to this wire with a velocity of 250 km/s in the same direction as the current, 2.00 cm from the wire. (a) Find the magnitude and direction of the electron's initial acceleration. (b) What should be the magnitude and direction of a uniform electric field that will allow the electron to continue to travel parallel to the wire? (c) Is it necessary to include the effects of gravity? Justify your answer.

28.64 • Two very long, straight wires carry currents as shown in Fig. P28.64. For each case, find all locations where the net magnetic field is zero.

Figure **P28.64**

(a)   (b)   (c)

28.65 •• CP Two identical circular, wire loops 40.0 cm in diameter each carry a current of 3.80 A in the same direction. These loops are parallel to each other and are 25.0 cm apart. Line ab is normal to the plane of the loops and passes through their centers.

A proton is fired at 2400 km/s perpendicular to line *ab* from a point midway between the centers of the loops. Find the magnitude of the magnetic force these loops exert on the proton just after it is fired.

28.66 • A negative point charge $q = -7.20$ mC is moving in a reference frame. When the point charge is at the origin, the magnetic field it produces at the point $x = 25.0$ cm, $y = 0$, $z = 0$ is $\vec{B} = (6.00 \ \mu\text{T})\hat{\jmath}$, and its speed is 800 m/s. (a) What are the x-, y-, and z-components of the velocity $\vec{v}_0$ of the charge? (b) At this same instant, what is the magnitude of the magnetic field that the charge produces at the point $x = 0$, $y = 25.0$ cm, $z = 0$?

28.67 • Two long, straight, parallel wires are 1.00 m apart (Fig. P28.67). The wire on the left carries a current I_1 of 6.00 A into the plane of the paper. (a) What must the magnitude and direction of the current I_2 be for the net field at point P to be zero? (b) Then what are the magnitude and direction of the net field at Q? (c) Then what is the magnitude of the net field at S?

Figure **P28.67**

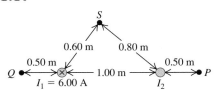

28.68 •• Figure P28.68 shows an end view of two long, parallel wires perpendicular to the *xy*-plane, each carrying a current *I* but in opposite directions. (a) Copy the diagram, and draw vectors to show the $\vec{B}$ field of each wire and the net $\vec{B}$ field at point *P*. (b) Derive the expression for the magnitude of $\vec{B}$ at any point on the *x*-axis in terms of the *x*-coordinate of the point. What is the direction of $\vec{B}$? (c) Graph the magnitude of $\vec{B}$ at points on the *x*-axis. (d) At what value of *x* is the magnitude of $\vec{B}$ a maximum? (e) What is the magnitude of $\vec{B}$ when $x \gg a$?

Figure **P28.68**

28.69 • Refer to the situation in Problem 28.68. Suppose that a third long, straight wire, parallel to the other two, passes through point *P* (see Fig. P28.68) and that each wire carries a current $I = 6.00$ A. Let $a = 40.0$ cm and $x = 60.0$ cm. Find the magnitude and direction of the force per unit length on the third wire, (a) if the current in it is directed into the plane of the figure, and (b) if the current in it is directed out of the plane of the figure.

28.70 •• **CP** A pair of long, rigid metal rods, each of length *L*, lie parallel to each other on a perfectly smooth table. Their ends are connected by identical, very light conducting springs of force constant *k* (Fig. P28.70) and negligible unstretched length. If a current *I* runs through this circuit, the springs will stretch. At what separation will the rods remain at rest? Assume that *k* is large enough so that the separation of the rods will be much less than *L*.

Figure **P28.70**

28.71 ••• **CP** Two long, parallel wires hang by 4.00-cm-long cords from a common axis (Fig. P28.71). The wires have a mass per unit length of 0.0125 kg/m and carry the same current in opposite directions. What is the current in each wire if the cords hang at an angle of 6.00° with the vertical?

Figure **P28.71**

28.72 • The long, straight wire *AB* shown in Fig. P28.72 carries a current of 14.0 A. The rectangular loop whose long edges are parallel to the wire carries a current of 5.00 A. Find the magnitude and direction of the net force exerted on the loop by the magnetic field of the wire.

Figure **P28.72**

28.73 •• **CP** A flat, round iron ring 5.00 cm in diameter has a current running through it that produces a magnetic field of 75.4 μT at its center. This ring is placed in a uniform external magnetic field of 0.375 T. What is the maximum torque the external field can exert on the ring? Show how the ring should be oriented relative to the field for the torque to have its maximum value.

28.74 • The wire semicircles shown in Fig. P28.74 have radii *a* and *b*. Calculate the net magnetic field (magnitude and direction) that the current in the wires produces at point *P*.

Figure **P28.74**

28.75 • **CALC** **Helmholtz Coils.** Figure 28.75 is a sectional view of two circular coils with radius *a*, each wound with *N* turns of wire carrying a current *I*, circulating in the same direction in both coils. The coils are separated by a distance *a* equal to their radii. In this configuration the coils are called Helmholtz coils; they produce a very uniform magnetic field in the region between them. (a) Derive the expression for the magnitude *B* of the magnetic field at a point on the axis a distance *x* to the right of point *P*, which is midway between the coils. (b) Graph *B* versus *x* for $x = 0$ to $x = a/2$. Compare this graph to one for the magnetic field due to the right-hand coil alone. (c) From part (a), obtain an expression for the magnitude of the magnetic field at point *P*. (d) Calculate the magnitude of the magnetic field at *P* if $N = 300$ turns, $I = 6.00$ A, and $a = 8.00$ cm. (e) Calculate dB/dx and d^2B/dx^2 at $P(x = 0)$. Discuss how your results show that the field is very uniform in the vicinity of *P*.

Figure **P28.75**

Figure **P28.76**

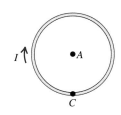

28.76 • A circular wire of diameter *D* lies on a horizontal table and carries a current *I*. In Fig. P28.76 point *A* marks the center of the circle and point *C* is on its rim. (a) Find the magnitude and direction of the magnetic field at point A. (b) The wire is now unwrapped so it is straight, centered on point C, and perpendicular to the line AC, but the same current is maintained in it. Now find the magnetic field at point A. (c) Which field is greater: the one in part (a) or in part (b)? By what factor? Why is this result physically reasonable?

28.77 • CALC A long, straight wire with a circular cross section of radius R carries a current I. Assume that the current density is not constant across the cross section of the wire, but rather varies as $J = \alpha r$, where α is a constant. (a) By the requirement that J integrated over the cross section of the wire gives the total current I, calculate the constant α in terms of I and R. (b) Use Ampere's law to calculate the magnetic field $B(r)$ for (i) $r \leq R$ and (ii) $r \geq R$. Express your answers in terms of I.

28.78 • CALC The wire shown in Fig. P28.78 is infinitely long and carries a current I. Calculate the magnitude and direction of the magnetic field that this current produces at point P.

Figure **P28.78**

28.79 • A conductor is made in the form of a hollow cylinder with inner and outer radii a and b, respectively. It carries a current I uniformly distributed over its cross section. Derive expressions for the magnitude of the magnetic field in the regions (a) $r < a$; (b) $a < r < b$; (c) $r > b$.

28.80 • A circular loop has radius R and carries current I_2 in a clockwise direction (Fig. P28.80). The center of the loop is a distance D above a long, straight wire. What are the magnitude and direction of the current I_1 in the wire if the magnetic field at the center of the loop is zero?

Figure **P28.80**

28.81 • CALC A long, straight, solid cylinder, oriented with its axis in the z-direction, carries a current whose current density is $\vec{J}$. The current density, although symmetric about the cylinder axis, is not constant but varies according to the relationship

$$\vec{J} = \frac{2I_0}{\pi a^2}\left[1 - \left(\frac{r}{a}\right)^2\right]\hat{k} \quad \text{for } r \leq a$$
$$= 0 \quad \text{for } r \geq a$$

where a is the radius of the cylinder, r is the radial distance from the cylinder axis, and I_0 is a constant having units of amperes. (a) Show that I_0 is the total current passing through the entire cross section of the wire. (b) Using Ampere's law, derive an expression for the magnitude of the magnetic field $\vec{B}$ in the region $r \geq a$. (c) Obtain an expression for the current I contained in a circular cross section of radius $r \leq a$ and centered at the cylinder axis. (d) Using Ampere's law, derive an expression for the magnitude of the magnetic field $\vec{B}$ in the region $r \leq a$. How do your results in parts (b) and (d) compare for $r = a$?

28.82 • A long, straight, solid cylinder, oriented with its axis in the z-direction, carries a current whose current density is $\vec{J}$. The current density, although symmetric about the cylinder axis, is not constant and varies according to the relationship

$$\vec{J} = \left(\frac{b}{r}\right)e^{(r-a)/\delta}\hat{k} \quad \text{for } r \leq a$$
$$= 0 \quad \text{for } r \geq a$$

where the radius of the cylinder is $a = 5.00$ cm, r is the radial distance from the cylinder axis, b is a constant equal to 600 A/m, and δ is a constant equal to 2.50 cm. (a) Let I_0 be the total current passing

through the entire cross section of the wire. Obtain an expression for I_0 in terms of b, δ, and a. Evaluate your expression to obtain a numerical value for I_0. (b) Using Ampere's law, derive an expression for the magnetic field $\vec{B}$ in the region $r \geq a$. Express your answer in terms of I_0 rather than b. (c) Obtain an expression for the current I contained in a circular cross section of radius $r \leq a$ and centered at the cylinder axis. Express your answer in terms of I_0 rather than b. (d) Using Ampere's law, derive an expression for the magnetic field $\vec{B}$ in the region $r \leq a$. (e) Evaluate the magnitude of the magnetic field at $r = \delta$, $r = a$, and $r = 2a$.

28.83 • **An Infinite Current Sheet.** Long, straight conductors with square cross sections and each carrying current I are laid side by side to form an infinite current sheet (Fig. P28.83). The conductors lie in the xy-plane, are parallel to the y-axis, and carry current in the +y-direction There are n conductors per unit length measured along the x-axis. (a) What are the magnitude and direction of the magnetic field a distance a below the current sheet? (b) What are the magnitude and direction of the magnetic field a distance a above the current sheet?

Figure **P28.83**

28.84 • Long, straight conductors with square cross section, each carrying current I, are laid side by side to form an infinite current sheet with current directed out of the plane of the page (Fig. P28.84). A second infinite current sheet is a distance d below the first and is parallel to it. The second sheet carries current into the plane of the page. Each sheet has n conductors per unit length. (Refer to Problem 28.83.) Calculate the magnitude and direction of the net magnetic field at (a) point P (above the upper sheet); (b) point R (midway between the two sheets); (c) point S (below the lower sheet).

Figure **P28.84**

28.85 • CP A piece of iron has magnetization $M = 6.50 \times 10^4$ A/m. Find the average magnetic dipole moment *per atom* in this piece of iron. Express your answer both in A·m² and in Bohr magnetons. The density of iron is given in Table 14.1, and the atomic mass of iron (in grams per mole) is given in Appendix D. The chemical symbol for iron is Fe.

CHALLENGE PROBLEMS

28.86 ••• A wide, long, insulating belt has a uniform positive charge per unit area σ on its upper surface. Rollers at each end move the belt to the right at a constant speed v. Calculate the magnitude and direction of the magnetic field produced by the moving belt at a point just above its surface. (*Hint:* At points near the surface and far from its edges or ends, the moving belt can be considered to be an infinite current sheet like that in Problem 28.83.)

28.87 ••• CP Two long, straight conducting wires with linear mass density λ are suspended from cords so that they are each horizontal, parallel to each other, and a distance d apart. The back ends of the wires are connected to each other by a slack, low-resistance connecting wire. A charged capacitor (capacitance C) is now added to the system; the positive plate of the capacitor (initial charge $+Q_0$) is connected to the front end of one of the wires, and the negative plate of the capacitor (initial charge $-Q_0$) is connected to the front end of the other wire (Fig. P28.87). Both of these connections are also made by slack, low-resistance wires. When the connection is made, the wires are pushed aside by the repulsive force between the wires, and each wire has an initial horizontal velocity of magnitude v_0. Assume that the time constant for the capacitor to discharge is negligible compared to the time it takes for any appreciable displacement in the position of the wires to occur. (a) Show that the initial speed v_0 of either wire is given by

Figure **P28.87**

$$v_0 = \frac{\mu_0 Q_0^2}{4\pi \lambda RCd}$$

where R is the total resistance of the circuit. (b) To what height h will each wire rise as a result of the circuit connection?

28.88 ••• **CALC** A wire in the shape of a semicircle with radius a is oriented in the yz-plane with its center of curvature at the origin (Fig. P28.88). If the current in the wire is I, calculate the magnetic-field components produced at point P, a distance x out along the x-axis. (*Note:* Do not forget the contribution from the straight wire at the bottom of the semicircle that runs from $z = -a$ to $z = +a$. You may use the fact that the fields of the two antiparallel currents at $z > a$ cancel, but you must explain *why* they cancel.)

Figure **P28.88**

Answers

Chapter Opening Question ?

There would be *no* change in the magnetic field strength. From Example 28.9 (Section 28.7), the field inside a solenoid has magnitude $B = \mu_0 nI$, where n is the number of turns of wire per unit length. Joining two solenoids end to end doubles both the number of turns and the length, so the number of turns per unit length is unchanged.

Test Your Understanding Questions

28.1 Answers: (a) (i), (b) (ii) The situation is the same as shown in Fig. 28.2 except that the upper proton has velocity $\vec{v}$ rather than $-\vec{v}$. The magnetic field due to the lower proton is the same as shown in Fig. 28.2, but the direction of the magnetic force $\vec{F} = q\vec{v} \times \vec{B}$ on the upper proton is reversed. Hence the magnetic force is attractive. Since the speed v is small compared to c, the magnetic force is much smaller in magnitude than the repulsive electric force and the net force is still repulsive.

28.2 Answer: (i) and (iii) (tie), (iv), (ii) From Eq. (28.5), the magnitude of the field dB due to a current element of length dl carrying current I is $dB = (\mu/4\pi)(I \, dl \sin\phi / r^2)$. In this expression r is the distance from the element to the field point, and ϕ is the angle between the direction of the current and a vector from the current element to the field point. All four points are the same distance $r = L$ from the current element, so the value of dB is proportional to the value of $\sin\phi$. For the four points the angle is (i) $\phi = 90°$, (ii) $\phi = 0$, (iii) $\phi = 90°$, and (iv) $\phi = 45°$, so the values of $\sin\phi$ are (i) 1, (ii) 0, (iii) 1, and (iv) $1/\sqrt{2}$.

28.3 Answer: A This orientation will cause current to flow clockwise around the circuit. Hence current will flow south through the wire that lies under the compass. From the right-hand rule for the magnetic field produced by a long, straight, current-carrying conductor, this will produce a magnetic field that points to the left at the position of the compass (which lies atop the wire). The combination of the northward magnetic field of the earth and the westward field produced by the current gives a net magnetic field to the northwest, so the compass needle will swing counterclockwise to align with this field.

28.4 Answers: (a) (i), (b) (iii), (c) (ii), (d) (iii) Current flows in the same direction in adjacent turns of the coil, so the magnetic forces between these turns are attractive. Current flows in opposite directions on opposite sides of the same turn, so the magnetic forces between these sides are repulsive. Thus the magnetic forces on the

solenoid turns squeeze them together in the direction along its axis but push them apart radially. The *electric* forces are zero because the wire is electrically neutral, with as much positive charge as there is negative charge.

28.5 Answers: (a) (ii), (b) (v) The vector $d\vec{B}$ is in the direction of $d\vec{l} \times \vec{r}$. For a segment on the negative y-axis, $d\vec{l} = -\hat{k} \, dl$ points in the negative z-direction and $\vec{r} = x\hat{i} + a\hat{j}$. Hence $d\vec{l} \times \vec{r} = (a \, dl)\hat{i} - (x \, dl)\hat{j}$, which has a positive x-component, a negative y-component, and zero z-component. For a segment on the negative z-axis, $d\vec{l} = \hat{j} \, dl$ points in the positive y-direction and $\vec{r} = x\hat{i} + a\hat{k}$. Hence $d\vec{l} \times \vec{r} = 1(a \, dl)\hat{i} - 1(x \, dl)\hat{k}$, which has a positive x-component, zero y-component, and a negative z-component.

28.6 Answer: (ii) Imagine carrying out the integral $\oint \vec{B} \cdot d\vec{l}$ along an integration path that goes counterclockwise around the red magnetic field line. At each point along the path the magnetic field $\vec{B}$ and the infinitesimal segment $d\vec{l}$ are both tangent to the path, so $\vec{B} \cdot d\vec{l}$ is positive at each point and the integral $\oint \vec{B} \cdot d\vec{l}$ is likewise positive. It follows from Ampere's law $\oint \vec{B} \cdot d\vec{l} = \mu_0 I_{encl}$ and the right-hand rule that the integration path encloses a current directed out of the plane of the page. There are no currents in the empty space outside the magnet, so there must be currents inside the magnet (see Section 28.8).

28.7 Answer: (iii) By symmetry, any $\vec{B}$ field outside the cable must circulate around the cable, with circular field lines like those surrounding the solid cylindrical conductor in Fig. 28.20. Choose an integration path like the one shown in Fig. 28.20 with radius $r > R$, so that the path completely encloses the cable. As in Example 28.8, the integral $\oint \vec{B} \cdot d\vec{l}$ for this path has magnitude $B(2\pi r)$. From Ampere's law this is equal to $\mu_0 I_{encl}$. The net enclosed current I_{encl} is zero because it includes two currents of equal magnitude but opposite direction: one in the central wire and one in the hollow cylinder. Hence $B(2\pi r) = 0$, and so $B = 0$ for any value of r outside the cable. (The field is nonzero *inside* the cable; see Exercise 28.45.)

28.8 Answer: (i), (iv) Sodium and uranium are paramagnetic materials and hence are attracted to a magnet, while bismuth and lead are diamagnetic materials that are repelled by a magnet. (See Table 28.1.)

Bridging Problem

Answer: $B = \dfrac{\mu_0 nQ}{a}$

ELECTROMAGNETIC INDUCTION

? When a credit card is "swiped" through a card reader, the information coded in a magnetic pattern on the back of the card is transmitted to the cardholder's bank. Why is it necessary to swipe the card rather than holding it motionless in the card reader's slot?

LEARNING GOALS

By studying this chapter, you will learn:

- The experimental evidence that a changing magnetic field induces an emf.

- How Faraday's law relates the induced emf in a loop to the change in magnetic flux through the loop.

- How to determine the direction of an induced emf.

- How to calculate the emf induced in a conductor moving through a magnetic field.

- How a changing magnetic flux generates an electric field that is very different from that produced by an arrangement of charges.

- The four fundamental equations that completely describe both electricity and magnetism.

Almost every modern device or machine, from a computer to a washing machine to a power drill, has electric circuits at its heart. We learned in Chapter 25 that an electromotive force (emf) is required for a current to flow in a circuit; in Chapters 25 and 26 we almost always took the source of emf to be a battery. But for the vast majority of electric devices that are used in industry and in the home (including any device that you plug into a wall socket), the source of emf is *not* a battery but an electric generating station. Such a station produces electric energy by converting other forms of energy: gravitational potential energy at a hydroelectric plant, chemical energy in a coal- or oil-fired plant, nuclear energy at a nuclear plant. But how is this energy conversion done?

The answer is a phenomenon known as *electromagnetic induction:* If the magnetic flux through a circuit changes, an emf and a current are induced in the circuit. In a power-generating station, magnets move relative to coils of wire to produce a changing magnetic flux in the coils and hence an emf. Other key components of electric power systems, such as transformers, also depend on magnetically induced emfs.

The central principle of electromagnetic induction, and the keystone of this chapter, is *Faraday's law.* This law relates induced emf to changing magnetic flux in any loop, including a closed circuit. We also discuss Lenz's law, which helps us to predict the directions of induced emfs and currents. These principles will allow us to understand electrical energy-conversion devices such as motors, generators, and transformers.

Electromagnetic induction tells us that a time-varying magnetic field can act as a source of electric field. We will also see how a time-varying *electric* field can act as a source of *magnetic* field. These remarkable results form part of a neat package of formulas, called *Maxwell's equations,* that describe the behavior of electric and magnetic fields in *any* situation. Maxwell's equations pave the way toward an understanding of electromagnetic waves, the topic of Chapter 32.

29.1 Induction Experiments

During the 1830s, several pioneering experiments with magnetically induced emf were carried out in England by Michael Faraday and in the United States by Joseph Henry (1797–1878), later the first director of the Smithsonian Institution. Figure 29.1 shows several examples. In Fig. 29.1a, a coil of wire is connected to a galvanometer. When the nearby magnet is stationary, the meter shows no current. This isn't surprising; there is no source of emf in the circuit. But when we *move* the magnet either toward or away from the coil, the meter shows current in the circuit, but *only* while the magnet is moving (Fig. 29.1b). If we keep the magnet stationary and move the coil, we again detect a current during the motion. We call this an **induced current,** and the corresponding emf required to cause this current is called an **induced emf.**

In Fig. 29.1c we replace the magnet with a second coil connected to a battery. When the second coil is stationary, there is no current in the first coil. However, when we move the second coil toward or away from the first or move the first toward or away from the second, there is current in the first coil, but again *only* while one coil is moving relative to the other.

Finally, using the two-coil setup in Fig. 29.1d, we keep both coils stationary and vary the current in the second coil, either by opening and closing the switch or by changing the resistance of the second coil with the switch closed (perhaps by changing the second coil's temperature). We find that as we open or close the switch, there is a momentary current pulse in the first circuit. When we vary the resistance (and thus the current) in the second coil, there is an induced current in the first circuit, but only while the current in the second circuit is changing.

To explore further the common elements in these observations, let's consider a more detailed series of experiments (Fig. 29.2). We connect a coil of wire to a galvanometer and then place the coil between the poles of an electromagnet whose magnetic field we can vary. Here's what we observe:

1. When there is no current in the electromagnet, so that $\vec{B} = 0$, the galvanometer shows no current.
2. When the electromagnet is turned on, there is a momentary current through the meter as $\vec{B}$ increases.
3. When $\vec{B}$ levels off at a steady value, the current drops to zero, no matter how large $\vec{B}$ is.
4. With the coil in a horizontal plane, we squeeze it so as to decrease the cross-sectional area of the coil. The meter detects current only *during* the

29.1 Demonstrating the phenomenon of induced current.

(a) A stationary magnet does NOT induce a current in a coil.

Meter shows zero current.

All these actions DO induce a current in the coil. What do they have in common?*

(b) Moving the magnet toward or away from the coil

Meter shows induced current.

(c) Moving a second, current-carrying coil toward or away from the coil

(d) Varying the current in the second coil (by closing or opening a switch)

*They cause the magnetic field through the coil to *change*.

deformation, not before or after. When we increase the area to return the coil to its original shape, there is current in the opposite direction, but only while the area of the coil is changing.

5. If we rotate the coil a few degrees about a horizontal axis, the meter detects current during the rotation, in the same direction as when we decreased the area. When we rotate the coil back, there is a current in the opposite direction during this rotation.

6. If we jerk the coil out of the magnetic field, there is a current during the motion, in the same direction as when we decreased the area.

7. If we decrease the number of turns in the coil by unwinding one or more turns, there is a current during the unwinding, in the same direction as when we decreased the area. If we wind more turns onto the coil, there is a current in the opposite direction during the winding.

8. When the magnet is turned off, there is a momentary current in the direction opposite to the current when it was turned on.

9. The faster we carry out any of these changes, the greater the current.

10. If all these experiments are repeated with a coil that has the same shape but different material and different resistance, the current in each case is inversely proportional to the total circuit resistance. This shows that the induced emfs that are causing the current do not depend on the material of the coil but only on its shape and the magnetic field.

The common element in all these experiments is changing *magnetic flux* Φ_B through the coil connected to the galvanometer. In each case the flux changes either because the magnetic field changes with time or because the coil is moving through a nonuniform magnetic field. Faraday's law of induction, the subject of the next section, states that in all of these situations the induced emf is proportional to the *rate of change* of magnetic flux Φ_B through the coil. The *direction* of the induced emf depends on whether the flux is increasing or decreasing. If the flux is constant, there is no induced emf.

Induced emfs are not mere laboratory curiosities but have a tremendous number of practical applications. If you are reading these words indoors, you are making use of induced emfs right now! At the power plant that supplies your neighborhood, an electric generator produces an emf by varying the magnetic flux through coils of wire. (In the next section we'll see in detail how this is done.) This emf supplies the voltage between the terminals of the wall sockets in your home, and this voltage supplies the power to your reading lamp. Indeed, any appliance that you plug into a wall socket makes use of induced emfs.

Magnetically induced emfs, just like the emfs discussed in Section 25.4, are the result of *nonelectrostatic* forces. We have to distinguish carefully between the electrostatic electric fields produced by charges (according to Coulomb's law) and the nonelectrostatic electric fields produced by changing magnetic fields. We'll return to this distinction later in this chapter and the next.

29.2 Faraday's Law

The common element in all induction effects is changing magnetic flux through a circuit. Before stating the simple physical law that summarizes all of the kinds of experiments described in Section 29.1, let's first review the concept of magnetic flux Φ_B (which we introduced in Section 27.3). For an infinitesimal-area element $d\vec{A}$ in a magnetic field $\vec{B}$ (Fig. 29.3), the magnetic flux $d\Phi_B$ through the area is

$$d\Phi_B = \vec{B} \cdot d\vec{A} = B_\perp \, dA = B \, dA \cos\phi$$

where $B_\perp$ is the component of $\vec{B}$ perpendicular to the surface of the area element and ϕ is the angle between $\vec{B}$ and $d\vec{A}$. (As in Chapter 27, be careful to distinguish

29.2 A coil in a magnetic field. When the $\vec{B}$ field is constant and the shape, location, and orientation of the coil do not change, no current is induced in the coil. A current is induced when any of these factors change.

29.3 Calculating the magnetic flux through an area element.

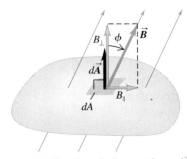

Magnetic flux through element of area $d\vec{A}$:
$d\Phi_B = \vec{B} \cdot d\vec{A} = B_\perp \, dA = B \, dA \cos\phi$

29.4 Calculating the flux of a uniform magnetic field through a flat area. (Compare to Fig. 22.6, which shows the rules for calculating the flux of a uniform *electric* field.)

Surface is face-on to magnetic field:
- $\vec{B}$ and $\vec{A}$ are parallel (the angle between $\vec{B}$ and $\vec{A}$ is $\phi = 0$).
- The magnetic flux $\Phi_B = \vec{B} \cdot \vec{A} = BA$.

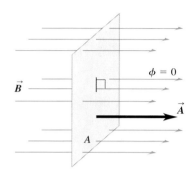

Surface is tilted from a face-on orientation by an angle ϕ:
- The angle between $\vec{B}$ and $\vec{A}$ is ϕ.
- The magnetic flux $\Phi_B = \vec{B} \cdot \vec{A} = BA \cos \phi$.

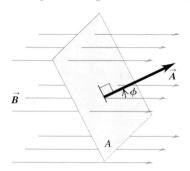

Surface is edge-on to magnetic field:
- $\vec{B}$ and $\vec{A}$ are perpendicular (the angle between $\vec{B}$ and $\vec{A}$ is $\phi = 90°$).
- The magnetic flux
  $\Phi_B = \vec{B} \cdot \vec{A} = BA \cos 90° = 0$.

between two quantities named "phi," ϕ and Φ_B.) The total magnetic flux Φ_B through a finite area is the integral of this expression over the area:

$$\Phi_B = \int \vec{B} \cdot d\vec{A} = \int B \, dA \cos \phi \qquad (29.1)$$

If $\vec{B}$ is uniform over a flat area $\vec{A}$, then

$$\Phi_B = \vec{B} \cdot \vec{A} = BA \cos \phi \qquad (29.2)$$

Figure 29.4 reviews the rules for using Eq. (29.2).

CAUTION **Choosing the direction of $d\vec{A}$ or $\vec{A}$** In Eqs. (29.1) and (29.2) we have to be careful to define the direction of the vector area $d\vec{A}$ or $\vec{A}$ unambiguously. There are always two directions perpendicular to any given area, and the sign of the magnetic flux through the area depends on which one we choose to be positive. For example, in Fig. 29.3 we chose $d\vec{A}$ to point upward so ϕ is less than 90° and $\vec{B} \cdot d\vec{A}$ is positive. We could have chosen instead to have $d\vec{A}$ point downward, in which case ϕ would have been greater than 90° and $\vec{B} \cdot d\vec{A}$ would have been negative. Either choice is equally good, but once we make a choice we must stick with it. ❚

Faraday's law of induction states:

The induced emf in a closed loop equals the negative of the time rate of change of magnetic flux through the loop.

In symbols, Faraday's law is

$$\mathcal{E} = -\frac{d\Phi_B}{dt} \qquad \text{(Faraday's law of induction)} \qquad (29.3)$$

To understand the negative sign, we have to introduce a sign convention for the induced emf $\mathcal{E}$. But first let's look at a simple example of this law in action.

Example 29.1 **Emf and current induced in a loop**

The magnetic field between the poles of the electromagnet in Fig. 29.5 is uniform at any time, but its magnitude is increasing at the rate of 0.020 T/s. The area of the conducting loop in the field is 120 cm², and the total circuit resistance, including the meter, is 5.0 Ω. (a) Find the induced emf and the induced current in the circuit. (b) If the loop is replaced by one made of an insulator, what effect does this have on the induced emf and induced current?

SOLUTION

IDENTIFY and SET UP: The magnetic flux Φ_B through the loop changes as the magnetic field changes. Hence there will be an induced emf $\mathcal{E}$ and an induced current I in the loop. We calculate Φ_B using Eq. (29.2), then find $\mathcal{E}$ using Faraday's law. Finally, we calculate I using $\mathcal{E} = IR$, where R is the total resistance of the circuit that includes the loop.

EXECUTE: (a) The area vector $\vec{A}$ for the loop is perpendicular to the plane of the loop; we take $\vec{A}$ to be vertically upward. Then $\vec{A}$ and $\vec{B}$ are parallel, and because $\vec{B}$ is uniform the magnetic flux through the loop is $\Phi_B = \vec{B} \cdot \vec{A} = BA \cos 0 = BA$. The area $A = 0.012\ \mathrm{m}^2$ is constant, so the rate of change of magnetic flux is

29.5 A stationary conducting loop in an increasing magnetic field.

$dB/dt = 0.020\ \mathrm{T/s}$

S

$\vec{A}$

$A = 120\ \mathrm{cm}^2 = 0.012\ \mathrm{m}^2$

a

b

I

N

Total resistance in circuit and meter $= 5.0\ \Omega$

$$\frac{d\Phi_B}{dt} = \frac{d(BA)}{dt} = \frac{dB}{dt} A = (0.020\ \mathrm{T/s})(0.012\ \mathrm{m}^2)$$
$$= 2.4 \times 10^{-4}\ \mathrm{V} = 0.24\ \mathrm{mV}$$

This, apart from a sign that we haven't discussed yet, is the induced emf $\mathcal{E}$. The corresponding induced current is

$$I = \frac{\mathcal{E}}{R} = \frac{2.4 \times 10^{-4}\ \mathrm{V}}{5.0\ \Omega} = 4.8 \times 10^{-5}\ \mathrm{A} = 0.048\ \mathrm{mA}$$

(b) By changing to an insulating loop, we've made the resistance of the loop very high. Faraday's law, Eq. (29.3), does not involve the resistance of the circuit in any way, so the induced *emf* does not change. But the *current* will be smaller, as given by the equation $I = \mathcal{E}/R$. If the loop is made of a perfect insulator with infinite resistance, the induced current is zero. This situation is analogous to an isolated battery whose terminals aren't connected to anything: An emf is present, but no current flows.

EVALUATE: Let's verify unit consistency in this calculation. One way to do this is to note that the magnetic-force relationship $\vec{F} = q\vec{v} \times \vec{B}$ implies that the units of $\vec{B}$ are the units of force divided by the units of (charge times velocity): $1\ \mathrm{T} = (1\ \mathrm{N})/(1\ \mathrm{C} \cdot \mathrm{m/s})$. The units of magnetic flux are then $(1\ \mathrm{T})(1\ \mathrm{m}^2) = 1\ \mathrm{N} \cdot \mathrm{s} \cdot \mathrm{m/C}$, and the rate of change of magnetic flux is $1\ \mathrm{N} \cdot \mathrm{m/C} = 1\ \mathrm{J/C} = 1\ \mathrm{V}$. Thus the unit of $d\Phi_B/dt$ is the volt, as required by Eq. (29.3). Also recall that the unit of magnetic flux is the weber (Wb): $1\ \mathrm{T} \cdot \mathrm{m}^2 = 1\ \mathrm{Wb}$, so $1\ \mathrm{V} = 1\ \mathrm{Wb/s}$.

Direction of Induced emf

We can find the direction of an induced emf or current by using Eq. (29.3) together with some simple sign rules. Here's the procedure:

1. Define a positive direction for the vector area $\vec{A}$.
2. From the directions of $\vec{A}$ and the magnetic field $\vec{B}$, determine the sign of the magnetic flux Φ_B and its rate of change $d\Phi_B/dt$. Figure 29.6 shows several examples.
3. Determine the sign of the induced emf or current. If the flux is increasing, so $d\Phi_B/dt$ is positive, then the induced emf or current is negative; if the flux is decreasing, $d\Phi_B/dt$ is negative and the induced emf or current is positive.
4. Finally, determine the direction of the induced emf or current using your right hand. Curl the fingers of your right hand around the $\vec{A}$ vector, with your right thumb in the direction of $\vec{A}$. If the induced emf or current in the circuit is *positive*, it is in the same direction as your curled fingers; if the induced emf or current is *negative*, it is in the opposite direction.

In Example 29.1, in which $\vec{A}$ is upward, a positive $\mathcal{E}$ would be directed counterclockwise around the loop, as seen from above. Both $\vec{A}$ and $\vec{B}$ are upward in this example, so Φ_B is positive; the magnitude B is increasing, so $d\Phi_B/dt$ is positive. Hence by Eq. (29.3), $\mathcal{E}$ in Example 29.1 is *negative*. Its actual direction is thus *clockwise* around the loop, as seen from above.

If the loop in Fig. 29.5 is a conductor, an induced current results from this emf; this current is also clockwise, as Fig. 29.5 shows. This induced current produces an additional magnetic field through the loop, and the right-hand rule described in Section 28.6 shows that this field is *opposite* in direction to the increasing field produced by the electromagnet. This is an example of a general rule called *Lenz's law,* which says that any induction effect tends to oppose the change that caused it; in this case the change is the increase in the flux of the

Application **Exploring the Brain with Induced emfs**
Transcranial magnetic stimulation (TMS) is a technique for studying the function of various parts of the brain. A coil held to the subject's head carries a varying electric current, and so produces a varying magnetic field. This field causes an induced emf, and that triggers electric activity in the region of the brain underneath the coil. By observing how the TMS subject responds (for instance, which muscles move as a result of stimulating a certain part of the brain), a physician can test for various neurological conditions.

29.6 The magnetic flux is becoming **(a)** more positive, **(b)** less positive, **(c)** more negative, and **(d)** less negative. Therefore Φ_B is increasing in **(a)** and **(d)** and decreasing in **(b)** and **(c)**. In **(a)** and **(d)** the emfs are negative (they are opposite to the direction of the curled fingers of your right hand when your right thumb points along $\vec{A}$). In **(b)** and **(c)** the emfs are positive (in the same direction as the curled fingers).

(a)

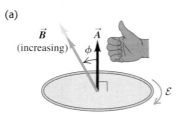

- Flux is positive ($\Phi_B > 0$) ...
- ... and becoming more positive ($d\Phi_B/dt > 0$).
- Induced emf is negative ($\mathcal{E} < 0$).

(b)

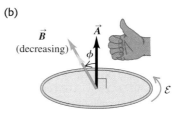

- Flux is positive ($\Phi_B > 0$) ...
- ... and becoming less positive ($d\Phi_B/dt < 0$).
- Induced emf is positive ($\mathcal{E} > 0$).

(c)

- Flux is negative ($\Phi_B < 0$) ...
- ... and becoming more negative ($d\Phi_B/dt < 0$).
- Induced emf is positive ($\mathcal{E} > 0$).

(d)

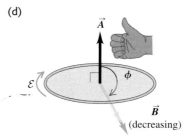

- Flux is negative ($\Phi_B < 0$) ...
- ... and becoming less negative ($d\Phi_B/dt > 0$).
- Induced emf is negative ($\mathcal{E} < 0$).

electromagnet's field through the loop. (We'll study this law in detail in the next section.)

You should check out the signs of the induced emfs and currents for the list of experiments in Section 29.1. For example, when the loop in Fig. 29.2 is in a constant field and we tilt it or squeeze it to *decrease* the flux through it, the induced emf and current are counterclockwise, as seen from above.

CAUTION **Induced emfs are caused by changes in flux** Since magnetic flux plays a central role in Faraday's law, it's tempting to think that *flux* is the cause of induced emf and that an induced emf will appear in a circuit whenever there is a magnetic field in the region bordered by the circuit. But Eq. (29.3) shows that only a *change* in flux through a circuit, not flux itself, can induce an emf in a circuit. If the flux through a circuit has a constant value, whether positive, negative, or zero, there is no induced emf.

If we have a coil with N identical turns, and if the flux varies at the same rate through each turn, the *total* rate of change through all the turns is N times as large as for a single turn. If Φ_B is the flux through each turn, the total emf in a coil with N turns is

$$\mathcal{E} = -N\frac{d\Phi_B}{dt} \tag{29.4}$$

As we discussed in this chapter's introduction, induced emfs play an essential role in the generation of electric power for commercial use. Several of the following examples explore different methods of producing emfs by the motion of a conductor relative to a magnetic field, giving rise to a changing flux through a circuit.

PhET: Faraday's Electromagnetic Lab
PhET: Faraday's Law
PhET: Generator

Problem-Solving Strategy 29.1 Faraday's Law

IDENTIFY *the relevant concepts:* Faraday's law applies when there is a changing magnetic flux. To use the law, identify an area through which there is a flux of magnetic field. This will usually be the area enclosed by a loop made of a conducting material (though not always—see part (b) of Example 29.1). Identify the target variables.

SET UP *the problem* using the following steps:
1. Faraday's law relates the induced emf to the rate of change of magnetic flux. To calculate this rate of change, you first have to understand what is making the flux change. Is the conductor moving? Is it changing orientation? Is the magnetic field changing? Remember that it's not the flux itself that counts, but its *rate of change*.
2. The area vector $\vec{A}$ (or $d\vec{A}$) must be perpendicular to the plane of the area. You always have two choices of its direction; for example, if the area is in a horizontal plane, $\vec{A}$ could point up or

down. Choose a direction and use it consistently throughout the problem.

EXECUTE *the solution* as follows:
1. Calculate the magnetic flux using Eq. (29.2) if $\vec{B}$ is uniform over the area of the loop or Eq. (29.1) if it isn't uniform. Remember the direction you chose for the area vector.
2. Calculate the induced emf using Eq. (29.3) or (if your conductor has N turns in a coil) Eq. (29.4). Apply the sign rule (described just after Example 29.1) to determine the positive direction of emf.
3. If the circuit resistance is known, you can calculate the magnitude of the induced current I using $\mathcal{E} = IR$.

EVALUATE *your answer:* Check your results for the proper units, and double-check that you have properly implemented the sign rules for magnetic flux and induced emf.

Example 29.2 Magnitude and direction of an induced emf

A 500-loop circular wire coil with radius 4.00 cm is placed between the poles of a large electromagnet. The magnetic field is uniform and makes an angle of 60° with the plane of the coil; it decreases at 0.200 T/s. What are the magnitude and direction of the induced emf?

SOLUTION

IDENTIFY and SET UP: Our target variable is the emf induced by a varying magnetic flux through the coil. The flux varies because the magnetic field decreases in amplitude. We choose the area vector $\vec{A}$ to be in the direction shown in Fig. 29.7. With this choice, the geometry is similar to that of Fig. 29.6b. That figure will help us determine the direction of the induced emf.

29.7 Our sketch for this problem.

EXECUTE: The magnetic field is uniform over the loop, so we can calculate the flux using Eq. (29.2): $\Phi_B = BA\cos\phi$, where $\phi = 30°$. In this expression, the only quantity that changes with time is the magnitude B of the field, so $d\Phi_B/dt = (dB/dt)A\cos\phi$.

CAUTION **Remember how ϕ is defined** You may have been tempted to say that $\phi = 60°$ in this problem. If so, remember that ϕ is the angle between $\vec{A}$ and $\vec{B}$, *not* the angle between $\vec{B}$ and the plane of the loop.

From Eq. (29.4), the induced emf in the coil of $N = 500$ turns is

$$\mathcal{E} = -N\frac{d\Phi_B}{dt} = N\frac{dB}{dt}A\cos\phi$$
$$= 500(-0.200 \text{ T/s})\pi(0.0400 \text{ m})^2(\cos 30°) = 0.435 \text{ V}$$

The positive answer means that when you point your right thumb in the direction of the area vector $\vec{A}$ (30° below the magnetic field $\vec{B}$ in Fig. 29.7), the positive direction for $\mathcal{E}$ is in the direction of the curled fingers of your right hand. If you viewed the coil from the left in Fig. 29.7 and looked in the direction of $\vec{A}$, the emf would be clockwise.

EVALUATE: If the ends of the wire are connected, the direction of current in the coil is in the same direction as the emf—that is, clockwise as seen from the left side of the coil. A clockwise current increases the magnetic flux through the coil, and therefore tends to oppose the decrease in total flux. This is an example of Lenz's law, which we'll discuss in Section 29.3.

Example 29.3 Generator I: A simple alternator

Figure 29.8a shows a simple *alternator,* a device that generates an emf. A rectangular loop is rotated with constant angular speed ω about the axis shown. The magnetic field $\vec{B}$ is uniform and constant. At time $t = 0$, $\phi = 0$. Determine the induced emf.

SOLUTION

IDENTIFY and SET UP: The magnetic field $\vec{B}$ and the area A of the loop are both constant, but the flux through the loop varies because the loop rotates and so the angle ϕ between $\vec{B}$ and the area vector

Continued

29.8 (a) Schematic diagram of an alternator. A conducting loop rotates in a magnetic field, producing an emf. Connections from each end of the loop to the external circuit are made by means of that end's slip ring. The system is shown at the time when the angle $\phi = \omega t = 90°$. (b) Graph of the flux through the loop and the resulting emf between terminals a and b, along with the corresponding positions of the loop during one complete rotation.

(a)

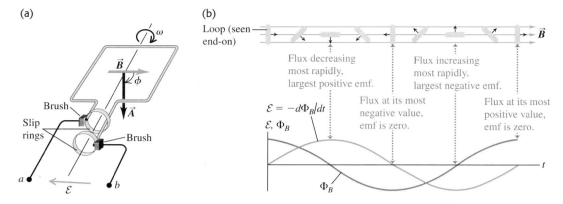

(b)

$\vec{A}$ changes (Fig. 29.8a). Because the angular speed is constant and $\phi = 0$ at $t = 0$, the angle as a function of time is given by $\phi = \omega t$.

EXECUTE: The magnetic field is uniform over the loop, so the magnetic flux is $\Phi_B = BA\cos\phi = BA\cos\omega t$. Hence, by Faraday's law [Eq. (29.3)] the induced emf is

$$\mathcal{E} = -\frac{d\Phi_B}{dt} = -\frac{d}{dt}(BA\cos\omega t) = \omega BA\sin\omega t$$

EVALUATE: The induced emf $\mathcal{E}$ varies sinusoidally with time (Fig. 29.8b). When the plane of the loop is perpendicular to $\vec{B}$ ($\phi = 0$ or 180°), Φ_B reaches its maximum and minimum values. At these times, its instantaneous rate of change is zero and $\mathcal{E}$ is zero. Conversely, $\mathcal{E}$ reaches its maximum and minimum values when the plane of the loop is parallel to $\vec{B}$ ($\phi = 90°$ or 270°) and Φ_B is changing most rapidly. We note that the induced emf does not depend on the *shape* of the loop, but only on its area.

We can use the alternator as a source of emf in an external circuit by using two *slip rings* that rotate with the loop, as shown in Fig. 29.8a. The rings slide against stationary contacts called *brushes,* which are connected to the output terminals a and b. Since the emf varies sinusoidally, the current that results in the circuit is an *alternating* current that also varies sinusoidally in magnitude and direction. The amplitude of the emf can be increased by increasing the rotation speed, the field magnitude, or the loop area or by using N loops instead of one, as in Eq. (29.4).

Alternators are used in automobiles to generate the currents in the ignition, the lights, and the entertainment system. The arrangement is a little different than in this example; rather than having a rotating loop in a magnetic field, the loop stays fixed and an electromagnet rotates. (The rotation is provided by a mechanical connection between the alternator and the engine.) But the result is the same; the flux through the loop varies sinusoidally, producing a sinusoidally varying emf. Larger alternators of this same type are used in electric power plants (Fig. 29.9).

29.9 A commercial alternator uses many loops of wire wound around a barrel-like structure called an armature. The armature and wire remain stationary while electromagnets rotate on a shaft (not shown) through the center of the armature. The resulting induced emf is far larger than would be possible with a single loop of wire.

Example 29.4 **Generator II: A DC generator and back emf in a motor**

The alternator in Example 29.3 produces a sinusoidally varying emf and hence an alternating current. Figure 29.10a shows a *direct-current* (dc) *generator* that produces an emf that always has the same sign. The arrangement of split rings, called a *commutator,* reverses the connections to the external circuit at angular positions at which the emf reverses. Figure 29.10b shows the resulting emf. Commercial dc generators have a large number of coils and commutator segments, smoothing out the bumps in the emf so that the terminal voltage is not only one-directional but also practically constant. This brush-and-commutator arrangement is the same as that in the direct-current motor discussed in Section 27.8. The

motor's *back emf* is just the emf induced by the changing magnetic flux through its rotating coil. Consider a motor with a square, 500-turn coil 10.0 cm on a side. If the magnetic field has magnitude 0.200 T, at what rotation speed is the *average* back emf of the motor equal to 112 V?

SOLUTION

IDENTIFY and SET UP: As far as the rotating loop is concerned, the situation is the same as in Example 29.3 except that we now have N turns of wire. Without the commutator, the emf would alternate between positive and negative values and have an average value of zero (see Fig. 29.8b). With the commutator, the emf is never negative and its average value is positive (Fig. 29.10b). We'll use our result from Example 29.3 to obtain an expression for this average value and solve it for the rotational speed ω.

EXECUTE: Comparison of Figs. 29.8b and 29.10b shows that the back emf of the motor is just N times the absolute value of the emf found for an alternator in Example 29.3, as in Eq. (29.4): $|\mathcal{E}| = N\omega BA|\sin\omega t|$. To find the *average* back emf, we must replace $|\sin\omega t|$ by its average value. We find this by integrating $|\sin\omega t|$ over half a cycle, from $t = 0$ to $t = T/2 = \pi/\omega$, and dividing by the elapsed time π/ω. During this half cycle, the sine function is positive, so $|\sin\omega t| = \sin\omega t$, and we find

$$(|\sin\omega t|)_{av} = \frac{\int_0^{\pi/\omega}\sin\omega t \, dt}{\pi/\omega} = \frac{2}{\pi}$$

The average back emf is then

$$\mathcal{E}_{av} = \frac{2N\omega BA}{\pi}$$

This confirms that the back emf is proportional to the rotation speed ω, as we stated without proof in Section 27.8. Solving for ω, we obtain

$$\omega = \frac{\pi\mathcal{E}_{av}}{2NBA}$$
$$= \frac{\pi(112 \text{ V})}{2(500)(0.200 \text{ T})(0.100 \text{ m})^2} = 176 \text{ rad/s}$$

(We used the unit relationships $1 \text{ V} = 1 \text{ Wb/s} = 1 \text{ T} \cdot \text{m}^2/\text{s}$ from Example 29.1.)

EVALUATE: The average back emf is directly proportional to ω. Hence the slower the rotation speed, the less the back emf and the greater the possibility of burning out the motor, as we described in Example 27.11 (Section 27.8).

29.10 (a) Schematic diagram of a dc generator, using a split-ring commutator. The ring halves are attached to the loop and rotate with it. (b) Graph of the resulting induced emf between terminals a and b. Compare to Fig. 29.8b.

Example 29.5 **Generator III: The slidewire generator**

Figure 29.11 shows a U-shaped conductor in a uniform magnetic field $\vec{B}$ perpendicular to the plane of the figure and directed *into* the page. We lay a metal rod (the "slidewire") with length L across the two arms of the conductor, forming a circuit, and move it to the right with constant velocity $\vec{v}$. This induces an emf and a current, which is why this device is called a *slidewire generator*. Find the magnitude and direction of the resulting induced emf.

SOLUTION

IDENTIFY and SET UP: The magnetic flux changes because the area of the loop—bounded on the right by the moving rod—is

29.11 A slidewire generator. The magnetic field $\vec{B}$ and the vector area $\vec{A}$ are both directed into the figure. The increase in magnetic flux (caused by an increase in area) induces the emf and current.

increasing. Our target variable is the emf $\mathcal{E}$ induced in this expanding loop. The magnetic field is uniform over the area of the loop, so we can find the flux using $\Phi_B = BA\cos\phi$. We choose the area vector $\vec{A}$ to point straight into the page, in the same direction as $\vec{B}$. With this choice a positive emf will be one that is directed clockwise around the loop. (You can check this with the right-hand rule: Using your right hand, point your thumb into the page and curl your fingers as in Fig. 29.6.)

EXECUTE: Since $\vec{B}$ and $\vec{A}$ point in the same direction, the angle $\phi = 0$ and $\Phi_B = BA$. The magnetic field magnitude B is constant, so the induced emf is

$$\mathcal{E} = -\frac{d\Phi_B}{dt} = -B\frac{dA}{dt}$$

To calculate dA/dt, note that in a time dt the sliding rod moves a distance $v \, dt$ (Fig. 29.11) and the loop area increases by an amount $dA = Lv \, dt$. Hence the induced emf is

$$\mathcal{E} = -B\frac{Lv \, dt}{dt} = -BLv$$

The minus sign tells us that the emf is directed *counterclockwise* around the loop. The induced current is also counterclockwise, as shown in the figure.

Continued

EVALUATE: The emf of a slidewire generator is constant if $\vec{v}$ is constant. Hence the slidewire generator is a *direct-current* generator. It's not a very practical device because the rod eventually moves beyond the U-shaped conductor and loses contact, after which the current stops.

Example 29.6 Work and power in the slidewire generator

In the slidewire generator of Example 29.5, energy is dissipated in the circuit owing to its resistance. Let the resistance of the circuit (made up of the moving slidewire and the U-shaped conductor that connects the ends of the slidewire) at a given point in the slidewire's motion be R. Find the rate at which energy is dissipated in the circuit and the rate at which work must be done to move the rod through the magnetic field.

SOLUTION

IDENTIFY and SET UP: Our target variables are the *rates* at which energy is dissipated and at which work is done. Energy is dissipated in the circuit at the rate $P_{\text{dissipated}} = I^2 R$. The current I in the circuit equals $|\mathcal{E}|/R$; we found an expression for the induced emf $\mathcal{E}$ in this circuit in Example 29.5. There is a magnetic force $\vec{F} = I\vec{L} \times \vec{B}$ on the rod, where $\vec{L}$ points along the rod in the direction of the current. Figure 29.12 shows that this force is opposite to the rod velocity $\vec{v}$; to maintain the motion, whoever is pushing the rod must apply a force of equal magnitude in the direction of $\vec{v}$. This force does work at the rate $P_{\text{applied}} = Fv$.

29.12 The magnetic force $\vec{F} = I\vec{L} \times \vec{B}$ that acts on the rod due to the induced current is to the left, opposite to $\vec{v}$.

EXECUTE: First we'll calculate $P_{\text{dissipated}}$. From Example 29.5, $\mathcal{E} = -BLv$, so the current in the rod is $I = |\mathcal{E}|/R = Blv/R$. Hence

$$P_{\text{dissipated}} = I^2 R = \left(\frac{BLv}{R}\right)^2 R = \frac{B^2 L^2 v^2}{R}$$

To calculate P_{applied}, we first calculate the magnitude of $\vec{F} = I\vec{L} \times \vec{B}$. Since $\vec{L}$ and $\vec{B}$ are perpendicular, this magnitude is

$$F = ILB = \frac{BLv}{R}LB = \frac{B^2 L^2 v}{R}$$

The applied force has the same magnitude and does work at the rate

$$P_{\text{applied}} = Fv = \frac{B^2 L^2 v^2}{R}$$

EVALUATE: The rate at which work is done is exactly *equal* to the rate at which energy is dissipated in the resistance.

CAUTION **You can't violate energy conservation** You might think that reversing the direction of $\vec{B}$ or of $\vec{v}$ might make it possible to have the magnetic force $\vec{F} = I\vec{L} \times \vec{B}$ be in the *same* direction as $\vec{v}$. This would be a pretty neat trick. Once the rod was moving, the changing magnetic flux would induce an emf and a current, and the magnetic force on the rod would make it move even faster, increasing the emf and current; this would go on until the rod was moving at tremendous speed and producing electric power at a prodigious rate. If this seems too good to be true, not to mention a violation of energy conservation, that's because it is. Reversing $\vec{B}$ also reverses the sign of the induced emf and current and hence the direction of $\vec{L}$, so the magnetic force still opposes the motion of the rod; a similar result holds true if we reverse $\vec{v}$. ∎

Generators As Energy Converters

Example 29.6 shows that the slidewire generator doesn't produce electric energy out of nowhere; the energy is supplied by whatever body exerts the force that keeps the rod moving. All that the generator does is *convert* that energy into a different form. The equality between the rate at which *mechanical* energy is supplied to a generator and the rate at which *electric* energy is generated holds for all types of generators. This is true in particular for the alternator described in Example 29.3. (We are neglecting the effects of friction in the bearings of an alternator or between the rod and the U-shaped conductor of a slidewire generator. If these are included, the conservation of energy demands that the energy lost to friction is not available for conversion to electric energy. In real generators the friction is kept to a minimum to keep the energy-conversion process as efficient as possible.)

In Chapter 27 we stated that the magnetic force on moving charges can never do work. But you might think that the magnetic force $\vec{F} = I\vec{L} \times \vec{B}$ in Example 29.6 *is* doing (negative) work on the current-carrying rod as it moves, contradicting our earlier statement. In fact, the work done by the magnetic force is actually zero. The moving charges that make up the current in the rod in Fig. 29.12 have a vertical component of velocity, causing a horizontal component of force on these charges. As a result, there is a horizontal displacement of charge within the rod, the left side acquiring a net positive charge and the right side a net negative charge. The result is a horizontal component of electric field, perpendicular to the length of the rod (analogous to the Hall effect, described in Section 27.9). It is this field, in the direction of motion of the rod, that does work on the mobile charges in the rod and hence indirectly on the atoms making up the rod.

Test Your Understanding of Section 29.2   The figure at right shows a wire coil being squeezed in a uniform magnetic field. (a) While the coil is being squeezed, is the induced emf in the coil (i) clockwise, (ii) counterclockwise, or (iii) zero? (b) Once the coil has reached its final squeezed shape, is the induced emf in the coil (i) clockwise, (ii) counterclockwise, or (iii) zero?

Circular wire coil   Coil squeezed into oval

29.3 Lenz's Law

Lenz's law is a convenient alternative method for determining the direction of an induced current or emf. Lenz's law is not an independent principle; it can be derived from Faraday's law. It always gives the same results as the sign rules we introduced in connection with Faraday's law, but it is often easier to use. Lenz's law also helps us gain intuitive understanding of various induction effects and of the role of energy conservation. H. F. E. Lenz (1804–1865) was a Russian scientist who duplicated independently many of the discoveries of Faraday and Henry. **Lenz's law** states:

> **The direction of any magnetic induction effect is such as to oppose the cause of the effect.**

The "cause" may be changing flux through a stationary circuit due to a varying magnetic field, changing flux due to motion of the conductors that make up the circuit, or any combination. If the flux in a stationary circuit changes, as in Examples 29.1 and 29.2, the induced current sets up a magnetic field of its own. Within the area bounded by the circuit, this field is *opposite* to the original field if the original field is *increasing* but is in the *same* direction as the original field if the latter is *decreasing*. That is, the induced current opposes the *change in flux* through the circuit (*not* the flux itself).

If the flux change is due to motion of the conductors, as in Examples 29.3 through 29.6, the direction of the induced current in the moving conductor is such that the direction of the magnetic-field force on the conductor is opposite in direction to its motion. Thus the motion of the conductor, which caused the induced current, is opposed. We saw this explicitly for the slidewire generator in Example 29.6. In all these cases the induced current tries to preserve the *status quo* by opposing motion or a change of flux.

Lenz's law is also directly related to energy conservation. If the induced current in Example 29.6 were in the direction opposite to that given by Lenz's law, the magnetic force on the rod would accelerate it to ever-increasing speed with no external energy source, even though electric energy is being dissipated in the circuit. This would be a clear violation of energy conservation and doesn't happen in nature.

Conceptual Example 29.7   Lenz's law and the slidewire generator

In Fig. 29.11, the induced current in the loop causes an additional magnetic field in the area bounded by the loop. The direction of the induced current is counterclockwise, so from the discussion of Section 28.2, this additional magnetic field is directed *out of* the plane of the figure. That direction is opposite that of the original magnetic field, so it tends to cancel the effect of that field. This is just what Lenz's law predicts.

Conceptual Example 29.8 Lenz's law and the direction of induced current

In Fig. 29.13 there is a uniform magnetic field $\vec{B}$ through the coil. The magnitude of the field is increasing, so there is an induced emf. Use Lenz's law to determine the direction of the resulting induced current.

SOLUTION

This situation is the same as in Example 29.1 (Section 29.2). By Lenz's law the induced current must produce a magnetic field $\vec{B}_{induced}$ inside the coil that is downward, opposing the change in flux. From the right-hand rule we described in Section 28.5 for the direction of the magnetic field produced by a circular loop, $\vec{B}_{induced}$ will be in the desired direction if the induced current flows as shown in Fig. 29.13.

Figure 29.14 shows several applications of Lenz's law to the similar situation of a magnet moving near a conducting loop. In each case, the induced current produces a magnetic field whose

29.13 The induced current due to the change in $\vec{B}$ is clockwise, as seen from above the loop. The added field $\vec{B}_{induced}$ that it causes is downward, opposing the change in the upward field $\vec{B}$.

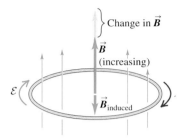

direction opposes the change in flux through the loop due to the magnet's motion.

29.14 Directions of induced currents as a bar magnet moves along the axis of a conducting loop. If the bar magnet is stationary, there is no induced current.

(a) Motion of magnet causes *increasing downward* flux through loop.

(b) Motion of magnet causes *decreasing upward* flux through loop.

(c) Motion of magnet causes *decreasing downward* flux through loop.

(d) Motion of magnet causes *increasing upward* flux through loop.

The induced magnetic field is *upward* to oppose the flux change. To produce this induced field, the induced current must be *counterclockwise* as seen from above the loop.

The induced magnetic field is *downward* to oppose the flux change. To produce this induced field, the induced current must be *clockwise* as seen from above the loop.

Lenz's Law and the Response to Flux Changes

Since an induced current always opposes any change in magnetic flux through a circuit, how is it possible for the flux to change at all? The answer is that Lenz's law gives only the *direction* of an induced current; the *magnitude* of the current depends on the resistance of the circuit. The greater the circuit resistance, the less the induced current that appears to oppose any change in flux and the easier it is for a flux change to take effect. If the loop in Fig. 29.14 were made out of wood (an insulator), there would be almost no induced current in response to changes in the flux through the loop.

Conversely, the less the circuit resistance, the greater the induced current and the more difficult it is to change the flux through the circuit. If the loop in Fig. 29.14 is a good conductor, an induced current flows as long as the magnet moves relative to the loop. Once the magnet and loop are no longer in relative motion, the induced current very quickly decreases to zero because of the nonzero resistance in the loop.

The extreme case occurs when the resistance of the circuit is *zero*. Then the induced current in Fig. 29.14 will continue to flow even after the induced emf has disappeared—that is, even after the magnet has stopped moving relative to the loop. Thanks to this *persistent current,* it turns out that the flux through the loop is exactly the same as it was before the magnet started to move, so the flux through a loop of zero resistance *never* changes. Exotic materials called *superconductors* do indeed have zero resistance; we discuss these further in Section 29.8.

Test Your Understanding of Section 29.3 (a) Suppose the magnet in Fig. 29.14a were stationary and the loop of wire moved upward. Would the induced current in the loop be (i) in the same direction as shown in Fig. 29.14a, (ii) in the direction opposite to that shown in Fig. 29.14a, or (iii) zero? (b) Suppose the magnet and loop of wire in Fig. 29.14a both moved downward at the same velocity. Would the induced current in the loop be (i) in the same direction as shown in Fig. 29.14a, (ii) in the direction opposite to that shown in Fig. 29.14a, or (iii) zero? ❙

29.4 Motional Electromotive Force

We've seen several situations in which a conductor moves in a magnetic field, as in the generators discussed in Examples 29.3 through 29.6. We can gain additional insight into the origin of the induced emf in these situations by considering the magnetic forces on mobile charges in the conductor. Figure 29.15a shows the same moving rod that we discussed in Example 29.5, separated for the moment from the U-shaped conductor. The magnetic field $\vec{B}$ is uniform and directed into the page, and we move the rod to the right at a constant velocity $\vec{v}$. A charged particle q in the rod then experiences a magnetic force $\vec{F} = q\vec{v} \times \vec{B}$ with magnitude $F = |q|vB$. We'll assume in the following discussion that q is positive; in that case the direction of this force is upward along the rod, from b toward a.

This magnetic force causes the free charges in the rod to move, creating an excess of positive charge at the upper end a and negative charge at the lower end b. This in turn creates an electric field $\vec{E}$ within the rod, in the direction from a toward b (opposite to the magnetic force). Charge continues to accumulate at the ends of the rod until $\vec{E}$ becomes large enough for the downward electric force (with magnitude qE) to cancel exactly the *upward* magnetic force (with magnitude qvB). Then $qE = qvB$ and the charges are in equilibrium.

The magnitude of the potential difference $V_{ab} = V_a - V_b$ is equal to the electric-field magnitude E multiplied by the length L of the rod. From the above discussion, $E = vB$, so

$$V_{ab} = EL = vBL \qquad (29.5)$$

with point a at higher potential than point b.

Now suppose the moving rod slides along a stationary U-shaped conductor, forming a complete circuit (Fig. 29.15b). No *magnetic* force acts on the charges in the stationary U-shaped conductor, but the charge that was near points a and b redistributes itself along the stationary conductor, creating an *electric* field within it. This field establishes a current in the direction shown. The moving rod has become a source of electromotive force; within it, charge moves from lower to higher potential, and in the remainder of the circuit, charge moves from higher to lower potential. We call this emf a **motional electromotive force,** denoted by $\mathcal{E}$. From the above discussion, the magnitude of this emf is

$$\mathcal{E} = vBL \qquad \begin{array}{l}\text{(motional emf; length and velocity}\\ \text{perpendicular to uniform } \vec{B})\end{array} \qquad (29.6)$$

corresponding to a force per unit charge of magnitude vB acting for a distance L along the moving rod. If the total circuit resistance of the U-shaped conductor and the sliding rod is R, the induced current I in the circuit is given by $vBL = IR$. This is the same result we obtained in Section 29.2 using Faraday's law, and indeed motional emf is a particular case of Faraday's law, one of the several examples described in Section 29.2.

The emf associated with the moving rod in Fig. 29.15 is analogous to that of a battery with its positive terminal at a and its negative terminal at b, although the origins of the two emfs are quite different. In each case a nonelectrostatic force acts on the charges in the device, in the direction from b to a, and the emf is the work per unit charge done by this force when a charge moves from b to a in the device. When the device is connected to an external circuit, the direction of

29.15 A conducting rod moving in a uniform magnetic field. (a) The rod, the velocity, and the field are mutually perpendicular. (b) Direction of induced current in the circuit.

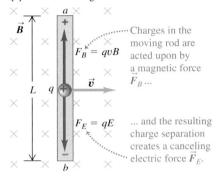

(a) Isolated moving rod

Charges in the moving rod are acted upon by a magnetic force $\vec{F}_B$ …

… and the resulting charge separation creates a canceling electric force $\vec{F}_E$.

(b) Rod connected to stationary conductor

The motional emf $\mathcal{E}$ in the moving rod creates an electric field in the stationary conductor.

Mastering**PHYSICS**

ActivPhysics 13.10: Motional EMF

current is from *b* to *a* in the device and from *a* to *b* in the external circuit. While we have discussed motional emf in terms of a closed circuit like that in Fig. 29.15b, a motional emf is also present in the isolated moving rod in Fig. 29.15a, in the same way that a battery has an emf even when it's not part of a circuit.

The direction of the induced emf in Fig. 29.15 can be deduced by using Lenz's law, even if (as in Fig. 29.15a) the conductor does not form a complete circuit. In this case we can mentally complete the circuit between the ends of the conductor and use Lenz's law to determine the direction of the current. From this we can deduce the polarity of the ends of the open-circuit conductor. The direction from the − end to the + end within the conductor is the direction the current would have if the circuit were complete.

You should verify that if we express *v* in meters per second, *B* in teslas, and *L* in meters, then $\mathcal{E}$ is in volts. (Recall that 1 V = 1 J/C.)

Motional emf: General Form

We can generalize the concept of motional emf for a conductor with *any* shape, moving in any magnetic field, uniform or not (assuming that the magnetic field at each point does not vary with time). For an element $d\vec{l}$ of the conductor, the contribution $d\mathcal{E}$ to the emf is the magnitude dl multiplied by the component of $\vec{v} \times \vec{B}$ (the magnetic force per unit charge) parallel to $d\vec{l}$; that is,

$$d\mathcal{E} = (\vec{v} \times \vec{B}) \cdot d\vec{l}$$

For any closed conducting loop, the total emf is

$$\mathcal{E} = \oint (\vec{v} \times \vec{B}) \cdot d\vec{l} \qquad \text{(motional emf; closed conducting loop)} \quad (29.7)$$

This expression looks very different from our original statement of Faraday's law, Eq. (29.3), which stated that $\mathcal{E} = -d\Phi_B/dt$. In fact, though, the two statements are equivalent. It can be shown that the rate of change of magnetic flux through a moving conducting loop is always given by the negative of the expression in Eq. (29.7). Thus this equation gives us an alternative formulation of Faraday's law. This alternative is often more convenient than the original one in problems with *moving* conductors. But when we have *stationary* conductors in changing magnetic fields, Eq. (29.7) *cannot* be used; in this case, $\mathcal{E} = -d\Phi_B/dt$ is the only correct way to express Faraday's law.

Example 29.9 | Motional emf in the slidewire generator

Suppose the moving rod in Fig. 29.15b is 0.10 m long, the velocity *v* is 2.5 m/s, the total resistance of the loop is 0.030 Ω, and *B* is 0.60 T. Find the motional emf, the induced current, and the force acting on the rod.

SOLUTION

IDENTIFY and SET UP: The first target variable is the motional emf $\mathcal{E}$ due to the rod's motion, which we'll find using Eq. (29.6). We'll find the current from the values of $\mathcal{E}$ and the resistance *R*. The force on the rod is a *magnetic* force, exerted by $\vec{B}$ on the current in the rod; we'll find this force using $\vec{F} = I\vec{L} \times \vec{B}$.

EXECUTE: From Eq. (29.6) the motional emf is

$$\mathcal{E} = vBL = (2.5 \text{ m/s})(0.60 \text{ T})(0.10 \text{ m}) = 0.15 \text{ V}$$

The induced current in the loop is

$$I = \frac{\mathcal{E}}{R} = \frac{0.15 \text{ V}}{0.030 \text{ Ω}} = 5.0 \text{ A}$$

In the expression for the magnetic force, $\vec{F} = I\vec{L} \times \vec{B}$, the vector $\vec{L}$ points in the same direction as the induced current in the rod (from *b* to *a* in Fig. 29.15). Applying the right-hand rule for vector products shows that this force is directed *opposite* to the rod's motion. Since $\vec{L}$ and $\vec{B}$ are perpendicular, the magnetic force has magnitude

$$F = ILB = (5.0 \text{ A})(0.10 \text{ m})(0.60 \text{ T}) = 0.30 \text{ N}$$

EVALUATE: We can check our answer for the direction of $\vec{F}$ by using Lenz's law. If we take the area vector $\vec{A}$ to point into the plane of the loop, the magnetic flux is positive and increasing as the rod moves to the right and increases the area of the loop. Lenz's law tells us that a force appears to oppose this increase in flux. Hence the force on the rod is to the left, opposite its motion.

Example 29.10 **The Faraday disk dynamo**

Figure 29.16 shows a conducting disk with radius R that lies in the xy-plane and rotates with constant angular velocity ω about the z-axis. The disk is in a uniform, constant $\vec{B}$ field in the z-direction. Find the induced emf between the center and the rim of the disk.

SOLUTION

IDENTIFY and SET UP: A motional emf arises because the conducting disk moves relative to $\vec{B}$. The complication is that different

29.16 A conducting disk with radius R rotating at an angular speed ω in a magnetic field $\vec{B}$. The emf is induced along radial lines of the disk and is applied to an external circuit through the two sliding contacts labeled b.

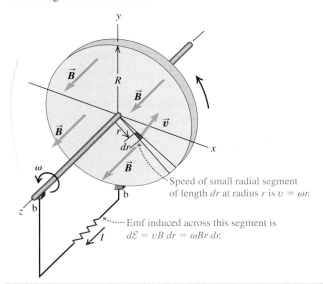

parts of the disk move at different speeds v, depending on their distance from the rotation axis. We'll address this by considering small segments of the disk and integrating their contributions to determine our target variable, the emf between the center and the rim. Consider the small segment of the disk shown in red in Fig. 29.16 and labeled by its velocity vector $\vec{v}$. The magnetic force per unit charge on this segment is $\vec{v} \times \vec{B}$, which points radially outward from the center of the disk. Hence the induced emf tends to make a current flow radially outward, which tells us that the moving conducting path to think about here is a straight line from the center to the rim. We can find the emf from each small disk segment along this line using $d\mathcal{E} = (\vec{v} \times \vec{B}) \cdot d\vec{l}$ and then integrate to find the total emf.

EXECUTE: The length vector $d\vec{l}$ (of length dr) associated with the segment points radially outward, in the same direction as $\vec{v} \times \vec{B}$. The vectors $\vec{v}$ and $\vec{B}$ are perpendicular, and the magnitude of $\vec{v}$ is $v = \omega r$. The emf from the segment is then $d\mathcal{E} = \omega B r\, dr$. The total emf is the integral of $d\mathcal{E}$ from the center $(r = 0)$ to the rim $(r = R)$:

$$\mathcal{E} = \int_0^R \omega B r\, dr = \tfrac{1}{2}\omega B R^2$$

EVALUATE: We can use this device as a source of emf in a circuit by completing the circuit through two stationary brushes (labeled b in the figure) that contact the disk and its conducting shaft as shown. Such a disk is called a *Faraday disk dynamo* or a *homopolar generator*. Unlike the alternator in Example 29.3, the Faraday disk dynamo is a direct-current generator; it produces an emf that is constant in time. Can you use Lenz's law to show that for the direction of rotation in Fig. 29.16, the current in the external circuit must be in the direction shown?

Test Your Understanding of Section 29.4 The earth's magnetic field points toward (magnetic) north. For simplicity, assume that the field has no vertical component (as is the case near the earth's equator). (a) If you hold a metal rod in your hand and walk toward the east, how should you orient the rod to get the maximum motional emf between its ends? (i) east-west; (ii) north-south; (iii) up-down; (iv) you get the same motional emf with all of these orientations. (b) How should you hold it to get *zero* emf as you walk toward the east? (i) east-west; (ii) north-south; (iii) up-down; (iv) none of these. (c) In which direction should you travel so that the motional emf across the rod is zero no matter how the rod is oriented? (i) west; (ii) north; (iii) south; (iv) straight up; (v) straight down.

29.5 Induced Electric Fields

When a conductor moves in a magnetic field, we can understand the induced emf on the basis of magnetic forces on charges in the conductor, as described in Section 29.4. But an induced emf also occurs when there is a changing flux through a stationary conductor. What is it that pushes the charges around the circuit in this type of situation?

As an example, let's consider the situation shown in Fig. 29.17. A long, thin solenoid with cross-sectional area A and n turns per unit length is encircled at its center by a circular conducting loop. The galvanometer G measures the current in the loop. A current I in the winding of the solenoid sets up a magnetic field $\vec{B}$ along the solenoid axis, as shown, with magnitude B as calculated in Example 28.9 (Section 28.7): $B = \mu_0 nI$, where n is the number of turns per unit length.

29.17 (a) The windings of a long sole-noid carry a current I that is increasing at a rate dI/dt. The magnetic flux in the sole-noid is increasing at a rate $d\Phi_B/dt$, and this changing flux passes through a wire loop. An emf $\mathcal{E} = -d\Phi_B/dt$ is induced in the loop, inducing a current I' that is measured by the galvanometer G. (b) Cross-sectional view.

(a)

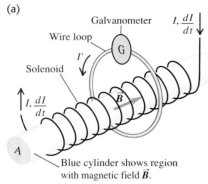

Galvanometer

Wire loop

Solenoid

I'

$I, \dfrac{dI}{dt}$

$\vec{B}$

$I, \dfrac{dI}{dt}$

A

Blue cylinder shows region with magnetic field $\vec{B}$.

(b)

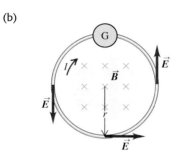

G

I'

$\vec{B}$

$\vec{E}$

$\vec{E}$

r

$\vec{E}$

$\vec{E}$

If we neglect the small field outside the solenoid and take the area vector $\vec{A}$ to point in the same direction as $\vec{B}$, then the magnetic flux Φ_B through the loop is

$$\Phi_B = BA = \mu_0 nIA$$

When the solenoid current I changes with time, the magnetic flux Φ_B also changes, and according to Faraday's law the induced emf in the loop is given by

$$\mathcal{E} = -\frac{d\Phi_B}{dt} = -\mu_0 nA \frac{dI}{dt} \qquad (29.8)$$

If the total resistance of the loop is R, the induced current in the loop, which we may call I', is $I' = \mathcal{E}/R$.

But what *force* makes the charges move around the wire loop? It can't be a magnetic force because the loop isn't even *in* a magnetic field. We are forced to conclude that there has to be an **induced electric field** in the conductor *caused by the changing magnetic flux*. This may be a little jarring; we are accustomed to thinking about electric field as being caused by electric charges, and now we are saying that a changing magnetic field somehow acts as a source of electric field. Furthermore, it's a strange sort of electric field. When a charge q goes once around the loop, the total work done on it by the electric field must be equal to q times the emf $\mathcal{E}$. That is, the electric field in the loop *is not conservative*, as we used the term in Chapter 23, because the line integral of $\vec{E}$ around a closed path is not zero. Indeed, this line integral, representing the work done by the induced $\vec{E}$ field per unit charge, is equal to the induced emf $\mathcal{E}$:

$$\oint \vec{E} \cdot d\vec{l} = \mathcal{E} \qquad (29.9)$$

From Faraday's law the emf $\mathcal{E}$ is also the negative of the rate of change of magnetic flux through the loop. Thus for this case we can restate Faraday's law as

$$\oint \vec{E} \cdot d\vec{l} = -\frac{d\Phi_B}{dt} \quad \text{(stationary integration path)} \qquad (29.10)$$

Note that Faraday's law is *always* true in the form $\mathcal{E} = -d\Phi_B/dt$; the form given in Eq. (29.10) is valid *only* if the path around which we integrate is *stationary*.

As an example of a situation to which Eq. (29.10) can be applied, consider the stationary circular loop in Fig. 29.17b, which we take to have radius r. Because of cylindrical symmetry, the electric field $\vec{E}$ has the same magnitude at every point on the circle and is tangent to it at each point. (Symmetry would also permit the field to be *radial*, but then Gauss's law would require the presence of a net charge inside the circle, and there is none.) The line integral in Eq. (29.10) becomes simply the magnitude E times the circumference $2\pi r$ of the loop, $\oint \vec{E} \cdot d\vec{l} = 2\pi rE$, and Eq. (29.10) gives

$$E = \frac{1}{2\pi r} \left| \frac{d\Phi_B}{dt} \right| \qquad (29.11)$$

The directions of $\vec{E}$ at points on the loop are shown in Fig. 29.17b. We know that $\vec{E}$ has to have the direction shown when $\vec{B}$ in the solenoid is increasing, because $\oint \vec{E} \cdot d\vec{l}$ has to be negative when $d\Phi_B/dt$ is positive. The same approach can be used to find the induced electric field *inside* the solenoid when the solenoid $\vec{B}$ field is changing; we leave the details to you (see Exercise 29.35).

Nonelectrostatic Electric Fields

Now let's summarize what we've learned. Faraday's law, Eq. (29.3), is valid for two rather different situations. In one, an emf is induced by magnetic forces on charges when a conductor moves through a magnetic field. In the other, a time-varying magnetic field induces an electric field in a stationary conductor and hence induces an emf; in fact, the $\vec{E}$ field is induced even when no conductor is present. This $\vec{E}$ field differs from an electro*static* field in an important way. It is *nonconservative;* the line integral $\oint \vec{E} \cdot d\vec{l}$ around a closed path is not zero, and when a charge moves around a closed path, the field does a nonzero amount of work on it. It follows that for such a field the concept of *potential* has no meaning. We call such a field a **nonelectrostatic field.** In contrast, an *electrostatic* field is *always* conservative, as we discussed in Section 23.1, and always has an associated potential function. Despite this difference, the fundamental effect of *any* electric field is to exert a force $\vec{F} = q\vec{E}$ on a charge q. This relationship is valid whether $\vec{E}$ is a conservative field produced by a charge distribution or a nonconservative field caused by changing magnetic flux.

So a changing magnetic field acts as a source of electric field of a sort that we *cannot* produce with any static charge distribution. This may seem strange, but it's the way nature behaves. What's more, we'll see in Section 29.7 that a changing *electric* field acts as a source of *magnetic* field. We'll explore this symmetry between the two fields in greater detail in our study of electromagnetic waves in Chapter 32.

If any doubt remains in your mind about the reality of magnetically induced electric fields, consider a few of the many practical applications (Fig. 29.18). Pickups in electric guitars use currents induced in stationary pickup coils by the vibration of nearby ferromagnetic strings. Alternators in most cars use rotating magnets to induce currents in stationary coils. Whether we realize it or not, magnetically induced electric fields play an important role in everyday life.

29.18 Applications of induced electric fields. (a) Data are stored on a computer hard disk in a pattern of magnetized areas on the surface of the disk. To read these data, a coil on a movable arm is placed next to the spinning disk. The coil experiences a changing magnetic flux, inducing a current whose characteristics depend on the pattern coded on the disk. (b) This hybrid automobile has both a gasoline engine and an electric motor. As the car comes to a halt, the spinning wheels run the motor backward so that it acts as a generator. The resulting induced current is used to recharge the car's batteries. (c) The rotating crankshaft of a piston-engine airplane spins a magnet, inducing an emf in an adjacent coil and generating the spark that ignites fuel in the engine cylinders. This keeps the engine running even if the airplane's other electrical systems fail.

(a)

(b)

(c)

Example 29.11 **Induced electric fields**

Suppose the long solenoid in Fig. 29.17a has 500 turns per meter and cross-sectional area 4.0 cm^2. The current in its windings is increasing at 100 A/s. (a) Find the magnitude of the induced emf in the wire loop outside the solenoid. (b) Find the magnitude of the induced electric field within the loop if its radius is 2.0 cm.

SOLUTION

IDENTIFY and SET UP: As in Fig. 29.17b, the increasing magnetic field inside the solenoid causes a change in the magnetic flux through the wire loop and hence induces an electric field $\vec{E}$ around the loop. Our target variables are the induced emf $\mathcal{E}$ and the electric-field magnitude E. We use Eq. (29.8) to determine the emf.

Determining the field magnitude E is simplified because the loop and the solenoid share the same central axis. Hence, by symmetry, the electric field is tangent to the loop and has the same magnitude all the way around its circumference. We can therefore use Eq. (29.9) to find E.

EXECUTE: (a) From Eq. (29.8), the induced emf is

$$\mathcal{E} = -\frac{d\Phi_B}{dt} = -\mu_0 nA \frac{dI}{dt}$$
$$= -(4\pi \times 10^{-7} \text{ Wb/A} \cdot \text{m})(500 \text{ turns/m})$$
$$\times (4.0 \times 10^{-4} \text{ m}^2)(100 \text{ A/s})$$
$$= -25 \times 10^{-6} \text{ Wb/s} = -25 \times 10^{-6} \text{ V} = -25 \, \mu\text{V}$$

Continued

(b) By symmetry the line integral $\oint \vec{E} \cdot d\vec{l}$ has absolute value $2\pi r E$ no matter which direction we integrate around the loop. This is equal to the absolute value of the emf, so

$$E = \frac{|\mathcal{E}|}{2\pi r} = \frac{25 \times 10^{-6}\,\text{V}}{2\pi(2.0 \times 10^{-2}\,\text{m})} = 2.0 \times 10^{-4}\,\text{V/m}$$

EVALUATE: In Fig. 29.17b the magnetic flux *into* the plane of the figure is increasing. According to the right-hand rule for induced emf (illustrated in Fig. 29.6), a positive emf would be clockwise around the loop; the negative sign of $\mathcal{E}$ shows that the emf is in the counterclockwise direction. Can you also show this using Lenz's law?

Test Your Understanding of Section 29.5 If you wiggle a magnet back and forth in your hand, are you generating an electric field? If so, is this electric field conservative?

29.6 Eddy Currents

29.19 Eddy currents induced in a rotating metal disk.

(a) Metal disk rotating through a magnetic field

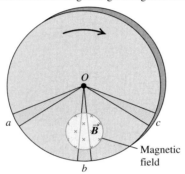

(b) Resulting eddy currents and braking force

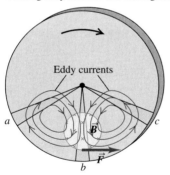

In the examples of induction effects that we have studied, the induced currents have been confined to well-defined paths in conductors and other components forming a circuit. However, many pieces of electrical equipment contain masses of metal moving in magnetic fields or located in changing magnetic fields. In situations like these we can have induced currents that circulate throughout the volume of a material. Because their flow patterns resemble swirling eddies in a river, we call these **eddy currents.**

As an example, consider a metallic disk rotating in a magnetic field perpendicular to the plane of the disk but confined to a limited portion of the disk's area, as shown in Fig. 29.19a. Sector Ob is moving across the field and has an emf induced in it. Sectors Oa and Oc are not in the field, but they provide return conducting paths for charges displaced along Ob to return from b to O. The result is a circulation of eddy currents in the disk, somewhat as sketched in Fig. 29.19b.

We can use Lenz's law to decide on the direction of the induced current in the neighborhood of sector Ob. This current must experience a magnetic force $\vec{F} = I\vec{L} \times \vec{B}$ that *opposes* the rotation of the disk, and so this force must be to the right in Fig. 29.19b. Since $\vec{B}$ is directed into the plane of the disk, the current and hence $\vec{L}$ have downward components. The return currents lie outside the field, so they do not experience magnetic forces. The interaction between the eddy currents and the field causes a braking action on the disk. Such effects can be used to stop the rotation of a circular saw quickly when the power is turned off. Some sensitive balances use this effect to damp out vibrations. Eddy current braking is used on some electrically powered rapid-transit vehicles. Electromagnets mounted in the cars induce eddy currents in the rails; the resulting magnetic fields cause braking forces on the electromagnets and thus on the cars.

Eddy currents have many other practical uses. The shiny metal disk in the electric power company's meter outside your house rotates as a result of eddy currents. These currents are induced in the disk by magnetic fields caused by sinusoidally varying currents in a coil. In induction furnaces, eddy currents are used to heat materials in completely sealed containers for processes in which it is essential to avoid the slightest contamination of the materials. The metal detectors used at airport security checkpoints (Fig. 29.20a) operate by detecting eddy currents induced in metallic objects. Similar devices (Fig. 29.20b) are used to find buried treasure such as bottlecaps and lost pennies.

Eddy currents also have undesirable effects. In an alternating-current transformer, coils wrapped around an iron core carry a sinusoidally varying current. The resulting eddy currents in the core waste energy through I^2R heating and themselves set up an unwanted opposing emf in the coils. To minimize these effects, the core is designed so that the paths for eddy currents are as narrow as possible. We'll describe how this is done when we discuss transformers in detail in Section 31.6.

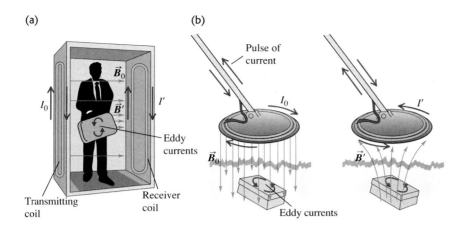

(a)

$\vec{B}_0$

I_0

$\vec{B}'$

I'

Eddy currents

Transmitting coil

Receiver coil

(b)

Pulse of current

I_0

I'

$\vec{B}_0$

$\vec{B}'$

Eddy currents

Test Your Understanding of Section 29.6 Suppose that the magnetic field in Fig. 29.19 were directed out of the plane of the figure and the disk were rotating counterclockwise. Compared to the directions of the force $\vec{F}$ and the eddy currents shown in Fig. 29.19b, what would the new directions be? (i) The force $\vec{F}$ and the eddy currents would both be in the same direction; (ii) the force $\vec{F}$ would be in the same direction, but the eddy currents would be in the opposite direction; (iii) the force $\vec{F}$ would be in the opposite direction, but the eddy currents would be in the same direction; (iv) the force $\vec{F}$ and the eddy currents would be in the opposite directions. ❙

29.7 Displacement Current and Maxwell's Equations

We have seen that a varying magnetic field gives rise to an induced electric field. In one of the more remarkable examples of the symmetry of nature, it turns out that a varying *electric* field gives rise to a *magnetic* field. This effect is of tremendous importance, for it turns out to explain the existence of radio waves, gamma rays, and visible light, as well as all other forms of electromagnetic waves.

Generalizing Ampere's Law

To see the origin of the relationship between varying electric fields and magnetic fields, let's return to Ampere's law as given in Section 28.6, Eq. (28.20):

$$\oint \vec{B} \cdot d\vec{l} = \mu_0 I_{\text{encl}}$$

The problem with Ampere's law in this form is that it is *incomplete*. To see why, let's consider the process of charging a capacitor (Fig. 29.21). Conducting wires lead current i_C into one plate and out of the other; the charge Q increases, and the electric field $\vec{E}$ between the plates increases. The notation i_C indicates *conduction* current to distinguish it from another kind of current we are about to encounter, called *displacement* current i_D. We use lowercase i's and v's to denote instantaneous values of currents and potential differences, respectively, that may vary with time.

Let's apply Ampere's law to the circular path shown. The integral $\oint \vec{B} \cdot d\vec{l}$ around this path equals $\mu_0 I_{\text{encl}}$. For the plane circular area bounded by the circle, I_{encl} is just the current i_C in the left conductor. But the surface that bulges out to the right is bounded by the same circle, and the current through that surface is zero. So $\oint \vec{B} \cdot d\vec{l}$ is equal to $\mu_0 i_C$, and at the same time it is equal to zero! This is a clear contradiction.

But something else is happening on the bulged-out surface. As the capacitor charges, the electric field $\vec{E}$ and the electric *flux* Φ_E through the surface are increasing. We can determine their rates of change in terms of the charge and

29.20 (a) A metal detector at an airport security checkpoint generates an alternating magnetic field $\vec{B}_0$. This induces eddy currents in a conducting object carried through the detector. The eddy currents in turn produce an alternating magnetic field $\vec{B}'$, and this field induces a current in the detector's receiver coil. (b) Portable metal detectors work on the same principle.

Application Eddy Currents Help Power Io's Volcanoes

Jupiter's moon Io is slightly larger than the earth's moon. It moves at more than 60,000 km/h through Jupiter's intense magnetic field (about ten times stronger than the earth's field), which sets up strong eddy currents within Io that dissipate energy at a rate of 10^{12} W. This dissipated energy helps to heat Io's interior and causes volcanic eruptions on its surface, as shown in the lower close-up image. (Gravitational effects from Jupiter cause even more heating.)

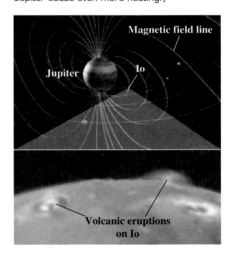

Magnetic field line

Jupiter

Io

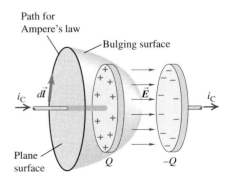

Volcanic eruptions on Io

29.21 Parallel-plate capacitor being charged. The conduction current through the plane surface is i_C, but there is no conduction current through the surface that bulges out to pass between the plates. The two surfaces have a common boundary, so this difference in I_{encl} leads to an apparent contradiction in applying Ampere's law.

Path for Ampere's law

Bulging surface

i_C

$d\vec{l}$

$\vec{E}$

i_C

Plane surface

Q

$-Q$

current. The instantaneous charge is $q = Cv$, where C is the capacitance and v is the instantaneous potential difference. For a parallel-plate capacitor, $C = \epsilon_0 A/d$, where A is the plate area and d is the spacing. The potential difference v between plates is $v = Ed$, where E is the electric-field magnitude between plates. (We neglect fringing and assume that $\vec{E}$ is uniform in the region between the plates.) If this region is filled with a material with permittivity ϵ, we replace ϵ_0 by ϵ everywhere; we'll use ϵ in the following discussion.

Substituting these expressions for C and v into $q = Cv$, we can express the capacitor charge q as

$$q = Cv = \frac{\epsilon A}{d}(Ed) = \epsilon EA = \epsilon \Phi_E \qquad (29.12)$$

where $\Phi_E = EA$ is the electric flux through the surface.

As the capacitor charges, the rate of change of q is the conduction current, $i_C = dq/dt$. Taking the derivative of Eq. (29.12) with respect to time, we get

$$i_C = \frac{dq}{dt} = \epsilon \frac{d\Phi_E}{dt} \qquad (29.13)$$

Now, stretching our imagination a little, we invent a fictitious **displacement current** i_D in the region between the plates, defined as

$$i_D = \epsilon \frac{d\Phi_E}{dt} \qquad \text{(displacement current)} \qquad (29.14)$$

That is, we imagine that the changing flux through the curved surface in Fig. 29.21 is somehow equivalent, in Ampere's law, to a conduction current through that surface. We include this fictitious current, along with the real conduction current i_C, in Ampere's law:

$$\oint \vec{B} \cdot d\vec{l} = \mu_0(i_C + i_D)_{encl} \qquad \text{(generalized Ampere's law)} \qquad (29.15)$$

Ampere's law in this form is obeyed no matter which surface we use in Fig. 29.21. For the flat surface, i_D is zero; for the curved surface, i_C is zero; and i_C for the flat surface equals i_D for the curved surface. Equation (29.15) remains valid in a magnetic material, provided that the magnetization is proportional to the external field and we replace μ_0 by μ.

The fictitious current i_D was invented in 1865 by the Scottish physicist James Clerk Maxwell (1831–1879), who called it displacement current. There is a corresponding *displacement current density* $j_D = i_D/A$; using $\Phi_E = EA$ and dividing Eq. (29.14) by A, we find

$$j_D = \epsilon \frac{dE}{dt} \qquad (29.16)$$

We have pulled the concept out of thin air, as Maxwell did, but we see that it enables us to save Ampere's law in situations such as that in Fig. 29.21.

Another benefit of displacement current is that it lets us generalize Kirchhoff's junction rule, discussed in Section 26.2. Considering the left plate of the capacitor, we have conduction current into it but none out of it. But when we include the displacement current, we have conduction current coming in one side and an equal displacement current coming out the other side. With this generalized meaning of the term "current," we can speak of current going *through* the capacitor.

The Reality of Displacement Current

You might well ask at this point whether displacement current has any real physical significance or whether it is just a ruse to satisfy Ampere's law and Kirchhoff's junction rule. Here's a fundamental experiment that helps to answer that question. We take a plane circular area between the capacitor plates (Fig. 29.22). If displacement current really plays the role in Ampere's law that we have claimed, then there ought to be a magnetic field in the region between the plates while the capacitor is charging. We can use our generalized Ampere's law, including displacement current, to predict what this field should be.

To be specific, let's picture round capacitor plates with radius R. To find the magnetic field at a point in the region between the plates at a distance r from the axis, we apply Ampere's law to a circle of radius r passing through the point, with $r < R$. This circle passes through points a and b in Fig. 29.22. The total current enclosed by the circle is j_D times its area, or $(i_D/\pi R^2)(\pi r^2)$. The integral $\oint \vec{B} \cdot d\vec{l}$ in Ampere's law is just B times the circumference $2\pi r$ of the circle, and because $i_D = i_C$ for the charging capacitor, Ampere's law becomes

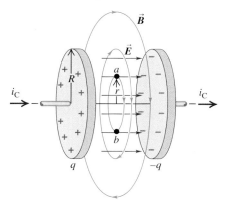

29.22 A capacitor being charged by a current i_C has a displacement current equal to i_C between the plates, with displacement-current density $j_D = \epsilon\, dE/dt$. This can be regarded as the source of the magnetic field between the plates.

$$\oint \vec{B} \cdot d\vec{l} = 2\pi r B = \mu_0 \frac{r^2}{R^2} i_C \quad \text{or}$$

$$B = \frac{\mu_0}{2\pi} \frac{r}{R^2} i_C \qquad (29.17)$$

This result predicts that in the region between the plates $\vec{B}$ is zero at the axis and increases linearly with distance from the axis. A similar calculation shows that *outside* the region between the plates (that is, for $r > R$), $\vec{B}$ is the same as though the wire were continuous and the plates not present at all.

When we *measure* the magnetic field in this region, we find that it really is there and that it behaves just as Eq. (29.17) predicts. This confirms directly the role of displacement current as a source of magnetic field. It is now established beyond reasonable doubt that displacement current, far from being just an artifice, is a fundamental fact of nature. Maxwell's discovery was the bold step of an extraordinary genius.

Maxwell's Equations of Electromagnetism

We are now in a position to wrap up in a single package *all* of the relationships between electric and magnetic fields and their sources. This package consists of four equations, called **Maxwell's equations.** Maxwell did not discover all of these equations single-handedly (though he did develop the concept of displacement current). But he did put them together and recognized their significance, particularly in predicting the existence of electromagnetic waves.

For now we'll state Maxwell's equations in their simplest form, for the case in which we have charges and currents in otherwise empty space. In Chapter 32 we'll discuss how to modify these equations if a dielectric or a magnetic material is present.

Two of Maxwell's equations involve an integral of $\vec{E}$ or $\vec{B}$ over a closed surface. The first is simply Gauss's law for electric fields, Eq. (22.8), which states that the surface integral of $E_\perp$ over any closed surface equals $1/\epsilon_0$ times the total charge Q_{encl} enclosed within the surface:

$$\oint \vec{E} \cdot d\vec{A} = \frac{Q_{encl}}{\epsilon_0} \qquad (\text{Gauss's law for } \vec{E}) \qquad (29.18)$$

The second is the analogous relationship for *magnetic* fields, Eq. (27.8), which states that the surface integral of $B_\perp$ over any closed surface is always zero:

$$\oint \vec{B} \cdot d\vec{A} = 0 \qquad (\text{Gauss's law for } \vec{B}) \qquad (29.19)$$

This statement means, among other things, that there are no magnetic monopoles (single magnetic charges) to act as sources of magnetic field.

The third equation is Ampere's law including displacement current. This states that both conduction current i_C and displacement current $\epsilon_0 d\Phi_E/dt$, where Φ_E is electric flux, act as sources of magnetic field:

$$\oint \vec{B} \cdot d\vec{l} = \mu_0 \left(i_C + \epsilon_0 \frac{d\Phi_E}{dt} \right)_{\text{encl}} \qquad \text{(Ampere's law)} \qquad (29.20)$$

The fourth and final equation is Faraday's law. It states that a changing magnetic field or magnetic flux induces an electric field:

$$\oint \vec{E} \cdot d\vec{l} = -\frac{d\Phi_B}{dt} \qquad \text{(Faraday's law)} \qquad (29.21)$$

If there is a changing magnetic flux, the line integral in Eq. (29.21) is not zero, which shows that the $\vec{E}$ field produced by a changing magnetic flux is not conservative. Recall that this line integral must be carried out over a *stationary* closed path.

It's worthwhile to look more carefully at the electric field $\vec{E}$ and its role in Maxwell's equations. In general, the total $\vec{E}$ field at a point in space can be the superposition of an electrostatic field $\vec{E}_c$ caused by a distribution of charges at rest and a magnetically induced, nonelectrostatic field $\vec{E}_n$. (The subscript c stands for Coulomb or conservative; the subscript n stands for non-Coulomb, nonelectrostatic, or nonconservative.) That is,

$$\vec{E} = \vec{E}_c + \vec{E}_n$$

The electrostatic part $\vec{E}_c$ is *always* conservative, so $\oint \vec{E}_c \cdot d\vec{l} = 0$. This conservative part of the field does not contribute to the integral in Faraday's law, so we can take $\vec{E}$ in Eq. (29.21) to be the *total* electric field $\vec{E}$, including both the part $\vec{E}_c$ due to charges and the magnetically induced part $\vec{E}_n$. Similarly, the nonconservative part $\vec{E}_n$ of the $\vec{E}$ field does not contribute to the integral in Gauss's law, because this part of the field is not caused by static charges. Hence $\oint \vec{E}_n \cdot d\vec{A}$ is always zero. We conclude that in all the Maxwell equations, $\vec{E}$ is the total electric field; these equations don't distinguish between conservative and nonconservative fields.

Symmetry in Maxwell's Equations

There is a remarkable symmetry in Maxwell's four equations. In empty space where there is no charge, the first two equations (Eqs. (29.18) and (29.19)) are identical in form, one containing $\vec{E}$ and the other containing $\vec{B}$. When we compare the second two equations, Eq. (29.20) says that a changing electric flux creates a magnetic field, and Eq. (29.21) says that a changing magnetic flux creates an electric field. In empty space, where there is no conduction current, $i_C = 0$ and the two equations have the same form, apart from a numerical constant and a negative sign, with the roles of $\vec{E}$ and $\vec{B}$ exchanged in the two equations.

We can rewrite Eqs. (29.20) and (29.21) in a different but equivalent form by introducing the definitions of electric and magnetic flux, $\Phi_E = \int \vec{E} \cdot d\vec{A}$ and $\Phi_B = \int \vec{B} \cdot d\vec{A}$, respectively. In empty space, where there is no charge or conduction current, $i_C = 0$ and $Q_{\text{encl}} = 0$, and we have

$$\oint \vec{B} \cdot d\vec{l} = \epsilon_0 \mu_0 \frac{d}{dt} \int \vec{E} \cdot d\vec{A} \qquad (29.22)$$

$$\oint \vec{E} \cdot d\vec{l} = -\frac{d}{dt} \int \vec{B} \cdot d\vec{A} \qquad (29.23)$$

Again we notice the symmetry between the roles of $\vec{E}$ and $\vec{B}$ in these expressions.

The most remarkable feature of these equations is that a time-varying field of *either* kind induces a field of the other kind in neighboring regions of space. Maxwell recognized that these relationships predict the existence of electromagnetic disturbances consisting of time-varying electric and magnetic fields that travel or *propagate* from one region of space to another, even if no matter is present in the intervening space. Such disturbances, called *electromagnetic waves,* provide the physical basis for light, radio and television waves, infrared, ultraviolet, x rays, and the rest of the electromagnetic spectrum. We will return to this vitally important topic in Chapter 32.

Although it may not be obvious, *all* the basic relationships between fields and their sources are contained in Maxwell's equations. We can derive Coulomb's law from Gauss's law, we can derive the law of Biot and Savart from Ampere's law, and so on. When we add the equation that defines the $\vec{E}$ and $\vec{B}$ fields in terms of the forces that they exert on a charge q, namely,

$$\vec{F} = q(\vec{E} + \vec{v} \times \vec{B}) \qquad (29.24)$$

we have *all* the fundamental relationships of electromagnetism!

Finally, we note that Maxwell's equations would have even greater symmetry between the $\vec{E}$ and $\vec{B}$ fields if single magnetic charges (magnetic monopoles) existed. The right side of Eq. (29.19) would contain the total *magnetic* charge enclosed by the surface, and the right side of Eq. (29.21) would include a magnetic monopole current term. Perhaps you can begin to see why some physicists wish that magnetic monopoles existed; they would help to perfect the mathematical poetry of Maxwell's equations.

The discovery that electromagnetism can be wrapped up so neatly and elegantly is a very satisfying one. In conciseness and generality, Maxwell's equations are in the same league with Newton's laws of motion and the laws of thermodynamics. Indeed, a major goal of science is learning how to express very broad and general relationships in a concise and compact form. Maxwell's synthesis of electromagnetism stands as a towering intellectual achievement, comparable to the Newtonian synthesis we described at the end of Section 13.5 and to the development of relativity and quantum mechanics in the 20th century.

Test Your Understanding of Section 29.7   (a) Which of Maxwell's equations explains how a credit card reader works? (b) Which one describes how a wire carrying a steady current generates a magnetic field? ❙

29.8 Superconductivity

The most familiar property of a superconductor is the sudden disappearance of all electrical resistance when the material is cooled below a temperature called the *critical temperature,* denoted by T_c. We discussed this behavior and the circumstances of its discovery in Section 25.2. But superconductivity is far more than just the absence of measurable resistance. As we'll see in this section, superconductors also have extraordinary *magnetic* properties.

The first hint of unusual magnetic properties was the discovery that for any superconducting material the critical temperature T_c changes when the material is placed in an externally produced magnetic field $\vec{B}_0$. Figure 29.23 shows this dependence for mercury, the first element in which superconductivity was observed. As the external field magnitude B_0 increases, the superconducting transition occurs at lower and lower temperature. When B_0 is greater than 0.0412 T, *no* superconducting transition occurs. The minimum magnitude of magnetic field that is needed to eliminate superconductivity at a temperature below T_c is called the *critical field,* denoted by B_c.

The Meissner Effect

Another aspect of the magnetic behavior of superconductors appears if we place a homogeneous sphere of a superconducting material in a uniform applied magnetic field $\vec{B}_0$ at a temperature T greater than T_c. The material is then in the normal phase, not the superconducting phase (Fig. 29.24a). Now we lower the temperature until the superconducting transition occurs. (We assume that the magnitude of $\vec{B}_0$ is not large enough to prevent the phase transition.) What happens to the field?

29.23 Phase diagram for pure mercury, showing the critical magnetic field B_c and its dependence on temperature. Superconductivity is impossible above the critical temperature T_c. The curves for other superconducting materials are similar but with different numerical values.

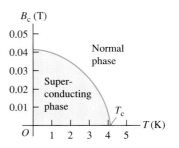

29.24 A superconducting material (a) above the critical temperature and (b), (c) below the critical temperature.

(a) Superconducting material in an external magnetic field $\vec{B}_0$ at $T > T_c$.

The field inside the material is very nearly equal to $\vec{B}_0$.

(b) The temperature is lowered to $T < T_c$, so the material becomes superconducting.

Magnetic flux is expelled from the material, and the field inside it is zero (Meissner effect).

(c) When the external field is turned off at $T < T_c$, the field is zero everywhere.

There is no change in magnetic flux in the material.

29.25 A superconductor (the black slab) exerts a repulsive force on a magnet (the metallic cylinder), supporting the magnet in midair.

Measurements of the field outside the sphere show that the field lines become distorted as in Fig. 29.24b. There is no longer any field inside the material, except possibly in a very thin surface layer a hundred or so atoms thick. If a coil is wrapped around the sphere, the emf induced in the coil shows that during the superconducting transition the magnetic flux through the coil decreases from its initial value to zero; this is consistent with the absence of field inside the material. Finally, if the field is now turned off while the material is still in its superconducting phase, no emf is induced in the coil, and measurements show no field outside the sphere (Fig. 29.24c).

We conclude that during a superconducting transition in the presence of the field $\vec{B}_0$, all of the magnetic flux is expelled from the bulk of the sphere, and the magnetic flux Φ_B through the coil becomes zero. This expulsion of magnetic flux is called the *Meissner effect*. As Fig. 29.24b shows, this expulsion crowds the magnetic field lines closer together to the side of the sphere, increasing $\vec{B}$ there.

Superconductor Levitation and Other Applications

The diamagnetic nature of a superconductor has some interesting *mechanical* consequences. A paramagnetic or ferromagnetic material is attracted by a permanent magnet because the magnetic dipoles in the material align with the nonuniform magnetic field of the permanent magnet. (We discussed this in Section 27.7.) For a diamagnetic material the magnetization is in the opposite sense, and a diamagnetic material is *repelled* by a permanent magnet. By Newton's third law the magnet is also repelled by the diamagnetic material. Figure 29.25 shows the repulsion between a specimen of a high-temperature superconductor and a magnet; the magnet is supported ("levitated") by this repulsive magnetic force.

The behavior we have described is characteristic of what are called *type-I superconductors*. There is another class of superconducting materials called *type-II superconductors*. When such a material in the superconducting phase is placed in a magnetic field, the bulk of the material remains superconducting, but thin filaments of material, running parallel to the field, may return to the normal phase. Currents circulate around the boundaries of these filaments, and there *is* magnetic flux inside them. Type-II superconductors are used for electromagnets because they usually have much larger values of B_c than do type-I materials, permitting much larger magnetic fields without destroying the superconducting state. Type-II superconductors have *two* critical magnetic fields: The first, B_{c1}, is the field at which magnetic flux begins to enter the material, forming the filaments just described, and the second, B_{c2}, is the field at which the material becomes normal.

Many important and exciting applications of superconductors are under development. Superconducting electromagnets have been used in research laboratories for several years. Their advantages compared to conventional electromagnets include greater efficiency, compactness, and greater field magnitudes. Once a current is established in the coil of a superconducting electromagnet, no additional power input is required because there is no resistive energy loss. The coils can also be made more compact because there is no need to provide channels for the circulation of cooling fluids. Superconducting magnets routinely attain steady fields of the order of 10 T, much larger than the maximum fields that are available with ordinary electromagnets.

Superconductors are attractive for long-distance electric power transmission and for energy-conversion devices, including generators, motors, and transformers. Very sensitive measurements of magnetic fields can be made with superconducting quantum interference devices (SQUIDs), which can detect changes in magnetic flux of less than 10^{-14} Wb; these devices have applications in medicine, geology, and other fields. The number of potential uses for superconductors has increased greatly since the discovery in 1987 of high-temperature superconductors. These materials have critical temperatures that are above the temperature of liquid nitrogen (about 77 K) and so are comparatively easy to attain. Development of practical applications of superconductor science promises to be an exciting chapter in contemporary technology.

Faraday's law: Faraday's law states that the induced emf in a closed loop equals the negative of the time rate of change of magnetic flux through the loop. This relationship is valid whether the flux change is caused by a changing magnetic field, motion of the loop, or both. (See Examples 29.1–29.6.)

$$\mathcal{E} = -\frac{d\Phi_B}{dt} \qquad (29.3)$$

The magnet's motion causes a *changing* magnetic field through the coil, inducing a current in the coil.

Lenz's law: Lenz's law states that an induced current or emf always tends to oppose or cancel out the change that caused it. Lenz's law can be derived from Faraday's law and is often easier to use. (See Examples 29.7 and 29.8.)

Change in $\vec{B}$
$\vec{B}$ (increasing)
$\mathcal{E}$ I
$\vec{B}_{induced}$

Motional emf: If a conductor moves in a magnetic field, a motional emf is induced. (See Examples 29.9 and 29.10.)

$$\mathcal{E} = vBL \qquad (29.6)$$

(conductor with length L moves in uniform $\vec{B}$ field, $\vec{L}$ and $\vec{v}$ both perpendicular to $\vec{B}$ and to each other)

$$\mathcal{E} = \oint (\vec{v} \times \vec{B}) \cdot d\vec{l} \qquad (29.7)$$

(all or part of a closed loop moves in a $\vec{B}$ field)

Induced electric fields: When an emf is induced by a changing magnetic flux through a stationary conductor, there is an induced electric field $\vec{E}$ of nonelectrostatic origin. This field is nonconservative and cannot be associated with a potential. (See Example 29.11.)

$$\oint \vec{E} \cdot d\vec{l} = -\frac{d\Phi_B}{dt} \qquad (29.10)$$

$\vec{E}$
$\vec{B}$ increasing
$\vec{E}$
$\vec{E}$

Displacement current and Maxwell's equations: A time-varying electric field generates a displacement current i_D, which acts as a source of magnetic field in exactly the same way as conduction current. The relationships between electric and magnetic fields and their sources can be stated compactly in four equations, called Maxwell's equations. Together they form a complete basis for the relationship of $\vec{E}$ and $\vec{B}$ fields to their sources.

$$i_D = \epsilon \frac{d\Phi_E}{dt} \qquad (29.14)$$

(displacement current)

$$\oint \vec{E} \cdot d\vec{A} = \frac{Q_{encl}}{\epsilon_0} \qquad (29.18)$$

(Gauss's law for $\vec{E}$ fields)

$$\oint \vec{B} \cdot d\vec{A} = 0 \qquad (29.19)$$

(Gauss's law for $\vec{B}$ fields)

$$\oint \vec{B} \cdot d\vec{l} = \mu_0 \left(i_C + \epsilon_0 \frac{d\Phi_E}{dt} \right)_{encl} \qquad (29.20)$$

(Ampere's law including displacement current)

$$\oint \vec{E} \cdot d\vec{l} = -\frac{d\Phi_B}{dt} \qquad (29.21)$$

(Faraday's law)

A Falling Square Loop

A vertically oriented square loop of copper wire falls from rest in a region in which the field $\vec{B}$ is horizontal, uniform, and perpendicular to the plane of the loop, into a field-free region. The side length of the loop is s and the wire diameter is d. The resistivity of copper is ρ_R and the density of copper is ρ_m. If the loop reaches its terminal speed while its upper segment is still in the magnetic-field region, find an expression for the terminal speed.

SOLUTION GUIDE

See MasteringPhysics® study area for a Video Tutor solution.

IDENTIFY and SET UP

1. The motion of the loop through the magnetic field induces an emf and a current in the loop. The field then gives rise to a magnetic force on this current that opposes the downward force of gravity.
2. Consider the case in which the entire loop is in the magnetic-field region. Is there an induced emf in this case? If so, what is its direction?

3. Consider the case in which only the upper segment of the loop is in the magnetic-field region. Is there an induced emf in this case? If so, what is its direction?
4. For the case in which there is an induced emf and hence an induced current, what is the direction of the magnetic force on each of the four sides of the loop? What is the direction of the *net* magnetic force on the loop?

EXECUTE

5. For the case in which the loop is falling at speed v and there is an induced emf, find (i) the emf, (ii) the induced current, and (iii) the magnetic force on the loop in terms of its resistance R.
6. Find R and the mass of the loop in terms of the given information about the loop.
7. Use your results from steps 5 and 6 to find an expression for the terminal speed.

EVALUATE

8. How does the terminal speed depend on the magnetic-field magnitude B? Explain why this makes sense.

Problems

•, ••, •••: Problems of increasing difficulty. **CP**: Cumulative problems incorporating material from earlier chapters. **CALC**: Problems requiring calculus. **BIO**: Biosciences problems.

DISCUSSION QUESTIONS

Q29.1 A sheet of copper is placed between the poles of an electromagnet with the magnetic field perpendicular to the sheet. When the sheet is pulled out, a considerable force is required, and the force required increases with speed. Explain.

Q29.2 In Fig. 29.8, if the angular speed ω of the loop is doubled, then the frequency with which the induced current changes direction doubles, and the maximum emf also doubles. Why? Does the torque required to turn the loop change? Explain.

Q29.3 Two circular loops lie side by side in the same plane. One is connected to a source that supplies an increasing current; the other is a simple closed ring. Is the induced current in the ring in the same direction as the current in the loop connected to the source, or opposite? What if the current in the first loop is decreasing? Explain.

Q29.4 For Eq. (29.6), show that if v is in meters per second, B in teslas, and L in meters, then the units of the right-hand side of the equation are joules per coulomb or volts (the correct SI units for $\mathcal{E}$).

Q29.5 A long, straight conductor passes through the center of a metal ring, perpendicular to its plane. If the current in the conductor increases, is a current induced in the ring? Explain.

Q29.6 A student asserted that if a permanent magnet is dropped down a vertical copper pipe, it eventually reaches a terminal velocity even if there is no air resistance. Why should this be? Or should it?

Q29.7 An airplane is in level flight over Antarctica, where the magnetic field of the earth is mostly directed upward away from the ground. As viewed by a passenger facing toward the front of the plane, is the left or the right wingtip at higher potential? Does your answer depend on the direction the plane is flying?

Q29.8 Consider the situation in Exercise 29.19. In part (a), find the direction of the force that the large circuit exerts on the small one. Explain how this result is consistent with Lenz's law.

Q29.9 A metal rectangle is close to a long, straight, current-carrying wire, with two of its sides parallel to the wire. If the current in the long wire is decreasing, is the rectangle repelled by or attracted to the wire? Explain why this result is consistent with Lenz's law.

Q29.10 A square conducting loop is in a region of uniform, constant magnetic field. Can the loop be rotated about an axis along one side and no emf be induced in the loop? Discuss, in terms of the orientation of the rotation axis relative to the magnetic-field direction.

Q29.11 Example 29.6 discusses the external force that must be applied to the slidewire to move it at constant speed. If there were a break in the left-hand end of the U-shaped conductor, how much force would be needed to move the slidewire at constant speed? As in the example, you can ignore friction.

Q29.12 In the situation shown in Fig. 29.17, would it be appropriate to ask how much *energy* an electron gains during a complete trip around the wire loop with current I'? Would it be appropriate to ask what *potential difference* the electron moves through during such a complete trip? Explain your answers.

Q29.13 A metal ring is oriented with the plane of its area perpendicular to a spatially uniform magnetic field that increases at a steady rate. If the radius of the ring is doubled, by what factor do (a) the emf induced in the ring and (b) the electric field induced in the ring change?

Q29.14 • A type-II superconductor in an external field between B_{c1} and B_{c2} has regions that contain magnetic flux and have resistance, and also has superconducting regions. What is the resistance of a long, thin cylinder of such material?

Q29.15 Can one have a displacement current as well as a conduction current within a conductor? Explain.

Q29.16 Your physics study partner asks you to consider a parallel-plate capacitor that has a dielectric completely filling the volume between the plates. He then claims that Eqs. (29.13) and (29.14) show that the conduction current in the dielectric equals the displacement current in the dielectric. Do you agree? Explain.

Q29.17 Match the mathematical statements of Maxwell's equations as given in Section 29.7 to these verbal statements. (a) Closed electric field lines are evidently produced only by changing magnetic flux. (b) Closed magnetic field lines are produced both by the motion of electric charge and by changing electric flux. (c) Electric field lines can start on positive charges and end on negative charges. (d) Evidently there are no magnetic monopoles on which to start and end magnetic field lines.

Q29.18 If magnetic monopoles existed, the right-hand side of Eq. (29.21) would include a term proportional to the current of magnetic monopoles. Suppose a steady monopole current is moving in a long straight wire. Sketch the *electric* field lines that such a current would produce.

EXERCISES

Section 29.2 Faraday's Law

29.1 • A single loop of wire with an area of 0.0900 m^2 is in a uniform magnetic field that has an initial value of 3.80 T, is perpendicular to the plane of the loop, and is decreasing at a constant rate of 0.190 T/s. (a) What emf is induced in this loop? (b) If the loop has a resistance of $0.600 \ \Omega$, find the current induced in the loop.

29.2 •• In a physics laboratory experiment, a coil with 200 turns enclosing an area of 12 cm^2 is rotated in 0.040 s from a position where its plane is perpendicular to the earth's magnetic field to a position where its plane is parallel to the field. The earth's magnetic field at the lab location is $6.0 \times 10^{-5} \text{ T}$. (a) What is the total magnetic flux through the coil before it is rotated? After it is rotated? (b) What is the average emf induced in the coil?

29.3 •• **Search Coils and Credit Cards.** One practical way to measure magnetic field strength uses a small, closely wound coil called a *search coil*. The coil is initially held with its plane perpendicular to a magnetic field. The coil is then either quickly rotated a quarter-turn about a diameter or quickly pulled out of the field. (a) Derive the equation relating the total charge Q that flows through a search coil to the magnetic-field magnitude B. The search coil has N turns, each with area A, and the flux through the coil is decreased from its initial maximum value to zero in a time Δt. The resistance of the coil is R, and the total charge is $Q = I\Delta t$, where I is the average current induced by the change in flux. (b) In a credit card reader, the magnetic strip on the back of a credit card is rapidly "swiped" past a coil within the reader. Explain, using the same ideas that underlie the operation of a search coil, how the reader can decode the information stored in the pattern of magnetization on the strip. (c) Is it necessary that the credit card be "swiped" through the reader at exactly the right speed? Why or why not?

29.4 • A closely wound search coil (see Exercise 29.3) has an area of 3.20 cm^2, 120 turns, and a resistance of $60.0 \ \Omega$. It is connected to a charge-measuring instrument whose resistance is $45.0 \ \Omega$. When the coil is rotated quickly from a position parallel to a uniform magnetic field to a position perpendicular to the field, the instrument indicates a charge of $3.56 \times 10^{-5} \text{ C}$. What is the magnitude of the field?

29.5 • A circular loop of wire with a radius of 12.0 cm and oriented in the horizontal xy-plane is located in a region of uniform magnetic field. A field of 1.5 T is directed along the positive z-direction, which is upward. (a) If the loop is removed from the field region in a time interval of 2.0 ms, find the average emf that will be induced in the wire loop during the extraction process. (b) If the coil is viewed looking down on it from above, is the induced current in the loop clockwise or counterclockwise?

29.6 • **CALC** A coil 4.00 cm in radius, containing 500 turns, is placed in a uniform magnetic field that varies with time according to $B = (0.0120 \text{ T/s})t + (3.00 \times 10^{-5} \text{ T/s}^4)t^4$. The coil is connected to a 600-Ω resistor, and its plane is perpendicular to the magnetic field. You can ignore the resistance of the coil. (a) Find the magnitude of the induced emf in the coil as a function of time. (b) What is the current in the resistor at time $t = 5.00 \text{ s}$?

29.7 • **CALC** The current in the long, straight wire AB shown in Fig. E29.7 is upward and is increasing steadily at a rate di/dt. (a) At an instant when the current is i, what are the magnitude and direction of the field $\vec{B}$ at a distance r to the right of the wire? (b) What is the flux $d\Phi_B$ through the narrow, shaded strip? (c) What is the total flux through the loop? (d) What is the induced emf in the loop? (e) Evaluate the numerical value of the induced emf if $a = 12.0 \text{ cm}$, $b = 36.0 \text{ cm}$, $L = 24.0 \text{ cm}$, and $di/dt = 9.60 \text{ A/s}$.

Figure **E29.7**

29.8 • **CALC** A flat, circular, steel loop of radius 75 cm is at rest in a uniform magnetic field, as shown in an edge-on view in Fig. E29.8. The field is changing with time, according to $B(t) = (1.4 \text{ T})e^{-(0.057 \text{ s}^{-1})t}$. (a) Find the emf induced in the loop as a function of time. (b) When is the induced emf equal to $\frac{1}{10}$ of its initial value? (c) Find the direction of the current induced in the loop, as viewed from above the loop.

Figure **E29.8**

29.9 • **Shrinking Loop.** A circular loop of flexible iron wire has an initial circumference of 165.0 cm, but its circumference is decreasing at a constant rate of 12.0 cm/s due to a tangential pull on the wire. The loop is in a constant, uniform magnetic field oriented perpendicular to the plane of the loop and with magnitude 0.500 T. (a) Find the emf induced in the loop at the instant when 9.0 s have passed. (b) Find the direction of the induced current in the loop as viewed looking along the direction of the magnetic field.

29.10 • A closely wound rectangular coil of 80 turns has dimensions of 25.0 cm by 40.0 cm. The plane of the coil is rotated from a position where it makes an angle of 37.0° with a magnetic field of 1.10 T to a position perpendicular to the field. The rotation takes 0.0600 s. What is the average emf induced in the coil?

29.11 • **CALC** In a region of space, a magnetic field points in the $+x$-direction (toward the right). Its magnitude varies with position according to the formula $B_x = B_0 + bx$, where B_0 and b are positive constants, for $x \geq 0$. A flat coil of area A moves with uniform speed v from right to left with the plane of its area always perpendicular to this field. (a) What is the emf induced in this coil while it is to the right of the origin? (b) As viewed from the origin, what is the direction (clockwise or counterclockwise) of the current induced in the coil? (c) If instead the coil moved from left to right, what would be the answers to parts (a) and (b)?

29.12 • **Back emf.** A motor with a brush-and-commutator arrangement, as described in Example 29.4, has a circular coil with radius 2.5 cm and 150 turns of wire. The magnetic field has magnitude 0.060 T, and the coil rotates at 440 rev/min. (a) What is the maximum emf induced in the coil? (b) What is the average back emf?

29.13 •• The armature of a small generator consists of a flat, square coil with 120 turns and sides with a length of 1.60 cm. The coil rotates in a magnetic field of 0.0750 T. What is the angular speed of the coil if the maximum emf produced is 24.0 mV?

29.14 • A flat, rectangular coil of dimensions l and w is pulled with uniform speed v through a uniform magnetic field B with the plane of its area perpendicular to the field (Fig. E29.14). (a) Find the emf induced in this coil. (b) If the speed and magnetic field are both tripled, what is the induced emf?

Figure **E29.14**

Section 29.3 Lenz's Law

29.15 • A circular loop of wire is in a region of spatially uniform magnetic field, as shown in Fig. E29.15. The magnetic field is directed into the plane of the figure. Determine the direction (clockwise or counterclockwise) of the induced current in the loop when (a) B is increasing; (b) B is decreasing; (c) B is constant with value B_0. Explain your reasoning.

Figure **E29.15**

29.16 • The current in Fig. E29.16 obeys the equation $I(t) = I_0 e^{-bt}$, where $b > 0$. Find the direction (clockwise or counterclockwise) of the current induced in the round coil for $t > 0$.

Figure **E29.16**

29.17 • Using Lenz's law, determine the direction of the current in resistor ab of Fig. E29.17 when (a) switch S is opened after having been closed for several minutes; (b) coil B is brought closer to coil A with the switch closed; (c) the resistance of R is decreased while the switch remains closed.

Figure **E29.17**

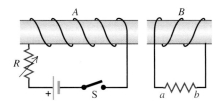

29.18 • A cardboard tube is wrapped with two windings of insulated wire wound in opposite directions, as shown in Fig. E29.18. Terminals a and b of winding A may be connected to a battery through a reversing switch. State whether the induced current in the resistor R is from left to right or from right to left in the following circumstances: (a) the current in winding A is from a to b and is increasing; (b) the current in winding A is from b to a and is decreasing; (c) the current in winding A is from b to a and is increasing.

Figure **E29.18**

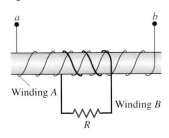

29.19 • A small, circular ring is inside a larger loop that is connected to a battery and a switch, as shown in Fig. E29.19. Use Lenz's law to find the direction of the current induced in the small ring (a) just after switch S is closed; (b) after S has been closed a long time; (c) just after S has been reopened after being closed a long time.

Figure **E29.19**

29.20 • A circular loop of wire with radius $r = 0.0480$ m and resistance $R = 0.160 \ \Omega$ is in a region of spatially uniform magnetic field, as shown in Fig. E29.20. The magnetic field is directed out of the plane of the figure. The magnetic field has an initial value of 8.00 T and is decreasing at a rate of $dB/dt = -0.680$ T/s. (a) Is the induced current in the loop clockwise or counterclockwise? (b) What is the rate at which electrical energy is being dissipated by the resistance of the loop?

Figure **E29.20**

29.21 • **CALC** A circular loop of wire with radius $r = 0.0250$ m and resistance $R = 0.390 \ \Omega$ is in a region of spatially uniform magnetic field, as shown in Fig. E29.21. The magnetic field is directed into the plane of the figure. At $t = 0$, $B = 0$. The magnetic field then begins increasing, with $B(t) = (0.380 \ \text{T/s}^3)t^3$. What is the current in the loop (magnitude and direction) at the instant when $B = 1.33$ T?

Figure **E29.21**

Section 29.4 Motional Electromotive Force

29.22 • A rectangular loop of wire with dimensions 1.50 cm by 8.00 cm and resistance $R = 0.600 \ \Omega$ is being pulled to the right out of a region of uniform magnetic field. The magnetic field has magnitude $B = 3.50$ T and is directed into the plane of Fig. E29.22. At

Figure **E29.22**

the instant when the speed of the loop is 3.00 m/s and it is still partially in the field region, what force (magnitude and direction) does the magnetic field exert on the loop?

29.23 • In Fig. E29.23 a conducting rod of length $L = 30.0$ cm moves in a magnetic field $\vec{B}$ of magnitude 0.450 T directed into the plane of the figure. The rod moves with speed $v = 5.00$ m/s in the direction shown. (a) What is the potential difference between the ends of the rod? (b) Which point, a or b, is at higher potential? (c) When the charges in the rod are in equilibrium, what are the magnitude and direction of the electric field within the rod? (d) When the charges in the rod are in equilibrium, which point, a or b, has an excess of positive charge? (e) What is the potential difference across the rod if it moves (i) parallel to ab and (ii) directly out of the page?

Figure **E29.23**

29.24 • A rectangle measuring 30.0 cm by 40.0 cm is located inside a region of a spatially uniform magnetic field of 1.25 T, with the field perpendicular to the plane of the coil (Fig. E29.24). The coil is pulled out at a steady rate of 2.00 cm/s traveling perpendicular to the field lines. The region of the field ends abruptly as shown. Find the emf induced in this coil when it is (a) all inside the field; (b) partly inside the field; (c) all outside the field.

Figure **E29.24**

29.25 • **Are Motional emfs a Practical Source of Electricity?** How fast (in m/s and mph) would a 5.00-cm copper bar have to move at right angles to a 0.650-T magnetic field to generate 1.50 V (the same as a AA battery) across its ends? Does this seem like a practical way to generate electricity?

29.26 • **Motional emfs in Transportation.** Airplanes and trains move through the earth's magnetic field at rather high speeds, so it is reasonable to wonder whether this field can have a substantial effect on them. We shall use a typical value of 0.50 G for the earth's field (a) The French TGV train and the Japanese "bullet train" reach speeds of up to 180 mph moving on tracks about 1.5 m apart. At top speed moving perpendicular to the earth's magnetic field, what potential difference is induced across the tracks as the wheels roll? Does this seem large enough to produce noticeable effects? (b) The Boeing 747-400 aircraft has a wingspan of 64.4 m and a cruising speed of 565 mph. If there is no wind blowing (so that this is also their speed relative to the ground), what is the maximum potential difference that could be induced between the opposite tips of the wings? Does this seem large enough to cause problems with the plane?

29.27 • The conducting rod ab shown in Fig. E29.27 makes contact with metal rails ca and db. The apparatus is in a uniform magnetic field of 0.800 T, perpendicular to the plane of the figure (a) Find the magnitude of the emf induced in the rod when it is moving toward the right with a speed 7.50 m/s. (b) In what direction does the current flow in the rod? (c) If the resistance of the circuit $abdc$ is 1.50 Ω (assumed to be constant), find the force (magnitude and direction) required to keep the rod moving to the right with a constant speed of 7.50 m/s. You can

Figure **E29.27**

ignore friction. (d) Compare the rate at which mechanical work is done by the force (Fv) with the rate at which thermal energy is developed in the circuit (I^2R).

29.28 • A 1.50-m-long metal bar is pulled to the right at a steady 5.0 m/s perpendicular to a uniform, 0.750-T magnetic field. The bar rides on parallel metal rails connected through a 25.0-Ω resistor, as shown in Fig. E29.28, so the apparatus makes a complete circuit. You can ignore the resistance of the bar and the rails. (a) Calculate the magnitude of the emf induced in the circuit. (b) Find the direction of the current induced in the circuit (i) using the magnetic force on the charges in the moving bar; (ii) using Faraday's law; (iii) using Lenz's law. (c) Calculate the current through the resistor.

Figure **E29.28**

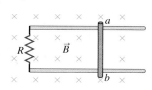

29.29 • A 0.360-m-long metal bar is pulled to the left by an applied force F. The bar rides on parallel metal rails connected through a 45.0-Ω resistor, as shown in Fig. E29.29, so the apparatus makes a complete circuit. You can ignore the resistance of the bar and rails. The circuit is in a uniform 0.650-T magnetic field that is directed out of the plane of the figure. At the instant when the bar is moving to the left at 5.90 m/s, (a) is the induced current in the circuit clockwise or counterclockwise and (b) what is the rate at which the applied force is doing work on the bar?

Figure **E29.29**

29.30 • Consider the circuit shown in Fig. E29.29, but with the bar moving to the right with speed v. As in Exercise 29.29, the bar has length 0.360 m, $R = 45.0$ Ω, and $B = 0.650$ T. (a) Is the induced current in the circuit clockwise or counterclockwise? (b) At an instant when the 45.0-Ω resistor is dissipating electrical energy at a rate of 0.840 J/s, what is the speed of the bar?

29.31 • A 0.250-m-long bar moves on parallel rails that are connected through a 6.00-Ω resistor, as shown in Fig. E29.31, so the apparatus makes a complete circuit. You can ignore the resistance of the bar and rails. The circuit is in a uniform magnetic field $B = 1.20$ T that is directed into the plane of the figure. At an instant when the induced current in the circuit is counterclockwise and equal to 1.75 A, what is the velocity of the bar (magnitude and direction)?

Figure **E29.31**

29.32 •• **BIO** **Measuring Blood Flow.** Blood contains positive and negative ions and thus is a conductor. A blood vessel, therefore, can be viewed as an electrical wire. We can even picture the flowing blood as a series of parallel conducting slabs whose thickness is the diameter d of the vessel moving with speed v. (See Fig. E29.32.) (a) If the blood vessel is placed in a magnetic field B perpendicular to the vessel, as in the figure, show that the motional potential difference induced across it is $\mathcal{E} = vBd$. (b) If you expect that the blood will be flowing at 15 cm/s for a vessel

Figure **E29.32**

5.0 mm in diameter, what strength of magnetic field will you need to produce a potential difference of 1.0 mV? (c) Show that the volume rate of flow (R) of the blood is equal to $R = \pi \mathcal{E} d / 4B$. (*Note:* Although the method developed here is useful in measuring the rate of blood flow in a vessel, it is limited to use in surgery because measurement of the potential $\mathcal{E}$ must be made directly across the vessel.)

29.33 • A 1.41-m bar moves through a uniform, 1.20-T magnetic field with a speed of 2.50 m/s (Fig. E29.33). In each case, find the emf induced between the ends of this bar and identify which, if any, end (*a* or *b*) is at the higher potential. The bar moves in the direction of (a) the +x-axis; (b) the −y-axis; (c) the +z-axis. (d) How should this bar move so that the emf across its ends has the greatest possible value with b at a higher potential than a, and what is this maximum emf?

Figure **E29.33**

29.34 •• A rectangular circuit is moved at a constant velocity of 3.0 m/s into, through, and then out of a uniform 1.25-T magnetic field, as shown in Fig. E29.34. The magnetic-field region is considerably wider than 50.0 cm. Find the magnitude and direction (clockwise or counterclockwise) of the current induced in the circuit as it is (a) going into the magnetic field; (b) totally within the magnetic field, but still moving; and (c) moving out of the field. (d) Sketch a graph of the current in this circuit as a function of time, including the preceding three cases.

Figure **E29.34**

3.0 m/s

$\vec{B}$ (1.25 T)

12.5 Ω   75.0 cm

50.0 cm

Section 29.5 Induced Electric Fields

29.35 • The magnetic field within a long, straight solenoid with a circular cross section and radius R is increasing at a rate of dB/dt. (a) What is the rate of change of flux through a circle with radius r_1 inside the solenoid, normal to the axis of the solenoid, and with center on the solenoid axis? (b) Find the magnitude of the induced electric field inside the solenoid, at a distance r_1 from its axis. Show the direction of this field in a diagram. (c) What is the magnitude of the induced electric field *outside* the solenoid, at a distance r_2 from the axis? (d) Graph the magnitude of the induced electric field as a function of the distance r from the axis from $r = 0$ to $r = 2R$. (e) What is the magnitude of the induced emf in a circular turn of radius $R/2$ that has its center on the solenoid axis? (f) What is the magnitude of the induced emf if the radius in part (e) is R? (g) What is the induced emf if the radius in part (e) is $2R$?

29.36 •• A long, thin solenoid has 900 turns per meter and radius 2.50 cm. The current in the solenoid is increasing at a uniform rate of 60.0 A/s. What is the magnitude of the induced electric field at a point near the center of the solenoid and (a) 0.500 cm from the axis of the solenoid; (b) 1.00 cm from the axis of the solenoid?

29.37 •• A long, thin solenoid has 400 turns per meter and radius 1.10 cm. The current in the solenoid is increasing at a uniform rate di/dt. The induced electric field at a point near the center of the solenoid and 3.50 cm from its axis is 8.00×10^{-6} V/m. Calculate di/dt.

29.38 • A metal ring 4.50 cm in diameter is placed between the north and south poles of large magnets with the plane of its area perpendicular to the magnetic field. These magnets produce an initial uniform field of 1.12 T between them but are gradually pulled apart, causing this field to remain uniform but decrease steadily at 0.250 T/s. (a) What is the magnitude of the electric field induced in the ring? (b) In which direction (clockwise or counterclockwise) does the current flow as viewed by someone on the south pole of the magnet?

29.39 • A long, straight solenoid with a cross-sectional area of 8.00 cm^2 is wound with 90 turns of wire per centimeter, and the windings carry a current of 0.350 A. A second winding of 12 turns encircles the solenoid at its center. The current in the solenoid is turned off such that the magnetic field of the solenoid becomes zero in 0.0400 s. What is the average induced emf in the second winding?

29.40 • The magnetic field $\vec{B}$ at all points within the colored circle shown in Fig. E29.15 has an initial magnitude of 0.750 T. (The circle could represent approximately the space inside a long, thin solenoid.) The magnetic field is directed into the plane of the diagram and is decreasing at the rate of -0.0350 T/s. (a) What is the shape of the field lines of the induced electric field shown in Fig. E29.15, within the colored circle? (b) What are the magnitude and direction of this field at any point on the circular conducting ring with radius 0.100 m? (c) What is the current in the ring if its resistance is 4.00 Ω? (d) What is the emf between points a and b on the ring? (e) If the ring is cut at some point and the ends are separated slightly, what will be the emf between the ends?

Section 29.7 Displacement Current and Maxwell's Equations

29.41 • CALC The electric flux through a certain area of a dielectric is $(8.76 \times 10^3 \, \text{V} \cdot \text{m/s}^4) t^4$. The displacement current through that area is 12.9 pA at time $t = 26.1$ ms. Calculate the dielectric constant for the dielectric.

29.42 • A parallel-plate, air-filled capacitor is being charged as in Fig. 29.22. The circular plates have radius 4.00 cm, and at a particular instant the conduction current in the wires is 0.280 A. (a) What is the displacement current density j_D in the air space between the plates? (b) What is the rate at which the electric field between the plates is changing? (c) What is the induced magnetic field between the plates at a distance of 2.00 cm from the axis? (d) At 1.00 cm from the axis?

29.43 • **Displacement Current in a Dielectric.** Suppose that the parallel plates in Fig. 29.22 have an area of 3.00 cm^2 and are separated by a 2.50-mm-thick sheet of dielectric that completely fills the volume between the plates. The dielectric has dielectric constant 4.70. (You can ignore fringing effects.) At a certain instant, the potential difference between the plates is 120 V and the conduction current i_C equals 6.00 mA. At this instant, what are (a) the charge q on each plate; (b) the rate of change of charge on the plates; (c) the displacement current in the dielectric?

29.44 • CALC In Fig. 29.22 the capacitor plates have area 5.00 cm^2 and separation 2.00 mm. The plates are in vacuum. The charging current i_C has a *constant* value of 1.80 mA. At $t = 0$ the charge on the plates is zero. (a) Calculate the charge on the plates, the electric field between the plates, and the potential difference between the plates when $t = 0.500$ μs. (b) Calculate dE/dt, the time rate of change of the electric field between the plates. Does dE/dt vary in time? (c) Calculate the displacement current density j_D between the plates, and from this the total displacement current i_D. How do i_C and i_D compare?

29.45 • **CALC** **Displacement Current in a Wire.** A long, straight, copper wire with a circular cross-sectional area of 2.1 mm² carries a current of 16 A. The resistivity of the material is $2.0 \times 10^{-8} \; \Omega \cdot m$. (a) What is the uniform electric field in the material? (b) If the current is changing at the rate of 4000 A/s, at what rate is the electric field in the material changing? (c) What is the displacement current density in the material in part (b)? (*Hint:* Since K for copper is very close to 1, use $\epsilon = \epsilon_0$.) (d) If the current is changing as in part (b), what is the magnitude of the magnetic field 6.0 cm from the center of the wire? Note that both the conduction current and the displacement current should be included in the calculation of B. Is the contribution from the displacement current significant?

Section 29.8 Superconductivity

29.46 • At temperatures near absolute zero, B_c approaches 0.142 T for vanadium, a type-I superconductor. The normal phase of vanadium has a magnetic susceptibility close to zero. Consider a long, thin vanadium cylinder with its axis parallel to an external magnetic field $\vec{B}_0$ in the $+x$-direction. At points far from the ends of the cylinder, by symmetry, all the magnetic vectors are parallel to the x-axis. At temperatures near absolute zero, what are the resultant magnetic field $\vec{B}$ and the magnetization $\vec{M}$ inside and outside the cylinder (far from the ends) for (a) $\vec{B}_0 = (0.130 \; \text{T})\hat{\imath}$ and (b) $\vec{B}_0 = (0.260 \; \text{T})\hat{\imath}$?

29.47 • The compound SiV_3 is a type-II superconductor. At temperatures near absolute zero the two critical fields are $B_{c1} = 55.0$ mT and $B_{c2} = 15.0$ T. The normal phase of SiV_3 has a magnetic susceptibility close to zero. A long, thin SiV_3 cylinder has its axis parallel to an external magnetic field $\vec{B}_0$ in the $+x$-direction. At points far from the ends of the cylinder, by symmetry, all the magnetic vectors are parallel to the x-axis. At a temperature near absolute zero, the external magnetic field is slowly increased from zero. What are the resultant magnetic field $\vec{B}$ and the magnetization $\vec{M}$ inside the cylinder at points far from its ends (a) just before the magnetic flux begins to penetrate the material, and (b) just after the material becomes completely normal?

PROBLEMS

29.48 ••• **CALC** **A Changing Magnetic Field.** You are testing a new data-acquisition system. This system allows you to record a graph of the current in a circuit as a function of time. As part of the test, you are using a circuit made up of a 4.00-cm-radius, 500-turn coil of copper wire connected in series to a 600-Ω resistor. Copper has resistivity $1.72 \times 10^{-8} \; \Omega \cdot m$, and the wire used for the coil has diameter 0.0300 mm. You place the coil on a table that is tilted 30.0° from the horizontal and that lies between the poles of an electromagnet. The electromagnet generates a vertically upward magnetic field that is zero for $t < 0$, equal to $(0.120 \; \text{T}) \times (1 - \cos \pi t)$ for $0 \le t \le 1.00$ s, and equal to 0.240 T for $t > 1.00$ s. (a) Draw the graph that should be produced by your data-acquisition system. (This is a full-featured system, so the graph will include labels and numerical values on its axes.) (b) If you were looking vertically downward at the coil, would the current be flowing clockwise or counterclockwise?

29.49 •• **CP CALC** In the circuit shown in Fig. P29.49 the capacitor has capacitance $C = 20 \; \mu\text{F}$ and is initially charged to 100 V with the polarity shown. The resistor R_0 has resistance 10 Ω. At time $t = 0$ the switch is closed. The small circuit is not connected in any way to the large one. The wire of the small circuit has a resistance of 1.0 Ω/m and contains 25 loops. The large circuit is a rectangle 2.0 m by 4.0 m, while the small one has dimensions $a = 10.0$ cm and $b = 20.0$ cm. The distance c is 5.0 cm. (The figure is not drawn to scale.) Both circuits are held stationary. Assume that only the wire nearest the small circuit produces an appreciable magnetic field through it. (a) Find the current in the large circuit 200 μs after S is closed. (b) Find the current in the small circuit 200 μs after S is closed. (*Hint:* See Exercise 29.7.) (c) Find the direction of the current in the small circuit. (d) Justify why we can ignore the magnetic field from all the wires of the large circuit except for the wire closest to the small circuit.

Figure **P29.49**

29.50 •• **CP CALC** In the circuit in Fig. P29.49, an emf of 90.0 V is added in series with the capacitor and the resistor, and the capacitor is initially uncharged. The emf is placed between the capacitor and the switch, with the positive terminal of the emf adjacent to the capacitor. Otherwise, the two circuits are the same as in Problem 29.49. The switch is closed at $t = 0$. When the current in the large circuit is 5.00 A, what are the magnitude and direction of the induced current in the small circuit?

29.51 •• **CALC** A very long, straight solenoid with a cross-sectional area of 2.00 cm² is wound with 90.0 turns of wire per centimeter. Starting at $t = 0$, the current in the solenoid is increasing according to $i(t) = (0.160 \; \text{A/s}^2)t^2$. A secondary winding of 5 turns encircles the solenoid at its center, such that the secondary winding has the same cross-sectional area as the solenoid. What is the magnitude of the emf induced in the secondary winding at the instant that the current in the solenoid is 3.20 A?

29.52 • A flat coil is oriented with the plane of its area at right angles to a spatially uniform magnetic field. The magnitude of this field varies with time according to the graph in Fig. P29.52. Sketch a qualitative (but accurate!) graph of the emf induced in the coil as a function of time. Be sure to identify the times t_1, t_2, and t_3 on your graph.

Figure **P29.52**

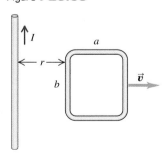

29.53 • In Fig. P29.53 the loop is being pulled to the right at constant speed v. A constant current I flows in the long wire, in the direction shown. (a) Calculate the magnitude of the net emf $\mathcal{E}$ induced in the loop. Do this two ways: (i) by using Faraday's law of induction (*Hint:* See Exercise 29.7) and (ii) by looking at the emf induced in each segment of the loop due to its motion. (b) Find the direction (clockwise or counterclockwise) of the current induced in the loop. Do this two ways: (i) using Lenz's law and (ii) using the magnetic force on charges in the loop. (c) Check your answer for the emf in part (a) in the following special cases to see whether it is physically reasonable: (i) The loop is stationary; (ii) the loop is very thin, so $a \to 0$; (iii) the loop gets very far from the wire.

Figure **P29.53**

29.54 • Suppose the loop in Fig. P29.54 is (a) rotated about the y-axis; (b) rotated about the x-axis; (c) rotated about an edge parallel to the z-axis. What is the maximum induced emf in each case if $A = 600$ cm^2, $\omega = 35.0$ rad/s, and $B = 0.450$ T?

Figure **P29.54**

29.55 ••• As a new electrical engineer for the local power company, you are assigned the project of designing a generator of sinusoidal ac voltage with a maximum voltage of 120 V. Besides plenty of wire, you have two strong magnets that can produce a constant uniform magnetic field of 1.5 T over a square area of 10.0 cm on a side when they are 12.0 cm apart. The basic design should consist of a square coil turning in the uniform magnetic field. To have an acceptable coil resistance, the coil can have at most 400 loops. What is the minimum rotation rate (in rpm) of the coil so it will produce the required voltage?

29.56 • **Make a Generator?** You are shipwrecked on a deserted tropical island. You have some electrical devices that you could operate using a generator but you have no magnets. The earth's magnetic field at your location is horizontal and has magnitude 8.0×10^{-5} T, and you decide to try to use this field for a generator by rotating a large circular coil of wire at a high rate. You need to produce a peak emf of 9.0 V and estimate that you can rotate the coil at 30 rpm by turning a crank handle. You also decide that to have an acceptable coil resistance, the maximum number of turns the coil can have is 2000. (a) What area must the coil have? (b) If the coil is circular, what is the maximum translational speed of a point on the coil as it rotates? Do you think this device is feasible? Explain.

29.57 • A flexible circular loop 6.50 cm in diameter lies in a magnetic field with magnitude 1.35 T, directed into the plane of the page as shown in Fig. P29.57. The loop is pulled at the points indicated by the arrows, forming a loop of zero area in 0.250 s. (a) Find the average induced emf in the circuit. (b) What is the direction of the current in R: from a to b or from b to a? Explain your reasoning.

Figure **P29.57**

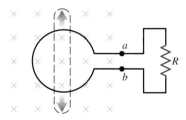

29.58 ••• CALC A conducting rod with length $L = 0.200$ m, mass $m = 0.120$ kg, and resistance $R = 80.0$ Ω moves without friction on metal rails as shown in Fig. 29.11. A uniform magnetic field with magnitude $B = 1.50$ T is directed into the plane of the figure. The rod is initially at rest, and then a constant force with magnitude $F = 1.90$ N and directed to the right is applied to the bar. How many seconds after the force is applied does the bar reach a speed of 25.0 m/s?

29.59 ••• **Terminal Speed.** A conducting rod with length L, mass m, and resistance R moves without friction on metal rails as shown in Fig. 29.11. A uniform magnetic field $\vec{B}$ is directed into the plane of the figure. The rod starts from rest and is acted on by a constant force $\vec{F}$ directed to the right. The rails are infinitely long and have negligible resistance. (a) Graph the speed of the rod as a function of time. (b) Find an expression for the terminal speed (the speed when the acceleration of the rod is zero).

29.60 •• CP CALC **Terminal Speed.** A bar of length $L = 0.36$ m is free to slide without friction on horizontal rails, as shown in Fig. P29.60. There is a uniform magnetic field $B = 1.5$ T directed into the plane of the figure. At one end of the rails there is a battery with emf $\mathcal{E} = 12$ V and a switch. The bar has mass 0.90 kg and resistance 5.0 Ω, and all other resistance in the circuit can be ignored. The switch is closed at time $t = 0$. (a) Sketch the speed of the bar as a function of time. (b) Just after the switch is closed, what is the acceleration of the bar? (c) What is the acceleration of the bar when its speed is 2.0 m/s? (d) What is the terminal speed of the bar?

Figure **P29.60**

29.61 • CP **Antenna emf.** A satellite, orbiting the earth at the equator at an altitude of 400 km, has an antenna that can be modeled as a 2.0-m-long rod. The antenna is oriented perpendicular to the earth's surface. At the equator, the earth's magnetic field is essentially horizontal and has a value of 8.0×10^{-5} T; ignore any changes in B with altitude. Assuming the orbit is circular, determine the induced emf between the tips of the antenna.

29.62 • **emf in a Bullet.** At the equator, the earth's magnetic field is approximately horizontal, is directed toward the north, and has a value of 8×10^{-5} T. (a) Estimate the emf induced between the top and bottom of a bullet shot horizontally at a target on the equator if the bullet is shot toward the east. Assume the bullet has a length of 1 cm and a diameter of 0.4 cm and is traveling at 300 m/s. Which is at higher potential: the top or bottom of the bullet? (b) What is the emf if the bullet travels south? (c) What is the emf induced between the front and back of the bullet for any horizontal velocity?

29.63 •• CALC A very long, cylindrical wire of radius R carries a current I_0 uniformly distributed across the cross section of the wire. Calculate the magnetic flux through a rectangle that has one side of length W running down the center of the wire and another side of length R, as shown in Fig. P29.63 (see Exercise 29.7).

Figure **P29.63**

29.64 • CALC A circular conducting ring with radius $r_0 = 0.0420$ m lies in the xy-plane in a region of uniform magnetic field $\vec{B} = B_0[1 - 3(t/t_0)^2 + 2(t/t_0)^3]\hat{k}$. In this expression, $t_0 = 0.0100$ s and is constant, t is time, $\hat{k}$ is the unit vector in the +z-direction, and $B_0 = 0.0800$ T and is constant. At points a and b (Fig. P29.64) there is a small gap in the ring with wires leading to an external circuit of resistance $R = 12.0$ Ω. There is no magnetic field at the location of the external circuit. (a) Derive an expression, as a function of time, for the total magnetic flux Φ_B through the ring. (b) Determine the emf

Figure **P29.64**

induced in the ring at time $t = 5.00 \times 10^{-3}$ s. What is the polarity of the emf? (c) Because of the internal resistance of the ring, the current through R at the time given in part (b) is only 3.00 mA. Determine the internal resistance of the ring. (d) Determine the emf in the ring at a time $t = 1.21 \times 10^{-2}$ s. What is the polarity of the emf? (e) Determine the time at which the current through R reverses its direction.

29.65 • **CALC** The long, straight wire shown in Fig. P29.65a carries constant current I. A metal bar with length L is moving at constant velocity $\vec{v}$, as shown in the figure. Point a is a distance d from the wire. (a) Calculate the emf induced in the bar. (b) Which point, a or b, is at higher potential? (c) If the bar is replaced by a rectangular wire loop of resistance R (Fig. P29.65b), what is the magnitude of the current induced in the loop?

Figure **P29.65**

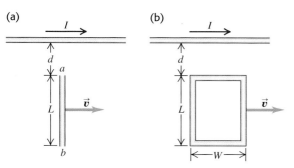

29.66 • The cube shown in Fig. P29.66, 50.0 cm on a side, is in a uniform magnetic field of 0.120 T, directed along the positive y-axis. Wires A, C, and D move in the directions indicated, each with a speed of 0.350 m/s. (Wire A moves parallel to the xy-plane, C moves at an angle of 45.0° below the xy-plane, and D moves parallel to the xz-plane.) What is the potential difference between the ends of each wire?

Figure **P29.66**

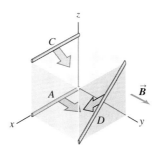

29.67 • **CALC** A slender rod, 0.240 m long, rotates with an angular speed of 8.80 rad/s about an axis through one end and perpendicular to the rod. The plane of rotation of the rod is perpendicular to a uniform magnetic field with a magnitude of 0.650 T. (a) What is the induced emf in the rod? (b) What is the potential difference between its ends? (c) Suppose instead the rod rotates at 8.80 rad/s about an axis through its center and perpendicular to the rod. In this case, what is the potential difference between the ends of the rod? Between the center of the rod and one end?

29.68 • **A Magnetic Exercise Machine.** You have designed a new type of exercise machine with an extremely simple mechanism (Fig. E29.28). A vertical bar of silver (chosen for its low resistivity and because it makes the machine look cool) with length $L = 3.0$ m is free to move left or right without friction on silver rails. The entire apparatus is placed in a horizontal, uniform magnetic field of strength 0.25 T. When you push the bar to the left or right, the bar's motion sets up a current in the circuit that includes the bar. The resistance of the bar and the rails can be neglected. The magnetic field exerts a force on the current-carrying bar, and this force opposes the bar's motion. The health benefit is from the exercise that you do in working against this force. (a) Your design

goal is that the person doing the exercise is to do work at the rate of 25 watts when moving the bar at a steady 2.0 m/s. What should be the resistance R? (b) You decide you want to be able to vary the power required from the person, to adapt the machine to the person's strength and fitness. If the power is to be increased to 50 W by altering R while leaving the other design parameters constant, should R be increased or decreased? Calculate the value of R for 50 W. (c) When you start to construct a prototype machine, you find it is difficult to produce a 0.25-T magnetic field over such a large area. If you decrease the length of the bar to 0.20 m while leaving B, v, and R the same as in part (a), what will be the power required of the person?

29.69 •• **CP CALC** A rectangular loop with width L and a slide wire with mass m are as shown in Fig. P29.69. A uniform magnetic field $\vec{B}$ is directed perpendicular to the plane of the loop into the plane of the figure. The slide wire is given an initial speed of v_0 and then released. There is no friction between the slide wire and the loop, and the resistance of the loop is negligible in comparison to the resistance R of the slide wire. (a) Obtain an expression for F, the magnitude of the force exerted on the wire while it is moving at speed v. (b) Show that the distance x that the wire moves before coming to rest is $x = mv_0R/a^2B^2$.

Figure **P29.69**

29.70 •• A 25.0-cm-long metal rod lies in the xy-plane and makes an angle of 36.9° with the positive x-axis and an angle of 53.1° with the positive y-axis. The rod is moving in the $+x$-direction with a speed of 6.80 m/s. The rod is in a uniform magnetic field $\vec{B} = (0.120 \text{ T})\hat{i} - (0.220 \text{ T})\hat{j} - (0.0900 \text{ T})\hat{k}$. (a) What is the magnitude of the emf induced in the rod? (b) Indicate in a sketch which end of the rod is at higher potential.

29.71 • The magnetic field $\vec{B}$, at all points within a circular region of radius R, is uniform in space and directed into the plane of the page as shown in Fig. P29.71. (The region could be a cross section inside the windings of a long, straight solenoid.) If the magnetic field is increasing at a rate dB/dt, what are the magnitude and direction of the force on a stationary positive point charge q located at points a, b, and c? (Point a is a distance r above the center of the region, point b is a distance r to the right of the center, and point c is at the center of the region.)

Figure **P29.71**

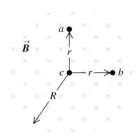

29.72 • **CALC** An airplane propeller of total length L rotates around its center with angular speed ω in a magnetic field that is perpendicular to the plane of rotation. Modeling the propeller as a thin, uniform bar, find the potential difference between (a) the center and either end of the propeller and (b) the two ends. (c) If the field is the earth's field of 0.50 G and the propeller turns at 220 rpm and is 2.0 m long, what is the potential difference between the middle and either end? It this large enough to be concerned about?

29.73 ••• **CALC** A dielectric of permittivity 3.5×10^{-11} F/m completely fills the volume between two capacitor plates. For $t > 0$ the electric flux through the dielectric is $(8.0 \times 10^3 \text{ V} \cdot \text{m/s}^3)t^3$. The dielectric is ideal and nonmagnetic; the conduction current in the dielectric is zero. At what time does the displacement current in the dielectric equal 21 μA?

29.74 •• CP CALC A capacitor has two parallel plates with area A separated by a distance d. The space between plates is filled with a material having dielectric constant K. The material is not a perfect insulator but has resistivity ρ. The capacitor is initially charged with charge of magnitude Q_0 on each plate that gradually discharges by conduction through the dielectric. (a) Calculate the conduction current density $j_C(t)$ in the dielectric. (b) Show that at any instant the displacement current density in the dielectric is equal in magnitude to the conduction current density but opposite in direction, so the total current density is zero at every instant.

29.75 •• CALC A rod of pure silicon (resistivity $\rho = 2300 \ \Omega \cdot m$) is carrying a current. The electric field varies sinusoidally with time according to $E = E_0 \sin \omega t$, where $E_0 = 0.450 \ \mathrm{V/m}$, $\omega = 2\pi f$, and the frequency $f = 120 \ \mathrm{Hz}$. (a) Find the magnitude of the maximum conduction current density in the wire. (b) Assuming $\mathcal{E} = \mathcal{E}_C$, find the maximum displacement current density in the wire, and compare with the result of part (a). (c) At what frequency f would the maximum conduction and displacement densities become equal if $\mathcal{E} = \mathcal{E}_0$ (which is not actually the case)? (d) At the frequency determined in part (c), what is the relative *phase* of the conduction and displacement currents?

CHALLENGE PROBLEMS

29.76 ••• CP CALC A square, conducting, wire loop of side L, total mass m, and total resistance R initially lies in the horizontal xy-plane, with corners at $(x, y, z) = (0, 0, 0)$, $(0, L, 0)$, $(L, 0, 0)$, and $(L, L, 0)$. There is a uniform, upward magnetic field $\vec{B} = B\hat{k}$ in the space within and around the loop. The side of the loop that extends from $(0, 0, 0)$ to $(L, 0, 0)$ is held in place on the x-axis; the rest of the loop is free to pivot around this axis. When the loop is released, it begins to rotate due to the gravitational torque. (a)

Find the *net* torque (magnitude and direction) that acts on the loop when it has rotated through an angle ϕ from its original orientation and is rotating downward at an angular speed ω. (b) Find the angular acceleration of the loop at the instant described in part (a). (c) Compared to the case with zero magnetic field, does it take the loop a longer or shorter time to rotate through 90°? Explain. (d) Is mechanical energy conserved as the loop rotates downward? Explain.

29.77 ••• A metal bar with length L, mass m, and resistance R is placed on frictionless metal rails that are inclined at an angle ϕ above the horizontal. The rails have negligible resistance. A uniform magnetic field of magnitude B is directed downward as shown in Fig. P29.77. The bar is released from rest and slides down the rails. (a) Is the direction of the current induced in the bar from a to b or from b to a? (b) What is the terminal speed of the bar? (c) What is the induced current in the bar when the terminal speed has been reached? (d) After the terminal speed has been reached, at what rate is electrical energy being converted to thermal energy in the resistance of the bar? (e) After the terminal speed has been reached, at what rate is work being done on the bar by gravity? Compare your answer to that in part (d).

Figure **P29.77**

Answers

Chapter Opening Question

As the magnetic stripe moves through the card reader, the coded pattern of magnetization in the stripe causes a varying magnetic flux and hence an induced current in the reader's circuits. If the card does not move, there is no induced emf or current and none of the credit card's information is read.

Test Your Understanding Questions

29.2 Answers: (a) (i), (b) (iii) (a) Initially there is magnetic flux into the plane of the page, which we call positive. While the loop is being squeezed, the flux is becoming less positive $(d\Phi_B/dt < 0)$ and so the induced emf is positive as in Fig. 29.6b $(\mathcal{E} = -d\Phi_B/dt > 0)$. If you point the thumb of your right hand into the page, your fingers curl clockwise, so this is the direction of positive induced emf. (b) Since the coil's shape is no longer changing, the magnetic flux is not changing and there is no induced emf.

29.3 Answers: (a) (i), (b) (iii) In (a), as in the original situation, the magnet and loop are approaching each other and the downward flux through the loop is increasing. Hence the induced emf and induced current are the same. In (b), since the magnet and loop are moving together, the flux through the loop is not changing and no emf is induced.

29.4 Answers: (a) (iii); (b) (i) or (ii); (c) (ii) or (iii) You will get the maximum motional emf if you hold the rod vertically, so that its length is perpendicular to both the magnetic field and the direc-

tion of motion. With this orientation, $\vec{L}$ is parallel to $\vec{v} \times \vec{B}$. If you hold the rod in any horizontal orientation, $\vec{L}$ will be perpendicular to $\vec{v} \times \vec{B}$ and no emf will be induced. If you walk due north or south, $\vec{v} \times \vec{B} = 0$ and no emf will be induced for any orientation of the rod.

29.5 Answers: yes, no The magnetic field at a fixed position changes as you move the magnet. Such induced electric fields are *not* conservative.

29.6 Answer: (iii) By Lenz's law, the force must oppose the motion of the disk through the magnetic field. Since the disk material is now moving to the right through the field region, the force $\vec{F}$ is to the left—that is, in the opposite direction to that shown in Fig. 29.19b. To produce a leftward magnetic force $\vec{F} = I\vec{L} \times \vec{B}$ on currents moving through a magnetic field $\vec{B}$ directed out of the plane of the figure, the eddy currents must be moving downward in the figure—that is, in the same direction shown in Fig. 29.19b.

29.7 Answers: (a) Faraday's law, (b) Ampere's law A credit card reader works by inducing currents in the reader's coils as the card's magnetized stripe is swiped (see the answer to the chapter opening question). Ampere's law describes how currents of all kinds (both conduction currents and displacement currents) give rise to magnetic fields.

Bridging Problem

Answer: $v_t = 16\rho_m \rho_R g / B^2$

INDUCTANCE

? Many traffic lights change when a car rolls up to the intersection. How does the light sense the presence of the car?

Take a length of copper wire and wrap it around a pencil to form a coil. If you put this coil in a circuit, does it behave any differently than a straight piece of wire? Remarkably, the answer is yes. In an ordinary gasoline-powered car, a coil of this kind makes it possible for the 12-volt car battery to provide thousands of volts to the spark plugs, which in turn makes it possible for the plugs to fire and make the engine run. Other coils of this type are used to keep fluorescent light fixtures shining. Larger coils placed under city streets are used to control the operation of traffic signals. All of these applications, and many others, involve the *induction* effects that we studied in Chapter 29.

A changing current in a coil induces an emf in an adjacent coil. The coupling between the coils is described by their *mutual inductance*. A changing current in a coil also induces an emf in that same coil. Such a coil is called an *inductor,* and the relationship of current to emf is described by the *inductance* (also called *self-inductance*) of the coil. If a coil is initially carrying a current, energy is released when the current decreases; this principle is used in automotive ignition systems. We'll find that this released energy was stored in the magnetic field caused by the current that was initially in the coil, and we'll look at some of the practical applications of magnetic-field energy.

We'll also take a first look at what happens when an inductor is part of a circuit. In Chapter 31 we'll go on to study how inductors behave in alternating-current circuits; in that chapter we'll learn why inductors play an essential role in modern electronics, including communication systems, power supplies, and many other devices.

30.1 Mutual Inductance

In Section 28.4 we considered the magnetic interaction between two wires carrying *steady* currents; the current in one wire causes a magnetic field, which exerts a force on the current in the second wire. But an additional interaction arises

30.1 A current i_1 in coil 1 gives rise to a magnetic flux through coil 2.

Mutual inductance: If the current in coil 1 is changing, the changing flux through coil 2 induces an emf in coil 2.

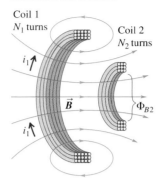

between two circuits when there is a *changing* current in one of the circuits. Consider two neighboring coils of wire, as in Fig. 30.1. A current flowing in coil 1 produces a magnetic field $\vec{B}$ and hence a magnetic flux through coil 2. If the current in coil 1 changes, the flux through coil 2 changes as well; according to Faraday's law, this induces an emf in coil 2. In this way, a change in the current in one circuit can induce a current in a second circuit.

Let's analyze the situation shown in Fig. 30.1 in more detail. We will use lowercase letters to represent quantities that vary with time; for example, a time-varying current is i, often with a subscript to identify the circuit. In Fig. 30.1 a current i_1 in coil 1 sets up a magnetic field (as indicated by the blue lines), and some of these field lines pass through coil 2. We denote the magnetic flux through *each* turn of coil 2, caused by the current i_1 in coil 1, as Φ_{B2}. (If the flux is different through different turns of the coil, then Φ_{B2} denotes the *average* flux.) The magnetic field is proportional to i_1, so Φ_{B2} is also proportional to i_1. When i_1 changes, Φ_{B2} changes; this changing flux induces an emf $\mathcal{E}_2$ in coil 2, given by

$$\mathcal{E}_2 = -N_2 \frac{d\Phi_{B2}}{dt} \tag{30.1}$$

We could represent the proportionality of Φ_{B2} and i_1 in the form $\Phi_{B2} = (\text{constant})i_1$, but instead it is more convenient to include the number of turns N_2 in the relationship. Introducing a proportionality constant M_{21}, called the **mutual inductance** of the two coils, we write

$$N_2 \Phi_{B2} = M_{21} i_1 \tag{30.2}$$

where Φ_{B2} is the flux through a *single* turn of coil 2. From this,

$$N_2 \frac{d\Phi_{B2}}{dt} = M_{21} \frac{di_1}{dt}$$

and we can rewrite Eq. (30.1) as

$$\mathcal{E}_2 = -M_{21} \frac{di_1}{dt} \tag{30.3}$$

That is, a change in the current i_1 in coil 1 induces an emf in coil 2 that is directly proportional to the rate of change of i_1 (Fig. 30.2).

We may also write the definition of mutual inductance, Eq. (30.2), as

$$M_{21} = \frac{N_2 \Phi_{B2}}{i_1}$$

If the coils are in vacuum, the flux Φ_{B2} through each turn of coil 2 is directly proportional to the current i_1. Then the mutual inductance M_{21} is a constant that depends only on the geometry of the two coils (the size, shape, number of turns, and orientation of each coil and the separation between the coils). If a magnetic material is present, M_{21} also depends on the magnetic properties of the material. If the material has nonlinear magnetic properties—that is, if the relative permeability K_{m} (defined in Section 28.8) is not constant and magnetization is not proportional to magnetic field—then Φ_{B2} is no longer directly proportional to i_1. In that case the mutual inductance also depends on the value of i_1. In this discussion we will assume that any magnetic material present has constant K_{m} so that flux *is* directly proportional to current and M_{21} depends on geometry only.

We can repeat our discussion for the opposite case in which a changing current i_2 in coil 2 causes a changing flux Φ_{B1} and an emf $\mathcal{E}_1$ in coil 1. We might expect that the corresponding constant M_{12} would be different from M_{21} because in general the two coils are not identical and the flux through them is not the same. It turns out, however, that M_{12} is *always* equal to M_{21}, even when the two coils are not symmetric. We call this common value simply the mutual inductance,

30.2 This electric toothbrush makes use of mutual inductance. The base contains a coil that is supplied with alternating current from a wall socket. This varying current induces an emf in a coil within the toothbrush itself, which is used to recharge the toothbrush battery.

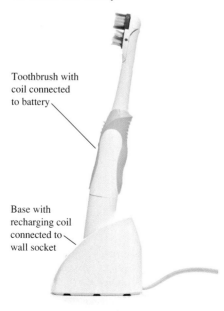

Toothbrush with coil connected to battery

Base with recharging coil connected to wall socket

denoted by the symbol M without subscripts; it characterizes completely the induced-emf interaction of two coils. Then we can write

$$\mathcal{E}_2 = -M\frac{di_1}{dt} \quad \text{and} \quad \mathcal{E}_1 = -M\frac{di_2}{dt} \qquad \text{(mutually induced emfs)} \qquad (30.4)$$

where the mutual inductance M is

$$M = \frac{N_2\Phi_{B2}}{i_1} = \frac{N_1\Phi_{B1}}{i_2} \qquad \text{(mutual inductance)} \qquad (30.5)$$

The negative signs in Eq. (30.4) are a reflection of Lenz's law. The first equation says that a change in current in coil 1 causes a change in flux through coil 2, inducing an emf in coil 2 that opposes the flux change; in the second equation the roles of the two coils are interchanged.

CAUTION **Only a time-varying current induces an emf** Note that only a *time-varying* current in a coil can induce an emf and hence a current in a second coil. Equations (30.4) show that the induced emf in each coil is directly proportional to the *rate of change* of the current in the other coil, not to the value of the current. A steady current in one coil, no matter how strong, cannot induce a current in a neighboring coil.

The SI unit of mutual inductance is called the **henry** (1 H), in honor of the American physicist Joseph Henry (1797–1878), one of the discoverers of electromagnetic induction. From Eq. (30.5), one henry is equal to *one weber per ampere*. Other equivalent units, obtained by using Eq. (30.4), are *one volt-second per ampere, one ohm-second,* and *one joule per ampere squared:*

$$1\text{ H} = 1\text{ Wb/A} = 1\text{ V}\cdot\text{s/A} = 1\text{ }\Omega\cdot\text{s} = 1\text{ J/A}^2$$

Just as the farad is a rather large unit of capacitance (see Section 24.1), the henry is a rather large unit of mutual inductance. As Example 30.1 shows, typical values of mutual inductance can be in the millihenry (mH) or microhenry (μH) range.

Drawbacks and Uses of Mutual Inductance

Mutual inductance can be a nuisance in electric circuits, since variations in current in one circuit can induce unwanted emfs in other nearby circuits. To minimize these effects, multiple-circuit systems must be designed so that M is as small as possible; for example, two coils would be placed far apart or with their planes perpendicular.

Happily, mutual inductance also has many useful applications. A *transformer,* used in alternating-current circuits to raise or lower voltages, is fundamentally no different from the two coils shown in Fig. 30.1. A time-varying alternating current in one coil of the transformer produces an alternating emf in the other coil; the value of M, which depends on the geometry of the coils, determines the amplitude of the induced emf in the second coil and hence the amplitude of the output voltage. (We'll describe transformers in more detail in Chapter 31 after we've discussed alternating current in greater depth.)

Example 30.1 Calculating mutual inductance

In one form of Tesla coil (a high-voltage generator popular in science museums), a long solenoid with length l and cross-sectional area A is closely wound with N_1 turns of wire. A coil with N_2 turns surrounds it at its center (Fig. 30.3). Find the mutual inductance M.

SOLUTION

IDENTIFY and SET UP: Mutual inductance occurs here because a current in either coil sets up a magnetic field that causes a flux through the other coil. From Example 28.9 (Section 28.7) we have

Continued

30.3 A long solenoid with cross-sectional area A and N_1 turns is surrounded at its center by a coil with N_2 turns.

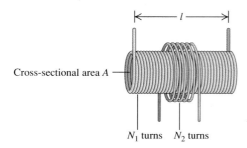

Cross-sectional area A

N_1 turns N_2 turns

an expression [Eq. (28.23)] for the field magnitude B_1 at the center of the solenoid (coil 1) in terms of the solenoid current i_1. This allows us to determine the flux through a cross section of the solenoid. Since there is no magnetic field outside a very long solenoid, this is also equal to the flux Φ_{B2} through each turn of the *outer* coil (2). We then use Eq. (30.5), in the form $M = N_2 \Phi_{B2}/i_1$, to determine M.

EXECUTE: Equation (28.23) is expressed in terms of the number of turns per unit length, which for solenoid (1) is $n_1 = N_1/L$. We then have

$$B_1 = \mu_0 n_1 i_1 = \frac{\mu_0 N_1 i_1}{l}$$

The flux through a cross section of the solenoid equals $B_1 A$. As we mentioned above, this also equals the flux Φ_{B2} through each turn of the outer coil, independent of its cross-sectional area. From Eq. (30.5), the mutual inductance M is then

$$M = \frac{N_2 \Phi_{B2}}{i_1} = \frac{N_2 B_1 A}{i_1} = \frac{N_2}{i_1} \frac{\mu_0 N_1 i_1}{l} A = \frac{\mu_0 A N_1 N_2}{l}$$

EVALUATE: The mutual inductance M of any two coils is proportional to the product $N_1 N_2$ of their numbers of turns. Notice that M depends only on the geometry of the two coils, not on the current.

Here's a numerical example to give you an idea of magnitudes. Suppose $l = 0.50$ m, $A = 10$ cm$^2 = 1.0 \times 10^{-3}$ m^2, $N_1 = 1000$ turns, and $N_2 = 10$ turns. Then

$$M = \frac{(4\pi \times 10^{-7} \text{ Wb/A} \cdot \text{m})(1.0 \times 10^{-3} \text{ m}^2)(1000)(10)}{0.50 \text{ m}}$$

$$= 25 \times 10^{-6} \text{ Wb/A} = 25 \times 10^{-6} \text{ H} = 25 \ \mu\text{H}$$

Example 30.2   **Emf due to mutual inductance**

In Example 30.1, suppose the current i_2 in the outer coil is given by $i_2 = (2.0 \times 10^6 \text{ A/s})t$. (Currents in wires can indeed increase this rapidly for brief periods.) (a) At $t = 3.0 \ \mu$s, what is the average magnetic flux through each turn of the solenoid (coil 1) due to the current in the outer coil? (b) What is the induced emf in the solenoid?

SOLUTION

IDENTIFY and SET UP: In Example 30.1 we found the mutual inductance by relating the current in the solenoid to the flux produced in the outer coil; to do that, we used Eq. (30.5) in the form $M = N_2 \Phi_{B2}/i_1$. Here we are given the current i_2 in the outer coil and want to find the resulting flux Φ_1 in the solenoid. The mutual inductance is the *same* in either case, and we have $M = 25 \ \mu$H from Example 30.1. We use Eq. (30.5) in the form $M = N_1 \Phi_{B1}/i_2$ to determine the average flux Φ_{B1} through each turn of the solenoid caused by a given current i_2 in the outer coil. We then use Eq. (30.4), to determine the emf induced in the solenoid by the time variation of i_2.

EXECUTE: (a) At $t = 3.0 \ \mu$s $= 3.0 \times 10^{-6}$ s, the current in the outer coil is $i_2 = (2.0 \times 10^6 \text{ A/s})(3.0 \times 10^{-6} \text{ s}) = 6.0$ A. We

solve Eq. (30.5) for the flux Φ_{B1} through each turn of the solenoid (coil 1):

$$\Phi_{B1} = \frac{Mi_2}{N_1} = \frac{(25 \times 10^{-6} \text{ H})(6.0 \text{ A})}{1000} = 1.5 \times 10^{-7} \text{ Wb}$$

We emphasize that this is an *average* value; the flux can vary considerably between the center and the ends of the solenoid.

(b) We are given $i_2 = (2.0 \times 10^6 \text{ A/s})t$, so $di_2/dt = 2.0 \times 10^6$ A/s; then, from Eq. (30.4), the induced emf in the solenoid is

$$\mathcal{E}_1 = -M \frac{di_2}{dt} = -(25 \times 10^{-6} \text{ H})(2.0 \times 10^6 \text{ A/s}) = -50 \text{ V}$$

EVALUATE: This is a substantial induced emf in response to a very rapid current change. In an operating Tesla coil, there is a high-frequency alternating current rather than a continuously increasing current as in this example; both di_2/dt and $\mathcal{E}_1$ alternate as well, with amplitudes that can be thousands of times larger than in this example.

Test Your Understanding of Section 30.1   Consider the Tesla coil described in Example 30.1. If you make the solenoid out of twice as much wire, so that it has twice as many turns and is twice as long, how much larger is the mutual inductance? (i) M is four times greater; (ii) M is twice as great; (iii) M is unchanged; (iv) M is $\frac{1}{2}$ as great; (v) M is $\frac{1}{4}$ as great.

30.2 Self-Inductance and Inductors

In our discussion of mutual inductance we considered two separate, independent circuits: A current in one circuit creates a magnetic field that gives rise to a flux through the second circuit. If the current in the first circuit changes, the flux through the second circuit changes and an emf is induced in the second circuit.

An important related effect occurs even if we consider only a *single* isolated circuit. When a current is present in a circuit, it sets up a magnetic field that causes a magnetic flux through the *same* circuit; this flux changes when the current changes. Thus any circuit that carries a varying current has an emf induced in it by the variation in *its own* magnetic field. Such an emf is called a **self-induced emf.** By Lenz's law, a self-induced emf always opposes the change in the current that caused the emf and so tends to make it more difficult for variations in current to occur. For this reason, self-induced emfs can be of great importance whenever there is a varying current.

Self-induced emfs can occur in *any* circuit, since there is always some magnetic flux through the closed loop of a current-carrying circuit. But the effect is greatly enhanced if the circuit includes a coil with N turns of wire (Fig. 30.4). As a result of the current i, there is an average magnetic flux Φ_B through each turn of the coil. In analogy to Eq. (30.5) we define the **self-inductance** L of the circuit as

$$L = \frac{N\Phi_B}{i} \quad \text{(self-inductance)} \qquad (30.6)$$

30.4 The current i in the circuit causes a magnetic field $\vec{B}$ in the coil and hence a flux through the coil.

Self-inductance: If the current i in the coil is changing, the changing flux through the coil induces an emf in the coil.

When there is no danger of confusion with mutual inductance, the self-inductance is called simply the **inductance.** Comparing Eqs. (30.5) and (30.6), we see that the units of self-inductance are the same as those of mutual inductance; the SI unit of self-inductance is the henry.

If the current i in the circuit changes, so does the flux Φ_B; from rearranging Eq. (30.6) and taking the derivative with respect to time, the rates of change are related by

$$N\frac{d\Phi_B}{dt} = L\frac{di}{dt}$$

From Faraday's law for a coil with N turns, Eq. (29.4), the self-induced emf is $\mathcal{E} = -N\,d\Phi_B/dt$, so it follows that

$$\mathcal{E} = -L\frac{di}{dt} \quad \text{(self-induced emf)} \qquad (30.7)$$

The minus sign in Eq. (30.7) is a reflection of Lenz's law; it says that the self-induced emf in a circuit opposes any change in the current in that circuit. (Later in this section we'll explore in greater depth the significance of this minus sign.)

Equation (30.7) also states that the self-inductance of a circuit is the magnitude of the self-induced emf per unit rate of change of current. This relationship makes it possible to measure an unknown self-inductance in a relatively simple way: Change the current in the circuit at a known rate di/dt, measure the induced emf, and take the ratio to determine L.

Inductors As Circuit Elements

A circuit device that is designed to have a particular inductance is called an **inductor,** or a *choke*. The usual circuit symbol for an inductor is

Like resistors and capacitors, inductors are among the indispensable circuit elements of modern electronics. Their purpose is to oppose any variations in the current through the circuit. An inductor in a direct-current circuit helps to maintain a steady current despite any fluctuations in the applied emf; in an alternating-current circuit, an inductor tends to suppress variations of the current that are more rapid than desired. In this chapter and the next we will explore the behavior and applications of inductors in circuits in more detail.

To understand the behavior of circuits containing inductors, we need to develop a general principle analogous to Kirchhoff's loop rule (discussed in

Application Inductors, Power Transmission, and Lightning Strikes
If lightning strikes part of an electrical power transmission system, it causes a sudden spike in voltage that can damage the components of the system as well as anything connected to that system (for example, home appliances). To minimize these effects, large inductors are incorporated into the transmission system. These use the principle that an inductor opposes and suppresses any rapid changes in the current.

30.5 A circuit containing a source of emf and an inductor. The source is variable, so the current i and its rate of change di/dt can be varied.

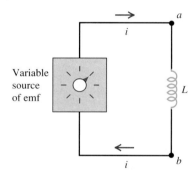

Variable source of emf

L

30.6 (a) The potential difference across a resistor depends on the current. (b), (c), (d) The potential difference across an inductor depends on the rate of change of the current.

(a) Resistor with current i flowing from a to b: potential drops from a to b.

$V_{ab} = iR > 0$

(b) Inductor with *constant* current i flowing from a to b: no potential difference.

i constant: $di/dt = 0$

$\mathcal{E} = 0$

$V_{ab} = L\dfrac{di}{dt} = 0$

(c) Inductor with *increasing* current i flowing from a to b: potential drops from a to b.

i increasing: $di/dt > 0$

$\mathcal{E}$

$V_{ab} = L\dfrac{di}{dt} > 0$

(d) Inductor with *decreasing* current i flowing from a to b: potential increases from a to b.

i decreasing: $di/dt < 0$

$\mathcal{E}$

$V_{ab} = L\dfrac{di}{dt} < 0$

Section 26.2). To apply that rule, we go around a conducting loop, measuring potential differences across successive circuit elements as we go. The algebraic sum of these differences around any closed loop must be zero because the electric field produced by charges distributed around the circuit is *conservative*. In Section 29.7 we denoted such a conservative field as $\vec{E}_c$.

When an inductor is included in the circuit, the situation changes. The magnetically induced electric field within the coils of the inductor is *not* conservative; as in Section 29.7, we'll denote it by $\vec{E}_n$. We need to think very carefully about the roles of the various fields. Let's assume we are dealing with an inductor whose coils have negligible resistance. Then a negligibly small electric field is required to make charge move through the coils, so the *total* electric field $\vec{E}_c + \vec{E}_n$ within the coils must be zero, even though neither field is individually zero. Because $\vec{E}_c$ is nonzero, there have to be accumulations of charge on the terminals of the inductor and the surfaces of its conductors to produce this field.

Consider the circuit shown in Fig. 30.5; the box contains some combination of batteries and variable resistors that enables us to control the current i in the circuit. According to Faraday's law, Eq. (29.10), the line integral of $\vec{E}_n$ around the circuit is the negative of the rate of change of flux through the circuit, which in turn is given by Eq. (30.7). Combining these two relationships, we get

$$\oint \vec{E}_n \cdot d\vec{l} = -L\frac{di}{dt}$$

where we integrate clockwise around the loop (the direction of the assumed current). But $\vec{E}_n$ is different from zero only within the inductor. Therefore the integral of $\vec{E}_n$ around the whole loop can be replaced by its integral only from a to b through the inductor; that is,

$$\int_a^b \vec{E}_n \cdot d\vec{l} = -L\frac{di}{dt}$$

Next, because $\vec{E}_c + \vec{E}_n = 0$ at each point within the inductor coils, we can rewrite this as

$$\int_a^b \vec{E}_c \cdot d\vec{l} = L\frac{di}{dt}$$

But this integral is just the potential V_{ab} of point a with respect to point b, so we finally obtain

$$V_{ab} = V_a - V_b = L\frac{di}{dt} \qquad (30.8)$$

We conclude that there is a genuine potential difference between the terminals of the inductor, associated with conservative, electrostatic forces, despite the fact that the electric field associated with the magnetic induction effect is nonconservative. Thus we are justified in using Kirchhoff's loop rule to analyze circuits that include inductors. Equation (30.8) gives the potential difference across an inductor in a circuit.

CAUTION **Self-induced emf opposes changes in current** Note that the self-induced emf does not oppose the current i itself; rather, it opposes any *change* (di/dt) in the current. Thus the circuit behavior of an inductor is quite different from that of a resistor. Figure 30.6 compares the behaviors of a resistor and an inductor and summarizes the sign relationships.

Applications of Inductors

Because an inductor opposes changes in current, it plays an important role in fluorescent light fixtures (Fig. 30.7). In such fixtures, current flows from the wiring into the gas that fills the tube, ionizing the gas and causing it to glow. However, an ionized gas or *plasma* is a highly nonohmic conductor: The greater the current, the more highly ionized the plasma becomes and the lower its resistance. If a sufficiently large voltage is applied to the plasma, the current can grow so much that it damages the circuitry outside the fluorescent tube. To prevent this problem, an inductor or *magnetic ballast* is put in series with the fluorescent tube to keep the current from growing out of bounds.

The ballast also makes it possible for the fluorescent tube to work with the alternating voltage provided by household wiring. This voltage oscillates sinusoidally with a frequency of 60 Hz, so that it goes momentarily to zero 120 times per second. If there were no ballast, the plasma in the fluorescent tube would rapidly deionize when the voltage went to zero and the tube would shut off. With a ballast present, a self-induced emf sustains the current and keeps the tube lit. Magnetic ballasts are also used for this purpose in streetlights (which obtain their light from a glowing vapor of mercury or sodium atoms) and in neon lights. (In compact fluorescent lamps, the magnetic ballast is replaced by a more complicated scheme for regulating current. This scheme utilizes transistors, discussed in Chapter 42.)

The self-inductance of a circuit depends on its size, shape, and number of turns. For N turns close together, it is always proportional to N^2. It also depends on the magnetic properties of the material enclosed by the circuit. In the following examples we will assume that the circuit encloses only vacuum (or air, which from the standpoint of magnetism is essentially vacuum). If, however, the flux is concentrated in a region containing a magnetic material with permeability μ, then in the expression for B we must replace μ_0 (the permeability of vacuum) by $\mu = K_m\mu_0$, as discussed in Section 28.8. If the material is diamagnetic or paramagnetic, this replacement makes very little difference, since K_m is very close to 1. If the material is *ferromagnetic,* however, the difference is of crucial importance. A solenoid wound on a soft iron core having $K_m = 5000$ can have an inductance approximately 5000 times as great as that of the same solenoid with an air core. Ferromagnetic-core inductors are very widely used in a variety of electronic and electric-power applications.

An added complication is that with ferromagnetic materials the magnetization is in general not a linear function of magnetizing current, especially as saturation is approached. As a result, the inductance is not constant but can depend on current in a fairly complicated way. In our discussion we will ignore this complication and assume always that the inductance is constant. This is a reasonable assumption even for a ferromagnetic material if the magnetization remains well below the saturation level.

Because automobiles contain steel, a ferromagnetic material, driving an automobile over a coil causes an appreciable increase in the coil's inductance. This effect is used in traffic light sensors, which use a large, current-carrying coil embedded under the road surface near an intersection. The circuitry connected to the coil detects the inductance change as a car drives over. When a preprogrammed number of cars have passed over the coil, the light changes to green to allow the cars through the intersection.

30.7 These fluorescent light tubes are wired in series with an inductor, or ballast, that helps to sustain the current flowing through the tubes.

Example 30.3 **Calculating self-inductance**

Determine the self-inductance of a toroidal solenoid with cross-sectional area A and mean radius r, closely wound with N turns of wire on a nonmagnetic core (Fig. 30.8). Assume that B is uniform across a cross section (that is, neglect the variation of B with distance from the toroid axis).

SOLUTION

IDENTIFY and SET UP: Our target variable is the self-inductance L of the toroidal solenoid. We can find L using Eq. (30.6), which requires knowing the flux Φ_B through each turn and the current i in

Continued

30.8 Determining the self-inductance of a closely wound toroidal solenoid. For clarity, only a few turns of the winding are shown. Part of the toroid has been cut away to show the cross-sectional area A and radius r.

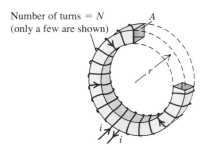

Number of turns = N
(only a few are shown)

the coil. For this, we use the results of Example 28.10 (Section 28.7), in which we found the magnetic field in the interior of a toroidal solenoid as a function of the current.

EXECUTE: From Eq. (30.6), the self-inductance is $L = N\Phi_B/i$. From Example 28.10, the field magnitude at a distance r from the toroid axis is $B = \mu_0 Ni/2\pi r$. If we assume that the field has this magnitude over the entire cross-sectional area A, then

$$\Phi_B = BA = \frac{\mu_0 NiA}{2\pi r}$$

The flux Φ_B is the same through each turn, and the self-inductance L is

$$L = \frac{N\Phi_B}{i} = \frac{\mu_0 N^2 A}{2\pi r} \quad \text{(self-inductance of a toroidal solenoid)}$$

EVALUATE: Suppose $N = 200$ turns, $A = 5.0 \text{ cm}^2 = 5.0 \times 10^{-4} \text{ m}^2$, and $r = 0.10$ m; then

$$L = \frac{(4\pi \times 10^{-7} \text{ Wb/A} \cdot \text{m})(200)^2(5.0 \times 10^{-4} \text{ m}^2)}{2\pi(0.10 \text{ m})}$$

$$= 40 \times 10^{-6} \text{ H} = 40 \ \mu\text{H}$$

Example 30.4   Calculating self-induced emf

If the current in the toroidal solenoid in Example 30.3 increases uniformly from 0 to 6.0 A in 3.0 μs, find the magnitude and direction of the self-induced emf.

SOLUTION

IDENTIFY and SET UP: We are given L, the self-inductance, and di/dt, the rate of change of the solenoid current. We find the magnitude of self-induced emf $\mathcal{E}$ using Eq. (30.7) and its direction using Lenz's law.

EXECUTE: We have $di/dt = (6.0 \text{ A})/(3.0 \times 10^{-6} \text{ s}) = 2.0 \times 10^6$ A/s. From Eq. (30.7), the magnitude of the induced emf is

$$|\mathcal{E}| = L\left|\frac{di}{dt}\right| = (40 \times 10^{-6} \text{ H})(2.0 \times 10^6 \text{ A/s}) = 80 \text{ V}$$

The current is increasing, so according to Lenz's law the direction of the emf is opposite to that of the current. This corresponds to the situation in Fig. 30.6c; the emf is in the direction from b to a, like a battery with a as the $+$ terminal and b the $-$ terminal, tending to oppose the current increase from the external circuit.

EVALUATE: This example shows that even a small inductance L can give rise to a substantial induced emf if the current changes rapidly.

Test Your Understanding of Section 30.2 Rank the following inductors in order of the potential difference v_{ab}, from most positive to most negative. In each case the inductor has zero resistance and the current flows from point a through the inductor to point b. (i) The current through a 2.0-μH inductor increases from 1.0 A to 2.0 A in 0.50 s; (ii) the current through a 4.0-μH inductor decreases from 3.0 A to 0 in 2.0 s; (iii) the current through a 1.0-μH inductor remains constant at 4.0 A; (iv) the current through a 1.0-μH inductor increases from 0 to 4.0 A in 0.25 s.

30.3 Magnetic-Field Energy

Establishing a current in an inductor requires an input of energy, and an inductor carrying a current has energy stored in it. Let's see how this comes about. In Fig. 30.5, an increasing current i in the inductor causes an emf $\mathcal{E}$ between its terminals and a corresponding potential difference V_{ab} between the terminals of the source, with point a at higher potential than point b. Thus the source must be adding energy to the inductor, and the instantaneous power P (rate of transfer of energy into the inductor) is $P = V_{ab}i$.

Energy Stored in an Inductor

We can calculate the total energy input U needed to establish a final current I in an inductor with inductance L if the initial current is zero. We assume that the inductor has zero resistance, so no energy is dissipated within the inductor. Let the current at some instant be i and let its rate of change be di/dt; the current is increasing, so $di/dt > 0$. The voltage between the terminals a and b of the inductor at this instant is $V_{ab} = L\,di/dt$, and the rate P at which energy is being delivered to the inductor (equal to the instantaneous power supplied by the external source) is

$$P = V_{ab}i = Li\frac{di}{dt}$$

The energy dU supplied to the inductor during an infinitesimal time interval dt is $dU = P\,dt$, so

$$dU = Li\,di$$

The total energy U supplied while the current increases from zero to a final value I is

$$U = L\int_0^I i\,di = \tfrac{1}{2}LI^2 \qquad \text{(energy stored in an inductor)} \qquad (30.9)$$

After the current has reached its final steady value I, $di/dt = 0$ and no more energy is input to the inductor. When there is no current, the stored energy U is zero; when the current is I, the energy is $\frac{1}{2}LI^2$.

When the current decreases from I to zero, the inductor acts as a source that supplies a total amount of energy $\frac{1}{2}LI^2$ to the external circuit. If we interrupt the circuit suddenly by opening a switch or yanking a plug from a wall socket, the current decreases very rapidly, the induced emf is very large, and the energy may be dissipated in an arc across the switch contacts. This large emf is the electrical analog of the large force exerted by a car running into a brick wall and stopping very suddenly.

CAUTION **Energy, resistors, and inductors** It's important not to confuse the behavior of resistors and inductors where energy is concerned (Fig. 30.9). Energy flows into a resistor whenever a current passes through it, whether the current is steady or varying; this energy is dissipated in the form of heat. By contrast, energy flows into an ideal, zero-resistance inductor only when the current in the inductor *increases*. This energy is not dissipated; it is stored in the inductor and released when the current *decreases*. When a steady current flows through an inductor, there is no energy flow in or out.

Magnetic Energy Density

The energy in an inductor is actually stored in the magnetic field within the coil, just as the energy of a capacitor is stored in the electric field between its plates. We can develop relationships for magnetic-field energy analogous to those we obtained for electric-field energy in Section 24.3 [Eqs. (24.9) and (24.11)]. We will concentrate on one simple case, the ideal toroidal solenoid. This system has the advantage that its magnetic field is confined completely to a finite region of space within its core. As in Example 30.3, we assume that the cross-sectional area A is small enough that we can pretend that the magnetic field is uniform over the area. The volume V enclosed by the toroidal solenoid is approximately equal to the circumference $2\pi r$ multiplied by the area A: $V = 2\pi rA$. From Example 30.3, the self-inductance of the toroidal solenoid with vacuum within its coils is

$$L = \frac{\mu_0 N^2 A}{2\pi r}$$

From Eq. (30.9), the energy U stored in the toroidal solenoid when the current is I is

$$U = \tfrac{1}{2}LI^2 = \tfrac{1}{2}\frac{\mu_0 N^2 A}{2\pi r}I^2$$

30.9 A resistor is a device in which energy is irrecoverably dissipated. By contrast, energy stored in a current-carrying inductor can be recovered when the current decreases to zero.

Resistor with current i: energy is *dissipated*.

Inductor with current i: energy is *stored*.

This composite of two images of the sun shows a coronal mass ejection, a dramatic event in which about 10^{12} kg (a billion tons) of material from the sun's outer atmosphere is ejected into space at speeds of 500 km/s or faster. Such ejections happen at intervals of a few hours to a few days. These immense eruptions are powered by the energy stored in the sun's magnetic field. Unlike the earth's relatively steady magnetic field, the sun's field is constantly changing, and regions of unusually strong field (and hence unusually high magnetic energy density) frequently form. A coronal mass ejection occurs when the energy stored in such a region is suddenly released.

The magnetic field and therefore this energy are localized in the volume $V = 2\pi rA$ enclosed by the windings. The energy *per unit volume*, or *magnetic energy density*, is $u = U/V$:

$$u = \frac{U}{2\pi rA} = \frac{1}{2}\mu_0 \frac{N^2 I^2}{(2\pi r)^2}$$

We can express this in terms of the magnitude B of the magnetic field inside the toroidal solenoid. From Eq. (28.24) in Example 28.10 (Section 28.7), this is

$$B = \frac{\mu_0 NI}{2\pi r}$$

and so

$$\frac{N^2 I^2}{(2\pi r)^2} = \frac{B^2}{\mu_0^2}$$

When we substitute this into the above equation for u, we finally find the expression for **magnetic energy density** in vacuum:

$$u = \frac{B^2}{2\mu_0} \qquad \text{(magnetic energy density in vacuum)} \qquad (30.10)$$

This is the magnetic analog of the energy per unit volume in an *electric* field in vacuum, $u = \frac{1}{2}\epsilon_0 E^2$, which we derived in Section 24.3. As an example, the energy density in the 1.5-T magnetic field of an MRI scanner (see Section 27.7) is $u = B^2/2\mu_0 = (1.5\text{ T})^2/(2 \times 4\pi \times 10^{-7}\text{ T}\cdot\text{m/A}) = 9.0 \times 10^5\text{ J/m}^3$.

When the material inside the toroid is not vacuum but a material with (constant) magnetic permeability $\mu = K_m\mu_0$, we replace μ_0 by μ in Eq. (30.10). The energy per unit volume in the magnetic field is then

$$u = \frac{B^2}{2\mu} \qquad \text{(magnetic energy density in a material)} \qquad (30.11)$$

Although we have derived Eq. (30.11) only for one special situation, it turns out to be the correct expression for the energy per unit volume associated with *any* magnetic-field configuration in a material with constant permeability. For vacuum, Eq. (30.11) reduces to Eq. (30.10). We will use the expressions for electric-field and magnetic-field energy in Chapter 32 when we study the energy associated with electromagnetic waves.

Magnetic-field energy plays an important role in the ignition systems of gasoline-powered automobiles. A primary coil of about 250 turns is connected to the car's battery and produces a strong magnetic field. This coil is surrounded by a secondary coil with some 25,000 turns of very fine wire. When it is time for a spark plug to fire (see Fig. 20.5 in Section 20.3), the current to the primary coil is interrupted, the magnetic field quickly drops to zero, and an emf of tens of thousands of volts is induced in the secondary coil. The energy stored in the magnetic field thus goes into a powerful pulse of current that travels through the secondary coil to the spark plug, generating the spark that ignites the fuel–air mixture in the engine's cylinders (Fig. 30.10).

30.10 The energy required to fire an automobile spark plug is derived from magnetic-field energy stored in the ignition coil.

Example 30.5 **Storing energy in an inductor**

The electric-power industry would like to find efficient ways to store electrical energy generated during low-demand hours to help meet customer requirements during high-demand hours. Could a large inductor be used? What inductance would be needed to store 1.00 kW·h of energy in a coil carrying a 200-A current?

SOLUTION

IDENTIFY and SET UP: We are given the required amount of stored energy U and the current $I = 200$ A. We use Eq. (30.9) to find the self-inductance L.

EXECUTE: We have $I = 200$ A and $U = 1.00$ kW·h $= (1.00 \times 10^3$ W$)(3600$ s$) = 3.60 \times 10^6$ J. Solving Eq. (30.9) for L, we find

$$L = \frac{2U}{I^2} = \frac{2(3.60 \times 10^6 \text{ J})}{(200 \text{ A})^2} = 180 \text{ H}$$

EVALUATE: The required inductance is more than a million times greater than the self-inductance of the toroidal solenoid of Example 30.3. Conventional wires that are to carry 200 A would have to be of large diameter to keep the resistance low and avoid unacceptable energy losses due to I^2R heating. As a result, a 180-H inductor using conventional wire would be very large (room-size). A superconducting inductor could be much smaller, since the resistance of a superconductor is zero and much thinner wires could be used; but the wires would have to be kept at low temperature to remain superconducting, and maintaining this temperature would itself require energy. This scheme is impractical with present technology.

Test Your Understanding of Section 30.3 The current in a solenoid is reversed in direction while keeping the same magnitude. (a) Does this change the magnetic field within the solenoid? (b) Does this change the magnetic energy density in the solenoid? ❙

30.4 The *R-L* Circuit

Let's look at some examples of the circuit behavior of an inductor. One thing is clear already; an inductor in a circuit makes it difficult for rapid changes in current to occur, thanks to the effects of self-induced emf. Equation (30.7) shows that the greater the rate of change of current di/dt, the greater the self-induced emf and the greater the potential difference between the inductor terminals. This equation, together with Kirchhoff's rules (see Section 26.2), gives us the principles we need to analyze circuits containing inductors.

ActivPhysics 14.1: The *RL* Circuit

Problem-Solving Strategy 30.1 **Inductors in Circuits**

IDENTIFY *the relevant concepts:* An inductor is just another circuit element, like a source of emf, a resistor, or a capacitor. One key difference is that when an inductor is included in a circuit, all the voltages, currents, and capacitor charges are in general functions of time, not constants as they have been in most of our previous circuit analysis. But Kirchhoff's rules (see Section 26.2) are still valid. When the voltages and currents vary with time, Kirchhoff's rules hold at each instant of time.

SET UP *the problem* using the following steps:
1. Follow the procedure described in Problem-Solving Strategy 26.2 (Section 26.2). Draw a circuit diagram and label all quantities, known and unknown. Apply the junction rule immediately so as to express the currents in terms of as few quantities as possible.
2. Determine which quantities are the target variables.

EXECUTE *the solution* as follows:
1. As in Problem-Solving Strategy 26.2, apply Kirchhoff's loop rule to each loop in the circuit.

2. Review the sign rules given in Problem-Solving Strategy 26.2. To get the correct sign for the potential difference between the terminals of an inductor, apply Lenz's law and the sign rule described in Section 30.2 in connection with Eq. (30.7) and Fig. 30.6. In Kirchhoff's loop rule, when we go through an inductor in the *same* direction as the assumed current, we encounter a voltage *drop* equal to $L\, di/dt$, so the corresponding term in the loop equation is $-L\, di/dt$. When we go through an inductor in the *opposite* direction from the assumed current, the potential difference is reversed and the term to use in the loop equation is $+L\, di/dt$.
3. Solve for the target variables.

EVALUATE *your answer:* Check whether your answer is consistent with the behavior of inductors. By Lenz's law, if the current through an inductor is changing, your result should indicate that the potential difference across the inductor opposes the change.

Current Growth in an *R-L* Circuit

We can learn several basic things about inductor behavior by analyzing the circuit of Fig. 30.11. A circuit that includes both a resistor and an inductor, and possibly a source of emf, is called an **R-L circuit.** The inductor helps to prevent rapid changes in current, which can be useful if a steady current is required but the external source has a fluctuating emf. The resistor R may be a separate circuit

30.11 An *R-L* circuit.

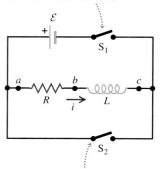

Closing switch S₁ connects the *R-L* combination in series with a source of emf $\mathcal{E}$.

Closing switch S₂ while opening switch S₁ disconnnects the combination from the source.

element, or it may be the resistance of the inductor windings; every real-life inductor has some resistance unless it is made of superconducting wire. By closing switch S₁, we can connect the *R-L* combination to a source with constant emf $\mathcal{E}$. (We assume that the source has zero internal resistance, so the terminal voltage equals the emf.)

Suppose both switches are open to begin with, and then at some initial time $t = 0$ we close switch S₁. The current cannot change suddenly from zero to some final value, since di/dt and the induced emf in the inductor would both be infinite. Instead, the current begins to grow at a rate that depends only on the value of L in the circuit.

Let i be the current at some time t after switch S₁ is closed, and let di/dt be its rate of change at that time. The potential difference v_{ab} across the resistor at that time is

$$v_{ab} = iR$$

and the potential difference v_{bc} across the inductor is

$$v_{bc} = L\frac{di}{dt}$$

Note that if the current is in the direction shown in Fig. 30.11 and is increasing, then both v_{ab} and v_{bc} are positive; a is at a higher potential than b, which in turn is at a higher potential than c. (Compare to Figs. 30.6a and c.) We apply Kirchhoff's loop rule, starting at the negative terminal and proceeding counterclockwise around the loop:

$$\mathcal{E} - iR - L\frac{di}{dt} = 0 \tag{30.12}$$

Solving this for di/dt, we find that the rate of increase of current is

$$\frac{di}{dt} = \frac{\mathcal{E} - iR}{L} = \frac{\mathcal{E}}{L} - \frac{R}{L}i \tag{30.13}$$

At the instant that switch S₁ is first closed, $i = 0$ and the potential drop across R is zero. The initial rate of change of current is

$$\left(\frac{di}{dt}\right)_{initial} = \frac{\mathcal{E}}{L}$$

As we would expect, the greater the inductance L, the more slowly the current increases.

As the current increases, the term $(R/L)i$ in Eq. (30.13) also increases, and the *rate* of increase of current given by Eq. (30.13) becomes smaller and smaller. This means that the current is approaching a final, steady-state value I. When the current reaches this value, its rate of increase is zero. Then Eq. (30.13) becomes

$$\left(\frac{di}{dt}\right)_{final} = 0 = \frac{\mathcal{E}}{L} - \frac{R}{L}I \quad \text{and}$$

$$I = \frac{\mathcal{E}}{R}$$

The *final* current I does not depend on the inductance L; it is the same as it would be if the resistance R alone were connected to the source with emf $\mathcal{E}$.

Figure 30.12 shows the behavior of the current as a function of time. To derive the equation for this curve (that is, an expression for current as a function of time), we proceed just as we did for the charging capacitor in Section 26.4. First we rearrange Eq. (30.13) to the form

$$\frac{di}{i - (\mathcal{E}/R)} = -\frac{R}{L}dt$$

30.12 Graph of i versus t for growth of current in an *R-L* circuit with an emf in series. The final current is $I = \mathcal{E}/R$; after one time constant τ, the current is $1 - 1/e$ of this value.

Switch S₁ is closed at $t = 0$.

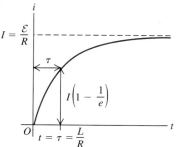

This separates the variables, with i on the left side and t on the right. Then we integrate both sides, renaming the integration variables i' and t' so that we can use i and t as the upper limits. (The lower limit for each integral is zero, corresponding to zero current at the initial time $t = 0$.) We get

$$\int_0^i \frac{di'}{i' - (\mathcal{E}/R)} = -\int_0^t \frac{R}{L}\,dt'$$

$$\ln\left(\frac{i - (\mathcal{E}/R)}{-\mathcal{E}/R}\right) = -\frac{R}{L}t$$

Now we take exponentials of both sides and solve for i. We leave the details for you to work out; the final result is

$$i = \frac{\mathcal{E}}{R}(1 - e^{-(R/L)t}) \qquad \text{(current in an } R\text{-}L \text{ circuit with emf)} \qquad (30.14)$$

This is the equation of the curve in Fig. 30.12. Taking the derivative of Eq. (30.14), we find

$$\frac{di}{dt} = \frac{\mathcal{E}}{L}e^{-(R/L)t} \qquad\qquad (30.15)$$

At time $t = 0$, $i = 0$ and $di/dt = \mathcal{E}/L$. As $t \to \infty$, $i \to \mathcal{E}/R$ and $di/dt \to 0$, as we predicted.

As Fig. 30.12 shows, the instantaneous current i first rises rapidly, then increases more slowly and approaches the final value $I = \mathcal{E}/R$ asymptotically. At a time equal to L/R, the current has risen to $(1 - 1/e)$, or about 63%, of its final value. The quantity L/R is therefore a measure of how quickly the current builds toward its final value; this quantity is called the **time constant** for the circuit, denoted by τ:

$$\tau = \frac{L}{R} \qquad \text{(time constant for an } R\text{-}L \text{ circuit)} \qquad (30.16)$$

In a time equal to 2τ, the current reaches 86% of its final value; in 5τ, 99.3%; and in 10τ, 99.995%. (Compare the discussion in Section 26.4 of charging a capacitor of capacitance C that was in series with a resistor of resistance R; the time constant for that situation was the product RC.)

The graphs of i versus t have the same general shape for all values of L. For a given value of R, the time constant τ is greater for greater values of L. When L is small, the current rises rapidly to its final value; when L is large, it rises more slowly. For example, if $R = 100\ \Omega$ and $L = 10\ \text{H}$,

$$\tau = \frac{L}{R} = \frac{10\ \text{H}}{100\ \Omega} = 0.10\ \text{s}$$

and the current increases to about 63% of its final value in 0.10 s. (Recall that $1\ \text{H} = 1\ \Omega \cdot \text{s}$.) But if $L = 0.010\ \text{H}$, $\tau = 1.0 \times 10^{-4}\ \text{s} = 0.10\ \text{ms}$, and the rise is much more rapid.

Energy considerations offer us additional insight into the behavior of an R-L circuit. The instantaneous rate at which the source delivers energy to the circuit is $P = \mathcal{E}i$. The instantaneous rate at which energy is dissipated in the resistor is i^2R, and the rate at which energy is stored in the inductor is $iv_{bc} = Li\,di/dt$ [or, equivalently, $(d/dt)\left(\frac{1}{2}Li^2\right) = Li\,di/dt$]. When we multiply Eq. (30.12) by i and rearrange, we find

$$\mathcal{E}i = i^2R + Li\frac{di}{dt} \qquad\qquad (30.17)$$

Of the power $\mathcal{E}i$ supplied by the source, part (i^2R) is dissipated in the resistor and part $(Li\,di/dt)$ goes to store energy in the inductor. This discussion is completely analogous to our power analysis for a charging capacitor, given at the end of Section 26.4.

Example 30.6 **Analyzing an *R-L* circuit**

A sensitive electronic device of resistance $R = 175 \ \Omega$ is to be connected to a source of emf (of negligible internal resistance) by a switch. The device is designed to operate with a 36-mA current, but to avoid damage to the device, the current can rise to no more than 4.9 mA in the first 58 μs after the switch is closed. An inductor is therefore connected in series with the device, as in Fig. 30.11; the switch in question is S_1. (a) What is the required source emf $\mathcal{E}$? (b) What is the required inductance L? (c) What is the *R-L* time constant τ?

SOLUTION

IDENTIFY and SET UP: This problem concerns current and current growth in an *R-L* circuit, so we can use the ideas of this section. Figure 30.12 shows the current i versus the time t that has elapsed since closing S_1. The graph shows that the final current is $I = \mathcal{E}/R$; we are given $R = 175 \ \Omega$, so the emf is determined by the requirement that the final current be $I = 36$ mA. The other requirement is that the current be no more than $i = 4.9$ mA at $t = 58 \ \mu$s; to satisfy this, we use Eq. (30.14) for the current as a function of time and solve for the inductance, which is the only unknown quantity. Equation (30.16) then tells us the time constant.

EXECUTE: (a) We solve $I = \mathcal{E}/R$ for $\mathcal{E}$:

$$\mathcal{E} = IR = (0.036 \text{ A})(175 \ \Omega) = 6.3 \text{ V}$$

(b) To find the required inductance, we solve Eq. (30.14) for L. First we multiply through by $(-R/\mathcal{E})$ and then add 1 to both sides to obtain

$$1 - \frac{iR}{\mathcal{E}} = e^{-(R/L)t}$$

Then we take natural logs of both sides, solve for L, and insert the numbers:

$$L = \frac{-Rt}{\ln(1 - iR/\mathcal{E})}$$

$$= \frac{-(175 \ \Omega)(58 \times 10^{-6} \text{ s})}{\ln[1 - (4.9 \times 10^{-3} \text{ A})(175 \ \Omega)/(6.3 \text{ V})]} = 69 \text{ mH}$$

(c) From Eq. (30.16),

$$\tau = \frac{L}{R} = \frac{69 \times 10^{-3} \text{ H}}{175 \ \Omega} = 3.9 \times 10^{-4} \text{ s} = 390 \ \mu\text{s}$$

EVALUATE: Note that 58 μs is much less than the time constant. In 58 μs the current builds up from zero to 4.9 mA, a small fraction of its final value of 36 mA; after 390 μs the current equals $(1 - 1/e)$ of its final value, or about $(0.63)(36 \text{ mA}) = 23$ mA.

30.13 Graph of i versus t for decay of current in an *R-L* circuit. After one time constant τ, the current is $1/e$ of its initial value.

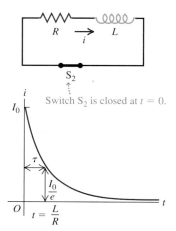

Current Decay in an *R-L* Circuit

Now suppose switch S_1 in the circuit of Fig. 30.11 has been closed for a while and the current has reached the value I_0. Resetting our stopwatch to redefine the initial time, we close switch S_2 at time $t = 0$, bypassing the battery. (At the same time we should open S_1 to save the battery from ruin.) The current through R and L does not instantaneously go to zero but decays smoothly, as shown in Fig. 30.13. The Kirchhoff's-rule loop equation is obtained from Eq. (30.12) by simply omitting the $\mathcal{E}$ term. We challenge you to retrace the steps in the above analysis and show that the current i varies with time according to

$$i = I_0 e^{-(R/L)t} \tag{30.18}$$

where I_0 is the initial current at time $t = 0$. The time constant, $\tau = L/R$, is the time for current to decrease to $1/e$, or about 37%, of its original value. In time 2τ it has dropped to 13.5%, in time 5τ to 0.67%, and in 10τ to 0.0045%.

The energy that is needed to maintain the current during this decay is provided by the energy stored in the magnetic field of the inductor. The detailed energy analysis is simpler this time. In place of Eq. (30.17) we have

$$0 = i^2R + Li\frac{di}{dt} \tag{30.19}$$

In this case, $Li \, di/dt$ is negative; Eq. (30.19) shows that the energy stored in the inductor *decreases* at a rate equal to the rate of dissipation of energy i^2R in the resistor.

This entire discussion should look familiar; the situation is very similar to that of a charging and discharging capacitor, analyzed in Section 26.4. It would be a good idea to compare that section with our discussion of the *R-L* circuit.

Example 30.7 **Energy in an *R-L* circuit**

When the current in an *R-L* circuit is decaying, what fraction of the original energy stored in the inductor has been dissipated after 2.3 time constants?

SOLUTION

IDENTIFY and SET UP: This problem concerns current decay in an *R-L* circuit as well as the relationship between the current in an inductor and the amount of stored energy. The current i at any time t is given by Eq. (30.18); the stored energy associated with this current is given by Eq. (30.9), $U = \frac{1}{2}Li^2$.

EXECUTE: From Eq. (30.18), the current i at any time t is

$$i = I_0 e^{-(R/L)t}$$

We substitute this into $U = \frac{1}{2}Li^2$ to obtain an expression for the stored energy at any time:

$$U = \frac{1}{2}LI_0^2 e^{-2(R/L)t} = U_0 e^{-2(R/L)t}$$

where $U_0 = \frac{1}{2}LI_0^2$ is the energy at the initial time $t = 0$. When $t = 2.3\tau = 2.3L/R$, we have

$$U = U_0 e^{-2(2.3)} = U_0 e^{-4.6} = 0.010U_0$$

That is, only 0.010 or 1.0% of the energy initially stored in the inductor remains, so 99.0% has been dissipated in the resistor.

EVALUATE: To get a sense of what this result means, consider the *R-L* circuit we analyzed in Example 30.6, for which $\tau = 390 \ \mu s$. With $L = 69$ mH and $I_0 = 36$ mA, we have $U_0 = \frac{1}{2}LI_0^2 = \frac{1}{2}(0.069 \ \text{H})(0.036 \ \text{A})^2 = 4.5 \times 10^{-5}$ J. Of this, 99.0% or 4.4×10^{-5} J is dissipated in $2.3(390 \ \mu s) = 9.0 \times 10^{-4}$ s $= 0.90$ ms. In other words, this circuit can be almost completely powered off (or powered on) in 0.90 ms, so the minimum time for a complete on–off cycle is 1.8 ms. Even shorter cycle times are required for many purposes, such as in fast switching networks for telecommunications. In such cases a smaller time constant $\tau = L/R$ is needed.

Test Your Understanding of Section 30.4   (a) In Fig. 30.11, what are the algebraic signs of the potential differences v_{ab} and v_{bc} when switch S_1 is closed and switch S_2 is open? (i) $v_{ab} > 0$, $v_{bc} > 0$; (ii) $v_{ab} > 0$, $v_{bc} < 0$; (iii) $v_{ab} < 0$, $v_{bc} > 0$; (iv) $v_{ab} < 0$, $v_{bc} < 0$. (b) What are the signs of v_{ab} and v_{bc} when S_1 is open, S_2 is closed, and current is flowing in the direction shown? (i) $v_{ab} > 0$, $v_{bc} > 0$; (ii) $v_{ab} > 0$, $v_{bc} < 0$; (iii) $v_{ab} < 0$, $v_{bc} > 0$; (iv) $v_{ab} < 0$, $v_{bc} < 0$. ❙

30.5 The *L-C* Circuit

ActivPhysics 14.2: AC Circuits: The *RLC* Oscillator (Questions 1–6)

A circuit containing an inductor and a capacitor shows an entirely new mode of behavior, characterized by *oscillating* current and charge. This is in sharp contrast to the *exponential* approach to a steady-state situation that we have seen with both *R-C* and *R-L* circuits. In the **L-C circuit** in Fig. 30.14a we charge the capacitor to a potential difference V_m and initial charge $Q = CV_m$ on its left-hand plate and then close the switch. What happens?

The capacitor begins to discharge through the inductor. Because of the induced emf in the inductor, the current cannot change instantaneously; it starts at zero and eventually builds up to a maximum value I_m. During this buildup the capacitor is discharging. At each instant the capacitor potential equals the induced emf, so as the capacitor discharges, the *rate of change* of current decreases. When the capacitor potential becomes zero, the induced emf is also zero, and the current has leveled off at its maximum value I_m. Figure 30.14b shows this situation; the capacitor has completely discharged. The potential difference between its terminals (and those of the inductor) has decreased to zero, and the current has reached its maximum value I_m.

During the discharge of the capacitor, the increasing current in the inductor has established a magnetic field in the space around it, and the energy that was initially stored in the capacitor's electric field is now stored in the inductor's magnetic field.

Although the capacitor is completely discharged in Fig. 30.14b, the current persists (it cannot change instantaneously), and the capacitor begins to charge with polarity opposite to that in the initial state. As the current decreases, the magnetic field also decreases, inducing an emf in the inductor in the *same* direction as the current; this slows down the decrease of the current. Eventually, the

30.14 In an oscillating L-C circuit, the charge on the capacitor and the current through the inductor both vary sinusoidally with time. Energy is transferred between magnetic energy in the inductor (U_B) and electric energy in the capacitor (U_E). As in simple harmonic motion, the total energy E remains constant. (Compare Fig. 14.14 in Section 14.3.)

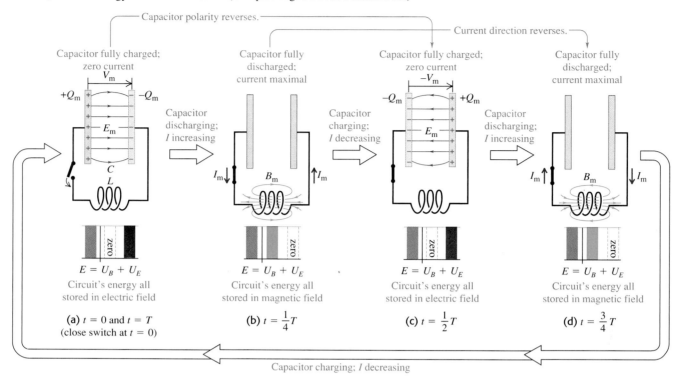

| (a) $t = 0$ and $t = T$ (close switch at $t = 0$) | (b) $t = \frac{1}{4}T$ | (c) $t = \frac{1}{2}T$ | (d) $t = \frac{3}{4}T$ |

current and the magnetic field reach zero, and the capacitor has been charged in the sense *opposite* to its initial polarity (Fig. 30.14c), with potential difference $-V_m$ and charge $-Q$ on its left-hand plate.

The process now repeats in the reverse direction; a little later, the capacitor has again discharged, and there is a current in the inductor in the opposite direction (Fig. 30.14d). Still later, the capacitor charge returns to its original value (Fig. 30.14a), and the whole process repeats. If there are no energy losses, the charges on the capacitor continue to oscillate back and forth indefinitely. This process is called an **electrical oscillation.**

From an energy standpoint the oscillations of an electrical circuit transfer energy from the capacitor's electric field to the inductor's magnetic field and back. The *total* energy associated with the circuit is constant. This is analogous to the transfer of energy in an oscillating mechanical system from potential energy to kinetic energy and back, with constant total energy. As we will see, this analogy goes much further.

Electrical Oscillations in an *L-C* Circuit

To study the flow of charge in detail, we proceed just as we did for the R-L circuit. Figure 30.15 shows our definitions of q and i.

30.15 Applying Kirchhoff's loop rule to the L-C circuit. The direction of travel around the loop in the loop equation is shown. Just after the circuit is completed and the capacitor first begins to discharge, as in Fig. 30.14a, the current is negative (opposite to the direction shown).

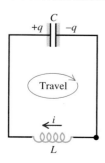

CAUTION   **Positive current in an *L-C* circuit** After examining Fig. 30.14, the positive direction for current in Fig. 30.15 may seem backward to you. In fact we've chosen this direction to simplify the relationship between current and capacitor charge. We define the current at each instant to be $i = dq/dt$, the rate of change of the charge on the left-hand capacitor plate. Hence if the capacitor is initially charged and begins to discharge as in Figs. 30.14a and 30.14b, then $dq/dt < 0$ and the initial current i is negative; the direction of the current is then opposite to the (positive) direction shown in Fig. 30.15.

We apply Kirchhoff's loop rule to the circuit in Fig. 30.15. Starting at the lower-right corner of the circuit and adding voltages as we go clockwise around the loop, we obtain

$$-L\frac{di}{dt} - \frac{q}{C} = 0$$

Since $i = dq/dt$, it follows that $di/dt = d^2q/dt^2$. We substitute this expression into the above equation and divide by $-L$ to obtain

$$\frac{d^2q}{dt^2} + \frac{1}{LC}q = 0 \qquad (L\text{-}C \text{ circuit}) \qquad (30.20)$$

Equation (30.20) has exactly the same form as the equation we derived for simple harmonic motion in Section 14.2, Eq. (14.4). That equation is $d^2x/dt^2 = -(k/m)x$, or

$$\frac{d^2x}{dt^2} + \frac{k}{m}x = 0$$

(You should review Section 14.2 before going on with this discussion.) In the *L-C* circuit the capacitor charge q plays the role of the displacement x, and the current $i = dq/dt$ is analogous to the particle's velocity $v_x = dx/dt$. The inductance L is analogous to the mass m, and the reciprocal of the capacitance, $1/C$, is analogous to the force constant k.

Pursuing this analogy, we recall that the angular frequency $\omega = 2\pi f$ of the harmonic oscillator is equal to $(k/m)^{1/2}$, and the position is given as a function of time by Eq. (14.13),

$$x = A\cos(\omega t + \phi)$$

where the amplitude A and the phase angle ϕ depend on the initial conditions. In the analogous electrical situation the capacitor charge q is given by

$$q = Q\cos(\omega t + \phi) \qquad (30.21)$$

and the angular frequency ω of oscillation is given by

$$\omega = \sqrt{\frac{1}{LC}} \qquad \begin{array}{l}\text{(angular frequency of oscillation}\\\text{in an } L\text{-}C \text{ circuit)}\end{array} \qquad (30.22)$$

You should verify that Eq. (30.21) satisfies the loop equation, Eq. (30.20), when ω has the value given by Eq. (30.22). In doing this, you will find that the instantaneous current $i = dq/dt$ is given by

$$i = -\omega Q\sin(\omega t + \phi) \qquad (30.23)$$

Thus the charge and current in an *L-C* circuit oscillate sinusoidally with time, with an angular frequency determined by the values of L and C. The ordinary frequency f, the number of cycles per second, is equal to $\omega/2\pi$ as always. The constants Q and ϕ in Eqs. (30.21) and (30.23) are determined by the initial conditions. If at time $t = 0$ the left-hand capacitor plate in Fig. 30.15 has its maximum charge Q and the current i is zero, then $\phi = 0$. If $q = 0$ at time $t = 0$, then $\phi = \pm\pi/2$ rad.

Energy in an *L-C* Circuit

We can also analyze the *L-C* circuit using an energy approach. The analogy to simple harmonic motion is equally useful here. In the mechanical problem a body with mass m is attached to a spring with force constant k. Suppose we displace the body a distance A from its equilibrium position and release it from rest at time $t = 0$. The kinetic energy of the system at any later time is $\frac{1}{2}mv_x^2$, and its elastic potential energy is $\frac{1}{2}kx^2$. Because the system is conservative, the sum of these energies equals the initial energy of the system, $\frac{1}{2}kA^2$. We find the velocity v_x at any position x just as we did in Section 14.3, Eq. (14.22):

$$v_x = \pm\sqrt{\frac{k}{m}}\sqrt{A^2 - x^2} \qquad (30.24)$$

The L-C circuit is also a conservative system. Again let Q be the maximum capacitor charge. The magnetic-field energy $\frac{1}{2}Li^2$ in the inductor at any time corresponds to the kinetic energy $\frac{1}{2}mv^2$ of the oscillating body, and the electric-field energy $q^2/2C$ in the capacitor corresponds to the elastic potential energy $\frac{1}{2}kx^2$ of the spring. The sum of these energies equals the total energy $Q^2/2C$ of the system:

$$\frac{1}{2}Li^2 + \frac{q^2}{2C} = \frac{Q^2}{2C} \qquad (30.25)$$

The total energy in the L-C circuit is *constant;* it oscillates between the magnetic and the electric forms, just as the constant total mechanical energy in simple harmonic motion is constant and oscillates between the kinetic and potential forms.

Solving Eq. (30.25) for i, we find that when the charge on the capacitor is q, the current i is

$$i = \pm\sqrt{\frac{1}{LC}}\sqrt{Q^2 - q^2} \qquad (30.26)$$

You can verify this equation by substituting q from Eq. (30.21) and i from Eq. (30.23). Comparing Eqs. (30.24) and (30.26), we see that current $i = dq/dt$ and charge q are related in the same way as are velocity $v_x = dx/dt$ and position x in the mechanical problem.

Table 30.1 summarizes the analogies between simple harmonic motion and L-C circuit oscillations. The striking parallels shown there are so close that we can solve complicated mechanical and acoustical problems by setting up analogous electric circuits and measuring the currents and voltages that correspond to the mechanical and acoustical quantities to be determined. This is the basic principle of many analog computers. This analogy can be extended to *damped* oscillations, which we consider in the next section. In Chapter 31 we will extend the analogy further to include *forced* electrical oscillations, which occur in all alternating-current circuits.

Table 30.1 Oscillation of a Mass-Spring System Compared with Electrical Oscillation in an *L-C* Circuit

Mass-Spring System

Kinetic energy $= \frac{1}{2}mv_x^2$

Potential energy $= \frac{1}{2}kx^2$

$\frac{1}{2}mv_x^2 + \frac{1}{2}kx^2 = \frac{1}{2}kA^2$

$v_x = \pm\sqrt{k/m}\sqrt{A^2 - x^2}$

$v_x = dx/dt$

$\omega = \sqrt{\dfrac{k}{m}}$

$x = A\cos(\omega t + \phi)$

Inductor-Capacitor Circuit

Magnetic energy $= \frac{1}{2}Li^2$

Electric energy $= q^2/2C$

$\frac{1}{2}Li^2 + q^2/2C = Q^2/2C$

$i = \pm\sqrt{1/LC}\sqrt{Q^2 - q^2}$

$i = dq/dt$

$\omega = \sqrt{\dfrac{1}{LC}}$

$q = Q\cos(\omega t + \phi)$

Example 30.8 An oscillating circuit

A 300-V dc power supply is used to charge a 25-μF capacitor. After the capacitor is fully charged, it is disconnected from the power supply and connected across a 10-mH inductor. The resistance in the circuit is negligible. (a) Find the frequency and period of oscillation of the circuit. (b) Find the capacitor charge and the circuit current 1.2 ms after the inductor and capacitor are connected.

SOLUTION

IDENTIFY and SET UP: Our target variables are the oscillation frequency f and period T, as well as the charge q and current i at a particular time t. We are given the capacitance C and the inductance L, from which we can calculate the frequency and period using Eq. (30.22). We find the charge and current using Eqs. (30.21) and (30.23). Initially the capacitor is fully charged and the current is zero, as in Fig. 30.14a, so the phase angle is $\phi = 0$ [see the discussion that follows Eq. (30.23)].

EXECUTE: (a) The natural angular frequency is

$$\omega = \sqrt{\frac{1}{LC}} = \sqrt{\frac{1}{(10 \times 10^{-3}\text{ H})(25 \times 10^{-6}\text{ F})}}$$

$$= 2.0 \times 10^3 \text{ rad/s}$$

The frequency f and period T are then

$$f = \frac{\omega}{2\pi} = \frac{2.0 \times 10^3 \text{ rad/s}}{2\pi \text{ rad/cycle}} = 320 \text{ Hz}$$

$$T = \frac{1}{f} = \frac{1}{320 \text{ Hz}} = 3.1 \times 10^{-3} \text{ s} = 3.1 \text{ ms}$$

(b) Since the period of the oscillation is $T = 3.1$ ms, $t = 1.2$ ms equals $0.38T$; this corresponds to a situation intermediate between Fig. 30.14b ($t = T/4$) and Fig. 30.14c ($t = T/2$). Comparing those figures with Fig. 30.15, we expect the capacitor charge q to be negative (that is, there will be negative charge on the left-hand plate of the capacitor) and the current i to be negative as well (that is, current will flow counterclockwise).

To find the value of q, we use Eq. (30.21), $q = Q \cos(\omega t + \phi)$. The charge is maximum at $t = 0$, so $\phi = 0$ and $Q = C\mathcal{E} = (25 \times 10^{-6}\ \text{F})(300\ \text{V}) = 7.5 \times 10^{-3}$ C. Hence Eq. (30.21) becomes

$$q = (7.5 \times 10^{-3}\ \text{C}) \cos \omega t$$

At time $t = 1.2 \times 10^{-3}$ s,

$$\omega t = (2.0 \times 10^3\ \text{rad/s})(1.2 \times 10^{-3}\ \text{s}) = 2.4\ \text{rad}$$

$$q = (7.5 \times 10^{-3}\ \text{C}) \cos(2.4\ \text{rad}) = -5.5 \times 10^{-3}\ \text{C}$$

From Eq. (30.23), the current i at any time is $i = -\omega Q \sin \omega t$. At $t = 1.2 \times 10^{-3}$ s,

$$i = -(2.0 \times 10^3\ \text{rad/s})(7.5 \times 10^{-3}\ \text{C}) \sin(2.4\ \text{rad}) = -10\ \text{A}$$

EVALUATE: The signs of q and i are both negative, as predicted.

Example 30.9 Energy in an oscillating circuit

For the L-C circuit of Example 30.8, find the magnetic and electric energies (a) at $t = 0$ and (b) at $t = 1.2$ ms.

SOLUTION

IDENTIFY and SET UP: We must calculate the magnetic energy U_B (stored in the inductor) and the electric energy U_E (stored in the capacitor) at two times during the L-C circuit oscillation. From Example 30.8 we know the values of the capacitor charge q and circuit current i for both times. We use them to calculate $U_B = \frac{1}{2}Li^2$ and $U_E = q^2/2C$.

EXECUTE: (a) At $t = 0$ there is no current and $q = Q$. Hence there is no magnetic energy, and all the energy in the circuit is in the form of electric energy in the capacitor:

$$U_B = \tfrac{1}{2}Li^2 = 0 \qquad U_E = \frac{Q^2}{2C} = \frac{(7.5 \times 10^{-3}\ \text{C})^2}{2(25 \times 10^{-6}\ \text{F})} = 1.1\ \text{J}$$

(b) From Example 30.8, at $t = 1.2$ ms we have $i = -10$ A and $q = -5.5 \times 10^{-3}$ C. Hence

$$U_B = \tfrac{1}{2}Li^2 = \tfrac{1}{2}(10 \times 10^{-3}\ \text{H})(-10\ \text{A})^2 = 0.5\ \text{J}$$

$$U_E = \frac{q^2}{2C} = \frac{(-5.5 \times 10^{-3}\ \text{C})^2}{2(25 \times 10^{-6}\ \text{F})} = 0.6\ \text{J}$$

EVALUATE: The magnetic and electric energies are the same at $t = 3T/8 = 0.375T$, halfway between the situations in Figs. 30.14b and 30.14c. We saw in Example 30.8 that the time considered in part (b), $t = 1.2$ ms, equals $0.38T$; this is slightly later than $0.375T$, so U_B is slightly less than U_E. At *all* times the *total* energy $E = U_B + U_E$ has the same value, 1.1 J. An L-C circuit without resistance is a conservative system; no energy is dissipated.

Test Your Understanding of Section 30.5   One way to think about the energy stored in an *L-C* circuit is to say that the circuit elements do positive or negative work on the charges that move back and forth through the circuit. (a) Between stages (a) and (b) in Fig. 30.14, does the capacitor do positive work or negative work on the charges? (b) What kind of force (electric or magnetic) does the capacitor exert on the charges to do this work? (c) During this process, does the inductor do positive or negative work on the charges? (d) What kind of force (electric or magnetic) does the inductor exert on the charges?

30.6 The *L-R-C* Series Circuit

In our discussion of the *L-C* circuit we assumed that there was no *resistance* in the circuit. This is an idealization, of course; every real inductor has resistance in its windings, and there may also be resistance in the connecting wires. Because of resistance, the electromagnetic energy in the circuit is dissipated and converted to other forms, such as internal energy of the circuit materials. Resistance in an electric circuit is analogous to friction in a mechanical system.

Suppose an inductor with inductance L and a resistor of resistance R are connected in series across the terminals of a charged capacitor, forming an **L-R-C series circuit.** As before, the capacitor starts to discharge as soon as the circuit is completed. But because of i^2R losses in the resistor, the magnetic-field energy acquired by the inductor when the capacitor is completely discharged is *less* than the original electric-field energy of the capacitor. In the same way, the energy of the capacitor when the magnetic field has decreased to zero is still smaller, and so on.

If the resistance R is relatively small, the circuit still oscillates, but with **damped harmonic motion** (Fig. 30.16a), and we say that the circuit is

ActivPhysics 14.2: AC Circuits: The *RLC* Oscillator (Questions 7–10)

30.16 Graphs of capacitor charge as a function of time in an *L-R-C* series circuit with initial charge *Q*.

(a) Underdamped circuit (small resistance *R*)

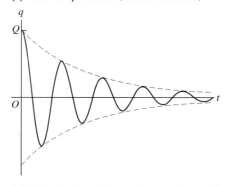

(b) Critically damped circuit (larger resistance *R*)

(c) Overdamped circuit (very large resistance *R*)

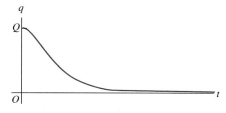

30.17 An *L-R-C* series circuit.

When switch S is in this position, the emf charges the capacitor.

When switch S is moved to this position, the capacitor discharges through the resistor and inductor.

underdamped. If we increase *R*, the oscillations die out more rapidly. When *R* reaches a certain value, the circuit no longer oscillates; it is **critically damped** (Fig. 30.16b). For still larger values of *R*, the circuit is **overdamped** (Fig. 30.16c), and the capacitor charge approaches zero even more slowly. We used these same terms to describe the behavior of the analogous mechanical system, the damped harmonic oscillator, in Section 14.7.

Analyzing an *L-R-C* Series Circuit

To analyze *L-R-C* series circuit behavior in detail, we consider the circuit shown in Fig. 30.17. It is like the *L-C* circuit of Fig. 30.15 except for the added resistor *R*; we also show the source that charges the capacitor initially. The labeling of the positive senses of *q* and *i* are the same as for the *L-C* circuit.

First we close the switch in the upward position, connecting the capacitor to a source of emf $\mathcal{E}$ for a long enough time to ensure that the capacitor acquires its final charge $Q = C\mathcal{E}$ and any initial oscillations have died out. Then at time *t* = 0 we flip the switch to the downward position, removing the source from the circuit and placing the capacitor in series with the resistor and inductor. Note that the initial current is negative, opposite to the direction of *i* shown in Fig. 30.17.

To find how *q* and *i* vary with time, we apply Kirchhoff's loop rule. Starting at point *a* and going around the loop in the direction *abcda*, we obtain the equation

$$-iR - L\frac{di}{dt} - \frac{q}{C} = 0$$

Replacing *i* with *dq/dt* and rearranging, we get

$$\frac{d^2q}{dt^2} + \frac{R}{L}\frac{dq}{dt} + \frac{1}{LC}q = 0 \qquad (30.27)$$

Note that when *R* = 0, this reduces to Eq. (30.20) for an *L-C* circuit.

There are general methods for obtaining solutions of Eq. (30.27). The form of the solution is different for the underdamped (small *R*) and overdamped (large *R*) cases. When R^2 is less than $4L/C$, the solution has the form

$$q = Ae^{-(R/2L)t}\cos\left(\sqrt{\frac{1}{LC} - \frac{R^2}{4L^2}}\,t + \phi\right) \qquad (30.28)$$

where *A* and ϕ are constants. We invite you to take the first and second derivatives of this function and show by direct substitution that it does satisfy Eq. (30.27).

This solution corresponds to the *underdamped* behavior shown in Fig. 30.16a; the function represents a sinusoidal oscillation with an exponentially decaying amplitude. (Note that the exponential factor $e^{-(R/2L)t}$ is *not* the same as the factor $e^{-(R/L)t}$ that we encountered in describing the *R-L* circuit in Section 30.4.) When *R* = 0, Eq. (30.28) reduces to Eq. (30.21) for the oscillations in an *L-C* circuit. If *R* is not zero, the angular frequency of the oscillation is *less* than $1/(LC)^{1/2}$ because of the term containing *R*. The angular frequency ω' of the damped oscillations is given by

$$\omega' = \sqrt{\frac{1}{LC} - \frac{R^2}{4L^2}} \qquad \text{(underdamped } L\text{-}R\text{-}C \text{ series circuit)} \quad (30.29)$$

When *R* = 0, this reduces to Eq. (30.22), $\omega = (1/LC)^{1/2}$. As *R* increases, ω' becomes smaller and smaller. When $R^2 = 4L/C$, the quantity under the radical becomes zero; the system no longer oscillates, and the case of *critical damping* (Fig. 30.16b) has been reached. For still larger values of *R* the system behaves as in Fig. 30.16c. In this case the circuit is *overdamped*, and *q* is given as a function of time by the sum of two decreasing exponential functions.

In the *underdamped* case the phase constant ϕ in the cosine function of Eq. (30.28) provides for the possibility of both an initial charge and an initial current at time $t = 0$, analogous to an underdamped harmonic oscillator given both an initial displacement and an initial velocity (see Exercise 30.40).

We emphasize once more that the behavior of the *L-R-C* series circuit is completely analogous to that of the damped harmonic oscillator studied in Section 14.7. We invite you to verify, for example, that if you start with Eq. (14.41) and substitute q for x, L for m, $1/C$ for k, and R for the damping constant b, the result is Eq. (30.27). Similarly, the cross-over point between underdamping and overdamping occurs at $b^2 = 4km$ for the mechanical system and at $R^2 = 4L/C$ for the electrical one. Can you find still other aspects of this analogy?

The practical applications of the *L-R-C* series circuit emerge when we include a sinusoidally varying source of emf in the circuit. This is analogous to the *forced oscillations* that we discussed in Section 14.7, and there are analogous *resonance* effects. Such a circuit is called an *alternating-current (ac) circuit;* the analysis of ac circuits is the principal topic of the next chapter.

Example 30.10   **An underdamped *L-R-C* series circuit**

What resistance R is required (in terms of L and C) to give an *L-R-C* series circuit a frequency that is one-half the undamped frequency?

SOLUTION

IDENTIFY and SET UP: This problem concerns an underdamped *L-R-C* series circuit (Fig. 30.16a). We want just enough resistance to reduce the oscillation frequency to one-half of the undamped value. Equation (30.29) gives the angular frequency ω' of an underdamped *L-R-C* series circuit; Eq. (30.22) gives the angular frequency ω of an undamped *L-C* circuit. We use these two equations to solve for R.

EXECUTE: From Eqs. (30.29) and (30.22), the requirement $\omega' = \omega/2$ yields

$$\sqrt{\frac{1}{LC} - \frac{R^2}{4L^2}} = \frac{1}{2}\sqrt{\frac{1}{LC}}$$

We square both sides and solve for R:

$$R = \sqrt{\frac{3L}{C}}$$

For example, adding $35\ \Omega$ to the circuit of Example 30.8 ($L = 10$ mH, $C = 25\ \mu$F) would reduce the frequency from 320 Hz to 160 Hz.

EVALUATE: The circuit becomes critically damped with no oscillations when $R = \sqrt{4L/C}$. Our result for R is smaller than that, as it should be; we want the circuit to be *under*damped.

Test Your Understanding of Section 30.6   An *L-R-C* series circuit includes a 2.0-Ω resistor. At $t = 0$ the capacitor charge is 2.0 μC. For which of the following values of the inductance and capacitance will the charge on the capacitor *not* oscillate? (i) $L = 3.0\ \mu$H, $C = 6.0\ \mu$F; (ii) $L = 6.0\ \mu$H, $C = 3.0\ \mu$F; (iii) $L = 3.0\ \mu$H, $C = 3.0\ \mu$F.

Mutual inductance: When a changing current i_1 in one circuit causes a changing magnetic flux in a second circuit, an emf $\mathcal{E}_2$ is induced in the second circuit. Likewise, a changing current i_2 in the second circuit induces an emf $\mathcal{E}_1$ in the first circuit. If the circuits are coils of wire with N_1 and N_2 turns, the mutual inductance M can be expressed in terms of the average flux Φ_{B2} through each turn of coil 2 caused by the current i_1 in coil 1, or in terms of the average flux Φ_{B1} through each turn of coil 1 caused by the current i_2 in coil 2. The SI unit of mutual inductance is the henry, abbreviated H. (See Examples 30.1 and 30.2.)

$$\mathcal{E}_2 = -M\frac{di_1}{dt} \quad \text{and}$$

$$\mathcal{E}_1 = -M\frac{di_2}{dt} \quad (30.4)$$

$$M = \frac{N_2 \Phi_{B2}}{i_1} = \frac{N_1 \Phi_{B1}}{i_2} \quad (30.5)$$

Self-inductance: A changing current i in any circuit causes a self-induced emf $\mathcal{E}$. The inductance (or self-inductance) L depends on the geometry of the circuit and the material surrounding it. The inductance of a coil of N turns is related to the average flux Φ_B through each turn caused by the current i in the coil. An inductor is a circuit device, usually including a coil of wire, intended to have a substantial inductance. (See Examples 30.3 and 30.4.)

$$\mathcal{E} = -L\frac{di}{dt} \quad (30.7)$$

$$L = \frac{N\Phi_B}{i} \quad (30.6)$$

Magnetic-field energy: An inductor with inductance L carrying current I has energy U associated with the inductor's magnetic field. The magnetic energy density u (energy per unit volume) is proportional to the square of the magnetic field magnitude. (See Example 30.5.)

$$U = \tfrac{1}{2}LI^2 \quad (30.9)$$

$$u = \frac{B^2}{2\mu_0} \quad \text{(in vacuum)} \quad (30.10)$$

$$u = \frac{B^2}{2\mu} \quad \begin{array}{l}\text{(in a material} \\ \text{with magnetic} \\ \text{permeability } \mu)\end{array} \quad (30.11)$$

Stored energy $U = \tfrac{1}{2}LI^2$ Energy density $u = B^2/2\mu_0$

R-L circuits: In a circuit containing a resistor R, an inductor L, and a source of emf, the growth and decay of current are exponential. The time constant τ is the time required for the current to approach within a fraction $1/e$ of its final value. (See Examples 30.6 and 30.7.)

$$\tau = \frac{L}{R} \quad (30.16)$$

L-C circuits: A circuit that contains inductance L and capacitance C undergoes electrical oscillations with an angular frequency ω that depends on L and C. This is analogous to a mechanical harmonic oscillator, with inductance L analogous to mass m, the reciprocal of capacitance $1/C$ to force constant k, charge q to displacement x, and current i to velocity v_x. (See Examples 30.8 and 30.9.)

$$\omega = \sqrt{\frac{1}{LC}} \quad (30.22)$$

L-R-C series circuits: A circuit that contains inductance, resistance, and capacitance undergoes damped oscillations for sufficiently small resistance. The frequency ω' of damped oscillations depends on the values of L, R, and C. As R increases, the damping increases; if R is greater than a certain value, the behavior becomes overdamped and no longer oscillates. (See Example 30.10.)

$$\omega' = \sqrt{\frac{1}{LC} - \frac{R^2}{4L^2}} \quad (30.29)$$

Underdamped circuit (small R)

BRIDGING PROBLEM   **Analyzing an *L-C* Circuit**

An *L-C* circuit consists of a 60.0-mH inductor and a 250-μF capacitor. The initial charge on the capacitor is 6.00 μC, and the initial current in the inductor is 0.400 mA. (a) What is the maximum energy stored in the inductor? (b) What is the maximum current in the inductor? (c) What is the maximum voltage across the capacitor? (d) When the current in the inductor has half its maximum value, what is the energy stored in the inductor and the voltage across the capacitor?

SOLUTION GUIDE

See MasteringPhysics® study area for a Video Tutor solution.

IDENTIFY and SET UP:

1. An *L-C* circuit is a conservative system because there is no resistance to dissipate energy. The energy oscillates between electric energy in the capacitor and magnetic energy stored in the inductor.

2. Which key equations are needed to describe the capacitor? To describe the inductor?

EXECUTE:

3. Find the initial total energy in the *L-C* circuit. Use this to determine the maximum energy stored in the inductor during the oscillation.

4. Use the result of step 3 to find the maximum current in the inductor.

5. Use the result of step 3 to find the maximum energy stored in the capacitor during the oscillation. Then use this to find the maximum capacitor voltage.

6. Find the energy in the inductor and the capacitor charge when the current has half the value that you found in step 4.

EVALUATE:

7. Initially, what fraction of the total energy is in the inductor? Is it possible to tell whether this is initially increasing or decreasing?

Problems   For instructor-assigned homework, go to www.masteringphysics.com

•, ••, •••: Problems of increasing difficulty. **CP**: Cumulative problems incorporating material from earlier chapters. **CALC**: Problems requiring calculus. **BIO**: Biosciences problems.

DISCUSSION QUESTIONS

Q30.1 In an electric trolley or bus system, the vehicle's motor draws current from an overhead wire by means of a long arm with an attachment at the end that slides along the overhead wire. A brilliant electric spark is often seen when the attachment crosses a junction in the wires where contact is momentarily lost. Explain this phenomenon.

Q30.2 From Eq. (30.5) 1 H = 1 Wb/A, and from Eq. (30.4) 1 H = 1 $\Omega \cdot$ s. Show that these two definitions are equivalent.

Q30.3 In Fig. 30.1, if coil 2 is turned 90° so that its axis is vertical, does the mutual inductance increase or decrease? Explain.

Q30.4 The tightly wound toroidal solenoid is one of the few configurations for which it is easy to calculate self-inductance. What features of the toroidal solenoid give it this simplicity?

Q30.5 Two identical, closely wound, circular coils, each having self-inductance *L*, are placed next to each other, so that they are coaxial and almost touching. If they are connected in series, what is the self-inductance of the combination? What if they are connected in parallel? Can they be connected so that the total inductance is zero? Explain.

Q30.6 Two closely wound circular coils have the same number of turns, but one has twice the radius of the other. How are the self-inductances of the two coils related? Explain your reasoning.

Q30.7 You are to make a resistor by winding a wire around a cylindrical form. To make the inductance as small as possible, it is proposed that you wind half the wire in one direction and the other half in the opposite direction. Would this achieve the desired result? Why or why not?

Q30.8 For the same magnetic field strength *B*, is the energy density greater in vacuum or in a magnetic material? Explain. Does

Eq. (30.11) imply that for a long solenoid in which the current is *I* the energy stored is proportional to $1/\mu$? And does this mean that for the same current less energy is stored when the solenoid is filled with a ferromagnetic material rather than with air? Explain.

Q30.9 In Section 30.5 Kirchhoff's loop rule is applied to an *L-C* circuit where the capacitor is initially fully charged and the equation $-L\, di/dt - q/C = 0$ is derived. But as the capacitor starts to discharge, the current increases from zero. The equation says $L\, di/dt = -q/C$, so it says $L\, di/dt$ is negative. Explain how $L\, di/dt$ can be negative when the current is increasing.

Q30.10 In Section 30.5 the relationship $i = dq/dt$ is used in deriving Eq. (30.20). But a flow of current corresponds to a decrease in the charge on the capacitor. Explain, therefore, why this is the correct equation to use in the derivation, rather than $i = -dq/dt$.

Q30.11 In the *R-L* circuit shown in Fig. 30.11, when switch S_1 is closed, the potential v_{ab} changes suddenly and discontinuously, but the current does not. Explain why the voltage can change suddenly but the current can't.

Q30.12 In the *R-L* circuit shown in Fig. 30.11, is the current in the resistor always the same as the current in the inductor? How do you know?

Q30.13 Suppose there is a steady current in an   u attempt to reduce the current to zero instantane   ly opening a switch, an arc can appear at the switch   ? Is it physically possible to stop the current instantaneously? Explain.

Q30.14 In an *L-R-C* series circuit, what criteria could be used to decide whether the system is overdamped or underdamped? For example, could we compare the maximum energy stored during one cycle to the energy dissipated during one cycle? Explain.

EXERCISES

Section 30.1 Mutual Inductance

30.1 • Two coils have mutual inductance $M = 3.25 \times 10^{-4}$ H. The current i_1 in the first coil increases at a uniform rate of 830 A/s. (a) What is the magnitude of the induced emf in the second coil? Is it constant? (b) Suppose that the current described is in the second coil rather than the first. What is the magnitude of the induced emf in the first coil?

30.2 • Two coils are wound around the same cylindrical form, like the coils in Example 30.1. When the current in the first coil is decreasing at a rate of -0.242 A/s, the induced emf in the second coil has magnitude 1.65×10^{-3} V. (a) What is the mutual inductance of the pair of coils? (b) If the second coil has 25 turns, what is the flux through each turn when the current in the first coil equals 1.20 A? (c) If the current in the second coil increases at a rate of 0.360 A/s, what is the magnitude of the induced emf in the first coil?

30.3 • A 10.0-cm-long solenoid of diameter 0.400 cm is wound uniformly with 800 turns. A second coil with 50 turns is wound around the solenoid at its center. What is the mutual inductance of the combination of the two coils?

30.4 • A solenoidal coil with 25 turns of wire is wound tightly around another coil with 300 turns (see Example 30.1). The inner solenoid is 25.0 cm long and has a diameter of 2.00 cm. At a certain time, the current in the inner solenoid is 0.120 A and is increasing at a rate of 1.75×10^3 A/s. For this time, calculate: (a) the average magnetic flux through each turn of the inner solenoid; (b) the mutual inductance of the two solenoids; (c) the emf induced in the outer solenoid by the changing current in the inner solenoid.

30.5 • Two toroidal solenoids are wound around the same form so that the magnetic field of one passes through the turns of the other. Solenoid 1 has 700 turns, and solenoid 2 has 400 turns. When the current in solenoid 1 is 6.52 A, the average flux through each turn of solenoid 2 is 0.0320 Wb. (a) What is the mutual inductance of the pair of solenoids? (b) When the current in solenoid 2 is 2.54 A, what is the average flux through each turn of solenoid 1?

30.6 •• A toroidal solenoid with mean radius r and cross-sectional area A is wound uniformly with N_1 turns. A second toroidal solenoid with N_2 turns is wound uniformly on top of the first, so that the two solenoids have the same cross-sectional area and mean radius. (a) What is the mutual inductance of the two solenoids? Assume that the magnetic field of the first solenoid is uniform across the cross section of the two solenoids. (b) If $N_1 = 500$ turns, $N_2 = 300$ turns, $r = 10.0$ cm, and $A = 0.800$ cm², what is the value of the mutual inductance?

Section 30.2 Self-Inductance and Inductors

30.7 • A 2.50-mH toroidal solenoid has an average radius of 6.00 cm and a cross-sectional area of 2.00 cm². (a) How many coils does it have? (Make the same assumption as in Example 30.3.) (b) At what rate must the current through it change so that a potential difference of 2.00 V is developed across its ends?

30.8 • A toroidal solenoid has 500 turns, cross-sectional area 6.25 cm², and mean radius 4.00 cm. (a) Calculate the coil's self-inductance. (b) If the current decreases uniformly from 5.00 A to 2.00 A in 3.00 ms, calculate the self-induced emf in the coil. (c) The current is directed from terminal a of the coil to terminal b. Is the direction of the induced emf from a to b or from b to a?

30.9 • At the instant when the current in an inductor is increasing at a rate of 0.0640 A/s, the magnitude of the self-induced emf is 0.0160 V. (a) What is the inductance of the inductor? (b) If the

inductor is a solenoid with 400 turns, what is the average magnetic flux through each turn when the current is 0.720 A?

30.10 •• When the current in a toroidal solenoid is changing at a rate of 0.0260 A/s, the magnitude of the induced emf is 12.6 mV. When the current equals 1.40 A, the average flux through each turn of the solenoid is 0.00285 Wb. How many turns does the solenoid have?

30.11 • The inductor in Fig. E30.11 has inductance 0.260 H and carries a current in the direction shown that is decreasing at a uniform rate, $di/dt = -0.0180$ A/s. (a) Find the self-induced emf. (b) Which end of the inductor, a or b, is at a higher potential?

Figure **E30.11**

30.12 • The inductor shown in Fig. E30.11 has inductance 0.260 H and carries a current in the direction shown. The current is changing at a constant rate. (a) The potential between points a and b is $V_{ab} = 1.04$ V, with point a at higher potential. Is the current increasing or decreasing? (b) If the current at $t = 0$ is 12.0 A, what is the current at $t = 2.00$ s?

30.13 •• A toroidal solenoid has mean radius 12.0 cm and cross-sectional area 0.600 cm². (a) How many turns does the solenoid have if its inductance is 0.100 mH? (b) What is the resistance of the solenoid if the wire from which it is wound has a resistance per unit length of 0.0760 Ω/m?

30.14 • A long, straight solenoid has 800 turns. When the current in the solenoid is 2.90 A, the average flux through each turn of the solenoid is 3.25×10^{-3} Wb. What must be the magnitude of the rate of change of the current in order for the self-induced emf to equal 7.50 mV?

30.15 •• **Inductance of a Solenoid.** (a) A long, straight solenoid has N turns, uniform cross-sectional area A, and length l. Show that the inductance of this solenoid is given by the equation $L = \mu_0 A N^2 / l$. Assume that the magnetic field is uniform inside the solenoid and zero outside. (Your answer is approximate because B is actually smaller at the ends than at the center. For this reason, your answer is actually an upper limit on the inductance.) (b) A metallic laboratory spring is typically 5.00 cm long and 0.150 cm in diameter and has 50 coils. If you connect such a spring in an electric circuit, how much self-inductance must you include for it if you model it as an ideal solenoid?

Section 30.3 Magnetic-Field Energy

30.16 • An inductor used in a dc power supply has an inductance of 12.0 H and a resistance of 180 Ω. It carries a current of 0.300 A. (a) What is the energy stored in the magnetic field? (b) At what rate is thermal energy developed in the inductor? (c) Does your answer to part (b) mean that the magnetic-field energy is decreasing with time? Explain.

30.17 • An air-filled toroidal solenoid has a mean radius of 15.0 cm and a cross-sectional area of 5.00 cm². When the current is 12.0 A, the energy stored is 0.390 J. How many turns does the winding have?

30.18 • An air-filled toroidal solenoid has 300 turns of wire, a mean radius of 12.0 cm, and a cross-sectional area of 4.00 cm². If the current is 5.00 A, calculate: (a) the magnetic field in the solenoid; (b) the self-inductance of the solenoid; (c) the energy stored in the magnetic field; (d) the energy density in the magnetic field. (e) Check your answer for part (d) by dividing your answer to part (c) by the volume of the solenoid.

30.19 •• A solenoid 25.0 cm long and with a cross-sectional area of 0.500 cm² contains 400 turns of wire and carries a current of 80.0 A. Calculate: (a) the magnetic field in the solenoid; (b) the energy density in the magnetic field if the solenoid is filled with air; (c) the total energy contained in the coil's magnetic field (assume the field is uniform); (d) the inductance of the solenoid.

30.20 • It has been proposed to use large inductors as energy storage devices. (a) How much electrical energy is converted to light and thermal energy by a 200-W light bulb in one day? (b) If the amount of energy calculated in part (a) is stored in an inductor in which the current is 80.0 A, what is the inductance?

30.21 •• In a proton accelerator used in elementary particle physics experiments, the trajectories of protons are controlled by bending magnets that produce a magnetic field of 4.80 T. What is the magnetic-field energy in a 10.0-cm^3 volume of space where $B = 4.80$ T?

30.22 • It is proposed to store 1.00 kW $\cdot$ h $= 3.60 \times 10^6$ J of electrical energy in a uniform magnetic field with magnitude 0.600 T. (a) What volume (in vacuum) must the magnetic field occupy to store this amount of energy? (b) If instead this amount of energy is to be stored in a volume (in vacuum) equivalent to a cube 40.0 cm on a side, what magnetic field is required?

Section 30.4 The *R-L* Circuit

30.23 • An inductor with an inductance of 2.50 H and a resistance of 8.00 Ω is connected to the terminals of a battery with an emf of 6.00 V and negligible internal resistance. Find (a) the initial rate of increase of current in the circuit; (b) the rate of increase of current at the instant when the current is 0.500 A; (c) the current 0.250 s after the circuit is closed; (d) the final steady-state current.

30.24 • In Fig. 30.11, $R = 15.0$ Ω and the battery emf is 6.30 V. With switch S_2 open, switch S_1 is closed. After several minutes, S_1 is opened and S_2 is closed. (a) At 2.00 ms after S_1 is opened, the current has decayed to 0.320 A. Calculate the inductance of the coil. (b) How long after S_1 is opened will the current reach 1.00% of its original value?

30.25 • A 35.0-V battery with negligible internal resistance, a 50.0-Ω resistor, and a 1.25-mH inductor with negligible resistance are all connected in series with an open switch. The switch is suddenly closed. (a) How long after closing the switch will the current through the inductor reach one-half of its maximum value? (b) How long after closing the switch will the energy stored in the inductor reach one-half of its maximum value?

30.26 • In Fig. 30.11, switch S_1 is closed while switch S_2 is kept open. The inductance is $L = 0.115$ H, and the resistance is $R = 120$ Ω. (a) When the current has reached its final value, the energy stored in the inductor is 0.260 J. What is the emf $\mathcal{E}$ of the battery? (b) After the current has reached its final value, S_1 is opened and S_2 is closed. How much time does it take for the energy stored in the inductor to decrease to 0.130 J, half the original value?

30.27 • In Fig. 30.11, suppose that $\mathcal{E} = 60.0$ V, $R = 240$ Ω, and $L = 0.160$ H. With switch S_2 open, switch S_1 is left closed until a constant current is established. Then S_2 is closed and S_1 opened, taking the battery out of the circuit. (a) What is the initial current in the resistor, just after S_2 is closed and S_1 is opened? (b) What is the current in the resistor at $t = 4.00 \times 10^{-4}$ s? (c) What is the potential difference between points b and c at $t = 4.00 \times 10^{-4}$ s? Which point is at a higher potential? (d) How long does it take the current to decrease to half its initial value?

30.28 • In Fig. 30.11, suppose that $\mathcal{E} = 60.0$ V, $R = 240$ Ω, and $L = 0.160$ H. Initially there is no current in the circuit. Switch S_2 is left open, and switch S_1 is closed. (a) Just after S_1 is closed, what are the potential differences v_{ab} and v_{bc}? (b) A long time (many time constants) after S_1 is closed, what are v_{ab} and v_{bc}? (c) What are v_{ab} and v_{bc} at an intermediate time when $i = 0.150$ A?

30.29 • Refer to the circuit in Exercise 30.23. (a) What is the power input to the inductor from the battery as a function of time if the circuit is completed at $t = 0$? (b) What is the rate of dissipation of energy in the resistance of the inductor as a function of time? (c) What is the rate at which the energy of the magnetic field in the inductor is increasing, as a function of time? (d) Compare the results of parts (a), (b), and (c).

30.30 • In Fig. 30.11 switch S_1 is closed while switch S_2 is kept open. The inductance is $L = 0.380$ H, the resistance is $R = 48.0$ Ω, and the emf of the battery is 18.0 V. At time t after S_1 is closed, the current in the circuit is increasing at a rate of $di/dt = 7.20$ A/s. At this instant what is v_{ab}, the voltage across the resistor?

Section 30.5 The *L-C* Circuit

30.31 • CALC Show that the differential equation of Eq. (30.20) is satisfied by the function $q = Q \cos(\omega t + \phi)$, with ω given by $1/\sqrt{LC}$.

30.32 •• A 20.0-μF capacitor is charged by a 150.0-V power supply, then disconnected from the power and connected in series with a 0.280-mH inductor. Calculate: (a) the oscillation frequency of the circuit; (b) the energy stored in the capacitor at time $t = 0$ ms (the moment of connection with the inductor); (c) the energy stored in the inductor at $t = 1.30$ ms.

30.33 • A 7.50-nF capacitor is charged up to 12.0 V, then disconnected from the power supply and connected in series through a coil. The period of oscillation of the circuit is then measured to be 8.60×10^{-5} s. Calculate: (a) the inductance of the coil; (b) the maximum charge on the capacitor; (c) the total energy of the circuit; (d) the maximum current in the circuit.

30.34 •• A 18.0-μF capacitor is placed across a 22.5-V battery for several seconds and is then connected across a 12.0-mH inductor that has no appreciable resistance. (a) After the capacitor and inductor are connected together, find the maximum current in the circuit. When the current is a maximum, what is the charge on the capacitor? (b) How long after the capacitor and inductor are connected together does it take for the capacitor to be completely discharged for the first time? For the second time? (c) Sketch graphs of the charge on the capacitor plates and the current through the inductor as functions of time.

30.35 • L-C Oscillations. A capacitor with capacitance 6.00×10^{-5} F is charged by connecting it to a 12.0-V battery. The capacitor is disconnected from the battery and connected across an inductor with $L = 1.50$ H. (a) What are the angular frequency ω of the electrical oscillations and the period of these oscillations (the time for one oscillation)? (b) What is the initial charge on the capacitor? (c) How much energy is initially stored in the capacitor? (d) What is the charge on the capacitor 0.0230 s after the connection to the inductor is made? Interpret the sign of your answer. (e) At the time given in part (d), what is the current in the inductor? Interpret the sign of your answer. (f) At the time given in part (d), how much electrical energy is stored in the capacitor and how much is stored in the inductor?

30.36 • A Radio Tuning Circuit. The minimum capacitance of a variable capacitor in a radio is 4.18 pF. (a) What is the inductance of a coil connected to this capacitor if the oscillation frequency of the L-C circuit is 1600×10^3 Hz, corresponding to one end of the AM radio broadcast band, when the capacitor is set to its minimum capacitance? (b) The frequency at the other end of the broadcast band is 540×10^3 Hz. What is the maximum capacitance of the capacitor if the oscillation frequency is adjustable over the range of the broadcast band?

30.37 •• An *L-C* circuit containing an 80.0-mH inductor and a 1.25-nF capacitor oscillates with a maximum current of 0.750 A. Calculate: (a) the maximum charge on the capacitor and (b) the oscillation frequency of the circuit. (c) Assuming the capacitor had its maximum charge at time $t = 0$, calculate the energy stored in the inductor after 2.50 ms of oscillation.

30.38 • In an *L-C* circuit, $L = 85.0$ mH and $C = 3.20$ μF. During the oscillations the maximum current in the inductor is 0.850 mA. (a) What is the maximum charge on the capacitor? (b) What is the magnitude of the charge on the capacitor at an instant when the current in the inductor has magnitude 0.500 mA?

Section 30.6 The *L-R-C* Series Circuit

30.39 • An *L-R-C* series circuit has $L = 0.450$ H, $C = 2.50 \times 10^{-5}$ F, and resistance *R*. (a) What is the angular frequency of the circuit when $R = 0$? (b) What value must *R* have to give a 5.0% decrease in angular frequency compared to the value calculated in part (a)?

30.40 • For the circuit of Fig. 30.17, let $C = 15.0$ nF, $L = 22$ mH, and $R = 75.0$ Ω. (a) Calculate the oscillation frequency of the circuit once the capacitor has been charged and the switch has been connected to point *a*. (b) How long will it take for the amplitude of the oscillation to decay to 10.0% of its original value? (c) What value of *R* would result in a critically damped circuit?

30.41 • CP (a) In Eq. (14.41), substitute *q* for *x*, *L* for *m*, $1/C$ for *k*, and *R* for the damping constant *b*. Show that the result is Eq. (30.27). (b) Make these same substitutions in Eq. (14.43) and show that Eq. (30.29) results. (c) Make these same substitutions in Eq. (14.42) and show that Eq. (30.28) results.

30.42 • CALC (a) Take first and second derivatives with respect to time of *q* given in Eq. (30.28), and show that it is a solution of Eq. (30.27). (b) At $t = 0$ the switch shown in Fig. 30.17 is thrown so that it connects points *d* and *a*; at this time, $q = Q$ and $i = dq/dt = 0$. Show that the constants ϕ and *A* in Eq. (30.28) are given by

$$\tan\phi = -\frac{R}{2L\sqrt{(1/LC) - (R^2/4L^2)}} \quad \text{and} \quad A = \frac{Q}{\cos\phi}$$

PROBLEMS

30.43 • One solenoid is centered inside another. The outer one has a length of 50.0 cm and contains 6750 coils, while the coaxial inner solenoid is 3.0 cm long and 0.120 cm in diameter and contains 15 coils. The current in the outer solenoid is changing at 49.2 A/s. (a) What is the mutual inductance of these solenoids? (b) Find the emf induced in the innner solenoid.

30.44 •• CALC A coil has 400 turns and self-inductance 4.80 mH. The current in the coil varies with time according to $i = (680 \text{ mA})\cos(\pi t/0.0250 \text{ s})$. (a) What is the maximum emf induced in the coil? (b) What is the maximum average flux through each turn of the coil? (c) At $t = 0.0180$ s, what is the magnitude of the induced emf?

30.45 • **A Differentiating Circuit.** The current in a resistanceless inductor is caused to vary with time as shown in the graph of Fig. P30.45. (a) Sketch the pattern that would be observed on the screen of an oscilloscope connected to the terminals of the inductor. (The oscilloscope spot sweeps horizontally across the screen at a constant speed, and its vertical deflection is proportional to the potential difference between

Figure **P30.45**

the inductor terminals.) (b) Explain why a circuit with an inductor can be described as a "differentiating circuit."

30.46 •• CALC A 0.250-H inductor carries a time-varying current given by the expression $i = (124 \text{ mA})\cos[(240\pi/\text{s})t]$. (a) Find an expression for the induced emf as a function of time. Graph the current and induced emf as functions of time for $t = 0$ to $t = \frac{1}{60}$ s. (b) What is the maximum emf? What is the current when the induced emf is a maximum? (c) What is the maximum current? What is the induced emf when the current is a maximum?

30.47 •• **Solar Magnetic Energy.** Magnetic fields within a sunspot can be as strong as 0.4 T. (By comparison, the earth's magnetic field is about $1/10,000$ as strong.) Sunspots can be as large as 25,000 km in radius. The material in a sunspot has a density of about 3×10^{-4} kg/m^3. Assume μ for the sunspot material is μ_0. If 100% of the magnetic-field energy stored in a sunspot could be used to eject the sunspot's material away from the sun's surface, at what speed would that material be ejected? Compare to the sun's escape speed, which is about 6×10^5 m/s. (*Hint:* Calculate the kinetic energy the magnetic field could supply to 1 m^3 of sunspot material.)

30.48 •• CP CALC **A Coaxial Cable.** A small solid conductor with radius *a* is supported by insulating, nonmagnetic disks on the axis of a thin-walled tube with inner radius *b*. The inner and outer conductors carry equal currents *i* in opposite directions. (a) Use Ampere's law to find the magnetic field at any point in the volume between the conductors. (b) Write the expression for the flux $d\Phi_B$ through a narrow strip of length *l* parallel to the axis, of width *dr*, at a distance *r* from the axis of the cable and lying in a plane containing the axis. (c) Integrate your expression from part (b) over the volume between the two conductors to find the total flux produced by a current *i* in the central conductor. (d) Show that the inductance of a length *l* of the cable is

$$L = l\frac{\mu_0}{2\pi}\ln\left(\frac{b}{a}\right)$$

(e) Use Eq. (30.9) to calculate the energy stored in the magnetic field for a length *l* of the cable.

30.49 •• CP CALC Consider the coaxial cable of Problem 30.48. The conductors carry equal currents *i* in opposite directions. (a) Use Ampere's law to find the magnetic field at any point in the volume between the conductors. (b) Use the energy density for a magnetic field, Eq. (30.10), to calculate the energy stored in a thin, cylindrical shell between the two conductors. Let the cylindrical shell have inner radius *r*, outer radius $r + dr$, and length *l*. (c) Integrate your result in part (b) over the volume between the two conductors to find the total energy stored in the magnetic field for a length *l* of the cable. (d) Use your result in part (c) and Eq. (30.9) to calculate the inductance *L* of a length *l* of the cable. Compare your result to *L* calculated in part (d) of Problem 30.48.

30.50 •• A toroidal solenoid has a mean radius *r* and a cross-sectional area *A* and is wound uniformly with N_1 turns. A second toroidal solenoid with N_2 turns is wound uniformly around the first. The two coils are wound in the same direction. (a) Derive an expression for the inductance L_1 when only the first coil is used and an expression for L_2 when only the second coil is used. (b) Show that $M^2 = L_1L_2$.

30.51 • (a) What would have to be the self-inductance of a solenoid for it to store 10.0 J of energy when a 2.00-A current runs through it? (b) If this solenoid's cross-sectional diameter is 4.00 cm, and if you could wrap its coils to a density of 10 coils/mm, how long would the solenoid be? (See Exercise 30.15.) Is this a realistic length for ordinary laboratory use?

30.52 • An inductor is connected to the terminals of a battery that has an emf of 12.0 V and negligible internal resistance. The current is 4.86 mA at 0.940 ms after the connection is completed. After a long time the current is 6.45 mA. What are (a) the resistance R of the inductor and (b) the inductance L of the inductor?

30.53 •• **CALC** Continuation of Exercises 30.23 and 30.29. (a) How much energy is stored in the magnetic field of the inductor one time constant after the battery has been connected? Compute this both by integrating the expression in Exercise 30.29(c) and by using Eq. (30.9), and compare the results. (b) Integrate the expression obtained in Exercise 30.29(a) to find the *total* energy supplied by the battery during the time interval considered in part (a). (c) Integrate the expression obtained in Exercise 30.29(b) to find the *total* energy dissipated in the resistance of the inductor during the same time period. (d) Compare the results obtained in parts (a), (b), and (c).

30.54 •• **CALC** Continuation of Exercise 30.27. (a) What is the total energy initially stored in the inductor? (b) At $t = 4.00 \times 10^{-4}$ s, at what rate is the energy stored in the inductor decreasing? (c) At $t = 4.00 \times 10^{-4}$ s, at what rate is electrical energy being converted into thermal energy in the resistor? (d) Obtain an expression for the rate at which electrical energy is being converted into thermal energy in the resistor as a function of time. Integrate this expression from $t = 0$ to $t = \infty$ to obtain the total electrical energy dissipated in the resistor. Compare your result to that of part (a).

30.55 • **CALC** The equation preceding Eq. (30.27) may be converted into an energy relationship. Multiply both sides of this equation by $-i = -dq/dt$. The first term then becomes $i^2 R$. Show that the second term can be written as $d\left(\frac{1}{2}Li^2\right)/dt$, and that the third term can be written as $d(q^2/2C)/dt$. What does the resulting equation say about energy conservation in the circuit?

30.56 • A 7.00-μF capacitor is initially charged to a potential of 16.0 V. It is then connected in series with a 3.75-mH inductor. (a) What is the total energy stored in this circuit? (b) What is the maximum current in the inductor? What is the charge on the capacitor plates at the instant the current in the inductor is maximal?

30.57 • **An Electromagnetic Car Alarm.** Your latest invention is a car alarm that produces sound at a particularly annoying frequency of 3500 Hz. To do this, the car-alarm circuitry must produce an alternating electric current of the same frequency. That's why your design includes an inductor and a capacitor in series. The maximum voltage across the capacitor is to be 12.0 V (the same voltage as the car battery). To produce a sufficiently loud sound, the capacitor must store 0.0160 J of energy. What values of capacitance and inductance should you choose for your car-alarm circuit?

30.58 • An L-C circuit consists of a 60.0-mH inductor and a 250-μF capacitor. The initial charge on the capacitor is 6.00 μC, and the initial current in the inductor is zero. (a) What is the maximum voltage across the capacitor? (b) What is the maximum current in the inductor? (c) What is the maximum energy stored in the inductor? (d) When the current in the inductor has half its maximum value, what is the charge on the capacitor and what is the energy stored in the inductor?

30.59 •• A 84.0-nF capacitor is charged to 12.0 V, then disconnected from the power supply and connected in series with a coil that has $L = 0.0420$ H and negligible resistance. At an instant when the charge on the capacitor is 0.650 μC, what is the magnitude of the current in the inductor and what is the magnitude of the rate of change of this current?

30.60 •• A charged capacitor with $C = 590$ μF is connected in series to an inductor that has $L = 0.330$ H and negligible resistance.

At an instant when the current in the inductor is $i = 2.50$ A, the current is increasing at a rate of $di/dt = 89.0$ A/s. During the current oscillations, what is the maximum voltage across the capacitor?

30.61 ••• **CP** In the circuit shown in Fig. P30.61, the switch has been open for a long time and is suddenly closed. Neither the battery nor the inductors have any appreciable resistance. (a) What do the ammeter and voltmeter read just after S is closed? (b) What do the ammeter and the voltmeter read after S has been closed a very long time? (c) What do the ammeter and the voltmeter read 0.115 ms after S is closed?

Figure **P30.61**

30.62 •• While studying a coil of unknown inductance and internal resistance, you connect it in series with a 25.0-V battery and a 150-Ω resistor. You then place an oscilloscope across one of these circuit elements and use the oscilloscope to measure the voltage across the circuit element as a function of time. The result is shown in Fig. P30.62. (a) Across which circuit element (coil or resistor) is the oscilloscope connected? How do you know this? (b) Find the inductance and the internal resistance of the coil. (c) Carefully make a quantitative sketch showing the voltage versus time you would observe if you put the oscilloscope across the other circuit element (resistor or coil).

Figure **P30.62**

30.63 •• In the lab, you are trying to find the inductance and internal resistance of a solenoid. You place it in series with a battery of negligible internal resistance, a 10.0-Ω resistor, and a switch. You then put an oscilloscope across one of these circuit elements to measure the voltage across that circuit element as a function of time. You close the switch, and the oscilloscope shows voltage versus time as shown in Fig. P30.63. (a) Across which circuit element (solenoid or resistor) is the oscilloscope connected? How do you know this? (b) Why doesn't the graph approach zero as $t \to \infty$? (c) What is the emf of the battery? (d) Find the maximum current in the circuit. (e) What are the internal resistance and self-inductance of the solenoid?

Figure **P30.63**

30.64 •• **CP** In the circuit shown in Fig. P30.64, find the reading in each ammeter and voltmeter (a) just after switch S is closed and (b) after S has been closed a very long time.

30.65 •• **CP** In the circuit shown in Fig. P30.65, switch S is closed at time $t = 0$ with no charge initially on the capacitor. (a) Find the reading of each ammeter and each voltmeter just after S is closed. (b) Find the

Figure **P30.64**

reading of each meter after a long time has elapsed. (c) Find the maximum charge on the capacitor. (d) Draw a qualitative graph of the reading of voltmeter V_2 as a function of time.

Figure **P30.65**

30.66 • In the circuit shown in Fig. P30.66 the battery and the inductor have no appreciable internal resistance and there is no current in the circuit. After the switch is closed, find the readings of the ammeter (A) and voltmeters (V_1 and V_2) (a) the instant after the switch is closed and (b) after the switch has been closed for a very long time. (c) Which answers in parts (a) and (b) would change if the inductance were 24.0 mH instead?

Figure **P30.66**

30.67 •• **CP** In the circuit shown in Fig. P30.67, switch S is closed at time $t = 0$. (a) Find the reading of each meter just after S is closed. (b) What does each meter read long after S is closed?

Figure **P30.67**

30.68 •• In the circuit shown in Fig. P30.68, switch S_1 has been closed for a long enough time so that the current reads a steady 3.50 A. Suddenly, switch S_2 is closed and S_1 is opened at the same instant. (a) What is the maximum charge that the capacitor will receive? (b) What is the current in the inductor at this time?

Figure **P30.68**

30.69 •• **CP** In the circuit shown in Fig. P30.69, $\mathcal{E} = 60.0$ V, $R_1 = 40.0$ Ω, $R_2 = 25.0$ Ω, and $L = 0.300$ H. Switch S is closed at $t = 0$. Just after the switch is closed, (a) what is the potential difference v_{ab} across the resistor R_1; (b) which point, a or b, is at a higher potential; (c) what is the

Figure **P30.69**

potential difference v_{cd} across the inductor L; (d) which point, c or d, is at a higher potential? The switch is left closed a long time and then opened. Just after the switch is opened, (e) what is the potential difference v_{ab} across the resistor R_1; (f) which point, a or b, is at a higher potential; (g) what is the potential difference v_{cd} across the inductor L; (h) which point, c or d, is at a higher potential?

30.70 •• **CP** In the circuit shown in Fig. P30.69, $\mathcal{E} = 60.0$ V, $R_1 = 40.0$ Ω, $R_2 = 25.0$ Ω, and $L = 0.300$ H. (a) Switch S is closed. At some time t afterward, the current in the inductor is increasing at a rate of $di/dt = 50.0$ A/s. At this instant, what are the current i_1 through R_1 and the current i_2 through R_2? (*Hint:* Analyze two separate loops: one containing $\mathcal{E}$ and R_1 and the other containing $\mathcal{E}$, R_2, and L.) (b) After the switch has been closed a long time, it is opened again. Just after it is opened, what is the current through R_1?

30.71 •• **CALC** Consider the circuit shown in Fig. P30.71. Let $\mathcal{E} = 36.0$ V, $R_0 = 50.0$ Ω, $R = 150$ Ω, and $L = 4.00$ H. (a) Switch S_1 is closed and switch S_2 is left open. Just after S_1 is closed, what are the current i_0 through R_0 and the potential differences v_{ac} and v_{cb}? (b) After S_1 has been closed a long time (S_2 is still open) so that the current has reached its final, steady value, what are i_0, v_{ac}, and v_{cb}? (c) Find the expressions for i_0, v_{ac}, and v_{cb} as functions of the time t since S_1 was closed. Your results should agree with part (a) when $t = 0$ and with part (b) when $t \to \infty$. Graph i_0, v_{ac}, and v_{cb} versus time.

Figure **P30.71**

30.72 •• After the current in the circuit of Fig. P30.71 has reached its final, steady value with switch S_1 closed and S_2 open, switch S_2 is closed, thus short-circuiting the inductor. (Switch S_1 remains closed. See Problem 30.71 for numerical values of the circuit elements.) (a) Just after S_2 is closed, what are v_{ac} and v_{cb}, and what are the currents through R_0, R, and S_2? (b) A long time after S_2 is closed, what are v_{ac} and v_{cb}, and what are the currents through R_0, R, and S_2? (c) Derive expressions for the currents through R_0, R, and S_2 as functions of the time t that has elapsed since S_2 was closed. Your results should agree with part (a) when $t = 0$ and with part (b) when $t \to \infty$. Graph these three currents versus time.

30.73 ••• **CP CALC** We have ignored the variation of the magnetic field across the cross section of a toroidal solenoid. Let's now examine the validity of that approximation. A certain toroidal solenoid has a rectangular cross section (Fig. P30.73). It has N uniformly spaced turns, with air inside. The magnetic field at a point inside the toroid is given by the equation derived in Example 28.10 (Section 28.7). Do not assume the field is uniform over the cross section. (a) Show that the magnetic flux through a cross section of the toroid is

Figure **P30.73**

$$\Phi_B = \frac{\mu_0 N i h}{2\pi} \ln\left(\frac{b}{a}\right)$$

(b) Show that the inductance of the toroidal solenoid is given by

$$L = \frac{\mu_0 N^2 h}{2\pi} \ln\left(\frac{b}{a}\right)$$

(c) The fraction b/a may be written as

$$\frac{b}{a} = \frac{a + b - a}{a} = 1 + \frac{b - a}{a}$$

Use the power series expansion $\ln(1 + z) = z + z^2/2 + \cdots$, valid for $|z| < 1$, to show that when $b - a$ is much less than a, the inductance is approximately equal to

$$L = \frac{\mu_0 N^2 h(b - a)}{2\pi a}$$

Compare this result with the result given in Example 30.3 (Section 30.2).

30.74 ••• **CP** In the circuit shown in Fig. P30.74, neither the battery nor the inductors have any appreciable resistance, the capacitors are initially uncharged, and the switch S has been in position 1 for a very long time. (a) What is the current in the circuit? (b) The switch is now suddenly flipped to position 2. Find the maximum charge that each capacitor will receive, and how much time after the switch is flipped it will take them to acquire this charge.

Figure **P30.74**

75.0 V
125.0 Ω
15.0 mH
5.0 mH
25.0 μF
35.0 μF

30.75 ••• **CP CALC** **Demonstrating Inductance.** A common demonstration of inductance employs a circuit such as the one shown in Fig. P30.69. Switch S is closed, and the light bulb (represented by resistance R_1) just barely glows. After a period of time, switch S is opened, and the bulb lights up brightly for a short period of time. To understand this effect, think of an inductor as a device that imparts an "inertia" to the current, preventing a discontinuous change in the current through it. (a) Derive, as explicit functions of time, expressions for i_1 (the current through the light bulb) and i_2 (the current through the inductor) after switch S is closed. (b) After a long period of time, the currents i_1 and i_2 reach their steady-state values. Obtain expressions for these steady-state currents. (c) Switch S is now opened. Obtain an expression for the current through the inductor and light bulb as an explicit function of time. (d) You have been asked to design a demonstration apparatus using the circuit shown in Fig. P30.69 with a 22.0-H inductor and a 40.0-W light bulb. You are to connect a resistor in series with the inductor, and R_2 represents the sum of that resistance plus the internal resistance of the inductor. When switch S is opened, a transient current is to be set up that starts at 0.600 A and is not to fall below 0.150 A until after 0.0800 s. For simplicity, assume that the resistance of the light bulb is constant and equals the resistance the bulb must have to dissipate 40.0 W at 120 V. Determine R_2 and $\mathcal{E}$ for the given design considerations. (e) With the numerical values determined in part (d), what is the current through the light bulb just before the switch is opened? Does this result confirm the qualitative description of what is observed in the demonstration?

CHALLENGE PROBLEMS

30.76 ••• **CP CALC** Consider the circuit shown in Fig. P30.76. The circuit elements are as follows: $\mathcal{E} = 32.0$ V, $L = 0.640$ H, $C = 2.00$ μF, and $R = 400$ Ω. At time $t = 0$, switch S is closed. The current through the inductor is i_1, the current through the capacitor branch is i_2, and the charge on the capacitor is q_2. (a) Using Kirchhoff's rules, verify the circuit equations

$$R(i_1 + i_2) + L\left(\frac{di_1}{dt}\right) = \mathcal{E}$$

$$R(i_1 + i_2) + \frac{q_2}{C} = \mathcal{E}$$

(b) What are the initial values of i_1, i_2, and q_2? (c) Show by direct substitution that the following solutions for i_1 and q_2 satisfy the circuit equations from part (a). Also, show that they satisfy the initial conditions

$$i_1 = \left(\frac{\mathcal{E}}{R}\right)[1 - e^{-\beta t}\{(2\omega RC)^{-1}\sin(\omega t) + \cos(\omega t)\}]$$

$$q_2 = \left(\frac{\mathcal{E}}{\omega R}\right)e^{-\beta t}\sin(\omega t)$$

where $\beta = (2RC)^{-1}$ and $\omega = [(LC)^{-1} - (2RC)^{-2}]^{1/2}$. (d) Determine the time t_1 at which i_2 first becomes zero.

Figure **P30.76**

30.77 ••• **CP** **A Volume Gauge.** A tank containing a liquid has turns of wire wrapped around it, causing it to act like an inductor. The liquid content of the tank can be measured by using its inductance to determine the height of the liquid in the tank. The inductance of the tank changes from a value of L_0 corresponding to a relative permeability of 1 when the tank is empty to a value of L_f corresponding to a relative permeability of K_m (the relative permeability of the liquid) when the tank is full. The appropriate electronic circuitry can determine the inductance to five significant figures and thus the effective relative permeability of the combined air and liquid within the rectangular cavity of the tank. The four sides of the tank each have width W and height D (Fig. P30.77). The height of the liquid in the tank is d. You can ignore any fringing effects and assume that the relative permeability of the material of which the tank is made can be ignored. (a) Derive an expression for d as a function of L, the inductance corresponding to a certain fluid height, L_0, L_f, and D. (b) What is the inductance (to five significant figures) for a tank $\frac{1}{4}$ full, $\frac{1}{2}$ full, $\frac{3}{4}$ full, and completely full if the tank contains liquid oxygen? Take $L_0 = 0.63000$ H. The magnetic susceptibility of liquid oxygen is $\chi_m = 1.52 \times 10^{-3}$. (c) Repeat part (b) for mercury. The magnetic susceptibility of mercury is given in Table 28.1. (d) For which material is this volume gauge more practical?

Figure **P30.77**

30.78 ••• Two coils are wrapped around each other as shown in Fig. 30.3. The current travels in the same sense around each coil. One coil has self-inductance L_1, and the other coil has self-inductance L_2. The mutual inductance of the two coils is M. (a) Show that if the two coils are connected in series, the equivalent inductance of the combination is $L_{eq} = L_1 + L_2 + 2M$. (b) Show that if the two coils are connected in parallel, the equivalent inductance of the combination is

$$L_{eq} = \frac{L_1 L_2 - M^2}{L_1 + L_2 - 2M}$$

30.79 ••• **CP CALC** Consider the circuit shown in Fig. P30.79. Switch S is closed at time $t = 0$, causing a current i_1 through the inductive branch and a current i_2 through the capacitive branch.

The initial charge on the capacitor is zero, and the charge at time t is q_2. (a) Derive expressions for i_1, i_2, and q_2 as functions of time. Express your answers in terms of $\mathcal{E}$, L, C, R_1, R_2, and t. For the remainder of the problem let the circuit elements have the following values: $\mathcal{E} = 48$ V, $L = 8.0$ H, $C = 20$ μF, $R_1 = 25$ Ω, and $R_2 = 5000$ Ω. (b) What is the initial current through the inductive branch? What is the initial current

Figure **P30.79**

through the capacitive branch? (c) What are the currents through the inductive and capacitive branches a long time after the switch has been closed? How long is a "long time"? Explain. (d) At what time t_1 (accurate to two significant figures) will the currents i_1 and i_2 be equal? (*Hint:* You might consider using series expansions for the exponentials.) (e) For the conditions given in part (d), determine i_1. (f) The total current through the battery is $i = i_1 + i_2$. At what time t_2 (accurate to two significant figures) will i equal one-half of its final value? (*Hint:* The numerical work is greatly simplified if one makes suitable approximations. A sketch of i_1 and i_2 versus t may help you decide what approximations are valid.)

Answers

Chapter Opening Question ?

As explained in Section 30.2, traffic light sensors work by measuring the change in inductance of a coil embedded under the road surface when a car drives over it.

Test Your Understanding Questions

30.1 Answer: (iii) Doubling both the length of the solenoid (l) and the number of turns of wire in the solenoid (N_1) would have *no* effect on the mutual inductance M. Example 30.1 shows that M depends on the ratio of these quantities, which would remain unchanged. This is because the magnetic field produced by the solenoid depends on the number of turns *per unit length,* and the proposed change has no effect on this quantity.

30.2 Answer: (iv), (i), (iii), (ii) From Eq. (30.8), the potential difference across the inductor is $V_{ab} = L\,di/dt$. For the four cases we find (i) $V_{ab} = (2.0\,\mu\text{H})(2.0\,\text{A} - 1.0\,\text{A})/(0.50\,\text{s}) = 4.0\,\mu\text{V}$; (ii) $V_{ab} = (4.0\,\mu\text{H})(0 - 3.0\,\text{A})/(2.0\,\text{s}) = -6.0\,\mu\text{V}$; (iii) $V_{ab} = 0$ because the rate of change of current is zero; and (iv) $V_{ab} = (1.0\,\mu\text{H})(4.0\,\text{A} - 0)/(0.25\,\text{s}) = 16\,\mu\text{V}$.

30.3 Answers: (a) yes, (b) no Reversing the direction of the current has no effect on the magnetic field magnitude, but it causes the direction of the magnetic field to reverse. It has no effect on the magnetic-field energy density, which is proportional to the square of the *magnitude* of the magnetic field.

30.4 Answers: (a) (i), (b) (ii) Recall that v_{ab} is the potential at a minus the potential at b, and similarly for v_{bc}. For either arrangement of the switches, current flows through the resistor from a to

b. The upstream end of the resistor is always at the higher potential, so v_{ab} is positive. With S_1 closed and S_2 open, the current through the inductor flows from b to c and is increasing. The self-induced emf opposes this increase and is therefore directed from c toward b, which means that b is at the higher potential. Hence v_{bc} is positive. With S_1 open and S_2 closed, the inductor current again flows from b to c but is now decreasing. The self-induced emf is directed from b to c in an effort to sustain the decaying current, so c is at the higher potential and v_{bc} is negative.

30.5 Answers: (a) positive, (b) electric, (c) negative, (d) electric The capacitor loses energy between stages (a) and (b), so it does positive work on the charges. It does this by exerting an electric force that pushes current away from the positively charged left-hand capacitor plate and toward the negatively charged right-hand plate. At the same time, the inductor gains energy and does negative work on the moving charges. Although the inductor stores magnetic energy, the force that the inductor exerts is *electric*. This force comes about from the inductor's self-induced emf (see Section 30.2).

30.6 Answer: (i) and (iii) There are no oscillations if $R^2 \geq 4L/C$. In each case $R^2 = (2.0\,\Omega)^2 = 4.0\,\Omega^2$. In case (i) $4L/C = 4(3.0\,\mu\text{H})/(6.0\,\mu\text{F}) = 2.0\,\Omega^2$, so there are no oscillations (the system is overdamped); in case (ii) $4L/C = 4(6.0\,\mu\text{H})/(3.0\,\mu\text{F}) = 8.0\,\Omega^2$, so there are oscillations (the system is underdamped); and in case (iii) $4L/C = 4(3.0\,\mu\text{H})/(3.0\,\mu\text{F}) = 4.0\,\Omega^2$, so there are no oscillations (the system is critically damped).

Bridging Problem

Answers: (a) 7.68×10^{-8} J **(b)** 1.60 mA **(c)** 24.8 mV
(d) 1.92×10^{-8} J, 21.5 mV

ALTERNATING CURRENT

LEARNING GOALS

By studying this chapter, you will learn:

- How phasors make it easy to describe sinusoidally varying quantities.

- How to use reactance to describe the voltage across a circuit element that carries an alternating current.

- How to analyze an *L-R-C* series circuit with a sinusoidal emf.

- What determines the amount of power flowing into or out of an alternating-current circuit.

- How an *L-R-C* series circuit responds to sinusoidal emfs of different frequencies.

- Why transformers are useful, and how they work.

? Waves from a broadcasting station produce an alternating current in the circuits of a radio (like the one in this classic car). If a radio is tuned to a station at a frequency of 1000 kHz, does it also detect the transmissions from a station broadcasting at 600 kHz?

During the 1880s in the United States there was a heated and acrimonious debate between two inventors over the best method of electric-power distribution. Thomas Edison favored direct current (dc)—that is, steady current that does not vary with time. George Westinghouse favored **alternating current (ac)**, with sinusoidally varying voltages and currents. He argued that transformers (which we will study in this chapter) can be used to step the voltage up and down with ac but not with dc; low voltages are safer for consumer use, but high voltages and correspondingly low currents are best for long-distance power transmission to minimize i^2R losses in the cables.

Eventually, Westinghouse prevailed, and most present-day household and industrial power-distribution systems operate with alternating current. Any appliance that you plug into a wall outlet uses ac, and many battery-powered devices such as radios and cordless telephones make use of the dc supplied by the battery to create or amplify alternating currents. Circuits in modern communication equipment, including pagers and television, also make extensive use of ac.

In this chapter we will learn how resistors, inductors, and capacitors behave in circuits with sinusoidally varying voltages and currents. Many of the principles that we found useful in Chapters 25, 28, and 30 are applicable, along with several new concepts related to the circuit behavior of inductors and capacitors. A key concept in this discussion is *resonance,* which we studied in Chapter 14 for mechanical systems.

31.1 Phasors and Alternating Currents

To supply an alternating current to a circuit, a source of alternating emf or voltage is required. An example of such a source is a coil of wire rotating with constant angular velocity in a magnetic field, which we discussed in Example 29.3 (Section 29.2). This develops a sinusoidal alternating emf and is the prototype of the commercial alternating-current generator or *alternator* (see Fig. 29.8).

We use the term **ac source** for any device that supplies a sinusoidally varying voltage (potential difference) v or current i. The usual circuit-diagram symbol for an ac source is

A sinusoidal voltage might be described by a function such as

$$v = V\cos\omega t \tag{31.1}$$

31.1 The voltage across a sinusoidal ac source.

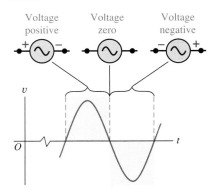

In this expression, v (lowercase) is the *instantaneous* potential difference; V (uppercase) is the maximum potential difference, which we call the **voltage amplitude;** and ω is the *angular frequency,* equal to 2π times the frequency f (Fig. 31.1).

In the United States and Canada, commercial electric-power distribution systems always use a frequency of $f = 60\,\text{Hz}$, corresponding to $\omega = (2\pi\,\text{rad})(60\,\text{s}^{-1}) = 377\,\text{rad/s}$; in much of the rest of the world, $f = 50\,\text{Hz}$ ($\omega = 314\,\text{rad/s}$) is used. Similarly, a sinusoidal current might be described as

$$i = I\cos\omega t \tag{31.2}$$

where i (lowercase) is the instantaneous current and I (uppercase) is the maximum current or **current amplitude.**

Phasor Diagrams

To represent sinusoidally varying voltages and currents, we will use rotating vector diagrams similar to those we used in the study of simple harmonic motion in Section 14.2 (see Figs. 14.5b and 14.6). In these diagrams the instantaneous value of a quantity that varies sinusoidally with time is represented by the *projection* onto a horizontal axis of a vector with a length equal to the amplitude of the quantity. The vector rotates counterclockwise with constant angular speed ω. These rotating vectors are called **phasors,** and diagrams containing them are called **phasor diagrams.** Figure 31.2 shows a phasor diagram for the sinusoidal current described by Eq. (31.2). The projection of the phasor onto the horizontal axis at time t is $I\cos\omega t$; this is why we chose to use the cosine function rather than the sine in Eq. (31.2).

31.2 A phasor diagram.

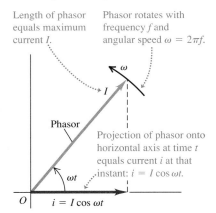

CAUTION *Just what is a phasor?* A phasor is not a real physical quantity with a direction in space, such as velocity, momentum, or electric field. Rather, it is a *geometric* entity that helps us to describe and analyze physical quantities that vary sinusoidally with time. In Section 14.2 we used a single phasor to represent the position of a point mass undergoing simple harmonic motion. In this chapter we will use phasors to *add* sinusoidal voltages and currents. Combining sinusoidal quantities with phase differences then becomes a matter of vector addition. We will find a similar use for phasors in Chapters 35 and 36 in our study of interference effects with light.

Rectified Alternating Current

How do we measure a sinusoidally varying current? In Section 26.3 we used a d'Arsonval galvanometer to measure steady currents. But if we pass a *sinusoidal* current through a d'Arsonval meter, the torque on the moving coil varies sinusoidally, with one direction half the time and the opposite direction the other half. The needle may wiggle a little if the frequency is low enough, but its average deflection is zero. Hence a d'Arsonval meter by itself isn't very useful for measuring alternating currents.

To get a measurable one-way current through the meter, we can use *diodes*, which we described in Section 25.3. A diode is a device that conducts better in one direction than in the other; an ideal diode has zero resistance for one direction of current and infinite resistance for the other. Figure 31.3a shows one possible arrangement, called a *full-wave rectifier circuit*. The current through the galvanometer G is always upward, regardless of the direction of the current from the ac source (i.e., which part of the cycle the source is in). The graph in Fig. 31.3b shows the current through G: It pulsates but always has the same direction, and the average meter deflection is *not* zero.

The **rectified average current** I_{rav} is defined so that during any whole number of cycles, the total charge that flows is the same as though the current were constant with a value equal to I_{rav}. The notation I_{rav} and the name *rectified average current* emphasize that this is *not* the average of the original sinusoidal current. In Fig. 31.3b the total charge that flows in time t corresponds to the area under the curve of i versus t (recall that $i = dq/dt$, so q is the integral of t); this area must equal the rectangular area with height I_{rav}. We see that I_{rav} is less than the maximum current I; the two are related by

$$I_{rav} = \frac{2}{\pi}I = 0.637I \qquad \text{(rectified average value of a sinusoidal current)} \qquad (31.3)$$

(The factor of $2/\pi$ is the average value of $|\cos\omega t|$ or of $|\sin\omega t|$; see Example 29.4 in Section 29.2.) The galvanometer deflection is proportional to I_{rav}. The galvanometer scale can be calibrated to read I, I_{rav}, or, most commonly, I_{rms} (discussed below).

Root-Mean-Square (rms) Values

A more useful way to describe a quantity that can be either positive or negative is the *root-mean-square (rms) value*. We used rms values in Section 18.3 in connection with the speeds of molecules in a gas. We *square* the instantaneous current i, take the *average* (mean) value of i^2, and finally take the *square root* of that average. This procedure defines the **root-mean-square current,** denoted as I_{rms} (Fig. 31.4). Even when i is negative, i^2 is always positive, so I_{rms} is never zero (unless i is zero at every instant).

Here's how we obtain I_{rms} for a sinusoidal current, like that shown in Fig. 31.4. If the instantaneous current is given by $i = I\cos\omega t$, then

$$i^2 = I^2\cos^2\omega t$$

Using a double-angle formula from trigonometry,

$$\cos^2 A = \tfrac{1}{2}(1 + \cos 2A)$$

we find

$$i^2 = I^2\tfrac{1}{2}(1 + \cos 2\omega t) = \tfrac{1}{2}I^2 + \tfrac{1}{2}I^2\cos 2\omega t$$

The average of $\cos 2\omega t$ is zero because it is positive half the time and negative half the time. Thus the average of i^2 is simply $I^2/2$. The square root of this is I_{rms}:

$$I_{rms} = \frac{I}{\sqrt{2}} \qquad \text{(root-mean-square value of a sinusoidal current)} \qquad (31.4)$$

31.3 (a) A full-wave rectifier circuit. (b) Graph of the resulting current through the galvanometer G.

(a) A full-wave rectifier circuit

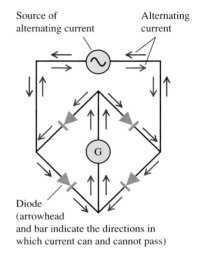

Diode
(arrowhead and bar indicate the directions in which current can and cannot pass)

(b) Graph of the full-wave rectified current and its average value, the rectified average current I_{rav}

31.4 Calculating the root-mean-square (rms) value of an alternating current.

Meaning of the rms value of a sinusoidal quantity (here, ac current with $I = 3$ A):

① Graph current i versus time.
② *Square* the instantaneous current i.
③ Take the *average* (mean) value of i^2.
④ Take the *square root* of that average.

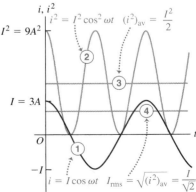

31.5 This wall socket delivers a root-mean-square voltage of 120 V. Sixty times per second, the instantaneous voltage across its terminals varies from $(\sqrt{2})(120\ \text{V}) = 170\ \text{V}$ to $-170\ \text{V}$ and back again.

In the same way, the root-mean-square value of a sinusoidal voltage with amplitude (maximum value) V is

$$V_{rms} = \frac{V}{\sqrt{2}} \qquad \text{(root-mean-square value of a sinusoidal voltage)} \qquad (31.5)$$

We can convert a rectifying ammeter into a voltmeter by adding a series resistor, just as for the dc case discussed in Section 26.3. Meters used for ac voltage and current measurements are nearly always calibrated to read rms values, not maximum or rectified average. Voltages and currents in power distribution systems are always described in terms of their rms values. The usual household power supply, "120-volt ac," has an rms voltage of 120 V (Fig. 31.5). The voltage amplitude is

$$V = \sqrt{2}V_{rms} = \sqrt{2}(120\ \text{V}) = 170\ \text{V}$$

Example 31.1   Current in a personal computer

The plate on the back of a personal computer says that it draws 2.7 A from a 120-V, 60-Hz line. For this computer, what are (a) the average current, (b) the average of the square of the current, and (c) the current amplitude?

SOLUTION

IDENTIFY and SET UP: This example is about alternating current. In part (a) we find the average, over a complete cycle, of the alternating current. In part (b) we recognize that the 2.7-A current draw of the computer is the rms value I_{rms}—that is, the *square root* of the *mean* (average) of the *square* of the current, $(i^2)_{av}$. In part (c) we use Eq. (31.4) to relate I_{rms} to the current amplitude.

EXECUTE: (a) The average of *any* sinusoidally varying quantity, over any whole number of cycles, is zero.

(b) We are given $I_{rms} = 2.7$ A. From the definition of rms value,

$$I_{rms} = \sqrt{(i^2)_{av}} \ \text{so} \ (i^2)_{av} = (I_{rms})^2 = (2.7\ \text{A})^2 = 7.3\ \text{A}^2$$

(c) From Eq. (31.4), the current amplitude I is

$$I = \sqrt{2}I_{rms} = \sqrt{2}(2.7\ \text{A}) = 3.8\ \text{A}$$

Figure 31.6 shows graphs of i and i^2 versus time t.

31.6 Our graphs of the current i and the square of the current i^2 versus time t.

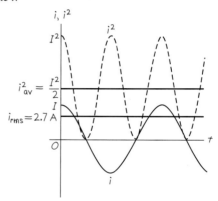

EVALUATE: Why would we be interested in the average of the square of the current? Recall that the rate at which energy is dissipated in a resistor R equals i^2R. This rate varies if the current is alternating, so it is best described by its average value $(i^2)_{av}R = I_{rms}^2R$. We'll use this idea in Section 31.4.

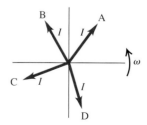

Test Your Understanding of Section 31.1 The figure at left shows four different current phasors with the same angular frequency ω. At the time shown, which phasor corresponds to (a) a positive current that is becoming more positive; (b) a positive current that is decreasing toward zero; (c) a negative current that is becoming more negative; (d) a negative current that is decreasing in magnitude toward zero?

31.2 Resistance and Reactance

In this section we will derive voltage–current relationships for individual circuit elements carrying a sinusoidal current. We'll consider resistors, inductors, and capacitors.

Resistor in an ac Circuit

First let's consider a resistor with resistance R through which there is a sinusoidal current given by Eq. (31.2): $i = I\cos\omega t$. The positive direction of current is counterclockwise around the circuit, as in Fig. 31.7a. The current amplitude (maximum current) is I. From Ohm's law the instantaneous potential v_R of point a with respect to point b (that is, the instantaneous voltage across the resistor) is

$$v_R = iR = (IR)\cos\omega t \qquad (31.6)$$

The maximum voltage V_R, the *voltage amplitude,* is the coefficient of the cosine function:

$$V_R = IR \qquad \text{(amplitude of voltage across a resistor, ac circuit)} \qquad (31.7)$$

Hence we can also write

$$v_R = V_R\cos\omega t \qquad (31.8)$$

The current i and voltage v_R are both proportional to $\cos\omega t$, so the current is *in phase* with the voltage. Equation (31.7) shows that the current and voltage amplitudes are related in the same way as in a dc circuit.

Figure 31.7b shows graphs of i and v_R as functions of time. The vertical scales for current and voltage are different, so the relative heights of the two curves are not significant. The corresponding phasor diagram is given in Fig. 31.7c. Because i and v_R are *in phase* and have the same frequency, the current and voltage phasors rotate together; they are parallel at each instant. Their projections on the horizontal axis represent the instantaneous current and voltage, respectively.

Inductor in an ac Circuit

Next, we replace the resistor in Fig. 31.7 with a pure inductor with self-inductance L and zero resistance (Fig. 31.8a). Again we assume that the current is $i = I\cos\omega t$, with the positive direction of current taken as counterclockwise around the circuit.

Although there is no resistance, there is a potential difference v_L between the inductor terminals a and b because the current varies with time, giving rise to a self-induced emf. The induced emf in the direction of i is given by Eq. (30.7), $\mathcal{E} = -L\,di/dt$; however, the voltage v_L is *not* simply equal to $\mathcal{E}$. To see why, notice that if the current in the inductor is in the positive (counterclockwise) direction from a to b and is increasing, then di/dt is positive and the induced emf is directed to the left to oppose the increase in current; hence point a is at higher potential than is point b. Thus the potential of point a with respect to point b is positive and is given by $v_L = +L\,di/dt$, the *negative* of the induced emf. (You

31.7 Resistance R connected across an ac source.

(a) Circuit with ac source and resistor

(b) Graphs of current and voltage versus time

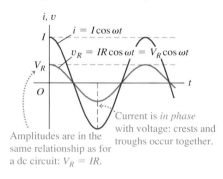

Amplitudes are in the same relationship as for a dc circuit: $V_R = IR$.

Current is *in phase* with voltage: crests and troughs occur together.

(c) Phasor diagram

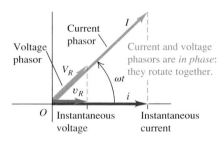

Current and voltage phasors are *in phase:* they rotate together.

31.8 Inductance L connected across an ac source.

(a) Circuit with ac source and inductor

(b) Graphs of current and voltage versus time

$$v_L = I\omega L\cos(\omega t + 90°)$$

Voltage curve *leads* current curve by a quarter-cycle (corresponding to $\phi = \pi/2$ rad $= 90°$).

(c) Phasor diagram

Voltage phasor *leads* current phasor by $\phi = \pi/2$ rad $= 90°$.

should convince yourself that this expression gives the correct sign of v_L in *all* cases, including *i* counterclockwise and decreasing, *i* clockwise and increasing, and *i* clockwise and decreasing; you should also review Section 30.2.) So we have

$$v_L = L\frac{di}{dt} = L\frac{d}{dt}(I\cos\omega t) = -I\omega L\sin\omega t \qquad (31.9)$$

The voltage v_L across the inductor at any instant is proportional to the *rate of change* of the current. The points of maximum voltage on the graph correspond to maximum steepness of the current curve, and the points of zero voltage are the points where the current curve instantaneously levels off at its maximum and minimum values (Fig. 31.8b). The voltage and current are "out of step" or *out of phase* by a quarter-cycle. Since the voltage peaks occur a quarter-cycle earlier than the current peaks, we say that the voltage *leads* the current by 90°. The phasor diagram in Fig. 31.8c also shows this relationship; the voltage phasor is ahead of the current phasor by 90°.

We can also obtain this phase relationship by rewriting Eq. (31.9) using the identity $\cos(A + 90°) = -\sin A$:

$$v_L = I\omega L\cos(\omega t + 90°) \qquad (31.10)$$

This result shows that the voltage can be viewed as a cosine function with a "head start" of 90° relative to the current.

As we have done in Eq. (31.10), we will usually describe the phase of the *voltage* relative to the *current,* not the reverse. Thus if the current *i* in a circuit is

$$i = I\cos\omega t$$

and the voltage *v* of one point with respect to another is

$$v = V\cos(\omega t + \phi)$$

we call ϕ the **phase angle;** it gives the phase of the *voltage* relative to the *current.* For a pure resistor, $\phi = 0$, and for a pure inductor, $\phi = 90°$.

From Eq. (31.9) or (31.10) the amplitude V_L of the inductor voltage is

$$V_L = I\omega L \qquad (31.11)$$

We define the **inductive reactance** X_L of an inductor as

$$X_L = \omega L \qquad \text{(inductive reactance)} \qquad (31.12)$$

Using X_L, we can write Eq. (31.11) in a form similar to Eq. (31.7) for a resistor ($V_R = IR$):

$$V_L = IX_L \qquad \text{(amplitude of voltage across an inductor, ac circuit)} \qquad (31.13)$$

Because X_L is the ratio of a voltage and a current, its SI unit is the ohm, the same as for resistance.

> **CAUTION** **Inductor voltage and current are not in phase** Keep in mind that Eq. (31.13) is a relationship between the *amplitudes* of the oscillating voltage and current for the inductor in Fig. 31.8a. It does *not* say that the voltage at any instant is equal to the current at that instant multiplied by X_L. As Fig. 31.8b shows, the voltage and current are 90° out of phase. Voltage and current are in phase only for resistors, as in Eq. (31.6).

The Meaning of Inductive Reactance

The inductive reactance X_L is really a description of the self-induced emf that opposes any change in the current through the inductor. From Eq. (31.13), for a given current amplitude *I* the voltage $v_L = +L\,di/dt$ across the inductor and the self-induced emf $\mathcal{E} = -L\,di/dt$ both have an amplitude V_L that is directly proportional to X_L. According to Eq. (31.12), the inductive reactance and self-induced emf increase with more rapid variation in current (that is, increasing angular frequency ω) and increasing inductance *L*.

If an oscillating voltage of a given amplitude V_L is applied across the inductor terminals, the resulting current will have a smaller amplitude I for larger values of X_L. Since X_L is proportional to frequency, a high-frequency voltage applied to the inductor gives only a small current, while a lower-frequency voltage of the same amplitude gives rise to a larger current. Inductors are used in some circuit applications, such as power supplies and radio-interference filters, to block high frequencies while permitting lower frequencies or dc to pass through. A circuit device that uses an inductor for this purpose is called a *low-pass filter* (see Problem 31.52).

Example 31.2   An inductor in an ac circuit

The current amplitude in a pure inductor in a radio receiver is to be 250 μA when the voltage amplitude is 3.60 V at a frequency of 1.60 MHz (at the upper end of the AM broadcast band). (a) What inductive reactance is needed? What inductance? (b) If the voltage amplitude is kept constant, what will be the current amplitude through this inductor at 16.0 MHz? At 160 kHz?

SOLUTION

IDENTIFY and SET UP: There may be other elements of this circuit, but in this example we don't care: All they do is provide the inductor with an oscillating voltage, so the other elements are lumped into the ac source shown in Fig. 31.8a. We are given the current amplitude I and the voltage amplitude V. Our target variables in part (a) are the inductive reactance X_L at 1.60 MHz and the inductance L, which we find using Eqs. (31.13) and (31.12). Knowing L, we use these equations in part (b) to find X_L and I at any frequency.

EXECUTE: (a) From Eq. (31.13),

$$X_L = \frac{V_L}{I} = \frac{3.60 \text{ V}}{250 \times 10^{-6} \text{ A}} = 1.44 \times 10^4 \ \Omega = 14.4 \text{ k}\Omega$$

From Eq. (31.12), with $\omega = 2\pi f$,

$$L = \frac{X_L}{2\pi f} = \frac{1.44 \times 10^4 \ \Omega}{2\pi(1.60 \times 10^6 \text{ Hz})}$$

$$= 1.43 \times 10^{-3} \text{ H} = 1.43 \text{ mH}$$

(b) Combining Eqs. (31.12) and (31.13), we find $I = V_L/X_L = V_L/\omega L = V_L/2\pi f L$. Thus the current amplitude is inversely proportional to the frequency f. Since $I = 250$ μA at $f = 1.60$ MHz, the current amplitudes at 16.0 MHz ($10f$) and 160 kHz = 0.160 MHz ($f/10$) will be, respectively, one-tenth as great (25.0 μA) and ten times as great (2500 μA = 2.50 mA).

EVALUATE: In general, the lower the frequency of an oscillating voltage applied across an inductor, the greater the amplitude of the resulting oscillating current.

Capacitor in an ac Circuit

Finally, we connect a capacitor with capacitance C to the source, as in Fig. 31.9a, producing a current $i = I\cos\omega t$ through the capacitor. Again, the positive direction of current is counterclockwise around the circuit.

CAUTION   **Alternating current through a capacitor** You may object that charge can't really move through the capacitor because its two plates are insulated from each other. True enough, but as the capacitor charges and discharges, there is at each instant a current i into one plate, an equal current out of the other plate, and an equal *displacement* current between the plates just as though the charge were being conducted through the capacitor. (You may want to review the discussion of displacement current in Section 29.7.) Thus we often speak about alternating current *through* a capacitor. ▌

To find the instantaneous voltage v_C across the capacitor—that is, the potential of point a with respect to point b—we first let q denote the charge on the left-hand plate of the capacitor in Fig. 31.9a (so $-q$ is the charge on the right-hand plate). The current i is related to q by $i = dq/dt$; with this definition, positive current corresponds to an increasing charge on the left-hand capacitor plate. Then

$$i = \frac{dq}{dt} = I\cos\omega t$$

Integrating this, we get

$$q = \frac{I}{\omega}\sin\omega t \qquad\qquad (31.14)$$

31.9 Capacitor C connected across an ac source.

(a) Circuit with ac source and capacitor

(b) Graphs of current and voltage versus time

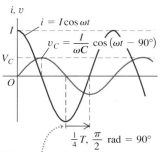

Voltage curve *lags* current curve by a quarter-cycle (corresponding to $\phi = -\pi/2$ rad $= -90°$).

(c) Phasor diagram

Also, from Eq. (24.1) the charge q equals the voltage v_C multiplied by the capacitance, $q = Cv_C$. Using this in Eq. (31.14), we find

$$v_C = \frac{I}{\omega C}\sin \omega t \qquad (31.15)$$

The instantaneous current i is equal to the rate of change dq/dt of the capacitor charge q; since $q = Cv_C$, i is also proportional to the rate of change of voltage. (Compare to an inductor, for which the situation is reversed and v_L is proportional to the rate of change of i.) Figure 31.9b shows v_C and i as functions of t. Because $i = dq/dt = C\,dv_C/dt$, the current has its greatest magnitude when the v_C curve is rising or falling most steeply and is zero when the v_C curve instantaneously levels off at its maximum and minimum values.

The capacitor voltage and current are out of phase by a quarter-cycle. The peaks of voltage occur a quarter-cycle *after* the corresponding current peaks, and we say that the voltage *lags* the current by 90°. The phasor diagram in Fig. 31.9c shows this relationship; the voltage phasor is behind the current phasor by a quarter-cycle, or 90°.

We can also derive this phase difference by rewriting Eq. (31.15) using the identity $\cos(A - 90°) = \sin A$:

$$v_C = \frac{I}{\omega C}\cos(\omega t - 90°) \qquad (31.16)$$

This corresponds to a phase angle $\phi = -90°$. This cosine function has a "late start" of 90° compared with the current $i = I\cos \omega t$.

Equations (31.15) and (31.16) show that the *maximum* voltage V_C (the voltage amplitude) is

$$V_C = \frac{I}{\omega C} \qquad (13.17)$$

To put this expression in a form similar to Eq. (31.7) for a resistor, $V_R = IR$, we define a quantity X_C, called the **capacitive reactance** of the capacitor, as

$$X_C = \frac{1}{\omega C} \qquad \text{(capacitive reactance)} \qquad (31.18)$$

Then

$$V_C = IX_C \qquad \text{(amplitude of voltage across a capacitor, ac circuit)} \qquad (31.19)$$

The SI unit of X_C is the ohm, the same as for resistance and inductive reactance, because X_C is the ratio of a voltage and a current.

CAUTION **Capacitor voltage and current are not in phase** Remember that Eq. (31.19) for a capacitor, like Eq. (31.13) for an inductor, is *not* a statement about the instantaneous values of voltage and current. The instantaneous values are actually 90° out of phase, as Fig. 31.9b shows. Rather, Eq. (31.19) relates the *amplitudes* of the voltage and current. ▌

The Meaning of Capacitive Reactance

The capacitive reactance of a capacitor is inversely proportional both to the capacitance C and to the angular frequency ω; the greater the capacitance and the higher the frequency, the *smaller* the capacitive reactance X_C. Capacitors tend to pass high-frequency current and to block low-frequency currents and dc, just the opposite of inductors. A device that preferentially passes signals of high frequency is called a *high-pass filter* (see Problem 31.51).

| Example 31.3 | A resistor and a capacitor in an ac circuit |

A 200-Ω resistor is connected in series with a 5.0-μF capacitor. The voltage across the resistor is $v_R = (1.20 \text{ V}) \cos(2500 \text{ rad/s})t$ (Fig. 31.10). (a) Derive an expression for the circuit current. (b) Determine the capacitive reactance of the capacitor. (c) Derive an expression for the voltage across the capacitor.

SOLUTION

IDENTIFY and SET UP: Since this is a series circuit, the current is the same through the capacitor as through the resistor. Our target variables are the current i, the capacitive reactance X_C, and the capacitor voltage v_C. We use Eq. (31.6) to find an expression for i in terms of the angular frequency $\omega = 2500$ rad/s, Eq. (31.18) to find X_C, Eq. (31.19) to find the capacitor voltage amplitude V_C, and Eq. (31.16) to write an expression for v_C.

31.10 Our sketch for this problem.

EXECUTE: (a) From Eq. (31.6), $v_R = iR$, we find

$$i = \frac{v_R}{R} = \frac{(1.20 \text{ V}) \cos(2500 \text{ rad/s})t}{200 \, \Omega}$$

$$= (6.0 \times 10^{-3} \text{ A}) \cos(2500 \text{ rad/s})t$$

(b) From Eq. (31.18), the capacitive reactance at $\omega = 2500$ rad/s is

$$X_C = \frac{1}{\omega C} = \frac{1}{(2500 \text{ rad/s})(5.0 \times 10^{-6} \text{ F})} = 80 \, \Omega$$

(c) From Eq. (31.19), the capacitor voltage amplitude is

$$V_C = IX_C = (6.0 \times 10^{-3} \text{ A})(80 \, \Omega) = 0.48 \text{ V}$$

(The 80-Ω reactance of the capacitor is 40% of the resistor's 200-Ω resistance, so V_C is 40% of V_R.) The instantaneous capacitor voltage is given by Eq. (31.16):

$$v_C = V_C \cos(\omega t - 90°)$$
$$= (0.48 \text{ V}) \cos[(2500 \text{ rad/s})t - \pi/2 \text{ rad}]$$

EVALUATE: Although the same *current* passes through both the capacitor and the resistor, the *voltages* across them are different in both amplitude and phase. Note that in the expression for v_C we converted the 90° to $\pi/2$ rad so that all the angular quantities have the same units. In ac circuit analysis, phase angles are often given in degrees, so be careful to convert to radians when necessary.

Comparing ac Circuit Elements

Table 31.1 summarizes the relationships of voltage and current amplitudes for the three circuit elements we have discussed. Note again that *instantaneous* voltage and current are proportional in a resistor, where there is zero phase difference between v_R and i (see Fig. 31.7b). The instantaneous voltage and current are *not* proportional in an inductor or capacitor, because there is a 90° phase difference in both cases (see Figs. 31.8b and 31.9b).

Figure 31.11 shows how the resistance of a resistor and the reactances of an inductor and a capacitor vary with angular frequency ω. Resistance R is independent of frequency, while the reactances X_L and X_C are not. If $\omega = 0$, corresponding to a dc circuit, there is *no* current through a capacitor because $X_C \to \infty$, and there is no inductive effect because $X_L = 0$. In the limit $\omega \to \infty$, X_L also approaches infinity, and the current through an inductor becomes vanishingly small; recall that the self-induced emf opposes rapid changes in current. In this same limit, X_C and the voltage across a capacitor both approach zero; the current changes direction so rapidly that no charge can build up on either plate.

Figure 31.12 shows an application of the above discussion to a loudspeaker system. Low-frequency sounds are produced by the *woofer*, which is a speaker with large diameter; the *tweeter*, a speaker with smaller diameter, produces high-frequency sounds. In order to route signals of different frequency to the appropriate speaker, the woofer and tweeter are connected in parallel across the amplifier

31.11 Graphs of R, X_L, and X_C as functions of angular frequency ω.

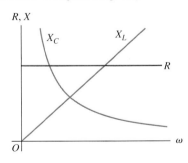

Table 31.1 Circuit Elements with Alternating Current

Circuit Element	Amplitude Relationship	Circuit Quantity	Phase of v
Resistor	$V_R = IR$	R	In phase with i
Inductor	$V_L = IX_L$	$X_L = \omega L$	Leads i by 90°
Capacitor	$V_C = IX_C$	$X_C = 1/\omega C$	Lags i by 90°

31.12 (a) The two speakers in this loud-speaker system are connected in parallel to the amplifier. (b) Graphs of current amplitude in the tweeter and woofer as functions of frequency for a given amplifier voltage amplitude.

(a) A crossover network in a loudspeaker system

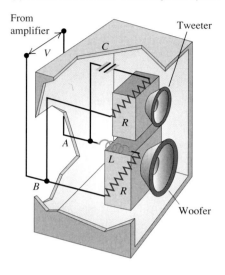

(b) Graphs of rms current as functions of frequency for a given amplifier voltage

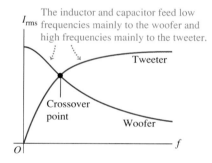

The inductor and capacitor feed low frequencies mainly to the woofer and high frequencies mainly to the tweeter.

output. The capacitor in the tweeter branch blocks the low-frequency components of sound but passes the higher frequencies; the inductor in the woofer branch does the opposite.

Test Your Understanding of Section 31.2 An oscillating voltage of fixed amplitude is applied across a circuit element. If the frequency of this voltage is increased, will the amplitude of the current through the element (i) increase, (ii) decrease, or (iii) remain the same if it is (a) a resistor, (b) an inductor, or (c) a capacitor?

31.3 The *L-R-C* Series Circuit

Many ac circuits used in practical electronic systems involve resistance, inductive reactance, and capacitive reactance. Figure 31.13a shows a simple example: A series circuit containing a resistor, an inductor, a capacitor, and an ac source. (In Section 30.6 we considered the behavior of the current in an *L-R-C* series circuit *without* a source.)

To analyze this and similar circuits, we will use a phasor diagram that includes the voltage and current phasors for each of the components. In this circuit, because of Kirchhoff's loop rule, the instantaneous *total* voltage v_{ad} across all three components is equal to the source voltage at that instant. We will show that the phasor representing this total voltage is the *vector sum* of the phasors for the individual voltages.

Figures 31.13b and 31.13c show complete phasor diagrams for the circuit of Fig. 31.13a. We assume that the source supplies a current i given by $i = I \cos \omega t$. Because the circuit elements are connected in series, the current at any instant is the same at every point in the circuit. Thus a *single phasor I*, with length proportional to the current amplitude, represents the current in *all* circuit elements.

As in Section 31.2, we use the symbols v_R, v_L, and v_C for the instantaneous voltages across R, L, and C, and the symbols V_R, V_L, and V_C for the maximum voltages. We denote the instantaneous and maximum *source* voltages by v and V. Then, in Fig. 31.13a, $v = v_{ad}$, $v_R = v_{ab}$, $v_L = v_{bc}$, and $v_C = v_{cd}$.

We have shown that the potential difference between the terminals of a resistor is *in phase* with the current in the resistor and that its maximum value V_R is given by Eq. (31.7):

$$V_R = IR$$

31.13 An *L-R-C* series circuit with an ac source.

(a) *L-R-C* series circuit

(b) Phasor diagram for the case $X_L > X_C$

Source voltage phasor is the vector sum of the V_R, V_L, and V_C phasors.

Inductor voltage phasor leads current phasor by 90°.

All circuit elements have the same current phasor.

Capacitor voltage phasor lags current phasor by 90°. It is thus always antiparallel to the V_L phasor.

Resistor voltage phasor is in phase with current phasor.

(c) Phasor diagram for the case $X_L < X_C$

If $X_L < X_C$, the source voltage phasor lags the current phasor, $X < 0$, and ϕ is a negative angle between 0 and −90°.

The phasor V_R in Fig. 31.13b, in phase with the current phasor I, represents the voltage across the resistor. Its projection onto the horizontal axis at any instant gives the instantaneous potential difference v_R.

The voltage across an inductor *leads* the current by 90°. Its voltage amplitude is given by Eq. (31.13):

$$V_L = IX_L$$

The phasor V_L in Fig. 31.13b represents the voltage across the inductor, and its projection onto the horizontal axis at any instant equals v_L.

The voltage across a capacitor *lags* the current by 90°. Its voltage amplitude is given by Eq. (31.19):

$$V_C = IX_C$$

The phasor V_C in Fig. 31.13b represents the voltage across the capacitor, and its projection onto the horizontal axis at any instant equals v_C.

The instantaneous potential difference v between terminals a and d is equal at every instant to the (algebraic) sum of the potential differences v_R, v_L, and v_C. That is, it equals the sum of the *projections* of the phasors V_R, V_L, and V_C. But the sum of the projections of these phasors is equal to the *projection* of their *vector sum*. So the vector sum V must be the phasor that represents the source voltage v and the instantaneous total voltage v_{ad} across the series of elements.

To form this vector sum, we first subtract the phasor V_C from the phasor V_L. (These two phasors always lie along the same line, with opposite directions.) This gives the phasor $V_L - V_C$. This is always at right angles to the phasor V_R, so from the Pythagorean theorem the magnitude of the phasor V is

$$V = \sqrt{V_R^2 + (V_L - V_C)^2} = \sqrt{(IR)^2 + (IX_L - IX_C)^2} \quad \text{or}$$
$$V = I\sqrt{R^2 + (X_L - X_C)^2} \tag{31.20}$$

We define the **impedance** Z of an ac circuit as the ratio of the voltage amplitude across the circuit to the current amplitude in the circuit. From Eq. (31.20) the impedance of the *L-R-C* series circuit is

$$Z = \sqrt{R^2 + (X_L - X_C)^2} \tag{31.21}$$

so we can rewrite Eq. (31.20) as

$$V = IZ \quad \text{(amplitude of voltage across an ac circuit)} \tag{31.22}$$

While Eq. (31.21) is valid only for an *L-R-C* series circuit, we can use Eq. (31.22) to define the impedance of *any* network of resistors, inductors, and capacitors as the ratio of the amplitude of the voltage across the network to the current amplitude. The SI unit of impedance is the ohm.

The Meaning of Impedance and Phase Angle

Equation (31.22) has a form similar to $V = IR$, with impedance Z in an ac circuit playing the role of resistance R in a dc circuit. Just as direct current tends to follow the path of least resistance, so alternating current tends to follow the path of lowest impedance (Fig. 31.14). Note, however, that impedance is actually a function of R, L, and C, as well as of the angular frequency ω. We can see this by substituting Eq. (31.12) for X_L and Eq. (31.18) for X_C into Eq. (31.21), giving the following complete expression for Z for a series circuit:

$$Z = \sqrt{R^2 + (X_L - X_C)^2}$$
$$= \sqrt{R^2 + [\omega L - (1/\omega C)]^2} \tag{31.23}$$

(impedance of an *L-R-C* series circuit)

31.14 This gas-filled glass sphere has an alternating voltage between its surface and the electrode at its center. The glowing streamers show the resulting alternating current that passes through the gas. When you touch the outside of the sphere, your fingertips and the inner surface of the sphere act as the plates of a capacitor, and the sphere and your body together form an *L-R-C* series circuit. The current (which is low enough to be harmless) is drawn to your fingers because the path through your body has a low impedance.

Hence for a given amplitude V of the source voltage applied to the circuit, the amplitude $I = V/Z$ of the resulting current will be different at different frequencies. We'll explore this frequency dependence in detail in Section 31.5.

In the phasor diagram shown in Fig. 31.13b, the angle ϕ between the voltage and current phasors is the phase angle of the source voltage v with respect to the current i; that is, it is the angle by which the source voltage leads the current. From the diagram,

$$\tan\phi = \frac{V_L - V_C}{V_R} = \frac{I(X_L - X_C)}{IR} = \frac{X_L - X_C}{R}$$

$$\tan\phi = \frac{\omega L - 1/\omega C}{R} \qquad \text{(phase angle of an } L\text{-}R\text{-}C \text{ series circuit)} \quad (31.24)$$

If the current is $i = I\cos\omega t$, then the source voltage v is

$$v = V\cos(\omega t + \phi) \qquad (31.25)$$

Figure 31.13b shows the behavior of a circuit in which $X_L > X_C$. Figure 31.13c shows the behavior when $X_L < X_C$; the voltage phasor V lies on the opposite side of the current phasor I and the voltage *lags* the current. In this case, $X_L - X_C$ is *negative*, tan ϕ is negative, and ϕ is a negative angle between 0 and $-90°$. Since X_L and X_C depend on frequency, the phase angle ϕ depends on frequency as well. We'll examine the consequences of this in Section 31.5.

All of the expressions that we've developed for an L-R-C series circuit are still valid if one of the circuit elements is missing. If the resistor is missing, we set $R = 0$; if the inductor is missing, we set $L = 0$. But if the capacitor is missing, we set $C = \infty$, corresponding to the absence of any potential difference $(v_C = q/C = 0)$ or any capacitive reactance $(X_C = 1/\omega C = 0)$.

In this entire discussion we have described magnitudes of voltages and currents in terms of their *maximum* values, the voltage and current *amplitudes*. But we remarked at the end of Section 31.1 that these quantities are usually described in terms of rms values, not amplitudes. For any sinusoidally varying quantity, the rms value is always $1/\sqrt{2}$ times the amplitude. All the relationships between voltage and current that we have derived in this and the preceding sections are still valid if we use rms quantities throughout instead of amplitudes. For example, if we divide Eq. (31.22) by $\sqrt{2}$, we get

$$\frac{V}{\sqrt{2}} = \frac{I}{\sqrt{2}}Z$$

which we can rewrite as

$$V_{\text{rms}} = I_{\text{rms}}Z \qquad (31.26)$$

We can translate Eqs. (31.7), (31.13), and (31.19) in exactly the same way.

We have considered only ac circuits in which an inductor, a resistor, and a capacitor are in series. You can do a similar analysis for an L-R-C *parallel* circuit; see Problem 31.56.

Finally, we remark that in this section we have been describing the *steady-state* condition of a circuit, the state that exists after the circuit has been connected to the source for a long time. When the source is first connected, there may be additional voltages and currents, called *transients*, whose nature depends on the time in the cycle when the circuit is initially completed. A detailed analysis of transients is beyond our scope. They always die out after a sufficiently long time, and they do not affect the steady-state behavior of the circuit. But they can cause dangerous and damaging surges in power lines, which is why delicate electronic systems such as computers are often provided with power-line surge protectors.

Problem-Solving Strategy 31.1 | Alternating-Current Circuits

IDENTIFY *the relevant concepts:* In analyzing ac circuits, we can apply all of the concepts used to analyze direct-current circuits, particularly those in Problem-Solving Strategies 26.1 and 26.2. But now we must distinguish between the amplitudes of alternating currents and voltages and their instantaneous values, and among resistance (for resistors), reactance (for inductors or capacitors), and impedance (for composite circuits).

SET UP *the problem* using the following steps:
1. Draw a diagram of the circuit and label all known and unknown quantities.
2. Identify the target variables.

EXECUTE *the solution* as follows:
1. Use the relationships derived in Sections 31.2 and 31.3 to solve for the target variables, using the following hints.
2. It's almost always easiest to work with angular frequency $\omega = 2\pi f$ rather than ordinary frequency f.
3. Keep in mind the following phase relationships: For a resistor, voltage and current are *in phase,* so the corresponding phasors always point in the same direction. For an inductor, the voltage *leads* the current by 90° (i.e., $\phi = +90° = \pi/2$ radians), so the voltage phasor points 90° counterclockwise from the current phasor. For a capacitor, the voltage *lags* the current by 90° (i.e., $\phi = -90° = -\pi/2$ radians), so the voltage phasor points 90° clockwise from the current phasor.

4. Kirchhoff's rules hold *at each instant.* For example, in a series circuit, the instantaneous current is the same in all circuit elements; in a parallel circuit, the instantaneous potential difference is the same across all circuit elements.
5. Inductive reactance, capacitive reactance, and impedance are analogous to resistance; each represents the ratio of voltage amplitude V to current amplitude I in a circuit element or combination of elements. However, phase relationships are crucial. In applying Kirchhoff's loop rule, you must combine the effects of resistance and reactance by *vector* addition of the corresponding voltage phasors, as in Figs. 31.13b and 31.13c. When you have several circuit elements in series, for example, you can't just *add* all the numerical values of resistance and reactance to get the impedance; that would ignore the phase relationships.

EVALUATE *your answer:* When working with an *L-R-C series* circuit, you can check your results by comparing the values of the inductive and capacitive reactances X_L and X_C. If $X_L > X_C$, then the voltage amplitude across the inductor is greater than that across the capacitor and the phase angle ϕ is positive (between 0 and 90°). If $X_L < X_C$, then the voltage amplitude across the inductor is less than that across the capacitor and the phase angle ϕ is negative (between 0 and −90°).

Example 31.4 | An *L-R-C* series circuit I

In the series circuit of Fig. 31.13a, suppose $R = 300 \, \Omega$, $L = 60 \, \text{mH}$, $C = 0.50 \, \mu\text{F}$, $V = 50 \, \text{V}$, and $\omega = 10{,}000 \, \text{rad/s}$. Find the reactances X_L and X_C, the impedance Z, the current amplitude I, the phase angle ϕ, and the voltage amplitude across each circuit element.

SOLUTION

IDENTIFY and SET UP: This problem uses the ideas developed in Section 31.2 and this section about the behavior of circuit elements in an ac circuit. We use Eqs. (31.12) and (31.18) to determine X_L and X_C, and Eq. (31.23) to find Z. We then use Eq. (31.22) to find the current amplitude and Eq. (31.24) to find the phase angle. The relationships in Table 31.1 then yield the voltage amplitudes.

EXECUTE: The inductive and capacitive reactances are

$$X_L = \omega L = (10{,}000 \, \text{rad/s})(60 \, \text{mH}) = 600 \, \Omega$$

$$X_C = \frac{1}{\omega C} = \frac{1}{(10{,}000 \, \text{rad/s})(0.50 \times 10^{-6} \, \text{F})} = 200 \, \Omega$$

The impedance Z of the circuit is then

$$Z = \sqrt{R^2 + (X_L - X_C)^2} = \sqrt{(300 \, \Omega)^2 + (600 \, \Omega - 200 \, \Omega)^2}$$
$$= 500 \, \Omega$$

With source voltage amplitude $V = 50 \, \text{V}$, the current amplitude I and phase angle ϕ are

$$I = \frac{V}{Z} = \frac{50 \, \text{V}}{500 \, \Omega} = 0.10 \, \text{A}$$

$$\phi = \arctan \frac{X_L - X_C}{R} = \arctan \frac{400 \, \Omega}{300 \, \Omega} = 53°$$

From Table 31.1, the voltage amplitudes V_R, V_L, and V_C across the resistor, inductor, and capacitor, respectively, are

$$V_R = IR = (0.10 \, \text{A})(300 \, \Omega) = 30 \, \text{V}$$
$$V_L = IX_L = (0.10 \, \text{A})(600 \, \Omega) = 60 \, \text{V}$$
$$V_C = IX_C = (0.10 \, \text{A})(200 \, \Omega) = 20 \, \text{V}$$

EVALUATE: As in Fig. 31.13b, $X_L > X_C$; hence the voltage amplitude across the inductor is greater than that across the capacitor and ϕ is positive. The value $\phi = 53°$ means that the voltage *leads* the current by 53°.

Note that the source voltage amplitude $V = 50 \, \text{V}$ is *not* equal to the sum of the voltage amplitudes across the separate circuit elements: $50 \, \text{V} \neq 30 \, \text{V} + 60 \, \text{V} + 20 \, \text{V}$. Instead, V is the *vector sum* of the V_R, V_L, and V_C phasors. If you draw the phasor diagram like Fig. 31.13b for this particular situation, you'll see that V_R, $V_L - V_C$, and V constitute a 3-4-5 right triangle.

Example 31.5 An *L-R-C* series circuit II

For the *L-R-C* series circuit of Example 31.4, find expressions for the time dependence of the instantaneous current i and the instantaneous voltages across the resistor (v_R), inductor (v_L), capacitor (v_C), and ac source (v).

SOLUTION

IDENTIFY and SET UP: We describe the current using Eq. (31.2), which assumes that the current is maximum at $t = 0$. The voltages are then given by Eq. (31.8) for the resistor, Eq. (31.10) for the inductor, Eq. (31.16) for the capacitor, and Eq. (31.25) for the source.

EXECUTE: The current and the voltages all oscillate with the same angular frequency, $\omega = 10{,}000$ rad/s, and hence with the same period, $2\pi/\omega = 2\pi/(10{,}000 \text{ rad/s}) = 6.3 \times 10^{-4}$ s $= 0.63$ ms. From Eq. (31.2), the current is

$$i = I\cos\omega t = (0.10 \text{ A})\cos(10{,}000 \text{ rad/s})t$$

The resistor voltage is *in phase* with the current, so

$$v_R = V_R\cos\omega t = (30 \text{ V})\cos(10{,}000 \text{ rad/s})t$$

The inductor voltage *leads* the current by 90°, so

$$v_L = V_L\cos(\omega t + 90°) = -V_L\sin\omega t$$
$$= -(60 \text{ V})\sin(10{,}000 \text{ rad/s})t$$

The capacitor voltage *lags* the current by 90°, so

$$v_C = V_C\cos(\omega t - 90°) = V_C\sin\omega t$$
$$= (20 \text{ V})\sin(10{,}000 \text{ rad/s})t$$

We found in Example 31.4 that the source voltage (equal to the voltage across the entire combination of resistor, inductor, and capacitor) *leads* the current by $\phi = 53°$, so

$$v = V\cos(\omega t + \phi)$$
$$= (50 \text{ V})\cos\left[(10{,}000 \text{ rad/s})t + \left(\frac{2\pi \text{ rad}}{360°}\right)(53°)\right]$$
$$= (50 \text{ V})\cos[(10{,}000 \text{ rad/s})t + 0.93 \text{ rad}]$$

EVALUATE: Figure 31.15 graphs the four voltages versus time. The inductor voltage has a larger amplitude than the capacitor voltage because $X_L > X_C$. The *instantaneous* source voltage v is always equal to the sum of the instantaneous voltages v_R, v_L, and v_C. You should verify this by measuring the values of the voltages shown in the graph at different values of the time t.

31.15 Graphs of the source voltage v, resistor voltage v_R, inductor voltage v_L, and capacitor voltage v_C as functions of time for the situation of Example 31.4. The current, which is not shown, is in phase with the resistor voltage.

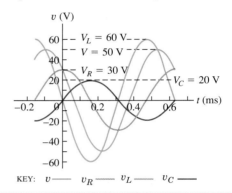

KEY: v —— v_R —— v_L —— v_C ——

Test Your Understanding of Section 31.3 Rank the following ac circuits in order of their current amplitude, from highest to lowest value. (i) the circuit in Example 31.4; (ii) the circuit in Example 31.4 with the capacitor and inductor both removed; (iii) the circuit in Example 31.4 with the resistor and capacitor both removed; (iv) the circuit in Example 31.4 with the resistor and inductor both removed.

31.4 Power in Alternating-Current Circuits

Alternating currents play a central role in systems for distributing, converting, and using electrical energy, so it's important to look at power relationships in ac circuits. For an ac circuit with instantaneous current i and current amplitude I, we'll consider an element of that circuit across which the instantaneous potential difference is v with voltage amplitude V. The instantaneous power p delivered to this circuit element is

$$p = vi$$

Let's first see what this means for individual circuit elements. We'll assume in each case that $i = I\cos\omega t$.

Power in a Resistor

Suppose first that the circuit element is a *pure resistor* R, as in Fig. 31.7a; then $v = v_R$ and i are *in phase*. We obtain the graph representing p by multiplying the heights of the graphs of v and i in Fig. 31.7b at each instant. This graph is shown by the black curve in Fig. 31.16a. The product vi is always positive because v and i are always either both positive or both negative. Hence energy is supplied *to* the resistor at every instant for both directions of i, although the power is not constant.

The power curve for a pure resistor is symmetrical about a value equal to one-half its maximum value VI, so the *average power* P_{av} is

$$P_{av} = \tfrac{1}{2}VI \qquad \text{(for a pure resistor)} \qquad (31.27)$$

An equivalent expression is

$$P_{av} = \frac{V}{\sqrt{2}} \frac{I}{\sqrt{2}} = V_{rms}I_{rms} \qquad \text{(for a pure resistor)} \qquad (31.28)$$

Also, $V_{rms} = I_{rms}R$, so we can express P_{av} by any of the equivalent forms

$$P_{av} = I_{rms}{}^2 R = \frac{V_{rms}{}^2}{R} = V_{rms}I_{rms} \qquad \text{(for a pure resistor)} \qquad (31.29)$$

Note that the expressions in Eq. (31.29) have the same form as the corresponding relationships for a dc circuit, Eq. (25.18). Also note that they are valid only for pure resistors, not for more complicated combinations of circuit elements.

Power in an Inductor

Next we connect the source to a pure inductor L, as in Fig. 31.8a. The voltage $v = v_L$ leads the current i by 90°. When we multiply the curves of v and i, the product vi is *negative* during the half of the cycle when v and i have *opposite* signs. The power curve, shown in Fig. 31.16b, is symmetrical about the horizontal axis; it is positive half the time and negative the other half, and the average power is zero. When p is positive, energy is being supplied to set up the magnetic field in the inductor; when p is negative, the field is collapsing and the inductor is returning energy to the source. The net energy transfer over one cycle is zero.

Power in a Capacitor

Finally, we connect the source to a pure capacitor C, as in Fig. 31.9a. The voltage $v = v_C$ lags the current i by 90°. Figure 31.16c shows the power curve; the average power is again zero. Energy is supplied to charge the capacitor and is returned

31.16 Graphs of current, voltage, and power as functions of time for (a) a pure resistor, (b) a pure inductor, (c) a pure capacitor, and (d) an arbitrary ac circuit that can have resistance, inductance, and capacitance.

(a) Pure resistor

For a resistor, $p = vi$ is always positive because v and i are either both positive or both negative at any instant.

(b) Pure inductor

(c) Pure capacitor

For an inductor or capacitor, $p = vi$ is alternately positive and negative, and the average power is zero.

(d) Arbitrary ac circuit

For an arbitrary combination of resistors, inductors, and capacitors, the average power is positive.

KEY: Instantaneous current, i ▬   Instantaneous voltage across device, v ▬   Instantaneous power input to device, p ▬

to the source when the capacitor discharges. The net energy transfer over one cycle is again zero.

Power in a General ac Circuit

In *any* ac circuit, with any combination of resistors, capacitors, and inductors, the voltage v across the entire circuit has some phase angle ϕ with respect to the current i. Then the instantaneous power p is given by

$$p = vi = [V\cos(\omega t + \phi)][I\cos\omega t] \qquad (31.30)$$

The instantaneous power curve has the form shown in Fig. 31.16d. The area between the positive loops and the horizontal axis is greater than the area between the negative loops and the horizontal axis, and the average power is positive.

We can derive from Eq. (31.30) an expression for the *average* power P_{av} by using the identity for the cosine of the sum of two angles:

$$p = [V(\cos\omega t\cos\phi - \sin\omega t\sin\phi)][I\cos\omega t]$$
$$= VI\cos\phi\cos^2\omega t - VI\sin\phi\cos\omega t\sin\omega t$$

From the discussion in Section 31.1 that led to Eq. (31.4), we see that the average value of $\cos^2\omega t$ (over one cycle) is $\frac{1}{2}$. The average value of $\cos\omega t\sin\omega t$ is zero because this product is equal to $\frac{1}{2}\sin 2\omega t$, whose average over a cycle is zero. So the average power P_{av} is

$$P_{av} = \tfrac{1}{2}VI\cos\phi = V_{rms}I_{rms}\cos\phi \qquad \begin{matrix}\text{(average power into a}\\ \text{general ac circuit)}\end{matrix} \qquad (31.31)$$

When v and i are in phase, so $\phi = 0$, the average power equals $\frac{1}{2}VI = V_{rms}I_{rms}$; when v and i are 90° out of phase, the average power is zero. In the general case, when v has a phase angle ϕ with respect to i, the average power equals $\frac{1}{2}I$ multiplied by $V\cos\phi$, the component of the voltage phasor that is *in phase* with the current phasor. Figure 31.17 shows the general relationship of the current and voltage phasors. For the L-R-C series circuit, Figs. 31.13b and 31.13c show that $V\cos\phi$ equals the voltage amplitude V_R for the resistor; hence Eq. (31.31) is the average power dissipated in the resistor. On average there is no energy flow into or out of the inductor or capacitor, so none of P_{av} goes into either of these circuit elements.

The factor $\cos\phi$ is called the **power factor** of the circuit. For a pure resistance, $\phi = 0$, $\cos\phi = 1$, and $P_{av} = V_{rms}I_{rms}$. For a pure inductor or capacitor, $\phi = \pm 90°$, $\cos\phi = 0$, and $P_{av} = 0$. For an L-R-C series circuit the power factor is equal to R/Z; we leave the proof of this statement to you (see Exercise 31.21).

A low power factor (large angle ϕ of lag or lead) is usually undesirable in power circuits. The reason is that for a given potential difference, a large current is needed to supply a given amount of power. This results in large i^2R losses in the transmission lines. Your electric power company may charge a higher rate to a client with a low power factor. Many types of ac machinery draw a *lagging* current; that is, the current drawn by the machinery lags the applied voltage. Hence the voltage leads the current, so $\phi > 0$ and $\cos\phi < 1$. The power factor can be corrected toward the ideal value of 1 by connecting a capacitor in parallel with the load. The current drawn by the capacitor *leads* the voltage (that is, the voltage across the capacitor lags the current), which compensates for the lagging current in the other branch of the circuit. The capacitor itself absorbs no net power from the line.

31.17 Using phasors to calculate the average power for an arbitrary ac circuit.

Average power $= \frac{1}{2}I(V\cos\phi)$, where $V\cos\phi$ is the component of V in phase with I.

Example 31.6 **Power in a hair dryer**

An electric hair dryer is rated at 1500 W (the *average* power) at 120 V (the *rms* voltage). Calculate (a) the resistance, (b) the rms current, and (c) the maximum instantaneous power. Assume that the dryer is a pure resistor. (The heating element acts as a resistor.)

Continued

SOLUTION

IDENTIFY and SET UP: We are given $P_{av} = 1500$ W and $V_{rms} = 120$ V. Our target variables are the resistance R, the rms current I_{rms}, and the maximum value p_{max} of the instantaneous power p. We solve Eq. (31.29) to find R, Eq. (31.28) to find I_{rms} from V_{rms} and P_{av}, and Eq. (31.30) to find p_{max}.

EXECUTE: (a) From Eq. (31.29), the resistance is

$$R = \frac{V_{rms}^2}{P_{av}} = \frac{(120 \text{ V})^2}{1500 \text{ W}} = 9.6 \ \Omega$$

(b) From Eq. (31.28),

$$I_{rms} = \frac{P_{av}}{V_{rms}} = \frac{1500 \text{ W}}{120 \text{ V}} = 12.5 \text{ A}$$

(c) For a pure resistor, the voltage and current are in phase and the phase angle ϕ is zero. Hence from Eq. (31.30), the instantaneous power is $p = VI\cos^2\omega t$ and the maximum instantaneous power is $p_{max} = VI$. From Eq. (31.27), this is twice the average power P_{av}, so

$$p_{max} = VI = 2P_{av} = 2(1500 \text{ W}) = 3000 \text{ W}$$

EVALUATE: We can confirm our result in part (b) by using Eq. (31.7): $I_{rms} = V_{rms}/R = (120 \text{ V})/(9.6 \ \Omega) = 12.5$ A. Note that some unscrupulous manufacturers of stereo amplifiers advertise the *peak* power output rather than the lower average value.

Example 31.7 **Power in an *L-R-C* series circuit**

For the *L-R-C* series circuit of Example 31.4, (a) calculate the power factor and (b) calculate the average power delivered to the entire circuit and to each circuit element.

SOLUTION

IDENTIFY and SET UP: We can use the results of Example 31.4. The power factor is the cosine of the phase angle ϕ, and we use Eq. (31.31) to find the average power delivered in terms of ϕ and the amplitudes of voltage and current.

EXECUTE: (a) The power factor is $\cos\phi = \cos 53° = 0.60$.

(b) From Eq. (31.31),

$$P_{av} = \tfrac{1}{2}VI\cos\phi = \tfrac{1}{2}(50 \text{ V})(0.10 \text{ A})(0.60) = 1.5 \text{ W}$$

EVALUATE: Although P_{av} is the average power delivered to the *L-R-C* combination, all of this power is dissipated in the *resistor*. As Figs. 31.16b and 31.16c show, the average power delivered to a pure inductor or pure capacitor is always zero.

Test Your Understanding of Section 31.4 Figure 31.16d shows that during part of a cycle of oscillation, the instantaneous power delivered to the circuit is negative. This means that energy is being extracted from the circuit. (a) Where is the energy extracted from? (i) the resistor; (ii) the inductor; (iii) the capacitor; (iv) the ac source; (v) more than one of these. (b) Where does the energy go? (i) the resistor; (ii) the inductor; (iii) the capacitor; (iv) the ac source; (v) more than one of these.

31.5 Resonance in Alternating-Current Circuits

ActivPhysics 14.3: AC Circuits: The Driven Oscillator (Questions 8, 9, and 11)

Much of the practical importance of *L-R-C* series circuits arises from the way in which such circuits respond to sources of different angular frequency ω. For example, one type of tuning circuit used in radio receivers is simply an *L-R-C* series circuit. A radio signal of any given frequency produces a current of the same frequency in the receiver circuit, but the amplitude of the current is *greatest* if the signal frequency equals the particular frequency to which the receiver circuit is "tuned." This effect is called *resonance*. The circuit is designed so that signals at other than the tuned frequency produce currents that are too small to make an audible sound come out of the radio's speakers.

To see how an *L-R-C* series circuit can be used in this way, suppose we connect an ac source with constant voltage amplitude V but adjustable angular frequency ω across an *L-R-C* series circuit. The current that appears in the circuit has the same angular frequency as the source and a current amplitude $I = V/Z$, where Z is the impedance of the *L-R-C* series circuit. This impedance depends on the frequency, as Eq. (31.23) shows. Figure 31.18a shows graphs of R, X_L, X_C, and Z as functions of ω. We have used a logarithmic angular frequency scale so that we can cover a wide range of frequencies. As the frequency increases, X_L increases and X_C decreases; hence there is always one frequency at which

31.18 How variations in the angular frequency of an ac circuit affect (a) reactance, resistance, and impedance, and (b) impedance, current amplitude, and phase angle.

(a) Reactance, resistance, and impedance as functions of angular frequency

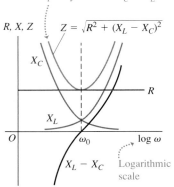

Impedance Z is least at the angular frequency at which $X_C = X_L$.

$Z = \sqrt{R^2 + (X_L - X_C)^2}$

Logarithmic scale

(b) Impedance, current, and phase angle as functions of angular frequency

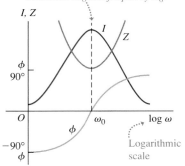

Current peaks at the angular frequency at which impedance is least. This is the *resonance angular frequency* ω_0.

Logarithmic scale

31.19 Graph of current amplitude I as a function of angular frequency ω for an L-R-C series circuit with $V = 100$ V, $L = 2.0$ H, $C = 0.50\ \mu$F, and three different values of the resistance R.

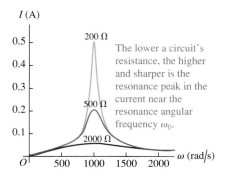

The lower a circuit's resistance, the higher and sharper is the resonance peak in the current near the resonance angular frequency ω_0.

X_L and X_C are equal and $X_L - X_C$ is zero. At this frequency the impedance $Z = \sqrt{R^2 + (X_L - X_C)^2}$ has its *smallest* value, equal simply to the resistance R.

Circuit Behavior at Resonance

As we vary the angular frequency ω of the source, the current amplitude $I = V/Z$ varies as shown in Fig. 31.18b; the *maximum* value of I occurs at the frequency at which the impedance Z is *minimum*. This peaking of the current amplitude at a certain frequency is called **resonance.** The angular frequency ω_0 at which the resonance peak occurs is called the **resonance angular frequency.** This is the angular frequency at which the inductive and capacitive reactances are equal, so at resonance,

$$X_L = X_C \qquad \omega_0 L = \frac{1}{\omega_0 C} \qquad \omega_0 = \frac{1}{\sqrt{LC}} \qquad \begin{array}{c}(L\text{-}R\text{-}C \text{ series circuit} \\ \text{at resonance})\end{array} \qquad (31.32)$$

Note that this is equal to the natural angular frequency of oscillation of an L-C circuit, which we derived in Section 30.5, Eq. (30.22). The **resonance frequency** f_0 is $\omega_0/2\pi$. This is the frequency at which the greatest current appears in the circuit for a given source voltage amplitude; in other words, f_0 is the frequency to which the circuit is "tuned."

It's instructive to look at what happens to the *voltages* in an L-R-C series circuit at resonance. The current at any instant is the same in L and C. The voltage across an inductor always *leads* the current by 90°, or $\frac{1}{4}$ cycle, and the voltage across a capacitor always *lags* the current by 90°. Therefore the instantaneous voltages across L and C always differ in phase by 180°, or $\frac{1}{2}$ cycle; they have opposite signs at each instant. At the resonance frequency, and *only* at the resonance frequency, $X_L = X_C$ and the voltage amplitudes $V_L = IX_L$ and $V_C = IX_C$ are *equal*; then the instantaneous voltages across L and C add to zero at each instant, and the *total* voltage v_{bd} across the L-C combination in Fig. 31.13a is exactly zero. The voltage across the resistor is then equal to the source voltage. So at the resonance frequency the circuit behaves as if the inductor and capacitor weren't there at all!

The *phase* of the voltage relative to the current is given by Eq. (31.24). At frequencies below resonance, X_C is greater than X_L; the capacitive reactance dominates, the voltage *lags* the current, and the phase angle ϕ is between zero and $-90°$. Above resonance, the inductive reactance dominates, the voltage *leads* the current, and the phase angle ϕ is between zero and $+90°$. Figure 31.18b shows this variation of ϕ with angular frequency.

Tailoring an ac Circuit

If we can vary the inductance L or the capacitance C of a circuit, we can also vary the resonance frequency. This is exactly how a radio or television receiving set is "tuned" to receive a particular station. In the early days of radio this was accomplished by the use of capacitors with movable metal plates whose overlap could be varied to change C. (This is what is being done with the radio tuning knob shown in the photograph that opens this chapter.) A more modern approach is to vary L by using a coil with a ferrite core that slides in or out.

In an L-R-C series circuit the impedance reaches its minimum value and the current its maximum value at the resonance frequency. The middle curve in Fig. 31.19 is a graph of current as a function of frequency for such a circuit, with source voltage amplitude $V = 100$ V, $L = 2.0$ H, $C = 0.50\ \mu$F, and $R = 500\ \Omega$. This curve is called a *response curve* or a *resonance curve*. The resonance angular frequency is $\omega_0 = (LC)^{-1/2} = 1000$ rad/s. As we expect, the curve has a peak at this angular frequency.

The resonance frequency is determined by L and C; what happens when we change R? Figure 31.19 also shows graphs of I as a function of ω for $R = 200\ \Omega$ and for $R = 2000\ \Omega$. The curves are similar for frequencies far away from resonance, where the impedance is dominated by X_L or X_C. But near resonance, where X_L and X_C nearly cancel each other, the curve is higher and more sharply peaked for small values of R and broader and flatter for large values of R. At resonance, $Z = R$ and $I = V/R$, so the maximum height of the curve is inversely proportional to R.

The shape of the response curve is important in the design of radio and television receiving circuits. The sharply peaked curve is what makes it possible to discriminate between two stations broadcasting on adjacent frequency bands. But if the peak is *too* sharp, some of the information in the received signal is lost, such as the high-frequency sounds in music. The shape of the resonance curve is also related to the overdamped and underdamped oscillations that we described in Section 30.6. A sharply peaked resonance curve corresponds to a small value of R and a lightly damped oscillating system; a broad, flat curve goes with a large value of R and a heavily damped system.

In this section we have discussed resonance in an *L-R-C series* circuit. Resonance can also occur in an ac circuit in which the inductor, resistor, and capacitor are connected in *parallel*. We leave the details to you (see Problem 31.57).

Resonance phenomena occur not just in ac circuits, but in all areas of physics. We discussed examples of resonance in *mechanical* systems in Sections 13.8 and 16.5. The amplitude of a mechanical oscillation peaks when the driving-force frequency is close to a natural frequency of the system; this is analogous to the peaking of the current in an *L-R-C* series circuit. We suggest that you review the sections on mechanical resonance now, looking for the analogies.

Example 31.8   Tuning a radio

The series circuit in Fig. 31.20 is similar to some radio tuning circuits. It is connected to a variable-frequency ac source with an rms terminal voltage of 1.0 V. (a) Find the resonance frequency. At the resonance frequency, find (b) the inductive reactance X_L, the capacitive reactance X_C, and the impedance Z; (c) the rms current I_{rms}; (d) the rms voltage across each circuit element.

SOLUTION

IDENTIFY and SET UP: Figure 31.20 shows an *L-R-C* series circuit, with ideal meters inserted to measure the rms current and voltages, our target variables. Equations (31.32) include the formula for the resonance angular frequency ω_0, from which we find the resonance frequency f_0. We use Eqs. (31.12) and (31.18) to find X_L and X_C, which are equal at resonance; at resonance, from Eq. (31.23), we

31.20 A radio tuning circuit at resonance. The circles denote rms current and voltages.

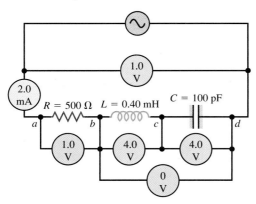

have $Z = R$. We use Eqs. (31.7), (31.13), and (31.19) to find the voltages across the circuit elements.

EXECUTE: (a) The values of ω_0 and f_0 are

$$\omega_0 = \frac{1}{\sqrt{LC}} = \frac{1}{\sqrt{(0.40 \times 10^{-3}\ \text{H})(100 \times 10^{-12}\ \text{F})}}$$

$$= 5.0 \times 10^6\ \text{rad/s}$$

$$f_0 = 8.0 \times 10^5\ \text{Hz} = 800\ \text{kHz}$$

This frequency is in the lower part of the AM radio band.
  (b) At this frequency,

$$X_L = \omega L = (5.0 \times 10^6\ \text{rad/s})(0.40 \times 10^{-3}\ \text{H}) = 2000\ \Omega$$

$$X_C = \frac{1}{\omega C} = \frac{1}{(5.0 \times 10^6\ \text{rad/s})(100 \times 10^{-12}\ \text{F})} = 2000\ \Omega$$

Since $X_L = X_C$ at resonance as stated above, $Z = R = 500\ \Omega$.
  (c) From Eq. (31.26) the rms current at resonance is

$$I_{rms} = \frac{V_{rms}}{Z} = \frac{V_{rms}}{R} = \frac{1.0\ \text{V}}{500\ \Omega} = 0.0020\ \text{A} = 2.0\ \text{mA}$$

  (d) The rms potential difference across the resistor is

$$V_{R\text{-}rms} = I_{rms}R = (0.0020\ \text{A})(500\ \Omega) = 1.0\ \text{V}$$

The rms potential differences across the inductor and capacitor are

$$V_{L\text{-}rms} = I_{rms}X_L = (0.0020\ \text{A})(2000\ \Omega) = 4.0\ \text{V}$$

$$V_{C\text{-}rms} = I_{rms}X_C = (0.0020\ \text{A})(2000\ \Omega) = 4.0\ \text{V}$$

EVALUATE: The potential differences across the inductor and the capacitor have equal rms values and amplitudes, but are 180° out of phase and so add to zero at each instant. Note also that at resonance, $V_{R\text{-}rms}$ is equal to the source voltage V_{rms}, while in this example, $V_{L\text{-}rms}$ and $V_{C\text{-}rms}$ are both considerably *larger* than V_{rms}.

Test Your Understanding of Section 31.5 How does the resonance frequency of an *L-R-C* series circuit change if the plates of the capacitor are brought closer together? (i) It increases; (ii) it decreases; (iii) it is unaffected.   ▮

31.6 Transformers

One of the great advantages of ac over dc for electric-power distribution is that it is much easier to step voltage levels up and down with ac than with dc. For long-distance power transmission it is desirable to use as high a voltage and as small a current as possible; this reduces i^2R losses in the transmission lines, and smaller wires can be used, saving on material costs. Present-day transmission lines routinely operate at rms voltages of the order of 500 kV. On the other hand, safety considerations and insulation requirements dictate relatively low voltages in generating equipment and in household and industrial power distribution. The standard voltage for household wiring is 120 V in the United States and Canada and 240 V in many other countries. The necessary voltage conversion is accomplished by the use of **transformers.**

How Transformers Work

Figure 31.21 shows an idealized transformer. The key components of the transformer are two coils or *windings,* electrically insulated from each other but wound on the same core. The core is typically made of a material, such as iron, with a very large relative permeability K_{m}. This keeps the magnetic field lines due to a current in one winding almost completely within the core. Hence almost all of these field lines pass through the other winding, maximizing the *mutual inductance* of the two windings (see Section 30.1). The winding to which power is supplied is called the **primary;** the winding from which power is delivered is called the **secondary.** The circuit symbol for a transformer with an iron core, such as those used in power distribution systems, is

Here's how a transformer works. The ac source causes an alternating current in the primary, which sets up an alternating flux in the core; this induces an emf in each winding, in accordance with Faraday's law. The induced emf in the secondary gives rise to an alternating current in the secondary, and this delivers energy to the device to which the secondary is connected. All currents and emfs have the same frequency as the ac source.

Let's see how the voltage across the secondary can be made larger or smaller in amplitude than the voltage across the primary. We neglect the resistance of the windings and assume that all the magnetic field lines are confined to the iron core, so at any instant the magnetic flux Φ_B is the same in each turn of the primary and secondary windings. The primary winding has N_1 turns and the secondary winding has N_2 turns. When the magnetic flux changes because of changing currents in the two coils, the resulting induced emfs are

$$\mathcal{E}_1 = -N_1\frac{d\Phi_B}{dt} \quad \text{and} \quad \mathcal{E}_2 = -N_2\frac{d\Phi_B}{dt} \qquad (31.33)$$

The flux *per turn* Φ_B is the same in both the primary and the secondary, so Eqs. (31.33) show that the induced emf *per turn* is the same in each. The ratio of the secondary emf $\mathcal{E}_2$ to the primary emf $\mathcal{E}_1$ is therefore equal at any instant to the ratio of secondary to primary turns:

$$\frac{\mathcal{E}_2}{\mathcal{E}_1} = \frac{N_2}{N_1} \qquad (31.34)$$

Since $\mathcal{E}_1$ and $\mathcal{E}_2$ both oscillate with the same frequency as the ac source, Eq. (31.34) also gives the ratio of the amplitudes or of the rms values of the induced

31.21 Schematic diagram of an idealized step-up transformer. The primary is connected to an ac source; the secondary is connected to a device with resistance R.

The induced emf *per turn* is the same in both coils, so we adjust the ratio of terminal voltages by adjusting the ratio of turns:

$$\frac{V_2}{V_1} = \frac{N_2}{N_1}$$

emfs. If the windings have zero resistance, the induced emfs $\mathcal{E}_1$ and $\mathcal{E}_2$ are equal to the terminal voltages across the primary and the secondary, respectively; hence

$$\frac{V_2}{V_1} = \frac{N_2}{N_1} \qquad \text{(terminal voltages of transformer primary and secondary)} \qquad (31.35)$$

where V_1 and V_2 are either the amplitudes or the rms values of the terminal voltages. By choosing the appropriate turns ratio N_2/N_1, we may obtain any desired secondary voltage from a given primary voltage. If $N_2 > N_1$, as in Fig. 31.21, then $V_2 > V_1$ and we have a *step-up* transformer; if $N_2 < N_1$, then $V_2 < V_1$ and we have a *step-down* transformer. At a power generating station, step-up transformers are used; the primary is connected to the power source and the secondary is connected to the transmission lines, giving the desired high voltage for transmission. Near the consumer, step-down transformers lower the voltage to a value suitable for use in home or industry (Fig. 31.22).

Even the relatively low voltage provided by a household wall socket is too high for many electronic devices, so a further step-down transformer is necessary. This is the role of an "ac adapter" such as those used to recharge a mobile phone or laptop computer from line voltage. Such adapters contain a step-down transformer that converts line voltage to a lower value, typically 3 to 12 volts, as well as diodes to convert alternating current to the direct current that small electronic devices require (Fig. 31.23).

Energy Considerations for Transformers

If the secondary circuit is completed by a resistance R, then the amplitude or rms value of the current in the secondary circuit is $I_2 = V_2/R$. From energy considerations, the power delivered to the primary equals that taken out of the secondary (since there is no resistance in the windings), so

$$V_1 I_1 = V_2 I_2 \qquad \text{(currents in transformer primary and secondary)} \qquad (31.36)$$

We can combine Eqs. (31.35) and (31.36) and the relationship $I_2 = V_2/R$ to eliminate V_2 and I_2; we obtain

$$\frac{V_1}{I_1} = \frac{R}{(N_2/N_1)^2} \qquad (31.37)$$

This shows that when the secondary circuit is completed through a resistance R, the result is the same as if the *source* had been connected directly to a resistance equal to R divided by the square of the turns ratio, $(N_2/N_1)^2$. In other words, the transformer "transforms" not only voltages and currents, but resistances as well. More generally, we can regard a transformer as "transforming" the *impedance* of the network to which the secondary circuit is completed.

Equation (31.37) has many practical consequences. The power supplied by a source to a resistor depends on the resistances of both the resistor and the source. It can be shown that the power transfer is greatest when the two resistances are *equal*. The same principle applies in both dc and ac circuits. When a high-impedance ac source must be connected to a low-impedance circuit, such as an audio amplifier connected to a loudspeaker, the source impedance can be *matched* to that of the circuit by the use of a transformer with an appropriate turns ratio N_2/N_1.

Real transformers always have some energy losses. (That's why an ac adapter like the one shown in Fig. 31.23 feels warm to the touch after it's been in use for a while; the transformer is heated by the dissipated energy.) The windings have some resistance, leading to i^2R losses. There are also energy losses through hysteresis in the core (see Section 28.8). Hysteresis losses are minimized by the use of soft iron with a narrow hysteresis loop.

Another important mechanism for energy loss in a transformer core involves eddy currents (see Section 29.6). Consider a section AA through an iron transformer core (Fig. 31.24a). Since iron is a conductor, any such section can be pictured as

31.22 The cylindrical can near the top of this power pole is a step-down transformer. It converts the high-voltage ac in the power lines to low-voltage (120 V) ac, which is then distributed to the surrounding homes and businesses.

31.23 An ac adapter like this one converts household ac into low-voltage dc for use in electronic devices. It contains a step-down transformer to lower the voltage and diodes to rectify the output current (see Fig. 31.3).

31.24 (a) Primary and secondary windings in a transformer. (b) Eddy currents in the iron core, shown in the cross section at *AA*. (c) Using a laminated core reduces the eddy currents.

(a) Schematic transformer

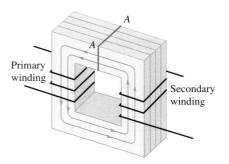

(b) Large eddy currents in solid core

(c) Smaller eddy currents in laminated core

several conducting circuits, one within the other (Fig. 31.24b). The flux through each of these circuits is continually changing, so eddy currents circulate in the entire volume of the core, with lines of flow that form planes perpendicular to the flux. These eddy currents are very undesirable; they waste energy through i^2R heating and themselves set up an opposing flux.

The effects of eddy currents can be minimized by the use of a *laminated* core—that is, one built up of thin sheets or laminae. The large electrical surface resistance of each lamina, due either to a natural coating of oxide or to an insulating varnish, effectively confines the eddy currents to individual laminae (Fig. 31.24c). The possible eddy-current paths are narrower, the induced emf in each path is smaller, and the eddy currents are greatly reduced. The alternating magnetic field exerts forces on the current-carrying laminae that cause them to vibrate back and forth; this vibration causes the characteristic "hum" of an operating transformer. You can hear this same "hum" from the magnetic ballast of a fluorescent light fixture (see Section 30.2).

Thanks to the use of soft iron cores and lamination, transformer efficiencies are usually well over 90%; in large installations they may reach 99%.

Example 31.9   **"Wake up and smell the (transformer)!"**

A friend returns to the United States from Europe with a 960-W coffeemaker, designed to operate from a 240-V line. (a) What can she do to operate it at the USA-standard 120 V? (b) What current will the coffeemaker draw from the 120-V line? (c) What is the resistance of the coffeemaker? (The voltages are rms values.)

SOLUTION

IDENTIFY and SET UP: Our friend needs a step-up transformer to convert 120-V ac to the 240-V ac that the coffeemaker requires. We use Eq. (31.35) to determine the transformer turns ratio N_2/N_1, $P_{av} = V_{rms}I_{rms}$ for a resistor to find the current draw, and Eq. (31.37) to calculate the resistance.

EXECUTE: (a) To get $V_2 = 240$ V from $V_1 = 120$ V, the required turns ratio is $N_2/N_1 = V_2/V_1 = (240\text{ V})/(120\text{ V}) = 2$. That is, the secondary coil (connected to the coffeemaker) should have twice as many turns as the primary coil (connected to the 120-V line).

(b) We find the rms current I_1 in the 120-V primary by using $P_{av} = V_1I_1$, where P_{av} is the average power drawn by the coffeemaker and hence the power supplied by the 120-V line. (We're assuming that no energy is lost in the transformer.) Hence $I_1 = P_{av}/V_1 = (960\text{ W})/(120\text{ V}) = 8.0$ A. The secondary current is then $I_2 = P_{av}/V_2 = (960\text{ W})/(240\text{ V}) = 4.0$ A.

(c) We have $V_1 = 120$ V, $I_1 = 8.0$ A, and $N_2/N_1 = 2$, so

$$\frac{V_1}{I_1} = \frac{120\text{ V}}{8.0\text{ A}} = 15\ \Omega$$

From Eq. (31.37),

$$R = 2^2(15\ \Omega) = 60\ \Omega$$

EVALUATE: As a check, $V_2/R = (240\text{ V})/(60\ \Omega) = 4.0\text{ A} = I_2$, the same value obtained previously. You can also check this result for R by using the expression $P_{av} = V_2^2/R$ for the power drawn by the coffeemaker.

Test Your Understanding of Section 31.6   Each of the following four transformers has 1000 turns in its primary coil. Rank the transformers from largest to smallest number of turns in the secondary coil. (i) converts 120-V ac into 6.0-V ac; (ii) converts 120-V ac into 240-V ac; (iii) converts 240-V ac into 6.0-V ac; (iv) converts 240-V ac into 120-V ac.

Phasors and alternating current: An alternator or ac source produces an emf that varies sinusoidally with time. A sinusoidal voltage or current can be represented by a phasor, a vector that rotates counterclockwise with constant angular velocity ω equal to the angular frequency of the sinusoidal quantity. Its projection on the horizontal axis at any instant represents the instantaneous value of the quantity.

For a sinusoidal current, the rectified average and rms (root-mean-square) currents are proportional to the current amplitude I. Similarly, the rms value of a sinusoidal voltage is proportional to the voltage amplitude V. (See Example 31.1.)

$$I_{\text{rav}} = \frac{2}{\pi}I = 0.637I \quad (31.3)$$

$$I_{\text{rms}} = \frac{I}{\sqrt{2}} \quad (31.4)$$

$$V_{\text{rms}} = \frac{V}{\sqrt{2}} \quad (31.5)$$

Voltage, current, and phase angle: In general, the instantaneous voltage between two points in an ac circuit is not in phase with the instantaneous current passing through those points. The quantity ϕ is called the phase angle of the voltage relative to the current.

$$i = I\cos\omega t \quad (31.2)$$

$$v = V\cos(\omega t + \phi)$$

Resistance and reactance: The voltage across a resistor R is in phase with the current. The voltage across an inductor L leads the current by 90° ($\phi = +90°$), while the voltage across a capacitor C lags the current by 90° ($\phi = -90°$). The voltage amplitude across each type of device is proportional to the current amplitude I. An inductor has inductive reactance $X_L = \omega L$, and a capacitor has capacitive reactance $X_C = 1/\omega C$. (See Examples 31.2 and 31.3.)

$$V_R = IR \quad (31.7)$$

$$V_L = IX_L \quad (31.13)$$

$$V_C = IX_C \quad (31.19)$$

Impedance and the *L-R-C* series circuit: In a general ac circuit, the voltage and current amplitudes are related by the circuit impedance Z. In an L-R-C series circuit, the values of L, R, C, and the angular frequency ω determine the impedance and the phase angle ϕ of the voltage relative to the current. (See Examples 31.4 and 31.5.)

$$V = IZ \quad (31.22)$$

$$Z = \sqrt{R^2 + (X_L - X_C)^2}$$

$$= \sqrt{R^2 + [\omega L - (1/\omega C)]^2} \quad (31.23)$$

$$\tan\phi = \frac{\omega L - 1/\omega C}{R} \quad (31.24)$$

Power in ac circuits: The average power input P_{av} to an ac circuit depends on the voltage and current amplitudes (or, equivalently, their rms values) and the phase angle ϕ of the voltage relative to the current. The quantity $\cos\phi$ is called the power factor. (See Examples 31.6 and 31.7.)

$$P_{\text{av}} = \tfrac{1}{2}VI\cos\phi \quad (31.31)$$

$$= V_{\text{rms}}I_{\text{rms}}\cos\phi$$

Resonance in ac circuits: In an L-R-C series circuit, the current becomes maximum and the impedance becomes minimum at an angular frequency called the resonance angular frequency. This phenomenon is called resonance. At resonance the voltage and current are in phase, and the impedance Z is equal to the resistance R. (See Example 31.8.)

$$\omega_0 = \frac{1}{\sqrt{LC}} \quad (31.32)$$

Transformers: A transformer is used to transform the voltage and current levels in an ac circuit. In an ideal transformer with no energy losses, if the primary winding has N_1 turns and the secondary winding has N_2 turns, the amplitudes (or rms values) of the two voltages are related by Eq. (31.35). The amplitudes (or rms values) of the primary and secondary voltages and currents are related by Eq. (31.36). (See Example 31.9.)

$$\frac{V_2}{V_1} = \frac{N_2}{N_1}$$ (31.35)

$$V_1 I_1 = V_2 I_2$$ (31.36)

BRIDGING PROBLEM | **An Alternating-Current Circuit**

A series circuit consists of a 1.50-mH inductor, a 125-Ω resistor, and a 25.0-nF capacitor connected across an ac source having an rms voltage of 35.0 V and variable frequency. (a) At what angular frequencies will the current amplitude be equal to $\frac{1}{3}$ of its maximum possible value? (b) At the frequencies in part (a), what are the current amplitude and the voltage amplitude across each circuit element (including the ac source)?

SOLUTION GUIDE

See MasteringPhysics® study area for a Video Tutor solution.

IDENTIFY and SET UP

1. The maximum current amplitude occurs at the resonance angular frequency. This problem concerns the angular frequencies at which the current amplitude is one-third of that maximum.
2. Choose the equation that will allow you to find the angular frequencies in question, and choose the equations that you will

then use to find the current and voltage amplitudes at each angular frequency.

EXECUTE

3. Find the impedance at the angular frequencies in part (a); then solve for the values of angular frequency.
4. Find the voltage amplitude across the source and the current amplitude for each of the angular frequencies in part (a). (*Hint:* Be careful to distinguish between *amplitude* and *rms value*.)
5. Use the results of steps 3 and 4 to find the reactances at each angular frequency. Then calculate the voltage amplitudes for the resistor, inductor, and capacitor.

EVALUATE

6. Are there any voltage amplitudes that are greater than the voltage amplitude of the source? If so, does this mean your results are in error?

Problems

For instructor-assigned homework, go to www.masteringphysics.com

•, ••, •••: Problems of increasing difficulty. **CP**: Cumulative problems incorporating material from earlier chapters. **CALC**: Problems requiring calculus. **BIO**: Biosciences problems.

DISCUSSION QUESTIONS

Q31.1 Household electric power in most of western Europe is supplied at 240 V, rather than the 120 V that is standard in the United States and Canada. What are the advantages and disadvantages of each system?

Q31.2 The current in an ac power line changes direction 120 times per second, and its average value is zero. Explain how it is possible for power to be transmitted in such a system.

Q31.3 In an ac circuit, why is the average power for an inductor and a capacitor zero, but not for a resistor?

Q31.4 Equation (31.14) was derived by using the relationship $i = dq/dt$ between the current and the charge on the capacitor. In Fig. 31.9a the positive counterclockwise current increases the charge on the capacitor. When the charge on the left plate is positive but decreasing in time, is $i = dq/dt$ still correct or should it be $i = -dq/dt$? Is $i = dq/dt$ still correct when the right-hand plate has positive charge that is increasing or decreasing in magnitude? Explain.

Q31.5 Fluorescent lights often use an inductor, called a ballast, to limit the current through the tubes. Why is it better to use an inductor rather than a resistor for this purpose?

Q31.6 Equation (31.9) says that $v_{ab} = L\, di/dt$ (see Fig. 31.8a). Using Faraday's law, explain why point a is at higher potential than point b when i is in the direction shown in Fig. 31.8a and is increasing in magnitude. When i is counterclockwise and decreasing in magnitude, is $v_{ab} = L\, di/dt$ still correct, or should it be $v_{ab} = -L\, di/dt$? Is $v_{ab} = L\, di/dt$ still correct when i is clockwise and increasing or decreasing in magnitude? Explain.

Q31.7 Is it possible for the power factor of an *L-R-C* series ac circuit to be zero? Justify your answer on *physical* grounds.

Q31.8 In an *L-R-C* series circuit, can the instantaneous voltage across the capacitor exceed the source voltage at that same instant? Can this be true for the instantaneous voltage across the inductor? Across the resistor? Explain.

Q31.9 In an *L-R-C* series circuit, what are the phase angle ϕ and power factor $\cos\phi$ when the resistance is much smaller than the inductive or capacitive reactance and the circuit is operated far from resonance? Explain.

Q31.10 When an L-R-C series circuit is connected across a 120-V ac line, the voltage rating of the capacitor may be exceeded even if it is rated at 200 or 400 V. How can this be?

Q31.11 In Example 31.6 (Section 31.4), a hair dryer is treated as a pure resistor. But because there are coils in the heating element and in the motor that drives the blower fan, a hair dryer also has inductance. Qualitatively, does including an inductance increase or decrease the values of R, I_{rms}, and P?

Q31.12 A light bulb and a parallel-plate capacitor with air between the plates are connected in series to an ac source. What happens to the brightness of the bulb when a dielectric is inserted between the plates of the capacitor? Explain.

Q31.13 A coil of wire wrapped on a hollow tube and a light bulb are connected in series to an ac source. What happens to the brightness of the bulb when an iron rod is inserted in the tube?

Q31.14 A circuit consists of a light bulb, a capacitor, and an inductor connected in series to an ac source. What happens to the brightness of the bulb when the inductor is removed? When the inductor is left in the circuit but the capacitor is removed? Explain.

Q31.15 A circuit consists of a light bulb, a capacitor, and an inductor connected in series to an ac source. Is it possible for both the capacitor and the inductor to be removed and the brightness of the bulb to remain the same? Explain.

Q31.16 Can a transformer be used with dc? Explain. What happens if a transformer designed for 120-V ac is connected to a 120-V dc line?

Q31.17 An ideal transformer has N_1 windings in the primary and N_2 windings in its secondary. If you double only the number of secondary windings, by what factor does (a) the voltage amplitude in the secondary change, and (b) the effective resistance of the secondary circuit change?

Q31.18 Some electrical appliances operate equally well on ac or dc, and others work only on ac or only on dc. Give examples of each, and explain the differences.

EXERCISES

Section 31.1 Phasors and Alternating Currents

31.1 • You have a special light bulb with a *very* delicate wire filament. The wire will break if the current in it ever exceeds 1.50 A, even for an instant. What is the largest root-mean-square current you can run through this bulb?

31.2 • A sinusoidal current $i = I\cos\omega t$ has an rms value $I_{rms} =$ 2.10 A. (a) What is the current amplitude? (b) The current is passed through a full-wave rectifier circuit. What is the rectified average current? (c) Which is larger: I_{rms} or I_{rav}? Explain, using graphs of i^2 and of the rectified current.

31.3 • The voltage across the terminals of an ac power supply varies with time according to Eq. (31.1). The voltage amplitude is $V = 45.0$ V. What are (a) the root-mean-square potential difference V_{rms} and (b) the average potential difference V_{av} between the two terminals of the power supply?

Section 31.2 Resistance and Reactance

31.4 • A capacitor is connected across an ac source that has voltage amplitude 60.0 V and frequency 80.0 Hz. (a) What is the phase angle ϕ for the source voltage relative to the current? Does the source voltage lag or lead the current? (b) What is the capacitance C of the capacitor if the current amplitude is 5.30 A?

31.5 • An inductor with $L = 9.50$ mH is connected across an ac source that has voltage amplitude 45.0 V. (a) What is the phase angle ϕ for the source voltage relative to the current? Does the source voltage lag or lead the current? (b) What value for the frequency of the source results in a current amplitude of 3.90 A?

31.6 • A capacitance C and an inductance L are operated at the same angular frequency. (a) At what angular frequency will they have the same reactance? (b) If $L = 5.00$ mH and $C = 3.50$ μF, what is the numerical value of the angular frequency in part (a), and what is the reactance of each element?

31.7 • **Kitchen Capacitance.** The wiring for a refrigerator contains a starter capacitor. A voltage of amplitude 170 V and frequency 60.0 Hz applied across the capacitor is to produce a current amplitude of 0.850 A through the capacitor. What capacitance C is required?

31.8 • (a) Compute the reactance of a 0.450-H inductor at frequencies of 60.0 Hz and 600 Hz. (b) Compute the reactance of a 2.50-μF capacitor at the same frequencies. (c) At what frequency is the reactance of a 0.450-H inductor equal to that of a 2.50-μF capacitor?

31.9 • (a) What is the reactance of a 3.00-H inductor at a frequency of 80.0 Hz? (b) What is the inductance of an inductor whose reactance is 120 Ω at 80.0 Hz? (c) What is the reactance of a 4.00-μF capacitor at a frequency of 80.0 Hz? (d) What is the capacitance of a capacitor whose reactance is 120 Ω at 80.0 Hz?

31.10 • **A Radio Inductor.** You want the current amplitude through a 0.450-mH inductor (part of the circuitry for a radio receiver) to be 2.60 mA when a sinusoidal voltage with amplitude 12.0 V is applied across the inductor. What frequency is required?

31.11 •• A 0.180-H inductor is connected in series with a 90.0-Ω resistor and an ac source. The voltage across the inductor is $v_L = -(12.0\text{ V})\sin[(480\text{ rad/s})t]$. (a) Derive an expression for the voltage v_R across the resistor. (b) What is v_R at $t = 2.00$ ms?

31.12 •• A 250-Ω resistor is connected in series with a 4.80-μF capacitor and an ac source. The voltage across the capacitor is $v_C = (7.60\text{ V})\sin[(120\text{ rad/s})t]$. (a) Determine the capacitive reactance of the capacitor. (b) Derive an expression for the voltage v_R across the resistor.

31.13 •• A 150-Ω resistor is connected in series with a 0.250-H inductor and an ac source. The voltage across the resistor is $v_R = (3.80\text{ V})\cos[(720\text{ rad/s})t]$. (a) Derive an expression for the circuit current. (b) Determine the inductive reactance of the inductor. (c) Derive an expression for the voltage v_L across the inductor.

Section 31.3 The L-R-C Series Circuit

31.14 • You have a 200-Ω resistor, a 0.400-H inductor, and a 6.00-μF capacitor. Suppose you take the resistor and inductor and make a series circuit with a voltage source that has voltage amplitude 30.0 V and an angular frequency of 250 rad/s. (a) What is the impedance of the circuit? (b) What is the current amplitude? (c) What are the voltage amplitudes across the resistor and across the inductor? (d) What is the phase angle ϕ of the source voltage with respect to the current? Does the source voltage lag or lead the current? (e) Construct the phasor diagram.

31.15 • The resistor, inductor, capacitor, and voltage source described in Exercise 31.14 are connected to form an L-R-C series circuit. (a) What is the impedance of the circuit? (b) What is the current amplitude? (c) What is the phase angle of the source voltage with respect to the current? Does the source voltage lag or lead the current? (d) What are the voltage amplitudes across the resistor, inductor, and capacitor? (e) Explain how it is possible for the voltage amplitude across the capacitor to be greater than the voltage amplitude across the source.

31.16 •• A 200-Ω resistor, a 0.900-H inductor, and a 6.00-μF capacitor are connected in series across a voltage source that has voltage amplitude 30.0 V and an angular frequency of 250 rad/s. (a) What are v, v_R, v_L, and v_C at $t = 20.0$ ms? Compare $v_R + v_L + v_C$ to v at this instant. (b) What are V_R, V_L, and V_C? Compare V to $V_R + V_L + V_C$. Explain why these two quantities are not equal.

31.17 • In an *L-R-C* series circuit, the rms voltage across the resistor is 30.0 V, across the capacitor it is 90.0 V, and across the inductor it is 50.0 V. What is the rms voltage of the source?

Section 31.4 Power in Alternating-Current Circuits

31.18 •• A resistor with $R = 300$ Ω and an inductor are connected in series across an ac source that has voltage amplitude 500 V. The rate at which electrical energy is dissipated in the resistor is 216 W. (a) What is the impedance Z of the circuit? (b) What is the amplitude of the voltage across the inductor? (c) What is the power factor?

31.19 • The power of a certain CD player operating at 120 V rms is 20.0 W. Assuming that the CD player behaves like a pure resistor, find (a) the maximum instantaneous power; (b) the rms current; (c) the resistance of this player.

31.20 •• In an *L-R-C* series circuit, the components have the following values: $L = 20.0$ mH, $C = 140$ nF, and $R = 350$ Ω. The generator has an rms voltage of 120 V and a frequency of 1.25 kHz. Determine (a) the power supplied by the generator and (b) the power dissipated in the resistor.

31.21 • (a) Show that for an *L-R-C* series circuit the power factor is equal to R/Z. (b) An *L-R-C* series circuit has phase angle $-31.5°$. The voltage amplitude of the source is 90.0 V. What is the voltage amplitude across the resistor?

31.22 • (a) Use the results of part (a) of Exercise 31.21 to show that the average power delivered by the source in an *L-R-C* series circuit is given by $P_{av} = I_{rms}^2R$. (b) An *L-R-C* series series circuit has $R = 96.0$ Ω, and the amplitude of the voltage across the resistor is 36.0 V. What is the average power delivered by the source?

31.23 • An *L-R-C* series circuit with $L = 0.120$ H, $R = 240$ Ω, and $C = 7.30$ μF carries an rms current of 0.450 A with a frequency of 400 Hz. (a) What are the phase angle and power factor for this circuit? (b) What is the impedance of the circuit? (c) What is the rms voltage of the source? (d) What average power is delivered by the source? (e) What is the average rate at which electrical energy is converted to thermal energy in the resistor? (f) What is the average rate at which electrical energy is dissipated (converted to other forms) in the capacitor? (g) In the inductor?

31.24 •• An *L-R-C* series circuit is connected to a 120-Hz ac source that has $V_{rms} = 80.0$ V. The circuit has a resistance of 75.0 Ω and an impedance at this frequency of 105 Ω. What average power is delivered to the circuit by the source?

31.25 •• A series ac circuit contains a 250-Ω resistor, a 15-mH inductor, a 3.5-μF capacitor, and an ac power source of voltage amplitude 45 V operating at an angular frequency of 360 rad/s, (a) What is the power factor of this circuit? (b) Find the average power delivered to the entire circuit. (c) What is the average power delivered to the resistor, to the capacitor, and to the inductor?

Section 31.5 Resonance in Alternating-Current Circuits

31.26 •• In an *L-R-C* series circuit the source is operated at its resonant angular frequency. At this frequency, the reactance X_C of

the capacitor is 200 Ω and the voltage amplitude across the capacitor is 600 V. The circuit has $R = 300$ Ω. What is the voltage amplitude of the source?

31.27 • **Analyzing an *L-R-C* Circuit.** You have a 200-Ω resistor, a 0.400-H inductor, a 5.00-μF capacitor, and a variable-frequency ac source with an amplitude of 3.00 V. You connect all four elements together to form a series circuit. (a) At what frequency will the current in the circuit be greatest? What will be the current amplitude at this frequency? (b) What will be the current amplitude at an angular frequency of 400 rad/s? At this frequency, will the source voltage lead or lag the current?

31.28 • An *L-R-C* series circuit is constructed using a 175-Ω resistor, a 12.5-μF capacitor, and an 8.00-mH inductor, all connected across an ac source having a variable frequency and a voltage amplitude of 25.0 V. (a) At what angular frequency will the impedance be smallest, and what is the impedance at this frequency? (b) At the angular frequency in part (a), what is the maximum current through the inductor? (c) At the angular frequency in part (a), find the potential difference across the ac source, the resistor, the capacitor, and the inductor at the instant that the current is equal to one-half its greatest positive value. (d) In part (c), how are the potential differences across the resistor, inductor, and capacitor related to the potential difference across the ac source?

31.29 • In an *L-R-C* series circuit, $R = 300$ Ω, $L = 0.400$ H, and $C = 6.00 \times 10^{-8}$ F. When the ac source operates at the resonance frequency of the circuit, the current amplitude is 0.500 A. (a) What is the voltage amplitude of the source? (b) What is the amplitude of the voltage across the resistor, across the inductor, and across the capacitor? (c) What is the average power supplied by the source?

31.30 • An *L-R-C* series circuit consists of a source with voltage amplitude 120 V and angular frequency 50.0 rad/s, a resistor with $R = 400$ Ω, an inductor with $L = 9.00$ H, and a capacitor with capacitance C. (a) For what value of C will the current amplitude in the circuit be a maximum? (b) When C has the value calculated in part (a), what is the amplitude of the voltage across the inductor?

31.31 • In an *L-R-C* series circuit, $R = 150$ Ω, $L = 0.750$ H, and $C = 0.0180$ μF. The source has voltage amplitude $V = 150$ V and a frequency equal to the resonance frequency of the circuit. (a) What is the power factor? (b) What is the average power delivered by the source? (c) The capacitor is replaced by one with $C = 0.0360$ μF and the source frequency is adjusted to the new resonance value. Then what is the average power delivered by the source?

31.32 • In an *L-R-C* series circuit, $R = 400$ Ω, $L = 0.350$ H, and $C = 0.0120$ μF. (a) What is the resonance angular frequency of the circuit? (b) The capacitor can withstand a peak voltage of 550 V. If the voltage source operates at the resonance frequency, what maximum voltage amplitude can it have if the maximum capacitor voltage is not exceeded?

31.33 • A series circuit consists of an ac source of variable frequency, a 115-Ω resistor, a 1.25-μF capacitor, and a 4.50-mH inductor. Find the impedance of this circuit when the angular frequency of the ac source is adjusted to (a) the resonance angular frequency; (b) twice the resonance angular frequency; (c) half the resonance angular frequency.

31.34 •• In an *L-R-C* series circuit, $L = 0.280$ H and $C = 4.00$ μF. The voltage amplitude of the source is 120 V. (a) What is the resonance angular frequency of the circuit? (b) When the source operates at the resonance angular frequency, the current amplitude in the circuit is 1.70 A. What is the resistance R of the resistor? (c) At the resonance angular frequency, what are the peak voltages across the inductor, the capacitor, and the resistor?

Section 31.6 Transformers

31.35 • **A Step-Down Transformer.** A transformer connected to a 120-V (rms) ac line is to supply 12.0 V (rms) to a portable electronic device. The load resistance in the secondary is 5.00 Ω. (a) What should the ratio of primary to secondary turns of the transformer be? (b) What rms current must the secondary supply? (c) What average power is delivered to the load? (d) What resistance connected directly across the 120-V line would draw the same power as the transformer? Show that this is equal to 5.00 Ω times the square of the ratio of primary to secondary turns.

31.36 • **A Step-Up Transformer.** A transformer connected to a 120-V (rms) ac line is to supply 13,000 V (rms) for a neon sign. To reduce shock hazard, a fuse is to be inserted in the primary circuit; the fuse is to blow when the rms current in the secondary circuit exceeds 8.50 mA. (a) What is the ratio of secondary to primary turns of the transformer? (b) What power must be supplied to the transformer when the rms secondary current is 8.50 mA? (c) What current rating should the fuse in the primary circuit have?

31.37 • **Off to Europe!** You plan to take your hair dryer to Europe, where the electrical outlets put out 240 V instead of the 120 V seen in the United States. The dryer puts out 1600 W at 120 V. (a) What could you do to operate your dryer via the 240-V line in Europe? (b) What current will your dryer draw from a European outlet? (c) What resistance will your dryer appear to have when operated at 240 V?

PROBLEMS

31.38 •• Figure 31.12a shows the crossover network in a loudspeaker system. One branch consists of a capacitor C and a resistor R in series (the tweeter). This branch is in parallel with a second branch (the woofer) that consists of an inductor L and a resistor R in series. The same source voltage with angular frequency ω is applied across each parallel branch. (a) What is the impedance of the tweeter branch? (b) What is the impedance of the woofer branch? (c) Explain why the currents in the two branches are equal when the impedances of the branches are equal. (d) Derive an expression for the frequency f that corresponds to the crossover point in Fig. 31.12b.

31.39 • A coil has a resistance of 48.0 Ω. At a frequency of 80.0 Hz the voltage across the coil leads the current in it by 52.3°. Determine the inductance of the coil.

31.40 •• Five infinite-impedance voltmeters, calibrated to read rms values, are connected as shown in Fig. P31.40. Let $R = 200\ \Omega$, $L = 0.400\ \text{H}$, $C = 6.00\ \mu\text{F}$, and $V = 30.0\ \text{V}$. What is the reading of each voltmeter if (a) $\omega = 200\ \text{rad/s}$ and (b) $\omega = 1000\ \text{rad/s}$?

Figure **P31.40**

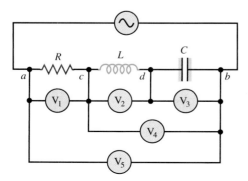

31.41 •• **CP** A parallel-plate capacitor having square plates 4.50 cm on each side and 8.00 mm apart is placed in series with an ac source of angular frequency 650 rad/s and voltage amplitude 22.5 V, a 75.0-Ω resistor, and an ideal solenoid that is 9.00 cm long, has a circular cross section 0.500 cm in diameter, and carries 125 coils per centimeter. What is the resonance angular frequency of this circuit? (See Exercise 30.15.)

31.42 •• **CP** A toroidal solenoid has 2900 closely wound turns, cross-sectional area 0.450 cm², mean radius 9.00 cm, and resistance $R = 2.80\ \Omega$. The variation of the magnetic field across the cross section of the solenoid can be neglected. What is the amplitude of the current in the solenoid if it is connected to an ac source that has voltage amplitude 24.0 V and frequency 365 Hz?

31.43 •• An L-R-C series circuit has $C = 4.80\ \mu\text{F}$, $L = 0.520\ \text{H}$, and source voltage amplitude $V = 56.0\ \text{V}$. The source is operated at the resonance frequency of the circuit. If the voltage across the capacitor has amplitude 80.0 V, what is the value of R for the resistor in the circuit?

31.44 • A large electromagnetic coil is connected to a 120-Hz ac source. The coil has resistance 400 Ω, and at this source frequency the coil has inductive reactance 250 Ω. (a) What is the inductance of the coil? (b) What must the rms voltage of the source be if the coil is to consume an average electrical power of 800 W?

31.45 •• A series circuit has an impedance of 60.0 Ω and a power factor of 0.720 at 50.0 Hz. The source voltage lags the current. (a) What circuit element, an inductor or a capacitor, should be placed in series with the circuit to raise its power factor? (b) What size element will raise the power factor to unity?

31.46 •• An L-R-C series circuit has $R = 300\ \Omega$. At the frequency of the source, the inductor has reactance $X_L = 900\ \Omega$ and the capacitor has reactance $X_C = 500\ \Omega$. The amplitude of the voltage across the inductor is 450 V. (a) What is the amplitude of the voltage across the resistor? (b) What is the amplitude of the voltage across the capacitor? (c) What is the voltage amplitude of the source? (d) What is the rate at which the source is delivering electrical energy to the circuit?

31.47 •• In an L-R-C series circuit, $R = 300\ \Omega$, $X_C = 300\ \Omega$, and $X_L = 500\ \Omega$. The average power consumed in the resistor is 60.0 W. (a) What is the power factor of the circuit? (b) What is the rms voltage of the source?

31.48 • A circuit consists of a resistor and a capacitor in series with an ac source that supplies an rms voltage of 240 V. At the frequency of the source the reactance of the capacitor is 50.0 Ω. The rms current in the circuit is 3.00 A. What is the average power supplied by the source?

31.49 • An L-R-C series circuit consists of a 50.0-Ω resistor, a 10.0-μF capacitor, a 3.50-mH inductor, and an ac voltage source of voltage amplitude 60.0 V operating at 1250 Hz. (a) Find the current amplitude and the voltage amplitudes across the inductor, the resistor, and the capacitor. Why can the voltage amplitudes add up to *more* than 60.0 V? (b) If the frequency is now doubled, but nothing else is changed, which of the quantities in part (a) will change? Find the new values for those that do change.

31.50 • At a frequency ω_1 the reactance of a certain capacitor equals that of a certain inductor. (a) If the frequency is changed to $\omega_2 = 2\omega_1$, what is the ratio of the reactance of the inductor to that of the capacitor? Which reactance is larger? (b) If the frequency is changed to $\omega_3 = \omega_1/3$, what is the ratio of the reactance of the inductor to that of the capacitor? Which reactance is larger? (c) If the capacitor and inductor are placed in series with a resistor of resistance R to form an L-R-C series circuit, what will be the resonance angular frequency of the circuit?

31.51 ·· **A High-Pass Filter.** Figure **P31.51**
One application of *L-R-C* series circuits is to high-pass or low-pass filters, which filter out either the low- or high-frequency components of a signal. A high-pass filter is shown in Fig. P31.51, where the output volt-

age is taken across the *L-R* combination. (The *L-R* combination represents an inductive coil that also has resistance due to the large length of wire in the coil.) Derive an expression for V_{out}/V_s, the ratio of the output and source voltage amplitudes, as a function of the angular frequency ω of the source. Show that when ω is small, this ratio is proportional to ω and thus is small, and show that the ratio approaches unity in the limit of large frequency.

31.52 ·· **A Low-Pass Filter.** Figure P31.52 shows a low-pass filter (see Problem 31.51); the output voltage is taken across the capacitor in an *L-R-C* series circuit. Derive an expression for V_{out}/V_s, the ratio of the output and source voltage amplitudes, as a function of the angular frequency ω of the source. Show that when ω is large, this ratio is proportional to ω^{-2} and thus is very small, and show that the ratio approaches unity in the limit of small frequency.

Figure **P31.52**

31.53 ··· An *L-R-C* series circuit is connected to an ac source of constant voltage amplitude *V* and variable angular frequency ω. (a) Show that the current amplitude, as a function of ω, is

$$I = \frac{V}{\sqrt{R^2 + (\omega L - 1/\omega C)^2}}$$

(b) Show that the average power dissipated in the resistor is

$$P = \frac{V^2 R/2}{R^2 + (\omega L - 1/\omega C)^2}$$

(c) Show that *I* and *P* are *both* maximum when $\omega = 1/\sqrt{LC}$, the resonance frequency of the circuit. (d) Graph *P* as a function of ω for *V* = 100 V, *R* = 200 Ω, *L* = 2.0 H, and *C* = 0.50 μF. Compare to the light purple curve in Fig. 31.19. Discuss the behavior of *I* and *P* in the limits $\omega = 0$ and $\omega \to \infty$.

31.54 ·· An *L-R-C* series circuit is connected to an ac source of constant voltage amplitude *V* and variable angular frequency ω. Using the results of Problem 31.53, find an expression for (a) the amplitude V_L of the voltage across the inductor as a function of ω and (b) the amplitude V_C of the voltage across the capacitor as a function of ω. (c) Graph V_L and V_C as functions of ω for *V* = 100 V, *R* = 200 Ω, *L* = 2.0 H, and *C* = 0.50 μF. (d) Discuss the behavior of V_L and V_C in the limits $\omega = 0$ and $\omega \to \infty$. For what value of ω is $V_L = V_C$? What is the significance of this value of ω?

31.55 ·· In an *L-R-C* series circuit the magnitude of the phase angle is 54.0°, with the source voltage lagging the current. The reactance of the capacitor is 350 Ω, and the resistor resistance is 180 Ω. The average power delivered by the source is 140 W. Find

(a) the reactance of the inductor; (b) the rms current; (c) the rms voltage of the source.

31.56 ·· **The *L-R-C* Parallel Circuit.** A resistor, inductor, and capacitor are connected in parallel to an ac source with voltage amplitude *V* and angular frequency ω. Let the source voltage be given by $v = V\cos\omega t$. (a) Show that the instantaneous voltages v_R, v_L, and v_C at any instant are each equal to v and that $i = i_R + i_L + i_C$, where *i* is the current through the source and i_R, i_L, and i_C are the currents through the resistor, the inductor, and the capacitor, respectively. (b) What are the phases of i_R, i_L, and i_C with respect to v? Use current phasors to represent i, i_R, i_L, and i_C. In a phasor diagram, show the phases of these four currents with respect to v. (c) Use the phasor diagram of part (b) to show that the current amplitude *I* for the current *i* through the source is given by $I = \sqrt{I_R^2 + (I_C - I_L)^2}$. (d) Show that the result of part (c) can be written as $I = V/Z$, with $1/Z = \sqrt{1/R^2 + (\omega C - 1/\omega L)^2}$.

31.57 ·· **Parallel Resonance.** The impedance of an *L-R-C* parallel circuit was derived in Problem 31.56. (a) Show that at the resonance angular frequency $\omega_0 = 1/\sqrt{LC}$, $I_C = I_L$, and *I* is a *minimum*. (b) Since *I* is a minimum at resonance, is it correct to say that the power delivered to the resistor is also a minimum at $\omega = \omega_0$? Explain. (c) At resonance, what is the phase angle of the source current with respect to the source voltage? How does this compare to the phase angle for an *L-R-C series* circuit at resonance? (d) Draw the circuit diagram for an *L-R-C* parallel circuit. Arrange the circuit elements in your diagram so that the resistor is closest to the ac source. Justify the following statement: When the angular frequency of the source is $\omega = \omega_0$, there is *no* current flowing between (i) the part of the circuit that includes the source and the resistor and (ii) the part that includes the inductor and the capacitor, so you could cut the wires connecting these two parts of the circuit without affecting the currents. (e) Is the statement in part (d) still valid if we consider that any real inductor or capacitor also has some resistance of its own? Explain.

31.58 ·· A 400-Ω resistor and a 6.00-μF capacitor are connected in parallel to an ac generator that supplies an rms voltage of 220 V at an angular frequency of 360 rad/s. Use the results of Problem 31.56. Note that since there is no inductor in the circuit, the $1/\omega L$ term is not present in the expression for *Z*. Find (a) the current amplitude in the resistor; (b) the current amplitude in the capacitor; (c) the phase angle of the source current with respect to the source voltage; (d) the amplitude of the current through the generator. (e) Does the source current lag or lead the source voltage?

31.59 ·· An *L-R-C* parallel circuit is connected to an ac source of constant voltage amplitude *V* and variable angular frequency ω. (a) Using the results of Problem 31.56, find expressions for the amplitudes I_R, I_L, and I_C of the currents through the resistor, inductor, and capacitor as functions of ω. (b) Graph I_R, I_L, and I_C as functions of ω for *V* = 100 V, *R* = 200 Ω, *L* = 2.0 H, and *C* = 0.50 μF. (c) Discuss the behavior of I_L and I_C in the limits $\omega = 0$ and $\omega \to \infty$. Explain why I_L and I_C behave as they do in these limits. (d) Calculate the resonance frequency (in Hz) of the circuit, and sketch the phasor diagram at the resonance frequency. (e) At the resonance frequency, what is the current amplitude through the source? (f) At the resonance frequency, what is the current amplitude through the resistor, through the inductor, and through the capacitor?

31.60 ·· A 100-Ω resistor, a 0.100-μF capacitor, and a 0.300-H inductor are connected in parallel to a voltage source with amplitude 240 V. (a) What is the resonance angular frequency? (b) What is the maximum current through the source at the resonance frequency? (c) Find the maximum current in the resistor at resonance. (d) What is the maximum current in the inductor at resonance. (e) What is the maximum current in the branch containing the capacitor at resonance? (f) Find the maximum energy stored in the inductor and in the capacitor at resonance.

31.61 • You want to double the resonance angular frequency of an *L-R-C* series circuit by changing only the *pertinent* circuit elements all by the same factor. (a) Which ones should you change? (b) By what factor should you change them?

31.62 ••• An *L-R-C* series circuit consists of a 2.50-μF capacitor, a 5.00-mH inductor, and a 75.0-Ω resistor connected across an ac source of voltage amplitude 15.0 V having variable frequency. (a) Under what circumstances is the average power delivered to the circuit equal to $\frac{1}{2}V_{rms}I_{rms}$? (b) Under the conditions of part (a), what is the average power delivered to each circuit element and what is the maximum current through the capacitor?

31.63 •• In an *L-R-C* series circuit, the source has a voltage amplitude of 120 V, $R = 80.0\ \Omega$, and the reactance of the capacitor is 480 Ω. The voltage amplitude across the capacitor is 360 V. (a) What is the current amplitude in the circuit? (b) What is the impedance? (c) What two values can the reactance of the inductor have? (d) For which of the two values found in part (c) is the angular frequency less than the resonance angular frequency? Explain.

31.64 • An *L-R-C* series circuit has $R = 500\ \Omega$, $L = 2.00$ H, $C = 0.500\ \mu$F, and $V = 100$ V. (a) For $\omega = 800$ rad/s, calculate V_R, V_L, V_C, and ϕ. Using a single set of axes, graph v, v_R, v_L, and v_C as functions of time. Include two cycles of v on your graph. (b) Repeat part (a) for $\omega = 1000$ rad/s. (c) Repeat part (a) for $\omega = 1250$ rad/s.

31.65 •• CALC The current in a certain circuit varies with time as shown in Fig. P31.65. Find the average current and the rms current in terms of I_0.

Figure **P31.65**

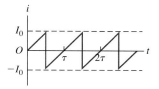

31.66 •• **The Resonance Width.** Consider an *L-R-C* series circuit with a 1.80-H inductor, a 0.900-μF capacitor, and a 300-Ω resistor. The source has terminal rms voltage $V_{rms} = 60.0$ V and variable angular frequency ω. (a) What is the resonance angular frequency ω_0 of the circuit? (b) What is the rms current through the circuit at resonance, I_{rms-0}?(c) For what two values of the angular frequency, ω_1 and ω_2, is the rms current half the resonance value? (d) The quantity $|\omega_1 - \omega_2|$ defines the *resonance width*. Calculate I_{rms-0} and the resonance width for $R = 300\ \Omega$, 30.0 Ω, and 3.00 Ω. Describe how your results compare to the discussion in Section 31.5.

31.67 •• An inductor, a capacitor, and a resistor are all connected in series across an ac source. If the resistance, inductance, and capacitance are all doubled, by what factor does each of the following quantities change? Indicate whether they increase or decrease: (a) the resonance angular frequency; (b) the inductive reactance; (c) the capacitive reactance. (d) Does the impedance double?

31.68 • A resistance R, capacitance C, and inductance L are connected in series to a voltage source with amplitude V and variable angular frequency ω. If $\omega = \omega_0$, the resonance angular frequency, find (a) the maximum current in the resistor; (b) the maximum voltage across the capacitor; (c) the maximum voltage across the inductor; (d) the maximum energy stored in the capacitor; (e) the maximum energy stored in the inductor. Give your answers in terms of R, C, L, and V.

31.69 • Repeat Problem 31.68 for the case $\omega = \omega_0/2$.

31.70 • Repeat Problem 31.68 for the case $\omega = 2\omega_0$.

31.71 • A transformer consists of 275 primary windings and 834 secondary windings. If the potential difference across the primary coil is 25.0 V, (a) what is the voltage across the secondary coil, and (b) what is the effective load resistance of the secondary coil if it is connected across a 125-Ω resistor?

31.72 •• An *L-R-C* series circuit draws 220 W from a 120-V (rms), 50.0-Hz ac line. The power factor is 0.560, and the source voltage leads the current. (a) What is the net resistance R of the circuit? (b) Find the capacitance of the series capacitor that will result in a power factor of unity when it is added to the original circuit. (c) What power will then be drawn from the supply line?

31.73 •• CALC In an *L-R-C* series circuit the current is given by $i = I\cos\omega t$. The voltage amplitudes for the resistor, inductor, and capacitor are V_R, V_L, and V_C. (a) Show that the instantaneous power into the resistor is $p_R = V_R I\cos^2\omega t = \frac{1}{2}V_R I(1 + \cos 2\omega t)$. What does this expression give for the average power into the resistor? (b) Show that the instantaneous power into the inductor is $p_L = -V_L I\sin\omega t\cos\omega t = -\frac{1}{2}V_L I\sin 2\omega t$. What does this expression give for the average power into the inductor? (c) Show that the instantaneous power into the capacitor is $p_C = V_C I\sin\omega t\cos\omega t = \frac{1}{2}V_C I\sin 2\omega t$. What does this expression give for the average power into the capacitor? (d) The instantaneous power delivered by the source is shown in Section 31.4 to be $p = VI\cos\omega t(\cos\phi\cos\omega t - \sin\phi\sin\omega t)$. Show that $p_R + p_L + p_C$ equals p at each instant of time.

CHALLENGE PROBLEMS

31.74 ••• CALC (a) At what angular frequency is the voltage amplitude across the *resistor* in an *L-R-C* series circuit at maximum value? (b) At what angular frequency is the voltage amplitude across the *inductor* at maximum value? (c) At what angular frequency is the voltage amplitude across the *capacitor* at maximum value? (You may want to refer to the results of Problem 31.53.)

31.75 ••• **Complex Numbers in a Circuit.** The voltage across a circuit element in an ac circuit is not necessarily in phase with the current through that circuit element. Therefore the voltage amplitudes across the circuit elements in a branch in an ac circuit do not add algebraically. A method that is commonly employed to simplify the analysis of an ac circuit driven by a sinusoidal source is to represent the impedance Z as a *complex* number. The resistance R is taken to be the real part of the impedance, and the reactance $X = X_L - X_C$ is taken to be the imaginary part. Thus, for a branch containing a resistor, inductor, and capacitor in series, the complex impedance is $Z_{cpx} = R + iX$, where $i^2 = -1$. If the voltage amplitude across the branch is V_{cpx}, we define a *complex* current amplitude by $I_{cpx} = V_{cpx}/Z_{cpx}$. The *actual* current amplitude is the absolute value of the complex current amplitude; that is, $I = (I_{cpx}{}^*I_{cpx})^{1/2}$. The phase angle ϕ of the current with respect to the source voltage is given by $\tan\phi = \text{Im}(I_{cpx})/\text{Re}(I_{cpx})$. The voltage amplitudes $V_{R\text{-}cpx}$, $V_{L\text{-}cpx}$, and $V_{C\text{-}cpx}$ across the resistance, inductance, and capacitance, respectively, are found by multiplying I_{cpx} by R, iX_L, and $-iX_C$, respectively. From the complex representation for the voltage amplitudes, the voltage across a branch is just the algebraic sum of the voltages across each circuit element: $V_{cpx} = V_{R\text{-}cpx} + V_{L\text{-}cpx} + V_{C\text{-}cpx}$. The actual value of any current amplitude or voltage amplitude is the absolute value of the corresponding complex

Figure **P31.75**

$L = 0.500$ H
$V = 200$ V
$\omega = 1000$ rad/s
$C = 1.25\ \mu$F
$R = 400\ \Omega$

quantity. Consider the *L-R-C* series circuit shown in Fig. P31.75. The values of the circuit elements, the source voltage amplitude, and the source angular frequency are as shown. Use the phasor diagram techniques presented in Section 31.1 to solve for (a) the current amplitude and (b) the phase angle ϕ of the current with respect to the source voltage. (Note that this angle is the negative of the phase angle defined in Fig. 31.13.) Now analyze the same circuit using the complex-number approach. (c) Determine the complex impedance of the circuit, Z_{cpx}. Take the absolute value to obtain *Z*, the actual

impedance of the circuit. (d) Take the voltage amplitude of the source, V_{cpx}, to be real, and find the complex current amplitude I_{cpx}. Find the actual current amplitude by taking the absolute value of I_{cpx}. (e) Find the phase angle ϕ of the current with respect to the source voltage by using the real and imaginary parts of I_{cpx}, as explained above. (f) Find the complex representations of the voltages across the resistance, the inductance, and the capacitance. (g) Adding the answers found in part (f), verify that the sum of these complex numbers is real and equal to 200 V, the voltage of the source.

Answers

Chapter Opening Question

Yes. In fact, the radio simultaneously detects transmissions at *all* frequencies. However, a radio is an *L-R-C* series circuit, and at any given time it is tuned to have a resonance at just one frequency. Hence the response of the radio to that frequency is much greater than its response to any other frequency, which is why you hear only one broadcasting station through the radio's speaker. (You can sometimes hear a second station if its frequency is sufficiently close to the tuned frequency.)

Test Your Understanding Questions

31.1 Answers: (a) D; (b) A; (c) B; (d) C For each phasor, the actual current is represented by the projection of that phasor onto the horizontal axis. The phasors all rotate counterclockwise around the origin with angular speed ω, so at the instant shown the projection of phasor A is positive but trending toward zero; the projection of phasor B is negative and becoming more negative; the projection of phasor C is negative but trending toward zero; and the projection of phasor D is positive and becoming more positive.

31.2 Answers: (a) (iii); (b) (ii); (c) (i) For a resistor, $V_R = IR$, so $I = V_R/R$. The voltage amplitude V_R and resistance *R* do not change with frequency, so the current amplitude *I* remains constant. For an inductor, $V_L = IX_L = I\omega L$, so $I = V_L/\omega L$. The voltage amplitude V_L and inductance *L* are constant, so the current amplitude *I* decreases as the frequency increases. For a capacitor, $V_C = IX_C = I/\omega C$, so $I = V_C\omega C$. The voltage amplitude V_C and capacitance *C* are constant, so the current amplitude *I* increases as the frequency increases.

31.3 Answer: (iv), (ii), (i), (iii) For the circuit in Example 31.4, $I = V/Z = (50 \text{ V})/(500 \, \Omega) = 0.10$ A. If the capacitor and inductor are removed so that only the ac source and resistor remain, the circuit is like that shown in Fig. 31.7a; then $I = V/R = (50 \text{ V})/(300 \, \Omega) = 0.17$ A. If the resistor and capacitor are removed so that only the ac source and inductor remain, the circuit is like that

shown in Fig. 31.8a; then $I = V/X_L = (50 \text{ V})/(600 \, \Omega) = 0.083$ A. Finally, if the resistor and inductor are removed so that only the ac source and capacitor remain, the circuit is like that shown in Fig. 31.9a; then $I = V/X_C = (50 \text{ V})/(200 \, \Omega) = 0.25$ A.

31.4 Answers: (a) (v); (b) (iv) The energy cannot be extracted from the resistor, since energy is dissipated in a resistor and cannot be recovered. Instead, the energy must be extracted from either the inductor (which stores magnetic-field energy) or the capacitor (which stores electric-field energy). Positive power means that energy is being transferred from the ac source to the circuit, so *negative* power implies that energy is being transferred back into the source.

31.5 Answer: (ii) The capacitance *C* increases if the plate spacing is decreased (see Section 24.1). Hence the resonance frequency $f_0 = \omega_0/2\pi = 1/2\pi\sqrt{LC}$ decreases.

31.6 Answer: (ii), (iv), (i), (iii) From Eq. (31.35) the turns ratio is $N_2/N_1 = V_2/V_1$, so the number of turns in the secondary is $N_2 = N_1 V_2/V_1$. Hence for the four cases we have (i) $N_2 = (1000)(6.0 \text{ V})/(120 \text{ V}) = 50$ turns; (ii) $N_2 = (1000)(240 \text{ V})/(120 \text{ V}) = 2000$ turns; (iii) $N_2 = (1000)(6.0 \text{ V})/(240 \text{ V}) = 25$ turns; and (iv) $N_2 = (1000)(120 \text{ V})/(240 \text{ V}) = 500$ turns. Note that (i), (iii), and (iv) are step-down transformers with fewer turns in the secondary than in the primary, while (ii) is a step-up transformer with more turns in the secondary than in the primary.

Bridging Problem

Answers: (a) 8.35×10^4 rad/s and 3.19×10^5 rad/s
(b) At 8.35×10^4 rad/s: $V_{\text{source}} = 49.5$ V,
$I = 0.132$ A, $V_R = 16.5$ V, $V_L = 16.5$ V,
$V_C = 63.2$ V.
At 3.19×10^5 rad/s: $V_{\text{source}} = 49.5$ V,
$I = 0.132$ A, $V_R = 16.5$ V, $V_L = 63.2$ V,
$V_C = 16.5$ V.

ELECTROMAGNETIC WAVES

? Metal objects reflect not only visible light but also radio waves. What aspect of metals makes them so reflective?

LEARNING GOALS

By studying this chapter, you will learn:

- Why there are both electric and magnetic fields in a light wave.

- How the speed of light is related to the fundamental constants of electricity and magnetism.

- How to describe the propagation of a sinusoidal electromagnetic wave.

- What determines the amount of power carried by an electromagnetic wave.

- How to describe standing electromagnetic waves.

W hat is light? This question has been asked by humans for centuries, but there was no answer until electricity and magnetism were unified into *electromagnetism,* as described by Maxwell's equations. These equations show that a time-varying magnetic field acts as a source of electric field and that a time-varying electric field acts as a source of magnetic field. These $\vec{E}$ and $\vec{B}$ fields can sustain each other, forming an *electromagnetic wave* that propagates through space. Visible light emitted by the glowing filament of a light bulb is one example of an electromagnetic wave; other kinds of electromagnetic waves are produced by TV and radio stations, x-ray machines, and radioactive nuclei.

In this chapter we'll use Maxwell's equations as the theoretical basis for understanding electromagnetic waves. We'll find that these waves carry both energy and momentum. In sinusoidal electromagnetic waves, the $\vec{E}$ and $\vec{B}$ fields are sinusoidal functions of time and position, with a definite frequency and wavelength. Visible light, radio, x rays, and other types of electromagnetic waves differ only in their frequency and wavelength. Our study of optics in the following chapters will be based in part on the electromagnetic nature of light.

Unlike waves on a string or sound waves in a fluid, electromagnetic waves do not require a material medium; the light that you see coming from the stars at night has traveled without difficulty across tens or hundreds of light-years of (nearly) empty space. Nonetheless, electromagnetic waves and mechanical waves have much in common and are described in much the same language. Before reading further in this chapter, you should review the properties of mechanical waves as discussed in Chapters 15 and 16.

32.1 Maxwell's Equations and Electromagnetic Waves

In the last several chapters we studied various aspects of electric and magnetic fields. We learned that when the fields don't vary with time, such as an electric field produced by charges at rest or the magnetic field of a steady current, we can analyze the electric and magnetic fields independently without considering interactions between them. But when the fields vary with time, they are no longer independent. Faraday's law (see Section 29.2) tells us that a time-varying magnetic field acts as a source of electric field, as shown by induced emfs in inductors and transformers. Ampere's law, including the displacement current discovered by Maxwell (see Section 29.7), shows that a time-varying electric field acts as a source of magnetic field. This mutual interaction between the two fields is summarized in Maxwell's equations, presented in Section 29.7.

Thus, when *either* an electric or a magnetic field is changing with time, a field of the other kind is induced in adjacent regions of space. We are led (as Maxwell was) to consider the possibility of an electromagnetic disturbance, consisting of time-varying electric and magnetic fields, that can propagate through space from one region to another, even when there is no matter in the intervening region. Such a disturbance, if it exists, will have the properties of a *wave,* and an appropriate term is **electromagnetic wave.**

Such waves do exist; radio and television transmission, light, x rays, and many other kinds of radiation are examples of electromagnetic waves. Our goal in this chapter is to see how such waves are explained by the principles of electromagnetism that we have studied thus far and to examine the properties of these waves.

Electricity, Magnetism, and Light

As often happens in the development of science, the theoretical understanding of electromagnetic waves evolved along a considerably more devious path than the one just outlined. In the early days of electromagnetic theory (the early 19th century), two different units of electric charge were used: one for electrostatics and the other for magnetic phenomena involving currents. In the system of units used at that time, these two units of charge had different physical dimensions. Their *ratio* had units of velocity, and measurements showed that the ratio had a numerical value that was precisely equal to the speed of light, 3.00×10^8 m/s. At the time, physicists regarded this as an extraordinary coincidence and had no idea how to explain it.

In searching to understand this result, Maxwell (Fig. 32.1) proved in 1865 that an electromagnetic disturbance should propagate in free space with a speed equal to that of light and hence that light waves were likely to be electromagnetic in nature. At the same time, he discovered that the basic principles of electromagnetism can be expressed in terms of the four equations that we now call **Maxwell's equations,** which we discussed in Section 29.7. These four equations are (1) Gauss's law for electric fields; (2) Gauss's law for magnetic fields, showing the absence of magnetic monopoles; (3) Ampere's law, including displacement current; and (4) Faraday's law:

$$\oint \vec{E} \cdot d\vec{A} = \frac{Q_{\text{encl}}}{\epsilon_0} \qquad \text{(Gauss's law)} \tag{29.18}$$

$$\oint \vec{B} \cdot d\vec{A} = 0 \qquad \text{(Gauss's law for magnetism)} \tag{29.19}$$

$$\oint \vec{B} \cdot d\vec{l} = \mu_0 \left(i_C + \epsilon_0 \frac{d\Phi_E}{dt} \right)_{\text{encl}} \qquad \text{(Ampere's law)} \tag{29.20}$$

$$\oint \vec{E} \cdot d\vec{l} = -\frac{d\Phi_B}{dt} \qquad \text{(Faraday's law)} \tag{29.21}$$

32.1 James Clerk Maxwell (1831–1879) was the first person to truly understand the fundamental nature of light. He also made major contributions to thermodynamics, optics, astronomy, and color photography. Albert Einstein described Maxwell's accomplishments as "the most profound and the most fruitful that physics has experienced since the time of Newton."

These equations apply to electric and magnetic fields *in vacuum*. If a material is present, the permittivity ϵ_0 and permeability μ_0 of free space are replaced by the permittivity ϵ and permeability μ of the material. If the values of ϵ and μ are different at different points in the regions of integration, then ϵ and μ have to be transferred to the left sides of Eqs. (29.18) and (29.20), respectively, and placed inside the integrals. The ϵ in Eq. (29.20) also has to be included in the integral that gives $d\Phi_E/dt$.

According to Maxwell's equations, a point charge at rest produces a static $\vec{E}$ field but no $\vec{B}$ field; a point charge moving with a constant velocity (see Section 28.1) produces both $\vec{E}$ and $\vec{B}$ fields. Maxwell's equations can also be used to show that in order for a point charge to produce electromagnetic waves, the charge must *accelerate*. In fact, it's a general result of Maxwell's equations that *every* accelerated charge radiates electromagnetic energy (Fig. 32.2).

Generating Electromagnetic Radiation

One way in which a point charge can be made to emit electromagnetic waves is by making it oscillate in simple harmonic motion, so that it has an acceleration at almost every instant (the exception is when the charge is passing through its equilibrium position). Figure 32.3 shows some of the electric field lines produced by such an oscillating point charge. Field lines are *not* material objects, but you may nonetheless find it helpful to think of them as behaving somewhat like strings that extend from the point charge off to infinity. Oscillating the charge up and down makes waves that propagate outward from the charge along these "strings." Note that the charge does not emit waves equally in all directions; the waves are strongest at 90° to the axis of motion of the charge, while there are *no* waves along this axis. This is just what the "string" picture would lead you to conclude. There is also a *magnetic* disturbance that spreads outward from the charge; this is not shown in Fig. 32.3. Because the electric and magnetic disturbances spread or radiate away from the source, the name **electromagnetic radiation** is used interchangeably with the phrase "electromagnetic waves."

Electromagnetic waves with macroscopic wavelengths were first produced in the laboratory in 1887 by the German physicist Heinrich Hertz. As a source of waves, he used charges oscillating in *L-C* circuits of the sort discussed in Section 30.5; he detected the resulting electromagnetic waves with other circuits tuned to the same frequency. Hertz also produced electromagnetic *standing waves* and measured the distance between adjacent nodes (one half-wavelength) to determine the wavelength. Knowing the resonant frequency of his circuits, he then found the speed of the waves from the wavelength–frequency relationship $v = \lambda f$. He established that their speed was the same as that of light; this verified Maxwell's theoretical prediction directly. The SI unit of frequency is named in honor of Hertz: One hertz (1 Hz) equals one cycle per second.

32.2 (Top) Every mobile phone, wireless modem, or radio transmitter emits signals in the form of electromagnetic waves that are made by accelerating charges. (Bottom) Power lines carry a strong alternating current, which means that a substantial amount of charge is accelerating back and forth and generating electromagnetic waves. These waves can produce a buzzing sound from your car radio when you drive near the lines.

32.3 Electric field lines of a point charge oscillating in simple harmonic motion, seen at five instants during an oscillation period T. The charge's trajectory is in the plane of the drawings. At $t = 0$ the point charge is at its maximum upward displacement. The arrow shows one "kink" in the lines of $\vec{E}$ as it propagates outward from the point charge. The magnetic field (not shown) comprises circles that lie in planes perpendicular to these figures and concentric with the axis of oscillation.

(a) $t = 0$

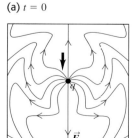

$\vec{E}$

(b) $t = T/4$

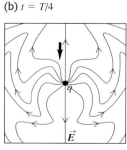

$\vec{E}$

(c) $t = T/2$

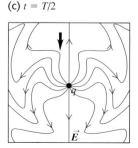

$\vec{E}$

(d) $t = 3T/4$

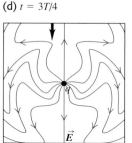

$\vec{E}$

(e) $t = T$

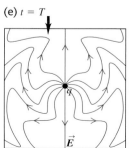

$\vec{E}$

The modern value of the speed of light, which we denote by the symbol c, is 299,792,458 m/s. (Recall from Section 1.3 that this value is the basis of our standard of length: One meter is defined to be the distance that light travels in 1/299,792,458 second.) For our purposes, $c = 3.00 \times 10^8$ m/s is sufficiently accurate.

The possible use of electromagnetic waves for long-distance communication does not seem to have occurred to Hertz. It was left to Marconi and others to make radio communication a familiar household experience. In a radio *transmitter*, electric charges are made to oscillate along the length of the conducting antenna, producing oscillating field disturbances like those shown in Fig. 32.3. Since many charges oscillate together in the antenna, the disturbances are much stronger than those of a single oscillating charge and can be detected at a much greater distance. In a radio *receiver* the antenna is also a conductor; the fields of the wave emanating from a distant transmitter exert forces on free charges within the receiver antenna, producing an oscillating current that is detected and amplified by the receiver circuitry.

For the remainder of this chapter our concern will be with electromagnetic waves themselves, not with the rather complex problem of how they are produced.

The Electromagnetic Spectrum

The **electromagnetic spectrum** encompasses electromagnetic waves of all frequencies and wavelengths. Figure 32.4 shows approximate wavelength and frequency ranges for the most commonly encountered portion of the spectrum. Despite vast differences in their uses and means of production, these are all electromagnetic waves with the same propagation speed (in vacuum) $c = 299,792,458$ m/s. Electromagnetic waves may differ in frequency f and wavelength λ, but the relationship $c = \lambda f$ in vacuum holds for each.

We can detect only a very small segment of this spectrum directly through our sense of sight. We call this range **visible light.** Its wavelengths range from about 380 to 750 nm (380 to 750×10^{-9} m), with corresponding frequencies from about 790 to 400 THz (7.9 to 4.0×10^{14} Hz). Different parts of the visible spectrum evoke in humans the sensations of different colors. Table 32.1 gives the approximate wavelengths for colors in the visible spectrum.

Ordinary white light includes all visible wavelengths. However, by using special sources or filters, we can select a narrow band of wavelengths within a range of a few nm. Such light is approximately *monochromatic* (single-color) light. Absolutely monochromatic light with only a single wavelength is an unattainable idealization. When we use the expression "monochromatic light with $\lambda = 550$ nm" with reference to a laboratory experiment, we really mean a small band

Table 32.1 Wavelengths of Visible Light

380–450 nm	Violet
450–495 nm	Blue
495–570 nm	Green
570–590 nm	Yellow
590–620 nm	Orange
620–750 nm	Red

32.4 The electromagnetic spectrum. The frequencies and wavelengths found in nature extend over such a wide range that we have to use a logarithmic scale to show all important bands. The boundaries between bands are somewhat arbitrary.

of wavelengths *around* 550 nm. Light from a *laser* is much more nearly monochromatic than is light obtainable in any other way.

Invisible forms of electromagnetic radiation are no less important than visible light. Our system of global communication, for example, depends on radio waves: AM radio uses waves with frequencies from 5.4×10^5 Hz to 1.6×10^6 Hz, while FM radio broadcasts are at frequencies from 8.8×10^7 Hz to 1.08×10^8 Hz. (Television broadcasts use frequencies that bracket the FM band.) Microwaves are also used for communication (for example, by cellular phones and wireless networks) and for weather radar (at frequencies near 3×10^9 Hz). Many cameras have a device that emits a beam of infrared radiation; by analyzing the properties of the infrared radiation reflected from the subject, the camera determines the distance to the subject and automatically adjusts the focus. X rays are able to penetrate through flesh, which makes them invaluable in dentistry and medicine. Gamma rays, the shortest-wavelength type of electromagnetic radiation, are used in medicine to destroy cancer cells.

Test Your Understanding of Section 32.1 (a) Is it possible to have a purely electric wave propagate through empty space—-that is, a wave made up of an electric field but no magnetic field? (b) What about a purely magnetic wave, with a magnetic field but no electric field?

32.2 Plane Electromagnetic Waves and the Speed of Light

We are now ready to develop the basic ideas of electromagnetic waves and their relationship to the principles of electromagnetism. Our procedure will be to postulate a simple field configuration that has wavelike behavior. We'll assume an electric field $\vec{E}$ that has only a *y*-component and a magnetic field $\vec{B}$ with only a *z*-component, and we'll assume that both fields move together in the +*x*-direction with a speed *c* that is initially unknown. (As we go along, it will become clear why we choose $\vec{E}$ and $\vec{B}$ to be perpendicular to the direction of propagation as well as to each other.) Then we will test whether these fields are physically possible by asking whether they are consistent with Maxwell's equations, particularly Ampere's law and Faraday's law. We'll find that the answer is yes, provided that *c* has a particular value. We'll also show that the *wave equation,* which we encountered during our study of mechanical waves in Chapter 15, can be derived from Maxwell's equations.

A Simple Plane Electromagnetic Wave

Using an *xyz*-coordinate system (Fig. 32.5), we imagine that all space is divided into two regions by a plane perpendicular to the *x*-axis (parallel to the *yz*-plane). At every point to the left of this plane there are a uniform electric field $\vec{E}$ in the +*y*-direction and a uniform magnetic field $\vec{B}$ in the +*z*-direction, as shown. Furthermore, we suppose that the boundary plane, which we call the *wave front,* moves to the right in the +*x*-direction with a constant speed *c*, the value of which we'll leave undetermined for now. Thus the $\vec{E}$ and $\vec{B}$ fields travel to the right into previously field-free regions with a definite speed. This is a rudimentary electromagnetic wave. A wave such as this, in which at any instant the fields are uniform over any plane perpendicular to the direction of propagation, is called a **plane wave.** In the case shown in Fig. 32.5, the fields are zero for planes to the right of the wave front and have the same values on all planes to the left of the wave front; later we will consider more complex plane waves.

We won't concern ourselves with the problem of actually *producing* such a field configuration. Instead, we simply ask whether it is consistent with the laws of electromagnetism—-that is, with Maxwell's equations. We'll consider each of these four equations in turn.

32.5 An electromagnetic wave front. The plane representing the wave front moves to the right (in the positive *x*-direction) with speed *c*.

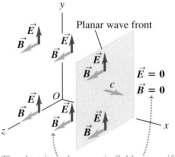

The electric and magnetic fields are uniform behind the advancing wave front and zero in front of it.

32.6 Gaussian surface for a transverse plane electromagnetic wave.

The electric field is the same on the top and bottom sides of the Gaussian surface, so the total electric flux through the surface is zero.

The magnetic field is the same on the left and right sides of the Gaussian surface, so the total magnetic flux through the surface is zero.

32.7 (a) Applying Faraday's law to a plane wave. (b) In a time dt, the magnetic flux through the rectangle in the xy-plane increases by an amount $d\Phi_B$. This increase equals the flux through the shaded rectangle with area $ac\,dt$; that is, $d\Phi_B = Bac\,dt$. Thus $d\Phi_B/dt = Bac$.

(a) In time dt, the wave front moves a distance $c\,dt$ in the $+x$-direction.

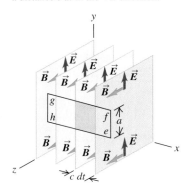

(b) Side view of situation in (a)

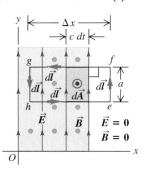

Let us first verify that our wave satisfies Maxwell's first and second equations—that is, Gauss's laws for electric and magnetic fields. To do this, we take as our Gaussian surface a rectangular box with sides parallel to the xy, xz, and yz coordinate planes (Fig. 32.6). The box encloses no electric charge. The total electric flux and magnetic flux through the box are both zero, even if part of the box is in the region where $E = B = 0$. This would *not* be the case if $\vec{E}$ or $\vec{B}$ had an x-component, parallel to the direction of propagation; if the wave front were inside the box, there would be flux through the left-hand side of the box (at $x = 0$) but not the right-hand side (at $x > 0$). Thus to satisfy Maxwell's first and second equations, the electric and magnetic fields must be perpendicular to the direction of propagation; that is, the wave must be **transverse.**

The next of Maxwell's equations to be considered is Faraday's law:

$$\oint \vec{E} \cdot d\vec{l} = -\frac{d\Phi_B}{dt} \tag{32.1}$$

To test whether our wave satisfies Faraday's law, we apply this law to a rectangle $efgh$ that is parallel to the xy-plane (Fig. 32.7a). As shown in Fig. 32.7b, a cross section in the xy-plane, this rectangle has height a and width Δx. At the time shown, the wave front has progressed partway through the rectangle, and $\vec{E}$ is zero along the side ef. In applying Faraday's law we take the vector area $d\vec{A}$ of rectangle $efgh$ to be in the $+z$-direction. With this choice the right-hand rule requires that we integrate $\vec{E} \cdot d\vec{l}$ *counterclockwise* around the rectangle. At every point on side ef, $\vec{E}$ is zero. At every point on sides fg and he, $\vec{E}$ is either zero or perpendicular to $d\vec{l}$. Only side gh contributes to the integral. On this side, $\vec{E}$ and $d\vec{l}$ are opposite, and we obtain

$$\oint \vec{E} \cdot d\vec{l} = -Ea \tag{32.2}$$

Hence, the left-hand side of Eq. (32.1) is nonzero.

To satisfy Faraday's law, Eq. (32.1), there must be a component of $\vec{B}$ in the z-direction (perpendicular to $\vec{E}$) so that there can be a nonzero magnetic flux Φ_B through the rectangle $efgh$ and a nonzero derivative $d\Phi_B/dt$. Indeed, in our wave, $\vec{B}$ has *only* a z-component. We have assumed that this component is in the *positive* z-direction; let's see whether this assumption is consistent with Faraday's law. During a time interval dt the wave front moves a distance $c\,dt$ to the right in Fig. 32.7b, sweeping out an area $ac\,dt$ of the rectangle $efgh$. During this interval the magnetic flux Φ_B through the rectangle $efgh$ increases by $d\Phi_B = B(ac\,dt)$, so the rate of change of magnetic flux is

$$\frac{d\Phi_B}{dt} = Bac \tag{32.3}$$

Now we substitute Eqs. (32.2) and (32.3) into Faraday's law, Eq. (32.1); we get

$$-Ea = -Bac$$

$$E = cB \quad \text{(electromagnetic wave in vacuum)} \tag{32.4}$$

This shows that our wave is consistent with Faraday's law only if the wave speed c and the magnitudes of the perpendicular vectors $\vec{E}$ and $\vec{B}$ are related as in Eq. (32.4). Note that if we had assumed that $\vec{B}$ was in the *negative* z-direction, there would have been an additional minus sign in Eq. (32.4); since E, c, and B are all positive magnitudes, no solution would then have been possible. Furthermore, any component of $\vec{B}$ in the y-direction (parallel to $\vec{E}$) would not contribute to the changing magnetic flux Φ_B through the rectangle $efgh$ (which is parallel to the xy-plane) and so would not be part of the wave.

Finally, we carry out a similar calculation using Ampere's law, the remaining member of Maxwell's equations. There is no conduction current ($i_C = 0$), so Ampere's law is

$$\oint \vec{B} \cdot d\vec{l} = \mu_0 \epsilon_0 \frac{d\Phi_E}{dt} \qquad (32.5)$$

To check whether our wave is consistent with Ampere's law, we move our rectangle so that it lies in the xz-plane, as shown in Fig. 32.8, and we again look at the situation at a time when the wave front has traveled partway through the rectangle. We take the vector area $d\vec{A}$ in the $+y$-direction, and so the right-hand rule requires that we integrate $\vec{B} \cdot d\vec{l}$ counterclockwise around the rectangle. The $\vec{B}$ field is zero at every point along side ef, and at each point on sides fg and he it is either zero or perpendicular to $d\vec{l}$. Only side gh, where $\vec{B}$ and $d\vec{l}$ are parallel, contributes to the integral, and we find

$$\oint \vec{B} \cdot d\vec{l} = Ba \qquad (32.6)$$

Hence, the left-hand side of Ampere's law, Eq. (32.5), is nonzero; the right-hand side must be nonzero as well. Thus $\vec{E}$ must have a y-component (perpendicular to $\vec{B}$) so that the electric flux Φ_E through the rectangle and the time derivative $d\Phi_E/dt$ can be nonzero. We come to the same conclusion that we inferred from Faraday's law: In an electromagnetic wave, $\vec{E}$ and $\vec{B}$ must be mutually perpendicular.

In a time interval dt the electric flux Φ_E through the rectangle increases by $d\Phi_E = E(ac\,dt)$. Since we chose $d\vec{A}$ to be in the $+y$-direction, this flux change is positive; the rate of change of electric field is

$$\frac{d\Phi_E}{dt} = Eac \qquad (32.7)$$

Substituting Eqs. (32.6) and (32.7) into Ampere's law, Eq. (32.5), we find

$$Ba = \epsilon_0 \mu_0 Eac$$

$$B = \epsilon_0 \mu_0 cE \qquad \text{(electromagnetic wave in vacuum)} \qquad (32.8)$$

Thus our assumed wave obeys Ampere's law only if B, c, and E are related as in Eq. (32.8).

Our electromagnetic wave must obey *both* Ampere's law and Faraday's law, so Eqs. (32.4) and (32.8) must both be satisfied. This can happen only if $\epsilon_0\mu_0 c = 1/c$, or

$$c = \frac{1}{\sqrt{\epsilon_0\mu_0}} \qquad \text{(speed of electromagnetic waves in vacuum)} \qquad (32.9)$$

Inserting the numerical values of these quantities, we find

$$c = \frac{1}{\sqrt{(8.85 \times 10^{-12} \text{ C}^2/\text{N} \cdot \text{m}^2)(4\pi \times 10^{-7} \text{ N/A}^2)}}$$

$$= 3.00 \times 10^8 \text{ m/s}$$

Our assumed wave is consistent with all of Maxwell's equations, provided that the wave front moves with the speed given above, which you should recognize as the speed of light! Note that the *exact* value of c is defined to be 299,792,458 m/s; the modern value of ϵ_0 is defined to agree with this when used in Eq. (32.9) (see Section 21.3).

32.8 (a) Applying Ampere's law to a plane wave. (Compare to Fig. 32.7a.) (b) In a time dt, the electric flux through the rectangle in the xz-plane increases by an amount $d\Phi_E$. This increase equals the flux through the shaded rectangle with area $ac\,dt$; that is, $d\Phi_E = Eac\,dt$. Thus $d\Phi_E/dt = Eac$.

(a) In time dt, the wave front moves a distance $c\,dt$ in the $+x$-direction.

(b) Top view of situation in (a)

32.9 A right-hand rule for electromagnetic waves relates the directions of $\vec{E}$ and $\vec{B}$ and the direction of propagation.

Right-hand rule for an electromagnetic wave:

① Point the thumb of your right hand in the wave's direction of propagation.

② Imagine rotating the $\vec{E}$-field vector 90° in the sense your fingers curl.

That is the direction of the $\vec{B}$ field.

Direction of propagation = direction of $\vec{E} \times \vec{B}$.

Key Properties of Electromagnetic Waves

We chose a simple wave for our study in order to avoid mathematical complications, but this special case illustrates several important features of *all* electromagnetic waves:

1. The wave is *transverse;* both $\vec{E}$ and $\vec{B}$ are perpendicular to the direction of propagation of the wave. The electric and magnetic fields are also perpendicular to each other. The direction of propagation is the direction of the vector product $\vec{E} \times \vec{B}$ (Fig. 32.9).
2. There is a definite ratio between the magnitudes of $\vec{E}$ and $\vec{B}$: $E = cB$.
3. The wave travels in vacuum with a definite and unchanging speed.
4. Unlike mechanical waves, which need the oscillating particles of a medium such as water or air to transmit a wave, electromagnetic waves require no medium.

We can generalize this discussion to a more realistic situation. Suppose we have several wave fronts in the form of parallel planes perpendicular to the x-axis, all of which are moving to the right with speed c. Suppose that the $\vec{E}$ and $\vec{B}$ fields are the same at all points within a single region between two planes, but that the fields differ from region to region. The overall wave is a plane wave, but one in which the fields vary in steps along the x-axis. Such a wave could be constructed by superposing several of the simple step waves we have just discussed (shown in Fig. 32.5). This is possible because the $\vec{E}$ and $\vec{B}$ fields obey the superposition principle in waves just as in static situations: When two waves are superposed, the total $\vec{E}$ field at each point is the vector sum of the $\vec{E}$ fields of the individual waves, and similarly for the total $\vec{B}$ field.

We can extend the above development to show that a wave with fields that vary in steps is also consistent with Ampere's and Faraday's laws, provided that the wave fronts all move with the speed c given by Eq. (32.9). In the limit that we make the individual steps infinitesimally small, we have a wave in which the $\vec{E}$ and $\vec{B}$ fields at any instant vary *continuously* along the x-axis. The entire field pattern moves to the right with speed c. In Section 32.3 we will consider waves in which $\vec{E}$ and $\vec{B}$ are *sinusoidal* functions of x and t. Because at each point the magnitudes of $\vec{E}$ and $\vec{B}$ are related by $E = cB$, the periodic variations of the two fields in any periodic traveling wave must be *in phase.*

Electromagnetic waves have the property of **polarization.** In the above discussion the choice of the y-direction for $\vec{E}$ was arbitrary. We could just as well have specified the z-axis for $\vec{E}$; then $\vec{B}$ would have been in the $-y$-direction. A wave in which $\vec{E}$ is always parallel to a certain axis is said to be **linearly polarized** along that axis. More generally, *any* wave traveling in the x-direction can be represented as a superposition of waves linearly polarized in the y- and z-directions. We will study polarization in greater detail in Chapter 33.

Derivation of the Electromagnetic Wave Equation

Here is an alternative derivation of Eq. (32.9) for the speed of electromagnetic waves. It is more mathematical than our other treatment, but it includes a derivation of the wave equation for electromagnetic waves. This part of the section can be omitted without loss of continuity in the chapter.

During our discussion of mechanical waves in Section 15.3, we showed that a function $y(x, t)$ that represents the displacement of any point in a mechanical wave traveling along the x-axis must satisfy a differential equation, Eq. (15.12):

$$\frac{\partial^2 y(x, t)}{\partial x^2} = \frac{1}{v^2} \frac{\partial^2 y(x, t)}{\partial t^2} \qquad (32.10)$$

This equation is called the **wave equation,** and v is the speed of propagation of the wave.

To derive the corresponding equation for an electromagnetic wave, we again consider a plane wave. That is, we assume that at each instant, E_y and B_z are uniform over any plane perpendicular to the x-axis, the direction of propagation. But now we let E_y and B_z vary continuously as we go along the x-axis; then each is a function of x and t. We consider the values of E_y and B_z on two planes perpendicular to the x-axis, one at x and one at $x + \Delta x$.

Following the same procedure as previously, we apply Faraday's law to a rectangle lying parallel to the xy-plane, as in Fig. 32.10. This figure is similar to Fig. 32.7. Let the left end gh of the rectangle be at position x, and let the right end ef be at position $(x + \Delta x)$. At time t, the values of E_y on these two sides are $E_y(x, t)$ and $E_y(x + \Delta x, t)$, respectively. When we apply Faraday's law to this rectangle, we find that instead of $\oint \vec{E} \cdot d\vec{l} = -Ea$ as before, we have

$$\oint \vec{E} \cdot d\vec{l} = -E_y(x, t)a + E_y(x + \Delta x, t)a$$
$$= a[E_y(x + \Delta x, t) - E_y(x, t)] \qquad (32.11)$$

To find the magnetic flux Φ_B through this rectangle, we assume that Δx is small enough that B_z is nearly uniform over the rectangle. In that case, $\Phi_B = B_z(x, t)A = B_z(x, t)a\,\Delta x$, and

$$\frac{d\Phi_B}{dt} = \frac{\partial B_z(x, t)}{\partial t} a\, \Delta x$$

We use partial-derivative notation because B_z is a function of both x and t. When we substitute this expression and Eq. (32.11) into Faraday's law, Eq. (32.1), we get

$$a[E_y(x + \Delta x, t) - E_y(x, t)] = -\frac{\partial B_z}{\partial t} a\, \Delta x$$
$$\frac{E_y(x + \Delta x, t) - E_y(x, t)}{\Delta x} = -\frac{\partial B_z}{\partial t}$$

Finally, imagine shrinking the rectangle down to a sliver so that Δx approaches zero. When we take the limit of this equation as $\Delta x \to 0$, we get

$$\frac{\partial E_y(x, t)}{\partial x} = -\frac{\partial B_z(x, t)}{\partial t} \qquad (32.12)$$

This equation shows that if there is a time-varying component B_z of magnetic field, there must also be a component E_y of electric field that varies with x, and conversely. We put this relationship on the shelf for now; we'll return to it soon.

Next we apply Ampere's law to the rectangle shown in Fig. 32.11. The line integral $\oint \vec{B} \cdot d\vec{l}$ becomes

$$\oint \vec{B} \cdot d\vec{l} = -B_z(x + \Delta x, t)a + B_z(x, t)a \qquad (32.13)$$

Again assuming that the rectangle is narrow, we approximate the electric flux Φ_E through it as $\Phi_E = E_y(x, t)A = E_y(x, t)a\,\Delta x$. The rate of change of Φ_E, which we need for Ampere's law, is then

$$\frac{d\Phi_E}{dt} = \frac{\partial E_y(x, t)}{\partial t} a\, \Delta x$$

Now we substitute this expression and Eq. (32.13) into Ampere's law, Eq. (32.5):

$$-B_z(x + \Delta x, t)a + B_z(x, t)a = \epsilon_0 \mu_0 \frac{\partial E_y(x, t)}{\partial t} a\, \Delta x$$

Again we divide both sides by $a\,\Delta x$ and take the limit as $\Delta x \to 0$. We find

$$-\frac{\partial B_z(x, t)}{\partial x} = \epsilon_0 \mu_0 \frac{\partial E_y(x, t)}{\partial t} \qquad (32.14)$$

32.10 Faraday's law applied to a rectangle with height a and width Δx parallel to the xy-plane.

(a)

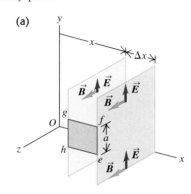

(b) Side view of the situation in (a)

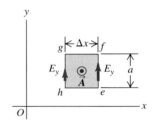

32.11 Ampere's law applied to a rectangle with height a and width Δx parallel to the xz-plane.

(a)

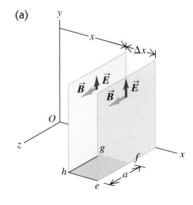

(b) Top view of the situation in (a)

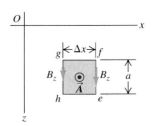

Now comes the final step. We take the partial derivatives with respect to x of both sides of Eq. (32.12), and we take the partial derivatives with respect to t of both sides of Eq. (32.14). The results are

$$-\frac{\partial^2 E_y(x, t)}{\partial x^2} = \frac{\partial^2 B_z(x, t)}{\partial x \partial t}$$

$$-\frac{\partial^2 B_z(x, t)}{\partial x \partial t} = \epsilon_0 \mu_0 \frac{\partial^2 E_y(x, t)}{\partial t^2}$$

Combining these two equations to eliminate B_z, we finally find

$$\frac{\partial^2 E_y(x, t)}{\partial x^2} = \epsilon_0 \mu_0 \frac{\partial^2 E_y(x, t)}{\partial t^2} \qquad \text{(electromagnetic wave equation in vacuum)} \qquad (32.15)$$

This expression has the same form as the general wave equation, Eq. (32.10). Because the electric field E_y must satisfy this equation, it behaves as a wave with a pattern that travels through space with a definite speed. Furthermore, comparison of Eqs. (32.15) and (32.10) shows that the wave speed v is given by

$$\frac{1}{v^2} = \epsilon_0 \mu_0 \qquad \text{or} \qquad v = \frac{1}{\sqrt{\epsilon_0 \mu_0}}$$

This agrees with Eq. (32.9) for the speed c of electromagnetic waves.

We can show that B_z also must satisfy the same wave equation as E_y, Eq. (32.15). To prove this, we take the partial derivative of Eq. (32.12) with respect to t and the partial derivative of Eq. (32.14) with respect to x and combine the results. We leave this derivation for you to carry out.

Test Your Understanding of Section 32.2   For each of the following electromagnetic waves, state the direction of the magnetic field. (a) The wave is propagating in the positive z-direction, and $\vec{E}$ is in the positive x-direction; (b) the wave is propagating in the positive y-direction, and $\vec{E}$ is in the negative z-direction; (c) the wave is propagating in the negative x-direction, and $\vec{E}$ is in the positive z-direction.   ❙

32.3 Sinusoidal Electromagnetic Waves

Sinusoidal electromagnetic waves are directly analogous to sinusoidal transverse mechanical waves on a stretched string, which we studied in Section 15.3. In a sinusoidal electromagnetic wave, $\vec{E}$ and $\vec{B}$ at any point in space are sinusoidal functions of time, and at any instant of time the *spatial* variation of the fields is also sinusoidal.

Some sinusoidal electromagnetic waves are *plane waves;* they share with the waves described in Section 32.2 the property that at any instant the fields are uniform over any plane perpendicular to the direction of propagation. The entire pattern travels in the direction of propagation with speed c. The directions of $\vec{E}$ and $\vec{B}$ are perpendicular to the direction of propagation (and to each other), so the wave is *transverse.* Electromagnetic waves produced by an oscillating point charge, shown in Fig. 32.3, are an example of sinusoidal waves that are *not* plane waves. But if we restrict our observations to a relatively small region of space at a sufficiently great distance from the source, even these waves are well approximated by plane waves (Fig. 32.12). In the same way, the curved surface of the (nearly) spherical earth appears flat to us because of our small size relative to the earth's radius. In this section we'll restrict our discussion to plane waves.

The frequency f, the wavelength λ, and the speed of propagation c of any periodic wave are related by the usual wavelength–frequency relationship $c = \lambda f$. If the frequency f is 10^8 Hz (100 MHz), typical of commercial FM radio broadcasts, the wavelength is

$$\lambda = \frac{3 \times 10^8 \text{ m/s}}{10^8 \text{ Hz}} = 3 \text{ m}$$

Figure 32.4 shows the inverse proportionality between wavelength and frequency.

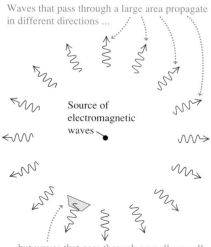

32.12 Waves passing through a small area at a sufficiently great distance from a source can be treated as plane waves.

Waves that pass through a large area propagate in different directions ...

Source of electromagnetic waves

... but waves that pass through a small area all propagate in nearly the same direction, so we can treat them as plane waves.

Fields of a Sinusoidal Wave

Figure 32.13 shows a linearly polarized sinusoidal electromagnetic wave traveling in the $+x$-direction. The $\vec{E}$ and $\vec{B}$ vectors are shown for only a few points on the positive x-axis. Note that the electric and magnetic fields oscillate in phase: $\vec{E}$ is maximum where $\vec{B}$ is maximum and $\vec{E}$ is zero where $\vec{B}$ is zero. Note also that where $\vec{E}$ is in the $+y$-direction, $\vec{B}$ is in the $+z$-direction; where $\vec{E}$ is in the $-y$-direction, $\vec{B}$ is in the $-z$-direction. At all points the vector product $\vec{E} \times \vec{B}$ is in the direction in which the wave is propagating (the $+x$-direction). We mentioned this in Section 32.2 in the list of characteristics of electromagnetic waves.

CAUTION **In a plane wave, $\vec{E}$ and $\vec{B}$ are everywhere** Figure 32.13 may give you the erroneous impression that the electric and magnetic fields exist only along the x-axis. In fact, in a sinusoidal plane wave there are electric and magnetic fields at *all* points in space. Imagine a plane perpendicular to the x-axis (that is, parallel to the yz-plane) at a particular point, at a particular time; the fields have the same values at all points in that plane. The values are different on different planes.

We can describe electromagnetic waves by means of *wave functions,* just as we did in Section 15.3 for waves on a string. One form of the wave function for a transverse wave traveling in the $+x$-direction along a stretched string is Eq. (15.7):

$$y(x, t) = A \cos(kx - \omega t)$$

where $y(x, t)$ is the transverse displacement from its equilibrium position at time t of a point with coordinate x on the string. The quantity A is the maximum displacement, or *amplitude,* of the wave; ω is its *angular frequency,* equal to 2π times the frequency f; and k is the *wave number,* equal to $2\pi/\lambda$, where λ is the wavelength.

Let $E_y(x, t)$ and $B_z(x, t)$ represent the instantaneous values of the y-component of $\vec{E}$ and the z-component of $\vec{B}$, respectively, in Fig. 32.13, and let E_{max} and B_{max} represent the maximum values, or *amplitudes,* of these fields. The wave functions for the wave are then

$$E_y(x, t) = E_{max} \cos(kx - \omega t) \qquad B_z(x, t) = B_{max} \cos(kx - \omega t) \qquad \text{(32.16)}$$

(sinusoidal electromagnetic plane wave, propagating in $+x$-direction)

We can also write the wave functions in vector form:

$$\vec{E}(x, t) = \hat{j} E_{max} \cos(kx - \omega t)$$
$$\vec{B}(x, t) = \hat{k} B_{max} \cos(kx - \omega t) \qquad \text{(32.17)}$$

CAUTION **The symbol k has two meanings** Note the two different k's: the unit vector $\hat{k}$ in the z-direction and the wave number k. Don't get these confused!

The sine curves in Fig. 32.13 represent instantaneous values of the electric and magnetic fields as functions of x at time $t = 0$—that is, $\vec{E}(x, t = 0)$ and $\vec{B}(x, t = 0)$. As time goes by, the wave travels to the right with speed c. Equations (32.16) and (32.17) show that at any point the sinusoidal oscillations of $\vec{E}$ and $\vec{B}$ are *in phase.* From Eq. (32.4) the amplitudes must be related by

$$E_{max} = cB_{max} \qquad \text{(electromagnetic wave in vacuum)} \qquad \text{(32.18)}$$

These amplitude and phase relationships are also required for $E(x, t)$ and $B(x, t)$ to satisfy Eqs. (32.12) and (32.14), which came from Faraday's law and Ampere's law, respectively. Can you verify this statement? (See Problem 32.38.)

32.13 Representation of the electric and magnetic fields as functions of x for a linearly polarized sinusoidal plane electromagnetic wave. One wavelength of the wave is shown at time $t = 0$. The fields are shown only for points along the x-axis.

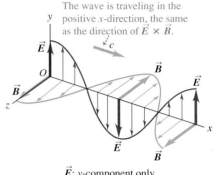

$\vec{E}$: y-component only
$\vec{B}$: z-component only

Mastering**PHYSICS**

PhET: Radio Waves & Electromagnetic Fields
ActivPhysics 10.1: Properties of Mechanical Waves

32.14 Representation of one wavelength of a linearly polarized sinusoidal plane electromagnetic wave traveling in the negative x-direction at $t = 0$. The fields are shown only for points along the x-axis. (Compare with Fig. 32.13.)

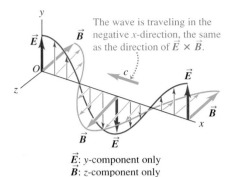

The wave is traveling in the negative x-direction, the same as the direction of $\vec{E} \times \vec{B}$.

$\vec{E}$: y-component only
$\vec{B}$: z-component only

Figure 32.14 shows the electric and magnetic fields of a wave traveling in the *negative x*-direction. At points where $\vec{E}$ is in the positive y-direction, $\vec{B}$ is in the negative z-direction; where $\vec{E}$ is in the negative y-direction, $\vec{B}$ is in the *positive* z-direction. The wave functions for this wave are

$$E_y(x, t) = E_{max}\cos(kx + \omega t) \quad B_z(x, t) = -B_{max}\cos(kx + \omega t) \quad (32.19)$$

(sinusoidal electromagnetic plane wave, propagating in $-x$-direction)

As with the wave traveling in the $+x$-direction, at any point the sinusoidal oscillations of the $\vec{E}$ and $\vec{B}$ fields are *in phase*, and the vector product $\vec{E} \times \vec{B}$ points in the direction of propagation.

The sinusoidal waves shown in Figs. 32.13 and 32.14 are both linearly polarized in the y-direction; the $\vec{E}$ field is always parallel to the y-axis. Example 32.1 concerns a wave that is linearly polarized in the z-direction.

Problem-Solving Strategy 32.1 Electromagnetic Waves

IDENTIFY *the relevant concepts:* Many of the same ideas that apply to mechanical waves apply to electromagnetic waves. One difference is that electromagnetic waves are described by two quantities (in this case, electric field $\vec{E}$ and magnetic field $\vec{B}$), rather than by a single quantity, such as the displacement of a string.

SET UP *the problem* using the following steps:
1. Draw a diagram showing the direction of wave propagation and the directions of $\vec{E}$ and $\vec{B}$.
2. Identify the target variables.

EXECUTE *the solution* as follows:
1. Review the treatment of sinusoidal mechanical waves in Chapters 15 and 16, and particularly the four problem-solving strategies suggested there.
2. Keep in mind the basic relationships for periodic waves: $v = \lambda f$ and $\omega = vk$. For electromagnetic waves in vacuum,

$v = c$. Distinguish between ordinary frequency f, usually expressed in hertz, and angular frequency $\omega = 2\pi f$, expressed in rad/s. Remember that the wave number is $k = 2\pi/\lambda$.
3. Concentrate on basic relationships, such as those between $\vec{E}$ and $\vec{B}$ (magnitude, direction, and relative phase), how the wave speed is determined, and the transverse nature of the waves.

EVALUATE *your answer:* Check that your result is reasonable. For electromagnetic waves in vacuum, the magnitude of the magnetic field in teslas is much smaller (by a factor of 3.00×10^8) than the magnitude of the electric field in volts per meter. If your answer suggests otherwise, you probably made an error using the relationship $E = cB$. (We'll see later in this section that the relationship between E and B is different for electromagnetic waves in a material medium.)

Example 32.1 Electric and magnetic fields of a laser beam

A carbon dioxide laser emits a sinusoidal electromagnetic wave that travels in vacuum in the negative x-direction. The wavelength is 10.6 μm (in the infrared; see Fig. 32.4) and the $\vec{E}$ field is parallel to the z-axis, with $E_{max} = 1.5$ MV/m. Write vector equations for $\vec{E}$ and $\vec{B}$ as functions of time and position.

SOLUTION

IDENTIFY and SET UP: Equations (32.19) describe a wave traveling in the negative x-direction with $\vec{E}$ along the y-axis—that is, a wave that is linearly polarized along the y-axis. By contrast, the wave in this example is linearly polarized along the z-axis. At points where $\vec{E}$ is in the positive z-direction, $\vec{B}$ must be in the positive y-direction for the vector product $\vec{E} \times \vec{B}$ to be in the negative x-direction (the direction of propagation). Figure 32.15 shows a wave that satisfies these requirements.

EXECUTE: A possible pair of wave functions that describe the wave shown in Fig. 32.15 are

32.15 Our sketch for this problem.

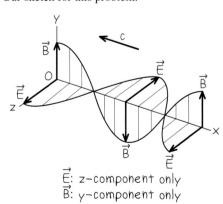

$\vec{E}$: z-component only
$\vec{B}$: y-component only

$$\vec{E}(x, t) = \hat{k}E_{max}\cos(kx + \omega t)$$
$$\vec{B}(x, t) = \hat{j}B_{max}\cos(kx + \omega t)$$

The plus sign in the arguments of the cosine functions indicates that the wave is propagating in the negative x-direction, as it should. Faraday's law requires that $E_{max} = cB_{max}$ [Eq. (32.18)], so

$$B_{max} = \frac{E_{max}}{c} = \frac{1.5 \times 10^6 \text{ V/m}}{3.0 \times 10^8 \text{ m/s}} = 5.0 \times 10^{-3} \text{ T}$$

To check unit consistency, note that $1 \text{ V} = 1 \text{ Wb/s}$ and $1 \text{ Wb/m}^2 = 1 \text{ T}$.

We have $\lambda = 10.6 \times 10^{-6}$ m, so the wave number and angular frequency are

$$k = \frac{2\pi}{\lambda} = \frac{2\pi \text{ rad}}{10.6 \times 10^{-6} \text{ m}} = 5.93 \times 10^5 \text{ rad/m}$$

$$\omega = ck = (3.00 \times 10^8 \text{ m/s})(5.93 \times 10^5 \text{ rad/m})$$
$$= 1.78 \times 10^{14} \text{ rad/s}$$

Substituting these values into the above wave functions, we get

$$\vec{E}(x, t) = \hat{k}(1.5 \times 10^6 \text{ V/m})$$
$$\times \cos[(5.93 \times 10^5 \text{ rad/m})x + (1.78 \times 10^{14} \text{ rad/s})t]$$

$$\vec{B}(x, t) = \hat{j}(5.0 \times 10^{-3} \text{ T})$$
$$\times \cos[(5.93 \times 10^5 \text{ rad/m})x + (1.78 \times 10^{14} \text{ rad/s})t]$$

EVALUATE: As we expect, the magnitude B_{max} in teslas is much smaller than the magnitude E_{max} in volts per meter. To check the directions of $\vec{E}$ and $\vec{B}$, note that $\vec{E} \times \vec{B}$ is in the direction of $\hat{k} \times \hat{j} = -\hat{i}$. This is as it should be for a wave that propagates in the negative x-direction.

Our expressions for $\vec{E}(x, t)$ and $\vec{B}(x, t)$ are not the only possible solutions. We could always add a phase angle ϕ to the arguments of the cosine function, so that $kx + \omega t$ would become $kx + \omega t + \phi$. To determine the value of ϕ we would need to know $\vec{E}$ and $\vec{B}$ either as functions of x at a given time t or as functions of t at a given coordinate x. However, the statement of the problem doesn't include this information.

Electromagnetic Waves in Matter

So far, our discussion of electromagnetic waves has been restricted to waves in *vacuum*. But electromagnetic waves can also travel in *matter;* think of light traveling through air, water, or glass. In this subsection we extend our analysis to electromagnetic waves in nonconducting materials—that is, *dielectrics*.

In a dielectric the wave speed is not the same as in vacuum, and we denote it by v instead of c. Faraday's law is unaltered, but in Eq. (32.4), derived from Faraday's law, the speed c is replaced by v. In Ampere's law the displacement current is given not by $\epsilon_0 \, d\Phi_E/dt$, where Φ_E is the flux of $\vec{E}$ through a surface, but by $\epsilon \, d\Phi_E/dt = K\epsilon_0 \, d\Phi_E/dt$, where K is the dielectric constant and ϵ is the permittivity of the dielectric. (We introduced these quantities in Section 24.4.) Also, the constant μ_0 in Ampere's law must be replaced by $\mu = K_m\mu_0$, where K_m is the relative permeability of the dielectric and μ is its permeability (see Section 28.8). Hence Eqs. (32.4) and (32.8) are replaced by

$$E = vB \quad \text{and} \quad B = \epsilon\mu vE \qquad (32.20)$$

Following the same procedure as for waves in vacuum, we find that the wave speed v is

$$v = \frac{1}{\sqrt{\epsilon\mu}} = \frac{1}{\sqrt{KK_m}} \frac{1}{\sqrt{\epsilon_0\mu_0}} = \frac{c}{\sqrt{KK_m}} \quad \begin{array}{l}\text{(speed of electromagnetic} \\ \text{waves in a dielectric)}\end{array} \qquad (32.21)$$

For most dielectrics the relative permeability K_m is very nearly equal to unity (except for insulating ferromagnetic materials). When $K_m \cong 1$,

$$v = \frac{1}{\sqrt{K}} \frac{1}{\sqrt{\epsilon_0\mu_0}} = \frac{c}{\sqrt{K}}$$

Because K is always greater than unity, the speed v of electromagnetic waves in a dielectric is always *less* than the speed c in vacuum by a factor of $1/\sqrt{K}$ (Fig. 32.16). The ratio of the speed c in vacuum to the speed v in a material is known in optics as the **index of refraction** n of the material. When $K_m \cong 1$,

$$\frac{c}{v} = n = \sqrt{KK_m} \cong \sqrt{K} \qquad (32.22)$$

Usually, we can't use the values of K in Table 24.1 in this equation because those values are measured using *constant* electric fields. When the fields oscillate rapidly,

32.16 The dielectric constant K of water is about 1.8 for visible light, so the speed of visible light in water is slower than in vacuum by a factor of $1/\sqrt{K} = 1/\sqrt{1.8} = 0.75$.

there is usually not time for the reorientation of electric dipoles that occurs with steady fields. Values of K with rapidly varying fields are usually much *smaller* than the values in the table. For example, K for water is 80.4 for steady fields but only about 1.8 in the frequency range of visible light. Thus the dielectric "constant" K is actually a function of frequency (the *dielectric function*).

Example 32.2 Electromagnetic waves in different materials

(a) Visiting a jewelry store one evening, you hold a diamond up to the light of a sodium-vapor street lamp. The heated sodium vapor emits yellow light with a frequency of 5.09×10^{14} Hz. Find the wavelength in vacuum and the wave speed and wavelength in diamond, for which $K = 5.84$ and $K_m = 1.00$ at this frequency. (b) A 90.0-MHz radio wave (in the FM radio band) passes from vacuum into an insulating ferrite (a ferromagnetic material used in computer cables to suppress radio interference). Find the wavelength in vacuum and the wave speed and wavelength in the ferrite, for which $K = 10.0$ and $K_m = 1000$ at this frequency.

SOLUTION

IDENTIFY and SET UP: In each case we find the wavelength in vacuum using $c = \lambda f$. To use the corresponding equation $v = \lambda f$ to find the wavelength in a material medium, we find the speed v of electromagnetic waves in the medium using Eq. (32.21), which relates v to the values of dielectric constant K and relative permeability K_m for the medium.

EXECUTE: (a) The wavelength in vacuum of the sodium light is

$$\lambda_{vacuum} = \frac{c}{f} = \frac{3.00 \times 10^8 \text{ m/s}}{5.09 \times 10^{14} \text{ Hz}} = 5.89 \times 10^{-7} \text{ m} = 589 \text{ nm}$$

The wave speed and wavelength in diamond are

$$v_{diamond} = \frac{c}{\sqrt{KK_m}} = \frac{3.00 \times 10^8 \text{ m/s}}{\sqrt{(5.84)(1.00)}} = 1.24 \times 10^8 \text{ m/s}$$

$$\lambda_{diamond} = \frac{v_{diamond}}{f} = \frac{1.24 \times 10^8 \text{ m/s}}{5.09 \times 10^{14} \text{ Hz}}$$
$$= 2.44 \times 10^{-7} \text{ m} = 244 \text{ nm}$$

(b) Following the same steps as in part (a), we find

$$\lambda_{vacuum} = \frac{c}{f} = \frac{3.00 \times 10^8 \text{ m/s}}{90.0 \times 10^6 \text{ Hz}} = 3.33 \text{ m}$$

$$v_{ferrite} = \frac{c}{\sqrt{KK_m}} = \frac{3.00 \times 10^8 \text{ m/s}}{\sqrt{(10.0)(1000)}} = 3.00 \times 10^6 \text{ m/s}$$

$$\lambda_{ferrite} = \frac{v_{ferrite}}{f} = \frac{3.00 \times 10^6 \text{ m/s}}{90.0 \times 10^6 \text{ Hz}}$$
$$= 3.33 \times 10^{-2} \text{ m} = 3.33 \text{ cm}$$

EVALUATE: The speed of light in transparent materials is typically between $0.2c$ and c; our result in part (a) shows that $v_{diamond} = 0.414c$. As our results in part (b) show, the speed of electromagnetic waves in dense materials like ferrite (for which $v_{ferrite} = 0.010c$) can be *far* slower than in vacuum.

Test Your Understanding of Section 32.3 The first of Eqs. (32.17) gives the electric field for a plane wave as measured at points along the *x*-axis. For this plane wave, how does the electric field at points *off* the *x*-axis differ from the expression in Eqs. (32.17)? (i) The amplitude is different; (ii) the phase is different; (iii) both the amplitude and phase are different; (iv) none of these.

32.4 Energy and Momentum in Electromagnetic Waves

It is a familiar fact that energy is associated with electromagnetic waves; think of the energy in the sun's radiation. Microwave ovens, radio transmitters, and lasers for eye surgery all make use of the energy that these waves carry. To understand how to utilize this energy, it's helpful to derive detailed relationships for the energy in an electromagnetic wave.

We begin with the expressions derived in Sections 24.3 and 30.3 for the **energy densities** in electric and magnetic fields; we suggest you review those derivations now. Equations (24.11) and (30.10) show that in a region of empty space where $\vec{E}$ and $\vec{B}$ fields are present, the total energy density u is given by

$$u = \tfrac{1}{2}\epsilon_0 E^2 + \frac{1}{2\mu_0}B^2 \tag{32.23}$$

where ϵ_0 and μ_0 are, respectively, the permittivity and permeability of free space. For electromagnetic waves in vacuum, the magnitudes E and B are related by

$$B = \frac{E}{c} = \sqrt{\epsilon_0 \mu_0}\, E \qquad (32.24)$$

Combining Eqs. (32.23) and (32.24), we can also express the energy density u in a simple electromagnetic wave in vacuum as

$$u = \tfrac{1}{2}\epsilon_0 E^2 + \frac{1}{2\mu_0}\left(\sqrt{\epsilon_0 \mu_0}\, E\right)^2 = \epsilon_0 E^2 \qquad (32.25)$$

This shows that in vacuum, the energy density associated with the $\vec{E}$ field in our simple wave is equal to the energy density of the $\vec{B}$ field. In general, the electric-field magnitude E is a function of position and time, as for the sinusoidal wave described by Eqs. (32.16); thus the energy density u of an electromagnetic wave, given by Eq. (32.25), also depends in general on position and time.

Electromagnetic Energy Flow and the Poynting Vector

Electromagnetic waves such as those we have described are *traveling* waves that transport energy from one region to another. We can describe this energy transfer in terms of energy transferred *per unit time per unit cross-sectional area,* or *power per unit area,* for an area perpendicular to the direction of wave travel.

To see how the energy flow is related to the fields, consider a stationary plane, perpendicular to the x-axis, that coincides with the wave front at a certain time. In a time dt after this, the wave front moves a distance $dx = c\, dt$ to the right of the plane. Considering an area A on this stationary plane (Fig. 32.17), we note that the energy in the space to the right of this area must have passed through the area to reach the new location. The volume dV of the relevant region is the base area A times the length $c\, dt$, and the energy dU in this region is the energy density u times this volume:

$$dU = u\, dV = (\epsilon_0 E^2)(Ac\, dt)$$

This energy passes through the area A in time dt. The energy flow per unit time per unit area, which we will call S, is

$$S = \frac{1}{A}\frac{dU}{dt} = \epsilon_0 c E^2 \qquad \text{(in vacuum)} \qquad (32.26)$$

Using Eqs. (32.4) and (32.9), we can derive the alternative forms

$$S = \frac{\epsilon_0}{\sqrt{\epsilon_0 \mu_0}} E^2 = \sqrt{\frac{\epsilon_0}{\mu_0}} E^2 = \frac{EB}{\mu_0} \qquad \text{(in vacuum)} \qquad (32.27)$$

We leave the derivation of Eq. (32.27) from Eq. (32.26) as an exercise for you. The units of S are energy per unit time per unit area, or power per unit area. The SI unit of S is $1\ \text{J/s}\cdot\text{m}^2$ or $1\ \text{W/m}^2$.

We can define a *vector* quantity that describes both the magnitude and direction of the energy flow rate:

$$\vec{S} = \frac{1}{\mu_0}\vec{E} \times \vec{B} \qquad \text{(Poynting vector in vacuum)} \qquad (32.28)$$

The vector $\vec{S}$ is called the **Poynting vector;** it was introduced by the British physicist John Poynting (1852–1914). Its direction is in the direction of propagation of the wave (Fig. 32.18). Since $\vec{E}$ and $\vec{B}$ are perpendicular, the magnitude of $\vec{S}$ is $S = EB/\mu_0$; from Eqs. (32.26) and (32.27) this is the energy flow per unit area and per unit time through a cross-sectional area perpendicular to the propagation direction. The total energy flow per unit time (power, P) out of any closed surface is the integral of $\vec{S}$ over the surface:

$$P = \oint \vec{S} \cdot d\vec{A}$$

32.17 A wave front at a time dt after it passes through the stationary plane with area A.

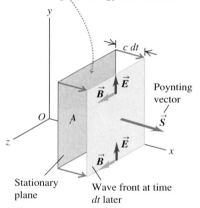

At time dt, the volume between the stationary plane and the wave front contains an amount of electromagnetic energy $dU = uAc\, dt$.

32.18 These rooftop solar panels are tilted to be face-on to the sun—that is, face-on to the Poynting vector of electromagnetic waves from the sun, so that the panels can absorb the maximum amount of wave energy.

For the sinusoidal waves studied in Section 32.3, as well as for other more complex waves, the electric and magnetic fields at any point vary with time, so the Poynting vector at any point is also a function of time. Because the frequencies of typical electromagnetic waves are very high, the time variation of the Poynting vector is so rapid that it's most appropriate to look at its *average* value. The magnitude of the average value of $\vec{S}$ at a point is called the **intensity** of the radiation at that point. The SI unit of intensity is the same as for S, 1 W/m^2 (watt per square meter).

Let's work out the intensity of the sinusoidal wave described by Eqs. (32.17). We first substitute $\vec{E}$ and $\vec{B}$ into Eq. (32.28):

$$\vec{S}(x, t) = \frac{1}{\mu_0}\vec{E}(x, t) \times \vec{B}(x, t)$$

$$= \frac{1}{\mu_0}[\hat{\jmath}E_{\max}\cos(kx - \omega t)] \times [\hat{k}B_{\max}\cos(kx - \omega t)]$$

The vector product of the unit vectors is $\hat{\jmath} \times \hat{k} = \hat{\imath}$ and $\cos^2(kx - \omega t)$ is never negative, so $\vec{S}(x, t)$ always points in the positive x-direction (the direction of wave propagation). The x-component of the Poynting vector is

$$S_x(x, t) = \frac{E_{\max}B_{\max}}{\mu_0}\cos^2(kx - \omega t) = \frac{E_{\max}B_{\max}}{2\mu_0}[1 + \cos 2(kx - \omega t)]$$

The time average value of $\cos 2(kx - \omega t)$ is zero because at any point, it is positive during one half-cycle and negative during the other half. So the average value of the Poynting vector over a full cycle is $\vec{S}_{\text{av}} = \hat{\imath}S_{\text{av}}$, where

$$S_{\text{av}} = \frac{E_{\max}B_{\max}}{2\mu_0}$$

That is, the magnitude of the average value of $\vec{S}$ for a sinusoidal wave (the intensity I of the wave) is $\frac{1}{2}$ the maximum value. By using the relationships $E_{\max} = B_{\max}c$ and $\epsilon_0\mu_0 = 1/c^2$, we can express the intensity in several equivalent forms:

$$I = S_{\text{av}} = \frac{E_{\max}B_{\max}}{2\mu_0} = \frac{E_{\max}^2}{2\mu_0 c}$$

$$= \frac{1}{2}\sqrt{\frac{\epsilon_0}{\mu_0}}E_{\max}^2 = \frac{1}{2}\epsilon_0 c E_{\max}^2$$

(intensity of a sinusoidal wave in vacuum)   (32.29)

We invite you to verify that these expressions are all equivalent.

For a wave traveling in the $-x$-direction, represented by Eqs. (32.19), the Poynting vector is in the $-x$-direction at every point, but its magnitude is the same as for a wave traveling in the $+x$-direction. Verifying these statements is left to you (see Exercise 32.24).

CAUTION **Poynting vector vs. intensity** At any point x, the magnitude of the Poynting vector varies with time. Hence, the *instantaneous* rate at which electromagnetic energy in a sinusoidal plane wave arrives at a surface is not constant. This may seem to contradict everyday experience; the light from the sun, a light bulb, or the laser in a grocery-store scanner appears steady and unvarying in strength. In fact the Poynting vector from these sources *does* vary in time, but the variation isn't noticeable because the oscillation frequency is so high (around 5×10^{14} Hz for visible light). All that you sense is the *average* rate at which energy reaches your eye, which is why we commonly use intensity (the average value of S) to describe the strength of electromagnetic radiation.

Throughout this discussion we have considered only electromagnetic waves propagating in vacuum. If the waves are traveling in a dielectric medium, however,

Application **Laser Surgery**
Lasers are used widely in medicine as ultra-precise, bloodless "scalpels." They can reach and remove tumors with minimal damage to neighboring healthy tissues, as in the brain surgery shown here. The power output of the laser is typically below 40 W, less than that of a typical light bulb. However, this power is concentrated into a spot from 0.1 to 2.0 mm in diameter, so the intensity of the light (equal to the average value of the Poynting vector) can be as high as 5×10^9 W/m^2.

the expressions for energy density [Eq. (32.23)], the Poynting vector [Eq. (32.28)], and the intensity of a sinusoidal wave [Eq. (32.29)] must be modified. It turns out that the required modifications are quite simple: Just replace ϵ_0 with the permittivity ϵ of the dielectric, replace μ_0 with the permeability μ of the dielectric, and replace c with the speed v of electromagnetic waves in the dielectric. Remarkably, the energy densities in the $\vec{E}$ and $\vec{B}$ fields are equal even in a dielectric.

Example 32.3 Energy in a nonsinusoidal wave

For the nonsinusoidal wave described in Section 32.2, suppose that $E = 100$ V/m $= 100$ N/C. Find the value of B, the energy density u, and the rate of energy flow per unit area S.

SOLUTION

IDENTIFY and SET UP: In this wave $\vec{E}$ and $\vec{B}$ are uniform behind the wave front (and zero ahead of it). Hence the target variables B, u, and S must also be uniform behind the wave front. Given the magnitude E, we use Eq. (32.4) to find B, Eq. (32.25) to find u, and Eq. (32.27) to find S. (We cannot use Eq. (32.29), which applies to sinusoidal waves only.)

EXECUTE: From Eq. (32.4),

$$B = \frac{E}{c} = \frac{100 \text{ V/m}}{3.00 \times 10^8 \text{ m/s}} = 3.33 \times 10^{-7} \text{ T}$$

From Eq. (32.25),

$$u = \epsilon_0 E^2 = (8.85 \times 10^{-12} \text{ C}^2/\text{N} \cdot \text{m}^2)(100 \text{ N/C})^2$$
$$= 8.85 \times 10^{-8} \text{ N/m}^2 = 8.85 \times 10^{-8} \text{ J/m}^3$$

The magnitude of the Poynting vector is

$$S = \frac{EB}{\mu_0} = \frac{(100 \text{ V/m})(3.33 \times 10^{-7} \text{ T})}{4\pi \times 10^{-7} \text{ T} \cdot \text{m/A}}$$
$$= 26.5 \text{ V} \cdot \text{A/m}^2 = 26.5 \text{ W/m}^2$$

EVALUATE: We can check our result for S by using Eq. (32.26):

$$S = \epsilon_0 c E^2 = (8.85 \times 10^{-12} \text{ C}^2/\text{N} \cdot \text{m}^2)(3.00 \times 10^8 \text{ m/s})$$
$$\times (100 \text{ N/C})^2 = 26.5 \text{ W/m}^2$$

Since $\vec{E}$ and $\vec{B}$ have the same values at all points behind the wave front, u and S likewise have the same value everywhere behind the wave front. In front of the wave front, $\vec{E} = 0$ and $\vec{B} = 0$, and so $u = 0$ and $S = 0$; where there are no fields, there is no field energy.

Example 32.4 Energy in a sinusoidal wave

A radio station on the earth's surface emits a sinusoidal wave with average total power 50 kW (Fig. 32.19). Assuming that the transmitter radiates equally in all directions above the ground (which is unlikely in real situations), find the electric-field and magnetic-field amplitudes E_{max} and B_{max} detected by a satellite 100 km from the antenna.

SOLUTION

IDENTIFY and SET UP: We are given the transmitter's average total power P. The intensity I is just the average power per unit area, so to find I at 100 km from the transmitter we divide P by the surface area of the hemisphere shown in Fig. 32.19. For a sinusoidal wave, I is also equal to the magnitude of the average value S_{av} of the Poynting vector, so we can use Eqs. (32.29) to find E_{max}; Eq. (32.4) then yields B_{max}.

32.19 A radio station radiates waves into the hemisphere shown.

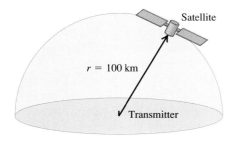

EXECUTE: The surface area of a hemisphere of radius $r = 100$ km $= 1.00 \times 10^5$ m is

$$A = 2\pi R^2 = 2\pi(1.00 \times 10^5 \text{ m})^2 = 6.28 \times 10^{10} \text{ m}^2$$

All the radiated power passes through this surface, so the average power per unit area (that is, the intensity) is

$$I = \frac{P}{A} = \frac{P}{2\pi R^2} = \frac{5.00 \times 10^4 \text{ W}}{6.28 \times 10^{10} \text{ m}^2} = 7.96 \times 10^{-7} \text{ W/m}^2$$

From Eqs. (32.29), $I = S_{av} = E_{max}^2/2\mu_0 c$, so

$$E_{max} = \sqrt{2\mu_0 c S_{av}}$$
$$= \sqrt{2(4\pi \times 10^{-7} \text{ T} \cdot \text{m/A})(3.00 \times 10^8 \text{ m/s})(7.96 \times 10^{-7} \text{ W/m}^2)}$$
$$= 2.45 \times 10^{-2} \text{ V/m}$$

Then from Eq. (32.4),

$$B_{max} = \frac{E_{max}}{c} = 8.17 \times 10^{-11} \text{ T}$$

EVALUATE: Note that E_{max} is comparable to fields commonly seen in the laboratory, but B_{max} is extremely small in comparison to $\vec{B}$ fields we saw in previous chapters. For this reason, most detectors of electromagnetic radiation respond to the effect of the electric field, not the magnetic field. Loop radio antennas are an exception (see the Bridging Problem at the end of this chapter).

Electromagnetic Momentum Flow and Radiation Pressure

By using the observation that energy is required to establish electric and magnetic fields, we have shown that electromagnetic waves transport energy. It can also be shown that electromagnetic waves carry *momentum p*, with a corresponding momentum density (momentum dp per volume dV) of magnitude

$$\frac{dp}{dV} = \frac{EB}{\mu_0 c^2} = \frac{S}{c^2} \tag{32.30}$$

This momentum is a property of the field; it is not associated with the mass of a moving particle in the usual sense.

There is also a corresponding momentum flow rate. The volume dV occupied by an electromagnetic wave (speed c) that passes through an area A in time dt is $dV = Ac\,dt$. When we substitute this into Eq. (32.30) and rearrange, we find that the momentum flow rate per unit area is

$$\frac{1}{A}\frac{dp}{dt} = \frac{S}{c} = \frac{EB}{\mu_0 c} \qquad \text{(flow rate of electromagnetic momentum)} \tag{32.31}$$

This is the momentum transferred per unit surface area per unit time. We obtain the *average* rate of momentum transfer per unit area by replacing S in Eq. (32.31) by $S_{av} = I$.

This momentum is responsible for **radiation pressure.** When an electromagnetic wave is completely absorbed by a surface, the wave's momentum is also transferred to the surface. For simplicity we'll consider a surface perpendicular to the propagation direction. Using the ideas developed in Section 8.1, we see that the rate dp/dt at which momentum is transferred to the absorbing surface equals the *force* on the surface. The average force per unit area due to the wave, or *radiation pressure* p_{rad}, is the average value of dp/dt divided by the absorbing area A. (We use the subscript "rad" to distinguish pressure from momentum, for which the symbol p is also used.) From Eq. (32.31) the radiation pressure is

$$p_{rad} = \frac{S_{av}}{c} = \frac{I}{c} \qquad \text{(radiation pressure, wave totally absorbed)} \tag{32.32}$$

If the wave is totally reflected, the momentum change is twice as great, and the pressure is

$$p_{rad} = \frac{2S_{av}}{c} = \frac{2I}{c} \qquad \text{(radiation pressure, wave totally reflected)} \tag{32.33}$$

For example, the value of I (or S_{av}) for direct sunlight, before it passes through the earth's atmosphere, is approximately $1.4\ \text{kW/m}^2$. From Eq. (32.32) the corresponding average pressure on a completely absorbing surface is

$$p_{rad} = \frac{I}{c} = \frac{1.4 \times 10^3\ \text{W/m}^2}{3.0 \times 10^8\ \text{m/s}} = 4.7 \times 10^{-6}\ \text{Pa}$$

From Eq. (32.33) the average pressure on a totally *reflecting* surface is twice this: $2I/c$ or 9.4×10^{-6} Pa. These are very small pressures, of the order of 10^{-10} atm, but they can be measured with sensitive instruments.

The radiation pressure of sunlight is much greater *inside* the sun than at the earth (see Problem 32.45). Inside stars that are much more massive and luminous than the sun, radiation pressure is so great that it substantially augments the gas pressure within the star and so helps to prevent the star from collapsing under its own gravity. In some cases the radiation pressure of stars can have dramatic effects on the material surrounding them (Fig. 32.20).

32.20 At the center of this interstellar gas cloud is a group of intensely luminous stars that exert tremendous radiation pressure on their surroundings. Aided by a "wind" of particles emanating from the stars, over the past million years the radiation pressure has carved out a bubble within the cloud 70 light-years across.

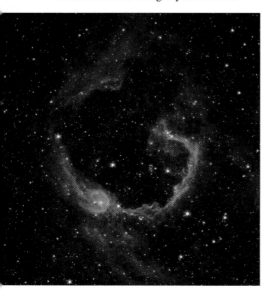

Example 32.5 **Power and pressure from sunlight**

An earth-orbiting satellite has solar energy–collecting panels with a total area of 4.0 m² (Fig. 32.21). If the sun's radiation is perpendicular to the panels and is completely absorbed, find the average solar power absorbed and the average radiation-pressure force.

SOLUTION

IDENTIFY and SET UP: This problem uses the relationships among intensity, power, radiation pressure, and force. In the above discussion we calculated the intensity I (power per unit area) of sunlight as well as the radiation pressure p_{rad} (force per unit area) of sunlight on an absorbing surface. (We calculated these values for

32.21 Solar panels on a satellite.

points above the atmosphere, which is where the satellite orbits.) Multiplying each value by the area of the solar panels gives the average power absorbed and the net radiation force on the panels.

EXECUTE: The intensity I (power per unit area) is 1.4×10^3 W/m². Although the light from the sun is not a simple sinusoidal wave, we can still use the relationship that the average power P is the intensity I times the area A:

$$P = IA = (1.4 \times 10^3 \text{ W/m}^2)(4.0 \text{ m}^2)$$
$$= 5.6 \times 10^3 \text{ W} = 5.6 \text{ kW}$$

The radiation pressure of sunlight on an absorbing surface is $p_{rad} = 4.7 \times 10^{-6}$ Pa $= 4.7 \times 10^{-6}$ N/m². The total force F is the pressure p_{rad} times the area A:

$$F = p_{rad}A = (4.7 \times 10^{-6} \text{ N/m}^2)(4.0 \text{ m}^2) = 1.9 \times 10^{-5} \text{ N}$$

EVALUATE: The absorbed power is quite substantial. Part of it can be used to power the equipment aboard the satellite; the rest goes into heating the panels, either directly or due to inefficiencies in the photocells contained in the panels.

The total radiation force is comparable to the weight (on earth) of a single grain of salt. Over time, however, this small force can have a noticeable effect on the orbit of a satellite like that in Fig. 32.21, and so radiation pressure must be taken into account.

Test Your Understanding of Section 32.4 Figure 32.13 shows one wavelength of a sinusoidal electromagnetic wave at time $t = 0$. For which of the following four values of x is (a) the energy density a maximum; (b) the energy density a minimum; (c) the magnitude of the instantaneous (not average) Poynting vector a maximum; (d) the magnitude of the instantaneous (not average) Poynting vector a minimum? (i) $x = 0$; (ii) $x = \lambda/4$; (iii) $x = \lambda/2$; (iv) $x = 3\lambda/4$.

32.5 Standing Electromagnetic Waves

Electromagnetic waves can be *reflected;* the surface of a conductor (like a polished sheet of metal) or of a dielectric (such as a sheet of glass) can serve as a reflector. The superposition principle holds for electromagnetic waves just as for electric and magnetic fields. The superposition of an incident wave and a reflected wave forms a **standing wave.** The situation is analogous to standing waves on a stretched string, discussed in Section 15.7; you should review that discussion.

Suppose a sheet of a perfect conductor (zero resistivity) is placed in the yz-plane of Fig. 32.22 and a linearly polarized electromagnetic wave, traveling in the negative x-direction, strikes it. As we discussed in Section 23.4, $\vec{E}$ cannot have a component parallel to the surface of a perfect conductor. Therefore in the present situation, $\vec{E}$ must be zero everywhere in the yz-plane. The electric field of the *incident* electromagnetic wave is *not* zero at all times in the yz-plane. But this incident wave induces oscillating currents on the surface of the conductor, and these currents give rise to an additional electric field. The *net* electric field, which is the vector sum of this field and the incident $\vec{E}$, *is* zero everywhere inside and on the surface of the conductor.

The currents induced on the surface of the conductor also produce a *reflected* wave that travels out from the plane in the $+x$-direction. Suppose the incident wave is described by the wave functions of Eqs. (32.19) (a sinusoidal wave traveling in the $-x$-direction) and the reflected wave by the negative of Eqs. (32.16) (a sinusoidal wave traveling in the $+x$-direction). We take the *negative* of the

32.22 Representation of the electric and magnetic fields of a linearly polarized electromagnetic standing wave when $\omega t = 3\pi/4$ rad. In any plane perpendicular to the x-axis, E is maximum (an antinode) where B is zero (a node), and vice versa. As time elapses, the pattern does *not* move along the x-axis; instead, at every point the $\vec{E}$ and $\vec{B}$ vectors simply oscillate.

wave given by Eqs. (32.16) so that the incident and reflected electric fields cancel at $x = 0$ (the plane of the conductor, where the total electric field must be zero). The superposition principle states that the total $\vec{E}$ field at any point is the vector sum of the $\vec{E}$ fields of the incident and reflected waves, and similarly for the $\vec{B}$ field. Therefore the wave functions for the superposition of the two waves are

$$E_y(x, t) = E_{max}[\cos(kx + \omega t) - \cos(kx - \omega t)]$$

$$B_z(x, t) = B_{max}[-\cos(kx + \omega t) - \cos(kx - \omega t)]$$

We can expand and simplify these expressions, using the identities

$$\cos(A \pm B) = \cos A \cos B \mp \sin A \sin B$$

The results are

$$E_y(x, t) = -2E_{max}\sin kx \sin \omega t \tag{32.34}$$

$$B_z(x, t) = -2B_{max}\cos kx \cos \omega t \tag{32.35}$$

Equation (32.34) is analogous to Eq. (15.28) for a stretched string. We see that at $x = 0$ the electric field $E_y(x = 0, t)$ is *always* zero; this is required by the nature of the ideal conductor, which plays the same role as a fixed point at the end of a string. Furthermore, $E_y(x, t)$ is zero at *all* times at points in those planes perpendicular to the x-axis for which $\sin kx = 0$—that is, $kx = 0,\ \pi,\ 2\pi,\dots$. Since $k = 2\pi/\lambda$, the positions of these planes are

$$x = 0, \frac{\lambda}{2}, \lambda, \frac{3\lambda}{2}, \dots \quad \text{(nodal planes of } \vec{E}\text{)} \tag{32.36}$$

These planes are called the **nodal planes** of the $\vec{E}$ field; they are the equivalent of the nodes, or nodal points, of a standing wave on a string. Midway between any two adjacent nodal planes is a plane on which $\sin kx = \pm 1$; on each such plane, the magnitude of $E(x, t)$ equals the maximum possible value of $2E_{max}$ twice per oscillation cycle. These are the **antinodal planes** of $\vec{E}$, corresponding to the antinodes of waves on a string.

The total magnetic field is zero at all times at points in planes on which $\cos kx = 0$. This occurs where

$$x = \frac{\lambda}{4}, \frac{3\lambda}{4}, \frac{5\lambda}{4}, \dots \quad \text{(nodal planes of } \vec{B}\text{)} \tag{32.37}$$

These are the nodal planes of the $\vec{B}$ field; there is an antinodal plane of $\vec{B}$ midway between any two adjacent nodal planes.

Figure 32.22 shows a standing-wave pattern at one instant of time. The magnetic field is *not* zero at the conducting surface ($x = 0$). The surface currents that must be present to make $\vec{E}$ exactly zero at the surface cause magnetic fields at the surface. The nodal planes of each field are separated by one half-wavelength. The nodal planes of one field are midway between those of the other; hence the nodes of $\vec{E}$ coincide with the antinodes of $\vec{B}$, and conversely. Compare this situation to the distinction between pressure nodes and displacement nodes in Section 16.4.

The total electric field is a *sine* function of t, and the total magnetic field is a *cosine* function of t. The sinusoidal variations of the two fields are therefore 90° out of phase at each point. At times when $\sin \omega t = 0$, the electric field is zero *everywhere,* and the magnetic field is maximum. When $\cos \omega t = 0$, the magnetic field is zero everywhere, and the electric field is maximum. This is in contrast to a wave traveling in one direction, as described by Eqs. (32.16) or (32.19) separately, in which the sinusoidal variations of $\vec{E}$ and $\vec{B}$ at any particular point are *in phase*. You can show that Eqs. (32.34) and (32.35) satisfy the wave equation, Eq. (32.15). You can also show that they satisfy Eqs. (32.12) and (32.14), the equivalents of Faraday's and Ampere's laws (see Exercise 32.36).

Standing Waves in a Cavity

Let's now insert a second conducting plane, parallel to the first and a distance L from it, along the $+x$-axis. The cavity between the two planes is analogous to a stretched string held at the points $x = 0$ and $x = L$. Both conducting planes must be nodal planes for $\vec{E}$; a standing wave can exist only when the second plane is placed at one of the positions where $E(x, t) = 0$, so L must be an integer multiple of $\lambda/2$. The wavelengths that satisfy this condition are

$$\lambda_n = \frac{2L}{n} \qquad (n = 1, 2, 3, \dots) \tag{32.38}$$

The corresponding frequencies are

$$f_n = \frac{c}{\lambda_n} = n\frac{c}{2L} \qquad (n = 1, 2, 3, \dots) \tag{32.39}$$

Thus there is a set of *normal modes*, each with a characteristic frequency, wave shape, and node pattern (Fig. 32.23). By measuring the node positions, we can measure the wavelength. If the frequency is known, the wave speed can be determined. This technique was first used by Hertz in the 1880s in his pioneering investigations of electromagnetic waves.

Conducting surfaces are not the only reflectors of electromagnetic waves. Reflections also occur at an interface between two insulating materials with different dielectric or magnetic properties. The mechanical analog is a junction of two strings with equal tension but different linear mass density. In general, a wave incident on such a boundary surface is partly transmitted into the second material and partly reflected back into the first. For example, light is transmitted through a glass window, but its surfaces also reflect light.

32.23 A typical microwave oven sets up a standing electromagnetic wave with $\lambda = 12.2$ cm, a wavelength that is strongly absorbed by the water in food. Because the wave has nodes spaced $\lambda/2 = 6.1$ cm apart, the food must be rotated while cooking. Otherwise, the portion that lies at a node—where the electric-field amplitude is zero—will remain cold.

Example 32.6   **Intensity in a standing wave**

Calculate the intensity of the standing wave represented by Eqs. (32.34) and (32.35).

SOLUTION

IDENTIFY and SET UP: The intensity I of the wave is the time-averaged value S_{av} of the magnitude of the Poynting vector $\vec{S}$. To find S_{av}, we first use Eq. (32.28) to find the instantaneous value of $\vec{S}$ and then average it over a whole number of cycles of the wave.

EXECUTE: Using the wave functions of Eqs. (32.34) and (32.35) in Eq. (32.28) for the Poynting vector $\vec{S}$, we find

$$\vec{S}(x, t) = \frac{1}{\mu_0}\vec{E}(x, t) \times \vec{B}(x, t)$$

$$= \frac{1}{\mu_0}[-2\hat{\jmath}E_{max}\sin kx \cos \omega t] \times [-2\hat{k}B_{max}\cos kx \sin \omega t]$$

$$= \hat{\imath}\frac{E_{max}B_{max}}{\mu_0}(2\sin kx \cos kx)(2\sin \omega t \cos \omega t)$$

$$= \hat{\imath}S_x(x, t)$$

Using the identity $\sin 2A = 2\sin A \cos A$, we can rewrite $S_x(x, t)$ as

$$S_x(x, t) = \frac{E_{max}B_{max}\sin 2kx \sin 2\omega t}{\mu_0}$$

The average value of a sine function over any whole number of cycles is zero. Thus *the time average of $\vec{S}$ at any point is zero;* $I = S_{av} = 0$.

EVALUATE: This result is what we should expect. The standing wave is a superposition of two waves with the same frequency and amplitude, traveling in opposite directions. All the energy transferred by one wave is cancelled by an equal amount transferred in the opposite direction by the other wave. When we use electromagnetic waves to transmit power, it is important to avoid reflections that give rise to standing waves.

Example 32.7   **Standing waves in a cavity**

Electromagnetic standing waves are set up in a cavity with two parallel, highly conducting walls 1.50 cm apart. (a) Calculate the longest wavelength λ and lowest frequency f of these standing waves. (b) For a standing wave of this wavelength, where in the cavity does $\vec{E}$ have maximum magnitude? Where is $\vec{E}$ zero? Where does $\vec{B}$ have maximum magnitude? Where is $\vec{B}$ zero?

Continued

SOLUTION

IDENTIFY and SET UP: Only certain normal modes are possible for electromagnetic waves in a cavity, just as only certain normal modes are possible for standing waves on a string. The longest possible wavelength and lowest possible frequency correspond to the $n = 1$ mode in Eqs. (32.38) and (32.39); we use these to find λ and f. Equations (32.36) and (32.37) then give the locations of the nodal planes of $\vec{E}$ and $\vec{B}$. The antinodal planes of each field are midway between adjacent nodal planes.

EXECUTE: (a) From Eqs. (32.38) and (32.39), the $n = 1$ wavelength and frequency are

$$\lambda_1 = 2L = 2(1.50 \text{ cm}) = 3.00 \text{ cm}$$

$$f_1 = \frac{c}{2L} = \frac{3.00 \times 10^8 \text{ m/s}}{2(1.50 \times 10^{-2} \text{ m})} = 1.00 \times 10^{10} \text{ Hz} = 10 \text{ GHz}$$

(b) With $n = 1$ there is a single half-wavelength between the walls. The electric field has nodal planes ($\vec{E} = \mathbf{0}$) at the walls and an antinodal plane (where $\vec{E}$ has its maximum magnitude) midway between them. The magnetic field has *antinodal* planes at the walls and a nodal plane midway between them.

EVALUATE: One application of such standing waves is to produce an oscillating $\vec{E}$ field of definite frequency, which is used to probe the behavior of a small sample of material placed in the cavity. To subject the sample to the strongest possible field, it should be placed near the center of the cavity, at the antinode of $\vec{E}$.

Test Your Understanding of Section 32.5 In the standing wave described in Example 32.7, is there any point in the cavity where the energy density is zero at all times? If so, where? If not, why not? ❙

Maxwell's equations and electromagnetic waves:
Maxwell's equations predict the existence of electromagnetic waves that propagate in vacuum at the speed of light c. The electromagnetic spectrum covers frequencies from at least 1 to 10^{24} Hz and a correspondingly broad range of wavelengths. Visible light, with wavelengths from 380 to 750 nm, is only a very small part of this spectrum. In a plane wave, $\vec{E}$ and $\vec{B}$ are uniform over any plane perpendicular to the propagation direction. Faraday's law and Ampere's law both give relationships between the magnitudes of $\vec{E}$ and $\vec{B}$; requiring both of these relationships to be satisfied gives an expression for c in terms of ϵ_0 and μ_0. Electromagnetic waves are transverse; the $\vec{E}$ and $\vec{B}$ fields are perpendicular to the direction of propagation and to each other. The direction of propagation is the direction of $\vec{E} \times \vec{B}$.

$$E = cB \tag{32.4}$$

$$B = \epsilon_0\mu_0 cE \tag{32.8}$$

$$c = \frac{1}{\sqrt{\epsilon_0\mu_0}} \tag{32.9}$$

Sinusoidal electromagnetic waves: Equations (32.17) and (32.18) describe a sinusoidal plane electromagnetic wave traveling in vacuum in the $+x$-direction. If the wave is propagating in the $-x$-direction, replace $kx - \omega t$ by $kx + \omega t$. (See Example 32.1.)

$$\vec{E}(x, t) = \hat{\jmath}E_{max}\cos(kx - \omega t)$$
$$\vec{B}(x, t) = \hat{k}B_{max}\cos(kx - \omega t) \tag{32.17}$$

$$E_{max} = cB_{max} \tag{32.18}$$

Electromagnetic waves in matter: When an electromagnetic wave travels through a dielectric, the wave speed v is less than the speed of light in vacuum c. (See Example 32.2.)

$$v = \frac{1}{\sqrt{\epsilon\mu}} = \frac{1}{\sqrt{KK_m}}\frac{1}{\sqrt{\epsilon_0\mu_0}}$$
$$= \frac{c}{\sqrt{KK_m}} \tag{32.21}$$

Energy and momentum in electromagnetic waves: The energy flow rate (power per unit area) in an electromagnetic wave in vacuum is given by the Poynting vector $\vec{S}$. The magnitude of the time-averaged value of the Poynting vector is called the intensity I of the wave. Electromagnetic waves also carry momentum. When an electromagnetic wave strikes a surface, it exerts a radiation pressure p_{rad}. If the surface is perpendicular to the wave propagation direction and is totally absorbing, $p_{rad} = I/c$; if the surface is a perfect reflector, $p_{rad} = 2I/c$. (See Examples 32.3–32.5.)

$$\vec{S} = \frac{1}{\mu_0}\vec{E} \times \vec{B} \tag{32.28}$$

$$I = S_{av} = \frac{E_{max}B_{max}}{2\mu_0} = \frac{E_{max}^2}{2\mu_0 c}$$

$$= \frac{1}{2}\sqrt{\frac{\epsilon_0}{\mu_0}}E_{max}^2$$

$$= \frac{1}{2}\epsilon_0 c E_{max}^2 \tag{32.29}$$

$$\frac{1}{A}\frac{dp}{dt} = \frac{S}{c} = \frac{EB}{\mu_0 c} \tag{32.31}$$

(flow rate of electromagnetic momentum)

Standing electromagnetic waves: If a perfect reflecting surface is placed at $x = 0$, the incident and reflected waves form a standing wave. Nodal planes for $\vec{E}$ occur at $kx = 0, \pi, 2\pi, \ldots$, and nodal planes for $\vec{B}$ at $kx = \pi/2, 3\pi/2, 5\pi/2, \ldots$. At each point, the sinusoidal variations of $\vec{E}$ and $\vec{B}$ with time are 90° out of phase. (See Examples 32.6 and 32.7.)

BRIDGING PROBLEM **Detecting Electromagnetic Waves**

A circular loop of wire can be used as a radio antenna. If an 18.0-cm-diameter antenna is located 2.50 km from a 95.0-MHz source with a total power of 55.0 kW, what is the maximum emf induced in the loop? Assume that the plane of the antenna loop is perpendicular to the direction of the radiation's magnetic field and that the source radiates uniformly in all directions.

SOLUTION GUIDE

See MasteringPhysics® study area for a Video Tutor solution.

IDENTIFY and SET UP:

1. The electromagnetic wave has an oscillating magnetic field. This causes a magnetic flux through the loop antenna that varies sinusoidally with time. By Faraday's law, this produces an emf equal in magnitude to the rate of change of the flux. The target variable is the magnitude of this emf.
2. Select the equations that you will need to find (i) the intensity of the wave at the position of the loop, a distance $r = 2.50$ km

from the source of power $P = 55.0$ kW; (ii) the amplitude of the sinusoidally varying magnetic field at that position; (iii) the magnetic flux through the loop as a function of time; and (iv) the emf produced by the flux.

EXECUTE

3. Find the wave intensity at the position of the loop.
4. Use your result from step 3 to write expressions for the time-dependent magnetic field at this position and the time-dependent magnetic flux through the loop.
5. Use the results of step 4 to find the time-dependent induced emf in the loop. The amplitude of this emf is your target variable.

EVALUATE

6. Is the induced emf large enough to detect? (If it is, a receiver connected to this antenna will be able to pick up signals from the source.)

Problems

For instructor-assigned homework, go to www.masteringphysics.com

•, ••, •••: Problems of increasing difficulty. **CP**: Cumulative problems incorporating material from earlier chapters. **CALC**: Problems requiring calculus. **BIO**: Biosciences problems.

DISCUSSION QUESTIONS

Q32.1 By measuring the electric and magnetic fields at a point in space where there is an electromagnetic wave, can you determine the direction from which the wave came? Explain.

Q32.2 According to Ampere's law, is it possible to have both a conduction current and a displacement current at the same time? Is it possible for the effects of the two kinds of current to cancel each other exactly so that *no* magnetic field is produced? Explain.

Q32.3 Give several examples of electromagnetic waves that are encountered in everyday life. How are they all alike? How do they differ?

Q32.4 Sometimes neon signs located near a powerful radio station are seen to glow faintly at night, even though they are not turned on. What is happening?

Q32.5 Is polarization a property of all electromagnetic waves, or is it unique to visible light? Can sound waves be polarized? What fundamental distinction in wave properties is involved? Explain.

Q32.6 Suppose that a positive point charge q is initially at rest on the x-axis, in the path of the electromagnetic plane wave described in Section 32.2. Will the charge move after the wave front reaches it? If not, why not? If the charge does move, describe its motion qualitatively. (Remember that $\vec{E}$ and $\vec{B}$ have the same value at all points behind the wave front.)

Q32.7 The light beam from a searchlight may have an electric-field magnitude of 1000 V/m, corresponding to a potential difference of 1500 V between the head and feet of a 1.5-m-tall person on whom the light shines. Does this cause the person to feel a strong electric shock? Why or why not?

Q32.8 For a certain sinusoidal wave of intensity I, the amplitude of the magnetic field is B. What would be the amplitude (in terms of B) in a similar wave of twice the intensity?

Q32.9 The magnetic-field amplitude of the electromagnetic wave from the laser described in Example 32.1 (Section 32.3) is about 100 times greater than the earth's magnetic field. If you illuminate a compass with the light from this laser, would you expect the compass to deflect? Why or why not?

Q32.10 Most automobiles have vertical antennas for receiving radio broadcasts. Explain what this tells you about the direction of polarization of $\vec{E}$ in the radio waves used in broadcasting.

Q32.11 If a light beam carries momentum, should a person holding a flashlight feel a recoil analogous to the recoil of a rifle when it is fired? Why is this recoil not actually observed?

Q32.12 A light source radiates a sinusoidal electromagnetic wave uniformly in all directions. This wave exerts an average pressure p on a perfectly reflecting surface a distance R away from it. What average pressure (in terms of p) would this wave exert on a perfectly absorbing surface that was twice as far from the source?

Q32.13 Does an electromagnetic *standing* wave have energy? Does it have momentum? Are your answers to these questions the same as for a *traveling* wave? Why or why not?

Q32.14 When driving on the upper level of the Bay Bridge, westbound from Oakland to San Francisco, you can easily pick up a number of radio stations on your car radio. But when driving eastbound on the lower level of the bridge, which has steel girders on either side to support the upper level, the radio reception is much worse. Why is there a difference?

EXERCISES

Section 32.2 Plane Electromagnetic Waves and the Speed of Light

32.1 • (a) How much time does it take light to travel from the moon to the earth, a distance of 384,000 km? (b) Light from the star Sirius takes 8.61 years to reach the earth. What is the distance from earth to Sirius in kilometers?

32.2 • Consider each of the electric- and magnetic-field orientations given next. In each case, what is the direction of propagation of the wave? (a) $\vec{E}$ in the $+x$-direction, $\vec{B}$ in the $+y$-direction; (b) $\vec{E}$ in the $-y$-direction, $\vec{B}$ in the $+x$-direction; (c) $\vec{E}$ in the $+z$-direction, $\vec{B}$ in the $-x$-direction; (d) $\vec{E}$ in the $+y$-direction, $\vec{B}$ in the $-z$-direction.

32.3 • A sinusoidal electromagnetic wave is propagating in vacuum in the $+z$-direction. If at a particular instant and at a certain point in space the electric field is in the $+x$-direction and has magnitude 4.00 V/m, what are the magnitude and direction of the magnetic field of the wave at this same point in space and instant in time?

32.4 • Consider each of the following electric- and magnetic-field orientations. In each case, what is the direction of propagation of the wave? (a) $\vec{E} = E\hat{\imath}$, $\vec{B} = -B\hat{\jmath}$; (b) $\vec{E} = E\hat{\jmath}$, $\vec{B} = B\hat{\imath}$; (c) $\vec{E} = -E\hat{k}$, $\vec{B} = -B\hat{\imath}$; (d) $\vec{E} = E\hat{\imath}$, $\vec{B} = -B\hat{k}$.

Section 32.3 Sinusoidal Electromagnetic Waves

32.5 • **BIO Medical X rays.** Medical x rays are taken with electromagnetic waves having a wavelength of around 0.10 nm. What are the frequency, period, and wave number of such waves?

32.6 • **BIO Ultraviolet Radiation.** There are two categories of ultraviolet light. Ultraviolet A (UVA) has a wavelength ranging from 320 nm to 400 nm. It is not harmful to the skin and is necessary for the production of vitamin D. UVB, with a wavelength between 280 nm and 320 nm, is much more dangerous because it causes skin cancer. (a) Find the frequency ranges of UVA and UVB. (b) What are the ranges of the wave numbers for UVA and UVB?

32.7 • A sinusoidal electromagnetic wave having a magnetic field of amplitude 1.25 μT and a wavelength of 432 nm is traveling in the $+x$-direction through empty space. (a) What is the frequency of this wave? (b) What is the amplitude of the associated electric field? (c) Write the equations for the electric and magnetic fields as functions of x and t in the form of Eqs. (32.17).

32.8 • An electromagnetic wave of wavelength 435 nm is traveling in vacuum in the $-z$-direction. The electric field has amplitude 2.70×10^{-3} V/m and is parallel to the x-axis. What are (a) the frequency and (b) the magnetic-field amplitude? (c) Write the vector equations for $\vec{E}(z, t)$ and $\vec{B}(z, t)$.

32.9 • Consider electromagnetic waves propagating in air. (a) Determine the frequency of a wave with a wavelength of (i) 5.0 km, (ii) 5.0 μm, (iii) 5.0 nm. (b) What is the wavelength (in meters and nanometers) of (i) gamma rays of frequency 6.50×10^{21} Hz and (ii) an AM station radio wave of frequency 590 kHz?

32.10 • The electric field of a sinusoidal electromagnetic wave obeys the equation $E = (375 \text{ V/m}) \cos[(1.99 \times 10^7 \text{ rad/m})x + (5.97 \times 10^{15} \text{ rad/s})t]$. (a) What are the amplitudes of the electric and magnetic fields of this wave? (b) What are the frequency, wavelength, and period of the wave? Is this light visible to humans? (c) What is the speed of the wave?

32.11 • An electromagnetic wave has an electric field given by $\vec{E}(y, t) = (3.10 \times 10^5 \text{ V/m})\hat{k} \cos[ky - (12.65 \times 10^{12} \text{ rad/s})t]$. (a) In which direction is the wave traveling? (b) What is the wavelength of the wave? (c) Write the vector equation for $\vec{B}(y, t)$.

32.12 • An electromagnetic wave has a magnetic field given by $\vec{B}(x, t) = -(8.25 \times 10^{-9} \text{ T})\hat{\jmath} \cos[(1.38 \times 10^4 \text{ rad/m})x + \omega t]$. (a) In which direction is the wave traveling? (b) What is the frequency f of the wave? (c) Write the vector equation for $\vec{E}(x, t)$.

32.13 • Radio station WCCO in Minneapolis broadcasts at a frequency of 830 kHz. At a point some distance from the transmitter, the magnetic-field amplitude of the electromagnetic wave from WCCO is 4.82×10^{-11} T. Calculate (a) the wavelength; (b) the wave number; (c) the angular frequency; (d) the electric-field amplitude.

32.14 • An electromagnetic wave with frequency 65.0 Hz travels in an insulating magnetic material that has dielectric constant 3.64 and relative permeability 5.18 at this frequency. The electric field has amplitude 7.20×10^{-3} V/m. (a) What is the speed of propagation of the wave? (b) What is the wavelength of the wave? (c) What is the amplitude of the magnetic field?

32.15 • An electromagnetic wave with frequency 5.70×10^{14} Hz propagates with a speed of 2.17×10^8 m/s in a certain piece of glass. Find (a) the wavelength of the wave in the glass; (b) the wavelength of a wave of the same frequency propagating in air; (c) the index of refraction n of the glass for an electromagnetic wave with this frequency; (d) the dielectric constant for glass at this frequency, assuming that the relative permeability is unity.

Section 32.4 Energy and Momentum in Electromagnetic Waves

32.16 • **BIO High-Energy Cancer Treatment.** Scientists are working on a new technique to kill cancer cells by zapping them with ultrahigh-energy (in the range of 10^{12} W) pulses of light that last for an extremely short time (a few nanoseconds). These short pulses scramble the interior of a cell without causing it to explode, as long pulses would do. We can model a typical such cell as a disk 5.0 μm in diameter, with the pulse lasting for 4.0 ns with an average power of 2.0×10^{12} W. We shall assume that the energy is spread uniformly over the faces of 100 cells for each pulse. (a) How much energy is given to the cell during this pulse? (b) What is the intensity (in W/m²) delivered to the cell? (c) What are the maximum values of the electric and magnetic fields in the pulse?

32.17 •• **Fields from a Light Bulb.** We can reasonably model a 75-W incandescent light bulb as a sphere 6.0 cm in diameter. Typically, only about 5% of the energy goes to visible light; the rest goes largely to nonvisible infrared radiation. (a) What is the visible-light intensity (in W/m²) at the surface of the bulb? (b) What are the amplitudes of the electric and magnetic fields at this surface, for a sinusoidal wave with this intensity?

32.18 •• A sinusoidal electromagnetic wave from a radio station passes perpendicularly through an open window that has area 0.500 m². At the window, the electric field of the wave has rms value 0.0200 V/m. How much energy does this wave carry through the window during a 30.0-s commercial?

32.19 •• **Testing a Space Radio Transmitter.** You are a NASA mission specialist on your first flight aboard the space shuttle. Thanks to your extensive training in physics, you have been assigned to evaluate the performance of a new radio transmitter on board the International Space Station (ISS). Perched on the shuttle's movable arm, you aim a sensitive detector at the ISS, which is 2.5 km away. You find that the electric-field amplitude of the radio waves coming from the ISS transmitter is 0.090 V/m and that the frequency of the waves is 244 MHz. Find the following: (a) the intensity of the radio wave at your location; (b) the magnetic-field amplitude of the wave at your location; (c) the total power output of the ISS radio transmitter. (d) What assumptions, if any, did you make in your calculations?

32.20 • The intensity of a cylindrical laser beam is 0.800 W/m^2. The cross-sectional area of the beam is $3.0 \times 10^{-4} \text{ m}^2$ and the intensity is uniform across the cross section of the beam. (a) What is the average power output of the laser? (b) What is the rms value of the electric field in the beam?

32.21 • A space probe 2.0×10^{10} m from a star measures the total intensity of electromagnetic radiation from the star to be $5.0 \times 10^3 \text{ W/m}^2$. If the star radiates uniformly in all directions, what is its total average power output?

32.22 • A sinusoidal electromagnetic wave emitted by a cellular phone has a wavelength of 35.4 cm and an electric-field amplitude of 5.40×10^{-2} V/m at a distance of 250 m from the phone. Calculate (a) the frequency of the wave; (b) the magnetic-field amplitude; (c) the intensity of the wave.

32.23 • A monochromatic light source with power output 60.0 W radiates light of wavelength 700 nm uniformly in all directions. Calculate E_{max} and B_{max} for the 700-nm light at a distance of 5.00 m from the source.

32.24 • For the electromagnetic wave represented by Eqs. (32.19), show that the Poynting vector (a) is in the same direction as the propagation of the wave and (b) has average magnitude given by Eqs. (32.29).

32.25 •• An intense light source radiates uniformly in all directions. At a distance of 5.0 m from the source, the radiation pressure on a perfectly absorbing surface is 9.0×10^{-6} Pa. What is the total average power output of the source?

32.26 • **Television Broadcasting.** Public television station KQED in San Francisco broadcasts a sinusoidal radio signal at a power of 316 kW. Assume that the wave spreads out uniformly into a hemisphere above the ground. At a home 5.00 km away from the antenna, (a) what average pressure does this wave exert on a totally reflecting surface, (b) what are the amplitudes of the electric and magnetic fields of the wave, and (c) what is the average density of the energy this wave carries? (d) For the energy density in part (c), what percentage is due to the electric field and what percentage is due to the magnetic field?

32.27 •• **BIO Laser Safety.** If the eye receives an average intensity greater than $1.0 \times 10^2 \text{ W/m}^2$, damage to the retina can occur. This quantity is called the *damage threshold* of the retina. (a) What is the largest average power (in mW) that a laser beam 1.5 mm in diameter can have and still be considered safe to view head-on? (b) What are the maximum values of the electric and magnetic fields for the beam in part (a)? (c) How much energy would the beam in part (a) deliver per second to the retina? (d) Express the damage threshold in W/cm^2.

32.28 • In the 25-ft Space Simulator facility at NASA's Jet Propulsion Laboratory, a bank of overhead arc lamps can produce light of intensity 2500 W/m^2 at the floor of the facility. (This simulates the intensity of sunlight near the planet Venus.) Find the average radiation pressure (in pascals and in atmospheres) on (a) a totally absorbing section of the floor and (b) a totally reflecting section of the floor. (c) Find the average momentum density (momentum per unit volume) in the light at the floor.

32.29 • **Laboratory Lasers.** He–Ne lasers are often used in physics demonstrations. They produce light of wavelength 633 nm and a power of 0.500 mW spread over a cylindrical beam 1.00 mm in diameter (although these quantities can vary). (a) What is the intensity of this laser beam? (b) What are the maximum values of the electric and magnetic fields? (c) What is the average energy density in the laser beam?

32.30 •• **Solar Sail 1.** During 2004, Japanese scientists successfully tested two solar sails. One had a somewhat complicated shape that we shall model as a disk 9.0 m in diameter and 7.5 μm thick. The intensity of solar energy at that location was about 1400 W/m^2. (a) What force did the sun's light exert on this sail, assuming that it struck perpendicular to the sail and that the sail was perfectly reflecting? (b) If the sail was made of magnesium, of density 1.74 g/cm^3, what acceleration would the sun's radiation give to the sail? (c) Does the acceleration seem large enough to be feasible for space flight? In what ways could the sail be modified to increase its acceleration?

Section 32.5 Standing Electromagnetic Waves

32.31 • **Microwave Oven.** The microwaves in a certain microwave oven have a wavelength of 12.2 cm. (a) How wide must this oven be so that it will contain five antinodal planes of the electric field along its width in the standing-wave pattern? (b) What is the frequency of these microwaves? (c) Suppose a manufacturing error occurred and the oven was made 5.0 cm longer than specified in part (a). In this case, what would have to be the frequency of the microwaves for there still to be five antinodal planes of the electric field along the width of the oven?

32.32 • An electromagnetic standing wave in air of frequency 750 MHz is set up between two conducting planes 80.0 cm apart. At which positions between the planes could a point charge be placed at rest so that it would *remain* at rest? Explain.

32.33 • A standing electromagnetic wave in a certain material has frequency 2.20×10^{10} Hz. The nodal planes of $\vec{B}$ are 3.55 mm apart. Find (a) the wavelength of the wave in this material; (b) the distance between adjacent nodal planes of the $\vec{E}$ field; (c) the speed of propagation of the wave.

32.34 • An electromagnetic standing wave in air has frequency 75.0 MHz. (a) What is the distance between nodal planes of the $\vec{E}$ field? (b) What is the distance between a nodal plane of $\vec{E}$ and the closest nodal plane of $\vec{B}$?

32.35 • An electromagnetic standing wave in a certain material has frequency 1.20×10^{10} Hz and speed of propagation 2.10×10^8 m/s. (a) What is the distance between a nodal plane of $\vec{B}$ and the closest antinodal plane of $\vec{B}$? (b) What is the distance between an antinodal plane of $\vec{E}$ and the closest antinodal plane of $\vec{B}$? (c) What is the distance between a nodal plane of $\vec{E}$ and the closest nodal plane of $\vec{B}$?

32.36 • **CALC** Show that the electric and magnetic fields for standing waves given by Eqs. (32.34) and (32.35) (a) satisfy the wave equation, Eq. (32.15), and (b) satisfy Eqs. (32.12) and (32.14).

PROBLEMS

32.37 •• **BIO Laser Surgery.** Very short pulses of high-intensity laser beams are used to repair detached portions of the retina of the eye. The brief pulses of energy absorbed by the retina weld the detached portions back into place. In one such procedure, a laser beam has a wavelength of 810 nm and delivers 250 mW of power spread over a circular spot 510 μm in diameter. The vitreous humor (the transparent fluid that fills most of the eye) has an index of refraction of 1.34. (a) If the laser pulses are each 1.50 ms long, how much energy is delivered to the retina with each pulse? (b) What average pressure does the pulse of the laser beam exert on the retina as it is fully absorbed by the circular spot? (c) What are the wavelength and frequency of the laser light inside the vitreous humor of the eye? (d) What are the maximum values of the electric and magnetic fields in the laser beam?

32.38 ••• **CALC** Consider a sinusoidal electromagnetic wave with fields $\vec{E} = E_{max}\hat{j}\cos(kx - \omega t)$ and $\vec{B} = B_{max}\hat{k}\cos(kx - \omega t + \phi)$, with $-\pi \le \phi \le \pi$. Show that if $\vec{E}$ and $\vec{B}$ are to satisfy Eqs. (32.12) and (32.14), then $E_{\text{max}} = cB_{\text{max}}$ and $\phi = 0$. (The result $\phi = 0$ means the $\vec{E}$ and $\vec{B}$ fields oscillate in phase.)

32.39 •• You want to support a sheet of fireproof paper horizontally, using only a vertical upward beam of light spread uniformly over the sheet. There is no other light on this paper. The sheet measures 22.0 cm by 28.0 cm and has a mass of 1.50 g. (a) If the paper is black and hence absorbs all the light that hits it, what must be the intensity of the light beam? (b) For the light in part (a), what are the amplitudes of its electric and magnetic fields? (c) If the paper is white and hence reflects all the light that hits it, what intensity of light beam is needed to support it? (d) To see if it is physically reasonable to expect to support a sheet of paper this way, calculate the intensity in a typical 0.500-mW laser beam that is 1.00 mm in diameter, and compare this value with your answer in part (a).

32.40 •• For a sinusoidal electromagnetic wave in vacuum, such as that described by Eq. (32.16), show that the *average* energy density in the electric field is the same as that in the magnetic field.

32.41 • A satellite 575 km above the earth's surface transmits sinusoidal electromagnetic waves of frequency 92.4 MHz uniformly in all directions, with a power of 25.0 kW. (a) What is the intensity of these waves as they reach a receiver at the surface of the earth directly below the satellite? (b) What are the amplitudes of the electric and magnetic fields at the receiver? (c) If the receiver has a totally absorbing panel measuring 15.0 cm by 40.0 cm oriented with its plane perpendicular to the direction the waves travel, what average force do these waves exert on the panel? Is this force large enough to cause significant effects?

32.42 • A plane sinusoidal electromagnetic wave in air has a wavelength of 3.84 cm and an $\vec{E}$-field amplitude of 1.35 V/m. (a) What is the frequency? (b) What is the $\vec{B}$-field amplitude? (c) What is the intensity? (d) What average force does this radiation exert on a totally absorbing surface with area 0.240 m² perpendicular to the direction of propagation?

32.43 • A small helium–neon laser emits red visible light with a power of 4.60 mW in a beam that has a diameter of 2.50 mm. (a) What are the amplitudes of the electric and magnetic fields of the light? (b) What are the average energy densities associated with the electric field and with the magnetic field? (c) What is the total energy contained in a 1.00-m length of the beam?

32.44 •• The electric-field component of a sinusoidal electromagnetic wave traveling through a plastic cylinder is given by the equation $E = (5.35 \text{ V/m}) \cos[(1.39 \times 10^7 \text{ rad/m})x - (3.02 \times 10^{15} \text{ rad/s})t]$. (a) Find the frequency, wavelength, and speed of this wave in the plastic. (b) What is the index of refraction of the plastic? (c) Assuming that the amplitude of the electric field does not change, write a comparable equation for the electric field if the light is traveling in air instead of in plastic.

32.45 • The sun emits energy in the form of electromagnetic waves at a rate of 3.9×10^{26} W. This energy is produced by nuclear reactions deep in the sun's interior. (a) Find the intensity of electromagnetic radiation and the radiation pressure on an absorbing object at the surface of the sun (radius $r = R = 6.96 \times 10^5$ km) and at $r = R/2$, in the sun's interior. Ignore any scattering of the waves as they move radially outward from the center of the sun. Compare to the values given in Section 32.4 for sunlight just before it enters the earth's atmosphere. (b) The gas pressure at the sun's surface is about 1.0×10^4 Pa; at $r = R/2$, the gas pressure is calculated from solar models to be about 4.7×10^{13} Pa. Comparing with your results in part (a), would you expect that radiation pressure is

an important factor in determining the structure of the sun? Why or why not?

32.46 •• A source of sinusoidal electromagnetic waves radiates uniformly in all directions. At 10.0 m from this source, the amplitude of the electric field is measured to be 1.50 N/C. What is the electric-field amplitude at a distance of 20.0 cm from the source?

32.47 •• CP Two square reflectors, each 1.50 cm on a side and of mass 4.00 g, are located at opposite ends of a thin, extremely light, 1.00-m rod that can rotate without friction and in vacuum about an axle perpendicular to it through its center (Fig. P32.47). These reflectors are small enough to be treated as point masses in moment-of-inertia calculations. Both reflectors are illuminated on one face by a sinusoidal light wave having an electric field of amplitude 1.25 N/C that falls uniformly on both surfaces and always strikes them perpendicular to the plane of their surfaces. One reflector is covered with a perfectly absorbing coating, and the other is covered with a perfectly reflecting coating. What is the angular acceleration of this device?

Figure **P32.47**

Axis of rotation

32.48 •• CP A circular loop of wire has radius 7.50 cm. A sinusoidal electromagnetic plane wave traveling in air passes through the loop, with the direction of the magnetic field of the wave perpendicular to the plane of the loop. The intensity of the wave at the location of the loop is 0.0195 W/m², and the wavelength of the wave is 6.90 m. What is the maximum emf induced in the loop?

32.49 • CALC CP A cylindrical conductor with a circular cross section has a radius a and a resistivity ρ and carries a constant current I. (a) What are the magnitude and direction of the electric-field vector $\vec{E}$ at a point just inside the wire at a distance a from the axis? (b) What are the magnitude and direction of the magnetic-field vector $\vec{B}$ at the same point? (c) What are the magnitude and direction of the Poynting vector $\vec{S}$ at the same point? (The direction of $\vec{S}$ is the direction in which electromagnetic energy flows into or out of the conductor.) (d) Use the result in part (c) to find the rate of flow of energy into the volume occupied by a length l of the conductor. (*Hint:* Integrate $\vec{S}$ over the surface of this volume.) Compare your result to the rate of generation of thermal energy in the same volume. Discuss why the energy dissipated in a current-carrying conductor, due to its resistance, can be thought of as entering through the cylindrical sides of the conductor.

32.50 • In a certain experiment, a radio transmitter emits sinusoidal electromagnetic waves of frequency 110.0 MHz in opposite directions inside a narrow cavity with reflectors at both ends, causing a standing-wave pattern to occur. (a) How far apart are the nodal planes of the magnetic field? (b) If the standing-wave pattern is determined to be in its eighth harmonic, how long is the cavity?

32.51 •• CP **Flashlight to the Rescue.** You are the sole crew member of the interplanetary spaceship *T:1339 Vorga*, which makes regular cargo runs between the earth and the mining colonies in the asteroid belt. You are working outside the ship one day while at a distance of 2.0 AU from the sun. [1 AU (astronomical unit) is the average distance from the earth to the sun, 149,600,000 km.] Unfortunately, you lose contact with the ship's hull and begin to drift away into space. You use your spacesuit's rockets to try to push yourself back toward the ship, but they run out of fuel and stop working before you can return to the ship. You find yourself in an awkward position, floating 16.0 m from the spaceship with zero velocity relative to it. Fortunately, you are carrying a 200-W flashlight. You turn on the flashlight and use its beam as a "light rocket" to push yourself back toward the ship. (a) If you, your spacesuit, and the flashlight have a combined mass of 150 kg, how long will it take you to get back to the ship? (b) Is there another way you could use the flashlight to accomplish the same job of returning you to the ship?

32.52 • The 19th-century inventor Nikola Tesla proposed to transmit electric power via sinusoidal electromagnetic waves. Suppose power is to be transmitted in a beam of cross-sectional area 100 m². What electric- and magnetic-field amplitudes are required to transmit an amount of power comparable to that handled by modern transmission lines (that carry voltages and currents of the order of 500 kV and 1000 A)?

32.53 •• **CP Global Positioning System (GPS).** The GPS network consists of 24 satellites, each of which makes two orbits around the earth per day. Each satellite transmits a 50.0-W (or even less) sinusoidal electromagnetic signal at two frequencies, one of which is 1575.42 MHz. Assume that a satellite transmits half of its power at each frequency and that the waves travel uniformly in a downward hemisphere. (a) What average intensity does a GPS receiver on the ground, directly below the satellite, receive? (*Hint:* First use Newton's laws to find the altitude of the satellite.) (b) What are the amplitudes of the electric and magnetic fields at the GPS receiver in part (a), and how long does it take the signal to reach the receiver? (c) If the receiver is a square panel 1.50 cm on a side that absorbs all of the beam, what average pressure does the signal exert on it? (d) What wavelength must the receiver be tuned to?

32.54 •• **CP Solar Sail 2.** NASA is giving serious consideration to the concept of *solar sailing*. A solar sailcraft uses a large, low-mass sail and the energy and momentum of sunlight for propulsion. (a) Should the sail be absorbing or reflective? Why? (b) The total power output of the sun is 3.9×10^{26} W. How large a sail is necessary to propel a 10,000-kg spacecraft against the gravitational force of the sun? Express your result in square kilometers. (c) Explain why your answer to part (b) is independent of the distance from the sun.

32.55 •• **CP** Interplanetary space contains many small particles referred to as *interplanetary dust*. Radiation pressure from the sun sets a lower limit on the size of such dust particles. To see the origin of this limit, consider a spherical dust particle of radius R and mass density ρ. (a) Write an expression for the gravitational force exerted on this particle by the sun (mass M) when the particle is a distance r from the sun. (b) Let L represent the luminosity of the sun, equal to the rate at which it emits energy in electromagnetic radiation. Find the force exerted on the (totally absorbing) particle due to solar radiation pressure, remembering that the intensity of the sun's radiation also depends on the distance r. The relevant area is the cross-sectional area of the particle, *not* the total surface area of the particle. As part of your answer, explain why this is so. (c) The mass density of a typical interplanetary dust particle is about 3000 kg/m³. Find the particle radius R such that the gravitational and radiation forces acting on the particle are equal in magnitude. The luminosity of the sun is 3.9×10^{26} W. Does your answer depend on the distance of the particle from the sun? Why or why not? (d) Explain why dust particles with a radius less than

that found in part (c) are unlikely to be found in the solar system. [*Hint:* Construct the ratio of the two force expressions found in parts (a) and (b).]

CHALLENGE PROBLEMS

32.56 ••• **CALC** Electromagnetic waves propagate much differently in *conductors* than they do in dielectrics or in vacuum. If the resistivity of the conductor is sufficiently low (that is, if it is a sufficiently good conductor), the oscillating electric field of the wave gives rise to an oscillating conduction current that is much larger than the displacement current. In this case, the wave equation for an electric field $\vec{E}(x, t) = E_y(x, t)\hat{j}$ propagating in the $+x$-direction within a conductor is

$$\frac{\partial^2 E_y (x, t)}{\partial x^2} = \frac{\mu}{\rho} \frac{\partial E_y(x, t)}{\partial t}$$

where μ is the permeability of the conductor and ρ is its resistivity. (a) A solution to this wave equation is

$$E_y(x, t) = E_{max} e^{-k_C x} \cos(k_C x - \omega t)$$

where $k_C = \sqrt{\omega\mu/2\rho}$. Verify this by substituting $E_y(x, t)$ into the above wave equation. (b) The exponential term shows that the electric field decreases in amplitude as it propagates. Explain why this happens. (*Hint:* The field does work to move charges within the conductor. The current of these moving charges causes $i^2 R$ heating within the conductor, raising its temperature. Where does the energy to do this come from?) (c) Show that the electric-field amplitude decreases by a factor of $1/e$ in a distance $1/k_C = \sqrt{2\rho/\omega\mu}$, and calculate this distance for a radio wave with frequency $f = 1.0$ MHz in copper (resistivity 1.72×10^{-8} $\Omega \cdot$m; permeability $\mu = \mu_0$). Since this distance is so short, electromagnetic waves of this frequency can hardly propagate at all into copper. Instead, they are reflected at the surface of the metal. This is why radio waves cannot penetrate through copper or other metals, and why radio reception is poor inside a metal structure.

32.57 ••• **CP** Electromagnetic radiation is emitted by accelerating charges. The rate at which energy is emitted from an accelerating charge that has charge q and acceleration a is given by

$$\frac{dE}{dt} = \frac{q^2 a^2}{6\pi\epsilon_0 c^3}$$

where c is the speed of light. (a) Verify that this equation is dimensionally correct. (b) If a proton with a kinetic energy of 6.0 MeV is traveling in a particle accelerator in a circular orbit of radius 0.750 m, what fraction of its energy does it radiate per second? (c) Consider an electron orbiting with the same speed and radius. What fraction of its energy does it radiate per second?

32.58 ••• **CP The Classical Hydrogen Atom.** The electron in a hydrogen atom can be considered to be in a circular orbit with a radius of 0.0529 nm and a kinetic energy of 13.6 eV. If the electron behaved classically, how much energy would it radiate per second (see Challenge Problem 32.57)? What does this tell you about the use of classical physics in describing the atom?

Answers

Chapter Opening Question

Metals are reflective because they are good conductors of electricity. When an electromagnetic wave strikes a conductor, the electric field of the wave sets up currents on the conductor surface that generate a reflected wave. For a perfect conductor, this reflected wave is just as intense as the incident wave. Tarnished metals are less shiny because their surface is oxidized and less conductive; polishing the metal removes the oxide and exposes the conducting metal.

Test Your Understanding Questions

32.1 Answers: (a) no, (b) no A purely electric wave would have a varying electric field. Such a field necessarily generates a magnetic field through Ampere's law, Eq. (29.20), so a purely electric wave is impossible. In the same way, a purely magnetic wave is impossible: The varying magnetic field in such a wave would automatically give rise to an electric field through Faraday's law, Eq. (29.21).

32.2 Answers: (a) positive y-direction, (b) negative x-direction, (c) positive y-direction You can verify these answers by using the right-hand rule to show that $\vec{E} \times \vec{B}$ in each case is in the direction of propagation, or by using the rule shown in Fig. 32.9.

32.3 Answer: (iv) In an ideal electromagnetic plane wave, at any instant the fields are the same anywhere in a plane perpendicular to the direction of propagation. The plane wave described by Eqs. (32.17) is propagating in the x-direction, so the fields depend on the coordinate x and time t but do *not* depend on the coordinates y and z.

32.4 Answers: (a) (i) and (iii), (b) (ii) and (iv), (c) (i) and (iii), (d) (ii) and (iv) Both the energy density u and the Poynting vector magnitude S are maximum where the $\vec{E}$ and $\vec{B}$ fields have their maximum magnitudes. (The directions of the fields doesn't matter.) From Fig. 32.13, this occurs at $x = 0$ and $x = \lambda/2$. Both u and S have a minimum value of zero; that occurs where $\vec{E}$ and $\vec{B}$ are both zero. From Fig. 32.13, this occurs at $x = \lambda/4$ and $x = 3\lambda/4$.

32.5 Answer: no There are places where $\vec{E} = 0$ at all times (at the walls) and the electric energy density $\frac{1}{2}\epsilon_0 E^2$ is always zero. There are also places where $\vec{B} = 0$ at all times (on the plane midway between the walls) and the magnetic energy density $B^2/2\mu_0$ is always zero. However, there are *no* locations where both $\vec{E}$ and $\vec{B}$ are always zero. Hence the energy density at any point in the standing wave is always nonzero.

Bridging Problem

Answer: 0.0368 V

33 THE NATURE AND PROPAGATION OF LIGHT

? These drafting tools are made of clear plastic, but a rainbow of colors appears when they are placed between two special filters called polarizers. How does this cause the colors?

Blue lakes, ochre deserts, green forests, and multicolored rainbows can be enjoyed by anyone who has eyes with which to see them. But by studying the branch of physics called **optics,** which deals with the behavior of light and other electromagnetic waves, we can reach a deeper appreciation of the visible world. A knowledge of the properties of light allows us to understand the blue color of the sky and the design of optical devices such as telescopes, microscopes, cameras, eyeglasses, and the human eye. The same basic principles of optics also lie at the heart of modern developments such as the laser, optical fibers, holograms, optical computers, and new techniques in medical imaging.

The importance of optics to physics, and to science and engineering in general, is so great that we will devote the next four chapters to its study. In this chapter we begin with a study of the laws of reflection and refraction and the concepts of dispersion, polarization, and scattering of light. Along the way we compare the various possible descriptions of light in terms of particles, rays, or waves, and we introduce Huygens's principle, an important link that connects the ray and wave viewpoints. In Chapter 34 we'll use the ray description of light to understand how mirrors and lenses work, and we'll see how mirrors and lenses are used in optical instruments such as cameras, microscopes, and telescopes. We'll explore the wave characteristics of light further in Chapters 35 and 36.

33.1 The Nature of Light

Until the time of Isaac Newton (1642–1727), most scientists thought that light consisted of streams of particles (called *corpuscles*) emitted by light sources. Galileo and others tried (unsuccessfully) to measure the speed of light. Around 1665, evidence of *wave* properties of light began to be discovered. By the early 19th century, evidence that light is a wave had grown very persuasive.

In 1873, James Clerk Maxwell predicted the existence of electromagnetic waves and calculated their speed of propagation, as we learned in Chapter 32. This development, along with the experimental work of Heinrich Hertz starting in 1887, showed conclusively that light is indeed an electromagnetic wave.

The Two Personalities of Light

The wave picture of light is not the whole story, however. Several effects associated with emission and absorption of light reveal a particle aspect, in that the energy carried by light waves is packaged in discrete bundles called *photons* or *quanta*. These apparently contradictory wave and particle properties have been reconciled since 1930 with the development of quantum electrodynamics, a comprehensive theory that includes *both* wave and particle properties. The *propagation* of light is best described by a wave model, but understanding emission and absorption requires a particle approach.

The fundamental sources of all electromagnetic radiation are electric charges in accelerated motion. All bodies emit electromagnetic radiation as a result of thermal motion of their molecules; this radiation, called *thermal radiation,* is a mixture of different wavelengths. At sufficiently high temperatures, all matter emits enough visible light to be self-luminous; a very hot body appears "red-hot" (Fig. 33.1) or "white-hot." Thus hot matter in any form is a light source. Familiar examples are a candle flame, hot coals in a campfire, the coils in an electric room heater, and an incandescent lamp filament (which usually operates at a temperature of about 3000°C).

Light is also produced during electrical discharges through ionized gases. The bluish light of mercury-arc lamps, the orange-yellow of sodium-vapor lamps, and the various colors of "neon" signs are familiar. A variation of the mercury-arc lamp is the *fluorescent* lamp (see Fig. 30.7). This light source uses a material called a *phosphor* to convert the ultraviolet radiation from a mercury arc into visible light. This conversion makes fluorescent lamps more efficient than incandescent lamps in transforming electrical energy into light.

In most light sources, light is emitted independently by different atoms within the source; in a *laser,* by contrast, atoms are induced to emit light in a cooperative, coherent fashion. The result is a very narrow beam of radiation that can be enormously intense and that is much more nearly *monochromatic,* or single-frequency, than light from any other source. Lasers are used by physicians for microsurgery, in a DVD or Blu-ray player to scan the information recorded on a video disc, in industry to cut through steel and to fuse high-melting-point materials, and in many other applications (Fig. 33.2).

No matter what its source, electromagnetic radiation travels in vacuum at the same speed. As we saw in Sections 1.3 and 32.1, the speed of light in vacuum is defined to be

$$c = 2.99792458 \times 10^8 \text{ m/s}$$

or 3.00×10^8 m/s to three significant figures. The duration of one second is defined by the cesium clock (see Section 1.3), so one meter is defined to be the distance that light travels in 1/299,792,458 s.

Waves, Wave Fronts, and Rays

We often use the concept of a **wave front** to describe wave propagation. We introduced this concept in Section 32.2 to describe the leading edge of a wave. More generally, we define a wave front as *the locus of all adjacent points at which the phase of vibration of a physical quantity associated with the wave is the same.* That is, at any instant, all points on a wave front are at the same part of the cycle of their variation.

When we drop a pebble into a calm pool, the expanding circles formed by the wave crests, as well as the circles formed by the wave troughs between

33.1 An electric heating element emits primarily infrared radiation. But if its temperature is high enough, it also emits a discernible amount of visible light.

33.2 Ophthalmic surgeons use lasers for repairing detached retinas and for cauterizing blood vessels in retinopathy. Pulses of blue-green light from an argon laser are ideal for this purpose, since they pass harmlessly through the transparent part of the eye but are absorbed by red pigments in the retina.

33.3 Spherical wave fronts of sound spread out uniformly in all directions from a point source in a motionless medium, such as still air, that has the same properties in all regions and in all directions. Electromagnetic waves in vacuum also spread out as shown here.

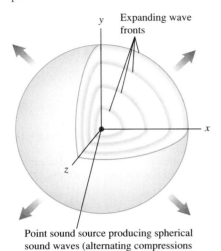

Point sound source producing spherical sound waves (alternating compressions and rarefactions of air)

33.4 Wave fronts (blue) and rays (purple).

(a)

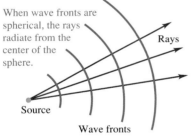

When wave fronts are spherical, the rays radiate from the center of the sphere.

Rays

Source

Wave fronts

(b)

When wave fronts are planar, the rays are perpendicular to the wave fronts and parallel to each other.

Rays

Wave fronts

ActivPhysics 15.1: Reflection and Refraction
ActivPhysics 15.3: Refraction Applications

them, are wave fronts. Similarly, when sound waves spread out in still air from a pointlike source, or when electromagnetic radiation spreads out from a pointlike emitter, any spherical surface that is concentric with the source is a wave front, as shown in Fig. 33.3. In diagrams of wave motion we usually draw only parts of a few wave fronts, often choosing consecutive wave fronts that have the same phase and thus are one wavelength apart, such as crests of water waves. Similarly, a diagram for sound waves might show only the "pressure crests," the surfaces over which the pressure is maximum, and a diagram for electromagnetic waves might show only the "crests" on which the electric or magnetic field is maximum.

We will often use diagrams that show the shapes of the wave fronts or their cross sections in some reference plane. For example, when electromagnetic waves are radiated by a small light source, we can represent the wave fronts as spherical surfaces concentric with the source or, as in Fig. 33.4a, by the circular intersections of these surfaces with the plane of the diagram. Far away from the source, where the radii of the spheres have become very large, a section of a spherical surface can be considered as a plane, and we have a *plane* wave like those discussed in Sections 32.2 and 32.3 (Fig, 33.4b).

To describe the directions in which light propagates, it's often convenient to represent a light wave by **rays** rather than by wave fronts. Rays were used to describe light long before its wave nature was firmly established. In a particle theory of light, rays are the paths of the particles. From the wave viewpoint *a ray is an imaginary line along the direction of travel of the wave.* In Fig. 33.4a the rays are the radii of the spherical wave fronts, and in Fig. 33.4b they are straight lines perpendicular to the wave fronts. When waves travel in a homogeneous isotropic material (a material with the same properties in all regions and in all directions), the rays are always straight lines normal to the wave fronts. At a boundary surface between two materials, such as the surface of a glass plate in air, the wave speed and the direction of a ray may change, but the ray segments in the air and in the glass are straight lines.

The next several chapters will give you many opportunities to see the interplay of the ray, wave, and particle descriptions of light. The branch of optics for which the ray description is adequate is called **geometric optics;** the branch dealing specifically with wave behavior is called **physical optics.** This chapter and the following one are concerned mostly with geometric optics. In Chapters 35 and 36 we will study wave phenomena and physical optics.

Test Your Understanding of Section 33.1 Some crystals are *not* isotropic: Light travels through the crystal at a higher speed in some directions than in others. In a crystal in which light travels at the same speed in the x- and z-directions but at a faster speed in the y-direction, what would be the shape of the wave fronts produced by a light source at the origin? (i) spherical, like those shown in Fig. 33.3; (ii) ellipsoidal, flattened along the y-axis; (iii) ellipsoidal, stretched out along the y-axis.

33.2 Reflection and Refraction

In this section we'll use the *ray* model of light to explore two of the most important aspects of light propagation: **reflection** and **refraction.** When a light wave strikes a smooth interface separating two transparent materials (such as air and glass or water and glass), the wave is in general partly *reflected* and partly *refracted* (transmitted) into the second material, as shown in Fig. 33.5a. For example, when you look into a restaurant window from the street, you see a reflection of the street scene, but a person inside the restaurant can look out through the window at the same scene as light reaches him by refraction.

33.5 (a) A plane wave is in part reflected and in part refracted at the boundary between two media (in this case, air and glass). The light that reaches the inside of the coffee shop is refracted twice, once entering the glass and once exiting the glass. (b), (c) How light behaves at the interface between the air outside the coffee shop (material *a*) and the glass (material *b*). For the case shown here, material *b* has a larger index of refraction than material $a(n_b > n_a)$ and the angle θ_b is smaller than θ_a.

(a) Plane waves reflected and refracted from a window

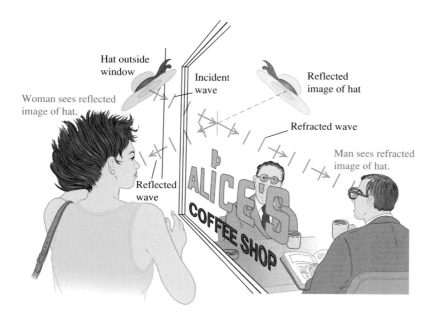

(b) The waves in the outside air and glass represented by rays

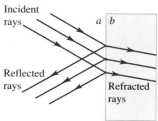

(c) The representation simplified to show just one set of rays

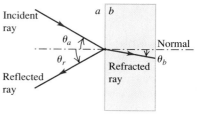

The segments of plane waves shown in Fig. 33.5a can be represented by bundles of rays forming *beams* of light (Fig. 33.5b). For simplicity we often draw only one ray in each beam (Fig. 33.5c). Representing these waves in terms of rays is the basis of geometric optics. We begin our study with the behavior of an individual ray.

We describe the directions of the incident, reflected, and refracted (transmitted) rays at a smooth interface between two optical materials in terms of the angles they make with the *normal* (perpendicular) to the surface at the point of incidence, as shown in Fig. 33.5c. If the interface is rough, both the transmitted light and the reflected light are scattered in various directions, and there is no single angle of transmission or reflection. Reflection at a definite angle from a very smooth surface is called **specular reflection** (from the Latin word for "mirror"); scattered reflection from a rough surface is called **diffuse reflection.** This distinction is shown in Fig. 33.6. Both kinds of reflection can occur with either transparent materials or *opaque* materials that do not transmit light. The vast majority of objects in your environment (including plants, other people, and this book) are visible to you because they reflect light in a diffuse manner from their surfaces. Our primary concern, however, will be with specular reflection from a very smooth surface such as highly polished glass or metal. Unless stated otherwise, when referring to "reflection" we will always mean *specular* reflection.

The **index of refraction** of an optical material (also called the **refractive index**), denoted by *n*, plays a central role in geometric optics. It is the ratio of the speed of light *c* in vacuum to the speed *v* in the material:

$$n = \frac{c}{v} \quad \text{(index of refraction)} \qquad (33.1)$$

Light always travels *more slowly* in a material than in vacuum, so the value of *n* in anything other than vacuum is always greater than unity. For vacuum, $n = 1$.

33.6 Two types of reflection.

(a) Specular reflection

(b) Diffuse reflection

Since n is a ratio of two speeds, it is a pure number without units. (The relationship of the value of n to the electric and magnetic properties of a material is described in Section 32.3.)

CAUTION **Wave speed and index of refraction** Keep in mind that the wave speed v is *inversely* proportional to the index of refraction n. The greater the index of refraction in a material, the *slower* the wave speed in that material. Failure to remember this point can lead to serious confusion! ▌

33.7 The laws of reflection and refraction.

1. The incident, reflected, and refracted rays and the normal to the surface all lie in the same plane.

Angles θ_a, θ_b, and θ_r are measured *from the normal*.

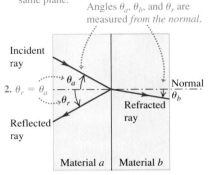

2. $\theta_r = \theta_a$

3. When a monochromatic light ray crosses the interface between two given materials a and b, the angles θ_a and θ_b are related to the indexes of refraction of a and b by

$$\frac{\sin\theta_a}{\sin\theta_b} = \frac{n_b}{n_a}$$

33.8 Refraction and reflection in three cases. (a) Material b has a larger index of refraction than material a. (b) Material b has a smaller index of refraction than material a. (c) The incident light ray is normal to the interface between the materials.

(a) A ray entering a material of *larger* index of refraction bends *toward* the normal.

(b) A ray entering a material of *smaller* index of refraction bends *away from* the normal.

(c) A ray oriented along the normal does not bend, regardless of the materials.

The Laws of Reflection and Refraction

Experimental studies of the directions of the incident, reflected, and refracted rays at a smooth interface between two optical materials lead to the following conclusions (Fig. 33.7):

1. **The incident, reflected, and refracted rays and the normal to the surface all lie in the same plane.** The plane of the three rays and the normal, called the **plane of incidence,** is perpendicular to the plane of the boundary surface between the two materials. We always draw ray diagrams so that the incident, reflected, and refracted rays are in the plane of the diagram.
2. **The angle of reflection θ_r is equal to the angle of incidence θ_a for all wavelengths and for any pair of materials.** That is, in Fig. 33.5c,

$$\theta_r = \theta_a \qquad \text{(law of reflection)} \qquad (33.2)$$

This relationship, together with the observation that the incident and reflected rays and the normal all lie in the same plane, is called the **law of reflection.**

3. For monochromatic light and for a given pair of materials, a and b, on opposite sides of the interface, **the ratio of the sines of the angles θ_a and θ_b, where both angles are measured from the normal to the surface, is equal to the inverse ratio of the two indexes of refraction:**

$$\frac{\sin\theta_a}{\sin\theta_b} = \frac{n_b}{n_a} \qquad (33.3)$$

or

$$n_a\sin\theta_a = n_b\sin\theta_b \qquad \text{(law of refraction)} \qquad (33.4)$$

This experimental result, together with the observation that the incident and refracted rays and the normal all lie in the same plane, is called the **law of refraction** or **Snell's law,** after the Dutch scientist Willebrord Snell (1591–1626). There is some doubt that Snell actually discovered it. The discovery that $n = c/v$ came much later.

While these results were first observed experimentally, they can be derived theoretically from a wave description of light. We do this in Section 33.7.

Equations (33.3) and (33.4) show that when a ray passes from one material (a) into another material (b) having a larger index of refraction ($n_b > n_a$) and hence a slower wave speed, the angle θ_b with the normal is *smaller* in the second material than the angle θ_a in the first; hence the ray is bent *toward* the normal (Fig. 33.8a). When the second material has a *smaller* index of refraction than the first material ($n_b < n_a$) and hence a faster wave speed, the ray is bent *away from* the normal (Fig. 33.8b).

No matter what the materials on either side of the interface, in the case of *normal* incidence the transmitted ray is not bent at all (Fig. 33.8c). In this case

33.9 (a) This ruler is actually straight, but it appears to bend at the surface of the water. (b) Light rays from any submerged object bend away from the normal when they emerge into the air. As seen by an observer above the surface of the water, the object appears to be much closer to the surface than it actually is.

(a) A straight ruler half-immersed in water

(b) Why the ruler appears bent

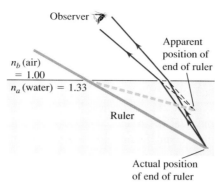

Observer

n_b (air) = 1.00

n_a (water) = 1.33

Ruler

Apparent position of end of ruler

Actual position of end of ruler

33.10 (a) The index of refraction of air is slightly greater than 1, so light rays from the setting sun bend downward when they enter our atmosphere. (The effect is exaggerated in this figure.) (b) Stronger refraction occurs for light coming from the lower limb of the sun (the part that appears closest to the horizon), which passes through denser air in the lower atmosphere. As a result, the setting sun appears flattened vertically. (See Problem 33.55.)

(a)

Atmosphere (not to scale)

Light ray from the sun

Earth

(b)

$\theta_a = 0$ and $\sin\theta_a = 0$, so from Eq. (33.4) θ_b is also equal to zero, so the transmitted ray is also normal to the interface. Equation (33.2) shows that θ_r, too, is equal to zero, so the reflected ray travels back along the same path as the incident ray.

The law of refraction explains why a partially submerged ruler or drinking straw appears bent; light rays coming from below the surface change in direction at the air–water interface, so the rays appear to be coming from a position above their actual point of origin (Fig. 33.9). A similar effect explains the appearance of the setting sun (Fig. 33.10).

An important special case is refraction that occurs at an interface between vacuum, for which the index of refraction is unity by definition, and a material. When a ray passes from vacuum into a material (b), so that $n_a = 1$ and $n_b > 1$, the ray is always bent *toward* the normal. When a ray passes from a material into vacuum, so that $n_a > 1$ and $n_b = 1$, the ray is always bent *away from* the normal.

The laws of reflection and refraction apply regardless of which side of the interface the incident ray comes from. If a ray of light approaches the interface in Fig. 33.8a or 33.8b from the right rather than from the left, there are again reflected and refracted rays; these two rays, the incident ray, and the normal to the surface again lie in the same plane. Furthermore, the path of a refracted ray is *reversible;* it follows the same path when going from b to a as when going from a to b. [You can verify this using Eq. (33.4).] Since reflected and incident rays make the same angle with the normal, the path of a reflected ray is also reversible. That's why when you see someone's eyes in a mirror, they can also see you.

The *intensities* of the reflected and refracted rays depend on the angle of incidence, the two indexes of refraction, and the polarization (that is, the direction of the electric-field vector) of the incident ray. The fraction reflected is smallest at normal incidence ($\theta_a = 0°$), where it is about 4% for an air–glass interface. This fraction increases with increasing angle of incidence to 100% at grazing incidence, when $\theta_a = 90°$.

It's possible to use Maxwell's equations to predict the amplitude, intensity, phase, and polarization states of the reflected and refracted waves. Such an analysis is beyond our scope, however.

The index of refraction depends not only on the substance but also on the wavelength of the light. The dependence on wavelength is called *dispersion;* we will consider it in Section 33.4. Indexes of refraction for several solids and liquids are given in Table 33.1 for a particular wavelength of yellow light.

Application Transparency and Index of Refraction
An eel in its larval stage is nearly as transparent as the seawater in which it swims. The larva in this photo is nonetheless easy to see because its index of refraction is higher than that of seawater, so that some of the light striking it is reflected instead of transmitted. The larva appears particularly shiny around its edges because the light reaching the camera from those points struck the larva at near-grazing incidence ($\theta_a = 90°$), resulting in almost 100% reflection.

Table 33.1 Index of Refraction for Yellow Sodium Light, $\lambda_0 = 589$ nm

Substance	Index of Refraction, n
Solids	
Ice (H_2O)	1.309
Fluorite (CaF_2)	1.434
Polystyrene	1.49
Rock salt (NaCl)	1.544
Quartz (SiO_2)	1.544
Zircon ($ZrO_2 \cdot SiO_2$)	1.923
Diamond (C)	2.417
Fabulite ($SrTiO_3$)	2.409
Rutile (TiO_2)	2.62
Glasses (typical values)	
Crown	1.52
Light flint	1.58
Medium flint	1.62
Dense flint	1.66
Lanthanum flint	1.80
Liquids at 20°C	
Methanol (CH_3OH)	1.329
Water (H_2O)	1.333
Ethanol (C_2H_5OH)	1.36
Carbon tetrachloride (CCl_4)	1.460
Turpentine	1.472
Glycerine	1.473
Benzene	1.501
Carbon disulfide (CS_2)	1.628

The index of refraction of air at standard temperature and pressure is about 1.0003, and we will usually take it to be exactly unity. The index of refraction of a gas increases as its density increases. Most glasses used in optical instruments have indexes of refraction between about 1.5 and 2.0. A few substances have larger indexes; one example is diamond, with 2.417.

Index of Refraction and the Wave Aspects of Light

We have discussed how the direction of a light ray changes when it passes from one material to another material with a different index of refraction. It's also important to see what happens to the *wave* characteristics of the light when this happens.

First, the frequency f of the wave does not change when passing from one material to another. That is, the number of wave cycles arriving per unit time must equal the number leaving per unit time; this is a statement that the boundary surface cannot create or destroy waves.

Second, the wavelength λ of the wave *is* different in general in different materials. This is because in any material, $v = \lambda f$; since f is the same in any material as in vacuum and v is always less than the wave speed c in vacuum, λ is also correspondingly reduced. Thus the wavelength λ of light in a material is *less than* the wavelength λ_0 of the same light in vacuum. From the above discussion, $f = c/\lambda_0 = v/\lambda$. Combining this with Eq. (33.1), $n = c/v$, we find

$$\lambda = \frac{\lambda_0}{n} \qquad \text{(wavelength of light in a material)} \qquad (33.5)$$

When a wave passes from one material into a second material with larger index of refraction, so that $n_b > n_a$, the wave speed decreases. The wavelength $\lambda_b = \lambda_0/n_b$ in the second material is then shorter than the wavelength $\lambda_a = \lambda_0/n_a$ in the first material. If instead the second material has a smaller index of refraction than the first material, so that $n_b < n_a$, then the wave speed increases. Then the wavelength λ_b in the second material is longer than the wavelength λ_a in the first material. This makes intuitive sense; the waves get "squeezed" (the wavelength gets shorter) if the wave speed decreases and get "stretched" (the wavelength gets longer) if the wave speed increases.

Problem-Solving Strategy 33.1   **Reflection and Refraction**

IDENTIFY *the relevant concepts:* Use geometric optics, discussed in this section, whenever light (or electromagnetic radiation of *any* frequency and wavelength) encounters a boundary between materials. In general, part of the light is reflected back into the first material and part is refracted into the second material.

SET UP *the problem* using the following steps:
1. In problems involving rays and angles, start by drawing a large, neat diagram. Label all known angles and indexes of refraction.
2. Identify the target variables.

EXECUTE *the solution* as follows:
1. Apply the laws of reflection, Eq. (33.2), and refraction, Eq. (33.4). Measure angles of incidence, reflection, and refraction with respect to the *normal* to the surface, *never* from the surface itself.

2. Apply geometry or trigonometry in working out angular relationships. Remember that the sum of the acute angles of a right triangle is 90° (they are *complementary*) and the sum of the interior angles in any triangle is 180°.
3. The frequency of the electromagnetic radiation does not change when it moves from one material to another; the wavelength changes in accordance with Eq. (33.5), $\lambda = \lambda_0/n$.

EVALUATE *your answer:* In problems that involve refraction, check that your results are consistent with Snell's law ($n_a \sin\theta_a = n_b \sin\theta_b$). If the second material has a higher index of refraction than the first, the angle of refraction must be *smaller* than the angle of incidence: The refracted ray bends toward the normal. If the first material has the higher index of refraction, the refracted angle must be larger than the incident angle: The refracted ray bends away from the normal.

Example 33.1 Reflection and refraction

In Fig. 33.11, material a is water and material b is glass with index of refraction 1.52. The incident ray makes an angle of 60.0° with the normal; find the directions of the reflected and refracted rays.

SOLUTION

IDENTIFY and SET UP: This is a problem in geometric optics. We are given the angle of incidence $\theta_a = 60.0°$ and the indexes of

33.11 Reflection and refraction of light passing from water to glass.

refraction $n_a = 1.33$ and $n_b = 1.52$. We must find the angles of reflection and refraction θ_r and θ_b; to do this we use Eqs. (33.2) and (33.4), respectively. Figure 33.11 shows the rays and angles; n_b is slightly greater than n_a, so by Snell's law [Eq. (33.4)] θ_b is slightly smaller than θ_a, as the figure shows.

EXECUTE: According to Eq. (33.2), the angle the reflected ray makes with the normal is the same as that of the incident ray, so $\theta_r = \theta_a = 60.0°$.

To find the direction of the refracted ray we use Snell's law, Eq. (33.4):

$$n_a \sin \theta_a = n_b \sin \theta_b$$
$$\sin \theta_b = \frac{n_a}{n_b} \sin \theta_a = \frac{1.33}{1.52} \sin 60.0° = 0.758$$
$$\theta_b = \arcsin(0.758) = 49.3°$$

EVALUATE: The second material has a larger refractive index than the first, as in Fig. 33.8a. Hence the refracted ray is bent toward the normal and $\theta_b < \theta_a$.

Example 33.2 Index of refraction in the eye

The wavelength of the red light from a helium-neon laser is 633 nm in air but 474 nm in the aqueous humor inside your eyeball. Calculate the index of refraction of the aqueous humor and the speed and frequency of the light in it.

SOLUTION

IDENTIFY and SET UP: The key ideas here are (i) the definition of index of refraction n in terms of the wave speed v in a medium and the speed c in vacuum, and (ii) the relationship between wavelength λ_0 in vacuum and wavelength λ in a medium of index n. We use Eq. (33.1), $n = c/v$; Eq. (33.5), $\lambda = \lambda_0/n$; and $v = \lambda f$.

EXECUTE: The index of refraction of air is very close to unity, so we assume that the wavelength λ_0 in vacuum is the same as that in air, 633 nm. Then from Eq. (33.5),

$$\lambda = \frac{\lambda_0}{n} \qquad n = \frac{\lambda_0}{\lambda} = \frac{633 \text{ nm}}{474 \text{ nm}} = 1.34$$

This is about the same index of refraction as for water. Then, using $n = c/v$ and $v = \lambda f$, we find

$$v = \frac{c}{n} = \frac{3.00 \times 10^8 \text{ m/s}}{1.34} = 2.25 \times 10^8 \text{ m/s}$$
$$f = \frac{v}{\lambda} = \frac{2.25 \times 10^8 \text{ m/s}}{474 \times 10^{-9} \text{ m}} = 4.74 \times 10^{14} \text{ Hz}$$

EVALUATE: Note that while the speed and wavelength have different values in air and in the aqueous humor, the *frequency* in air, f_0, is the same as the frequency f in the aqueous humor:

$$f_0 = \frac{c}{\lambda_0} = \frac{3.00 \times 10^8 \text{ m/s}}{633 \times 10^{-9} \text{ m}} = 4.74 \times 10^{14} \text{ Hz}$$

When a light wave passes from one material into another, the wave speed and wavelength both change but the wave frequency is unchanged.

Example 33.3 A twice-reflected ray

Two mirrors are perpendicular to each other. A ray traveling in a plane perpendicular to both mirrors is reflected from one mirror, then the other, as shown in Fig. 33.12. What is the ray's final direction relative to its original direction?

SOLUTION

IDENTIFY and SET UP: This problem involves the law of reflection, which we must apply twice (once for each mirror).

EXECUTE: For mirror 1 the angle of incidence is θ_1, and this equals the angle of reflection. The sum of interior angles in the triangle shown in the figure is 180°, so we see that the angles of incidence and reflection for mirror 2 are both $90° - \theta_1$. The total change in direction of the ray after both reflections is therefore $2(90° - \theta_1) + 2\theta_1 = 180°$. That is, the ray's final direction is opposite to its original direction.

Continued

33.12 A ray moving in the *xy*-plane. The first reflection changes the sign of the *y*-component of its velocity, and the second reflection changes the sign of the *x*-component. For a different ray with a *z*-component of velocity, a third mirror (perpendicular to the two shown) could be used to change the sign of that component.

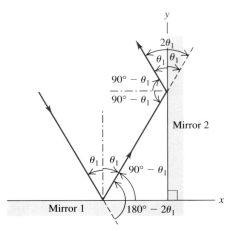

EVALUATE: An alternative viewpoint is that reflection reverses the sign of the component of light velocity perpendicular to the surface but leaves the other components unchanged. We invite you to verify this in detail. You should also be able to use this result to show that when a ray of light is successively reflected by three mirrors forming a corner of a cube (a "corner reflector"), its final direction is again opposite to its original direction. This principle is widely used in tail-light lenses and bicycle reflectors to improve their night-time visibility. Apollo astronauts placed arrays of corner reflectors on the moon. By use of laser beams reflected from these arrays, the earth–moon distance has been measured to within 0.15 m.

Test Your Understanding of Section 33.2   You are standing on the shore of a lake. You spot a tasty fish swimming some distance below the lake surface. (a) If you want to spear the fish, should you aim the spear (i) above, (ii) below, or (iii) directly at the apparent position of the fish? (b) If instead you use a high-power laser to simultaneously kill and cook the fish, should you aim the laser (i) above, (ii) below, or (iii) directly at the apparent position of the fish?   ❙

ActivPhysics 15.2: Total Internal Reflection

33.3 Total Internal Reflection

We have described how light is partially reflected and partially transmitted at an interface between two materials with different indexes of refraction. Under certain circumstances, however, *all* of the light can be reflected back from the interface, with none of it being transmitted, even though the second material is transparent. Figure 33.13a shows how this can occur. Several rays are shown radiating from a point source in material *a* with index of refraction n_a. The rays

33.13 (a) Total internal reflection. The angle of incidence for which the angle of refraction is $90°$ is called the critical angle: This is the case for ray 3. The reflected portions of rays 1, 2, and 3 are omitted for clarity. (b) Rays of laser light enter the water in the fishbowl from above; they are reflected at the bottom by mirrors tilted at slightly different angles. One ray undergoes total internal reflection at the air–water interface.

(a) Total internal reflection

(b) Total internal reflection demonstrated with a laser, mirrors, and water in a fishbowl

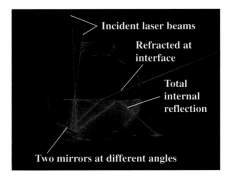

strike the surface of a second material b with index n_b, where $n_a > n_b$. (Materials a and b could be water and air, respectively.) From Snell's law of refraction,

$$\sin\theta_b = \frac{n_a}{n_b}\sin\theta_a$$

Because n_a/n_b is greater than unity, $\sin\theta_b$ is larger than $\sin\theta_a$; the ray is bent *away from* the normal. Thus there must be some value of θ_a *less than* 90° for which $\sin\theta_b = 1$ and $\theta_b = 90°$. This is shown by ray 3 in the diagram, which emerges just grazing the surface at an angle of refraction of 90°. Compare Fig. 33.13a to the photograph of light rays in Fig. 33.13b.

The angle of incidence for which the refracted ray emerges tangent to the surface is called the **critical angle,** denoted by θ_{crit}. (A more detailed analysis using Maxwell's equations shows that as the incident angle approaches the critical angle, the transmitted intensity approaches zero.) If the angle of incidence is *larger* than the critical angle, the sine of the angle of refraction, as computed by Snell's law, would have to be greater than unity, which is impossible. Beyond the critical angle, the ray *cannot* pass into the upper material; it is trapped in the lower material and is completely reflected at the boundary surface. This situation, called **total internal reflection,** occurs only when a ray in material a is incident on a second material b whose index of refraction is *smaller* than that of material a (that is, $n_b < n_a$).

We can find the critical angle for two given materials a and b by setting $\theta_b = 90°(\sin\theta_b = 1)$ in Snell's law. We then have

$$\sin\theta_{\text{crit}} = \frac{n_b}{n_a} \qquad \text{(critical angle for total internal reflection)} \qquad (33.6)$$

Total internal reflection will occur if the angle of incidence θ_a is larger than or equal to θ_{crit}.

Applications of Total Internal Reflection

Total internal reflection finds numerous uses in optical technology. As an example, consider glass with index of refraction $n = 1.52$. If light propagating within this glass encounters a glass–air interface, the critical angle is

$$\sin\theta_{\text{crit}} = \frac{1}{1.52} = 0.658 \qquad \theta_{\text{crit}} = 41.1°$$

The light will be *totally reflected* if it strikes the glass–air surface at an angle of 41.1° or larger. Because the critical angle is slightly smaller than 45°, it is possible to use a prism with angles of 45°−45°−90° as a totally reflecting surface. As reflectors, totally reflecting prisms have some advantages over metallic surfaces such as ordinary coated-glass mirrors. While no metallic surface reflects 100% of the light incident on it, light can be *totally* reflected by a prism. These reflecting properties of a prism are permanent and unaffected by tarnishing.

A 45°−45°−90° prism, used as in Fig. 33.14a, is called a *Porro* prism. Light enters and leaves at right angles to the hypotenuse and is totally reflected at each of the shorter faces. The total change of direction of the rays is 180°. Binoculars often use combinations of two Porro prisms, as in Fig. 33.14b.

When a beam of light enters at one end of a transparent rod (Fig. 33.15), the light can be totally reflected internally if the index of refraction of the rod is greater than that of the surrounding material. The light is "trapped" within the rod even if it is curved, provided that the curvature is not too great. Such a

33.14 (a) Total internal reflection in a Porro prism. (b) A combination of two Porro prisms in binoculars.

(a) Total internal reflection in a Porro prism

If the incident beam is oriented as shown, total internal reflection occurs on the 45° faces (because, for a glass–air interface, $\theta_{\text{crit}} = 41.1$).

(b) Binoculars use Porro prisms to reflect the light to each eyepiece.

Porro prisms

33.15 A transparent rod with refractive index greater than that of the surrounding material.

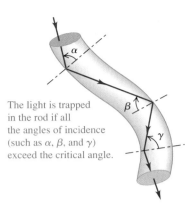

The light is trapped in the rod if all the angles of incidence (such as α, β, and γ) exceed the critical angle.

33.16 This colored x-ray image of a patient's abdomen shows an endoscope winding through the colon.

33.17 To maximize their brilliance, diamonds are cut so that there is total internal reflection on their back surfaces.

rod is sometimes called a *light pipe*. A bundle of fine glass or plastic fibers behaves in the same way and has the advantage of being flexible. A bundle may consist of thousands of individual fibers, each of the order of 0.002 to 0.01 mm in diameter. If the fibers are assembled in the bundle so that the relative positions of the ends are the same (or mirror images) at both ends, the bundle can transmit an image.

Fiber-optic devices have found a wide range of medical applications in instruments called *endoscopes*, which can be inserted directly into the bronchial tubes, the bladder, the colon, and other organs for direct visual examination (Fig. 33.16). A bundle of fibers can even be enclosed in a hypodermic needle for studying tissues and blood vessels far beneath the skin.

Fiber optics also have applications in communication systems, in which they are used to transmit a modulated laser beam. The rate at which information can be transmitted by a wave (light, radio, or whatever) is proportional to the frequency. To see qualitatively why this is so, consider modulating (modifying) the wave by chopping off some of the wave crests. Suppose each crest represents a binary digit, with a chopped-off crest representing a zero and an unmodified crest representing a one. The number of binary digits we can transmit per unit time is thus proportional to the frequency of the wave. Infrared and visible-light waves have much higher frequency than do radio waves, so a modulated laser beam can transmit an enormous amount of information through a single fiber-optic cable.

Another advantage of optical fibers is that they can be made thinner than conventional copper wire, so more fibers can be bundled together in a cable of a given diameter. Hence more distinct signals (for instance, different phone lines) can be sent over the same cable. Because fiber-optic cables are electrical insulators, they are immune to electrical interference from lightning and other sources, and they don't allow unwanted currents between source and receiver. For these and other reasons, fiber-optic cables play an important role in long-distance telephone, television, and Internet communication.

Total internal reflection also plays an important role in the design of jewelry. The brilliance of diamond is due in large measure to its very high index of refraction ($n = 2.417$) and correspondingly small critical angle. Light entering a cut diamond is totally internally reflected from facets on its back surface, and then emerges from its front surface (Fig. 33.17). "Imitation diamond" gems, such as cubic zirconia, are made from less expensive crystalline materials with comparable indexes of refraction.

Conceptual Example 33.4 **A leaky periscope**

A submarine periscope uses two totally reflecting 45°−45°−90° prisms with total internal reflection on the sides adjacent to the 45° angles. Explain why the periscope will no longer work if it springs a leak and the bottom prism is covered with water.

SOLUTION

The critical angle for water ($n_b = 1.33$) on glass ($n_a = 1.52$) is

$$\theta_{\text{crit}} = \arcsin\frac{1.33}{1.52} = 61.0°$$

The 45° angle of incidence for a totally reflecting prism is *smaller* than this new 61° critical angle, so total internal reflection does not occur at the glass–water interface. Most of the light is transmitted into the water, and very little is reflected back into the prism.

Test Your Understanding of Section 33.3 In which of the following situations is there total internal reflection? (i) Light propagating in water ($n = 1.33$) strikes a water–air interface at an incident angle of 70°; (ii) light propagating in glass ($n = 1.52$) strikes a glass–water interface at an incident angle of 70°; (iii) light propagating in water strikes a water–glass interface at an incident angle of 70°.

33.4 Dispersion

Ordinary white light is a superposition of waves with wavelengths extending throughout the visible spectrum. The speed of light *in vacuum* is the same for all wavelengths, but the speed in a material substance is different for different wavelengths. Therefore the index of refraction of a material depends on wavelength. The dependence of wave speed and index of refraction on wavelength is called **dispersion.**

Figure 33.18 shows the variation of index of refraction n with wavelength for some common optical materials. Note that the horizontal axis of this figure is the wavelength of the light *in vacuum,* λ_0; the wavelength in the material is given by Eq. (33.5), $\lambda = \lambda_0/n$. In most materials the value of n *decreases* with increasing wavelength and decreasing frequency, and thus n *increases* with decreasing wavelength and increasing frequency. In such a material, light of longer wavelength has greater speed than light of shorter wavelength.

Figure 33.19 shows a ray of white light incident on a prism. The deviation (change of direction) produced by the prism increases with increasing index of refraction and frequency and decreasing wavelength. Violet light is deviated most, and red is deviated least; other colors are in intermediate positions. When it comes out of the prism, the light is spread out into a fan-shaped beam, as shown. The light is said to be *dispersed* into a spectrum. The amount of dispersion depends on the *difference* between the refractive indexes for violet light and for red light. From Fig. 33.18 we can see that for a substance such as fluorite, the difference between the indexes for red and violet is small, and the dispersion will also be small. A better choice of material for a prism whose purpose is to produce a spectrum would be silicate flint glass, for which there is a larger difference in the value of n between red and violet.

33.18 Variation of index of refraction n with wavelength for different transparent materials. The horizontal axis shows the wavelength λ_0 of the light *in vacuum;* the wavelength in the material is equal to $\lambda = \lambda_0/n$.

33.19 Dispersion of light by a prism. The band of colors is called a spectrum.

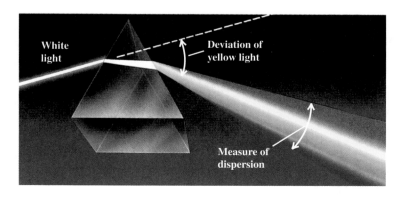

As we mentioned in Section 33.3, the brilliance of diamond is due in part to its unusually large refractive index; another important factor is its large dispersion, which causes white light entering a diamond to emerge as a multicolored spectrum. Crystals of rutile and of strontium titanate, which can be produced synthetically, have about eight times the dispersion of diamond.

Rainbows

When you experience the beauty of a rainbow, as in Fig. 33.20a, you are seeing the combined effects of dispersion, refraction, and reflection. Sunlight comes from behind you, enters a water droplet, is (partially) reflected from the back surface of the droplet, and is refracted again upon exiting the droplet (Fig. 33.20b). A light ray that enters the middle of the raindrop is reflected straight back. All other rays

33.20 How rainbows form.

(a) A double rainbow

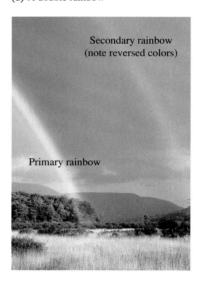

Secondary rainbow (note reversed colors)

Primary rainbow

(b) The paths of light rays entering the upper half of a raindrop

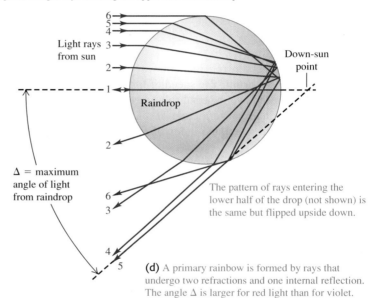

Light rays from sun

Down-sun point

Raindrop

Δ = maximum angle of light from raindrop

The pattern of rays entering the lower half of the drop (not shown) is the same but flipped upside down.

(c) Forming a rainbow. The sun in this illustration is directly behind the observer at P.

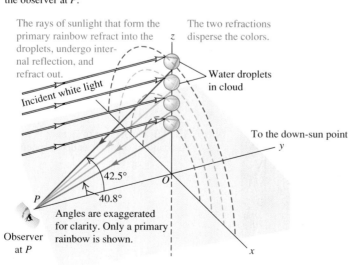

The rays of sunlight that form the primary rainbow refract into the droplets, undergo internal reflection, and refract out.

The two refractions disperse the colors.

Incident white light

Water droplets in cloud

To the down-sun point

42.5°

40.8°

Angles are exaggerated for clarity. Only a primary rainbow is shown.

Observer at P

(d) A primary rainbow is formed by rays that undergo two refractions and one internal reflection. The angle Δ is larger for red light than for violet.

Light from sun

$\Delta = 40.8°$ (violet) to 42.5° (red)

(e) A secondary rainbow is formed by rays that undergo two refractions and *two* internal reflections. The angle Δ is larger for violet light than for red.

Light from sun

$\Delta = 50.1°$ (red) to 53.2° (violet)

exit the raindrop within an angle Δ of that middle ray, with many rays "piling up" at the angle Δ. What you see is a disk of light of angular radius Δ centered on the down-sun point (the point in the sky opposite the sun); due to the "piling up" of light rays, the disk is brightest around its rim, which we see as a rainbow (Fig. 33.20c). Because no light reaches your eye from angles larger than Δ, the sky looks dark outside the rainbow (see Fig. 33.20a). The value of the angle Δ depends on the index of refraction of the water that makes up the raindrops, which in turn depends on the wavelength (Fig. 33.20d). The bright disk of red light is slightly larger than that for orange light, which in turn is slightly larger than that for yellow light, and so on. As a result, you see the rainbow as a band of colors.

In many cases you can see a second, larger rainbow. It is the result of dispersion, refraction, and *two* reflections from the back surface of the droplet (Fig. 33.20e). Each time a light ray hits the back surface, part of the light is refracted out of the drop (not shown in Fig. 33.20); after two such hits, relatively little light is left inside the drop, which is why the secondary rainbow is noticeably fainter than the primary rainbow. Just as a mirror held up to a book reverses the printed letters, so the second reflection reverses the sequence of colors in the secondary rainbow. You can see this effect in Fig. 33.20a.

33.5 Polarization

Polarization is a characteristic of all transverse waves. This chapter is about light, but to introduce some basic polarization concepts, let's go back to the transverse waves on a string that we studied in Chapter 15. For a string that in equilibrium lies along the x-axis, the displacements may be along the y-direction, as in Fig. 33.21a. In this case the string always lies in the xy-plane. But the displacements might instead be along the z-axis, as in Fig. 33.21b; then the string always lies in the xz-plane.

When a wave has only y-displacements, we say that it is **linearly polarized** in the y-direction; a wave with only z-displacements is linearly polarized in the z-direction. For mechanical waves we can build a **polarizing filter,** or **polarizer,** that permits only waves with a certain polarization direction to pass. In Fig. 33.21c the string can slide vertically in the slot without friction, but no horizontal motion is possible. This filter passes waves that are polarized in the y-direction but blocks those that are polarized in the z-direction.

This same language can be applied to electromagnetic waves, which also have polarization. As we learned in Chapter 32, an electromagnetic wave is a *transverse* wave; the fluctuating electric and magnetic fields are perpendicular to each other and to the direction of propagation. We always define the direction of polarization of an electromagnetic wave to be the direction of the *electric*-field vector $\vec{E}$, not the magnetic field, because many common electromagnetic-wave detectors respond to the electric forces on electrons in materials, not the magnetic forces. Thus the electromagnetic wave described by Eq. (32.17),

$$\vec{E}(x, t) = \hat{\jmath}E_{max}\cos(kx - \omega t)$$
$$\vec{B}(x, t) = \hat{k}B_{max}\cos(kx - \omega t)$$

ActivPhysics 16.9: Physical Optics: Polarization

33.21 (a), (b) Polarized waves on a string. (c) Making a polarized wave on a string from an unpolarized one using a polarizing filter.

(a) Transverse wave linearly polarized in the y-direction

(b) Transverse wave linearly polarized in the z-direction

(c) The slot functions as a polarizing filter, passing only components polarized in the y-direction.

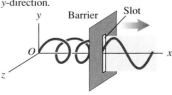

33.22 (a) Electrons in the red and white broadcast antenna oscillate vertically, producing vertically polarized electromagnetic waves that propagate away from the antenna in the horizontal direction. (The small gray antennas are for relaying cellular phone signals.) (b) No matter how this light bulb is oriented, the random motion of electrons in the filament produces unpolarized light waves.

(a)

(b)

is said to be polarized in the *y*-direction because the electric field has only a *y*-component.

CAUTION **The meaning of "polarization"** It's unfortunate that the same word "polarization" that is used to describe the direction of $\vec{E}$ in an electromagnetic wave is also used to describe the shifting of electric charge within a body, such as in response to a nearby charged body; we described this latter kind of polarization in Section 21.2 (see Fig. 21.7). You should remember that while these two concepts have the same name, they do not describe the same phenomenon.

Polarizing Filters

Waves emitted by a radio transmitter are usually linearly polarized. The vertical antennas that are used for radio broadcasting emit waves that, in a horizontal plane around the antenna, are polarized in the vertical direction (parallel to the antenna) (Fig. 33.22a).

The situation is different for visible light. Light from incandescent light bulbs and fluorescent light fixtures is *not* polarized (Fig. 33.22b). The "antennas" that radiate light waves are the molecules that make up the sources. The waves emitted by any one molecule may be linearly polarized, like those from a radio antenna. But any actual light source contains a tremendous number of molecules with random orientations, so the emitted light is a random mixture of waves linearly polarized in all possible transverse directions. Such light is called **unpolarized light** or **natural light.** To create polarized light from unpolarized natural light requires a filter that is analogous to the slot for mechanical waves in Fig. 33.21c.

Polarizing filters for electromagnetic waves have different details of construction, depending on the wavelength. For microwaves with a wavelength of a few centimeters, a good polarizer is an array of closely spaced, parallel conducting wires that are insulated from each other. (Think of a barbecue grill with the outer metal ring replaced by an insulating one.) Electrons are free to move along the length of the conducting wires and will do so in response to a wave whose $\vec{E}$ field is parallel to the wires. The resulting currents in the wires dissipate energy by I^2R heating; the dissipated energy comes from the wave, so whatever wave passes through the grid is greatly reduced in amplitude. Waves with $\vec{E}$ oriented perpendicular to the wires pass through almost unaffected, since electrons cannot move through the air between the wires. Hence a wave that passes through such a filter will be predominantly polarized in the direction perpendicular to the wires.

The most common polarizing filter for visible light is a material known by the trade name Polaroid, widely used for sunglasses and polarizing filters for camera lenses. Developed originally by the American scientist Edwin H. Land, this material incorporates substances that have **dichroism,** a selective absorption in which one of the polarized components is absorbed much more strongly than the other (Fig. 33.23). A Polaroid filter transmits 80% or more of the intensity of a wave that is polarized parallel to a certain axis in the material, called the **polarizing**

33.23 A Polaroid filter is illuminated by unpolarized natural light (shown by $\vec{E}$ vectors that point in all directions perpendicular to the direction of propagation). The transmitted light is linearly polarized along the polarizing axis (shown by $\vec{E}$ vectors along the polarization direction only).

Filter only partially absorbs vertically polarized component of light.

Incident unpolarized light

Polarizing axis

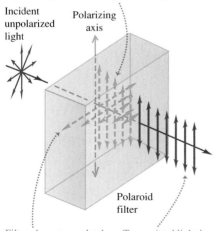

Polaroid filter

Filter almost completely absorbs horizontally polarized component of light.

Transmitted light is linearly polarized in the vertical direction.

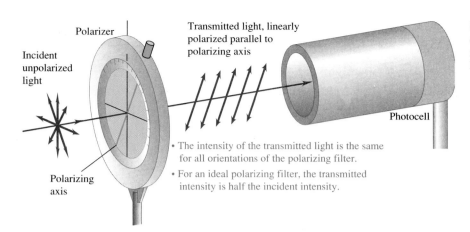

Unpolarized natural light is incident on the polarizing filter. The photocell measures the intensity of the transmitted linearly polarized light.

axis, but only 1% or less for waves that are polarized perpendicular to this axis. In one type of Polaroid filter, long-chain molecules within the filter are oriented with their axis perpendicular to the polarizing axis; these molecules preferentially absorb light that is polarized along their length, much like the conducting wires in a polarizing filter for microwaves.

Using Polarizing Filters

An *ideal* polarizing filter (polarizer) passes 100% of the incident light that is polarized parallel to the filter's polarizing axis but completely blocks all light that is polarized perpendicular to this axis. Such a device is an unattainable idealization, but the concept is useful in clarifying the basic ideas. In the following discussion we will assume that all polarizing filters are ideal. In Fig. 33.24 unpolarized light is incident on a flat polarizing filter. The $\vec{E}$ vector of the incident wave can be represented in terms of components parallel and perpendicular to the polarizer axis (shown in blue); only the component of $\vec{E}$ parallel to the polarizing axis is transmitted. Hence the light emerging from the polarizer is linearly polarized parallel to the polarizing axis.

When unpolarized light is incident on an ideal polarizer as in Fig. 33.24, the intensity of the transmitted light is *exactly half* that of the incident unpolarized light, no matter how the polarizing axis is oriented. Here's why: We can resolve the $\vec{E}$ field of the incident wave into a component parallel to the polarizing axis and a component perpendicular to it. Because the incident light is a random mixture of all states of polarization, these two components are, on average, equal. The ideal polarizer transmits only the component that is parallel to the polarizing axis, so half the incident intensity is transmitted.

What happens when the linearly polarized light emerging from a polarizer passes through a second polarizer, or *analyzer*, as in Fig. 33.25? Suppose the polarizing axis of the analyzer makes an angle ϕ with the polarizing axis of the

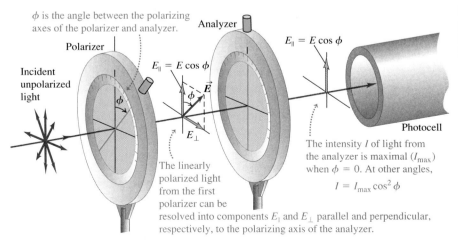

An ideal analyzer transmits only the electric field component parallel to its transmission direction (that is, its polarizing axis).

33.26 These photos show the view through Polaroid sunglasses whose polarizing axes are (left) aligned ($\phi = 0$) and (right) perpendicular ($\phi = 90°$). The transmitted intensity is greatest when the axes are aligned; it is zero when the axes are perpendicular.

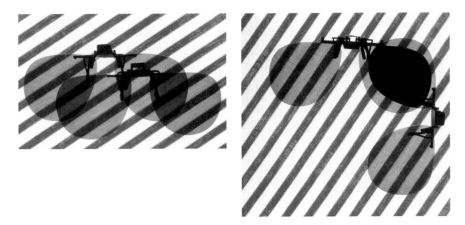

first polarizer. We can resolve the linearly polarized light that is transmitted by the first polarizer into two components, as shown in Fig. 33.25, one parallel and the other perpendicular to the axis of the analyzer. Only the parallel component, with amplitude $E\cos\phi$, is transmitted by the analyzer. The transmitted intensity is greatest when $\phi = 0$, and it is zero when the polarizer and analyzer are *crossed* so that $\phi = 90°$ (Fig. 33.26). To determine the direction of polarization of the light transmitted by the first polarizer, rotate the analyzer until the photocell in Fig. 33.25 measures zero intensity; the polarization axis of the first polarizer is then perpendicular to that of the analyzer.

To find the transmitted intensity at intermediate values of the angle ϕ, we recall from our energy discussion in Section 32.4 that the intensity of an electromagnetic wave is proportional to the *square* of the amplitude of the wave [see Eq. (32.29)]. The ratio of transmitted to incident *amplitude* is $\cos\phi$, so the ratio of transmitted to incident *intensity* is $\cos^2\phi$. Thus the intensity of the light transmitted through the analyzer is

$$I = I_{\text{max}}\cos^2\phi \qquad \begin{array}{l}\text{(Malus's law, polarized light}\\ \text{passing through an analyzer)}\end{array} \qquad (33.7)$$

where I_{max} is the maximum intensity of light transmitted (at $\phi = 0$) and I is the amount transmitted at angle ϕ. This relationship, discovered experimentally by Etienne Louis Malus in 1809, is called **Malus's law.** Malus's law applies *only* if the incident light passing through the analyzer is already linearly polarized.

Problem-Solving Strategy 33.2   Linear Polarization

IDENTIFY *the relevant concepts:* In all electromagnetic waves, including light waves, the direction of polarization is the direction of the $\vec{E}$ field and is perpendicular to the propagation direction. Problems about polarizers are therefore about the components of $\vec{E}$ parallel and perpendicular to the polarizing axis.

SET UP *the problem* using the following steps:
1. Start by drawing a large, neat diagram. Label all known angles, including the angles of all polarizing axes.
2. Identify the target variables.

EXECUTE *the solution* as follows:
1. Remember that a polarizer lets pass only electric-field components parallel to its polarizing axis.
2. If the incident light is linearly polarized and has amplitude E and intensity I_{max}, the light that passes through an ideal polarizer has amplitude $E\cos\phi$ and intensity $I_{\text{max}}\cos^2\phi$, where ϕ is the angle between the incident polarization direction and the filter's polarizing axis.
3. Unpolarized light is a random mixture of all possible polarization states, so on the average it has equal components in any two perpendicular directions. When passed through an ideal polarizer, unpolarized light becomes linearly polarized light with half the incident intensity. Partially linearly polarized light is a superposition of linearly polarized and unpolarized light.
4. The intensity (average power per unit area) of a wave is proportional to the *square* of its amplitude. If you find that two waves differ in amplitude by a certain factor, their intensities differ by the square of that factor.

EVALUATE *your answer:* Check your answer for any obvious errors. If your results say that light emerging from a polarizer has greater intensity than the incident light, something's wrong: A polarizer can't add energy to a light wave.

Example 33.5 Two polarizers in combination

In Fig. 33.25 the incident unpolarized light has intensity I_0. Find the intensities transmitted by the first and second polarizers if the angle between the axes of the two filters is 30°.

SOLUTION

IDENTIFY and SET UP: This problem involves a polarizer (a polarizing filter on which unpolarized light shines, producing polarized light) and an analyzer (a second polarizing filter on which the polarized light shines). We are given the intensity I_0 of the incident light and the angle $\phi = 30°$ between the axes of the polarizers. We use Malus's law, Eq. (33.7), to solve for the intensities of the light emerging from each polarizer.

EXECUTE: The incident light is unpolarized, so the intensity of the linearly polarized light transmitted by the first polarizer is $I_0/2$. From Eq. (33.7) with $\phi = 30°$, the second polarizer reduces the intensity by a further factor of $\cos^2 30° = \frac{3}{4}$. Thus the intensity transmitted by the second polarizer is

$$\left(\frac{I_0}{2}\right)\left(\tfrac{3}{4}\right) = \tfrac{3}{8} I_0$$

EVALUATE: Note that the intensity decreases after each passage through a polarizer. The only situation in which the transmitted intensity does *not* decrease is if the polarizer is ideal (so it absorbs none of the light that passes through it) and if the incident light is linearly polarized along the polarizing axis, so $\phi = 0$.

33.27 When light is incident on a reflecting surface at the polarizing angle, the reflected light is linearly polarized.

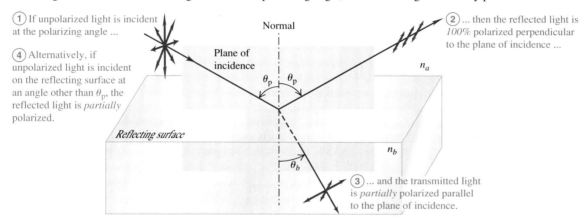

(1) If unpolarized light is incident at the polarizing angle ...

(4) Alternatively, if unpolarized light is incident on the reflecting surface at an angle other than θ_p, the reflected light is *partially* polarized.

(2) ... then the reflected light is *100%* polarized perpendicular to the plane of incidence ...

(3) ... and the transmitted light is *partially* polarized parallel to the plane of incidence.

Polarization by Reflection

Unpolarized light can be polarized, either partially or totally, by *reflection*. In Fig. 33.27, unpolarized natural light is incident on a reflecting surface between two transparent optical materials. For most angles of incidence, waves for which the electric-field vector $\vec{E}$ is perpendicular to the plane of incidence (that is, parallel to the reflecting surface) are reflected more strongly than those for which $\vec{E}$ lies in this plane. In this case the reflected light is *partially polarized* in the direction perpendicular to the plane of incidence.

But at one particular angle of incidence, called the **polarizing angle** θ_p, the light for which $\vec{E}$ lies in the plane of incidence is *not reflected at all* but is completely refracted. At this same angle of incidence the light for which $\vec{E}$ is perpendicular to the plane of incidence is partially reflected and partially refracted. The *reflected* light is therefore *completely* polarized perpendicular to the plane of incidence, as shown in Fig. 33.27. The *refracted* (transmitted) light is *partially* polarized parallel to this plane; the refracted light is a mixture of the component parallel to the plane of incidence, all of which is refracted, and the remainder of the perpendicular component.

In 1812 the British scientist Sir David Brewster discovered that when the angle of incidence is equal to the polarizing angle θ_p, the reflected ray and the refracted ray are perpendicular to each other (Fig. 33.28). In this case the angle of refraction θ_b equals $90° - \theta_p$. From the law of refraction,

$$n_a \sin\theta_p = n_b \sin\theta_b$$

33.28 The significance of the polarizing angle. The open circles represent a component of $\vec{E}$ that is perpendicular to the plane of the figure (the plane of incidence) and parallel to the surface between the two materials.

Note: This is a side view of the situation shown in Fig. 33.27.

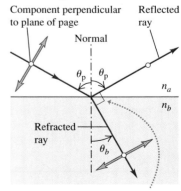

When light strikes a surface at the polarizing angle, the reflected and refracted rays are perpendicular to each other and

$$\tan\theta_p = \frac{n_b}{n_a}$$

so we find

$$n_a \sin\theta_p = n_b \sin(90° - \theta_p) = n_b \cos\theta_p$$

$$\tan\theta_p = \frac{n_b}{n_a} \quad \text{(Brewster's law for the polarizing angle)} \quad (33.8)$$

This relationship is known as **Brewster's law.** Although discovered experimentally, it can also be *derived* from a wave model using Maxwell's equations.

Polarization by reflection is the reason polarizing filters are widely used in sunglasses (Fig. 33.26). When sunlight is reflected from a horizontal surface, the plane of incidence is vertical, and the reflected light contains a preponderance of light that is polarized in the horizontal direction. When the reflection occurs at a smooth asphalt road surface or the surface of a lake, it causes unwanted glare. Vision can be improved by eliminating this glare. The manufacturer makes the polarizing axis of the lens material vertical, so very little of the horizontally polarized light reflected from the road is transmitted to the eyes. The glasses also reduce the overall intensity of the transmitted light to somewhat less than 50% of the intensity of the unpolarized incident light.

Example 33.6   **Reflection from a swimming pool's surface**

Sunlight reflects off the smooth surface of a swimming pool. (a) For what angle of reflection is the reflected light completely polarized? (b) What is the corresponding angle of refraction? (c) At night, an underwater floodlight is turned on in the pool. Repeat parts (a) and (b) for rays from the floodlight that strike the surface from below.

SOLUTION

IDENTIFY and SET UP: This problem involves polarization by reflection at an air–water interface in parts (a) and (b) and at a water–air interface in part (c). Figure 33.29 shows our sketches.

33.29 Our sketches for this problem.

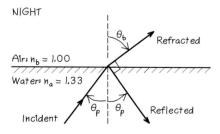

For both cases our first target variable is the polarizing angle θ_p, which we find using Brewster's law, Eq. (33.8). For this angle of reflection, the angle of refraction θ_b is the complement of θ_p (that is, $\theta_b = 90° - \theta_p$).

EXECUTE: (a) During the day (shown in the upper part of Fig. 33.29) the light moves in air toward water, so $n_a = 1.00$ (air) and $n_b = 1.33$ (water). From Eq. (33.8),

$$\theta_p = \arctan\frac{n_b}{n_a} = \arctan\frac{1.33}{1.00} = 53.1°$$

(b) The incident light is at the polarizing angle, so the reflected and refracted rays are perpendicular; hence

$$\theta_b = 90° - \theta_p = 90° - 53.1° = 36.9°$$

(c) At night (shown in the lower part of Fig. 33.29) the light moves in water toward air, so now $n_a = 1.33$ and $n_b = 1.00$. Again using Eq. (33.8), we have

$$\theta_p = \arctan\frac{1.00}{1.33} = 36.9°$$
$$\theta_b = 90° - 36.9° = 53.1°$$

EVALUATE: We check our answer in part (b) by using Snell's law, $n_a \sin\theta_a = n_b \sin\theta_b$, to solve for θ_b:

$$\sin\theta_b = \frac{n_a \sin\theta_p}{n_b} = \frac{1.00\sin 53.1°}{1.33} = 0.600$$
$$\theta_b = \arcsin(0.600) = 36.9°$$

Note that the two polarizing angles found in parts (a) and (c) add to 90°. This is *not* an accident; can you see why?

Circular and Elliptical Polarization

Light and other electromagnetic radiation can also have *circular* or *elliptical* polarization. To introduce these concepts, let's return once more to mechanical waves on a stretched string. In Fig. 33.21, suppose the two linearly polarized waves in parts (a) and (b) are in phase and have equal amplitude. When they are superposed, each point in the string has simultaneous y- and z-displacements of equal magnitude. A little thought shows that the resultant wave lies in a plane oriented at 45° to the y- and z-axes (i.e., in a plane making a 45° angle with the xy- and xz-planes). The amplitude of the resultant wave is larger by a factor of $\sqrt{2}$ than that of either component wave, and the resultant wave is linearly polarized.

But now suppose the two equal-amplitude waves differ in phase by a quarter-cycle. Then the resultant motion of each point corresponds to a superposition of two simple harmonic motions at right angles, with a quarter-cycle phase difference. The y-displacement at a point is greatest at times when the z-displacement is zero, and vice versa. The motion of the string as a whole then no longer takes place in a single plane. It can be shown that each point on the rope moves in a *circle* in a plane parallel to the yz-plane. Successive points on the rope have successive phase differences, and the overall motion of the string has the appearance of a rotating helix. This is shown to the left of the polarizing filter in Fig. 33.21c. This particular superposition of two linearly polarized waves is called **circular polarization.**

Figure 33.30 shows the analogous situation for an electromagnetic wave. Two sinusoidal waves of equal amplitude, polarized in the y- and z-directions and with a quarter-cycle phase difference, are superposed. The result is a wave in which the $\vec{E}$ vector at each point has a constant magnitude but *rotates* around the direction of propagation. The wave in Fig. 33.30 is propagating toward you and the $\vec{E}$ vector appears to be rotating clockwise, so it is called a *right circularly polarized* electromagnetic wave. If instead the $\vec{E}$ vector of a wave coming toward you appears to be rotating counterclockwise, it is called a *left circularly polarized* electromagnetic wave.

If the phase difference between the two component waves is something other than a quarter-cycle, or if the two component waves have different amplitudes, then each point on the string traces out not a circle but an *ellipse*. The resulting wave is said to be **elliptically polarized.**

For electromagnetic waves with radio frequencies, circular or elliptical polarization can be produced by using two antennas at right angles, fed from the same

33.30 Circular polarization of an electromagnetic wave moving toward you parallel to the x-axis. The y-component of $\vec{E}$ lags the z-component by a quarter-cycle. This phase difference results in right circular polarization.

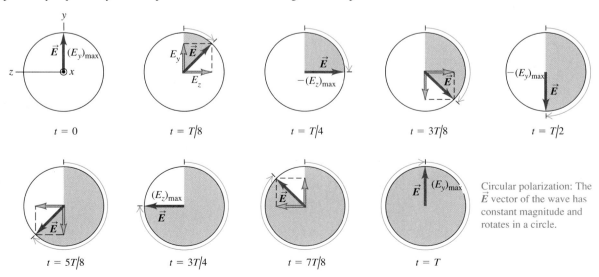

Circular polarization: The $\vec{E}$ vector of the wave has constant magnitude and rotates in a circle.

transmitter but with a phase-shifting network that introduces the appropriate phase difference. For light, the phase shift can be introduced by use of a material that exhibits *birefringence*—that is, has different indexes of refraction for different directions of polarization. A common example is calcite ($CaCO_3$). When a calcite crystal is oriented appropriately in a beam of unpolarized light, its refractive index (for a wavelength in vacuum of 589 nm) is 1.658 for one direction of polarization and 1.486 for the perpendicular direction. When two waves with equal amplitude and with perpendicular directions of polarization enter such a material, they travel with different speeds. If they are in phase when they enter the material, then in general they are no longer in phase when they emerge. If the crystal is just thick enough to introduce a quarter-cycle phase difference, then the crystal converts linearly polarized light to circularly polarized light. Such a crystal is called a *quarter-wave plate*. Such a plate also converts circularly polarized light to linearly polarized light. Can you prove this?

Photoelasticity

Some optical materials that are not normally birefringent become so when they are subjected to mechanical stress. This is the basis of the science of *photoelasticity*. Stresses in girders, boiler plates, gear teeth, and cathedral pillars can be analyzed by constructing a transparent model of the object, usually of a plastic material, subjecting it to stress, and examining it between a polarizer and an analyzer in the crossed position. Very complicated stress distributions can be studied by these optical methods.

Figure 33.31 is a photograph of a photoelastic model under stress. The polarized light that enters the model can be thought of as having a component along each of the two directions of the birefringent plastic. Since these two components travel through the plastic at different speeds, the light that emerges from the other side of the model can have a different overall direction of polarization. Hence some of this transmitted light will be able to pass through the analyzer even though its polarization axis is at a 90° angle to the polarizer's axis, and the stressed areas in the plastic will appear as bright spots. The amount of birefringence is different for different wavelengths and hence different colors of light; the color that appears at each location in Fig. 33.31 is that for which the transmitted light is most nearly polarized along the analyzer's polarization axis.

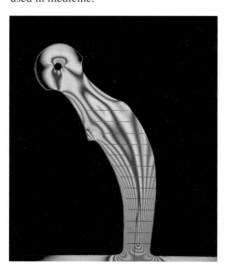

33.31 This plastic model of an artificial hip joint was photographed between two polarizing filters (a polarizer and an analyzer) with perpendicular polarizing axes. The colored interference pattern reveals the direction and magnitude of stresses in the model. Engineers use these results to help design the metal artificial hip joint used in medicine.

Test Your Understanding of Section 33.5   You are taking a photograph of a sunlit high-rise office building. In order to minimize the reflections from the building's windows, you place a polarizing filter on the camera lens. How should you orient the filter? (i) with the polarizing axis vertical; (ii) with the polarizing axis horizontal; (iii) either orientation will minimize the reflections just as well; (iv) neither orientation will have any effect.

33.6 Scattering of Light

The sky is blue. Sunsets are red. Skylight is partially polarized; that's why the sky looks darker from some angles than from others when it is viewed through Polaroid sunglasses. As we will see, a single phenomenon is responsible for all of these effects.

When you look at the daytime sky, the light that you see is sunlight that has been absorbed and then re-radiated in a variety of directions. This process is called **scattering.** (If the earth had no atmosphere, the sky would appear as black in the daytime as it does at night, just as it does to an astronaut in space or on the moon.) Figure 33.32 shows some of the details of the scattering process. Sunlight, which is unpolarized, comes from the left along the x-axis and passes over an observer looking vertically upward along the y-axis. (We are viewing the situation

33.32 When the sunbathing observer on the left looks up, he sees blue, polarized sunlight that has been scattered by air molecules. The observer on the right sees reddened, unpolarized light when he looks at the sun.

Incident white light, *y* unpolarized

Electric charges in air molecules at *O* oscillate in the direction of the $\vec{E}$ field of the incident light from the sun, acting as antennas that produce scattered light. The scattered light that reaches the observer directly below *O* is polarized in the *z*-direction.

Air molecules scatter blue light more effectively than red light; we see the sky overhead by scattered light, so it looks blue.

This observer sees reddened sunlight because most of the blue light has been scattered out.

from the side.) Consider the molecules of the earth's atmosphere located at point *O*. The electric field in the beam of sunlight sets the electric charges in these molecules into vibration. Since light is a transverse wave, the direction of the electric field in any component of the sunlight lies in the *yz*-plane, and the motion of the charges takes place in this plane. There is no field, and hence no motion of charges, in the direction of the *x*-axis.

An incident light wave sets the electric charges in the molecules at point *O* vibrating along the line of $\vec{E}$. We can resolve this vibration into two components, one along the *y*-axis and the other along the *z*-axis. Each component in the incident light produces the equivalent of two molecular "antennas," oscillating with the same frequency as the incident light and lying along the *y*- and *z*-axes.

We mentioned in Chapter 32 that an oscillating charge, like those in an antenna, does not radiate in the direction of its oscillation. (See Fig. 32.3 in Section 32.1.) Thus the "antenna" along the *y*-axis does not send any light to the observer directly below it, although it does emit light in other directions. Therefore the only light reaching this observer comes from the other molecular "antenna," corresponding to the oscillation of charge along the *z*-axis. This light is linearly polarized, with its electric field along the *z*-axis (parallel to the "antenna"). The red vectors on the *y*-axis below point *O* in Fig. 33.32 show the direction of polarization of the light reaching the observer.

As the original beam of sunlight passes though the atmosphere, its intensity decreases as its energy goes into the scattered light. Detailed analysis of the scattering process shows that the intensity of the light scattered from air molecules increases in proportion to the fourth power of the frequency (inversely to the fourth power of the wavelength). Thus the intensity ratio for the two ends of the visible spectrum is $(750 \text{ nm}/380 \text{ nm})^4 = 15$. Roughly speaking, scattered light contains 15 times as much blue light as red, and that's why the sky is blue.

Clouds contain a high concentration of water droplets or ice crystals, which also scatter light. Because of this high concentration, light passing through the cloud has many more opportunities for scattering than does light passing through a clear sky. Thus light of *all* wavelengths is eventually scattered out of the cloud, so the cloud looks white (Fig. 33.33). Milk looks white for the same reason; the scattering is due to fat globules in the milk.

Near sunset, when sunlight has to travel a long distance through the earth's atmosphere, a substantial fraction of the blue light is removed by scattering. White light minus blue light looks yellow or red. This explains the yellow or red hue that we so often see from the setting sun (and that is seen by the observer at the far right of Fig. 33.32).

Application **Bee Vision and Polarized Light from the Sky**
The eyes of a bee can detect the polarization of light. Bees use this to help them navigate between the hive and food sources. As Fig. 33.32 shows, a bee sees unpolarized light if it looks directly toward the sun and sees completely polarized light if it looks 90° away from the sun. These polarizations are unaffected by the presence of clouds, so a bee can navigate relative to the sun even on an overcast day.

Eyes

33.33 Clouds are white because they efficiently scatter sunlight of all wavelengths.

33.7 Huygens's Principle

The laws of reflection and refraction of light rays that we introduced in Section 33.2 were discovered experimentally long before the wave nature of light was firmly established. However, we can *derive* these laws from wave considerations and show that they are consistent with the wave nature of light.

We begin with a principle called **Huygens's principle.** This principle, stated originally by the Dutch scientist Christiaan Huygens in 1678, is a geometrical method for finding, from the known shape of a wave front at some instant, the shape of the wave front at some later time. Huygens assumed that **every point of a wave front may be considered the source of secondary wavelets that spread out in all directions with a speed equal to the speed of propagation of the wave.** The new wave front at a later time is then found by constructing a surface *tangent* to the secondary wavelets or, as it is called, the *envelope* of the wavelets. All the results that we obtain from Huygens's principle can also be obtained from Maxwell's equations. Thus it is not an independent principle, but it is often very convenient for calculations with wave phenomena.

Huygens's principle is shown in Fig. 33.34. The original wave front AA' is traveling outward from a source, as indicated by the arrows. We want to find the shape of the wave front after a time interval t. We assume that v, the speed of propagation of the wave, is the same at all points. Then in time t the wave front travels a distance vt. We construct several circles (traces of spherical wavelets) with radius $r = vt$, centered at points along AA'. The trace of the envelope of these wavelets, which is the new wave front, is the curve BB'.

Reflection and Huygens's Principle

To derive the law of reflection from Huygens's principle, we consider a plane wave approaching a plane reflecting surface. In Fig. 33.35a the lines AA', OB', and NC' represent successive positions of a wave front approaching the surface MM'. Point A on the wave front AA' has just arrived at the reflecting surface. We can use Huygens's principle to find the position of the wave front after a time interval t. With points on AA' as centers, we draw several secondary wavelets with radius vt. The wavelets that originate near the upper end of AA' spread out unhindered, and their envelope gives the portion OB' of the new wave front. If the reflecting surface were not there, the wavelets originating near the lower end of AA' would similarly reach the positions shown by the broken circular arcs. Instead, these wavelets strike the reflecting surface.

The effect of the reflecting surface is to *change the direction* of travel of those wavelets that strike it, so the part of a wavelet that would have penetrated the surface actually lies to the left of it, as shown by the full lines. The first such wavelet is centered at point A; the envelope of all such reflected wavelets is the portion OB of the wave front. The trace of the entire wave front at this instant is the bent line BOB'. A similar construction gives the line CNC' for the wave front after another interval t.

From plane geometry the angle θ_a between the incident *wave front* and the *surface* is the same as that between the incident *ray* and the *normal* to the surface and is therefore the angle of incidence. Similarly, θ_r is the angle of reflection. To find the relationship between these angles, we consider Fig. 33.35b. From O we draw $OP = vt$, perpendicular to AA'. Now OB, by construction, is tangent to a circle of radius vt with center at A. If we draw AQ from A to the point of tangency, the triangles APO and OQA are congruent because they are right triangles with the side AO in common and with $AQ = OP = vt$. The angle θ_a therefore equals the angle θ_r, and we have the law of reflection.

Refraction and Huygens's Principle

We can derive the law of *refraction* by a similar procedure. In Fig. 33.36a we consider a wave front, represented by line AA', for which point A has just

33.34 Applying Huygens's principle to wave front AA' to construct a new wave front BB'.

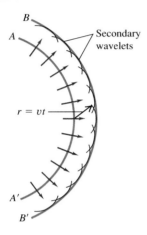

33.35 Using Huygens's principle to derive the law of reflection.

(a) Successive positions of a plane wave AA' as it is reflected from a plane surface

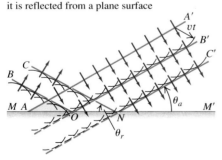

(b) Magnified portion of **(a)**

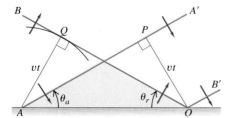

arrived at the boundary surface SS' between two transparent materials a and b, with indexes of refraction n_a and n_b and wave speeds v_a and v_b. (The *reflected* waves are not shown in the figure; they proceed as in Fig. 33.35.) We can apply Huygens's principle to find the position of the refracted wave fronts after a time t.

With points on AA' as centers, we draw several secondary wavelets. Those originating near the upper end of AA' travel with speed v_a and, after a time interval t, are spherical surfaces of radius $v_a t$. The wavelet originating at point A, however, is traveling in the second material b with speed v_b and at time t is a spherical surface of radius $v_b t$. The envelope of the wavelets from the original wave front is the plane whose trace is the bent line BOB'. A similar construction leads to the trace CPC' after a second interval t.

The angles θ_a and θ_b between the surface and the incident and refracted wave fronts are the angle of incidence and the angle of refraction, respectively. To find the relationship between these angles, refer to Fig. 33.36b. We draw $OQ = v_a t$, perpendicular to AQ, and we draw $AB = v_b t$, perpendicular to BO. From the right triangle AOQ,

$$\sin\theta_a = \frac{v_a t}{AO}$$

and from the right triangle AOB,

$$\sin\theta_b = \frac{v_b t}{AO}$$

Combining these, we find

$$\frac{\sin\theta_a}{\sin\theta_b} = \frac{v_a}{v_b} \qquad (33.9)$$

We have defined the index of refraction n of a material as the ratio of the speed of light c in vacuum to its speed v in the material: $n_a = c/v_a$ and $n_b = c/v_b$. Thus

$$\frac{n_b}{n_a} = \frac{c/v_b}{c/v_a} = \frac{v_a}{v_b}$$

and we can rewrite Eq. (33.9) as

$$\frac{\sin\theta_a}{\sin\theta_b} = \frac{n_b}{n_a} \quad \text{or}$$

$$n_a \sin\theta_a = n_b \sin\theta_b$$

which we recognize as Snell's law, Eq. (33.4). So we have derived Snell's law from a wave theory. Alternatively, we may choose to regard Snell's law as an experimental result that defines the index of refraction of a material; in that case this analysis helps to confirm the relationship $v = c/n$ for the speed of light in a material.

Mirages offer an interesting example of Huygens's principle in action. When the surface of pavement or desert sand is heated intensely by the sun, a hot, less dense, smaller-n layer of air forms near the surface. The speed of light is slightly greater in the hotter air near the ground, the Huygens wavelets have slightly larger radii, the wave fronts tilt slightly, and rays that were headed toward the surface with a large angle of incidence (near 90°) can be bent up as shown in Fig. 33.37. Light farther from the ground is bent less and travels nearly in a straight line. The observer sees the object in its natural position, with an inverted image below it, as though seen in a horizontal reflecting surface. The mind of a thirsty traveler can interpret the apparent reflecting surface as a sheet of water.

33.36 Using Huygens's principle to derive the law of refraction. The case $v_b < v_a$ ($n_b > n_a$) is shown.

(a) Successive positions of a plane wave AA' as it is refracted by a plane surface

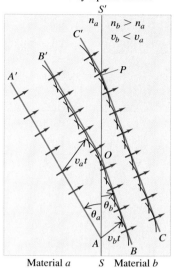

(b) Magnified portion of **(a)**

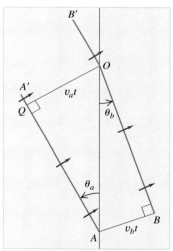

33.37 How mirages are formed.

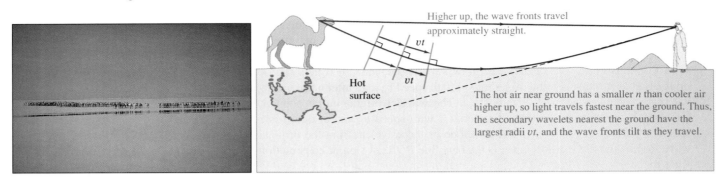

Higher up, the wave fronts travel approximately straight.

Hot surface

vt

vt

The hot air near ground has a smaller n than cooler air higher up, so light travels fastest near the ground. Thus, the secondary wavelets nearest the ground have the largest radii vt, and the wave fronts tilt as they travel.

It is important to keep in mind that Maxwell's equations are the fundamental relationships for electromagnetic wave propagation. But Huygens's principle provides a convenient way to visualize this propagation.

Test Your Understanding of Section 33.7 Sound travels faster in warm air than in cold air. Imagine a weather front that runs north-south, with warm air to the west of the front and cold air to the east. A sound wave traveling in a northeast direction in the warm air encounters this front. How will the direction of this sound wave change when it passes into the cold air? (i) The wave direction will deflect toward the north; (ii) the wave direction will deflect toward the east; (iii) the wave direction will be unchanged. ❙

Light and its properties: Light is an electromagnetic wave. When emitted or absorbed, it also shows particle properties. It is emitted by accelerated electric charges.

A wave front is a surface of constant phase; wave fronts move with a speed equal to the propagation speed of the wave. A ray is a line along the direction of propagation, perpendicular to the wave fronts.

When light is transmitted from one material to another, the frequency of the light is unchanged, but the wavelength and wave speed can change. The index of refraction n of a material is the ratio of the speed of light in vacuum c to the speed v in the material. If λ_0 is the wavelength in vacuum, the same wave has a shorter wavelength λ in a medium with index of refraction n. (See Example 33.2.)

$$n = \frac{c}{v} \qquad (33.1)$$

$$\lambda = \frac{\lambda_0}{n} \qquad (33.5)$$

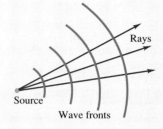

Reflection and refraction: At a smooth interface between two optical materials, the incident, reflected, and refracted rays and the normal to the interface all lie in a single plane called the plane of incidence. The law of reflection states that the angles of incidence and reflection are equal. The law of refraction relates the angles of incidence and refraction to the indexes of refraction of the materials. (See Examples 33.1 and 33.3.)

$$\theta_r = \theta_a \qquad (33.2)$$
(law of reflection)

$$n_a \sin\theta_a = n_b \sin\theta_b \qquad (33.4)$$
(law of refraction)

Total internal reflection: When a ray travels in a material of greater index of refraction n_a toward a material of smaller index n_b, total internal reflection occurs at the interface when the angle of incidence exceeds a critical angle θ_{crit}. (See Example 33.4.)

$$\sin\theta_{crit} = \frac{n_b}{n_a} \qquad (33.6)$$

Polarization of light: The direction of polarization of a linearly polarized electromagnetic wave is the direction of the $\vec{E}$ field. A polarizing filter passes waves that are linearly polarized along its polarizing axis and blocks waves polarized perpendicularly to that axis. When polarized light of intensity I_{max} is incident on a polarizing filter used as an analyzer, the intensity I of the light transmitted through the analyzer depends on the angle ϕ between the polarization direction of the incident light and the polarizing axis of the analyzer. (See Example 33.5.)

$$I = I_{max} \cos^2\phi \qquad (33.7)$$
(Malus's law)

Polarization by reflection: When unpolarized light strikes an interface between two materials, Brewster's law states that the reflected light is completely polarized perpendicular to the plane of incidence (parallel to the interface) if the angle of incidence equals the polarizing angle θ_p. (See Example 33.6.)

$$\tan\theta_p = \frac{n_b}{n_a} \qquad (33.8)$$
(Brewster's law)

Huygens's principle: Huygens's principle states that if the position of a wave front at one instant is known, then the position of the front at a later time can be constructed by imagining the front as a source of secondary wavelets. Huygens's principle can be used to derive the laws of reflection and refraction.

BRIDGING PROBLEM | **Reflection and Refraction**

Figure 33.38 shows a rectangular glass block that has a metal reflector on one face and water on an adjoining face. A light beam strikes the reflector as shown. You gradually increase the angle θ of the light beam. If $\theta \geq 59.2°$, no light enters the water. What is the speed of light in this glass?

SOLUTION GUIDE

See MasteringPhysics® study area for a Video Tutor solution.

IDENTIFY and SET UP

1. Specular reflection occurs where the light ray in the glass strikes the reflector. If no light is to enter the water, we require that there be reflection only and no refraction where this ray strikes the glass–water interface—that is, there must be total internal reflection.

2. The target variable is the speed of light v in the glass, which you can determine from the index of refraction n of the glass. (Table 33.1 gives the index of refraction of water.) Write down the equations you will use to find n and v.

33.38

EXECUTE

3. Use the figure to find the angle of incidence of the ray at the glass–water interface.

4. Use the result of step 3 to find n.

5. Use the result of step 4 to find v.

EVALUATE

6. How does the speed of light in the glass compare to the speed in water? Does this make sense?

Problems

For instructor-assigned homework, go to www.masteringphysics.com

•, ••, •••: Problems of increasing difficulty. **CP**: Cumulative problems incorporating material from earlier chapters. **CALC**: Problems requiring calculus. **BIO**: Biosciences problems.

DISCUSSION QUESTIONS

Q33.1 Light requires about 8 minutes to travel from the sun to the earth. Is it delayed appreciably by the earth's atmosphere? Explain.

Q33.2 Sunlight or starlight passing through the earth's atmosphere is always bent toward the vertical. Why? Does this mean that a star is not really where it appears to be? Explain.

Q33.3 A beam of light goes from one material into another. On *physical* grounds, explain *why* the wavelength changes but the frequency and period do not.

Q33.4 A student claimed that, because of atmospheric refraction (see Discussion Question Q33.2), the sun can be seen after it has set and that the day is therefore longer than it would be if the earth had no atmosphere. First, what does she mean by saying that the sun can be seen after it has set? Second, comment on the validity of her conclusion.

Q33.5 When hot air rises from a radiator or heating duct, objects behind it appear to shimmer or waver. What causes this?

Q33.6 Devise straightforward experiments to measure the speed of light in a given glass using (a) Snell's law; (b) total internal reflection; (c) Brewster's law.

Q33.7 Sometimes when looking at a window, you see two reflected images slightly displaced from each other. What causes this?

Q33.8 If you look up from underneath toward the surface of the water in your aquarium, you may see an upside-down reflection of your pet fish in the surface of the water. Explain how this can happen.

Q33.9 A ray of light in air strikes a glass surface. Is there a range of angles for which total reflection occurs? Explain.

Q33.10 When light is incident on an interface between two materials, the angle of the refracted ray depends on the wavelength, but the angle of the reflected ray does not. Why should this be?

Q33.11 A salesperson at a bargain counter claims that a certain pair of sunglasses has Polaroid filters; you suspect that the glasses are just tinted plastic. How could you find out for sure?

Q33.12 Does it make sense to talk about the polarization of a *longitudinal* wave, such as a sound wave? Why or why not?

Q33.13 How can you determine the direction of the polarizing axis of a single polarizer?

Q33.14 It has been proposed that automobile windshields and headlights should have polarizing filters to reduce the glare of oncoming lights during night driving. Would this work? How should the polarizing axes be arranged? What advantages would this scheme have? What disadvantages?

Q33.15 When a sheet of plastic food wrap is placed between two crossed polarizers, no light is transmitted. When the sheet is stretched in one direction, some light passes through the crossed polarizers. What is happening?

Q33.16 If you sit on the beach and look at the ocean through Polaroid sunglasses, the glasses help to reduce the glare from sunlight reflecting off the water. But if you lie on your side on the beach, there is little reduction in the glare. Explain why there is a difference.

Q33.17 When unpolarized light is incident on two crossed polarizers, no light is transmitted. A student asserted that if a third polarizer is inserted between the other two, some transmission will occur. Does this make sense? How can adding a third filter *increase* transmission?

Q33.18 For the old "rabbit-ear" style TV antennas, it's possible to alter the quality of reception considerably simply by changing the orientation of the antenna. Why?

Q33.19 In Fig. 33.32, since the light that is scattered out of the incident beam is polarized, why is the transmitted beam not also partially polarized?

Q33.20 You are sunbathing in the late afternoon when the sun is relatively low in the western sky. You are lying flat on your back, looking straight up through Polaroid sunglasses. To minimize the amount of sky light reaching your eyes, how should you lie: with your feet pointing north, east, south, west, or in some other direction? Explain your reasoning.

Q33.21 Light scattered from blue sky is strongly polarized because of the nature of the scattering process described in Section 33.6. But light scattered from white clouds is usually *not* polarized. Why not?

Q33.22 Atmospheric haze is due to water droplets or smoke particles ("smog"). Such haze reduces visibility by scattering light, so that the light from distant objects becomes randomized and images become indistinct. Explain why visibility through haze can be improved by wearing red-tinted sunglasses, which filter out blue light.

Q33.23 The explanation given in Section 33.6 for the color of the setting sun should apply equally well to the *rising* sun, since sunlight travels the same distance through the atmosphere to reach your eyes at either sunrise or sunset. Typically, however, sunsets are redder than sunrises. Why? (*Hint:* Particles of all kinds in the atmosphere contribute to scattering.)

Q33.24 Huygens's principle also applies to sound waves. During the day, the temperature of the atmosphere decreases with increasing altitude above the ground. But at night, when the ground cools, there is a layer of air just above the surface in which the temperature *increases* with altitude. Use this to explain why sound waves from distant sources can be heard more clearly at night than in the daytime. (*Hint:* The speed of sound increases with increasing temperature. Use the ideas displayed in Fig. 33.37 for light.)

Q33.25 Can water waves be reflected and refracted? Give examples. Does Huygens's principle apply to water waves? Explain.

EXERCISES

Section 33.2 Reflection and Refraction

33.1 • Two plane mirrors intersect at right angles. A laser beam strikes the first of them at a point 11.5 cm from their point of intersection, as shown in Fig. E33.1 For what angle of incidence at the first mirror will this ray strike the midpoint of the second mirror (which is 28.0 cm long) after reflecting from the first mirror?

Figure **E33.1**

33.2 • **BIO** **Light Inside the Eye.** The vitreous humor, a transparent, gelatinous fluid that fills most of the eyeball, has an index of refraction of 1.34. Visible light ranges in wavelength from 380 nm (violet) to 750 nm (red), as measured in air. This light travels through the vitreous humor and strikes the rods and cones at the surface of the retina. What are the ranges of (a) the wavelength, (b) the frequency, and (c) the speed of the light just as it approaches the retina within the vitreous humor?

33.3 • A beam of light has a wavelength of 650 nm in vacuum. (a) What is the speed of this light in a liquid whose index of refraction at this wavelength is 1.47? (b) What is the wavelength of these waves in the liquid?

33.4 • Light with a frequency of 5.80×10^{14} Hz travels in a block of glass that has an index of refraction of 1.52. What is the wavelength of the light (a) in vacuum and (b) in the glass?

33.5 • A light beam travels at 1.94×10^8 m/s in quartz. The wavelength of the light in quartz is 355 nm. (a) What is the index of refraction of quartz at this wavelength? (b) If this same light travels through air, what is its wavelength there?

33.6 •• Light of a certain frequency has a wavelength of 438 nm in water. What is the wavelength of this light in benzene?

33.7 •• A parallel beam of light in air makes an angle of 47.5° with the surface of a glass plate having a refractive index of 1.66. (a) What is the angle between the reflected part of the beam and the surface of the glass? (b) What is the angle between the refracted beam and the surface of the glass?

33.8 •• A laser beam shines along the surface of a block of transparent material (see Fig. E33.8.). Half of the beam goes straight to a detector, while the other half travels through the block and then hits the detector. The time delay between the arrival of the two light beams at the detector is 6.25 ns. What is the index of refraction of this material?

Figure **E33.8**

33.9 • Light traveling in air is incident on the surface of a block of plastic at an angle of 62.7° to the normal and is bent so that it makes a 48.1° angle with the normal in the plastic. Find the speed of light in the plastic.

33.10 • (a) A tank containing methanol has walls 2.50 cm thick made of glass of refractive index 1.550. Light from the outside air strikes the glass at a 41.3° angle with the normal to the glass. Find the angle the light makes with the normal in the methanol. (b) The tank is emptied and refilled with an unknown liquid. If light incident at the same angle as in part (a) enters the liquid in the tank at an angle of 20.2° from the normal, what is the refractive index of the unknown liquid?

33.11 •• As shown in Fig. E33.11, a layer of water covers a slab of material X in a beaker. A ray of light traveling upward follows the path indicated. Using the information on the figure, find (a) the index of refraction of material X and (b) the angle the light makes with the normal in the *air.*

Figure **E33.11**

33.12 •• A horizontal, parallel-sided plate of glass having a refractive index of 1.52 is in contact with the surface of water in a tank. A ray coming from above in air makes an angle of incidence of 35.0° with the normal to the top surface of the glass. (a) What angle does the ray refracted into the water make with the normal to the surface? (b) What is the dependence of this angle on the refractive index of the glass?

33.13 •• In a material having an index of refraction n, a light ray has frequency f, wavelength λ, and speed v. What are the frequency, wavelength, and speed of this light (a) in vacuum and

(b) in a material having refractive index n'? In each case, express your answers in terms of *only* f, λ, v, n, and n'.

33.14 • A ray of light traveling in water is incident on an interface with a flat piece of glass. The wavelength of the light in the water is 726 nm and its wavelength in the glass is 544 nm. If the ray in water makes an angle of 42.0° with respect to the normal to the interface, what angle does the refracted ray in the glass make with respect to the normal?

33.15 • A ray of light is incident on a plane surface separating two sheets of glass with refractive indexes 1.70 and 1.58. The angle of incidence is 62.0°, and the ray originates in the glass with $n = 1.70$. Compute the angle of refraction.

Section 33.3 Total Internal Reflection

33.16 • A flat piece of glass covers the top of a vertical cylinder that is completely filled with water. If a ray of light traveling in the glass is incident on the interface with the water at an angle of $\theta_a = 36.2°$, the ray refracted into the water makes an angle of 49.8° with the normal to the interface. What is the smallest value of the incident angle θ_a for which none of the ray refracts into the water?

33.17 • **Light Pipe.** Light enters a solid pipe made of plastic having an index of refraction of 1.60. The light travels parallel to the upper part of the pipe (Fig. E33.17). You want to cut the face AB so that all the light will reflect back into the pipe after it first strikes that face. (a) What is the largest that θ can be if the pipe is in air? (b) If the pipe is immersed in water of refractive index 1.33, what is the largest that θ can be?

Figure **E33.17**

33.18 • A beam of light is traveling inside a solid glass cube having index of refraction 1.53. It strikes the surface of the cube from the inside. (a) If the cube is in air, at what minimum angle with the normal inside the glass will this light *not* enter the air at this surface? (b) What would be the minimum angle in part (a) if the cube were immersed in water?

33.19 •• The critical angle for total internal reflection at a liquid–air interface is 42.5°. (a) If a ray of light traveling in the liquid has an angle of incidence at the interface of 35.0°, what angle does the refracted ray in the air make with the normal? (b) If a ray of light traveling in air has an angle of incidence at the interface of 35.0°, what angle does the refracted ray in the liquid make with the normal?

33.20 • At the very end of Wagner's series of operas *Ring of the Nibelung,* Brünnhilde takes the golden ring from the finger of the dead Siegfried and throws it into the Rhine, where it sinks to the bottom of the river. Assuming that the ring is small enough compared to the depth of the river to be treated as a point and that the Rhine is 10.0 m deep where the ring goes in, what is the area of the largest circle at the surface of the water over which light from the ring could escape from the water?

33.21 • A ray of light is traveling in a glass cube that is totally immersed in water. You find that if the ray is incident on the glass–water interface at an angle to the normal larger than 48.7°, no light is refracted into the water. What is the refractive index of the glass?

33.22 • Light is incident along the normal on face AB of a glass prism of refractive index 1.52, as shown in Fig. E33.22. Find the

largest value the angle α can have without any light refracted out of the prism at face AC if (a) the prism is immersed in air and (b) the prism is immersed in water.

Figure **E33.22**

33.23 • A piece of glass with a flat surface is at the bottom of a tank of water. If a ray of light traveling in the glass is incident on the interface with the water at an angle with respect to the normal that is greater than 62.0°, no light is refracted into the water. For smaller angles of incidence, part of the ray is refracted into the water. If the light has wavelength 408 nm in the glass, what is the wavelength of the light in the water?

33.24 •• We define the index of refraction of a material for sound waves to be the ratio of the speed of sound in air to the speed of sound in the material. Snell's law then applies to the refraction of sound waves. The speed of a sound wave is 344 m/s in air and 1320 m/s in water. (a) Which medium has the higher index of refraction for sound? (b) What is the critical angle for a sound wave incident on the surface between air and water? (c) For total internal reflection to occur, must the sound wave be traveling in the air or in the water? (d) Use your results to explain why it is possible to hear people on the opposite shore of a river or small lake extremely clearly.

Section 33.4 Dispersion

33.25 •• A narrow beam of white light strikes one face of a slab of silicate flint glass. The light is traveling parallel to the two adjoining faces, as shown in Fig. E33.25. For the transmitted light inside the glass, through what angle $\Delta\theta$ is the portion of the visible spectrum between 400 nm and 700 nm dispersed? (Consult the graph in Fig. 33.18.)

Figure **E33.25**

33.26 • A beam of light strikes a sheet of glass at an angle of 57.0° with the normal in air. You observe that red light makes an angle of 38.1° with the normal in the glass, while violet light makes a 36.7° angle. (a) What are the indexes of refraction of this glass for these colors of light? (b) What are the speeds of red and violet light in the glass?

Section 33.5 Polarization

33.27 • Unpolarized light with intensity I_0 is incident on two polarizing filters. The axis of the first filter makes an angle of 60.0° with the vertical, and the axis of the second filter is horizontal. What is the intensity of the light after it has passed through the second filter?

33.28 •• (a) At what angle above the horizontal is the sun if sunlight reflected from the surface of a calm lake is completely polarized? (b) What is the plane of the electric-field vector in the reflected light?

33.29 •• A beam of unpolarized light of intensity I_0 passes through a series of ideal polarizing filters with their polarizing directions turned to various angles as shown in Fig. E33.29. (a) What is the light intensity (in terms of I_0) at points A, B, and C? (b) If we remove the middle filter, what will be the light intensity at point C?

Figure **E33.29**

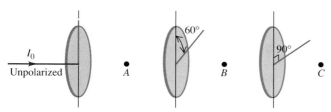

33.30 • Light traveling in water strikes a glass plate at an angle of incidence of 53.0°; part of the beam is reflected and part is refracted. If the reflected and refracted portions make an angle of 90.0° with each other, what is the index of refraction of the glass?

33.31 • A parallel beam of unpolarized light in air is incident at an angle of 54.5° (with respect to the normal) on a plane glass surface. The reflected beam is completely linearly polarized. (a) What is the refractive index of the glass? (b) What is the angle of refraction of the transmitted beam?

33.32 •• Light of original intensity I_0 passes through two ideal polarizing filters having their polarizing axes oriented as shown in Fig. E33.32. You want to adjust the angle ϕ so that the intensity at point P is equal to $I_0/10$. (a) If the original light is unpolarized, what should ϕ be? (b) If the original light is linearly polarized in the same direction as the polarizing axis of the first polarizer the light reaches, what should ϕ be?

Figure **E33.32**

33.33 •• A beam of polarized light passes through a polarizing filter. When the angle between the polarizing axis of the filter and the direction of polarization of the light is θ, the intensity of the emerging beam is I. If you now want the intensity to be $I/2$, what should be the angle (in terms of θ) between the polarizing angle of the filter and the original direction of polarization of the light?

33.34 • The refractive index of a certain glass is 1.66. For what incident angle is light reflected from the surface of this glass completely polarized if the glass is immersed in (a) air and (b) water?

33.35 •• Unpolarized light of intensity 20.0 W/cm² is incident on two polarizing filters. The axis of the first filter is at an angle of 25.0° counterclockwise from the vertical (viewed in the direction the light is traveling), and the axis of the second filter is at 62.0° counterclockwise from the vertical. What is the intensity of the light after it has passed through the second polarizer?

33.36 ••• Three polarizing filters are stacked, with the polarizing axis of the second and third filters at 23.0° and 62.0°, respectively, to that of the first. If unpolarized light is incident on the stack, the light has intensity 75.0 W/cm² after it passes through the stack. If the incident intensity is kept constant, what is the intensity of the light after it has passed through the stack if the second polarizer is removed?

33.37 • **Three Polarizing Filters.** Three polarizing filters are stacked with the polarizing axes of the second and third at 45.0° and 90.0°, respectively, with that of the first. (a) If unpolarized light of intensity I_0 is incident on the stack, find the intensity and

state of polarization of light emerging from each filter. (b) If the second filter is removed, what is the intensity of the light emerging from each remaining filter?

Section 33.6 Scattering of Light

33.38 • A beam of white light passes through a uniform thickness of air. If the intensity of the scattered light in the middle of the green part of the visible spectrum is I, find the intensity (in terms of I) of scattered light in the middle of (a) the red part of the spectrum and (b) the violet part of the spectrum. Consult Table 32.1.

PROBLEMS

33.39 •• **The Corner Reflector.** An inside corner of a cube is lined with mirrors to make a corner reflector (see Example 33.3 in Section 33.2). A ray of light is reflected successively from each of three mutually perpendicular mirrors; show that its final direction is always exactly opposite to its initial direction.

33.40 • A light beam is directed parallel to the axis of a hollow cylindrical tube. When the tube contains only air, it takes the light 8.72 ns to travel the length of the tube, but when the tube is filled with a transparent jelly, it takes the light 2.04 ns longer to travel its length. What is the refractive index of this jelly?

33.41 •• **BIO** **Heart Sonogram.** Physicians use high-frequency ($f = 1-5$ MHz) sound waves, called ultrasound, to image internal organs. The speed of these ultrasound waves is 1480 m/s in muscle and 344 m/s in air. We define the index of refraction of a material for sound waves to be the ratio of the speed of sound in air to the speed of sound in the material. Snell's law then applies to the refraction of sound waves. (a) At what angle from the normal does an ultrasound beam enter the heart if it leaves the lungs at an angle of 9.73° from the normal to the heart wall? (Assume that the speed of sound in the lungs is 344 m/s.) (b) What is the critical angle for sound waves in air incident on muscle?

33.42 ••• In a physics lab, light with wavelength 490 nm travels in air from a laser to a photocell in 17.0 ns. When a slab of glass 0.840 m thick is placed in the light beam, with the beam incident along the normal to the parallel faces of the slab, it takes the light 21.2 ns to travel from the laser to the photocell. What is the wavelength of the light in the glass?

33.43 •• A ray of light is incident in air on a block of a transparent solid whose index of refraction is n. If $n = 1.38$, what is the *largest* angle of incidence θ_a for which total internal reflection will occur at the vertical face (point A shown in Fig. P33.43)?

Figure **P33.43**

33.44 • A light ray in air strikes the right-angle prism shown in Fig. P33.44. The prism angle at B is 30.0°. This ray consists of two different wavelengths. When it emerges at face AB, it has been split into two different rays that diverge from each other by 8.50°. Find the index of refraction of the prism for each of the two wavelengths.

33.45 •• A ray of light traveling *in* a block of glass ($n = 1.52$) is incident on the top surface at an angle of 57.2° with respect to the normal in the glass. If a layer of oil is placed on the top surface

Figure **P33.44**

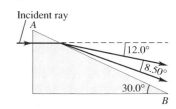

of the glass, the ray is totally reflected. What is the maximum possible index of refraction of the oil?

33.46 ••• A glass plate 2.50 mm thick, with an index of refraction of 1.40, is placed between a point source of light with wavelength 540 nm (in vacuum) and a screen. The distance from source to screen is 1.80 cm. How many wavelengths are there between the source and the screen?

33.47 •• Old photographic plates were made of glass with a light-sensitive emulsion on the front surface. This emulsion was somewhat transparent. When a bright point source is focused on the front of the plate, the developed photograph will show a halo around the image of the spot. If the glass plate is 3.10 mm thick and the halos have an inner radius of 5.34 mm, what is the index of refraction of the glass? (*Hint:* Light from the spot on the front surface is scattered in all directions by the emulsion. Some of it is then totally reflected at the back surface of the plate and returns to the front surface.)

33.48 • After a long day of driving you take a late-night swim in a motel swimming pool. When you go to your room, you realize that you have lost your room key in the pool. You borrow a powerful flashlight and walk around the pool, shining the light into it. The light shines on the key, which is lying on the bottom of the pool, when the flashlight is held 1.2 m above the water surface and is directed at the surface a horizontal distance of 1.5 m from the edge (Fig. P33.48). If the water here is 4.0 m deep, how far is the key from the edge of the pool?

Figure **P33.48**

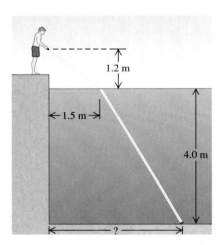

33.49 • You sight along the rim of a glass with vertical sides so that the top rim is lined up with the opposite edge of the bottom (Fig. P33.49a). The glass is a thin-walled, hollow cylinder 16.0 cm high. The diameter of the top and bottom of the glass is 8.0 cm. While you keep your eye in the same position, a friend fills the glass with a transparent liquid, and you then see a dime that is lying at the center of the bottom of the glass (Fig. P33.49b). What is the index of refraction of the liquid?

Figure **P33.49**

(a)   (b)

33.50 •• A 45°−45°−90° prism is immersed in water. A ray of light is incident normally on one of its shorter faces. What is the minimum index of refraction that the prism must have if this ray is to be totally reflected within the glass at the long face of the prism?

33.51 • A thin layer of ice ($n = 1.309$) floats on the surface of water ($n = 1.333$) in a bucket. A ray of light from the bottom of the bucket travels upward through the water. (a) What is the largest angle with respect to the normal that the ray can make at the ice–water interface and still pass out into the air above the ice? (b) What is this angle after the ice melts?

33.52 •• Light is incident normally on the short face of a 30°−60°−90° prism (Fig. P33.52). A drop of liquid is placed on the hypotenuse of the prism. If the index of refraction of the prism is 1.62, find the maximum index that the liquid may have if the light is to be totally reflected.

Figure **P33.52**

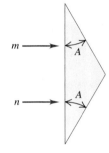

33.53 •• The prism shown in Fig. P33.53 has a refractive index of 1.66, and the angles A are 25.0°. Two light rays m and n are parallel as they enter the prism. What is the angle between them after they emerge?

Figure **P33.53**

33.54 •• A horizontal cylindrical tank 2.20 m in diameter is half full of water. The space above the water is filled with a pressurized gas of unknown refractive index. A small laser can move along the curved bottom of the water and aims a light beam toward the center of the water surface (Fig. P33.54). You observe that when the laser has moved a distance $S = 1.09$ m or more (measured along the curved surface) from the lowest point in the water, no light enters the gas. (a) What is the index of refraction of the gas? (b) What minimum time does it take the light beam to travel from the laser to the rim of the tank when (i) $S > 1.09$ m and (ii) $S < 1.09$ m?

Figure **P33.54**

33.55 •• When the sun is either rising or setting and appears to be just on the horizon, it is in fact *below* the horizon. The explanation for this seeming paradox is that light from the sun bends slightly when entering the earth's atmosphere, as shown in Fig. P33.55. Since our perception is based on the idea that light travels in straight lines, we perceive the light to be coming from an apparent position that is an angle δ above the sun's true position. (a) Make the simplifying assumptions that the atmosphere has uniform density, and hence uniform index of refraction n, and extends to a height h above the earth's surface, at which point it abruptly stops. Show that the angle δ is given by

$$\delta = \arcsin\left(\frac{nR}{R + h}\right) - \arcsin\left(\frac{R}{R + h}\right)$$

where $R = 6378$ km is the radius of the earth. (b) Calculate δ using $n = 1.0003$ and $h = 20$ km. How does this compare to the angular radius of the sun, which is about one quarter of a degree?

(In actuality a light ray from the sun bends gradually, not abruptly, since the density and refractive index of the atmosphere change gradually with altitude.)

Figure **P33.55**

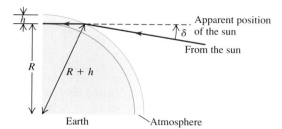

33.56 •• **CALC Fermat's Principle of Least Time.** A ray of light traveling with speed c leaves point 1 shown in Fig. P33.56 and is reflected to point 2. The ray strikes the reflecting surface a horizontal distance x from point 1. (a) Show that the time t required for the light to travel from 1 to 2 is

$$ t = \frac{\sqrt{y_1^2 + x^2} + \sqrt{y_2^2 + (l - x)^2}}{c} $$

(b) Take the derivative of t with respect to x. Set the derivative equal to zero to show that this time reaches its *minimum* value when $\theta_1 = \theta_2$, which is the law of reflection and corresponds to the actual path taken by the light. This is an example of Fermat's *principle of least time,* which states that among all possible paths between two points, the one actually taken by a ray of light is that for which the time of travel is a *minimum.* (In fact, there are some cases in which the time is a maximum rather than a minimum.)

Figure **P33.56**

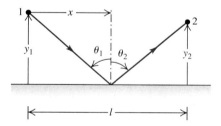

33.57 •• **CALC** A ray of light goes from point A in a medium in which the speed of light is v_1 to point B in a medium in which the speed is v_2 (Fig. P33.57). The ray strikes the interface a horizontal distance x to the right of point A. (a) Show that the time required for the light to go from A to B is

Figure **P33.57**

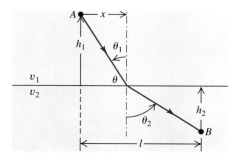

$$ t = \frac{\sqrt{h_1^2 + x^2}}{v_1} + \frac{\sqrt{h_2^2 + (l - x)^2}}{v_2} $$

(b) Take the derivative of t with respect to x. Set this derivative equal to zero to show that this time reaches its *minimum* value when $n_1 \sin\theta_1 = n_2 \sin\theta_2$. This is Snell's law and corresponds to the actual path taken by the light. This is another example of Fermat's principle of least time (see Problem 33.56).

33.58 •• Light is incident in air at an angle θ_a (Fig. P33.58) on the upper surface of a transparent plate, the surfaces of the plate being plane and parallel to each other. (a) Prove that $\theta_a = \theta_a'$. (b) Show that this is true for any number of different parallel plates. (c) Prove that the lateral displacement d of the emergent beam is given by the relationship

$$ d = t \frac{\sin(\theta_a - \theta_b')}{\cos\theta_b'} $$

where t is the thickness of the plate. (d) A ray of light is incident at an angle of 66.0° on one surface of a glass plate 2.40 cm thick with an index of refraction of 1.80. The medium on either side of the plate is air. Find the lateral displacement between the incident and emergent rays.

Figure **P33.58**

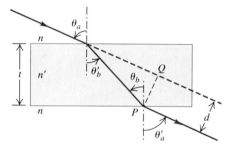

33.59 •• **Angle of Deviation.** The incident angle θ_a shown in Fig. P33.59 is chosen so that the light passes symmetrically through the prism, which has refractive index n and apex angle A. (a) Show that the angle of deviation δ (the angle between the initial and final directions of the ray) is given by

$$ \sin\frac{A + \delta}{2} = n \sin\frac{A}{2} $$

(When the light passes through symmetrically, as shown, the angle of deviation is a minimum.) (b) Use the result of part (a) to find the angle of deviation for a ray of light passing symmetrically through a prism having three equal angles ($A = 60.0°$) and $n = 1.52$. (c) A certain glass has a refractive index of 1.61 for red light (700 nm) and 1.66 for violet light (400 nm). If both colors pass through symmetrically, as described in part (a), and if $A = 60.0°$, find the difference between the angles of deviation for the two colors.

Figure **P33.59**

33.60 • A thin beam of white light is directed at a flat sheet of silicate flint glass at an angle of 20.0° to the surface of the sheet. Due to dispersion in the glass, the beam is spread out in a spectrum as shown in Fig. P33.60. The refractive index of silicate flint glass versus wavelength is graphed in Fig. 33.18. (a) The rays a and b shown in Fig. P33.60 correspond to the extreme wavelengths shown in Fig. 33.18. Which corresponds to red and which to violet? Explain your reasoning. (b) For what thickness d of the glass sheet will the spectrum be 1.0 mm wide, as shown (see Problem 33.58)?

Figure **P33.60**

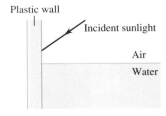

33.61 • A beam of light traveling horizontally is made of an unpolarized component with intensity I_0 and a polarized component with intensity I_p. The plane of polarization of the polarized component is oriented at an angle of θ with respect to the vertical. The data in the table give the intensity measured through a polarizer with an orientation of ϕ with respect to the vertical. (a) What is the orientation of the polarized component? (That is, what is the angle θ?) (b) What are the values of I_0 and I_p?

$\phi\,(°)$	$I_{total}\,(\mathrm{W/m^2})$	$\phi\,(°)$	$I_{total}\,(\mathrm{W/m^2})$
0	18.4	100	8.6
10	21.4	110	6.3
20	23.7	120	5.2
30	24.8	130	5.2
40	24.8	140	6.3
50	23.7	150	8.6
60	21.4	160	11.6
70	18.4	170	15.0
80	15.0	180	18.4
90	11.6		

33.62 •• **BIO** **Optical Activity of Biological Molecules.** Many biologically important molecules are optically active. When linearly polarized light traverses a solution of compounds containing these molecules, its plane of polarization is rotated. Some compounds rotate the polarization clockwise; others rotate the polarization counterclockwise. The amount of rotation depends on the amount of material in the path of the light. The following data give the amount of rotation through two amino acids over a path length of 100 cm:

	Rotation (°)	
l-leucine	*d*-glutamic acid	Concentration (g/100 mL)
−0.11	0.124	1.0
−0.22	0.248	2.0
−0.55	0.620	5.0
−1.10	1.24	10.0
−2.20	2.48	20.0
−5.50	6.20	50.0
−11.0	12.4	100.0

From these data, find the relationship between the concentration C (in grams per 100 mL) and the rotation of the polarization (in degrees) of each amino acid. (*Hint:* Graph the concentration as a function of the rotation angle for each amino acid.)

33.63 •• A beam of unpolarized sunlight strikes the vertical plastic wall of a water tank at an unknown angle. Some of the light reflects from the wall and enters the water (Fig. P33.63). The refractive index of the plastic wall is 1.61. If the light that has been reflected from the wall into the water is observed to be completely polarized, what angle does this beam make with the normal inside the water?

Figure **P33.63**

33.64 •• A certain birefringent material has indexes of refraction n_1 and n_2 for the two perpendicular components of linearly polarized light passing through it. The corresponding wavelengths are $\lambda_1 = \lambda_0/n_1$ and λ_0/n_2, where λ_0 is the wavelength in vacuum. (a) If the crystal is to function as a quarter-wave plate, the number of wavelengths of each component within the material must differ by $\frac{1}{4}$. Show that the minimum thickness for a quarter-wave plate is

$$d = \frac{\lambda_0}{4(n_1 - n_2)}$$

(b) Find the minimum thickness of a quarter-wave plate made of siderite ($FeO \cdot CO_2$) if the indexes of refraction are $n_1 = 1.875$ and $n_2 = 1.635$ and the wavelength in vacuum is $\lambda_0 = 589$ nm.

CHALLENGE PROBLEMS

33.65 ••• Consider two vibrations of equal amplitude and frequency but differing in phase, one along the x-axis,

$$x = a \sin(\omega t - \alpha)$$

and the other along the y-axis,

$$y = a \sin(\omega t - \beta)$$

These can be written as follows:

$$\frac{x}{a} = \sin \omega t \cos \alpha - \cos \omega t \sin \alpha \qquad (1)$$

$$\frac{y}{a} = \sin \omega t \cos \beta - \cos \omega t \sin \beta \qquad (2)$$

(a) Multiply Eq. (1) by $\sin \beta$ and Eq. (2) by $\sin \alpha$, and then subtract the resulting equations. (b) Multiply Eq. (1) by $\cos \beta$ and Eq. (2) by $\cos \alpha$, and then subtract the resulting equations. (c) Square and add the results of parts (a) and (b). (d) Derive the equation $x^2 + y^2 - 2xy \cos \delta = a^2 \sin^2 \delta$, where $\delta = \alpha - \beta$. (e) Use the above result to justify each of the diagrams in Fig. P33.65. In the figure, the angle given is the phase difference between two simple harmonic motions of the same frequency and amplitude, one horizontal (along the x-axis) and the other vertical (along the y-axis). The figure thus shows the resultant motion from the superposition of the two perpendicular harmonic motions.

Figure **P33.65**

0	$\frac{\pi}{4}$	$\frac{\pi}{2}$	$\frac{3\pi}{4}$	π	$\frac{5\pi}{4}$	$\frac{3\pi}{2}$	$\frac{7\pi}{4}$	2π
/	⬭	◯	⬭	\	⬭	◯	⬭	/

33.66 ••• **CALC** A rainbow is produced by the reflection of sunlight by spherical drops of water in the air. Figure P33.66 shows a ray that refracts into a drop at point A, is reflected from the back surface of the drop at point B, and refracts back into the air at point C. The angles of incidence and refraction, θ_a and θ_b, are shown at points A and C, and the angles of incidence and reflection, θ_a and θ_r, are shown at point B. (a) Show that $\theta_a{}^B = \theta_b{}^A$, $\theta_a{}^C = \theta_b{}^A$, and $\theta_b{}^C = \theta_a{}^A$. (b) Show that the angle in radians between the ray before it enters the drop at A and after it exits at C (the total angular deflection of the ray) is $\Delta = 2\theta_a{}^A - 4\theta_b{}^A + \pi$. (*Hint:* Find the angular deflections that occur at A, B, and C, and add them to get Δ.) (c) Use Snell's law to write Δ in terms of $\theta_a{}^A$ and n, the

Figure **P33.66**

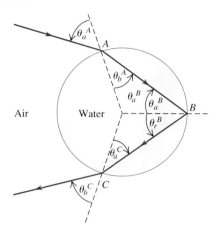

refractive index of the water in the drop. (d) A rainbow will form when the angular deflection Δ is *stationary* in the incident angle $\theta_a{}^A$—that is, when $d\Delta/d\theta_a{}^A = 0$. If this condition is satisfied, all the rays with incident angles close to $\theta_a{}^A$ will be sent back in the same direction, producing a bright zone in the sky. Let θ_1 be the value of $\theta_a{}^A$ for which this occurs. Show that $\cos^2\theta_1 = \frac{1}{3}(n^2 - 1)$. (*Hint:* You may find the derivative formula $d(\arcsin u(x))/dx = (1 - u^2)^{-1/2}(du/dx)$ helpful.) (e) The index of refraction in water is 1.342 for violet light and 1.330 for red light. Use the results of parts (c) and (d) to find θ_1 and Δ for violet and red light. Do your results agree with the angles shown in Fig. 33.20d? When you view the rainbow, which color, red or violet, is higher above the horizon?

33.67 ••• **CALC** A *secondary rainbow* is formed when the incident light undergoes two internal reflections in a spherical drop of water as shown in Fig. 33.20e. (See Challenge Problem 33.66.) (a) In terms of the incident angle $\theta_a{}^A$ and the refractive index n of the drop, what is the angular deflection Δ of the ray? That is, what is the angle between the ray before it enters the drop and after it exits? (b) What is the incident angle θ_2 for which the derivative of Δ with respect to the incident angle $\theta_a{}^A$ is zero? (c) The indexes of refraction for red and violet light in water are given in part (e) of Challenge Problem 33.66. Use the results of parts (a) and (b) to find θ_2 and Δ for violet and red light. Do your results agree with the angles shown in Fig. 33.20e? When you view a secondary rainbow, is red or violet higher above the horizon? Explain.

Answers

Chapter Opening Question ?

This is the same effect as shown in Fig. 33.31. The drafting tools are placed between two polarizing filters whose polarizing axes are perpendicular. In places where the clear plastic is under stress, the plastic becomes birefringent; that is, light travels through it at a speed that depends on its polarization. The result is that the light that emerges from the plastic has a different polarization than the light that enters. A spot on the plastic appears bright if the emerging light has the same polarization as the second polarizing filter. The amount of birefringence depends on the wavelength of the light as well as the amount of stress on the plastic, so different colors are seen at different locations on the plastic.

Test Your Understanding Questions

33.1 Answer: (iii) The waves go farther in the y-direction in a given amount of time than in the other directions, so the wave fronts are elongated in the y-direction.

33.2 Answers: (a) (ii), (b) (iii) As shown in the figure, light rays coming from the fish bend away from the normal when they pass from the water ($n = 1.33$) into the air ($n = 1.00$). As a result, the

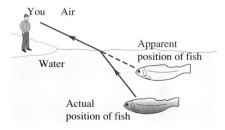

fish appears to be higher in the water than it actually is. Hence you should aim a spear *below* the apparent position of the fish. If you use a laser beam, you should aim *at* the apparent position of the fish: The beam of laser light takes the same path from you to the fish as ordinary light takes from the fish to you (though in the opposite direction).

33.3 Answers: (i), (ii) Total internal reflection can occur only if two conditions are met: n_b must be less than n_a, and the critical angle θ_{crit} (where $\sin\theta_{crit} = n_b/n_a$) must be smaller than the angle of incidence θ_a. In the first two cases both conditions are met: The critical angles are (i) $\theta_{crit} = \sin^{-1}(1/1.33) = 48.8°$ and (ii) $\theta_{crit} = \sin^{-1}(1.33/1.52) = 61.0°$, both of which are smaller than $\theta_a = 70°$. In the third case $n_b = 1.52$ is greater than $n_a = 1.33$, so total internal reflection cannot occur for any incident angle.

33.5 Answer: (ii) The sunlight reflected from the windows of the high-rise building is partially polarized in the vertical direction, since each window lies in a vertical plane. The Polaroid filter in front of the lens is oriented with its polarizing axis perpendicular to the dominant direction of polarization of the reflected light.

33.7 Answer: (ii) Huygens's principle applies to waves of all kinds, including sound waves. Hence this situation is exactly like that shown in Fig. 33.36, with material a representing the warm air, material b representing the cold air in which the waves travel more slowly, and the interface between the materials representing the weather front. North is toward the top of the figure and east is toward the right, so Fig. 33.36 shows that the rays (which indicate the direction of propagation) deflect toward the east.

Bridging Problem

Answer: 1.93×10^8 m/s

? How do magnifying lenses work? At what distance from the object being examined do they provide the sharpest view?

Your reflection in the bathroom mirror, the view of the moon through a telescope, the patterns seen in a kaleidoscope—all of these are examples of *images.* In each case the object that you're looking at appears to be in a different place than its actual position: Your reflection is on the other side of the mirror, the moon appears to be much closer when seen through a telescope, and objects seen in a kaleidoscope seem to be in many places at the same time. In each case, light rays that come from a point on an object are deflected by reflection or refraction (or a combination of the two), so they converge toward or appear to diverge from a point called an *image point.* Our goal in this chapter is to see how this is done and to explore the different kinds of images that can be made with simple optical devices.

To understand images and image formation, all we need are the ray model of light, the laws of reflection and refraction, and some simple geometry and trigonometry. The key role played by geometry in our analysis is the reason for the name *geometric optics* that is given to the study of how light rays form images. We'll begin our analysis with one of the simplest image-forming optical devices, a plane mirror. We'll go on to study how images are formed by curved mirrors, by refracting surfaces, and by thin lenses. Our results will lay the foundation for understanding many familiar optical instruments, including camera lenses, magnifiers, the human eye, microscopes, and telescopes.

ActivPhysics 15.4: Geometric Optics: Plane Mirrors

34.1 Reflection and Refraction at a Plane Surface

Before discussing what is meant by an image, we first need the concept of **object** as it is used in optics. By an *object* we mean anything from which light rays radiate. This light could be emitted by the object itself if it is *self-luminous,* like the glowing filament of a light bulb. Alternatively, the light could be emitted by another source (such as a lamp or the sun) and then reflected from the object; an example is the light you see coming from the pages of this book. Figure 34.1 shows light rays radiating in all directions from an object at a point *P*. For an observer to see this object directly, there must be no obstruction between the object and the observer's eyes. Note that light rays from the object reach the observer's left and right eyes at different angles; these differences are processed by the observer's brain to infer the *distance* from the observer to the object.

The object in Fig. 34.1 is a **point object** that has no physical extent. Real objects with length, width, and height are called **extended objects.** To start with, we'll consider only an idealized point object, since we can always think of an extended object as being made up of a very large number of point objects.

Suppose some of the rays from the object strike a smooth, plane reflecting surface (Fig. 34.2). This could be the surface of a material with a different index of refraction, which reflects part of the incident light, or a polished metal surface that reflects almost 100% of the light that strikes it. We will always draw the reflecting surface as a black line with a shaded area behind it, as in Fig. 34.2. Bathroom mirrors have a thin sheet of glass that lies in front of and protects the reflecting surface; we'll ignore the effects of this thin sheet.

According to the law of reflection, all rays striking the surface are reflected at an angle from the normal equal to the angle of incidence. Since the surface is plane, the normal is in the same direction at all points on the surface, and we have *specular* reflection. After the rays are reflected, their directions are the same as though they had come from point *P'*. We call point *P* an *object point* and point *P'* the corresponding *image point,* and we say that the reflecting surface forms an **image** of point *P*. An observer who can see only the rays reflected from the surface, and who doesn't know that he's seeing a reflection, *thinks* that the rays originate from the image point *P'*. The image point is therefore a convenient way to describe the directions of the various reflected rays, just as the object point *P* describes the directions of the rays arriving at the surface *before* reflection.

If the surface in Fig. 34.2 were *not* smooth, the reflection would be *diffuse,* and rays reflected from different parts of the surface would go in uncorrelated directions (see Fig. 33.6b). In this case there would not be a definite image point *P'* from which all reflected rays seem to emanate. You can't see your reflection in the surface of a tarnished piece of metal because its surface is rough; polishing the metal smoothes the surface so that specular reflection occurs and a reflected image becomes visible.

An image is also formed by a plane *refracting* surface, as shown in Fig. 34.3. Rays coming from point *P* are refracted at the interface between two optical materials. When the angles of incidence are small, the final directions of the rays after refraction are the same as though they had come from point *P'*, as shown, and again we call *P'* an *image point.* In Section 33.2 we described how this effect makes underwater objects appear closer to the surface than they really are (see Fig. 33.9).

In both Figs. 34.2 and 34.3 the rays do not actually pass through the image point *P'*. Indeed, if the mirror in Fig. 34.2 is opaque, there is no light at all on its right side. If the outgoing rays don't actually pass through the image point, we call the image a **virtual image.** Later we will see cases in which the outgoing rays really *do* pass through an image point, and we will call the resulting image a **real image.** The images that are formed on a projection screen, on the photographic film in a camera, and on the retina of your eye are real images.

Image Formation by a Plane Mirror

Let's concentrate for now on images produced by *reflection;* we'll return to refraction later in the chapter. To find the precise location of the virtual image *P'* that a plane mirror forms of an object at *P*, we use the construction shown in Fig. 34.4. The figure shows two rays diverging from an object point *P* at a

34.1 Light rays radiate from a point object *P* in all directions.

34.2 Light rays from the object at point *P* are reflected from a plane mirror. The reflected rays entering the eye look as though they had come from image point *P'*.

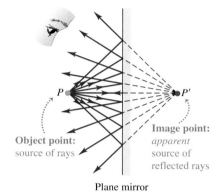

Object point: source of rays

Image point: *apparent* source of reflected rays

Plane mirror

34.3 Light rays from the object at point *P* are refracted at the plane interface. The refracted rays entering the eye look as though they had come from image point *P'*.

When $n_a > n_b$, *P'* is closer to the surface than *P*; for $n_a < n_b$, the reverse is true.

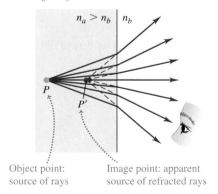

$n_a > n_b$ | n_b

Object point: source of rays

Image point: apparent source of refracted rays

34.4 Construction for determining the location of the image formed by a plane mirror. The image point P' is as far behind the mirror as the object point P is in front of it.

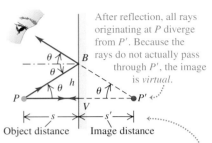

After reflection, all rays originating at P diverge from P'. Because the rays do not actually pass through P', the image is *virtual*.

Object distance | Image distance

Triangles PVB and $P'VB$ are congruent, so $|s| = |s'|$.

34.5 For both of these situations, the object distance s is positive (rule 1) and the image distance s' is negative (rule 2).

(a) Plane mirror

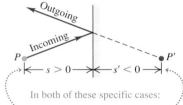

In both of these specific cases:

Object distance s is *positive* because the object is on the same side as the incoming light.

Image distance s' is *negative* because the image is NOT on the same side as the outgoing light.

(b) Plane refracting interface

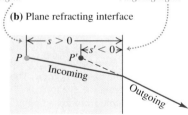

34.6 Construction for determining the height of an image formed by reflection at a plane reflecting surface.

For a plane mirror, PQV and $P'Q'V$ are congruent, so $y = y'$ and the object and image are the same size (the lateral magnification is 1).

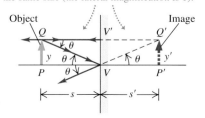

distance s to the left of a plane mirror. We call s the **object distance.** The ray PV is incident normally on the mirror (that is, it is perpendicular to the mirror surface), and it returns along its original path.

The ray PB makes an angle θ with PV. It strikes the mirror at an angle of incidence θ and is reflected at an equal angle with the normal. When we extend the two reflected rays backward, they intersect at point P', at a distance s' behind the mirror. We call s' the **image distance.** The line between P and P' is perpendicular to the mirror. The two triangles PVB and $P'VB$ are congruent, so P and P' are at equal distances from the mirror, and s and s' have equal magnitudes. The image point P' is located exactly opposite the object point P as far *behind* the mirror as the object point is from the front of the mirror.

We can repeat the construction of Fig. 34.4 for each ray diverging from P. The directions of *all* the outgoing reflected rays are the same as though they had originated at point P', confirming that P' is the *image* of P. No matter where the observer is located, she will always see the image at the point P'.

Sign Rules

Before we go further, let's introduce some general sign rules. These may seem unnecessarily complicated for the simple case of an image formed by a plane mirror, but we want to state the rules in a form that will be applicable to *all* the situations we will encounter later. These will include image formation by a plane or spherical reflecting or refracting surface, or by a pair of refracting surfaces forming a lens. Here are the rules:

1. **Sign rule for the object distance:** When the object is on the same side of the reflecting or refracting surface as the incoming light, the object distance s is positive; otherwise, it is negative.
2. **Sign rule for the image distance:** When the image is on the same side of the reflecting or refracting surface as the outgoing light, the image distance s' is positive; otherwise, it is negative.
3. **Sign rule for the radius of curvature of a spherical surface:** When the center of curvature C is on the same side as the outgoing light, the radius of curvature is positive; otherwise, it is negative.

Figure 34.5 illustrates rules 1 and 2 for two different situations. For a mirror the incoming and outgoing sides are always the same; for example, in Figs. 34.2, 34.4, and 34.5a they are both on the left side. For the refracting surfaces in Figs. 34.3 and 34.5b the incoming and outgoing sides are on the left and right sides, respectively, of the interface between the two materials. (Note that other textbooks may use different rules.)

In Figs. 34.4 and 34.5a the object distance s is *positive* because the object point P is on the incoming side (the left side) of the reflecting surface. The image distance s' is *negative* because the image point P' is *not* on the outgoing side (the left side) of the surface. The object and image distances s and s' are related simply by

$$s = -s' \quad \text{(plane mirror)} \tag{34.1}$$

For a plane reflecting or refracting surface, the radius of curvature is infinite and not a particularly interesting or useful quantity; in these cases we really don't need sign rule 3. But this rule will be of great importance when we study image formation by *curved* reflecting and refracting surfaces later in the chapter.

Image of an Extended Object: Plane Mirror

Next we consider an *extended* object with finite size. For simplicity we often consider an object that has only one dimension, like a slender arrow, oriented parallel to the reflecting surface; an example is the arrow PQ in Fig. 34.6. The distance from the head to the tail of an arrow oriented in this way is called its *height;* in Fig. 34.6 the height is y. The image formed by such an extended object is an extended image; to each point on the object, there corresponds a point on the image. Two of the rays from Q are shown; *all* the rays from Q appear to diverge from its image point Q' after reflection. The image of the arrow is the line $P'Q'$, with height y'. Other points of the object PQ have image points between P' and Q'. The triangles PQV and $P'Q'V$ are congruent, so the object PQ and image $P'Q'$ have the same size and orientation, and $y = y'$.

The ratio of image height to object height, y'/y, in *any* image-forming situation is called the **lateral magnification** m; that is,

$$m = \frac{y'}{y} \qquad \text{(lateral magnification)} \qquad (34.2)$$

Thus for a plane mirror the lateral magnification m is unity. When you look at yourself in a plane mirror, your image is the same size as the real you.

In Fig. 34.6 the image arrow points in the *same* direction as the object arrow; we say that the image is **erect.** In this case, y and y' have the same sign, and the lateral magnification m is positive. The image formed by a plane mirror is always erect, so y and y' have both the same magnitude and the same sign; from Eq. (34.2) the lateral magnification of a plane mirror is always $m = +1$. Later we will encounter situations in which the image is **inverted;** that is, the image arrow points in the direction *opposite* to that of the object arrow. For an inverted image, y and y' have *opposite* signs, and the lateral magnification m is *negative.*

The object in Fig. 34.6 has only one dimension. Figure 34.7 shows a *three-dimensional* object and its three-dimensional virtual image formed by a plane mirror. The object and image are related in the same way as a left hand and a right hand.

CAUTION   Reflections in a plane mirror At this point, you may be asking, "Why does a plane mirror reverse images left and right but not top and bottom?" This question is quite misleading! As Fig. 34.7 shows, the up-down image $P'Q'$ and the left-right image $P'S'$ are parallel to their objects and are not reversed at all. Only the front-back image $P'R'$ is reversed relative to PR. Hence it's most correct to say that a plane mirror reverses *back to front.* To verify this object-image relationship, point your thumbs along PR and $P'R'$, your forefingers along PQ and $P'Q'$, and your middle fingers along PS and $P'S'$. When an object and its image are related in this way, the image is said to be **reversed;** this means that *only* the front-back dimension is reversed. ▮

The reversed image of a three-dimensional object formed by a plane mirror is the same *size* as the object in all its dimensions. When the transverse dimensions of object and image are in the same direction, the image is erect. Thus a plane mirror always forms an erect but reversed image. Figure 34.8 illustrates this point.

An important property of all images formed by reflecting or refracting surfaces is that an *image* formed by one surface or optical device can serve as the *object* for a second surface or device. Figure 34.9 shows a simple example. Mirror 1 forms an image P'_1 of the object point P, and mirror 2 forms another image P'_2, each in the way we have just discussed. But in addition, the image P'_1 formed by mirror 1 serves an object for mirror 2, which then forms an image of this object at point P'_3 as shown. Similarly, mirror 1 uses the image P'_2 formed by mirror 2 as an object and forms an image of it. We leave it to you to show that this image point is also at P'_3. The idea that an image formed by one device can act as the object for a second device is of great importance in geometric optics. We will use it later in this chapter to locate the image formed by two successive curved-surface refractions in a lens. This idea will help us to understand image formation by combinations of lenses, as in a microscope or a refracting telescope.

34.7 The image formed by a plane mirror is virtual, erect, and reversed. It is the same size as the object.

An image made by a plane mirror is reversed back to front: the image thumb $P'R'$ and object thumb PR point in opposite directions (toward each other).

34.8 The image formed by a plane mirror is reversed; the image of a right hand is a left hand, and so on. (The hand is resting on a horizontal mirror.) Are images of the letters H and A reversed?

34.9 Images P'_1 and P'_2 are formed by a single reflection of each ray from the object at P. Image P'_3, located by treating either of the other images as an object, is formed by a double reflection of each ray.

34.2 Reflection at a Spherical Surface

A plane mirror produces an image that is the same size as the object. But there are many applications for mirrors in which the image and object must be of different sizes. A magnifying mirror used when applying makeup gives an image that is *larger* than the object, and surveillance mirrors (used in stores to help spot shoplifters) give an image that is *smaller* than the object. There are also applications of mirrors in which a *real* image is desired, so light rays do indeed pass through the image point P'. A plane mirror by itself cannot perform any of these tasks. Instead, *curved* mirrors are used.

Image of a Point Object: Spherical Mirror

We'll consider the special (and easily analyzed) case of image formation by a *spherical* mirror. Figure 34.10a shows a spherical mirror with radius of curvature R, with its concave side facing the incident light. The **center of curvature** of the surface (the center of the sphere of which the surface is a part) is at C, and the **vertex** of the mirror (the center of the mirror surface) is at V. The line CV is called the **optic axis**. Point P is an object point that lies on the optic axis; for the moment, we assume that the distance from P to V is greater than R.

Ray PV, passing through C, strikes the mirror normally and is reflected back on itself. Ray PB, at an angle α with the axis, strikes the mirror at B, where the angles of incidence and reflection are θ. The reflected ray intersects the axis at point P'. We will show shortly that *all* rays from P intersect the axis at the *same* point P', as in Fig. 34.10b, provided that the angle α is small. Point P' is therefore the *image* of object point P. Unlike the reflected rays in Fig. 34.1, the reflected rays in Fig. 34.10b actually do intersect at point P', then diverge from P' *as if* they had originated at this point. Thus P' is a *real* image.

To see the usefulness of having a real image, suppose that the mirror is in a darkened room in which the only source of light is a self-luminous object at P. If you place a small piece of photographic film at P', all the rays of light coming from point P that reflect off the mirror will strike the same point P' on the film; when developed, the film will show a single bright spot, representing a sharply focused image of the object at point P. This principle is at the heart of most astronomical telescopes, which use large concave mirrors to make photographs of celestial objects. With a *plane* mirror like that in Fig. 34.2, placing a piece of film at the image point P' would be a waste of time; the light rays never actually pass through the image point, and the image can't be recorded on film. Real images are *essential* for photography.

Let's now find the location of the real image point P' in Fig. 34.10a and prove the assertion that all rays from P intersect at P' (provided that their angle with the optic axis is small). The object distance, measured from the vertex V, is s; the image distance, also measured from V, is s'. The signs of s, s', and the radius of curvature R are determined by the sign rules given in Section 34.1. The object point P is on the same side as the incident light, so according to sign rule 1, s is positive. The image point P' is on the same side as the reflected light, so according to sign rule 2, the image distance s' is also positive. The center of curvature C is on the same side as the reflected light, so according to sign rule 3, R, too, is positive; R is always positive when reflection occurs at the *concave* side of a surface (Fig. 34.11).

We now use the following theorem from plane geometry: An exterior angle of a triangle equals the sum of the two opposite interior angles. Applying this theorem to triangles PBC and $P'BC$ in Fig. 34.10a, we have

34.10 (a) A concave spherical mirror forms a real image of a point object P on the mirror's optic axis. (b) The eye sees some of the outgoing rays and perceives them as having come from P'.

(a) Construction for finding the position P' of an image formed by a concave spherical mirror

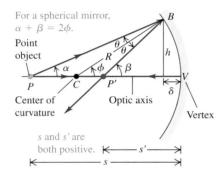

For a spherical mirror, $\alpha + \beta = 2\phi$.

(b) The paraxial approximation, which holds for rays with small α

All rays from P that have a small angle α pass through P', forming a real image.

34.11 The sign rule for the radius of a spherical mirror.

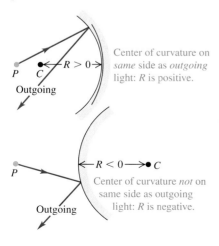

Center of curvature on *same* side as *outgoing* light: R is positive.

Center of curvature *not* on same side as outgoing light: R is negative.

$$\phi = \alpha + \theta \qquad \beta = \phi + \theta$$

Eliminating θ between these equations gives

$$\alpha + \beta = 2\phi \qquad (34.3)$$

We may now compute the image distance s'. Let h represent the height of point B above the optic axis, and let δ represent the short distance from V to the foot of this vertical line. We now write expressions for the tangents of α, β, and ϕ, remembering that s, s', and R are all positive quantities:

$$\tan \alpha = \frac{h}{s - \delta} \qquad \tan \beta = \frac{h}{s' - \delta} \qquad \tan \phi = \frac{h}{R - \delta}$$

These trigonometric equations cannot be solved as simply as the corresponding algebraic equations for a plane mirror. However, *if the angle α is small,* the angles β and ϕ are also small. The tangent of an angle that is much less than one radian is nearly equal to the angle itself (measured in radians), so we can replace $\tan \alpha$ by α, and so on, in the equations above. Also, if α is small, we can neglect the distance δ compared with s', s, and R. So for small angles we have the following approximate relationships:

$$\alpha = \frac{h}{s} \qquad \beta = \frac{h}{s'} \qquad \phi = \frac{h}{R}$$

Substituting these into Eq. (34.3) and dividing by h, we obtain a general relationship among s, s', and R:

$$\frac{1}{s} + \frac{1}{s'} = \frac{2}{R} \qquad \text{(object–image relationship, spherical mirror)} \qquad (34.4)$$

This equation does not contain the angle α. Hence *all* rays from P that make sufficiently small angles with the axis intersect at P' after they are reflected; this verifies our earlier assertion. Such rays, nearly parallel to the axis and close to it, are called **paraxial rays.** (The term **paraxial approximation** is often used for the approximations we have just described.) Since all such reflected light rays converge on the image point, a concave mirror is also called a *converging mirror.*

Be sure you understand that Eq. (34.4), as well as many similar relationships that we will derive later in this chapter and the next, is only *approximately* correct. It results from a calculation containing approximations, and it is valid only for paraxial rays. If we increase the angle α that a ray makes with the optic axis, the point P' where the ray intersects the optic axis moves somewhat closer to the vertex than for a paraxial ray. As a result, a spherical mirror, unlike a plane mirror, does not form a precise point image of a point object; the image is "smeared out." This property of a spherical mirror is called **spherical aberration.** When the primary mirror of the Hubble Space Telescope (Fig. 34.12a) was manufactured, tiny errors were made in its shape that led to an unacceptable amount of spherical aberration (Fig. 34.12b). The performance of the telescope improved dramatically after the installation of corrective optics (Fig. 34.12c).

If the radius of curvature becomes infinite ($R = \infty$), the mirror becomes *plane,* and Eq. (34.4) reduces to Eq. (34.1) for a plane reflecting surface.

Focal Point and Focal Length

When the object point P is very far from the spherical mirror ($s = \infty$), the incoming rays are parallel. (The star shown in Fig. 34.12c is an example of such a distant object.) From Eq. (34.4) the image distance s' in this case is given by

$$\frac{1}{\infty} + \frac{1}{s'} = \frac{2}{R} \qquad s' = \frac{R}{2}$$

34.12 (a), (b) Soon after the Hubble Space Telescope (HST) was placed in orbit in 1990, it was discovered that the concave primary mirror (also called the *objective mirror*) was too shallow by about $\frac{1}{50}$ the width of a human hair, leading to spherical aberration of the star's image. (c) After corrective optics were installed in 1993, the effects of spherical aberration were almost completely eliminated.

(a) The 2.4-m-diameter primary mirror of the Hubble Space Telescope

(b) A star seen with the original mirror

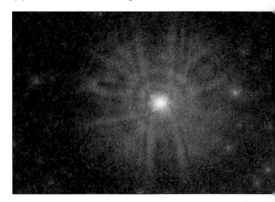

(c) The same star with corrective optics

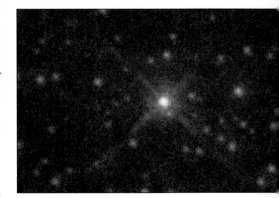

34.13 The focal point and focal length of a concave mirror.

(a) All parallel rays incident on a spherical mirror reflect through the focal point.

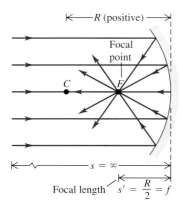

(b) Rays diverging from the focal point reflect to form parallel outgoing rays.

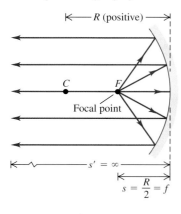

The situation is shown in Fig. 34.13a. The beam of incident parallel rays converges, after reflection from the mirror, to a point F at a distance $R/2$ from the vertex of the mirror. The point F at which the incident parallel rays converge is called the **focal point**; we say that these rays are brought to a focus. The distance from the vertex to the focal point, denoted by f, is called the **focal length.** We see that f is related to the radius of curvature R by

$$f = \frac{R}{2} \quad \text{(focal length of a spherical mirror)} \tag{34.5}$$

The opposite situation is shown in Fig. 34.13b. Now the *object* is placed at the focal point F, so the object distance is $s = f = R/2$. The image distance s' is again given by Eq. (34.4):

$$\frac{2}{R} + \frac{1}{s'} = \frac{2}{R} \qquad \frac{1}{s'} = 0 \qquad s' = \infty$$

With the object at the focal point, the reflected rays in Fig. 34.13b are parallel to the optic axis; they meet only at a point infinitely far from the mirror, so the image is at infinity.

Thus the focal point F of a spherical mirror has the properties that (1) any incoming ray parallel to the optic axis is reflected through the focal point and (2) any incoming ray that passes through the focal point is reflected parallel to the optic axis. For spherical mirrors these statements are true only for paraxial rays. For parabolic mirrors these statements are *exactly* true; this is why parabolic mirrors are preferred for astronomical telescopes. Spherical or parabolic mirrors are used in flashlights and headlights to form the light from the bulb into a parallel beam. Some solar-power plants use an array of plane mirrors to simulate an approximately spherical concave mirror; light from the sun is collected by the mirrors and directed to the focal point, where a steam boiler is placed. (The concepts of focal point and focal length also apply to lenses, as we'll see in Section 34.4.)

We will usually express the relationship between object and image distances for a mirror, Eq. (34.4), in terms of the focal length f:

$$\frac{1}{s} + \frac{1}{s'} = \frac{1}{f} \quad \text{(object–image relationship, spherical mirror)} \tag{34.6}$$

Image of an Extended Object: Spherical Mirror

Now suppose we have an object with *finite* size, represented by the arrow PQ in Fig. 34.14, perpendicular to the optic axis CV. The image of P formed by paraxial rays is at P'. The object distance for point Q is very nearly equal to that for point P, so the image $P'Q'$ is nearly straight and perpendicular to the axis. Note that the object and image arrows have different sizes, y and y', respectively, and that they have opposite orientation. In Eq. (34.2) we defined the *lateral magnification m* as the ratio of image size y' to object size y:

$$m = \frac{y'}{y}$$

34.14 Construction for determining the position, orientation, and height of an image formed by a concave spherical mirror.

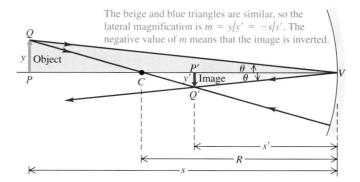

Because triangles PVQ and $P'VQ'$ in Fig. 34.14 are *similar*, we also have the relationship $y/s = -y'/s'$. The negative sign is needed because object and image are on opposite sides of the optic axis; if y is positive, y' is negative. Therefore

$$m = \frac{y'}{y} = -\frac{s'}{s} \quad \text{(lateral magnification, spherical mirror)} \quad (34.7)$$

If m is positive, the image is erect in comparison to the object; if m is negative, the image is *inverted* relative to the object, as in Fig. 34.14. For a *plane* mirror, $s = -s'$, so $y' = y$ and $m = +1$; since m is positive, the image is erect, and since $|m| = 1$, the image is the same size as the object.

CAUTION **Lateral magnification can be less than 1** Although the ratio of image size to object size is called the *lateral magnification,* the image formed by a mirror or lens may be larger than, smaller than, or the same size as the object. If it is smaller, then the lateral magnification is less than unity in absolute value: $|m| < 1$. The image formed by an astronomical telescope mirror or a camera lens is usually *much* smaller than the object. For example, the image of the bright star shown in Fig. 34.12c is just a few millimeters across, while the star itself is hundreds of thousands of kilometers in diameter. ▮

In our discussion of concave mirrors we have so far considered only objects that lie *outside* or at the focal point, so that the object distance s is greater than or equal to the (positive) focal length f. In this case the image point is on the same side of the mirror as the outgoing rays, and the image is real and inverted. If an object is placed *inside* the focal point of a concave mirror, so that $s < f$, the resulting image is *virtual* (that is, the image point is on the opposite side of the mirror from the object), *erect,* and *larger* than the object. Mirrors used when applying makeup (referred to at the beginning of this section) are concave mirrors; in use, the distance from the face to the mirror is less than the focal length, and an enlarged, erect image is seen. You can prove these statements about concave mirrors by applying Eqs. (34.6) and (34.7) (see Exercise 34.11). We'll also be able to verify these results later in this section, after we've learned some graphical methods for relating the positions and sizes of the object and the image.

MasteringPHYSICS

ActivPhysics 15.5: Spherical Mirrors: Ray Diagrams
ActivPhysics 15.6: Spherical Mirrors: The Mirror Equation
ActivPhysics 15.7: Spherical Mirrors: Linear Magnification
ActivPhysics 15.8: Spherical Mirrors: Problems

Example 34.1 **Image formation by a concave mirror I**

A concave mirror forms an image, on a wall 3.00 m in front of the mirror, of a headlamp filament 10.0 cm in front of the mirror. (a) What are the radius of curvature and focal length of the mirror? (b) What is the lateral magnification? What is the image height if the object height is 5.00 mm?

SOLUTION

IDENTIFY and SET UP: Figure 34.15 shows our sketch. Our target variables are the radius of curvature R, focal length f, lateral mag-

nification m, and image height y'. We are given the distances from the mirror to the object (s) and from the mirror to the image (s'). We solve Eq. (34.4) for R, and then use Eq. (34.5) to find f. Equation (34.7) yields both m and y'.

EXECUTE: (a) Both the object and the image are on the concave (reflective) side of the mirror, so both s and s' are positive; we have $s = 10.0$ cm and $s' = 300$ cm. We solve Eq. (34.4) for R:

$$\frac{1}{10.0 \text{ cm}} + \frac{1}{300 \text{ cm}} = \frac{2}{R}$$

$$R = 2\left(\frac{1}{10.0 \text{ cm}} + \frac{1}{300 \text{ cm}}\right)^{-1} = 19.4 \text{ cm}$$

The focal length of the mirror is $f = R/2 = 9.7$ cm.

(b) From Eq. (34.7) the lateral magnification is

$$m = -\frac{s'}{s} = -\frac{300 \text{ cm}}{10.0 \text{ cm}} = -30.0$$

Because m is negative, the image is inverted. The height of the image is 30.0 times the height of the object, or $(30.0)(5.00 \text{ mm}) = 150$ mm.

34.15 Our sketch for this problem.

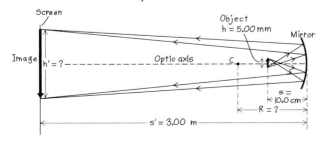

Continued

EVALUATE: Our sketch indicates that the image is inverted; our calculations agree. Note that the object (at $s = 10.0$ cm) is just outside the focal point ($f = 9.7$ cm). This is very similar to what is done in automobile headlights. With the filament close to the focal point, the concave mirror produces a beam of nearly parallel rays.

Conceptual Example 34.2 **Image formation by a concave mirror II**

In Example 34.1, suppose that the lower half of the mirror's reflecting surface is covered with nonreflective soot. What effect will this have on the image of the filament?

SOLUTION

It would be natural to guess that the image would now show only half of the filament. But in fact the image will still show the *entire* filament. You can see why by examining Fig. 34.10b. Light rays coming from any object point P are reflected from *all* parts of the mirror and converge on the corresponding image point P'. If part of the mirror surface is made nonreflective (or is removed altogether), rays from the remaining reflective surface still form an image of every part of the object.

Reducing the reflecting area reduces the light energy reaching the image point, however: The image becomes *dimmer*. If the area is reduced by one-half, the image will be one-half as bright. Conversely, *increasing* the reflective area makes the image brighter. To make reasonably bright images of faint stars, astronomical telescopes use mirrors that are up to several meters in diameter (see Fig. 34.12a).

Convex Mirrors

In Fig. 34.16a the *convex* side of a spherical mirror faces the incident light. The center of curvature is on the side opposite to the outgoing rays; according to sign rule 3 in Section 34.1, R is negative (see Fig. 34.11). Ray PB is reflected, with the angles of incidence and reflection both equal to θ. The reflected ray, projected backward, intersects the axis at P'. As with a concave mirror, *all* rays from P that are reflected by the mirror diverge from the same point P', provided that the angle α is small. Therefore P' is the image of P. The object distance s is positive, the image distance s' is negative, and the radius of curvature R is *negative* for a *convex* mirror.

Figure 34.16b shows two rays diverging from the head of the arrow PQ and the virtual image $P'Q'$ of this arrow. The same procedure that we used for a concave mirror can be used to show that for a convex mirror,

$$\frac{1}{s} + \frac{1}{s'} = \frac{2}{R}$$

and the lateral magnification is

$$m = \frac{y'}{y} = -\frac{s'}{s}$$

34.16 Image formation by a convex mirror.

(a) Construction for finding the position of an image formed by a convex mirror

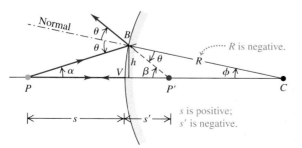

(b) Construction for finding the magnification of an image formed by a convex mirror

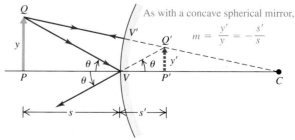

(a) Paraxial rays incident on a convex spherical mirror diverge from a virtual focal point.

(b) Rays aimed at the virtual focal point are parallel to the axis after reflection.

34.17 The focal point and focal length of a convex mirror.

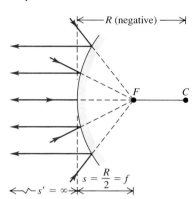

These expressions are exactly the same as Eqs. (34.4) and (34.7) for a concave mirror. Thus when we use our sign rules consistently, Eqs. (34.4) and (34.7) are valid for both concave and convex mirrors.

When R is negative (convex mirror), incoming rays that are parallel to the optic axis are not reflected through the focal point F. Instead, they diverge as though they had come from the point F at a distance f *behind* the mirror, as shown in Fig. 34.17a. In this case, f is the focal length, and F is called a *virtual focal point*. The corresponding image distance s' is negative, so both f and R are negative, and Eq. (34.5), $f = R/2$, holds for convex as well as concave mirrors. In Fig. 34.17b the incoming rays are converging as though they would meet at the virtual focal point F, and they are reflected parallel to the optic axis.

In summary, Eqs. (34.4) through (34.7), the basic relationships for image formation by a spherical mirror, are valid for both concave and convex mirrors, provided that we use the sign rules consistently.

Example 34.3   **Santa's image problem**

Santa checks himself for soot, using his reflection in a silvered Christmas tree ornament 0.750 m away (Fig. 34.18a). The diameter of the ornament is 7.20 cm. Standard reference texts state that he is a "right jolly old elf," so we estimate his height to be 1.6 m. Where and how tall is the image of Santa formed by the ornament? Is it erect or inverted?

SOLUTION

IDENTIFY and SET UP: Figure 34.18b shows the situation. Santa is the object, and the surface of the ornament closest to him acts as a convex mirror. The relationships among object distance, image distance, focal length, and magnification are the same as for

34.18 **(a)** The ornament forms a virtual, reduced, erect image of Santa. **(b)** Our sketch of two of the rays forming the image.

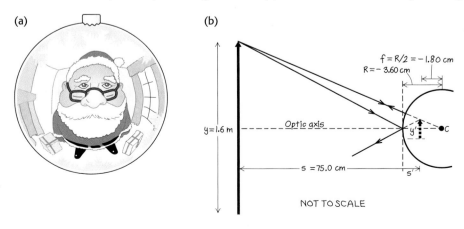

Continued

concave mirrors, provided we use the sign rules consistently. The radius of curvature and the focal length of a convex mirror are *negative*. The object distance is $s = 0.750$ m $= 75.0$ cm, and Santa's height is $y = 1.6$ m. We solve Eq. (34.6) to find the image distance s', and then use Eq. (34.7) to find the lateral magnification m and the image height y'. The sign of m tells us whether the image is erect or inverted.

EXECUTE: The radius of the mirror (half the diameter) is $R = -(7.20$ cm$)/2 = -3.60$ cm, and the focal length is $f = R/2 = -1.80$ cm. From Eq. (34.6),

$$\frac{1}{s'} = \frac{1}{f} - \frac{1}{s} = \frac{1}{-1.80 \text{ cm}} - \frac{1}{75.0 \text{ cm}}$$

$$s' = -1.76 \text{ cm}$$

Because s' is negative, the image is behind the mirror—that is, on the side opposite to the outgoing light (Fig. 34.18b)—and it is virtual.

The image is about halfway between the front surface of the ornament and its center.

From Eq. (34.7), the lateral magnification and the image height are

$$m = \frac{y'}{y} = -\frac{s'}{s} = -\frac{-1.76 \text{ cm}}{75.0 \text{ cm}} = 0.0234$$

$$y' = my = (0.0234)(1.6 \text{ m}) = 3.8 \times 10^{-2} \text{ m} = 3.8 \text{ cm}$$

EVALUATE: Our sketch indicates that the image is erect so both m and y' are positive; our calculations agree. When the object distance s is positive, a convex mirror *always* forms an erect, virtual, reduced, reversed image. For this reason, convex mirrors are used at blind intersections, for surveillance in stores, and as wide-angle rear-view mirrors for cars and trucks. (Many such mirrors read "Objects in mirror are closer than they appear.")

Graphical Methods for Mirrors

In Examples 34.1 and 34.3, we used Eqs. (34.6) and (34.7) to find the position and size of the image formed by a mirror. We can also determine the properties of the image by a simple *graphical* method. This method consists of finding the point of intersection of a few particular rays that diverge from a point of the object (such as point Q in Fig. 34.19) and are reflected by the mirror. Then (neglecting aberrations) *all* rays from this object point that strike the mirror will intersect at the same point. For this construction we always choose an object point that is *not* on the optic axis. Four rays that we can usually draw easily are shown in Fig. 34.19. These are called **principal rays.**

1. *A ray parallel to the axis,* after reflection, passes through the focal point F of a concave mirror or appears to come from the (virtual) focal point of a convex mirror.
2. *A ray through (or proceeding toward) the focal point F* is reflected parallel to the axis.
3. *A ray along the radius* through or away from the center of curvature C intersects the surface normally and is reflected back along its original path.
4. *A ray to the vertex V* is reflected forming equal angles with the optic axis.

34.19 The graphical method of locating an image formed by a spherical mirror. The colors of the rays are for identification only; they do not refer to specific colors of light.

(a) Principal rays for concave mirror

(b) Principal rays for convex mirror

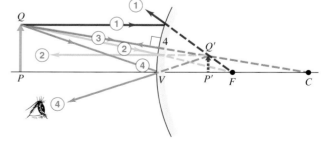

① Ray parallel to axis reflects through focal point.

② Ray through focal point reflects parallel to axis.

③ Ray through center of curvature intersects the surface normally and reflects along its original path.

④ Ray to vertex reflects symmetrically around optic axis.

① Reflected parallel ray appears to come from focal point.

② Ray toward focal point reflects parallel to axis.

③ As with concave mirror: Ray radial to center of curvature intersects the surface normally and reflects along its original path.

④ As with concave mirror: Ray to vertex reflects symmetrically around optic axis.

Once we have found the position of the image point by means of the intersection of any two of these principal rays $(1, 2, 3, 4)$, we can draw the path of any other ray from the object point to the same image point.

CAUTION **Principal rays are not the only rays** Although we've emphasized the principal rays, in fact *any* ray from the object that strikes the mirror will pass through the image point (for a real image) or appear to originate from the image point (for a virtual image). Usually, you only need to draw the principal rays, because these are all you need to locate the image.

Problem-Solving Strategy 34.1 **Image Formation by Mirrors**

IDENTIFY *the relevant concepts:* Problems involving image formation by mirrors can be solved in two ways: using principal-ray diagrams and using equations. A successful problem solution uses *both* approaches.

SET UP *the problem:* Identify the target variables. One of them is likely to be the focal length, the object distance, or the image distance, with the other two quantities given.

EXECUTE *the solution* as follows:
1. Draw a large, clear principal-ray diagram if you have enough information.
2. Orient your diagram so that incoming rays go from left to right. Draw only the principal rays; color-code them as in Fig. 34.19. If possible, use graph paper or quadrille-ruled paper. Use a ruler and measure distances carefully! A freehand sketch will *not* give good results.
3. If your principal rays don't converge at a real image point, you may have to extend them straight backward to locate a virtual

image point, as in Fig. 34.19b. We recommend drawing the extensions with broken lines.
4. Measure the resulting diagram to obtain the magnitudes of the target variables.
5. Solve for the target variables using Eq. (34.6), $1/s + 1/s' = 1/f$, and the lateral magnification equation, Eq. (34.7), as appropriate. Apply the sign rules given in Section 34.1 to object and image distances, radii of curvature, and object and image heights.
6. Use the sign rules to interpret the results that you deduced from your ray diagram and calculations. Note that the *same* sign rules (given in Section 34.1) work for all four cases in this chapter: reflection and refraction from plane and spherical surfaces.

EVALUATE *your answer:* Check that the results of your calculations agree with your ray-diagram results for image position, image size, and whether the image is real or virtual.

Example 34.4 **Concave mirror with various object distances**

A concave mirror has a radius of curvature with absolute value 20 cm. Find graphically the image of an object in the form of an arrow perpendicular to the axis of the mirror at object distances of (a) 30 cm, (b) 20 cm, (c) 10 cm, and (d) 5 cm. Check the construction by *computing* the size and lateral magnification of each image.

SOLUTION

IDENTIFY and SET UP: We must use graphical methods *and* calculations to analyze the image made by a mirror. The mirror is concave, so its radius of curvature is $R = +20$ cm and its focal length is $f = R/2 = +10$ cm. Our target variables are the image distances s' and lateral magnifications m corresponding to four cases with successively smaller object distances s. In each case we solve Eq. (34.6) for s' and use $m = -s'/s$ to find m.

EXECUTE: Figure 34.20 shows the principal-ray diagrams for the four cases. Study each of these diagrams carefully and confirm that each numbered ray is drawn in accordance with the rules given earlier (under "Graphical Methods for Mirrors"). Several points are worth noting. First, in case (b) the object and image distances are equal. Ray 3 cannot be drawn in this case because a ray from Q through the center of curvature C does not strike the mirror. In case (c), ray 2 cannot be drawn because a ray from Q through F does

not strike the mirror. In this case the outgoing rays are parallel, corresponding to an infinite image distance. In case (d), the outgoing rays diverge; they have been extended backward to the *virtual image point* Q', from which they appear to diverge. Case (d) illustrates the general observation that an object placed inside the focal point of a concave mirror produces a virtual image.

Measurements of the figures, with appropriate scaling, give the following approximate image distances: (a) 15 cm; (b) 20 cm; (c) ∞ or $-\infty$ (because the outgoing rays are parallel and do not converge at any finite distance); (d) -10 cm. To *compute* these distances, we solve Eq. (34.6) for s' and insert $f = 10$ cm:

(a) $\dfrac{1}{30 \text{ cm}} + \dfrac{1}{s'} = \dfrac{1}{10 \text{ cm}}$ $\quad s' = 15$ cm

(b) $\dfrac{1}{20 \text{ cm}} + \dfrac{1}{s'} = \dfrac{1}{10 \text{ cm}}$ $\quad s' = 20$ cm

(c) $\dfrac{1}{10 \text{ cm}} + \dfrac{1}{s'} = \dfrac{1}{10 \text{ cm}}$ $\quad s' = \infty$ (or $-\infty$)

(d) $\dfrac{1}{5 \text{ cm}} + \dfrac{1}{s'} = \dfrac{1}{10 \text{ cm}}$ $\quad s' = -10$ cm

The signs of s' tell us that the image is real in cases (a) and (b) and virtual in case (d).

Continued

The lateral magnifications measured from the figures are approximately (a) $-\frac{1}{2}$; (b) -1; (c) ∞ or $-\infty$; (d) $+2$. From Eq. (34.7),

(a) $m = -\dfrac{15 \text{ cm}}{30 \text{ cm}} = -\dfrac{1}{2}$

(b) $m = -\dfrac{20 \text{ cm}}{20 \text{ cm}} = -1$

(c) $m = -\dfrac{\infty \text{ cm}}{10 \text{ cm}} = -\infty \ (\text{or} \ +\infty)$

(d) $m = -\dfrac{-10 \text{ cm}}{5 \text{ cm}} = +2$

The signs of m tell us that the image is inverted in cases (a) and (b) and erect in case (d).

EVALUATE: Notice the trend of the results in the four cases. When the object is far from the mirror, as in Fig. 34.20a, the image is smaller than the object, inverted, and real. As the object distance s decreases, the image moves farther from the mirror and gets larger (Fig. 34.20b). When the object is at the focal point, the image is at infinity (Fig. 34.20c). When the object is inside the focal point, the image becomes larger than the object, erect, and virtual (Fig. 34.20d). You can confirm these conclusions by looking at objects reflected in the concave bowl of a shiny metal spoon.

34.20 Using principal-ray diagrams to locate the image $P'Q'$ made by a concave mirror.

(a) Construction for $s = 30$ cm

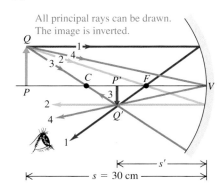

(b) Construction for $s = 20$ cm

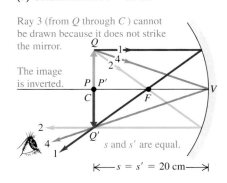

(c) Construction for $s = 10$ cm

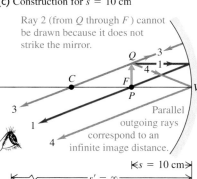

(d) Construction for $s = 5$ cm

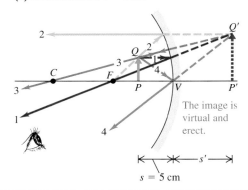

Test Your Understanding of Section 34.2 A cosmetics mirror is designed so that your reflection appears right-side up and enlarged. (a) Is the mirror concave or convex? (b) To see an enlarged image, what should be the distance from the mirror (of focal length f) to your face? (i) $|f|$; (ii) less than $|f|$; (iii) greater than $|f|$. ❙

34.3 Refraction at a Spherical Surface

As we mentioned in Section 34.1, images can be formed by refraction as well as by reflection. To begin with, let's consider refraction at a spherical surface—that is, at a spherical interface between two optical materials with different indexes of refraction. This analysis is directly applicable to some real optical systems, such as the human eye. It also provides a stepping-stone for the analysis of lenses, which usually have *two* spherical (or nearly spherical) surfaces.

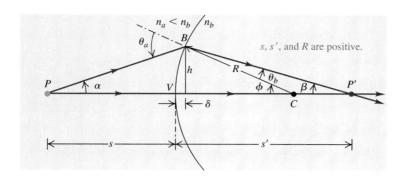

34.21 Construction for finding the position of the image point P' of a point object P formed by refraction at a spherical surface. The materials to the left and right of the interface have refractive indexes n_a and n_b, respectively. In the case shown here, $n_a < n_b$.

Image of a Point Object: Spherical Refracting Surface

In Fig. 34.21 a spherical surface with radius R forms an interface between two materials with different indexes of refraction n_a and n_b. The surface forms an image P' of an object point P; we want to find how the object and image distances (s and s') are related. We will use the same sign rules that we used for spherical mirrors. The center of curvature C is on the outgoing side of the surface, so R is positive. Ray PV strikes the vertex V and is perpendicular to the surface (that is, to the plane that is tangent to the surface at the point of incidence V). It passes into the second material without deviation. Ray PB, making an angle α with the axis, is incident at an angle θ_a with the normal and is refracted at an angle θ_b. These rays intersect at P', a distance s' to the right of the vertex. The figure is drawn for the case $n_a < n_b$. The object and image distances are both positive.

We are going to prove that if the angle α is small, *all* rays from P intersect at the same point P', so P' is the *real image* of P. We use much the same approach as we did for spherical mirrors in Section 34.2. We again use the theorem that an exterior angle of a triangle equals the sum of the two opposite interior angles; applying this to the triangles PBC and $P'BC$ gives

$$\theta_a = \alpha + \phi \qquad \phi = \beta + \theta_b \qquad (34.8)$$

From the law of refraction,

$$n_a \sin \theta_a = n_b \sin \theta_b$$

Also, the tangents of α, β, and ϕ are

$$\tan \alpha = \frac{h}{s + \delta} \qquad \tan \beta = \frac{h}{s' - \delta} \qquad \tan \phi = \frac{h}{R - \delta} \qquad (34.9)$$

For paraxial rays, θ_a and θ_b are both small in comparison to a radian, and we may approximate both the sine and tangent of either of these angles by the angle itself (measured in radians). The law of refraction then gives

$$n_a \theta_a = n_b \theta_b$$

Combining this with the first of Eqs. (34.8), we obtain

$$\theta_b = \frac{n_a}{n_b}(\alpha + \phi)$$

When we substitute this into the second of Eqs. (34.8), we get

$$n_a \alpha + n_b \beta = (n_b - n_a)\phi \qquad (34.10)$$

Now we use the approximations $\tan \alpha = \alpha$, and so on, in Eqs. (34.9) and also neglect the small distance δ; those equations then become

$$\alpha = \frac{h}{s} \qquad \beta = \frac{h}{s'} \qquad \phi = \frac{h}{R}$$

34.22 Construction for determining the height of an image formed by refraction at a spherical surface. In the case shown here, $n_a < n_b$.

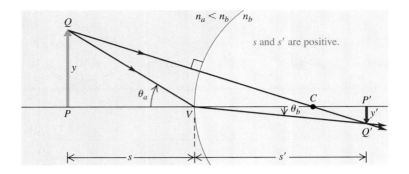

Finally, we substitute these into Eq. (34.10) and divide out the common factor h. We obtain

$$\frac{n_a}{s} + \frac{n_b}{s'} = \frac{n_b - n_a}{R} \qquad \text{(object–image relationship,} \atop \text{spherical refracting surface)} \qquad \text{(34.11)}$$

This equation does not contain the angle α, so the image distance is the same for *all* paraxial rays emanating from P; this proves our assertion that P' is the image of P.

To obtain the lateral magnification m for this situation, we use the construction in Fig. 34.22. We draw two rays from point Q, one through the center of curvature C and the other incident at the vertex V. From the triangles PQV and $P'Q'V$,

$$\tan\theta_a = \frac{y}{s} \qquad \tan\theta_b = \frac{-y'}{s'}$$

and from the law of refraction,

$$n_a \sin\theta_a = n_b \sin\theta_b$$

For small angles,

$$\tan\theta_a = \sin\theta_a \qquad \tan\theta_b = \sin\theta_b$$

so finally

$$\frac{n_a y}{s} = -\frac{n_b y'}{s'} \qquad \text{or}$$

$$m = \frac{y'}{y} = -\frac{n_a s'}{n_b s} \qquad \text{(lateral magnification,} \atop \text{spherical refracting surface)} \qquad \text{(34.12)}$$

Equations (34.11) and (34.12) can be applied to both convex and concave refracting surfaces, provided that you use the sign rules consistently. It doesn't matter whether n_b is greater or less than n_a. To verify these statements, you should construct diagrams like Figs. 34.21 and 34.22 for the following three cases: (i) $R > 0$ and $n_a > n_b$, (ii) $R < 0$ and $n_a < n_b$, and (iii) $R < 0$ and $n_a > n_b$. Then in each case, use your diagram to again derive Eqs. (34.11) and (34.12).

Here's a final note on the sign rule for the radius of curvature R of a surface. For the convex reflecting surface in Fig. 34.16, we considered R negative, but the convex *refracting* surface in Fig. 34.21 has a *positive* value of R. This may seem inconsistent, but it isn't. The rule is that R is positive if the center of curvature C is on the outgoing side of the surface and negative if C is on the other side. For the convex reflecting surface in Fig. 34.16, R is negative because point C is to the right of the surface but outgoing rays are to the left. For the convex refracting surface in Fig. 34.21, R is positive because both C and the outgoing rays are to the right of the surface.

Refraction at a curved surface is one reason gardeners avoid watering plants at midday. As sunlight enters a water drop resting on a leaf (Fig. 34.23), the light rays are refracted toward each other as in Figs. 34.21 and 34.22. The sunlight that strikes the leaf is therefore more concentrated and able to cause damage.

An important special case of a spherical refracting surface is a *plane* surface between two optical materials. This corresponds to setting $R = \infty$ in Eq. (34.11). In this case,

$$\frac{n_a}{s} + \frac{n_b}{s'} = 0 \qquad \text{(plane refracting surface)} \qquad (34.13)$$

To find the lateral magnification m for this case, we combine this equation with the general relationship, Eq. (34.12), obtaining the simple result

$$m = 1$$

That is, the image formed by a *plane* refracting surface always has the same lateral size as the object, and it is always erect.

An example of image formation by a plane refracting surface is the appearance of a partly submerged drinking straw or canoe paddle. When viewed from some angles, the object appears to have a sharp bend at the water surface because the submerged part appears to be only about three-quarters of its actual distance below the surface. (We commented on the appearance of a submerged object in Section 33.2; see Fig. 33.9.)

34.23 Light rays refract as they pass through the curved surfaces of these water droplets.

Example 34.5 | Image formation by refraction I

A cylindrical glass rod (Fig. 34.24) has index of refraction 1.52. It is surrounded by air. One end is ground to a hemispherical surface with radius $R = 2.00$ cm. A small object is placed on the axis of the rod, 8.00 cm to the left of the vertex. Find (a) the image distance and (b) the lateral magnification.

SOLUTION

IDENTIFY and SET UP: This problem uses the ideas of refraction at a curved surface. Our target variables are the image distance s' and the lateral magnification m. Here material a is air ($n_a = 1.00$) and

material b is the glass of which the rod is made ($n_b = 1.52$). We are given $s = 8.00$ cm. The center of curvature of the spherical surface is on the outgoing side of the surface, so the radius is positive: $R = +2.00$ cm. We solve Eq. (34.11) for s', and we use Eq. (34.12) to find m.

EXECUTE: (a) From Eq. (34.11),

$$\frac{1.00}{8.00 \text{ cm}} + \frac{1.52}{s'} = \frac{1.52 - 1.00}{+2.00 \text{ cm}}$$

$$s' = +11.3 \text{ cm}$$

(b) From Eq. (34.12),

$$m = -\frac{n_a s'}{n_b s} = -\frac{(1.00)(11.3 \text{ cm})}{(1.52)(8.00 \text{ cm})} = -0.929$$

34.24 The glass rod in air forms a real image.

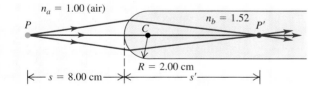

EVALUATE: Because the image distance s' is positive, the image is formed 11.3 cm to the *right* of the vertex (on the outgoing side), as Fig. 34.24 shows. The value of m tells us that the image is somewhat smaller than the object and that it is inverted. If the object is an arrow 1.000 mm high, pointing upward, the image is an arrow 0.929 mm high, pointing downward.

Example 34.6 | Image formation by refraction II

The glass rod of Example 34.5 is immersed in water, which has index of refraction $n = 1.33$ (Fig. 34.25). The object distance is again 8.00 cm. Find the image distance and lateral magnification.

SOLUTION

IDENTIFY and SET UP: The situation is the same as in Example 34.5 except that now $n_a = 1.33$. We again use Eqs. (34.11) and (34.12) to determine s' and m, respectively.

EXECUTE: Our solution of Eq. (34.11) in Example 34.5 yields

$$\frac{1.33}{8.00 \text{ cm}} + \frac{1.52}{s'} = \frac{1.52 - 1.33}{+2.00 \text{ cm}}$$

$$s' = -21.3 \text{ cm}$$

Continued

34.25 When immersed in water, the glass rod forms a virtual image.

The lateral magnification in this case is

$$m = -\frac{(1.33)(-21.3 \text{ cm})}{(1.52)(8.00 \text{ cm})} = +2.33$$

EVALUATE: The negative value of s' means that the refracted rays do not converge, but appear to diverge from a point 21.3 cm to the

left of the vertex. We saw a similar case in the reflection of light from a convex mirror; in both cases we call the result a *virtual image*. The vertical image is erect (because m is positive) and 2.33 times as large as the object.

Example 34.7 Apparent depth of a swimming pool

If you look straight down into a swimming pool where it is 2.00 m deep, how deep does it appear to be?

SOLUTION

IDENTIFY and SET UP: Figure 34.26 shows the situation. The surface of the water acts as a plane refracting surface. To determine the pool's apparent depth, we imagine an arrow PQ painted on the bottom. The pool's refracting surface forms a virtual image $P'Q'$ of this arrow. We solve Eq. (34.13) to find the image depth s'; that's the pool's apparent depth.

EXECUTE: The object distance is the actual depth of the pool, $s = 2.00$ m. Material a is water ($n_a = 1.33$) and material b is air ($n_b = 1.00$). From Eq. (34.13),

$$\frac{n_a}{s} + \frac{n_b}{s'} = \frac{1.33}{2.00 \text{ m}} + \frac{1.00}{s'} = 0$$
$$s' = -1.50 \text{ m}$$

The image distance is negative. By the sign rules in Section 34.1, this means that the image is virtual and on the incoming side of the refracting surface—that is, on the same side as the object, namely underwater. The pool's apparent depth is 1.50 m, or just 75% of its true depth.

EVALUATE: Recall that the lateral magnification for a plane refracting surface is $m = 1$. Hence the image $P'Q'$ of the arrow has the same *horizontal length* as the actual arrow PQ (Fig. 34.27). Only its depth is different from that of PQ.

34.26 Arrow $P'Q'$ is the virtual image of the underwater arrow PQ. The angles of the ray with the vertical are exaggerated for clarity.

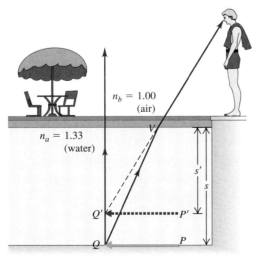

34.27 The submerged portion of this straw appears to be at a shallower depth (closer to the surface) than it actually is.

Test Your Understanding of Section 34.3 The water droplets in Fig. 34.23 have radius of curvature R and index of refraction $n = 1.33$. Can they form an image of the sun on the leaf?

34.4 Thin Lenses

The most familiar and widely used optical device (after the plane mirror) is the *lens.* A lens is an optical system with two refracting surfaces. The simplest lens has two *spherical* surfaces close enough together that we can neglect the distance between them (the thickness of the lens); we call this a **thin lens.** If you wear eyeglasses or contact lenses while reading, you are viewing these words through a pair of thin lenses. We can analyze thin lenses in detail using the results of Section 34.3 for refraction by a single spherical surface. However, we postpone this analysis until later in the section so that we can first discuss the properties of thin lenses.

Properties of a Lens

A lens of the shape shown in Fig. 34.28 has the property that when a beam of rays parallel to the axis passes through the lens, the rays converge to a point F_2 (Fig. 34.28a) and form a real image at that point. Such a lens is called a **converging lens.** Similarly, rays passing through point F_1 emerge from the lens as a beam of parallel rays (Fig. 34.28b). The points F_1 and F_2 are called the first and second *focal points,* and the distance f (measured from the center of the lens) is called the *focal length.* Note the similarities between the two focal points of a converging lens and the single focal point of a concave mirror (see Fig. 34.13). As for a concave mirror, the focal length of a converging lens is defined to be a *positive* quantity, and such a lens is also called a *positive lens.*

The central horizontal line in Fig. 34.28 is called the *optic axis,* as with spherical mirrors. The centers of curvature of the two spherical surfaces lie on and define the optic axis. The two focal lengths in Fig. 34.28, both labeled f, *are always equal* for a thin lens, even when the two sides have different curvatures. We will derive this somewhat surprising result later in the section, when we derive the relationship of f to the index of refraction of the lens and the radii of curvature of its surfaces.

Image of an Extended Object: Converging Lens

Like a concave mirror, a converging lens can form an image of an extended object. Figure 34.29 shows how to find the position and lateral magnification of an image made by a thin converging lens. Using the same notation and sign rules as before, we let s and s' be the object and image distances, respectively, and let y and y' be the object and image heights. Ray QA, parallel to the optic axis before refraction, passes through the second focal point F_2 after refraction. Ray QOQ' passes undeflected straight through the center of the lens because at the center the two surfaces are parallel and (we have assumed) very close together. There is refraction where the ray enters and leaves the material but no net change in direction.

34.28 F_1 and F_2 are the first and second focal points of a converging thin lens. The numerical value of f is positive.

(a)

Optic axis (passes through centers of curvature of both lens surfaces)

Second focal point: the point to which incoming parallel rays converge

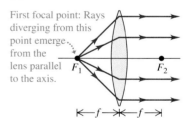

Focal length ·······
• Measured from lens center
• Always the same on both sides of the lens
• Positive for a converging thin lens

(b)

First focal point: Rays diverging from this point emerge from the lens parallel to the axis.

34.29 Construction used to find image position for a thin lens. To emphasize that the lens is assumed to be very thin, the ray QAQ' is shown as bent at the midplane of the lens rather than at the two surfaces and ray QOQ' is shown as a straight line.

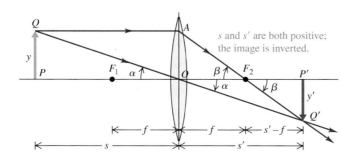

s and s' are both positive; the image is inverted.

The two angles labeled α in Fig. 34.29 are equal. Therefore the two right triangles PQO and $P'Q'O$ are *similar*, and ratios of corresponding sides are equal. Thus

$$\frac{y}{s} = -\frac{y'}{s'} \quad \text{or} \quad \frac{y'}{y} = -\frac{s'}{s} \tag{34.14}$$

(The reason for the negative sign is that the image is below the optic axis and y' is negative.) Also, the two angles labeled β are equal, and the two right triangles OAF_2 and $P'Q'F_2$ are similar, so

$$\frac{y}{f} = -\frac{y'}{s'-f} \quad \text{or}$$

$$\frac{y'}{y} = -\frac{s'-f}{f} \tag{34.15}$$

We now equate Eqs. (34.14) and (34.15), divide by s', and rearrange to obtain

$$\frac{1}{s} + \frac{1}{s'} = \frac{1}{f} \qquad \text{(object–image relationship, thin lens)} \tag{34.16}$$

This analysis also gives the lateral magnification $m = y'/y$ for the lens; from Eq. (34.14),

$$m = -\frac{s'}{s} \qquad \text{(lateral magnification, thin lens)} \tag{34.17}$$

The negative sign tells us that when s and s' are both positive, as in Fig. 34.29, the image is *inverted,* and y and y' have opposite signs.

Equations (34.16) and (34.17) are the basic equations for thin lenses. They are *exactly* the same as the corresponding equations for spherical mirrors, Eqs. (34.6) and (34.7). As we will see, the same sign rules that we used for spherical mirrors are also applicable to lenses. In particular, consider a lens with a positive focal length (a converging lens). When an object is outside the first focal point F_1 of this lens (that is, when $s > f$), the image distance s' is positive (that is, the image is on the same side as the outgoing rays); this image is real and inverted, as in Fig. 34.29. An object placed inside the first focal point of a converging lens, so that $s < f$, produces an image with a negative value of s'; this image is located on the same side of the lens as the object and is virtual, erect, and larger than the object. You can verify these statements algebraically using Eqs. (34.16) and (34.17); we'll also verify them in the next section, using graphical methods analogous to those introduced for mirrors in Section 34.2.

Figure 34.30 shows how a lens forms a three-dimensional image of a three-dimensional object. Point R is nearer the lens than point P. From Eq. (34.16), image point R' is farther from the lens than is image point P', and the image $P'R'$

34.30 The image $S'P'Q'R'$ of a three-dimensional object $SPQR$ is not reversed by a lens.

A real image made by a converging lens is inverted but *not* reversed back to front: the image thumb $P'R'$ and object thumb PR point in the same direction.

points in the same direction as the object *PR*. Arrows *P'S'* and *P'Q'* are reversed relative to *PS* and *PQ*.

Let's compare Fig. 34.30 with Fig. 34.7, which shows the image formed by a plane *mirror*. We note that the image formed by the lens is inverted, but it is *not* reversed front to back along the optic axis. That is, if the object is a left hand, its image is also a left hand. You can verify this by pointing your left thumb along *PR*, your left forefinger along *PQ*, and your left middle finger along *PS*. Then rotate your hand 180°, using your thumb as an axis; this brings the fingers into coincidence with *P'Q'* and *P'S'*. In other words, an *inverted* image is equivalent to an image that has been rotated by 180° about the lens axis.

Diverging Lenses

So far we have been discussing *converging* lenses. Figure 34.31 shows a **diverging lens;** the beam of parallel rays incident on this lens *diverges* after refraction. The focal length of a diverging lens is a negative quantity, and the lens is also called a *negative lens*. The focal points of a negative lens are reversed, relative to those of a positive lens. The second focal point, F_2, of a negative lens is the point from which rays that are originally parallel to the axis *appear to diverge* after refraction, as in Fig. 34.31a. Incident rays converging toward the first focal point F_1, as in Fig. 34.31b, emerge from the lens parallel to its axis. Comparing with Section 34.2, you can see that a diverging lens has the same relationship to a converging lens as a convex mirror has to a concave mirror.

Equations (34.16) and (34.17) apply to *both* positive and negative lenses. Figure 34.32 shows various types of lenses, both converging and diverging. Here's an important observation: *Any lens that is thicker at its center than at its edges is a converging lens with positive f; and any lens that is thicker at its edges than at its center is a diverging lens with negative f* (provided that the lens has a greater index of refraction than the surrounding material). We can prove this using the *lensmaker's equation,* which it is our next task to derive.

The Lensmaker's Equation

We'll now derive Eq. (34.16) in more detail and at the same time derive the *lensmaker's equation,* which is a relationship among the focal length f, the index of refraction n of the lens, and the radii of curvature R_1 and R_2 of the lens surfaces. We use the principle that an image formed by one reflecting or refracting surface can serve as the object for a second reflecting or refracting surface.

We begin with the somewhat more general problem of two spherical interfaces separating three materials with indexes of refraction n_a, n_b, and n_c, as shown in Fig. 34.33. The object and image distances for the first surface are s_1 and s'_1, and those for the second surface are s_2 and s'_2. We assume that the lens is thin, so that the distance t between the two surfaces is small in comparison with the object and image distances and can therefore be neglected. This is usually the case with eyeglass lenses (Fig. 34.34). Then s_2 and s'_1 have the same magnitude but opposite sign. For example, if the first image is on the outgoing side of the first surface, s'_1 is positive. But when viewed as an object for the second surface, the first image is *not* on the incoming side of that surface. So we can say that $s_2 = -s'_1$.

We need to use the single-surface equation, Eq. (34.11), twice, once for each surface. The two resulting equations are

$$\frac{n_a}{s_1} + \frac{n_b}{s'_1} = \frac{n_b - n_a}{R_1}$$

$$\frac{n_b}{s_2} + \frac{n_c}{s'_2} = \frac{n_c - n_b}{R_2}$$

Ordinarily, the first and third materials are air or vacuum, so we set $n_a = n_c = 1$. The second index n_b is that of the lens, which we can call simply n. Substituting these values and the relationship $s_2 = -s'_1$, we get

34.31 F_2 and F_1 are the second and first focal points of a diverging thin lens, respectively. The numerical value of f is negative.

(a)

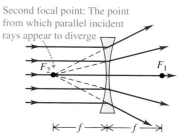

Second focal point: The point from which parallel incident rays appear to diverge

For a diverging thin lens, *f* is negative.

(b)

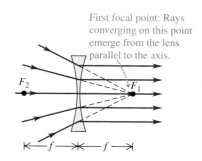

First focal point: Rays converging on this point emerge from the lens parallel to the axis.

34.32 Various types of lenses.

(a)   **Converging lenses**

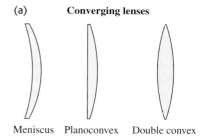

Meniscus   Planoconvex   Double convex

(b)   **Diverging lenses**

Meniscus   Planoconcave   Double concave

34.33 The image formed by the first surface of a lens serves as the object for the second surface. The distances s_1' and s_2 are taken to be equal; this is a good approximation if the lens thickness t is small.

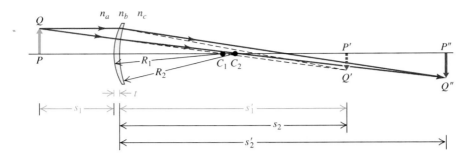

34.34 These eyeglass lenses satisfy the thin-lens approximation: Their thickness is small compared to the object and image distances.

$$\frac{1}{s_1} + \frac{n}{s_1'} = \frac{n-1}{R_1}$$

$$-\frac{n}{s_1'} + \frac{1}{s_2'} = \frac{1-n}{R_2}$$

To get a relationship between the initial object position s_1 and the final image position s_2', we add these two equations. This eliminates the term n/s_1', and we obtain

$$\frac{1}{s_1} + \frac{1}{s_2'} = (n-1)\left(\frac{1}{R_1} - \frac{1}{R_2}\right)$$

Finally, thinking of the lens as a single unit, we call the object distance simply s instead of s_1, and we call the final image distance s' instead of s_2'. Making these substitutions, we have

$$\frac{1}{s} + \frac{1}{s'} = (n-1)\left(\frac{1}{R_1} - \frac{1}{R_2}\right) \tag{34.18}$$

Now we compare this with the other thin-lens equation, Eq. (34.16). We see that the object and image distances s and s' appear in exactly the same places in both equations and that the focal length f is given by

$$\frac{1}{f} = (n-1)\left(\frac{1}{R_1} - \frac{1}{R_2}\right) \quad \text{(lensmaker's equation for a thin lens)} \tag{34.19}$$

This is the **lensmaker's equation.** In the process of rederiving the relationship among object distance, image distance, and focal length for a thin lens, we have also derived an expression for the focal length f of a lens in terms of its index of refraction n and the radii of curvature R_1 and R_2 of its surfaces. This can be used to show that all the lenses in Fig. 34.32a are converging lenses with positive focal lengths and that all the lenses in Fig. 34.32b are diverging lenses with negative focal lengths.

We use all our sign rules from Section 34.1 with Eqs. (34.18) and (34.19). For example, in Fig. 34.35, s, s', and R_1 are positive, but R_2 is negative.

It is not hard to generalize Eq. (34.19) to the situation in which the lens is immersed in a material with an index of refraction greater than unity. We invite you to work out the lensmaker's equation for this more general situation.

We stress that the paraxial approximation is indeed an approximation! Rays that are at sufficiently large angles to the optic axis of a spherical lens will not be brought to the same focus as paraxial rays; this is the same problem of spherical aberration that plagues spherical *mirrors* (see Section 34.2). To avoid this and other limitations of thin spherical lenses, lenses of more complicated shape are used in precision optical instruments.

34.35 A converging thin lens with a positive focal length f.

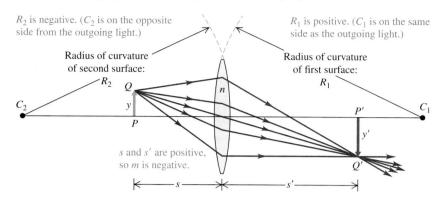

Example 34.8   Determining the focal length of a lens

(a) Suppose the absolute values of the radii of curvature of the lens surfaces in Fig. 34.35 are both equal to 10 cm and the index of refraction of the glass is $n = 1.52$. What is the focal length f of the lens? (b) Suppose the lens in Fig. 34.31 also has $n = 1.52$ and the absolute values of the radii of curvature of its lens surfaces are also both equal to 10 cm. What is the focal length of this lens?

SOLUTION

IDENTIFY and SET UP: We are asked to find the focal length f of (a) a lens that is convex on both sides (Fig. 34.35) and (b) a lens that is concave on both sides (Fig. 34.31). In both cases we solve the lensmaker's equation, Eq. (34.19), to determine f. We apply the sign rules given in Section 34.1 to the radii of curvature R_1 and R_2 to take account of whether the surfaces are convex or concave.

EXECUTE: (a) The lens in Fig. 34.35 is *double convex:* The center of curvature of the first surface (C_1) is on the outgoing side of the lens, so R_1 is positive, and the center of curvature of the second surface (C_2) is on the *incoming* side, so R_2 is negative. Hence $R_1 = +10$ cm and $R_2 = -10$ cm. Then from Eq. (34.19),

$$\frac{1}{f} = (1.52 - 1)\left(\frac{1}{+10 \text{ cm}} - \frac{1}{-10 \text{ cm}}\right)$$

$$f = 9.6 \text{ cm}$$

(b) The lens in Fig. 34.31 is *double concave:* The center of curvature of the first surface is on the *incoming* side, so R_1 is negative, and the center of curvature of the second surface is on the outgoing side, so R_2 is positive. Hence in this case $R_1 = -10$ cm and $R_2 = +10$ cm. Again using Eq. (34.19),

$$\frac{1}{f} = (1.52 - 1)\left(\frac{1}{-10 \text{ cm}} - \frac{1}{+10 \text{ cm}}\right)$$

$$f = -9.6 \text{ cm}$$

EVALUATE: In part (a) the focal length is *positive,* so this is a converging lens; this makes sense, since the lens is thicker at its center than at its edges. In part (b) the focal length is *negative,* so this is a diverging lens; this also makes sense, since the lens is thicker at its edges than at its center.

Graphical Methods for Lenses

We can determine the position and size of an image formed by a thin lens by using a graphical method very similar to the one we used in Section 34.2 for spherical mirrors. Again we draw a few special rays called *principal rays* that diverge from a point of the object that is *not* on the optic axis. The intersection of these rays, after they pass through the lens, determines the position and size of the image. In using this graphical method, we will consider the entire deviation of a ray as occurring at the midplane of the lens, as shown in Fig. 34.36. This is consistent with the assumption that the distance between the lens surfaces is negligible.

The three principal rays whose paths are usually easy to trace for lenses are shown in Fig. 34.36:

1. *A ray parallel to the axis* emerges from the lens in a direction that passes through the second focal point F_2 of a converging lens, or appears to come from the second focal point of a diverging lens.
2. *A ray through the center of the lens* is not appreciably deviated; at the center of the lens the two surfaces are parallel, so this ray emerges at essentially the same angle at which it enters and along essentially the same line.
3. *A ray through (or proceeding toward) the first focal point F_1* emerges parallel to the axis.

34.36 The graphical method of locating an image formed by a thin lens. The colors of the rays are for identification only; they do not refer to specific colors of light. (Compare Fig. 34.19 for spherical mirrors.)

(a) Converging lens

(b) Diverging lens

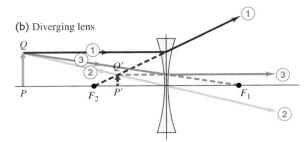

① Parallel incident ray refracts to pass through second focal point F_2.
② Ray through center of lens does not deviate appreciably.
③ Ray through the first focal point F_1 emerges parallel to the axis.

① Parallel incident ray appears after refraction to have come from the second focal point F_2.
② Ray through center of lens does not deviate appreciably.
③ Ray aimed at the first focal point F_1 emerges parallel to the axis.

When the image is real, the position of the image point is determined by the intersection of any two rays 1, 2, and 3 (Fig. 34.36a). When the image is virtual, we extend the diverging outgoing rays backward to their intersection point to find the image point (Fig. 34.36b).

> **CAUTION**   **Principal rays are not the only rays**   Keep in mind that *any* ray from the object that strikes the lens will pass through the image point (for a real image) or appear to originate from the image point (for a virtual image). (We made a similar comment about image formation by mirrors in Section 34.2.) We've emphasized the principal rays because they're the only ones you need to draw to locate the image. ❚

Figure 34.37 shows principal-ray diagrams for a converging lens for several object distances. We suggest you study each of these diagrams very carefully, comparing each numbered ray with the above description.

34.37 Formation of images by a thin converging lens for various object distances. The principal rays are numbered. (Compare Fig. 34.20 for a concave spherical mirror.)

(a) Object *O* is outside focal point; image *I* is real.

(b) Object *O* is closer to focal point; image *I* is real and farther away.

(c) Object *O* is even closer to focal point; image *I* is real and even farther away.

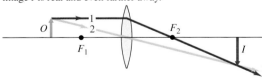

(d) Object *O* is at focal point; image *I* is at infinity.

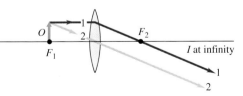

(e) Object *O* is inside focal point; image *I* is virtual and larger than object.

(f) A virtual object *O* (light rays are *converging* on lens)

Parts (a), (b), and (c) of Fig. 34.37 help explain what happens in focusing a camera. For a photograph to be in sharp focus, the film must be at the position of the real image made by the camera's lens. The image distance increases as the object is brought closer, so the film is moved farther behind the lens (i.e., the lens is moved farther in front of the film). In Fig. 34.37d the object is at the focal point; ray 3 can't be drawn because it doesn't pass through the lens. In Fig. 34.37e the object distance is less than the focal length. The outgoing rays are divergent, and the image is *virtual;* its position is located by extending the outgoing rays backward, so the image distance s' is negative. Note also that the image is erect and larger than the object. (We'll see the usefulness of this in Section 34.6.) Figure 34.37f corresponds to a *virtual object.* The incoming rays do not diverge from a real object, but are *converging* as though they would meet at the tip of the virtual object O on the right side; the object distance s is negative in this case. The image is real and is located between the lens and the second focal point. This situation can arise if the rays that strike the lens in Fig. 34.37f emerge from another converging lens (not shown) to the left of the figure.

Problem-Solving Strategy 34.2 **Image Formation by Thin Lenses**

IDENTIFY *the relevant concepts:* Review Problem-Solving Strategy 34.1 (Section 34.2) for mirrors, which is equally applicable here. As for mirrors, you should solve problems involving image formation by lenses using *both* principal-ray diagrams and equations.

SET UP *the problem:* Identify the target variables.

EXECUTE *the solution* as follows:
1. Draw a large principal-ray diagram if you have enough information, using graph paper or quadrille-ruled paper. Orient your diagram so that incoming rays go from left to right. Draw the rays with a ruler, and measure distances carefully.
2. Draw the principal rays so they change direction at the midplane of the lens, as in Fig. 34.36. For a lens there are only three principal rays (compared to four for a mirror). Draw all three whenever possible; the intersection of any two rays determines the image location, but the third ray should pass through the same point.

3. If the outgoing principal rays diverge, extend them backward to find the virtual image point on the *incoming* side of the lens, as in Fig. 34.27e.
4. Solve Eqs. (34.16) and (34.17), as appropriate, for the target variables. Make sure that you carefully use the sign rules given in Section 34.1.
5. The *image* from a first lens or mirror may serve as the *object* for a second lens or mirror. In finding the object and image distances for this intermediate image, be sure you include the distance between the two elements (lenses and/or mirrors) correctly.

EVALUATE *your answer:* Your calculated results must be consistent with your ray-diagram results. Check that they give the same image position and image size, and that they agree on whether the image is real or virtual.

Example 34.9 **Image position and magnification with a converging lens**

Use ray diagrams to find the image position and magnification for an object at each of the following distances from a converging lens with a focal length of 20 cm: (a) 50 cm; (b) 20 cm; (c) 15 cm; (d) −40 cm. Check your results by calculating the image position and lateral magnification using Eqs. (34.16) and (34.17), respectively.

SOLUTION

IDENTIFY and SET UP: We are given the focal length $f = 20$ cm and four object distances s. Our target variables are the corresponding image distances s' and lateral magnifications m. We solve Eq. (34.16) for s', and find m from Eq. (34.17), $m = -s'/s$.

EXECUTE: Figures 34.37a, d, e, and f, respectively, show the appropriate principal-ray diagrams. You should be able to reproduce these without referring to the figures. Measuring these diagrams yields the approximate results: $s' = 35$ cm, $-\infty$, -40 cm, and 15 cm, and $m = -\frac{2}{3}$, $+\infty$, $+3$, and $+\frac{1}{3}$, respectively.

Calculating the image distances from Eq. (34.16), we find

(a) $\dfrac{1}{50\ \text{cm}} + \dfrac{1}{s'} = \dfrac{1}{20\ \text{cm}}$ $s' = 33.3\ \text{cm}$

(b) $\dfrac{1}{20\ \text{cm}} + \dfrac{1}{s'} = \dfrac{1}{20\ \text{cm}}$ $s' = \pm\infty$

(c) $\dfrac{1}{15\ \text{cm}} + \dfrac{1}{s'} = \dfrac{1}{20\ \text{cm}}$ $s' = -60\ \text{cm}$

(d) $\dfrac{1}{-40\ \text{cm}} + \dfrac{1}{s'} = \dfrac{1}{20\ \text{cm}}$ $s' = 13.3\ \text{cm}$

The graphical results are fairly close to these except for part (c); the accuracy of the diagram in Fig. 34.37e is limited because the rays extended backward have nearly the same direction.

From Eq. (34.17),

(a) $m = -\dfrac{33.3\ \text{cm}}{50\ \text{cm}} = -\dfrac{2}{3}$ (b) $m = -\dfrac{\pm\infty\ \text{cm}}{20\ \text{cm}} = \pm\infty$

(c) $m = -\dfrac{-60\ \text{cm}}{15\ \text{cm}} = +4$ (d) $m = -\dfrac{13.3\ \text{cm}}{-40\ \text{cm}} = +\frac{1}{3}$

Continued

EVALUATE: Note that the image distance s' is positive in parts (a) and (d) but negative in part (c). This makes sense: The image is real in parts (a) and (d) but virtual in part (c). The light rays that emerge from the lens in part (b) are parallel and never converge, so the image can be regarded as being at either $+\infty$ or $-\infty$.

The values of magnification m tell us that the image is inverted in part (a) and erect in parts (c) and (d), in agreement with the principal-ray diagrams. The infinite value of magnification in part (b) is another way of saying that the image is formed infinitely far away.

Example 34.10 Image formation by a diverging lens

A beam of parallel rays spreads out after passing through a thin diverging lens, as if the rays all came from a point 20.0 cm from the center of the lens. You want to use this lens to form an erect, virtual image that is $\frac{1}{3}$ the height of the object. (a) Where should the object be placed? Where will the image be? (b) Draw a principal-ray diagram.

SOLUTION

IDENTIFY and SET UP: The result with parallel rays shows that the focal length is $f = -20$ cm. We want the lateral magnification to be $m = +\frac{1}{3}$ (positive because the image is to be erect). Our target variables are the object distance s and the image distance s'. In part (a), we solve the magnification equation, Eq. (34.17), for s' in terms of s; we then use the object–image relationship, Eq. (34.16), to find s and s' individually.

EXECUTE: (a) From Eq. (34.17), $m = +\frac{1}{3} = -s'/s$, so $s' = -s/3$. We insert this result into Eq. (34.16) and solve for the object distance s:

$$\frac{1}{s} + \frac{1}{-s/3} = \frac{1}{s} - \frac{3}{s} = -\frac{2}{s} = \frac{1}{f}$$

$$s = -2f = -2(-20.0 \text{ cm}) = 40.0 \text{ cm}$$

The object should be 40.0 cm from the lens. The image distance will be

$$s' = -\frac{s}{3} = -\frac{40.0 \text{ cm}}{3} = -13.3 \text{ cm}$$

The image distance is negative, so the object and image are on the same side of the lens.

(b) Figure 34.38 is a principal-ray diagram for this problem, with the rays numbered as in Fig. 34.36b.

EVALUATE: You should be able to draw a principal-ray diagram like Fig. 34.38 without referring to the figure. From your diagram, you can confirm our results in part (a) for the object and image distances. You can also check our results for s and s' by substituting them back into Eq. (34.16).

34.38 Principal-ray diagram for an image formed by a thin diverging lens.

Example 34.11 An image of an image

Converging lenses A and B, of focal lengths 8.0 cm and 6.0 cm, respectively, are placed 36.0 cm apart. Both lenses have the same optic axis. An object 8.0 cm high is placed 12.0 cm to the left of lens A. Find the position, size, and orientation of the image produced by the lenses in combination. (Such combinations are used in telescopes and microscopes, to be discussed in Section 34.7.)

SOLUTION

IDENTIFY and SET UP: Figure 34.39 shows the situation. The object O lies outside the first focal point F_1 of lens A, which therefore produces a real image I. The light rays that strike lens B diverge from this real image just as if I was a material object; image I therefore acts as an *object* for lens B. Our goal is to determine the properties of the image I' made by lens B. We use both ray-diagram and computational methods to do this.

EXECUTE: In Fig. 34.39 we have drawn principal rays 1, 2, and 3 from the head of the object arrow O to find the position of the image I made by lens A, and principal rays 1′, 2′, and 3′ from the head of I to find the position of the image I' made by lens B (even though rays 2′ and 3′ don't actually exist in this case). The image

34.39 Principal-ray diagram for a combination of two converging lenses. The first lens (A) makes a real image of the object. This real image acts as an object for the second lens (B).

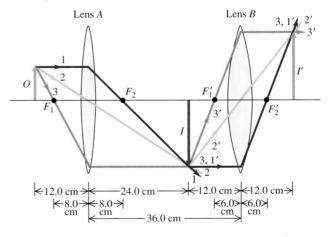

is inverted *twice,* once by each lens, so the second image I' has the same orientation as the original object.

We first find the position and size of the first image I. Applying Eq. (34.16), $1/s + 1/s' = 1/f$, to lens A gives

$$\frac{1}{12.0 \text{ cm}} + \frac{1}{s'_{I,A}} = \frac{1}{8.0 \text{ cm}} \qquad s'_{I,A} = +24.0 \text{ cm}$$

Image I is 24.0 cm to the right of lens A. The lateral magnification is $m_A = -(24.0 \text{ cm})/(12.0 \text{ cm}) = -2.00$, so image I is inverted and twice as tall as object O.

Image I is 36.0 cm $-$ 24.0 cm $=$ 12.0 cm to the left of lens B, so the object distance for lens B is $+12.0$ cm. Applying Eq. (34.16) to lens B then gives

$$\frac{1}{12.0 \text{ cm}} + \frac{1}{s'_{I',B}} = \frac{1}{6.0 \text{ cm}} \qquad s'_{I',B} = +12.0 \text{ cm}$$

The final image I' is 12.0 cm to the right of lens B. The magnification produced by lens B is $m_B = -(12.0 \text{ cm})/(12.0 \text{ cm}) = -1.00$.

EVALUATE: The value of m_B means that the final image I' is just as large as the first image I but has the opposite orientation. The *overall* magnification is $m_A m_B = (-2.00)(-1.00) = +2.00$. Hence the final image I' is $(2.00)(8.0 \text{ cm}) = 16$ cm tall and has the same orientation as the original object O, just as Fig. 34.39 shows.

Test Your Understanding of Section 34.4 A diverging lens and an object are positioned as shown in the figure at right. Which of the rays A, B, C, and D could emanate from point Q at the top of the object?

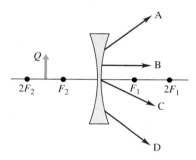

34.5 Cameras

The concept of *image,* which is so central to understanding simple mirror and lens systems, plays an equally important role in the analysis of optical instruments (also called *optical devices*). Among the most common optical devices are cameras, which make an image of an object and record it either electronically or on film.

The basic elements of a **camera** are a light-tight box ("camera" is a Latin word meaning "a room or enclosure"), a converging lens, a shutter to open the lens for a prescribed length of time, and a light-sensitive recording medium (Fig. 34.40). In a digital camera this is an electronic detector called a charge-coupled device (CCD) array; in an older camera, this is photographic film. The lens forms an inverted real image on the recording medium of the object being photographed. High-quality camera lenses have several elements, permitting partial correction of various *aberrations,* including the dependence of index of refraction on wavelength and the limitations imposed by the paraxial approximation.

When the camera is in proper *focus,* the position of the recording medium coincides with the position of the real image formed by the lens. The resulting photograph will then be as sharp as possible. With a converging lens, the image distance increases as the object distance decreases (see Figs. 34.41a, 34.41b, and 34.41c, and the discussion in Section 34.4). Hence in "focusing" the camera, we move the lens closer to the film for a distant object and farther from the film for a nearby object.

34.40 Key elements of a digital camera.

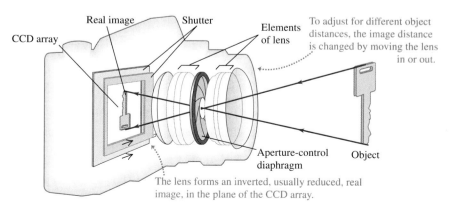

34.41 (a), (b), (c) Three photographs taken with the same camera from the same position in the Boston Public Garden using lenses with focal lengths $f = 28$ mm, 105 mm, and 300 mm. Increasing the focal length increases the image size proportionately. (d) The larger the value of f, the smaller the angle of view. The angles shown here are for a camera with image area 24 mm × 36 mm (corresponding to 35-mm film) and refer to the angle of view along the diagonal dimension of the film.

(a) $f = 28$ mm

(b) $f = 105$ mm

(c) $f = 300$ mm

(d) The angles of view for the photos in (a)–(c)

Camera Lenses: Focal Length

The choice of the focal length f for a camera lens depends on the film size and the desired angle of view. Figure 34.41 shows three photographs taken on 35-mm film with the same camera at the same position, but with lenses of different focal lengths. A lens of long focal length, called a *telephoto* lens, gives a small angle of view and a large image of a distant object (such as the statue in Fig. 34.41c); a lens of short focal length gives a small image and a wide angle of view (as in Fig. 34.41a) and is called a *wide-angle* lens. To understand this behavior, recall that the focal length is the distance from the lens to the image when the object is infinitely far away. In general, for *any* object distance, using a lens of longer focal length gives a greater image distance. This also increases the height of the image; as was discussed in Section 34.4, the ratio of the image height y' to the object height y (the *lateral magnification*) is equal in absolute value to the ratio of image distance s' to the object distance s [Eq. (34.17)]:

$$m = \frac{y'}{y} = -\frac{s'}{s}$$

With a lens of short focal length, the ratio s'/s is small, and a distant object gives only a small image. When a lens with a long focal length is used, the image of this same object may entirely cover the area of the film. Hence the longer the focal length, the narrower the angle of view (Fig. 34.41d).

Camera Lenses: f-Number

For the film to record the image properly, the total light energy per unit area reaching the film (the "exposure") must fall within certain limits. This is controlled by the *shutter* and the *lens aperture*. The shutter controls the time interval during which light enters the lens. This is usually adjustable in steps corresponding to factors of about 2, often from 1 s to $\frac{1}{1000}$ s.

The intensity of light reaching the film is proportional to the area viewed by the camera lens and to the effective area of the lens. The size of the area that the lens "sees" is proportional to the square of the angle of view of the lens, and so is roughly proportional to $1/f^2$. The effective area of the lens is controlled by means of an adjustable lens aperture, or *diaphragm,* a nearly circular hole with variable diameter D; hence the effective area is proportional to D^2. Putting these factors together, we see that the intensity of light reaching the film with a particular lens is proportional to D^2/f^2. The light-gathering capability of a lens is commonly expressed by photographers in terms of the ratio f/D, called the **f-number** of the lens:

$$f\text{-number} = \frac{\text{Focal length}}{\text{Aperture diameter}} = \frac{f}{D} \qquad (34.20)$$

For example, a lens with a focal length $f = 50$ mm and an aperture diameter $D = 25$ mm is said to have an f-number of 2, or "an aperture of $f/2$." The light intensity reaching the film is *inversely* proportional to the square of the f-number.

For a lens with a variable-diameter aperture, increasing the diameter by a factor of $\sqrt{2}$ changes the f-number by $1/\sqrt{2}$ and increases the intensity at the film by a factor of 2. Adjustable apertures usually have scales labeled with successive numbers (often called *f-stops*) related by factors of $\sqrt{2}$, such as

$$f/2 \quad f/2.8 \quad f/4 \quad f/5.6 \quad f/8 \quad f/11 \quad f/16$$

and so on. The larger numbers represent smaller apertures and exposures, and each step corresponds to a factor of 2 in intensity (Fig. 34.42). The actual *exposure* (total amount of light reaching the film) is proportional to both the aperture area and the time of exposure. Thus $f/4$ and $\frac{1}{500}$ s, $f/5.6$ and $\frac{1}{250}$ s, and $f/8$ and $\frac{1}{125}$ s all correspond to the same exposure.

Zoom Lenses and Projectors

Many photographers use a *zoom lens*, which is not a single lens but a complex collection of several lens elements that give a continuously variable focal length, often over a range as great as 10 to 1. Figures 34.43a and 34.43b show a simple system with variable focal length, and Fig. 34.43c shows a typical zoom lens for a single-lens reflex camera. Zoom lenses give a range of image sizes of a given object. It is an enormously complex problem in optical design to keep the image in focus and maintain a constant f-number while the focal length changes. When you vary the focal length of a typical zoom lens, two groups of elements move within the lens and a diaphragm opens and closes.

A *projector* for viewing slides, digital images, or motion pictures operates very much like a camera in reverse. In a movie projector, a lamp shines on the film, which acts as an object for the projection lens. The lens forms a real, enlarged, inverted image of the film on the projection screen. Because the image is inverted, the film goes through the projector upside down so that the image on the screen appears right-side up.

Application Inverting an Inverted Image

A camera lens makes an inverted image on the camera's light-sensitive electronic detector. The internal software of the camera then inverts the image again so it appears the right way around on the camera's display. A similar thing happens with your vision: The image formed on the retina of your eye is inverted, but your brain's "software" erects the image so you see the world right-side up.

34.42 A camera lens with an adjustable diaphragm.

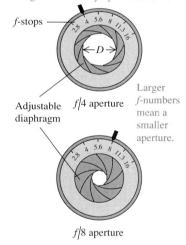

Changing the diameter by a factor of $\sqrt{2}$ changes the intensity by a factor of 2.

f-stops

2.8 4 5.6 8 11.3 16

D

Adjustable diaphragm

$f/4$ aperture

Larger f-numbers mean a smaller aperture.

2.8 4 5.6 8 11.3 16

$f/8$ aperture

34.43 A simple zoom lens uses a converging lens and a diverging lens in tandem. (a) When the two lenses are close together, the combination behaves like a single lens of long focal length. (b) If the two lenses are moved farther apart, the combination behaves like a short-focal-length lens. (c) A typical zoom lens for a single-lens reflex camera, containing twelve elements arranged in four groups.

(a) Zoom lens set for long focal length

Image

4 cm   24 cm

(b) Zoom lens set for short focal length

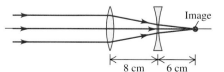

Image

8 cm   6 cm

(c) A practical zoom lens

Example 34.12 **Photographic exposures**

A common telephoto lens for a 35-mm camera has a focal length of 200 mm; its f-stops range from $f/2.8$ to $f/22$. (a) What is the corresponding range of aperture diameters? (b) What is the corresponding range of image intensities on the film?

SOLUTION

IDENTIFY and SET UP: Part (a) of this problem uses the relationship among lens focal length f, aperture diameter D, and f-number. Part (b) uses the relationship between intensity and aperture diameter. We use Eq. (34.20) to relate D (the target variable) to the f-number and the focal length $f = 200$ mm. The intensity of the light reaching the film is proportional to D^2/f^2; since f is the same in each case, we conclude that the intensity in this case is proportional to D^2, the square of the aperture diameter.

EXECUTE: (a) From Eq. (34.20), the diameter ranges from

$$D = \frac{f}{f\text{-number}} = \frac{200 \text{ mm}}{2.8} = 71 \text{ mm}$$

to

$$D = \frac{200 \text{ mm}}{22} = 9.1 \text{ mm}$$

(b) Because the intensity is proportional to D^2, the ratio of the intensity at $f/2.8$ to the intensity at $f/22$ is

$$\left(\frac{71 \text{ mm}}{9.1 \text{ mm}}\right)^2 = \left(\frac{22}{2.8}\right)^2 = 62 \quad \text{(about } 2^6\text{)}$$

EVALUATE: If the correct exposure time at $f/2.8$ is $\frac{1}{1000}$ s, then the exposure at $f/22$ is $(62)\left(\frac{1}{1000} \text{ s}\right) = \frac{1}{16}$ s to compensate for the lower intensity. In general, the smaller the aperture and the larger the f-number, the longer the required exposure. Nevertheless, many photographers prefer to use small apertures so that only the central part of the lens is used to make the image. This minimizes aberrations that occur near the edges of the lens and gives the sharpest possible image.

Test Your Understanding of Section 34.5 When used with 35-mm film (image area 24 mm × 36 mm), a lens with $f = 50$ mm gives a 45° angle of view and is called a "normal lens." When used with a CCD array that measures 5 mm × 5 mm, this same lens is (i) a wide-angle lens; (ii) a normal lens; (iii) a telephoto lens.

MasteringPHYSICS

PhET: Color Vision

34.6 The Eye

The optical behavior of the eye is similar to that of a camera. The essential parts of the human eye, considered as an optical system, are shown in Fig. 34.44a. The eye is nearly spherical and about 2.5 cm in diameter. The front portion is somewhat more sharply curved and is covered by a tough, transparent membrane called the *cornea*. The region behind the cornea contains a liquid called the *aqueous humor*. Next comes the *crystalline lens,* a capsule containing a fibrous jelly, hard at the center and progressively softer at the outer portions. The crystalline lens is

---

34.44 (a) The eye. (b) There are two types of light-sensitive cells on the retina. The rods are more sensitive to light than the cones, but only the cones are sensitive to differences in color. A typical human eye contains about 1.3×10^8 rods and about 7×10^6 cones.

(a) Diagram of the eye

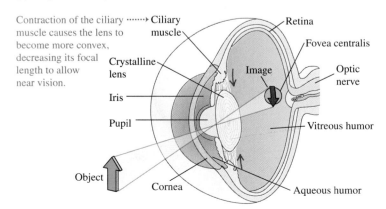

Contraction of the ciliary muscle causes the lens to become more convex, decreasing its focal length to allow near vision.

Ciliary muscle
Crystalline lens
Iris
Pupil
Object
Cornea
Retina
Fovea centralis
Image
Optic nerve
Vitreous humor
Aqueous humor

(b) Scanning electron micrograph showing retinal rods and cones in different colors

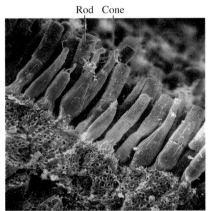

Rod Cone

held in place by ligaments that attach it to the ciliary muscle, which encircles it. Behind the lens, the eye is filled with a thin watery jelly called the *vitreous humor*. The indexes of refraction of both the aqueous humor and the vitreous humor are about 1.336, nearly equal to that of water. The crystalline lens, while not homogeneous, has an average index of 1.437. This is not very different from the indexes of the aqueous and vitreous humors. As a result, most of the refraction of light entering the eye occurs at the outer surface of the cornea.

Refraction at the cornea and the surfaces of the lens produces a *real image* of the object being viewed. This image is formed on the light-sensitive *retina*, lining the rear inner surface of the eye. The retina plays the same role as the film in a camera. The *rods* and *cones* in the retina act like an array of miniature photocells (Fig. 34.44b); they sense the image and transmit it via the *optic nerve* to the brain. Vision is most acute in a small central region called the *fovea centralis*, about 0.25 mm in diameter.

In front of the lens is the *iris*. It contains an aperture with variable diameter called the *pupil*, which opens and closes to adapt to changing light intensity. The receptors of the retina also have intensity adaptation mechanisms.

For an object to be seen sharply, the image must be formed exactly at the location of the retina. The eye adjusts to different object distances s by changing the focal length f of its lens; the lens-to-retina distance, corresponding to s', does not change. (Contrast this with focusing a camera, in which the focal length is fixed and the lens-to-film distance is changed.) For the normal eye, an object at infinity is sharply focused when the ciliary muscle is relaxed. To permit sharp imaging on the retina of closer objects, the tension in the ciliary muscle surrounding the lens increases, the ciliary muscle contracts, the lens bulges, and the radii of curvature of its surfaces decrease; this decreases the focal length. This process is called *accommodation*.

The extremes of the range over which distinct vision is possible are known as the *far point* and the *near point* of the eye. The far point of a normal eye is at infinity. The position of the near point depends on the amount by which the ciliary muscle can increase the curvature of the crystalline lens. The range of accommodation gradually diminishes with age because the crystalline lens grows throughout a person's life (it is about 50% larger at age 60 than at age 20) and the ciliary muscles are less able to distort a larger lens. For this reason, the near point gradually recedes as one grows older. This recession of the near point is called *presbyopia*. Table 34.1 shows the approximate position of the near point for an average person at various ages. For example, an average person 50 years of age cannot focus on an object that is closer than about 40 cm.

Defects of Vision

Several common defects of vision result from incorrect distance relationships in the eye. A normal eye forms an image on the retina of an object at infinity when the eye is relaxed (Fig. 34.45a). In the *myopic* (nearsighted) eye, the eyeball is too long from front to back in comparison with the radius of curvature of the cornea (or the cornea is too sharply curved), and rays from an object at infinity are focused in front of the retina (Fig. 34.45b). The most distant object for which an image can be formed on the retina is then nearer than infinity. In the *hyperopic* (farsighted) eye, the eyeball is too short or the cornea is not curved enough, and the image of an infinitely distant object is behind the retina (Fig. 34.45c). The myopic eye produces *too much* convergence in a parallel bundle of rays for an image to be formed on the retina; the hyperopic eye, *not enough* convergence.

All of these defects can be corrected by the use of corrective lenses (eyeglasses or contact lenses). The near point of either a presbyopic or a hyperopic eye is *farther* from the eye than normal. To see clearly an object at normal reading distance (often assumed to be 25 cm), we need a lens that forms a virtual image of the object at or beyond the near point. This can be accomplished by a

Table 34.1 Receding of Near Point with Age

Age (years)	Near Point (cm)
10	7
20	10
30	14
40	22
50	40
60	200

34.45 Refractive errors for (a) a normal eye, (b) a myopic (nearsighted) eye, and (c) a hyperopic (farsighted) eye viewing a very distant object. The dashed blue curve indicates the required position of the retina.

(a) Normal eye

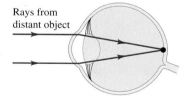

(b) Myopic (nearsighted) eye

Eye too long or cornea too sharply curved . . .   . . . rays focus in front of the retina.

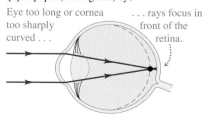

(c) Hyperopic (farsighted) eye

Eye too short or cornea not curved enough . . .   . . . rays focus behind the retina.

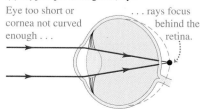

34.46 (a) An uncorrected hyperopic (farsighted) eye. (b) A positive (converging) lens gives the extra convergence needed for a hyperopic eye to focus the image on the retina.

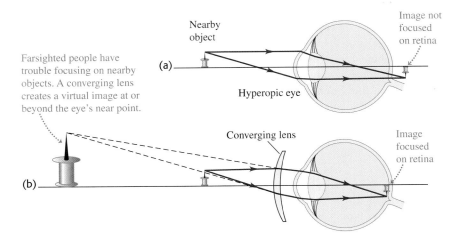

Farsighted people have trouble focusing on nearby objects. A converging lens creates a virtual image at or beyond the eye's near point.

Application Focusing in the Animal Kingdom

The crystalline lens and ciliary muscle found in humans and other mammals are among a number of focusing mechanisms used by animals. Birds can change the shape not only of their lens but also of the corneal surface. In aquatic animals the corneal surface is not very useful for focusing because its refractive index is close to that of water. Thus, focusing is accomplished entirely by the lens, which is nearly spherical. Fish focus by using a muscle to move the lens either inward or outward. Whales and dolphins achieve the same effect by filling or emptying a fluid chamber behind the lens to move the lens in or out.

converging (positive) lens, as shown in Fig. 34.46. In effect the lens moves the object farther away from the eye to a point where a sharp retinal image can be formed. Similarly, correcting the myopic eye involves using a diverging (negative) lens to move the image closer to the eye than the actual object, as shown in Fig. 34.47.

Astigmatism is a different type of defect in which the surface of the cornea is not spherical but rather more sharply curved in one plane than in another. As a result, horizontal lines may be imaged in a different plane from vertical lines (Fig. 34.48a). Astigmatism may make it impossible, for example, to focus clearly on both the horizontal and vertical bars of a window at the same time.

Astigmatism can be corrected by use of a lens with a *cylindrical* surface. For example, suppose the curvature of the cornea in a horizontal plane is correct to focus rays from infinity on the retina but the curvature in the vertical plane is too great to form a sharp retinal image. When a cylindrical lens with its axis horizontal is placed before the eye, the rays in a horizontal plane are unaffected, but the additional divergence of the rays in a vertical plane causes these to be sharply imaged on the retina (Fig. 34.48b).

Lenses for vision correction are usually described in terms of the **power,** defined as the reciprocal of the focal length expressed in meters. The unit of power is the **diopter.** Thus a lens with $f = 0.50$ m has a power of 2.0 diopters, $f = -0.25$ m corresponds to -4.0 diopters, and so on. The numbers on a prescription for glasses

34.47 (a) An uncorrected myopic (nearsighted) eye. (b) A negative (diverging) lens spreads the rays farther apart to compensate for the excessive convergence of the myopic eye.

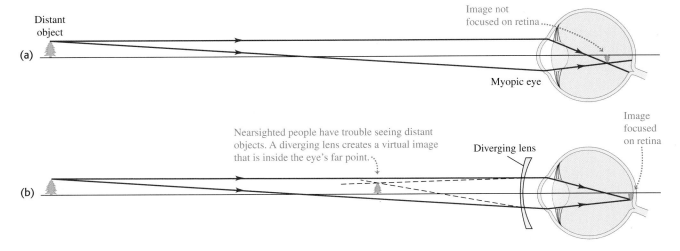

Nearsighted people have trouble seeing distant objects. A diverging lens creates a virtual image that is inside the eye's far point.

(a) Vertical lines are imaged in front of the retina.

Shape of eyeball or lens causes vertical and horizontal elements to focus at different distances.

(b) A cylindrical lens corrects for astigmatism.

This cylindrical lens is curved in the vertical, but not the horizontal, direction; it changes the focal length of vertical elements.

34.48 One type of astigmatism and how it is corrected.

are usually powers expressed in diopters. When the correction involves both astigmatism and myopia or hyperopia, there are three numbers: one for the spherical power, one for the cylindrical power, and an angle to describe the orientation of the cylinder axis.

Example 34.13 | **Correcting for farsightedness**

The near point of a certain hyperopic eye is 100 cm in front of the eye. Find the focal length and power of the contact lens that will permit the wearer to see clearly an object that is 25 cm in front of the eye.

SOLUTION

IDENTIFY and SET UP: Figure 34.49 shows the situation. We want the lens to form a virtual image of the object at the near point of the eye, 100 cm from it. The contact lens (which we treat as having negligible thickness) is at the surface of the cornea, so the object distance is $s = 25$ cm. The virtual image is on the incoming side of the contact lens, so the image distance is $s' = -100$ cm. We use Eq. (34.16) to determine the required focal length f of the contact lens; the corresponding power is $1/f$.

EXECUTE: From Eq. (34.16),

$$\frac{1}{f} = \frac{1}{s} + \frac{1}{s'} = \frac{1}{+25 \text{ cm}} + \frac{1}{-100 \text{ cm}}$$

$$f = +33 \text{ cm}$$

34.49 Using a contact lens to correct for farsightedness. For clarity, the eye and contact lens are shown much larger than the scale of the figure; the 2.5-cm diameter of the eye is actually much smaller than the focal length f of the contact lens.

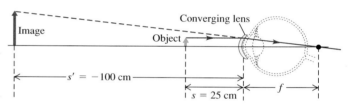

We need a converging lens with focal length $f = 33$ cm and power $1/(0.33 \text{ m}) = +3.0$ diopters.

EVALUATE: In this example we used a contact lens to correct hyperopia. Had we used eyeglasses, we would have had to account for the separation between the eye and the eyeglass lens, and a somewhat different power would have been required (see Example 34.14).

Example 34.14 | **Correcting for nearsightedness**

The far point of a certain myopic eye is 50 cm in front of the eye. Find the focal length and power of the eyeglass lens that will permit the wearer to see clearly an object at infinity. Assume that the lens is worn 2 cm in front of the eye.

SOLUTION

IDENTIFY and SET UP: Figure 34.50 shows the situation. The far point of a myopic eye is nearer than infinity. To see clearly objects

34.50 Using an eyeglass lens to correct for nearsightedness. For clarity, the eye and eyeglass lens are shown much larger than the scale of the figure.

Continued

beyond the far point, we need a lens that forms a virtual image of such objects no farther from the eye than the far point. Assume that the virtual image of the object at infinity is formed at the far point, 50 cm in front of the eye (48 cm in front of the eyeglass lens). Then when the object distance is $s = \infty$, we want the image distance to be $s' = -48$ cm. As in Example 34.13, we use the values of s and s' to calculate the required focal length.

EXECUTE: From Eq. (34.16),

$$\frac{1}{f} = \frac{1}{s} + \frac{1}{s'} = \frac{1}{\infty} + \frac{1}{-48 \text{ cm}}$$

$$f = -48 \text{ cm}$$

We need a *diverging* lens with focal length $f = -48$ cm and power $1/(-0.48 \text{ m}) = -2.1$ diopters.

EVALUATE: If a *contact* lens were used to correct this myopia, we would need $f = -50$ cm and a power of -2.0 diopters. Can you see why?

Test Your Understanding of Section 34.6 A certain eyeglass lens is thin at its center, even thinner at its top and bottom edges, and relatively thick at its left and right edges. What defects of vision is this lens intended to correct? (i) hyperopia for objects oriented both vertically and horizontally; (ii) myopia for objects oriented both vertically and horizontally; (iii) hyperopia for objects oriented vertically and myopia for objects oriented horizontally; (iv) hyperopia for objects oriented horizontally and myopia for objects oriented vertically. ❚

34.7 The Magnifier

The apparent size of an object is determined by the size of its image on the retina. If the eye is unaided, this size depends on the *angle θ* subtended by the object at the eye, called its **angular size** (Fig. 34.51a).

To look closely at a small object, such as an insect or a crystal, you bring it close to your eye, making the subtended angle and the retinal image as large as possible. But your eye cannot focus sharply on objects that are closer than the near point, so the angular size of an object is greatest (that is, it subtends the largest possible viewing angle) when it is placed at the near point. In the following discussion we will assume an average viewer for whom the near point is 25 cm from the eye.

A converging lens can be used to form a virtual image that is larger and farther from the eye than the object itself, as shown in Fig. 34.51b. Then the object can be moved closer to the eye, and the angular size of the image may be substantially larger than the angular size of the object at 25 cm without the lens. A lens used in this way is called a **magnifier,** otherwise known as a *magnifying glass* or a *simple magnifier.* The virtual image is most comfortable to view when it is placed at infinity, so that the ciliary muscle of the eye is relaxed; this means that the object is placed at the focal point F_1 of the magnifier. In the following discussion we assume that this is done.

34.51 (a) The angular size θ is largest when the object is at the near point. (b) The magnifier gives a virtual image at infinity. This virtual image appears to the eye to be a real object subtending a larger angle θ' at the eye.

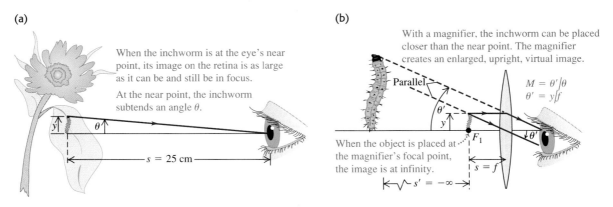

(a) When the inchworm is at the eye's near point, its image on the retina is as large as it can be and still be in focus.

At the near point, the inchworm subtends an angle θ.

$s = 25$ cm

(b) With a magnifier, the inchworm can be placed closer than the near point. The magnifier creates an enlarged, upright, virtual image.

Parallel

$M = \theta'/\theta$
$\theta' = y/f$

When the object is placed at the magnifier's focal point, the image is at infinity.

F_1
$s = f$
$s' = -\infty$

In Fig. 34.51a the object is at the near point, where it subtends an angle θ at the eye. In Fig. 34.51b a magnifier in front of the eye forms an image at infinity, and the angle subtended at the magnifier is θ'. The usefulness of the magnifier is given by the ratio of the angle θ' (with the magnifier) to the angle θ (without the magnifier). This ratio is called the **angular magnification** M:

$$M = \frac{\theta'}{\theta} \quad \text{(angular magnification)} \tag{34.21}$$

CAUTION **Angular magnification vs. lateral magnification** Don't confuse the *angular* magnification M with the *lateral* magnification m. Angular magnification is the ratio of the *angular* size of an image to the angular size of the corresponding object; lateral magnification refers to the ratio of the *height* of an image to the height of the corresponding object. For the situation shown in Fig. 34.51b, the angular magnification is about $3\times$, since the inchworm subtends an angle about three times larger than that in Fig. 34.51a; hence the inchworm will look about three times larger to the eye. The *lateral* magnification $m = -s'/s$ in Fig. 34.51b is *infinite* because the virtual image is at infinity, but that doesn't mean that the inchworm looks infinitely large through the magnifier! (That's why we didn't attempt to draw an infinitely large inchworm in Fig. 34.51b.) When dealing with a magnifier, M is useful but m is not.

To find the value of M, we first assume that the angles are small enough that each angle (in radians) is equal to its sine and its tangent. Using Fig. 34.451a and drawing the ray in Fig. 34.51b that passes undeviated through the center of the lens, we find that θ and θ' (in radians) are

$$\theta = \frac{y}{25 \text{ cm}} \qquad \theta' = \frac{y}{f}$$

Combining these expressions with Eq. (34.21), we find

$$M = \frac{\theta'}{\theta} = \frac{y/f}{y/25 \text{ cm}} = \frac{25 \text{ cm}}{f} \quad \begin{array}{l}\text{(angular magnification} \\ \text{for a simple magnifier)}\end{array} \tag{34.22}$$

It may seem that we can make the angular magnification as large as we like by decreasing the focal length f. In fact, the aberrations of a simple double-convex lens set a limit to M of about $3\times$ to $4\times$. If these aberrations are corrected, the angular magnification may be made as great as $20\times$. When greater magnification than this is needed, we usually use a compound microscope, discussed in the next section.

Test Your Understanding of Section 34.7 You are examining a gem using a magnifier. If you change to a different magnifier with twice the focal length of the first one, (i) you will have to hold the object at twice the distance and the angular magnification will be twice as great; (ii) you will have to hold the object at twice the distance and the angular magnification will be $\frac{1}{2}$ as great; (iii) you will have to hold the object at $\frac{1}{2}$ the distance and the angular magnification will be twice as great; (iv) you will have to hold the object at $\frac{1}{2}$ the distance and the angular magnification will be $\frac{1}{2}$ as great.

34.8 Microscopes and Telescopes

Cameras, eyeglasses, and magnifiers use a single lens to form an image. Two important optical devices that use *two* lenses are the microscope and the telescope. In each device a primary lens, or *objective,* forms a real image, and a second lens, or *eyepiece,* is used as a magnifier to make an enlarged, virtual image.

Microscopes

When we need greater magnification than we can get with a simple magnifier, the instrument that we usually use is the **microscope,** sometimes called a *compound*

Mastering**PHYSICS**

ActivPhysics 15.12: Two-Lens Optical Systems

34.52 (a) Elements of a microscope. (b) The object O is placed just outside the first focal point of the objective (the distance s_1 has been exaggerated for clarity). (c) This microscope image shows single-celled organisms about 2×10^{-4} m (0.2 mm) across. Typical light microscopes can resolve features as small as 2×10^{-7} m, comparable to the wavelength of light.

(a) Elements of a microscope

(b) Microscope optics

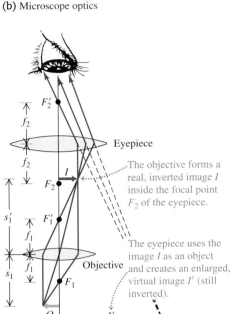

The objective forms a real, inverted image I inside the focal point F_2 of the eyepiece.

The eyepiece uses the image I as an object and creates an enlarged, virtual image I' (still inverted).

(c) Single-celled freshwater algae (*Micrasterias denticulata*)

microscope. The essential elements of a microscope are shown in Fig. 34.52a. To analyze this system, we use the principle that an image formed by one optical element such as a lens or mirror can serve as the object for a second element. We used this principle in Section 34.4 when we derived the thin-lens equation by repeated application of the single-surface refraction equation; we used this principle again in Example 34.11 (Section 34.4), in which the image formed by a lens was used as the object of a second lens.

The object O to be viewed is placed just beyond the first focal point F_1 of the **objective,** a converging lens that forms a real and enlarged image I (Fig. 34.52b). In a properly designed instrument this image lies just inside the first focal point F_1' of a second converging lens called the **eyepiece** or *ocular.* (The reason the image should lie just *inside* F_1' is left for you to discover; see Problem 34.108.) The eyepiece acts as a simple magnifier, as discussed in Section 34.7, and forms a final virtual image I' of I. The position of I' may be anywhere between the near and far points of the eye. Both the objective and the eyepiece of an actual microscope are highly corrected compound lenses with several optical elements, but for simplicity we show them here as simple thin lenses.

As for a simple magnifier, what matters when viewing through a microscope is the *angular* magnification M. The overall angular magnification of the compound microscope is the product of two factors. The first factor is the *lateral* magnification m_1 of the objective, which determines the linear size of the real image I; the second factor is the *angular* magnification M_2 of the eyepiece, which relates the angular size of the virtual image seen through the eyepiece to the angular size that the real image I would have if you viewed it *without* the eyepiece. The first of these factors is given by

$$m_1 = -\frac{s_1'}{s_1} \tag{34.23}$$

where s_1 and s_1' are the object and image distances, respectively, for the objective lens. Ordinarily, the object is very close to the focal point, and the resulting image distance s_1' is very great in comparison to the focal length f_1 of the objective lens. Thus s_1 is approximately equal to f_1, and we can write $m_1 = -s_1'/f_1$.

The real image I is close to the focal point F_1' of the eyepiece, so to find the eyepiece angular magnification, we can use Eq. (34.22): $M_2 = (25 \text{ cm})/f_2$, where f_2 is the focal length of the eyepiece (considered as a simple lens). The overall angular magnification M of the compound microscope (apart from a negative sign, which is customarily ignored) is the product of the two magnifications:

$$M = m_1 M_2 = \frac{(25 \text{ cm})s_1'}{f_1 f_2} \qquad \begin{array}{l}\text{(angular magnification} \\ \text{for a microscope)}\end{array} \tag{34.24}$$

where s_1', f_1, and f_2 are measured in centimeters. The final image is inverted with respect to the object. Microscope manufacturers usually specify the values of m_1 and M_2 for microscope components rather than the focal lengths of the objective and eyepiece.

Equation (34.24) shows that the angular magnification of a microscope can be increased by using an objective of shorter focal length f_1, thereby increasing m_1 and the size of the real image I. Most optical microscopes have a rotating "turret" with three or more objectives of different focal lengths so that the same object can be viewed at different magnifications. The eyepiece should also have a short focal length f_2 to help to maximize the value of M.

To take a photograph using a microscope (called a *photomicrograph* or *micrograph*), the eyepiece is removed and a camera placed so that the real image I falls on the camera's CCD array or film. Figure 34.52c shows such a photograph. In this case what matters is the *lateral* magnification of the microscope as given by Eq. (34.23).

Telescopes

The optical system of a **telescope** is similar to that of a compound microscope. In both instruments the image formed by an objective is viewed through an eyepiece. The key difference is that the telescope is used to view large objects at large distances and the microscope is used to view small objects close at hand. Another difference is that many telescopes use a curved mirror, not a lens, as an objective.

Figure 34.53 shows an *astronomical telescope*. Because this telescope uses a lens as an objective, it is called a *refracting telescope* or *refractor*. The objective lens forms a real, reduced image I of the object. This image is the object for the eyepiece lens, which forms an enlarged, virtual image of I. Objects that are viewed with a telescope are usually so far away from the instrument that the first image I is formed very nearly at the second focal point of the objective lens. If the final image I' formed by the eyepiece is at infinity (for most comfortable viewing by a normal eye), the first image must also be at the first focal point of the eyepiece. The distance between objective and eyepiece, which is the length of the telescope, is therefore the *sum* of the focal lengths of objective and eyepiece, $f_1 + f_2$.

The angular magnification M of a telescope is defined as the ratio of the angle subtended at the eye by the final image I' to the angle subtended at the (unaided) eye by the object. We can express this ratio in terms of the focal lengths of objective and eyepiece. In Fig. 34.53 the ray passing through F_1, the first focal point of the objective, and through F_2', the second focal point of the eyepiece, is shown in red. The object (not shown) subtends an angle θ at the objective and would subtend essentially the same angle at the unaided eye. Also, since the observer's eye is placed just to the right of the focal point F_2', the angle subtended at the eye by the final image is very nearly equal to the angle θ'. Because bd is parallel to the

34.53 Optical system of an astronomical refracting telescope.

optic axis, the distances *ab* and *cd* are equal to each other and also to the height y' of the real image *I*. Because the angles θ and θ' are small, they may be approximated by their tangents. From the right triangles F_1ab and F'_2cd,

$$\theta = \frac{-y'}{f_1} \qquad \theta' = \frac{y'}{f_2}$$

and the angular magnification *M* is

$$M = \frac{\theta'}{\theta} = -\frac{y'/f_2}{y'/f_1} = -\frac{f_1}{f_2} \qquad \text{(angular magnification for a telescope)} \qquad (34.25)$$

The angular magnification *M* of a telescope is equal to the ratio of the focal length of the objective to that of the eyepiece. The negative sign shows that the final image is inverted. Equation (34.25) shows that to achieve good angular magnification, a *telescope* should have a *long* objective focal length f_1. By contrast, Eq. (34.24) shows that a *microscope* should have a *short* objective focal length. However, a telescope objective with a long focal length should also have a large diameter *D* so that the *f*-number f_1/D will not be too large; as described in Section 34.5, a large *f*-number means a dim, low-intensity image. Telescopes typically do not have interchangeable objectives; instead, the magnification is varied by using different eyepieces with different focal lengths f_2. Just as for a microscope, smaller values of f_2 give larger angular magnifications.

An inverted image is no particular disadvantage for astronomical observations. When we use a telescope or binoculars—essentially a pair of telescopes mounted side by side—to view objects on the earth, though, we want the image to be right-side up. In prism binoculars, this is accomplished by reflecting the light several times along the path from the objective to the eyepiece. The combined effect of the reflections is to flip the image both horizontally and vertically. Binoculars are usually described by two numbers separated by a multiplication sign, such as 7 × 50. The first number is the angular magnification *M*, and the second is the diameter of the objective lenses (in millimeters). The diameter helps to determine the light-gathering capacity of the objective lenses and thus the brightness of the image.

In the *reflecting telescope* (Fig. 34.54a) the objective lens is replaced by a concave mirror. In large telescopes this scheme has many advantages. Mirrors are

34.54 (a), (b), (c) Three designs for reflecting telescopes. (d) This photo shows the interior of the Gemini North telescope, which uses the design shown in (c). The objective mirror is 8 meters in diameter.

(a)

Starlight

Cage

Concave
objective mirror

The cage at the
focal point may
contain a camera.

(b)

Starlight

Planar
secondary
mirror

Eyepiece

Concave
objective mirror

This is a common
design for the telescopes
of amateur astronomers.

(c)

Starlight

Planar
secondary
mirror

Concave
objective mirror

Eyepiece

This is a common design
for large modern telescopes.
A camera or other instrument
package is typically used
instead of an eyepiece.

(d)

Secondary
mirror (in
housing)

Objective
mirror

Hole in
objective
mirror

Reflection of
secondary
mirror

inherently free of chromatic aberrations (dependence of focal length on wavelength), and spherical aberrations (associated with the paraxial approximation) are easier to correct than with a lens. The reflecting surface is sometimes parabolic rather than spherical. The material of the mirror need not be transparent, and it can be made more rigid than a lens, which has to be supported only at its edges.

The largest reflecting telescopes in the world, the Keck telescopes atop Mauna Kea in Hawaii, each have an objective mirror of overall diameter 10 m made up of 36 separate hexagonal reflecting elements.

One challenge in designing reflecting telescopes is that the image is formed in front of the objective mirror, in a region traversed by incoming rays. Isaac Newton devised one solution to this problem. A flat secondary mirror oriented at 45° to the optic axis causes the image to be formed in a hole on the side of the telescope, where it can be magnified with an eyepiece (Fig. 34.54b). Another solution uses a secondary mirror that causes the focused light to pass through a hole in the objective mirror (Fig. 34.54c). Large research telescopes, as well as many amateur telescopes, use this design (Fig. 34.54d).

Like a microscope, when a telescope is used for photography the eyepiece is removed and a CCD array or photographic film is placed at the position of the real image formed by the objective. (Some long-focal-length "lenses" for photography are actually reflecting telescopes used in this way.) Most telescopes used for astronomical research are never used with an eyepiece.

Test Your Understanding of Section 34.8 Which gives a lateral magnification of greater absolute value: (i) the objective lens in a microscope (Fig. 34.52); (ii) the objective lens in a refracting telescope (Fig. 34.53); or (iii) not enough information is given to decide? ❙

Reflection or refraction at a plane surface: When rays diverge from an object point P and are reflected or refracted, the directions of the outgoing rays are the same as though they had diverged from a point P' called the image point. If they actually converge at P' and diverge again beyond it, P' is a real image of P; if they only appear to have diverged from P', it is a virtual image. Images can be either erect or inverted.

Plane mirror

Lateral magnification: The lateral magnification m in any reflecting or refracting situation is defined as the ratio of image height y' to object height y. When m is positive, the image is erect; when m is negative, the image is inverted.

$$m = \frac{y'}{y} \qquad (34.2)$$

Focal point and focal length: The focal point of a mirror is the point where parallel rays converge after reflection from a concave mirror, or the point from which they appear to diverge after reflection from a convex mirror. Rays diverging from the focal point of a concave mirror are parallel after reflection; rays converging toward the focal point of a convex mirror are parallel after reflection. The distance from the focal point to the vertex is called the focal length, denoted as f. The focal points of a lens are defined similarly.

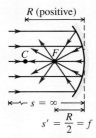

$$s' = \frac{R}{2} = f$$

Relating object and image distances: The formulas for object distance s and image distance s' for plane and spherical mirrors and single refracting surfaces are summarized in the table. The equation for a plane surface can be obtained from the corresponding equation for a spherical surface by setting $R = \infty$. (See Examples 34.1–34.7.)

	Plane Mirror	**Spherical Mirror**	**Plane Refracting Surface**	**Spherical Refracting Surface**
Object and image distances	$\dfrac{1}{s} + \dfrac{1}{s'} = 0$	$\dfrac{1}{s} + \dfrac{1}{s'} = \dfrac{2}{R} = \dfrac{1}{f}$	$\dfrac{n_a}{s} + \dfrac{n_b}{s'} = 0$	$\dfrac{n_a}{s} + \dfrac{n_b}{s'} = \dfrac{n_b - n_a}{R}$
Lateral magnification	$m = -\dfrac{s'}{s} = 1$	$m = -\dfrac{s'}{s}$	$m = -\dfrac{n_a s'}{n_b s} = 1$	$m = -\dfrac{n_a s'}{n_b s}$

Object–image relationships derived in this chapter are valid only for rays close to and nearly parallel to the optic axis; these are called paraxial rays. Nonparaxial rays do not converge precisely to an image point. This effect is called spherical aberration.

Thin lenses: The object–image relationship, given by Eq. (34.16), is the same for a thin lens as for a spherical mirror. Equation (34.19), the lensmaker's equation, relates the focal length of a lens to its index of refraction and the radii of curvature of its surfaces. (See Examples 34.8–34.11.)

$$\frac{1}{s} + \frac{1}{s'} = \frac{1}{f} \qquad (34.16)$$

$$\frac{1}{f} = (n - 1)\left(\frac{1}{R_1} - \frac{1}{R_2} \right) \qquad (34.19)$$

Sign rules: The following sign rules are used with all plane and spherical reflecting and refracting surfaces.

- $s > 0$ when the object is on the incoming side of the surface (a real object); $s < 0$ otherwise.

- $s' > 0$ when the image is on the outgoing side of the surface (a real image); $s' < 0$ otherwise.
- $R > 0$ when the center of curvature is on the outgoing side of the surface; $R < 0$ otherwise.
- $m > 0$ when the image is erect; $m < 0$ when inverted.

Cameras: A camera forms a real, inverted, reduced image of the object being photographed on a light-sensitive surface. The amount of light striking this surface is controlled by the shutter speed and the aperture. The intensity of this light is inversely proportional to the square of the f-number of the lens. (See Example 34.12.)

$$f\text{-number} = \frac{\text{Focal length}}{\text{Aperture diameter}}$$

$$= \frac{f}{D} \qquad (34.20)$$

Inverted, real image

The eye: In the eye, refraction at the surface of the cornea forms a real image on the retina. Adjustment for various object distances is made by squeezing the lens, thereby making it bulge and decreasing its focal length. A nearsighted eye is too long for its lens; a farsighted eye is too short. The power of a corrective lens, in diopters, is the reciprocal of the focal length in meters. (See Examples 34.13 and 34.14.)

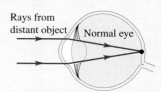

Rays from distant object / Normal eye

The simple magnifier: The simple magnifier creates a virtual image whose angular size θ' is larger than the angular size θ of the object itself at a distance of 25 cm, the nominal closest distance for comfortable viewing. The angular magnification M of a simple magnifier is the ratio of the angular size of the virtual image to that of the object at this distance.

$$M = \frac{\theta'}{\theta} = \frac{25 \text{ cm}}{f} \qquad (34.22)$$

Microscopes and telescopes: In a compound microscope, the objective lens forms a first image in the barrel of the instrument, and the eyepiece forms a final virtual image, often at infinity, of the first image. The telescope operates on the same principle, but the object is far away. In a reflecting telescope, the objective lens is replaced by a concave mirror, which eliminates chromatic aberrations.

Eyepiece / Objective

BRIDGING PROBLEM   **Image Formation by a Wine Goblet**

A thick-walled wine goblet can be considered to be a hollow glass sphere with an outer radius of 4.00 cm and an inner radius of 3.40 cm. The index of refraction of the goblet glass is 1.50. (a) A beam of parallel light rays enters the side of the empty goblet along a horizontal radius. Where, if anywhere, will an image be formed? (b) The goblet is filled with white wine ($n = 1.37$). Where is the image formed?

SOLUTION GUIDE

See MasteringPhysics® study area for a Video Tutor solution.

IDENTIFY and SET UP

1. The goblet is *not* a thin lens, so you cannot use the thin-lens formula. Instead, you must think of the inner and outer surfaces of the goblet walls as spherical refracting surfaces. The image formed by one surface serves as the object for the next surface.
2. Choose the appropriate equation that relates the image and object distances for a spherical refracting surface.

EXECUTE

3. For the empty goblet, each refracting surface has glass on one side and air on the other. Find the position of the image formed by the first surface, the outer wall of the goblet. Use this as the object for the second surface (the inner wall of the same side of the goblet) and find the position of the second image. (*Hint:* Be sure to account for the thickness of the goblet wall.)
4. Continue the process of step 3. Consider the refractions at the inner and outer surfaces of the glass on the opposite side of the goblet, and find the position of the final image. (*Hint:* Be sure to account for the distance between the two sides of the goblet.)
5. Repeat steps 3 and 4 for the case in which the goblet is filled with wine.

EVALUATE

6. Are the images real or virtual? How can you tell?

•, ••, •••: Problems of increasing difficulty. **CP**: Cumulative problems incorporating material from earlier chapters. **CALC**: Problems requiring calculus. **BIO**: Biosciences problems.

DISCUSSION QUESTIONS

Q34.1 A spherical mirror is cut in half horizontally. Will an image be formed by the bottom half of the mirror? If so, where will the image be formed?

Q34.2 For the situation shown in Fig. 34.3, is the image distance s' positive or negative? Is the image real or virtual? Explain your answers.

Q34.3 The laws of optics also apply to electromagnetic waves invisible to the eye. A satellite TV dish is used to detect radio waves coming from orbiting satellites. Why is a curved reflecting surface (a "dish") used? The dish is always concave, never convex; why? The actual radio receiver is placed on an arm and suspended in front of the dish. How far in front of the dish should it be placed?

Q34.4 Explain why the focal length of a *plane* mirror is infinite, and explain what it means for the focal point to be at infinity.

Q34.5 If a spherical mirror is immersed in water, does its focal length change? Explain.

Q34.6 For what range of object positions does a concave spherical mirror form a real image? What about a convex spherical mirror?

Q34.7 When a room has mirrors on two opposite walls, an infinite series of reflections can be seen. Discuss this phenomenon in terms of images. Why do the distant images appear fainter?

Q34.8 For a spherical mirror, if $s = f$, then $s' = \infty$, and the lateral magnification m is infinite. Does this make sense? If so, what does it mean?

Q34.9 You may have noticed a small convex mirror next to your bank's ATM. Why is this mirror convex, as opposed to flat or concave? What considerations determine its radius of curvature?

Q34.10 A student claims that she can start a fire on a sunny day using just the sun's rays and a concave mirror. How is this done? Is the concept of image relevant? Can she do the same thing with a convex mirror? Explain.

Q34.11 A person looks at his reflection in the concave side of a shiny spoon. Is it right side up or inverted? Does it matter how far his face is from the spoon? What if he looks in the convex side? (Try this yourself!)

Q34.12 In Example 34.4 (Section 34.2), there appears to be an ambiguity for the case $s = 10$ cm as to whether s' is $+\infty$ or $-\infty$ and whether the image is erect or inverted. How is this resolved? Or is it?

Q34.13 Suppose that in the situation of Example 34.7 of Section 34.3 (see Fig. 34.26) a vertical arrow 2.00 m tall is painted on the side of the pool beneath the water line. According to the calculations in the example, this arrow would appear to the person shown in Fig. 34.26 to be 1.50 m long. But the discussion following Eq. (34.13) states that the magnification for a plane refracting surface is $m = 1$, which suggests that the arrow would appear to the person to be 2.00 m long. How can you resolve this apparent contradiction?

Q34.14 The bottom of the passenger-side mirror on your car notes, "Objects in mirror are closer than they appear." Is this true? Why?

Q34.15 How could you very quickly make an approximate measurement of the focal length of a converging lens? Could the same method be applied if you wished to use a diverging lens? Explain.

Q34.16 The focal length of a simple lens depends on the color (wavelength) of light passing through it. Why? Is it possible for a lens to have a positive focal length for some colors and negative for others? Explain.

Q34.17 When a converging lens is immersed in water, does its focal length increase or decrease in comparison with the value in air? Explain.

Q34.18 A spherical air bubble in water can function as a lens. Is it a converging or diverging lens? How is its focal length related to its radius?

Q34.19 Can an image formed by one reflecting or refracting surface serve as an object for a second reflection or refraction? Does it matter whether the first image is real or virtual? Explain.

Q34.20 If a piece of photographic film is placed at the location of a real image, the film will record the image. Can this be done with a virtual image? How might one record a virtual image?

Q34.21 According to the discussion in Section 34.2, light rays are reversible. Are the formulas in the table in this chapter's Summary still valid if object and image are interchanged? What does reversibility imply with respect to the *forms* of the various formulas?

Q34.22 You've entered a survival contest that will include building a crude telescope. You are given a large box of lenses. Which two lenses do you pick? How do you quickly identify them?

Q34.23 **BIO** You can't see clearly underwater with the naked eye, but you *can* if you wear a face mask or goggles (with air between your eyes and the mask or goggles). Why is there a difference? Could you instead wear eyeglasses (with water between your eyes and the eyeglasses) in order to see underwater? If so, should the lenses be converging or diverging? Explain.

Q34.24 You take a lens and mask it so that light can pass through only the bottom half of the lens. How does the image formed by the masked lens compare to the image formed before masking?

EXERCISES

Section 34.1 Reflection and Refraction at a Plane Surface

34.1 • A candle 4.85 cm tall is 39.2 cm to the left of a plane mirror. Where is the image formed by the mirror, and what is the height of this image?

34.2 • The image of a tree just covers the length of a plane mirror 4.00 cm tall when the mirror is held 35.0 cm from the eye. The tree is 28.0 m from the mirror. What is its height?

34.3 • A pencil that is 9.0 cm long is held perpendicular to the surface of a plane mirror with the tip of the pencil lead 12.0 cm from the mirror surface and the end of the eraser 21.0 cm from the mirror surface. What is the length of the image of the pencil that is formed by the mirror? Which end of the image is closer to the mirror surface: the tip of the lead or the end of the eraser?

Section 34.2 Reflection at a Spherical Surface

34.4 • A concave mirror has a radius of curvature of 34.0 cm. (a) What is its focal length? (b) If the mirror is immersed in water (refractive index 1.33), what is its focal length?

34.5 • An object 0.600 cm tall is placed 16.5 cm to the left of the vertex of a concave spherical mirror having a radius of curvature of 22.0 cm. (a) Draw a principal-ray diagram showing the formation of the image. (b) Determine the position, size, orientation, and nature (real or virtual) of the image.

34.6 • Repeat Exercise 34.5 for the case in which the mirror is convex.

34.7 •• The diameter of Mars is 6794 km, and its minimum distance from the earth is 5.58×10^7 km. When Mars is at this distance, find the diameter of the image of Mars formed by a spherical, concave telescope mirror with a focal length of 1.75 m.

34.8 •• An object is 24.0 cm from the center of a silvered spherical glass Christmas tree ornament 6.00 cm in diameter. What are the position and magnification of its image?

34.9 • A coin is placed next to the convex side of a thin spherical glass shell having a radius of curvature of 18.0 cm. Reflection from the surface of the shell forms an image of the 1.5-cm-tall coin that is 6.00 cm behind the glass shell. Where is the coin located? Determine the size, orientation, and nature (real or virtual) of the image.

34.10 • You hold a spherical salad bowl 90 cm in front of your face with the bottom of the bowl facing you. The salad bowl is made of polished metal with a 35-cm radius of curvature. (a) Where is the image of your 2.0-cm-tall nose located? (b) What are the image's size, orientation, and nature (real or virtual)?

34.11 • (a) Show that Eq. (34.6) can be written as $s' = sf/(s - f)$ and hence the lateral magnification given by Eq. (34.7) can be expressed as $m = f/(f - s)$. (b) A concave spherical mirror has focal length $f = +14.0$ cm. What is the nonzero distance of the object from the mirror vertex if the image has the same height as the object? In this case, is the image erect or inverted? (c) A convex spherical mirror has $f = -8.00$ cm. What is the nonzero distance of the object from the mirror vertex if the height of the image is one-half the height of the object?

34.12 • The thin glass shell shown in Fig. E34.12 has a spherical shape with a radius of curvature of 12.0 cm, and both of its surfaces can act as mirrors. A seed 3.30 mm high is placed 15.0 cm from the center of the mirror along the optic axis, as shown in the figure. (a) Calculate the location and height of the image of this seed. (b) Suppose now that the shell is reversed. Find the location and height of the seed's image.

Figure **E34.12**

3.30 mm ↕
← 15.0 cm →

34.13 • **Dental Mirror.** A dentist uses a curved mirror to view teeth on the upper side of the mouth. Suppose she wants an erect image with a magnification of 2.00 when the mirror is 1.25 cm from a tooth. (Treat this problem as though the object and image lie along a straight line.) (a) What kind of mirror (concave or convex) is needed? Use a ray diagram to decide, without performing any calculations. (b) What must be the focal length and radius of curvature of this mirror? (c) Draw a principal-ray diagram to check your answer in part (b).

34.14 • A spherical, concave shaving mirror has a radius of curvature of 32.0 cm. (a) What is the magnification of a person's face when it is 12.0 cm to the left of the vertex of the mirror? (b) Where is the image? Is the image real or virtual? (c) Draw a principal-ray diagram showing the formation of the image.

Section 34.3 Refraction at a Spherical Surface

34.15 • A speck of dirt is embedded 3.50 cm below the surface of a sheet of ice ($n = 1.309$). What is its apparent depth when viewed at normal incidence?

34.16 •• A tank whose bottom is a mirror is filled with water to a depth of 20.0 cm. A small fish floats motionless 7.0 cm under the surface of the water. (a) What is the apparent depth of the fish when viewed at normal incidence? (b) What is the apparent depth of the image of the fish when viewed at normal incidence?

34.17 • A person swimming 0.80 m below the surface of the water in a swimming pool looks at the diving board that is directly overhead and sees the image of the board that is formed by refraction at the surface of the water. This image is a height of 5.20 m above the swimmer. What is the actual height of the diving board above the surface of the water?

34.18 • A person is lying on a diving board 3.00 m above the surface of the water in a swimming pool. The person looks at a penny that is on the bottom of the pool directly below her. The penny appears to the person to be a distance of 8.00 m from her. What is the depth of the water at this point?

34.19 •• **A Spherical Fish Bowl.** A small tropical fish is at the center of a water-filled, spherical fish bowl 28.0 cm in diameter. (a) Find the apparent position and magnification of the fish to an observer outside the bowl. The effect of the thin walls of the bowl may be ignored. (b) A friend advised the owner of the bowl to keep it out of direct sunlight to avoid blinding the fish, which might swim into the focal point of the parallel rays from the sun. Is the focal point actually within the bowl?

34.20 • The left end of a long glass rod 6.00 cm in diameter has a convex hemispherical surface 3.00 cm in radius. The refractive index of the glass is 1.60. Determine the position of the image if an object is placed in air on the axis of the rod at the following distances to the left of the vertex of the curved end: (a) infinitely far, (b) 12.0 cm; (c) 2.00 cm.

34.21 •• The glass rod of Exercise 34.20 is immersed in oil ($n = 1.45$). An object placed to the left of the rod on the rod's axis is to be imaged 1.20 m inside the rod. How far from the left end of the rod must the object be located to form the image?

34.22 •• The left end of a long glass rod 8.00 cm in diameter, with an index of refraction of 1.60, is ground and polished to a convex hemispherical surface with a radius of 4.00 cm. An object in the form of an arrow 1.50 mm tall, at right angles to the axis of the rod, is located on the axis 24.0 cm to the left of the vertex of the convex surface. Find the position and height of the image of the arrow formed by paraxial rays incident on the convex surface. Is the image erect or inverted?

34.23 •• Repeat Exercise 34.22 for the case in which the end of the rod is ground to a *concave* hemispherical surface with radius 4.00 cm.

34.24 •• The glass rod of Exercise 34.23 is immersed in a liquid. An object 14.0 cm from the vertex of the left end of the rod and on its axis is imaged at a point 9.00 cm from the vertex inside the liquid. What is the index of refraction of the liquid?

Section 34.4 Thin Lenses

34.25 • An insect 3.75 mm tall is placed 22.5 cm to the left of a thin planoconvex lens. The left surface of this lens is flat, the right surface has a radius of curvature of magnitude 13.0 cm, and the index of refraction of the lens material is 1.70. (a) Calculate the location and size of the image this lens forms of the insect. Is it real or virtual? Erect or inverted? (b) Repeat part (a) if the lens is reversed.

34.26 • A lens forms an image of an object. The object is 16.0 cm from the lens. The image is 12.0 cm from the lens on the same side as the object. (a) What is the focal length of the lens? Is the lens converging or diverging? (b) If the object is 8.50 mm tall, how tall is the image? Is it erect or inverted? (c) Draw a principal-ray diagram.

34.27 • A converging meniscus lens (see Fig. 34.32a) with a refractive index of 1.52 has spherical surfaces whose radii are 7.00 cm and 4.00 cm. What is the position of the image if an object is placed 24.0 cm to the left of the lens? What is the magnification?

34.28 • A converging lens with a focal length of 90.0 cm forms an image of a 3.20-cm-tall real object that is to the left of the lens. The image is 4.50 cm tall and inverted. Where are the object and image located in relation to the lens? Is the image real or virtual?

34.29 •• A converging lens forms an image of an 8.00-mm-tall real object. The image is 12.0 cm to the left of the lens, 3.40 cm tall, and erect. What is the focal length of the lens? Where is the object located?

34.30 • A photographic slide is to the left of a lens. The lens projects an image of the slide onto a wall 6.00 m to the right of the slide. The image is 80.0 times the size of the slide. (a) How far is the slide from the lens? (b) Is the image erect or inverted? (c) What is the focal length of the lens? (d) Is the lens converging or diverging?

34.31 •• A double-convex thin lens has surfaces with equal radii of curvature of magnitude 2.50 cm. Looking through this lens, you observe that it forms an image of a very distant tree at a distance of 1.87 cm from the lens. What is the index of refraction of the lens?

34.32 • BIO **The Lens of the Eye.** The crystalline lens of the human eye is a double-convex lens made of material having an index of refraction of 1.44 (although this varies). Its focal length in air is about 8.0 mm, which also varies. We shall assume that the radii of curvature of its two surfaces have the same magnitude. (a) Find the radii of curvature of this lens. (b) If an object 16 cm tall is placed 30.0 cm from the eye lens, where would the lens focus it and how tall would the image be? Is this image real or virtual? Is it erect or inverted? (*Note:* The results obtained here are not strictly accurate because the lens is embedded in fluids having refractive indexes different from that of air.)

34.33 • BIO **The Cornea As a Simple Lens.** The cornea behaves as a thin lens of focal length approximately 1.8 cm, although this varies a bit. The material of which it is made has an index of refraction of 1.38, and its front surface is convex, with a radius of curvature of 5.0 mm. (a) If this focal length is in air, what is the radius of curvature of the back side of the cornea? (b) The closest distance at which a typical person can focus on an object (called the near point) is about 25 cm, although this varies considerably with age. Where would the cornea focus the image of an 8.0-mm-tall object at the near point? (c) What is the height of the image in part (b)? Is this image real or virtual? Is it erect or inverted? (*Note:* The results obtained here are not strictly accurate because, on one side, the cornea has a fluid with a refractive index different from that of air.)

34.34 • A converging lens with a focal length of 7.00 cm forms an image of a 4.00-mm-tall real object that is to the left of the lens. The image is 1.30 cm tall and erect. Where are the object and image located? Is the image real or virtual?

34.35 • For each thin lens shown in Fig. E34.35, calculate the location of the image of an object that is 18.0 cm to the left of the lens. The lens material has a refractive index of 1.50, and the radii of curvature shown are only the magnitudes.

Figure **E34.35**

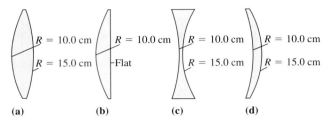

(a) (b) (c) (d)

34.36 • A converging lens with a focal length of 12.0 cm forms a virtual image 8.00 mm tall, 17.0 cm to the right of the lens. Determine the position and size of the object. Is the image erect or inverted? Are the object and image on the same side or opposite sides of the lens? Draw a principal-ray diagram for this situation.

34.37 • Repeat Exercise 34.36 for the case in which the lens is diverging, with a focal length of −48.0 cm.

34.38 • An object is 16.0 cm to the left of a lens. The lens forms an image 36.0 cm to the right of the lens. (a) What is the focal length of the lens? Is the lens converging or diverging? (b) If the object is 8.00 mm tall, how tall is the image? Is it erect or inverted? (c) Draw a principal-ray diagram.

34.39 •• **Combination of Lenses I.** A 1.20-cm-tall object is 50.0 cm to the left of a converging lens of focal length 40.0 cm. A second converging lens, this one having a focal length of 60.0 cm, is located 300.0 cm to the right of the first lens along the same optic axis. (a) Find the location and height of the image (call it I_1) formed by the lens with a focal length of 40.0 cm. (b) I_1 is now the object for the second lens. Find the location and height of the image produced by the second lens. This is the final image produced by the combination of lenses.

34.40 •• **Combination of Lenses II.** Repeat Problem 34.39 using the same lenses except for the following changes: (a) The second lens is a *diverging* lens having a focal length of magnitude 60.0 cm. (b) The first lens is a *diverging* lens having a focal length of magnitude 40.0 cm. (c) Both lenses are diverging lenses having focal lengths of the same *magnitudes* as in Problem 34.39.

34.41 •• **Combination of Lenses III.** Two thin lenses with a focal length of magnitude 12.0 cm, the first diverging and the second converging, are located 9.00 cm apart. An object 2.50 mm tall is placed 20.0 cm to the left of the first (diverging) lens. (a) How far from this first lens is the final image formed? (b) Is the final image real or virtual? (c) What is the height of the final image? Is it erect or inverted? (*Hint:* See the preceding two problems.)

Section 34.5 Cameras

34.42 • You wish to project the image of a slide on a screen 9.00 m from the lens of a slide projector. (a) If the slide is placed 15.0 cm from the lens, what focal length lens is required? (b) If the dimensions of the picture on a 35-mm color slide are 24 mm × 36 mm, what is the minimum size of the projector screen required to accommodate the image?

34.43 •• A camera lens has a focal length of 200 mm. How far from the lens should the subject for the photo be if the lens is 20.4 cm from the film?

34.44 • When a camera is focused, the lens is moved away from or toward the film. If you take a picture of your friend, who is standing 3.90 m from the lens, using a camera with a lens with a 85-mm focal length, how far from the film is the lens? Will the whole image of your friend, who is 175 cm tall, fit on film that is 24 × 36 mm?

34.45 • Figure 34.41 shows photographs of the same scene taken with the same camera with lenses of different focal length. If the object is 200 m from the lens, what is the magnitude of the lateral magnification for a lens of focal length (a) 28 mm; (b) 105 mm; (c) 300 mm?

34.46 • A photographer takes a photograph of a Boeing 747 airliner (length 70.7 m) when it is flying directly overhead at an altitude of 9.50 km. The lens has a focal length of 5.00 m. How long is the image of the airliner on the film?

34.47 • **Choosing a Camera Lens.** The picture size on ordinary 35-mm camera film is 24 mm × 36 mm. Focal lengths of lenses available for 35-mm cameras typically include 28, 35, 50 (the "normal" lens), 85, 100, 135, 200, and 300 mm, among others. Which of these lenses should be used to photograph the following objects, assuming that the object is to fill most of the picture area? (a) a building 240 m tall and 160 m wide at a distance of 600 m, and (b) a mobile home 9.6 m in length at a distance of 40.0 m.

34.48 • **Zoom Lens.** Consider the simple model of the zoom lens shown in Fig. 34.43a. The converging lens has focal length $f_1 = 12$ cm, and the diverging lens has focal length $f_2 = -12$ cm. The lenses are separated by 4 cm as shown in Fig. 34.43a. (a) For a distant object, where is the image of the converging lens? (b) The image of the converging lens serves as the object for the diverging lens. What is the object distance for the diverging lens? (c) Where is the final image? Compare your answer to Fig. 34.43a. (d) Repeat parts (a), (b), and (c) for the situation shown in Fig. 34.43b, in which the lenses are separated by 8 cm.

34.49 •• A camera lens has a focal length of 180.0 mm and an aperture diameter of 16.36 mm. (a) What is the f-number of the lens? (b) If the correct exposure of a certain scene is $\frac{1}{30}$ s at $f/11$, what is the correct exposure at $f/2.8$?

34.50 •• Recall that the intensity of light reaching film in a camera is proportional to the effective area of the lens. Camera A has a lens with an aperture diameter of 8.00 mm. It photographs an object using the correct exposure time of $\frac{1}{30}$ s. What exposure time should be used with camera B in photographing the same object with the same film if this camera has a lens with an aperture diameter of 23.1 mm?

34.51 • **Photography.** A 35-mm camera has a standard lens with focal length 50 mm and can focus on objects between 45 cm and infinity. (a) Is the lens for such a camera a concave or a convex lens? (b) The camera is focused by rotating the lens, which moves it on the camera body and changes its distance from the film. In what range of distances between the lens and the film plane must the lens move to focus properly over the 45 cm to infinity range?

Section 34.6 The Eye

34.52 •• **BIO** **Curvature of the Cornea.** In a simplified model of the human eye, the aqueous and vitreous humors and the lens all have a refractive index of 1.40, and all the refraction occurs at the cornea, whose vertex is 2.60 cm from the retina. What should be the radius of curvature of the cornea such that the image of an object 40.0 cm from the cornea's vertex is focused on the retina?

34.53 •• **BIO** (a) Where is the near point of an eye for which a contact lens with a power of +2.75 diopters is prescribed? (b) Where is the far point of an eye for which a contact lens with a power of −1.30 diopters is prescribed for distant vision?

34.54 • **BIO** **Contact Lenses.** Contact lenses are placed right on the eyeball, so the distance from the eye to an object (or image) is the same as the distance from the lens to that object (or image). A certain person can see distant objects well, but his near point is 45.0 cm from his eyes instead of the usual 25.0 cm. (a) Is this person nearsighted or farsighted? (b) What type of lens (converging or diverging) is needed to correct his vision? (c) If the correcting

lenses will be contact lenses, what focal length lens is needed and what is its power in diopters?

34.55 •• **BIO** **Ordinary Glasses.** Ordinary glasses are worn in front of the eye and usually 2.0 cm in front of the eyeball. Suppose that the person in Problem 34.54 prefers ordinary glasses to contact lenses. What focal length lenses are needed to correct his vision, and what is their power in diopters?

34.56 • **BIO** A person can see clearly up close but cannot focus on objects beyond 75.0 cm. She opts for contact lenses to correct her vision. (a) Is she nearsighted or farsighted? (b) What type of lens (converging or diverging) is needed to correct her vision? (c) What focal length contact lens is needed, and what is its power in diopters?

34.57 •• **BIO** If the person in Problem 34.56 chooses ordinary glasses over contact lenses, what power lens (in diopters) does she need to correct her vision if the lenses are 2.0 cm in front of the eye?

Section 34.7 The Magnifier

34.58 •• A thin lens with a focal length of 6.00 cm is used as a simple magnifier. (a) What angular magnification is obtainable with the lens if the object is at the focal point? (b) When an object is examined through the lens, how close can it be brought to the lens? Assume that the image viewed by the eye is at the near point, 25.0 cm from the eye, and that the lens is very close to the eye.

34.59 • The focal length of a simple magnifier is 8.00 cm. Assume the magnifier is a thin lens placed very close to the eye. (a) How far in front of the magnifier should an object be placed if the image is formed at the observer's near point, 25.0 cm in front of her eye? (b) If the object is 1.00 mm high, what is the height of its image formed by the magnifier?

34.60 • You want to view an insect 2.00 mm in length through a magnifier. If the insect is to be at the focal point of the magnifier, what focal length will give the image of the insect an angular size of 0.025 radian?

Section 34.8 Microscopes and Telescopes

34.61 • A certain microscope is provided with objectives that have focal lengths of 16 mm, 4 mm, and 1.9 mm and with eyepieces that have angular magnifications of 5× and 10×. Each objective forms an image 120 mm beyond its second focal point. Determine (a) the largest overall angular magnification obtainable and (b) the smallest overall angular magnification obtainable.

34.62 •• **Resolution of a Microscope.** The image formed by a microscope objective with a focal length of 5.00 mm is 160 mm from its second focal point. The eyepiece has a focal length of 26.0 mm. (a) What is the angular magnification of the microscope? (b) The unaided eye can distinguish two points at its near point as separate if they are about 0.10 mm apart. What is the minimum separation between two points that can be observed (or resolved) through this microscope?

34.63 •• The focal length of the eyepiece of a certain microscope is 18.0 mm. The focal length of the objective is 8.00 mm. The distance between objective and eyepiece is 19.7 cm. The final image formed by the eyepiece is at infinity. Treat all lenses as thin. (a) What is the distance from the objective to the object being viewed? (b) What is the magnitude of the linear magnification produced by the objective? (c) What is the overall angular magnification of the microscope?

34.64 •• The eyepiece of a refracting telescope (see Fig. 34.53) has a focal length of 9.00 cm. The distance between objective and eyepiece is 1.80 m, and the final image is at infinity. What is the angular magnification of the telescope?

34.65 •• A telescope is constructed from two lenses with focal lengths of 95.0 cm and 15.0 cm, the 95.0-cm lens being used as the objective. Both the object being viewed and the final image are at infinity. (a) Find the angular magnification for the telescope. (b) Find the height of the image formed by the objective of a building 60.0 m tall, 3.00 km away. (c) What is the angular size of the final image as viewed by an eye very close to the eyepiece?

34.66 •• Saturn is viewed through the Lick Observatory refracting telescope (objective focal length 18 m). If the diameter of the image of Saturn produced by the objective is 1.7 mm, what angle does Saturn subtend from when viewed from earth?

34.67 •• A reflecting telescope (Fig. E34.67) is to be made by using a spherical mirror with a radius of curvature of 1.30 m and an eyepiece with a focal length of 1.10 cm. The final image is at infinity. (a) What should the distance between the eyepiece and the mirror vertex be if the object is taken to be at infinity? (b) What will the angular magnification be?

Figure **E34.67**

PROBLEMS

34.68 • Where must you place an object in front of a concave mirror with radius R so that the image is erect and $2\frac{1}{2}$ times the size of the object? Where is the image?

34.69 • If you run away from a plane mirror at 3.60 m/s, at what speed does your image move away from you?

34.70 • An object is placed between two plane mirrors arranged at right angles to each other at a distance d_1 from the surface of one mirror and a distance d_2 from the other. (a) How many images are formed? Show the location of the images in a diagram. (b) Draw the paths of rays from the object to the eye of an observer.

34.71 •• What is the size of the smallest vertical plane mirror in which a woman of height h can see her full-length image?

34.72 • A light bulb is 3.00 m from a wall. You are to use a concave mirror to project an image of the bulb on the wall, with the image 2.25 times the size of the object. How far should the mirror be from the wall? What should its radius of curvature be?

34.73 •• A concave mirror is to form an image of the filament of a headlight lamp on a screen 8.00 m from the mirror. The filament is 6.00 mm tall, and the image is to be 24.0 cm tall. (a) How far in front of the vertex of the mirror should the filament be placed? (b) What should be the radius of curvature of the mirror?

34.74 •• **Rear-View Mirror.** A mirror on the passenger side of your car is convex and has a radius of curvature with magnitude 18.0 cm. (a) Another car is behind your car, 9.00 m from the mirror, and this car is viewed in the mirror by your passenger. If this car is 1.5 m tall, what is the height of the image? (b) The mirror has a warning attached that objects viewed in it are closer than they appear. Why is this so?

34.75 • Suppose the lamp filament shown in Example 34.1 (Section 34.2) is moved to a position 8.0 cm in front of the mirror. (a) Where is the image located now? Is it real or virtual? (b) What is the height of the image? Is it erect or inverted? (c) In Example 34.1, the filament is 10.0 cm in front of the mirror, and an image of the filament is formed on a wall 3.00 m from the mirror. If the filament is 8.0 cm from the mirror, can a wall be placed so that an image is formed on it? If so, where should the wall be placed? If not, why not?

34.76 •• A layer of benzene ($n = 1.50$) 4.20 cm deep floats on water ($n = 1.33$) that is 6.50 cm deep. What is the apparent distance from the upper benzene surface to the bottom of the water layer when it is viewed at normal incidence?

34.77 •• **CP CALC** You are in your car driving on a highway at 25 m/s when you glance in the passenger-side mirror (a convex mirror with radius of curvature 150 cm) and notice a truck approaching. If the image of the truck is approaching the vertex of the mirror at a speed of 1.9 m/s when the truck is 2.0 m from the mirror, what is the speed of the truck relative to the highway?

34.78 •• Figure P34.78 shows a small plant near a thin lens. The ray shown is one of the principal rays for the lens. Each square is 2.0 cm along the horizontal direction, but the vertical direction is not to the same scale. Use information from the diagram for the following: (a) Using only the ray shown, decide what type of lens (converging or diverging) this is. (b) What is the focal length of the lens? (c) Locate the image by drawing the other two principal rays. (d) Calculate where the image should be, and compare this result with the graphical solution in part (c).

Figure **P34.78**

34.79 •• **Pinhole Camera.** A pinhole camera is just a rectangular box with a tiny hole in one face. The film is on the face opposite this hole, and that is where the image is formed. The camera forms an image *without* a lens. (a) Make a clear ray diagram to show how a pinhole camera can form an image on the film without using a lens. (*Hint:* Put an object outside the hole, and then draw rays passing through the hole to the opposite side of the box.) (b) A certain pinhole camera is a box that is 25 cm square and 20.0 cm deep, with the hole in the middle of one of the 25 cm × 25 cm faces. If this camera is used to photograph a fierce chicken that is 18 cm high and 1.5 m in front of the camera, how large is the image of this bird on the film? What is the magnification of this camera?

34.80 ••• A microscope is focused on the upper surface of a glass plate. A second plate is then placed over the first. To focus on the bottom surface of the second plate, the microscope must be raised 0.780 mm. To focus on the upper surface, it must be raised another 2.50 mm. Find the index of refraction of the second plate.

34.81 •• What should be the index of refraction of a transparent sphere in order for paraxial rays from an infinitely distant object to be brought to a focus at the vertex of the surface opposite the point of incidence?

34.82 •• **A Glass Rod.** Both ends of a glass rod with index of refraction 1.60 are ground and polished to convex hemispherical surfaces. The radius of curvature at the left end is 6.00 cm, and the radius of curvature at the right end is 12.0 cm. The length of the rod between vertices is 40.0 cm. The object for the surface at the left end is an arrow that lies 23.0 cm to the left of the vertex of this surface. The arrow is 1.50 mm tall and at right angles to the axis. (a) What constitutes the object for the surface at the right end of the rod? (b) What is the object distance for this surface? (c) Is the object for this surface real or virtual? (d) What is the position of the final image? (e) Is the final image real or virtual? Is it erect or inverted with respect to the original object? (f) What is the height of the final image?

34.83 •• The rod in Problem 34.82 is shortened to a distance of 25.0 cm between its vertices; the curvatures of its ends remain the same. As in Problem 34.82, the object for the surface at the left end is an arrow that lies 23.0 cm to the left of the vertex of this surface. The arrow is 1.50 mm tall and at right angles to the axis. (a) What is the object distance for the surface at the right end of the rod? (b) Is the object for this surface real or virtual? (c) What is the position of the final image? (d) Is the final image real or virtual? Is it erect or inverted with respect to the original object? (e) What is the height of the final image?

34.84 • Figure P34.84 shows an object and its image formed by a thin lens. (a) What is the focal length of the lens, and what type of lens (converging or diverging) is it? (b) What is the height of the image? Is it real or virtual?

Figure **P34.84**

34.85 • Figure P34.85 shows an object and its image formed by a thin lens. (a) What is the focal length of the lens, and what type of lens (converging or diverging) is it? (b) What is the height of the image? Is it real or virtual?

Figure **P34.85**

34.86 ••• A transparent rod 30.0 cm long is cut flat at one end and rounded to a hemispherical surface of radius 10.0 cm at the other end. A small object is embedded within the rod along its axis and halfway between its ends, 15.0 cm from the flat end and 15.0 cm from the vertex of the curved end. When viewed from the flat end of the rod, the apparent depth of the object is 9.50 cm from the flat end. What is its apparent depth when viewed from the curved end?

34.87 • **BIO** **Focus of the Eye.** The cornea of the eye has a radius of curvature of approximately 0.50 cm, and the aqueous humor behind it has an index of refraction of 1.35. The thickness of the cornea itself is small enough that we shall neglect it. The depth of a typical human eye is around 25 mm. (a) What would have to be the radius of curvature of the cornea so that it alone would focus the image of a distant mountain on the retina, which is at the back of the eye opposite the cornea? (b) If the cornea focused the mountain correctly on the retina as described in part (a), would it also focus the text from a computer screen on the retina if that screen were 25 cm in front of the eye? If not, where would it focus that text: in front of or behind the retina? (c) Given that the cornea has a radius of curvature of about 5.0 mm, where does it actually focus the mountain? Is this in front of or behind the retina? Does this help you see why the eye needs help from a lens to complete the task of focusing?

34.88 ••• A transparent rod 50.0 cm long and with a refractive index of 1.60 is cut flat at the right end and rounded to a hemispherical surface with a 15.0-cm radius at the left end. An object is

placed on the axis of the rod 12.0 cm to the left of the vertex of the hemispherical end. (a) What is the position of the final image? (b) What is its magnification?

34.89 ••• A glass rod with a refractive index of 1.55 is ground and polished at both ends to hemispherical surfaces with radii of 6.00 cm. When an object is placed on the axis of the rod, 25.0 cm to the left of the left-hand end, the final image is formed 65.0 cm to the right of the right-hand end. What is the length of the rod measured between the vertices of the two hemispherical surfaces?

34.90 • The radii of curvature of the surfaces of a thin converging meniscus lens are $R_1 = +12.0$ cm and $R_2 = +28.0$ cm. The index of refraction is 1.60. (a) Compute the position and size of the image of an object in the form of an arrow 5.00 mm tall, perpendicular to the lens axis, 45.0 cm to the left of the lens. (b) A second converging lens with the same focal length is placed 3.15 m to the right of the first. Find the position and size of the final image. Is the final image erect or inverted with respect to the original object? (c) Repeat part (b) except with the second lens 45.0 cm to the right of the first.

34.91 • An object to the left of a lens is imaged by the lens on a screen 30.0 cm to the right of the lens. When the lens is moved 4.00 cm to the right, the screen must be moved 4.00 cm to the left to refocus the image. Determine the focal length of the lens.

34.92 • An object is placed 18.0 cm from a screen. (a) At what two points between object and screen may a converging lens with a 3.00-cm focal length be placed to obtain an image on the screen? (b) What is the magnification of the image for each position of the lens?

34.93 •• A convex mirror and a concave mirror are placed on the same optic axis, separated by a distance $L = 0.600$ m. The radius of curvature of each mirror has a magnitude of 0.360 m. A light source is located a distance x from the concave mirror, as shown in Fig. P34.93.

Figure **P34.93**

(a) What distance x will result in the rays from the source returning to the source after reflecting first from the convex mirror and then from the concave mirror? (b) Repeat part (a), but now let the rays reflect first from the concave mirror and then from the convex one.

34.94 •• As shown in Fig. P34.94 the candle is at the center of curvature of the concave mirror, whose focal length is 10.0 cm. The converging lens has a focal length of 32.0 cm and is 85.0 cm to the right of the candle. The candle is viewed looking through the lens from the right. The lens forms two images of the candle. The first is formed by light passing directly through the lens. The second image is formed from the light that goes from the candle to the mirror, is reflected, and then passes through the lens. (a) For each of these two images, draw a principal-ray diagram that locates the image. (b) For each image, answer the following questions: (i) Where is the image? (ii) Is the image real or virtual? (iii) Is the image erect or inverted with respect to the original object?

Figure **P34.94**

34.95 ••• One end of a long glass rod is ground to a convex hemispherical shape. This glass has an index of refraction of 1.55. When a small leaf is placed 20.0 cm in front of the center of the hemisphere along the optic axis, an image is formed inside the glass 9.12 cm from the spherical surface. Where would the image be formed if the glass were now immersed in water (refractive index 1.33) but nothing else were changed?

34.96 •• **Two Lenses in Contact.** (a) Prove that when two thin lenses with focal lengths f_1 and f_2 are placed *in contact*, the focal length f of the combination is given by the relationship

$$\frac{1}{f} = \frac{1}{f_1} + \frac{1}{f_2}$$

(b) A converging meniscus lens (see Fig. 34.32a) has an index of refraction of 1.55 and radii of curvature for its surfaces of magnitudes 4.50 cm and 9.00 cm. The concave surface is placed upward and filled with carbon tetrachloride (CCl_4), which has $n = 1.46$. What is the focal length of the CCl_4–glass combination?

34.97 ••• Rays from a lens are converging toward a point image P located to the right of the lens. What thickness t of glass with index of refraction 1.60 must be interposed between the lens and P for the image to be formed at P', located 0.30 cm to the right of P? The locations of the piece of glass and of points P and P' are shown in Fig. P34.97.

Figure **P34.97**

34.98 •• **A Lens in a Liquid.** A lens obeys Snell's law, bending light rays at each surface an amount determined by the index of refraction of the lens and the index of the medium in which the lens is located. (a) Equation (34.19) assumes that the lens is surrounded by air. Consider instead a thin lens immersed in a liquid with refractive index n_{liq}. Prove that the focal length f' is then given by Eq. (34.19) with n replaced by n/n_{liq}. (b) A thin lens with index n has focal length f in vacuum. Use the result of part (a) to show that when this lens is immersed in a liquid of index n_{liq}, it will have a new focal length given by

$$f' = \left[\frac{n_{\text{liq}}(n - 1)}{n - n_{\text{liq}}} \right] f$$

34.99 ••• When an object is placed at the proper distance to the left of a converging lens, the image is focused on a screen 30.0 cm to the right of the lens. A diverging lens is now placed 15.0 cm to the right of the converging lens, and it is found that the screen must be moved 19.2 cm farther to the right to obtain a sharp image. What is the focal length of the diverging lens?

34.100 ••• A convex spherical mirror with a focal length of magnitude 24.0 cm is placed 20.0 cm to the left of a plane mirror. An object 0.250 cm tall is placed midway between the surface of the plane mirror and the vertex of the spherical mirror. The spherical mirror forms multiple images of the object. Where are the two images of the object formed by the spherical mirror that are closest to the spherical mirror, and how tall is each image?

34.101 ••• A glass plate 3.50 cm thick, with an index of refraction of 1.55 and plane parallel faces, is held with its faces horizontal and its lower face 6.00 cm above a printed page. Find the position of the image of the page formed by rays making a small angle with the normal to the plate.

34.102 •• A symmetric, double-convex, thin lens made of glass with index of refraction 1.52 has a focal length in air of 40.0 cm. The lens is sealed into an opening in the left-hand end of a tank filled with water. At the right-hand end of the tank, opposite the lens, is a plane mirror 90.0 cm from the lens. The index of refraction of the water is $\frac{4}{3}$. (a) Find the position of the image formed by the lens–water–mirror system of a small object outside the tank on the lens axis and 70.0 cm to the left of the lens. (b) Is the image real or virtual? (c) Is it erect or inverted? (d) If the object has a height of 4.00 mm, what is the height of the image?

34.103 • You have a camera with a 35.0-mm-focal-length lens and 36.0-mm-wide film. You wish to take a picture of a 12.0-m-long sailboat but find that the image of the boat fills only $\frac{1}{4}$ of the width of the film. (a) How far are you from the boat? (b) How much closer must the boat be to you for its image to fill the width of the film?

34.104 •• **BIO** **What Is the Smallest Thing We Can See?** The smallest object we can resolve with our eye is limited by the size of the light receptor cells in the retina. In order for us to distinguish any detail in an object, its image cannot be any smaller than a single retinal cell. Although the size depends on the type of cell (rod or cone), a diameter of a few microns (μm) is typical near the center of the eye. We shall model the eye as a sphere 2.50 cm in diameter with a single thin lens at the front and the retina at the rear, with light receptor cells 5.0 μm in diameter. (a) What is the smallest object you can resolve at a near point of 25 cm? (b) What angle is subtended by this object at the eye? Express your answer in units of minutes ($1° = 60$ min), and compare it with the typical experimental value of about 1.0 min. (*Note:* There are other limitations, such as the bending of light as it passes through the pupil, but we shall ignore them here.)

34.105 • Three thin lenses, each with a focal length of 40.0 cm, are aligned on a common axis; adjacent lenses are separated by 52.0 cm. Find the position of the image of a small object on the axis, 80.0 cm to the left of the first lens.

34.106 •• A camera with a 90-mm-focal-length lens is focused on an object 1.30 m from the lens. To refocus on an object 6.50 m from the lens, by how much must the distance between the lens and the film be changed? To refocus on the more distant object, is the lens moved toward or away from the film?

34.107 •• The derivation of the expression for angular magnification, Eq. (34.22), assumed a near point of 25 cm. In fact, the near point changes with age as shown in Table 34.1. In order to achieve an angular magnification of 2.0×, what focal length should be used by a person of (a) age 10; (b) age 30; (c) age 60? (d) If the lens that gives $M = 2.0$ for a 10-year-old is used by a 60-year-old, what angular magnification will the older viewer obtain? (e) Does your answer in part (d) mean that older viewers are able to see more highly magnified images than younger viewers? Explain.

34.108 •• **Angular Magnification.** In deriving Eq. (34.22) for the angular magnification of a magnifier, we assumed that the object is placed at the focal point of the magnifier so that the virtual image is formed at infinity. Suppose instead that the object is placed so that the virtual image appears at an average viewer's near point of 25 cm, the closest point at which the viewer can bring an object into focus. (a) Where should the object be placed to achieve this? Give your answer in terms of the magnifier focal length f. (b) What angle θ' will an object of height y subtend at the position found in part (a)? (c) Find the angular magnification M with the object at the position found in part (a). The angle θ is the same as in Fig. 34.51a, since it refers to viewing the object *without* the magnifier. (d) For a convex lens with $f = +10.0$ cm, what is the value of M with the object at the position found in part (a)? How many times greater is M in this case than in the case where the image is formed at infinity? (e) In the description of a compound microscope in Section 34.8, it is stated that in a properly designed instrument, the real image formed by the objective lies *just inside* the first focal point F_1' of the eyepiece. What advantages are gained by having the image formed by the objective be just inside F_1', as opposed to precisely at F_1'? What happens if the image formed by the objective is *just outside* F_1'?

34.109 •• **BIO** In one form of cataract surgery the person's natural lens, which has become cloudy, is replaced by an artificial lens. The refracting properties of the replacement lens can be chosen so that the person's eye focuses on distant objects. But there is no accommodation, and glasses or contact lenses are needed for close vision. What is the power, in diopters, of the corrective contact lenses that will enable a person who has had such surgery to focus on the page of a book at a distance of 24 cm?

34.110 •• **BIO** **A Nearsighted Eye.** A certain very nearsighted person cannot focus on anything farther than 36.0 cm from the eye. Consider the simplified model of the eye described in Exercise 34.52. If the radius of curvature of the cornea is 0.75 cm when the eye is focusing on an object 36.0 cm from the cornea vertex and the indexes of refraction are as described in Exercise 34.52, what is the distance from the cornea vertex to the retina? What does this tell you about the shape of the nearsighted eye?

34.111 •• **BIO** A person with a near point of 85 cm, but excellent distant vision, normally wears corrective glasses. But he loses them while traveling. Fortunately, he has his old pair as a spare. (a) If the lenses of the old pair have a power of +2.25 diopters, what is his near point (measured from his eye) when he is wearing the old glasses if they rest 2.0 cm in front of his eye? (b) What would his near point be if his old glasses were contact lenses instead?

34.112 •• **The Galilean Telescope.** Figure P34.112 is a diagram of a *Galilean telescope,* or *opera glass,* with both the object and its final image at infinity. The image *I* serves as a virtual object for the eyepiece. The final image is virtual and erect. (a) Prove that the angular magnification is $M = -f_1/f_2$. (b) A Galilean telescope is to be constructed with the same objective lens as in Exercise 34.65. What focal length should the eyepiece have if this telescope is to have the same magnitude of angular magnification as the one in Exercise 34.65? (c) Compare the lengths of the telescopes.

Figure **P34.112**

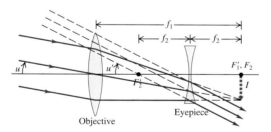

Objective

34.113 ••• **Focal Length of a Zoom Lens.** Figure P34.113 shows a simple version of a zoom lens. The converging lens has focal length f_1, and the diverging lens has focal length $f_2 = -|f_2|$. The two lenses are separated by a variable distance d that is always less than f_1. Also, the magnitude of the focal length of the diverging lens satisfies the inequality $|f_2| > (f_1 - d)$. To determine the effective focal length of the combination lens, consider a bundle of parallel rays of radius r_0 entering the converging lens. (a) Show that the radius of the ray bundle decreases to $r_0' = r_0(f_1 - d)/f_1$ at the point that it enters the diverging lens. (b) Show that the final image I' is formed a distance $s_2' = |f_2|(f_1 - d)/(|f_2| - f_1 + d)$ to the right of the diverging lens. (c) If the rays that emerge from the diverging lens and reach the final image point are extended

backward to the left of the diverging lens, they will eventually expand to the original radius r_0 at some point Q. The distance from the final image I' to the point Q is the *effective focal length* f of the lens combination; if the combination were replaced by a single lens of focal length f placed at Q, parallel rays would still be brought to a focus at I'. Show that the effective focal length is given by $f = f_1|f_2|/(|f_2| - f_1 + d)$. (d) If $f_1 = 12.0$ cm, $f_2 = -18.0$ cm, and the separation d is adjustable between 0 and 4.0 cm, find the maximum and minimum focal lengths of the combination. What value of d gives $f = 30.0$ cm?

Figure **P34.113**

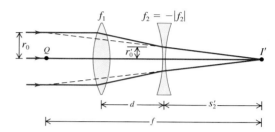

34.114 • A certain reflecting telescope, constructed as shown in Fig. E34.67, has a spherical mirror with a radius of curvature of 96.0 cm and an eyepiece with a focal length of 1.20 cm. If the angular magnification has a magnitude of 36 and the object is at infinity, find the position of the eyepiece and the position and nature (real or virtual) of the final image. (*Note:* $|M|$ is *not* equal to $|f_1|/|f_2|$, so the image formed by the eyepiece is *not* at infinity.)

34.115 • A microscope with an objective of focal length 8.00 mm and an eyepiece of focal length 7.50 cm is used to project an image on a screen 2.00 m from the eyepiece. Let the image distance of the objective be 18.0 cm. (a) What is the lateral magnification of the image? (b) What is the distance between the objective and the eyepiece?

CHALLENGE PROBLEMS

34.116 ••• *Spherical aberration* is a blurring of the image formed by a spherical mirror. It occurs because parallel rays striking the mirror far from the optic axis are focused at a different point than are rays near the axis. This problem is usually minimized by using only the center of a spherical mirror. (a) Show that for a spherical concave mirror, the focus moves toward the mirror as the parallel rays move toward the outer edge of the mirror. (*Hint:* Derive an analytic expression for the distance from the vertex to the focus of the ray for a particular parallel ray. This expression should be in terms of (i) the radius of curvature R of the mirror and (ii) the angle θ between the incident ray and a line connecting the center of curvature of the mirror with the point where the ray strikes the mirror.) (b) What value of θ produces a 2% change in the location of the focus, compared to the location for θ very close to zero?

34.117 ••• **CALC** (a) For a lens with focal length f, find the smallest distance possible between the object and its real image. (b) Graph the distance between the object and the real image as a function of the distance of the object from the lens. Does your graph agree with the result you found in part (a)?

34.118 ••• **An Object at an Angle.** A 16.0-cm-long pencil is placed at a 45.0° angle, with its center 15.0 cm above the optic axis and 45.0 cm from a lens with a 20.0-cm focal length as shown in Fig. P34.118. (Note that the figure is not drawn to scale.) Assume that the diameter of the lens is large enough for the paraxial approximation to be valid. (a) Where is the image of the pencil? (Give the location of the images of the points *A, B,* and *C* on the object, which are located at the eraser, point, and center of the pencil, respectively.) (b) What is the length of the image (that is, the distance between the images of points *A* and *B*)? (c) Show the orientation of the image in a sketch.

34.119 ••• **BIO** People with normal vision cannot focus their eyes underwater if they aren't

Figure **P34.118**

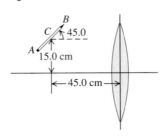

wearing a face mask or goggles and there is water in contact with their eyes (see Discussion Question Q34.23). (a) Why not? (b) With the simplified model of the eye described in Exercise 34.52, what corrective lens (specified by focal length as measured in air) would be needed to enable a person underwater to focus an infinitely distant object? (Be careful—the focal length of a lens underwater is *not* the same as in air! See Problem 34.98. Assume that the corrective lens has a refractive index of 1.62 and that the lens is used in eyeglasses, not goggles, so there is water on both sides of the lens. Assume that the eyeglasses are 2.00 cm in front of the eye.)

Answers

Chapter Opening Question ?

A magnifying lens (simple magnifier) produces a virtual image with a large angular size that is infinitely far away, so you can see it in sharp focus with your eyes relaxed. (A surgeon doing micro-surgery would not appreciate having to strain his eyes while working.) The object should be at the focal point of the lens, so the object and lens are separated by one focal length.

Test Your Understanding Questions

34.1 Answer: (iv) When you are a distance *s* from the mirror, your image is a distance *s* on the other side of the mirror and the distance from you to your image is 2*s*. As you move toward the mirror, the distance 2*s* changes at twice the rate of the distance *s*, so your image moves toward you at speed 2*v*.

34.2 Answers: (a) concave, (b) (ii) A convex mirror always produces an erect image, but that image is smaller than the object (see Fig. 34.16b). Hence a concave mirror must be used. The image will be erect and enlarged only if the distance from the object (your face) to the mirror is less than the focal length of the mirror, as in Fig. 34.20d.

34.3 Answer: no The sun is very far away, so the object distance is essentially infinite: $s = \infty$ and $1/s = 0$. Material *a* is air ($n_a = 1.00$) and material *b* is water ($n_b = 1.33$), so the image position s' is given by

$$\frac{n_a}{s} + \frac{n_b}{s'} = \frac{n_b - n_a}{R} \quad \text{or} \quad 0 + \frac{1.33}{s'} = \frac{1.33 - 1.00}{R}$$

$$s' = \frac{1.33}{0.33}R = 4.0R$$

The image would be formed 4.0 drop radii from the front surface of the drop. But since each drop is only a part of a complete sphere, the distance from the front to the back of the drop is less than 2*R*. Thus the rays of sunlight never reach the image point, and the drops do not form an image of the sun on the leaf. While the rays are not focused to a point, they are nonetheless concentrated and can cause damage to the leaf.

34.4 Answers: A and C When rays A and D are extended backward, they pass through focal point F_2; thus, before they passed through the lens, they were parallel to the optic axis. The figures show that ray A emanated from point *Q*, but ray D did not. Ray B is parallel to the optic axis, so before it passed through the lens, it was directed toward focal point F_1. Hence it cannot have come from point *Q*. Ray C passes through the center of the lens and hence is not deflected by its passage; tracing the ray backward shows that it emanates from point *Q*.

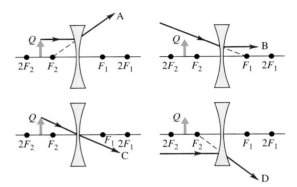

34.5 Answer: (iii) The smaller image area of the CCD array means that the angle of view is decreased for a given focal length. Individual objects make images of the same size in either case; when a smaller light-sensitive area is used, fewer images fit into the area and the field of view is narrower.

34.6 Answer: (iii) This lens is designed to correct for a type of astigmatism. Along the vertical axis, the lens is configured as a converging lens; along the horizontal axis, the lens is configured as a diverging lens. Hence the eye is hyperopic (see Fig. 34.46) for objects that are oriented vertically but myopic for objects that are oriented horizontally (see Fig. 34.47). Without correction, the eye focuses vertical objects behind the retina but horizontal objects in front of the retina.

34.7 Answer: (ii) The object must be held at the focal point, which is twice as far away if the focal length *f* is twice as great. Equation (24.22) shows that the angular magnification *M* is inversely proportional to *f*, so doubling the focal length makes *M* $\frac{1}{2}$ as great. To improve the magnification, you should use a magnifier with a *shorter* focal length.

34.8 Answer: (i) The objective lens of a microscope is designed to make enlarged images of small objects, so the absolute value of its lateral magnification *m* is greater than 1. By contrast, the objective lens of a refracting telescope is designed to make *reduced* images. For example, the moon is thousands of kilometers in diameter, but its image may fit on a CCD array a few centimeters across. Thus |*m*| is much less than 1 for a refracting telescope. (In both cases *m* is negative because the objective makes an inverted image, which is why the question asks about the absolute value of *m*.)

Bridging Problem

Answers: **(a)** 29.9 cm to the left of the goblet
(b) 3.73 cm to the right of the goblet

INTERFERENCE

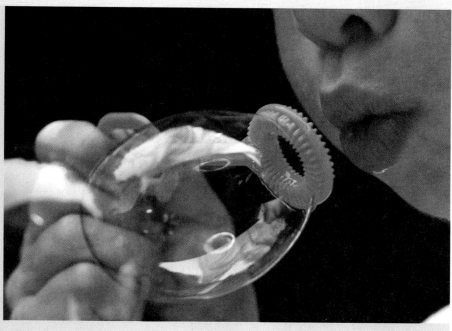

LEARNING GOALS

By studying this chapter, you will learn:

- What happens when two waves combine, or interfere, in space.

- How to understand the interference pattern formed by the interference of two coherent light waves.

- How to calculate the intensity at various points in an interference pattern.

- How interference occurs when light reflects from the two surfaces of a thin film.

- How interference makes it possible to measure extremely small distances.

? Soapy water is colorless, but when blown into bubbles it shows vibrant colors. How does the thickness of the bubble walls determine the particular colors that appear?

An ugly black oil spot on the pavement can become a thing of beauty after a rain, when the oil reflects a rainbow of colors. Multicolored reflections can also be seen from the surfaces of soap bubbles and DVDs. How is it possible for colorless objects to produce these remarkable colors?

In our discussion of lenses, mirrors, and optical instruments we used the model of *geometric optics,* in which we represent light as *rays,* straight lines that are bent at a reflecting or refracting surface. But many aspects of the behavior of light *can't* be understood on the basis of rays. We have already learned that light is fundamentally a *wave,* and in some situations we have to consider its wave properties explicitly. If two or more light waves of the same frequency overlap at a point, the total effect depends on the *phases* of the waves as well as their amplitudes. The resulting patterns of light are a result of the *wave* nature of light and cannot be understood on the basis of rays. Optical effects that depend on the wave nature of light are grouped under the heading **physical optics.**

In this chapter we'll look at *interference* phenomena that occur when two waves combine. The colors seen in oil films and soap bubbles are a result of interference between light reflected from the front and back surfaces of a thin film of oil or soap solution. Effects that occur when *many* sources of waves are present are called *diffraction* phenomena; we'll study these in Chapter 36. In that chapter we'll see that diffraction effects occur whenever a wave passes through an aperture or around an obstacle. They are important in practical applications of physical optics such as diffraction gratings, x-ray diffraction, and holography.

While our primary concern is with light, interference and diffraction can occur with waves of *any* kind. As we go along, we'll point out applications to other types of waves such as sound and water waves.

35.1 Interference and Coherent Sources

As we discussed in Chapter 15, the term **interference** refers to any situation in which two or more waves overlap in space. When this occurs, the total wave at any point at any instant of time is governed by the **principle of superposition,** which we introduced in Section 15.6 in the context of waves on a string. This principle also applies to electromagnetic waves and is the most important principle in all of physical optics. The principle of superposition states:

When two or more waves overlap, the resultant displacement at any point and at any instant is found by adding the instantaneous displacements that would be produced at the point by the individual waves if each were present alone.

(In some special situations, such as electromagnetic waves propagating in a crystal, this principle may not apply. A discussion of these is beyond our scope.)

We use the term "displacement" in a general sense. With waves on the surface of a liquid, we mean the actual displacement of the surface above or below its normal level. With sound waves, the term refers to the excess or deficiency of pressure. For electromagnetic waves, we usually mean a specific component of electric or magnetic field.

Interference in Two or Three Dimensions

We have already discussed one important case of interference, in which two identical waves propagating in opposite directions combine to produce a *standing wave*. We saw this in Chapters 15 and 16 for transverse waves on a string and for longitudinal waves in a fluid filling a pipe; we described the same phenomenon for electromagnetic waves in Section 32.5. In all of these cases the waves propagated along only a single axis: along a string, along the length of a fluid-filled pipe, or along the propagation direction of an electromagnetic plane wave. But light waves can (and do) travel in *two* or *three* dimensions, as can any kind of wave that propagates in a two- or three-dimensional medium. In this section we'll see what happens when we combine waves that spread out in two or three dimensions from a pair of identical wave sources.

Interference effects are most easily seen when we combine *sinusoidal* waves with a single frequency f and wavelength λ. Figure 35.1 shows a "snapshot" of a *single* source S_1 of sinusoidal waves and some of the wave fronts produced by this source. The figure shows only the wave fronts corresponding to wave *crests,* so the spacing between successive wave fronts is one wavelength. The material surrounding S_1 is uniform, so the wave speed is the same in all directions, and there is no refraction (and hence no bending of the wave fronts). If the waves are two-dimensional, like waves on the surface of a liquid, the circles in Fig. 35.1 represent circular wave fronts; if the waves propagate in three dimensions, the circles represent spherical wave fronts spreading away from S_1.

In optics, sinusoidal waves are characteristic of **monochromatic light** (light of a single color). While it's fairly easy to make water waves or sound waves of a single frequency, common sources of light *do not* emit monochromatic (single-frequency) light. For example, incandescent light bulbs and flames emit a continuous distribution of wavelengths. By far the most nearly monochromatic source that is available at present is the *laser.* An example is the helium–neon laser, which emits red light at 632.8 nm with a wavelength range of the order of ± 0.000001 nm, or about one part in 10^9. As we analyze interference and diffraction effects in this chapter and the next, we will assume that we are working with monochromatic waves (unless we explicitly state otherwise).

Constructive and Destructive Interference

Two identical sources of monochromatic waves, S_1 and S_2, are shown in Fig. 35.2a. The two sources produce waves of the same amplitude and the same wavelength λ.

35.1 A "snapshot" of sinusoidal waves of frequency f and wavelength λ spreading out from source S_1 in all directions.

Wave fronts: crests of the wave (frequency f) separated by one wavelength λ

The wave fronts move outward from source S_1 at the wave speed $v = f\lambda$.

In addition, the two sources are permanently *in phase;* they vibrate in unison. They might be two loudspeakers driven by the same amplifier, two radio antennas powered by the same transmitter, or two small slits in an opaque screen, illuminated by the same monochromatic light source. We will see that if there were not a constant phase relationship between the two sources, the phenomena we are about to discuss would not occur. Two monochromatic sources of the same frequency and with a constant phase relationship (not necessarily in phase) are said to be **coherent.** We also use the term *coherent waves* (or, for light waves, *coherent light*) to refer to the waves emitted by two such sources.

If the waves emitted by the two coherent sources are *transverse,* like electromagnetic waves, then we will also assume that the wave disturbances produced by both sources have the same *polarization* (that is, they lie along the same line). For example, the sources S_1 and S_2 in Fig. 35.2a could be two radio antennas in the form of long rods oriented parallel to the z-axis (perpendicular to the plane of the figure); at any point in the xy-plane the waves produced by both antennas have $\vec{E}$ fields with only a z-component. Then we need only a single scalar function to describe each wave; this makes the analysis much easier.

We position the two sources of equal amplitude, equal wavelength, and (if the waves are transverse) the same polarization along the y-axis in Fig. 35.2a, equidistant from the origin. Consider a point a on the x-axis. From symmetry the two distances from S_1 to a and from S_2 to a are *equal;* waves from the two sources thus require equal times to travel to a. Hence waves that leave S_1 and S_2 in phase arrive at a in phase. The two waves add, and the total amplitude at a is *twice* the amplitude of each individual wave. This is true for *any* point on the x-axis.

Similarly, the distance from S_2 to point b is exactly two wavelengths *greater* than the distance from S_1 to b. A wave crest from S_1 arrives at b exactly two cycles earlier than a crest emitted at the same time from S_2, and again the two waves arrive in phase. As at point a, the total amplitude is the sum of the amplitudes of the waves from S_1 and S_2.

In general, when waves from two or more sources arrive at a point *in phase,* they reinforce each other: The amplitude of the resultant wave is the *sum* of the amplitudes of the individual waves. This is called **constructive interference** (Fig. 35.2b). Let the distance from S_1 to any point P be r_1, and let the distance from S_2 to P be r_2. For constructive interference to occur at P, the path difference $r_2 - r_1$ for the two sources must be an integral multiple of the wavelength λ:

$$r_2 - r_1 = m\lambda \quad (m = 0, \pm1, \pm2, \pm3, \dots)$$
(constructive interference, sources in phase) (35.1)

In Fig. 35.2a, points a and b satisfy Eq. (35.1) with $m = 0$ and $m = +2$, respectively.

Something different occurs at point c in Fig. 35.2a. At this point, the path difference $r_2 - r_1 = -2.50\lambda$, which is a *half-integral* number of wavelengths. Waves from the two sources arrive at point c exactly a half-cycle out of phase. A crest of one wave arrives at the same time as a crest in the opposite direction (a "trough") of the other wave (Fig. 35.2c). The resultant amplitude is the *difference* between the two individual amplitudes. If the individual amplitudes are equal, then the total amplitude is *zero!* This cancellation or partial cancellation of the individual waves is called **destructive interference.** The condition for destructive interference in the situation shown in Fig. 35.2a is

$$r_2 - r_1 = \left(m + \tfrac{1}{2}\right)\lambda \quad (m = 0, \pm1, \pm2, \pm3, \dots)$$
(destructive interference, sources in phase) (35.2)

The path difference at point c in Fig. 35.2a satisfies Eq. (35.2) with $m = -3$.

35.2 (a) A "snapshot" of sinusoidal waves spreading out from two coherent sources S_1 and S_2. Constructive interference occurs at point a (equidistant from the two sources) and (b) at point b. (c) Destructive interference occurs at point c.

(a) Two coherent wave sources separated by a distance 4λ

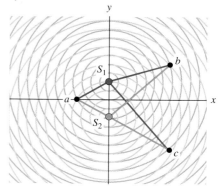

(b) Conditions for constructive interference: Waves interfere constructively if their path lengths differ by an integral number of wavelengths: $r_2 - r_1 = m\lambda$.

(c) Conditions for destructive interference: Waves interfere destructively if their path lengths differ by a half-integral number of wavelengths: $r_2 - r_1 = \left(m + \tfrac{1}{2}\right)\lambda$.

35.3 The same as Fig. 35.2a, but with red antinodal curves (curves of maximum amplitude) superimposed. All points on each curve satisfy Eq. (35.1) with the value of m shown. The nodal curves (not shown) lie between each adjacent pair of antinodal curves.

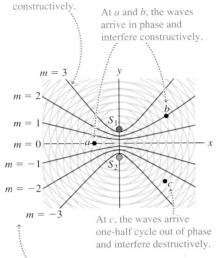

Antinodal curves (red) mark positions where the waves from S_1 and S_2 interfere constructively.

At a and b, the waves arrive in phase and interfere constructively.

At c, the waves arrive one-half cycle out of phase and interfere destructively.

m = the number of wavelengths λ by which the path lengths from S_1 and S_2 differ.

Figure 35.3 shows the same situation as in Fig. 35.2a, but with red curves that show all positions where *constructive* interference occurs. On each curve, the path difference $r_2 - r_1$ is equal to an integer m times the wavelength, as in Eq. (35.1). These curves are called **antinodal curves.** They are directly analogous to *antinodes* in the standing-wave patterns described in Chapters 15 and 16 and Section 32.5. In a standing wave formed by interference between waves propagating in opposite directions, the antinodes are points at which the amplitude is maximum; likewise, the wave amplitude in the situation of Fig. 35.3 is maximum along the antinodal curves. Not shown in Fig. 35.3 are the **nodal curves,** which are the curves that show where *destructive* interference occurs in accordance with Eq. (35.2); these are analogous to the *nodes* in a standing-wave pattern. A nodal curve lies between each two adjacent antinodal curves in Fig. 35.3; one such curve, corresponding to $r_2 - r_1 = -2.50\lambda$, passes through point c.

In some cases, such as two loudspeakers or two radio-transmitter antennas, the interference pattern is three-dimensional. Think of rotating the color curves of Fig. 35.3 around the y-axis; then maximum constructive interference occurs at all points on the resulting surfaces of revolution.

CAUTION   **Interference patterns are not standing waves** The interference patterns in Figs. 35.2a and 35.3 are *not* standing waves, though they have some similarities to the standing-wave patterns described in Chapters 15 and 16 and Section 32.5. In a standing wave, the interference is between two waves propagating in opposite directions; there is *no* net energy flow in either direction (the energy in the wave is left "standing"). In the situations shown in Figs. 35.2a and 35.3, there is likewise a stationary pattern of antinodal and nodal curves, but there is a net flow of energy *outward* from the two sources. All that interference does is to "channel" the energy flow so that it is greatest along the antinodal curves and least along the nodal curves. ▮

For Eqs. (35.1) and (35.2) to hold, the two sources must have the same wavelength and must *always* be in phase. These conditions are rather easy to satisfy for sound waves. But with *light* waves there is no practical way to achieve a constant phase relationship (coherence) with two independent sources. This is because of the way light is emitted. In ordinary light sources, atoms gain excess energy by thermal agitation or by impact with accelerated electrons. Such an "excited" atom begins to radiate energy and continues until it has lost all the energy it can, typically in a time of the order of 10^{-8} s. The many atoms in a source ordinarily radiate in an unsynchronized and random phase relationship, and the light that is emitted from *two* such sources has no definite phase relationship.

However, the light from a single source can be split so that parts of it emerge from two or more regions of space, forming two or more *secondary sources*. Then any random phase change in the source affects these secondary sources equally and does not change their *relative* phase.

The distinguishing feature of light from a *laser* is that the emission of light from many atoms is synchronized in frequency and phase. As a result, the random phase changes mentioned above occur much less frequently. Definite phase relationships are preserved over correspondingly much greater lengths in the beam, and laser light is much more coherent than ordinary light.

Test Your Understanding of Section 35.1   Consider a point in Fig. 35.3 on the positive y-axis above S_1. Does this point lie on (i) an antinodal curve; (ii) a nodal curve; or (iii) neither? (*Hint:* The distance between S_1 and S_2 is 4λ.)

35.2 Two-Source Interference of Light

The interference pattern produced by two coherent sources of *water* waves of the same wavelength can be readily seen in a ripple tank with a shallow layer of water (Fig. 35.4). This pattern is not directly visible when the interference is between *light* waves, since light traveling in a uniform medium cannot be seen. (A shaft of afternoon sunlight in a room is made visible by scattering from airborne dust particles.)

One of the earliest quantitative experiments to reveal the interference of light from two sources was performed in 1800 by the English scientist Thomas Young. We will refer back to this experiment several times in this and later chapters, so it's important to understand it in detail. Young's apparatus is shown in perspective in Fig. 35.5a. A light source (not shown) emits monochromatic light; however, this light is not suitable for use in an interference experiment because emissions from different parts of an ordinary source are not synchronized. To remedy this, the light is directed at a screen with a narrow slit S_0, 1 μm or so wide. The light emerging from the slit originated from only a small region of the light source; thus slit S_0 behaves more nearly like the idealized source shown in Fig. 35.1. (In modern versions of the experiment, a laser is used as a source of coherent light, and the slit S_0 isn't needed.) The light from slit S_0 falls on a screen with two other narrow slits S_1 and S_2, each 1 μm or so wide and a few tens or hundreds of micrometers apart. Cylindrical wave fronts spread out from slit S_0 and reach slits S_1 and S_2 *in phase* because they travel equal distances from S_0. The waves *emerging* from slits S_1 and S_2 are therefore also always in phase, so S_1 and S_2 are *coherent* sources. The interference of waves from S_1 and S_2 produces a pattern in space like that to the right of the sources in Figs. 35.2a and 35.3.

To visualize the interference pattern, a screen is placed so that the light from S_1 and S_2 falls on it (Fig. 35.5b). The screen will be most brightly illuminated at points P, where the light waves from the slits interfere constructively, and will be darkest at points where the interference is destructive.

To simplify the analysis of Young's experiment, we assume that the distance R from the slits to the screen is so large in comparison to the distance d between the slits that the lines from S_1 and S_2 to P are very nearly parallel, as in Fig. 35.5c. This is usually the case for experiments with light; the slit separation is typically a few millimeters, while the screen may be a meter or more away. The difference in path length is then given by

35.4 The concepts of constructive interference and destructive interference apply to these water waves as well as to light waves and sound waves.

(a) Interference of light waves passing through two slits

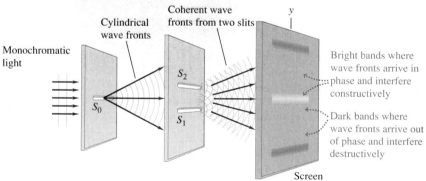

Bright bands where wave fronts arrive in phase and interfere constructively

Dark bands where wave fronts arrive out of phase and interfere destructively

Screen

35.5 **(a)** Young's experiment to show interference of light passing through two slits. A pattern of bright and dark areas appears on the screen (see Fig. 35.6). **(b)** Geometrical analysis of Young's experiment. For the case shown, $r_2 > r_1$ and both y and θ are positive. If point P is on the other side of the screen's center, $r_2 < r_1$ and both y and θ are negative. **(c)** Approximate geometry when the distance R to the screen is much greater than the distance d between the slits.

(b) Actual geometry (seen from the side)

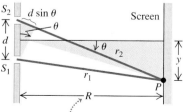

In real situations, the distance R to the screen is usually very much greater than the distance d between the slits ...

(c) Approximate geometry

... so we can treat the rays as parallel, in which case the path-length difference is simply $r_2 - r_1 = d \sin \theta$.

$$r_2 - r_1 = d\sin\theta \qquad (35.3)$$

where θ is the angle between a line from slits to screen (shown in blue in Fig. 35.5c) and the normal to the plane of the slits (shown as a thin black line).

Constructive and Destructive Two-Slit Interference

We found in Section 35.1 that constructive interference (reinforcement) occurs at points where the path difference is an integral number of wavelengths, $m\lambda$, where $m = 0, \pm 1, \pm 2, \pm 3, \ldots$. So the bright regions on the screen in Fig. 35.5a occur at angles θ for which

$$d\sin\theta = m\lambda \qquad (m = 0, \pm 1, \pm 2, \ldots) \qquad \text{(constructive interference, two slits)} \qquad (35.4)$$

Similarly, destructive interference (cancellation) occurs, forming dark regions on the screen, at points for which the path difference is a half-integral number of wavelengths, $\left(m + \frac{1}{2}\right)\lambda$:

$$d\sin\theta = \left(m + \frac{1}{2}\right)\lambda \qquad (m = 0, \pm 1, \pm 2, \ldots) \qquad \text{(destructive interference, two slits)} \qquad (35.5)$$

35.6 Photograph of interference fringes produced on a screen in Young's double-slit experiment.

m (constructive interference, bright regions)	$m + 1/2$ (destructive interference, dark regions)

	← 11/2
5 →	
	← 9/2
4 →	
	← 7/2
3 →	
	← 5/2
2 →	
	← 3/2
1 →	
	← 1/2
0 →	
	← −1/2
−1 →	
	← −3/2
−2 →	
	← −5/2
−3 →	
	← −7/2
−4 →	
	← −9/2
−5 →	
	← −11/2

Thus the pattern on the screen of Figs. 35.5a and 35.5b is a succession of bright and dark bands, or **interference fringes,** parallel to the slits S_1 and S_2. A photograph of such a pattern is shown in Fig. 35.6. The center of the pattern is a bright band corresponding to $m = 0$ in Eq. (35.4); this point on the screen is equidistant from the two slits.

We can derive an expression for the positions of the centers of the bright bands on the screen. In Fig. 35.5b, y is measured from the center of the pattern, corresponding to the distance from the center of Fig. 35.6. Let y_m be the distance from the center of the pattern $(\theta = 0)$ to the center of the mth bright band. Let θ_m be the corresponding value of θ; then

$$y_m = R\tan\theta_m$$

In experiments such as this, the distances y_m are often much smaller than the distance R from the slits to the screen. Hence θ_m is very small, $\tan\theta_m$ is very nearly equal to $\sin\theta_m$, and

$$y_m = R\sin\theta_m$$

Combining this with Eq. (35.4), we find that *for small angles only,*

$$y_m = R\frac{m\lambda}{d} \qquad \text{(constructive interference in Young's experiment)} \qquad (35.6)$$

We can measure R and d, as well as the positions y_m of the bright fringes, so this experiment provides a direct measurement of the wavelength λ. Young's experiment was in fact the first direct measurement of wavelengths of light.

CAUTION **Equation (35.6) is for small angles only** While Eqs. (35.4) and (35.5) are valid for any angle, Eq. (35.6) is valid only for *small* angles. It can be used *only* if the distance R from slits to screen is much greater than the slit separation d and if R is much greater than the distance y_m from the center of the interference pattern to the mth bright fringe. ▮

The distance between adjacent bright bands in the pattern is *inversely* proportional to the distance d between the slits. The closer together the slits are, the more the pattern spreads out. When the slits are far apart, the bands in the pattern are closer together.

While we have described the experiment that Young performed with visible light, the results given in Eqs. (35.4) and (35.5) are valid for *any* type of wave, provided that the resultant wave from two coherent sources is detected at a point that is far away in comparison to the separation d.

Example 35.1   Two-slit interference

Figure 35.7 shows a two-slit interference experiment in which the slits are 0.200 mm apart and the screen is 1.00 m from the slits. The $m = 3$ bright fringe in the figure is 9.49 mm from the central fringe. Find the wavelength of the light.

35.7 Using a two-slit interference experiment to measure the wavelength of light.

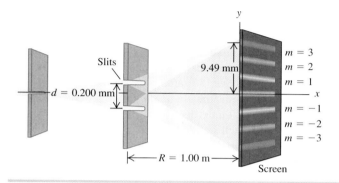

SOLUTION

IDENTIFY and SET UP: Our target variable in this two-slit interference problem is the wavelength λ. We are given the slit separation $d = 0.200$ mm, the distance from slits to screen $R = 1.00$ m, and the distance $y_3 = 9.49$ mm on the screen from the center of the interference pattern to the $m = 3$ bright fringe. We may use Eq. (35.6) to find λ, since the value of R is so much greater than the values of d or y_3.

EXECUTE: We solve Eq. (35.6) for λ for the case $m = 3$:

$$\lambda = \frac{y_m d}{mR} = \frac{(9.49 \times 10^{-3}\,\text{m})(0.200 \times 10^{-3}\,\text{m})}{(3)(1.00\,\text{m})}$$

$$= 633 \times 10^{-9}\,\text{m} = 633\,\text{nm}$$

EVALUATE: This bright fringe could also correspond to $m = -3$. Can you show that this gives the same result for λ?

Example 35.2   Broadcast pattern of a radio station

It is often desirable to radiate most of the energy from a radio transmitter in particular directions rather than uniformly in all directions. Pairs or rows of antennas are often used to produce the desired radiation pattern. As an example, consider two identical vertical antennas 400 m apart, operating at 1500 kHz $= 1.5 \times 10^6$ Hz (near the top end of the AM broadcast band) and oscillating in phase. At distances much greater than 400 m, in what directions is the intensity from the two antennas greatest?

SOLUTION

IDENTIFY and SET UP: The antennas, shown in Fig. 35.8, correspond to sources S_1 and S_2 in Fig. 35.5. Hence we can apply

35.8 Two radio antennas broadcasting in phase. The purple arrows indicate the directions of maximum intensity. The waves that are emitted toward the lower half of the figure are not shown.

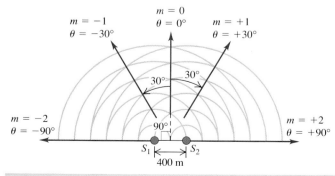

the ideas of two-slit interference to this problem. Since the resultant wave is detected at distances much greater than $d = 400$ m, we may use Eq. (35.4) to give the directions of the intensity maxima, the values of θ for which the path difference is zero or a whole number of wavelengths.

EXECUTE: The wavelength is $\lambda = c/f = 200$ m. From Eq. (35.4) with $m = 0$, ± 1, and ± 2, the intensity maxima are given by

$$\sin\theta = \frac{m\lambda}{d} = \frac{m(200\,\text{m})}{400\,\text{m}} = \frac{m}{2} \qquad \theta = 0,\ \pm 30°,\ \pm 90°$$

In this example, values of m greater than 2 or less than -2 give values of $\sin\theta$ greater than 1 or less than -1, which is impossible. There is *no* direction for which the path difference is three or more wavelengths, so values of m of ± 3 or beyond have no meaning in this example.

EVALUATE: We can check our result by calculating the angles for *minimum* intensity, using Eq. (35.5). There should be one intensity minimum between each pair of intensity maxima, just as in Fig. 35.6. From Eq. (35.5), with $m = -2, -1, 0$, and 1,

$$\sin\theta = \frac{(m + \frac{1}{2})\lambda}{d} = \frac{m + \frac{1}{2}}{2} \qquad \theta = \pm 14.5°,\ \pm 48.6°$$

These angles fall between the angles for intensity maxima, as they should. The angles are not small, so the angles for the minima are *not* exactly halfway between the angles for the maxima.

Test Your Understanding of Section 35.2 You shine a tunable laser (whose wavelength can be adjusted by turning a knob) on a pair of closely spaced slits. The light emerging from the two slits produces an interference pattern on a screen like that shown in Fig. 35.6. If you adjust the wavelength so that the laser light changes from red to blue, how will the spacing between bright fringes change? (i) The spacing increases; (ii) the spacing decreases; (iii) the spacing is unchanged; (iv) not enough information is given to decide.

35.3 Intensity in Interference Patterns

In Section 35.2 we found the positions of maximum and minimum intensity in a two-source interference pattern. Let's now see how to find the intensity at *any* point in the pattern. To do this, we have to combine the two sinusoidally varying fields (from the two sources) at a point P in the radiation pattern, taking proper account of the phase difference of the two waves at point P, which results from the path difference. The intensity is then proportional to the square of the result-ant electric-field amplitude, as we learned in Chapter 32.

To calculate the intensity, we will assume that the two sinusoidal functions (corresponding to waves from the two sources) have equal amplitude E and that the $\vec{E}$ fields lie along the same line (have the same polarization). This assumes that the sources are identical and neglects the slight amplitude difference caused by the unequal path lengths (the amplitude decreases with increasing distance from the source). From Eq. (32.29), each source by itself would give an intensity $\frac{1}{2}\epsilon_0 cE^2$ at point P. If the two sources are in phase, then the waves that arrive at P differ in phase by an amount proportional to the difference in their path lengths, $(r_2 - r_1)$. If the phase angle between these arriving waves is ϕ, then we can use the following expressions for the two electric fields superposed at P:

$$E_1(t) = E\cos(\omega t + \phi)$$

$$E_2(t) = E\cos\omega t$$

The superposition of the two fields at P is a sinusoidal function with some amplitude E_P that depends on E and the phase difference ϕ. First we'll work on finding the amplitude E_P if E and ϕ are known. Then we'll find the intensity I of the resultant wave, which is proportional to E_P^2. Finally, we'll relate the phase difference ϕ to the path difference, which is determined by the geometry of the situation.

Amplitude in Two-Source Interference

To add the two sinusoidal functions with a phase difference, we use the same *phasor* representation that we used for simple harmonic motion (see Section 14.2) and for voltages and currents in ac circuits (see Section 31.1). We suggest that you review these sections now. Each sinusoidal function is represented by a rotating vector (phasor) whose projection on the horizontal axis at any instant represents the instantaneous value of the sinusoidal function.

In Fig. 35.9, E_1 is the horizontal component of the phasor representing the wave from source S_1, and E_2 is the horizontal component of the phasor for the wave from S_2. As shown in the diagram, both phasors have the same magnitude E, but E_1 is *ahead* of E_2 in phase by an angle ϕ. Both phasors rotate counter-clockwise with constant angular speed ω, and the sum of the projections on the horizontal axis at any time gives the instantaneous value of the total E field at point P. Thus the amplitude E_P of the resultant sinusoidal wave at P is the mag-nitude of the dark red phasor in the diagram (labeled E_P); this is the *vector sum* of the other two phasors. To find E_P, we use the law of cosines and the trigonomet-ric identity $\cos(\pi - \phi) = -\cos\phi$:

$$E_P^2 = E^2 + E^2 - 2E^2\cos(\pi - \phi)$$
$$= E^2 + E^2 + 2E^2\cos\phi$$

35.9 Phasor diagram for the superposi-tion at a point P of two waves of equal amplitude E with a phase difference ϕ.

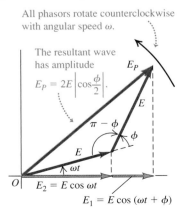

All phasors rotate counterclockwise with angular speed ω.

The resultant wave has amplitude E_P.

$E_P = 2E\left|\cos\dfrac{\phi}{2}\right|$.

$E_2 = E\cos\omega t$

$E_1 = E\cos(\omega t + \phi)$

Then, using the identity $1 + \cos\phi = 2\cos^2(\phi/2)$, we obtain

$$E_P{}^2 = 2E^2(1 + \cos\phi) = 4E^2\cos^2\left(\frac{\phi}{2}\right)$$

$$E_P = 2E\left|\cos\frac{\phi}{2}\right| \qquad \text{(amplitude in two-source interference)} \qquad (35.7)$$

You can also obtain this result without using phasors (see Problem 35.50).

When the two waves are in phase, $\phi = 0$ and $E_P = 2E$. When they are exactly a half-cycle out of phase, $\phi = \pi$ rad $= 180°$, $\cos(\phi/2) = \cos(\pi/2) = 0$, and $E_P = 0$. Thus the superposition of two sinusoidal waves with the same frequency and amplitude but with a phase difference yields a sinusoidal wave with the same frequency and an amplitude between zero and twice the individual amplitudes, depending on the phase difference.

Intensity in Two-Source Interference

To obtain the intensity I at point P, we recall from Section 32.4 that I is equal to the average magnitude of the Poynting vector, S_{av}. For a sinusoidal wave with electric-field amplitude E_P, this is given by Eq. (32.29) with E_{max} replaced by E_P. Thus we can express the intensity in several equivalent forms:

$$I = S_{\text{av}} = \frac{E_P{}^2}{2\mu_0 c} = \frac{1}{2}\sqrt{\frac{\epsilon_0}{\mu_0}}E_P{}^2 = \frac{1}{2}\epsilon_0 c E_P{}^2 \qquad (35.8)$$

The essential content of these expressions is that I is proportional to $E_P{}^2$. When we substitute Eq. (35.7) into the last expression in Eq. (35.8), we get

$$I = \frac{1}{2}\epsilon_0 c E_P{}^2 = 2\epsilon_0 c E^2 \cos^2\frac{\phi}{2} \qquad (35.9)$$

In particular, the *maximum* intensity I_0, which occurs at points where the phase difference is zero ($\phi = 0$), is

$$I_0 = 2\epsilon_0 c E^2$$

Note that the maximum intensity I_0 is *four times* (not twice) as great as the intensity $\frac{1}{2}\epsilon_0 c E^2$ from each individual source.

Substituting the expression for I_0 into Eq. (35.9), we can express the intensity I at any point very simply in terms of the maximum intensity I_0:

$$I = I_0\cos^2\frac{\phi}{2} \qquad \text{(intensity in two-source interference)} \qquad (35.10)$$

For some phase angles ϕ the intensity is I_0, four times as great as for an individual wave source, but for other phase angles the intensity is zero. If we average Eq. (35.10) over all possible phase differences, the result is $I_0/2 = \epsilon_0 c E^2$ (the average of $\cos^2(\phi/2)$ is $\frac{1}{2}$). This is just twice the intensity from each individual source, as we should expect. The total energy output from the two sources isn't changed by the interference effects, but the energy is redistributed (as we mentioned in Section 35.1).

Phase Difference and Path Difference

Our next task is to find the phase difference ϕ between the two fields at any point P. We know that ϕ is proportional to the difference in path length from the two sources to point P. When the path difference is one wavelength, the phase difference is one cycle, and $\phi = 2\pi$ rad $= 360°$. When the path difference is

$\lambda/2$, $\phi = \pi$ rad $= 180°$, and so on. That is, the ratio of the phase difference ϕ to 2π is equal to the ratio of the path difference $r_2 - r_1$ to λ:

$$\frac{\phi}{2\pi} = \frac{r_2 - r_1}{\lambda}$$

Thus a path difference $(r_2 - r_1)$ causes a phase difference given by

$$\phi = \frac{2\pi}{\lambda}(r_2 - r_1) = k(r_2 - r_1) \qquad \text{(phase difference related to path difference)} \qquad (35.11)$$

where $k = 2\pi/\lambda$ is the *wave number* introduced in Section 15.3.

If the material in the space between the sources and P is anything other than vacuum, we must use the wavelength *in the material* in Eq. (35.11). If the material has index of refraction n, then

$$\lambda = \frac{\lambda_0}{n} \qquad \text{and} \qquad k = nk_0 \qquad (35.12)$$

where λ_0 and k_0 are the wavelength and the wave number, respectively, in vacuum.

Finally, if the point P is far away from the sources in comparison to their separation d, the path difference is given by Eq. (35.3):

$$r_2 - r_1 = d\sin\theta$$

Combining this with Eq. (35.11), we find

$$\phi = k(r_2 - r_1) = kd\sin\theta = \frac{2\pi d}{\lambda}\sin\theta \qquad (35.13)$$

When we substitute this into Eq. (35.10), we find

$$I = I_0\cos^2\left(\tfrac{1}{2}kd\sin\theta\right) = I_0\cos^2\left(\frac{\pi d}{\lambda}\sin\theta\right) \qquad \text{(intensity far from two sources)} \qquad (35.14)$$

The directions of *maximum* intensity occur when the cosine has the values ±1—that is, when

$$\frac{\pi d}{\lambda}\sin\theta = m\pi \qquad (m = 0, \pm1, \pm2, \ldots)$$

or

$$d\sin\theta = m\lambda$$

in agreement with Eq. (35.4). You can also derive Eq. (35.5) for the zero-intensity directions from Eq. (35.14).

As we noted in Section 35.2, in experiments with light we visualize the interference pattern due to two slits by using a screen placed at a distance R from the slits. We can describe positions on the screen with the coordinate y; the positions of the bright fringes are given by Eq. (35.6), where ordinarily $y \ll R$. In that case, $\sin\theta$ is approximately equal to y/R, and we obtain the following expressions for the intensity at *any* point on the screen as a function of y:

$$I = I_0\cos^2\left(\frac{kdy}{2R}\right) = I_0\cos^2\left(\frac{\pi dy}{\lambda R}\right) \qquad \text{(intensity in two-slit interference)} \qquad (35.15)$$

Figure 35.10 shows a graph of Eq. (35.15); we can compare this with the photographically recorded pattern of Fig. 35.6. The peaks in Fig. 35.10 all have the same intensity, while those in Fig. 35.6 fade off as we go away from the center. We'll explore the reasons for this variation in peak intensity in Chapter 36.

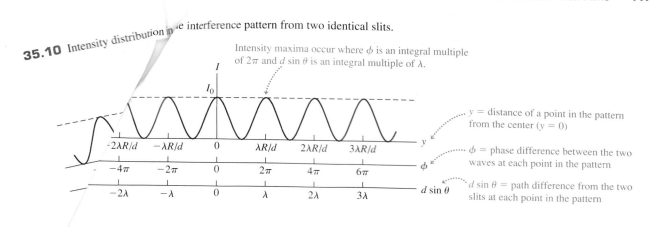

35.10 Intensity distribution in the interference pattern from two identical slits.

Intensity maxima occur where ϕ is an integral multiple of 2π and $d \sin\theta$ is an integral multiple of λ.

y = distance of a point in the pattern from the center ($y = 0$)

ϕ = phase difference between the two waves at each point in the pattern

$d \sin\theta$ = path difference from the two slits at each point in the pattern

35.3 A directional transmitting antenna array

the two identical radio antennas of Fig. 35.8 are moved to 10.0 m apart and the broadcast frequency is increased to 60.0 MHz. At a distance of 700 m from the point midway between the antennas and in the direction $\theta = 0$ (see Fig. 35.8), the intensity is $I_0 = 0.020$ W/m². At this same distance, find (a) the intensity in the direction $\theta = 4.0°$; (b) the direction near $\theta = 0$ for which the intensity is $I_0/2$; and (c) the directions in which the intensity is zero.

SOLUTION

IDENTIFY and SET UP: This problem involves the intensity distribution as a function of angle. Because the 700-m distance from the antennas to the point at which the intensity is measured is much greater than the distance $d = 10.0$ m between the antennas, the amplitudes of the waves from the two antennas are very nearly equal. Hence we can use Eq. (35.14) to relate intensity I and angle θ.

EXECUTE: The wavelength is $\lambda = c/f = 5.00$ m. The spacing $d = 10.0$ m between the antennas is just twice the wavelength (as was the case in Example 35.2), so $d/\lambda = 2.00$ and Eq. (35.14) becomes

$$I = I_0 \cos^2\left(\frac{\pi d}{\lambda}\sin\theta\right) = I_0 \cos^2[(2.00\pi \text{ rad})\sin\theta]$$

(a) When $\theta = 4.0°$,

$$I = I_0 \cos^2[(2.00\pi \text{ rad})\sin 4.0°] = 0.82I_0$$
$$= (0.82)(0.020 \text{ W/m}^2) = 0.016 \text{ W/m}^2$$

(b) The intensity I equals $I_0/2$ when the cosine in Eq. (35.14) has the value $\pm 1/\sqrt{2}$. The smallest angles at which this occurs correspond to $2.00\pi \sin\theta = \pm\pi/4$ rad, so that $\sin\theta = \pm(1/8.00) = \pm 0.125$ and $\theta = \pm 7.2°$.

(c) The intensity is zero when $\cos[(2.00\pi \text{ rad})\sin\theta] = 0$. This occurs for $2.00\pi \sin\theta = \pm\pi/2, \pm 3\pi/2, \pm 5\pi/2,\ldots$, or $\sin\theta = \pm 0.250, \pm 0.750, \pm 1.25,\ldots$. Values of $\sin\theta$ greater than 1 have no meaning, so the answers are

$$\theta = \pm 14.5°, \pm 48.6°$$

EVALUATE: The condition in part (b) that $I = I_0/2$, so that $(2.00\pi \text{ rad})\sin\theta = \pm\pi/4$ rad, is also satisfied when $\sin\theta = \pm 0.375, \pm 0.625$, or ± 0.875 so that $\theta = \pm 22.0°, \pm 38.7°$, or $\pm 61.0°$. (Can you verify this?) It would be incorrect to include these angles in the solution, however, because the problem asked for the angle *near* $\theta = 0$ at which $I = I_0/2$. These additional values of θ aren't the ones we're looking for.

Test Your Understanding of Section 35.3 A two-slit interference experiment uses coherent light of wavelength 5.00×10^{-7} m. Rank the following points in the interference pattern according to the intensity at each point, from highest to lowest. (i) a point that is closer to one slit than the other by 4.00×10^{-7} m; (ii) a point where the light waves received from the two slits are out of phase by 4.00 rad; (iii) a point that is closer to one slit than the other by 7.50×10^{-7} m; (iv) a point where the light waves received by the two slits are out of phase by 2.00 rad. ❚

35.4 Interference in Thin Films

You often see bright bands of color when light reflects from a thin layer of oil floating on water or from a soap bubble (see the photograph that opens this chapter). These are the results of interference. Light waves are reflected from the front and back surfaces of such thin films, and constructive interference between the two reflected waves (with different path lengths) occurs in different

35.11 (a) A diagram and (b) a photograph showing interference of light reflected from a thin film.

(a) Interference between rays reflected from the two surfaces of a thin film

Light reflected from the upper and lower surfaces of the film comes together in the eye at P and undergoes interference.

Some colors interfere constructively and others destructively, creating the color bands we see.

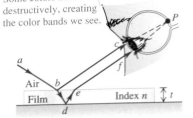

(b) The rainbow fringes of an oil slick on water

35.12 Interference between light waves reflected from the two sides of an air wedge separating two glass plates. The angles and the thickness of the air wedge have been exaggerated for clarity; in the text we assume that the light strikes the upper plate at normal incidence and that the distances h and t are much less than l.

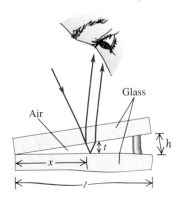

places for different wavelengths. Figure 35.11a shows the situation. Light shining on the upper surface of a thin film with thickness is partly reflected at the upper surface (path abc). Light *transmitted* through the upper surface is partly reflected at the lower surface (path $abdef$). The two reflected waves come together at point P on the retina of the eye. Depending on the phase relation, they may interfere constructively or destructively. Different colors have different wavelengths, so the interference may be constructive for some colors and destructive for others. That's why we see colored rings or fringes in Fig. 35.11b (which a thin film of oil floating on water) and in the photograph that opens this chapter shows thin films of soap solution that make up the bubble walls). The shapes of the colored rings in each photograph result from variations in thickness of the film.

Thin-Film Interference and Phase Shifts During Reflection

Let's look at a simplified situation in which *monochromatic* light reflects from two nearly parallel surfaces at nearly normal incidence. Figure 35.12 shows two plates of glass separated by a thin wedge, or film, of air. We want to consider interference between the two light waves reflected from the surfaces adjacent to the air wedge, as shown. (Reflections also occur at the top surface of the upper plate and the bottom surface of the lower plate; to keep our discussion simple, we won't include these.) The situation is the same as in Fig. 35.11a except that the film (wedge) thickness is not uniform. The path difference between the two waves is just twice the thickness t of the air wedge at each point. At points where $2t$ is an integer number of wavelengths, we expect to see constructive interference and a bright area; where it is a half-integer number of wavelengths, we expect to see destructive interference and a dark area. Along the line where the plates are in contact, there is practically *no* path difference, and we expect a bright area.

When we carry out the experiment, the bright and dark fringes appear, but they are interchanged! Along the line where the plates are in contact, we find a *dark* fringe, not a bright one. This suggests that one or the other of the reflected waves has undergone a half-cycle phase shift during its reflection. In that case the two waves that are reflected at the line of contact are a half-cycle out of phase even though they have the same path length.

In fact, this phase shift can be predicted from Maxwell's equations and the electromagnetic nature of light. The details of the derivation are beyond our scope, but here is the result. Suppose a light wave with electric-field amplitude E_i is traveling in an optical material with index of refraction n_a. It strikes, at normal incidence, an interface with another optical material with index n_b. The amplitude E_r of the wave reflected from the interface is proportional to the amplitude E_i of the incident wave and is given by

$$E_r = \frac{n_a - n_b}{n_a + n_b} E_i \quad \text{(normal incidence)} \tag{35.16}$$

This result shows that the incident and reflected amplitudes have the same sign when n_a is larger than n_b and opposite sign when n_b is larger than n_a. We can distinguish three cases, as shown in Fig. 35.13:

Figure 35.13a: When $n_a > n_b$, light travels more slowly in the first material than in the second. In this case, E_r and E_i have the same sign, and the phase shift of the reflected wave relative to the incident wave is zero. This is analogous to reflection of a transverse mechanical wave on a heavy rope at a point where it is tied to a lighter rope or a ring that can move vertically without friction.

Figure 35.13b: When $n_a = n_b$, the amplitude E_r of the reflected wave is zero. The incident light wave can't "see" the interface, and there is *no* reflected wave.

35.13 Upper figures: electromagnetic waves striking an interface between optical materials at normal incidence (shown as a small angle for clarity). Lower figures: mechanical wave pulses on ropes.

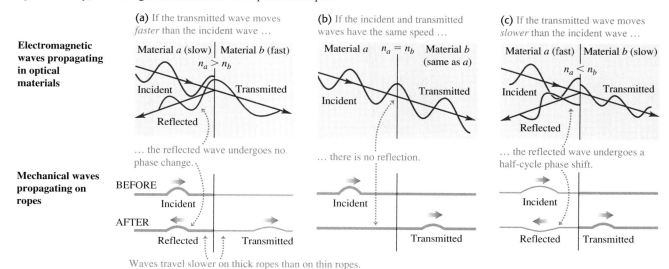

(a) If the transmitted wave moves *faster* than the incident wave …

(b) If the incident and transmitted waves have the same speed …

(c) If the transmitted wave moves *slower* than the incident wave …

Electromagnetic waves propagating in optical materials

… the reflected wave undergoes no phase change.

… there is no reflection.

… the reflected wave undergoes a half-cycle phase shift.

Mechanical waves propagating on ropes

Waves travel slower on thick ropes than on thin ropes.

Figure 35.13c: When $n_a < n_b$, light travels more slowly in the second material than in the first. In this case, E_r and E_i have opposite signs, and the phase shift of the reflected wave relative to the incident wave is π rad (180° or a half-cycle). This is analogous to reflection (with inversion) of a transverse mechanical wave on a light rope at a point where it is tied to a heavier rope or a rigid support.

Let's compare with the situation of Fig. 35.12. For the wave reflected from the upper surface of the air wedge, n_a (glass) is greater than n_b, so this wave has zero phase shift. For the wave reflected from the lower surface, n_a (air) is less than n_b (glass), so this wave has a half-cycle phase shift. Waves that are reflected from the line of contact have no path difference to give additional phase shifts, and they interfere destructively; this is what we observe. You can use the above principle to show that for normal incidence, the wave reflected at point b in Fig. 35.11a is shifted by a half-cycle, while the wave reflected at d is not (if there is air below the film).

We can summarize this discussion mathematically. If the film has thickness t, the light is at normal incidence and has wavelength λ in the film; if neither or both of the reflected waves from the two surfaces have a half-cycle reflection phase shift, the conditions for constructive and destructive interference are

$$2t = m\lambda \quad (m = 0, 1, 2, \dots)$$

(constructive reflection from thin film, no relative phase shift) (35.17a)

$$2t = \left(m + \tfrac{1}{2}\right)\lambda \quad (m = 0, 1, 2, \dots)$$

(destructive reflection from thin film, no relative phase shift) (35.17b)

If *one* of the two waves has a half-cycle reflection phase shift, the conditions for constructive and destructive interference are reversed:

$$2t = \left(m + \tfrac{1}{2}\right)\lambda \quad (m = 0, 1, 2, \dots)$$

(constructive reflection from thin film, half-cycle relative phase shift) (35.18a)

$$2t = m\lambda \quad (m = 0, 1, 2, \dots)$$

(destructive reflection from thin film, half-cycle relative phase shift) (35.18b)

35.14 (a) Light reflecting from a thin film produces a steady interference pattern, but (b) light reflecting from a thick film does not.

(a) Light reflecting from a thin film

Bursts of light a few μm long

The waves reflected from the two surfaces are part of the same burst and are coherent.

Thin film

(b) Light reflecting from a thick film

The waves reflected from the two surfaces are from different bursts and are *not* coherent.

Thick film

Thin and Thick Films

We have emphasized *thin* films in our discussion because of a principle we introduced in Section 35.1: In order for two waves to cause a steady interference pattern, the waves must be *coherent*, with a definite and constant phase relationship. The sun and light bulbs emit light in a stream of short bursts, each of which is only a few micrometers long (1 micrometer $= 1 \mu m = 10^{-6}$ m). If light reflects from the two surfaces of a thin film, the two reflected waves are part of the same burst (Fig. 35.14a). Hence these waves are coherent and interference occurs as we have described. If the film is too thick, however, the two reflected waves will belong to different bursts (Fig. 35.14b). There is no definite phase relationship between different light bursts, so the two waves are incoherent and there is no fixed interference pattern. That's why you see interference colors in light reflected from an oil slick a few micrometers thick (see Fig. 35.11b), but you do *not* see such colors in the light reflected from a pane of window glass with a thickness of a few millimeters (a thousand times greater).

Problem-Solving Strategy 35.1 **Interference in Thin Films**

IDENTIFY *the relevant concepts:* Problems with thin films involve interference of two waves, one reflected from the film's front surface and one reflected from the back surface. Typically you will be asked to relate the wavelength, the film thickness, and the index of refraction of the film.

SET UP *the problem* using the following steps:
1. Make a drawing showing the geometry of the film. Identify the materials that adjoin the film; their properties determine whether one or both of the reflected waves have a half-cycle phase shift.
2. Identify the target variable.

EXECUTE *the solution* as follows:
1. Apply the rule for phase changes to each reflected wave: There is a half-cycle phase shift when $n_b > n_a$ and none when $n_b < n_a$.

2. If *neither* reflected wave undergoes a phase shift, or if *both* do, use Eqs. (35.17). If only one reflected wave undergoes a phase shift, use Eqs. (35.18).
3. Solve the resulting equation for the target variable. Use the wavelength $\lambda = \lambda_0/n$ of light *in the film* in your calculations, where n is the index of refraction of the film. (For air, $n = 1.000$ to four-figure precision.)
4. If you are asked about the wave that is transmitted through the film, remember that minimum intensity in the reflected wave corresponds to maximum *transmitted* intensity, and vice versa.

EVALUATE *your answer:* Interpret your results by examining what would happen if the wavelength were changed or if the film had a different thickness.

Example 35.4 **Thin-film interference I**

Suppose the two glass plates in Fig. 35.12 are two microscope slides 10.0 cm long. At one end they are in contact; at the other end they are separated by a piece of paper 0.0200 mm thick. What is the spacing of the interference fringes seen by reflection? Is the fringe at the line of contact bright or dark? Assume monochromatic light with a wavelength in air of $\lambda = \lambda_0 = 500$ nm.

SOLUTION

IDENTIFY and SET UP: Figure 35.15 depicts the situation. We'll consider only interference between the light reflected from the upper and lower surfaces of the air wedge between the microscope slides. [The top slide has a relatively great thickness, about 1 mm,

35.15 Our sketch for this problem.

so we can ignore interference between the light reflected from its upper and lower surfaces (see Fig. 35.14b).] Light travels more slowly in the glass of the slides than it does in air. Hence the wave reflected from the upper surface of the air wedge has no phase shift (see Fig. 35.13a), while the wave reflected from the lower surface has a half-cycle phase shift (see Fig. 35.13c).

EXECUTE: Since only one of the reflected waves undergoes a phase shift, the condition for *destructive* interference (a dark fringe) is Eq. (35.18b):

$$2t = m\lambda_0 \quad (m = 0, 1, 2, \dots)$$

From similar triangles in Fig. 35.15 the thickness t of the air wedge at each point is proportional to the distance x from the line of contact:

$$\frac{t}{x} = \frac{h}{l}$$

Combining this with Eq. (35.18b), we find

$$\frac{2xh}{l} = m\lambda_0$$

$$x = m\frac{l\lambda_0}{2h} = m\frac{(0.100 \text{ m})(500 \times 10^{-9} \text{ m})}{(2)(0.0200 \times 10^{-3} \text{ m})} = m(1.25 \text{ mm})$$

Successive dark fringes, corresponding to $m = 1, 2, 3, \dots$, are spaced 1.25 mm apart. Substituting $m = 0$ into this equation gives $x = 0$, which is where the two slides touch (at the left-hand side of Fig. 35.15). Hence there is a dark fringe at the line of contact.

EVALUATE: Our result shows that the fringe spacing is proportional to the wavelength of the light used; the fringes would be farther apart with red light (larger λ_0) than with blue light (smaller λ_0). If we use white light, the reflected light at any point is a mixture of wavelengths for which constructive interference occurs; the wavelengths that interfere destructively are weak or absent in the reflected light. (This same effect explains the colors seen when an oil film on water is illuminated by white light, as in Fig. 35.11b.)

Example 35.5 **Thin-film interference II**

Suppose the glass plates of Example 35.4 have $n = 1.52$ and the space between plates contains water ($n = 1.33$) instead of air. What happens now?

SOLUTION

IDENTIFY and SET UP: The index of refraction of the water wedge is still less than that of the glass on either side of it, so the phase shifts are the same as in Example 35.4. Once again we use Eq. (35.18b) to find the positions of the dark fringes; the only difference is that the wavelength λ in this equation is now the wavelength in water instead of in air.

EXECUTE: In the film of water ($n = 1.33$), the wavelength is $\lambda = \lambda_0/n = (500 \text{ nm})/(1.33) = 376 \text{ nm}$. When we replace λ_0 by λ in the expression from Example 35.4 for the position x of the mth dark fringe, we find that the fringe spacing is reduced by the same factor of 1.33 and is equal to 0.940 mm. There is still a dark fringe at the line of contact.

EVALUATE: Can you see that to obtain the same fringe spacing as in Example 35.4, the dimension h in Fig. 35.15 would have to be reduced to $(0.0200 \text{ mm})/1.33 = 0.0150 \text{ mm}$? This shows that what matters in thin-film interference is the *ratio* t/λ between film thickness and wavelength. [You can see this by considering Eqs. (35.17) and (35.18).]

Example 35.6 **Thin-film interference III**

Suppose the upper of the two plates of Example 35.4 is a plastic with $n = 1.40$, the wedge is filled with a silicone grease with $n = 1.50$, and the bottom plate is a dense flint glass with $n = 1.60$. What happens now?

SOLUTION

IDENTIFY and SET UP: The geometry is again the same as shown in Fig. 35.15, but now half-cycle phase shifts occur at *both* surfaces of the grease wedge (see Fig. 35.13c). Hence there is no *relative* phase shift and we must use Eq. (35.17b) to find the positions of the dark fringes.

EXECUTE: The value of λ to use in Eq. (35.17b) is the wavelength in the silicone grease, $\lambda = \lambda_0/n = (500 \text{ nm})/1.50 = 333 \text{ nm}$. You can readily show that the fringe spacing is 0.833 mm. Note that the two reflected waves from the line of contact are in phase (they both undergo the same phase shift), so the line of contact is at a *bright* fringe.

EVALUATE: What would happen if you carefully removed the upper microscope slide so that the grease wedge retained its shape? There would still be half-cycle phase changes at the upper and lower surfaces of the wedge, so the pattern of fringes would be the same as with the upper slide present.

35.16 (a) Air film between a convex lens and a plane surface. The thickness of the film *t* increases from zero as we move out from the center, giving (b) a series of alternating dark and bright rings for monochromatic light.

(a) A convex lens in contact with a glass plane

(b) Newton's rings: circular interference fringes

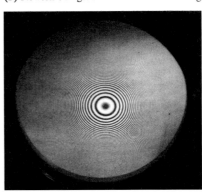

Newton's Rings

Figure 35.16a shows the convex surface of a lens in contact with a plane glass plate. A thin film of air is formed between the two surfaces. When you view the setup with monochromatic light, you see circular interference fringes (Fig. 35.16b). These were studied by Newton and are called **Newton's rings.**

We can use interference fringes to compare the surfaces of two optical parts by placing the two in contact and observing the interference fringes. Figure 35.17 is a photograph made during the grinding of a telescope objective lens. The lower, larger-diameter, thicker disk is the correctly shaped master, and the smaller, upper disk is the lens under test. The "contour lines" are Newton's interference fringes; each one indicates an additional distance between the specimen and the master of one half-wavelength. At 10 lines from the center spot the distance between the two surfaces is five wavelengths, or about 0.003 mm. This isn't very good; high-quality lenses are routinely ground with a precision of less than one wavelength. The surface of the primary mirror of the Hubble Space Telescope was ground to a precision of better than $\frac{1}{50}$ wavelength. Unfortunately, it was ground to incorrect specifications, creating one of the most precise errors in the history of optical technology (see Section 34.2).

35.17 The surface of a telescope objective lens under inspection during manufacture.

Fringes map lack of fit between lens and master.

Master   Lens being tested

Nonreflective and Reflective Coatings

Nonreflective coatings for lens surfaces make use of thin-film interference. A thin layer or film of hard transparent material with an index of refraction smaller than that of the glass is deposited on the lens surface, as in Fig. 35.18. Light is reflected from both surfaces of the layer. In both reflections the light is reflected from a medium of greater index than that in which it is traveling, so the same phase change occurs in both reflections. If the film thickness is a quarter (one-fourth) of the wavelength *in the film* (assuming normal incidence), the total path difference is a half-wavelength. Light reflected from the first surface is then a half-cycle out of phase with light reflected from the second, and there is destructive interference.

The thickness of the nonreflective coating can be a quarter-wavelength for only one particular wavelength. This is usually chosen in the central yellow-green portion of the spectrum ($\lambda = 550$ nm), where the eye is most sensitive. Then there is somewhat more reflection at both longer (red) and shorter (blue) wavelengths, and the reflected light has a purple hue. The overall reflection from a lens or prism surface can be reduced in this way from 4–5% to less than 1%. This also increases the net amount of light that is *transmitted* through the lens, since light that is not reflected will be transmitted. The same principle is used to minimize reflection from silicon photovoltaic solar cells ($n = 3.5$) by use of a thin surface layer of silicon monoxide (SiO, $n = 1.45$); this helps to increase the amount of light that actually reaches the solar cells.

35.18 A nonreflective coating has an index of refraction intermediate between those of glass and air.

Destructive interference occurs when
• the film is about $\frac{1}{4}\lambda$ thick and
• the light undergoes a phase change at both reflecting surfaces,

so that the two reflected waves emerge from the film about $\frac{1}{2}$ cycle out of phase.

$n_{\text{glass}} > n_{\text{film}} > n_{\text{air}}$

"Nonreflecting" film

Air

Film

Glass

$t = \frac{1}{4}\lambda$

If a quarter-wavelength thickness of a material with an index of refraction *greater* than that of glass is deposited on glass, then the reflectivity is *increased,* and the deposited material is called a **reflective coating.** In this case there is a half-cycle phase shift at the air–film interface but none at the film–glass interface, and reflections from the two sides of the film interfere constructively. For example, a coating with refractive index 2.5 causes 38% of the incident energy to be reflected, compared with 4% or so with no coating. By use of multiple-layer coatings, it is possible to achieve nearly 100% transmission or reflection for particular wavelengths. Some practical applications of these coatings are for color separation in television cameras and for infrared "heat reflectors" in motion-picture projectors, solar cells, and astronauts' visors.

Example 35.7 A nonreflective coating

A common lens coating material is magnesium fluoride (MgF_2), with $n = 1.38$. What thickness should a nonreflective coating have for 550-nm light if it is applied to glass with $n = 1.52$?

SOLUTION

IDENTIFY and SET UP: This coating is of the sort shown in Fig. 35.18. The thickness must be one-quarter of the wavelength of this light *in the coating.*

EXECUTE: The wavelength in air is $\lambda_0 = 550$ nm, so its wavelength in the MgF_2 coating is $\lambda = \lambda_0/n = (550\text{ nm})/1.38 = 400$ nm. The coating thickness should be one-quarter of this, or $\lambda/4 = 100$ nm.

EVALUATE: This is a very thin film, no more than a few hundred molecules thick. Note that this coating is *reflective* for light whose wavelength is *twice* the coating thickness; light of that wavelength reflected from the coating's lower surface travels one wavelength farther than light reflected from the upper surface, so the two waves are in phase and interfere constructively. This occurs for light with a wavelength in MgF_2 of 200 nm and a wavelength in air of $(200\text{ nm})(1.38) = 276$ nm. This is an ultraviolet wavelength (see Section 32.1), so designers of optical lenses with nonreflective coatings need not worry about such enhanced reflection.

Test Your Understanding of Section 35.4 A thin layer of benzene ($n = 1.501$) ties on top of a sheet of fluorite ($n = 1.434$). It is illuminated from above with light whose wavelength in benzene is 400 nm. Which of the following possible thicknesses of the benzene layer will maximize the brightness of the reflected light? (i) 100 nm; (ii) 200 nm; (iii) 300 nm; (iv) 400 nm.

35.5 The Michelson Interferometer

An important experimental device that uses interference is the **Michelson interferometer.** Michelson interferometers are used to make precise measurements of wavelengths and of very small distances, such as the minute changes in thickness of an axon when a nerve impulse propagates along its length. Like the Young two-slit experiment, a Michelson interferometer takes monochromatic light from a single source and divides it into two waves that follow different paths. In Young's experiment, this is done by sending part of the light through one slit and part through another; in a Michelson interferometer a device called a *beam splitter* is used. Interference occurs in both experiments when the two light waves are recombined.

How a Michelson Interferometer Works

Figure 35.19 shows the principal components of a Michelson interferometer. A ray of light from a monochromatic source A strikes the beam splitter C, which is a glass plate with a thin coating of silver on its right side. Part of the light (ray 1) passes through the silvered surface and the compensator plate D and is reflected from mirror M_1. It then returns through D and is reflected from the silvered surface of C to the observer. The remainder of the light (ray 2) is reflected from the silvered surface at point P to the mirror M_2 and back through C to the observer's eye.

35.19 A schematic Michelson interferometer. The observer sees an interference pattern that results from the difference in path lengths for rays 1 and 2.

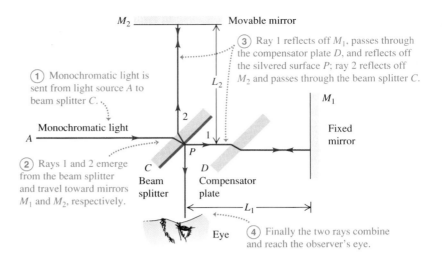

① Monochromatic light is sent from light source A to beam splitter C.

② Rays 1 and 2 emerge from the beam splitter and travel toward mirrors M_1 and M_2, respectively.

③ Ray 1 reflects off M_1, passes through the compensator plate D, and reflects off the silvered surface P; ray 2 reflects off M_2 and passes through the beam splitter C.

④ Finally the two rays combine and reach the observer's eye.

Application Imaging Cells with a Michelson Interferometer

This false-color image of a human colon cancer cell was made using a microscope that was mated to a Michelson interferometer. The cell is in one arm of the interferometer, and light passing through the cell undergoes a phase shift that depends on the cell thickness and the organelles within the cell. The fringe pattern can then be used to construct a three-dimensional view of the cell. Scientists have used this technique to observe how different types of cells behave when prodded by microscopic probes. Cancer cells turn out to be "softer" than normal cells, a distinction that may make cancer stem cells easier to identify.

The purpose of the compensator plate D is to ensure that rays 1 and 2 pass through the same thickness of glass; plate D is cut from the same piece of glass as plate C, so their thicknesses are identical to within a fraction of a wavelength.

The whole apparatus in Fig. 35.19 is mounted on a very rigid frame, and the position of mirror M_2 can be adjusted with a fine, very accurate micrometer screw. If the distances L_1 and L_2 are exactly equal and the mirrors M_1 and M_2 are exactly at right angles, the virtual image of M_1 formed by reflection at the silvered surface of plate C coincides with mirror M_2. If L_1 and L_2 are *not* exactly equal, the image of M_1 is displaced slightly from M_2; and if the mirrors are not exactly perpendicular, the image of M_1 makes a slight angle with M_2. Then the mirror M_2 and the virtual image of M_1 play the same roles as the two surfaces of a wedge-shaped thin film (see Section 35.4), and light reflected from these surfaces forms the same sort of interference fringes.

Suppose the angle between mirror M_2 and the virtual image of M_1 is just large enough that five or six vertical fringes are present in the field of view. If we now move the mirror M_2 slowly either backward or forward a distance $\lambda/2$, the difference in path length between rays 1 and 2 changes by λ, and each fringe moves to the left or right a distance equal to the fringe spacing. If we observe the fringe positions through a telescope with a crosshair eyepiece and m fringes cross the crosshairs when we move the mirror a distance y, then

$$y = m\frac{\lambda}{2} \quad \text{or} \quad \lambda = \frac{2y}{m} \quad (35.19)$$

If m is several thousand, the distance y is large enough that it can be measured with good accuracy, and we can obtain an accurate value for the wavelength λ. Alternatively, if the wavelength is known, a distance y can be measured by simply counting fringes when M_2 is moved by this distance. In this way, distances that are comparable to a wavelength of light can be measured with relative ease.

The Michelson-Morley Experiment

The original application of the Michelson interferometer was to the historic **Michelson-Morley experiment.** Before the electromagnetic theory of light became established, most physicists thought that the propagation of light waves occurred in a medium called the **ether,** which was believed to permeate all space. In 1887 the American scientists Albert Michelson and Edward Morley used the Michelson interferometer in an attempt to detect the motion of the earth through the ether. Suppose the interferometer in Fig. 35.19 is moving from left to right relative to the ether. According to the ether theory, this would lead to changes in the speed of light in the portions of the path shown as horizontal lines in the figure. There would be fringe shifts relative to the positions that the fringes would have if the instrument were at rest in the ether. Then when the entire instrument was rotated 90°, the other portions of the paths would be similarly affected, giving a fringe shift in the opposite direction.

Michelson and Morley expected that the motion of the earth through the ether would cause a shift of about four-tenths of a fringe when the instrument was rotated. The shift that was actually observed was less than a hundredth of a fringe and, within the limits of experimental uncertainty, appeared to be exactly zero. Despite its orbital motion around the sun, the earth appeared to be *at rest* relative to the ether. This negative result baffled physicists until 1905, when Albert Einstein developed the special theory of relativity (which we will study in detail in Chapter 37). Einstein postulated that the speed of a light wave in vacuum has the same magnitude c relative to *all* inertial reference frames, no matter what their velocity may be relative to each other. The presumed ether then plays no role, and the concept of an ether has been abandoned.

Test Your Understanding of Section 35.5   You are observing the pattern of fringes in a Michelson interferometer like that shown in Fig. 35.19. If you change the index of refraction (but not the thickness) of the compensator plate, will the pattern change?   ❙

Interference and coherent sources: Monochromatic light is light with a single frequency. Coherence is a definite, unchanging phase relationship between two waves. The overlap of waves from two coherent sources of monochromatic light forms an interference pattern. The principle of superposition states that the total wave disturbance at any point is the sum of the disturbances from the separate waves.

Two-source interference of light: When two sources are in phase, constructive interference occurs where the difference in path length from the two sources is zero or an integer number of wavelengths; destructive interference occurs where the path difference is a half-integer number of wavelengths. If two sources separated by a distance d are both very far from a point P, and the line from the sources to P makes an angle θ with the line perpendicular to the line of the sources, then the condition for constructive interference at P is Eq. (35.4). The condition for destructive interference is Eq. (35.5). When θ is very small, the position y_m of the mth bright fringe on a screen located a distance R from the sources is given by Eq. (35.6). (See Examples 35.1 and 35.2.)

$$d\sin\theta = m\lambda \quad (m = 0, \pm1, \pm2, \ldots)$$
$$\text{(constructive interference)} \quad (35.4)$$

$$d\sin\theta = \left(m + \tfrac{1}{2}\right)\lambda$$
$$(m = 0, \pm1, \pm2, \ldots) \quad (35.5)$$
$$\text{(destructive interference)}$$

$$y_m = R\frac{m\lambda}{d} \quad (35.6)$$
$$\text{(bright fringes)}$$

Intensity in interference patterns: When two sinusoidal waves with equal amplitude E and phase difference ϕ are superimposed, the resultant amplitude E_P and intensity I are given by Eqs. (35.7) and (35.10), respectively. If the two sources emit in phase, the phase difference ϕ at a point P (located a distance r_1 from source 1 and a distance r_2 from source 2) is directly proportional to the difference in path length $r_2 - r_1$. (See Example 35.3.)

$$E_P = 2E\left|\cos\frac{\phi}{2}\right| \quad (35.7)$$

$$I = I_0\cos^2\frac{\phi}{2} \quad (35.10)$$

$$\phi = \frac{2\pi}{\lambda}(r_2 - r_1) = k(r_2 - r_1) \quad (35.11)$$

Interference in thin films: When light is reflected from both sides of a thin film of thickness t and no phase shift occurs at either surface, constructive interference between the reflected waves occurs when $2t$ is equal to an integral number of wavelengths. If a half-cycle phase shift occurs at one surface, this is the condition for destructive interference. A half-cycle phase shift occurs during reflection whenever the index of refraction in the second material is greater than that in the first. (See Examples 35.4–35.7.)

$$2t = m\lambda \quad (m = 0, 1, 2, \ldots)$$
(constructive reflection from thin film, no relative phase shift) (35.17a)

$$2t = \left(m + \tfrac{1}{2}\right)\lambda \quad (m = 0, 1, 2, \ldots)$$
(destructive reflection from thin film, no relative phase shift) (35.17b)

$$2t = \left(m + \tfrac{1}{2}\right)\lambda \quad (m = 0, 1, 2, \ldots)$$
(constructive reflection from thin film, half-cycle relative phase shift) (35.18a)

$$2t = m\lambda \quad (m = 0, 1, 2, \ldots)$$
(destructive reflection from thin film, half-cycle relative phase shift) (35.18b)

Michelson interferometer: The Michelson interferometer uses a monochromatic light source and can be used for high-precision measurements of wavelengths. Its original purpose was to detect motion of the earth relative to a hypothetical ether, the supposed medium for electromagnetic waves. The ether has never been detected, and the concept has been abandoned; the speed of light is the same relative to all observers. This is part of the foundation of the special theory of relativity.

| BRIDGING PROBLEM | **Modifying a Two-Slit Experiment** |

An oil tanker spills a large amount of oil ($n = 1.45$) into the sea ($n = 1.33$). (a) If you look down onto the oil spill from overhead, what predominant wavelength of light do you see at a point where the oil is 380 nm thick? What color is the light? (*Hint:* See Table 32.1.) (b) In the water under the slick, what visible wavelength (as measured in air) is predominant in the transmitted light at the same place in the slick as in part (a)?

SOLUTION GUIDE

See MasteringPhysics® study area for a Video Tutor solution.

IDENTIFY and SET UP

1. The oil layer acts as a thin film, so we must consider interference between light that reflects from the top and bottom surfaces of the oil. If a wavelength is prominent in the *transmitted* light, there is destructive interference for that wavelength in the *reflected* light.

2. Choose the appropriate interference equations that relate the thickness of the oil film and the wavelength of light. Take account of the indexes of refraction of the air, oil, and water.

EXECUTE

3. For part (a), find the wavelengths for which there is constructive interference as seen from above the oil film. Which of these are in the visible spectrum?

4. For part (b), find the visible wavelength for which there is destructive interference as seen from above the film. (This will ensure that there is substantial transmitted light at the wavelength.)

EVALUATE

5. If a diver below the water's surface shines a light up at the bottom of the oil film, at what wavelengths would there be constructive interference in the light that reflects back downward?

| **Problems** | For instructor-assigned homework, go to www.masteringphysics.com |

•, ••, •••: Problems of increasing difficulty. **CP**: Cumulative problems incorporating material from earlier chapters. **CALC**: Problems requiring calculus. **BIO**: Biosciences problems.

DISCUSSION QUESTIONS

Q35.1 A two-slit interference experiment is set up, and the fringes are displayed on a screen. Then the whole apparatus is immersed in the nearest swimming pool. How does the fringe pattern change?

Q35.2 Could an experiment similar to Young's two-slit experiment be performed with sound? How might this be carried out? Does it matter that sound waves are longitudinal and electromagnetic waves are transverse? Explain.

Q35.3 Monochromatic coherent light passing through two thin slits is viewed on a distant screen. Are the bright fringes equally spaced on the screen? If so, why? If not, which ones are closest to being equally spaced?

Q35.4 In a two-slit interference pattern on a distant screen, are the bright fringes midway between the dark fringes? Is this ever a good approximation?

Q35.5 Would the headlights of a distant car form a two-source interference pattern? If so, how might it be observed? If not, why not?

Q35.6 The two sources S_1 and S_2 shown in Fig. 35.3 emit waves of the same wavelength λ and are in phase with each other. Suppose S_1 is a weaker source, so that the waves emitted by S_1 have half the amplitude of the waves emitted by S_2. How would this affect the positions of the antinodal lines and nodal lines? Would there be total reinforcement at points on the antinodal curves? Would there be total cancellation at points on the nodal curves? Explain your answers.

Q35.7 Could the Young two-slit interference experiment be performed with gamma rays? If not, why not? If so, discuss differences in the experimental design compared to the experiment with visible light.

Q35.8 Coherent red light illuminates two narrow slits that are 25 cm apart. Will a two-slit interference pattern be observed when the light from the slits falls on a screen? Explain.

Q35.9 Coherent light with wavelength λ falls on two narrow slits separated by a distance d. If d is less than some minimum value, no dark fringes are observed. Explain. In terms of λ, what is this minimum value of *d*?

Q35.10 A fellow student, who values memorizing equations above understanding them, combines Eqs. (35.4) and (35.13) to "prove" that φ can *only* equal $2\pi m$. How would you explain to this student that φ can have values other than $2\pi m$?

Q35.11 If the monochromatic light shown in Fig. 35.5a were replaced by white light, would a two-slit interference pattern be seen on the screen? Explain.

Q35.12 In using the superposition principle to calculate intensities in interference patterns, could you add the intensities of the waves instead of their amplitudes? Explain.

Q35.13 A glass windowpane with a thin film of water on it reflects less than when it is perfectly dry. Why?

Q35.14 A *very* thin soap film ($n = 1.33$), whose thickness is much less than a wavelength of visible light, looks black; it appears to reflect no light at all. Why? By contrast, an equally thin layer of soapy water ($n = 1.33$) on glass ($n = 1.50$) appears quite shiny. Why is there a difference?

Q35.15 Interference can occur in thin films. Why is it important that the films be *thin*? Why don't you get these effects with a relatively *thick* film? Where should you put the dividing line between "thin" and "thick"? Explain your reasoning.

Q35.16 If we shine white light on an air wedge like that shown in Fig. 35.12, the colors that are weak in the light *reflected* from any point along the wedge are strong in the light *transmitted* through the wedge. Explain why this should be so.

Q35.17 Monochromatic light is directed at normal incidence on a thin film. There is destructive interference for the reflected light, so the intensity of the reflected light is very low. What happened to the energy of the incident light?

Q35.18 When a thin oil film spreads out on a puddle of water, the thinnest part of the film looks dark in the resulting interference pattern. What does this tell you about the relative magnitudes of the refractive indexes of oil and water?

EXERCISES

Section 35.1 Interference and Coherent Sources

35.1 • Two small stereo speakers *A* and *B* that are 1.40 m apart are sending out sound of wavelength 34 cm in all directions and all in phase. A person at point *P* starts out equidistant from both speakers and walks so that he is always 1.50 m from speaker *B* (Fig. E35.1). For what values of *x* will the sound this person hears be (a) maximally reinforced, (b) cancelled? Limit your solution to the cases where $x \le 1.50$ m.

Figure **E35.1**

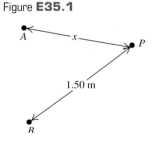

35.2 •• Two speakers that are 15.0 m apart produce in-phase sound waves of frequency 250.0 Hz in a room where the speed of sound is 340.0 m/s. A woman starts out at the midpoint between the two speakers. The room's walls and ceiling are covered with absorbers to eliminate reflections, and she listens with only one ear for best precision. (a) What does she hear: constructive or destructive interference? Why? (b) She now walks slowly toward one of the speakers. How far from the center must she walk before she first hears the sound reach a minimum intensity? (c) How far from the center must she walk before she first hears the sound maximally enhanced?

35.3 •• Two identical audio speakers connected to the same amplifier produce in-phase sound waves with a single frequency that can be varied between 300 and 600 Hz. The speed of sound is 340 m/s. You find that where you are standing, you hear minimum-intensity sound. (a) Explain why you hear minimum-intensity sound. (b) If one of the speakers is moved 39.8 cm toward you, the sound you hear has maximum intensity. What is the frequency of the sound? (c) How much closer to you from the position in part (b) must the speaker be moved to the next position where you hear maximum intensity?

35.4 • **Radio Interference.** Two radio antennas *A* and *B* radiate in phase. Antenna *B* is 120 m to the right of antenna *A*. Consider point *Q* along the extension of the line connecting the antennas, a horizontal distance of 40 m to the right of antenna *B*. The frequency, and hence the wavelength, of the emitted waves can be varied. (a) What is the longest wavelength for which there will be destructive interference at point *Q*? (b) What is the longest wavelength for which there will be constructive interference at point *Q*?

35.5 •• A radio transmitting station operating at a frequency of 120 MHz has two identical antennas that radiate in phase. Antenna *B* is 9.00 m to the right of antenna *A*. Consider point *P* between the antennas and along the line connecting them, a horizontal distance *x* to the right of antenna *A*. For what values of *x* will constructive interference occur at point *P*?

35.6 • Two light sources can be adjusted to emit monochromatic light of any visible wavelength. The two sources are coherent, 2.04 μm apart, and in line with an observer, so that one source is 2.04 μm farther from the observer than the other. (a) For what visible wavelengths (380 to 750 nm) will the observer see the brightest light, owing to constructive interference? (b) How would your answers to part (a) be affected if the two sources were not in line with the observer, but were still arranged so that one source is 2.04 μm farther away from the observer than the other? (c) For what visible wavelengths will there be *destructive* interference at the location of the observer?

35.7 • Two speakers, emitting identical sound waves of wavelength 2.0 m in phase with each other, and an observer are located as shown in Fig. E35.7. (a) At the observer's location, what is the path difference for waves from the two speakers? (b) Will the sound waves interfere constructively or destructively at the observer's location—or something in between constructive and destructive? (c) Suppose the observer now increases her distance from the closest speaker to 17.0 m, staying directly in front of the same speaker as initially. Answer the questions of parts (a) and (b) for this new situation.

Figure **E35.7**

35.8 •• Figure 35.3 shows the wave pattern produced by two identical, coherent sources emitting waves with wavelength λ and separated by a distance $d = 4\lambda$. (a) Explain why the positive *y*-axis above S_1 constitutes an antinodal curve with $m = +4$ and why the negative *y*-axis below S_2 constitutes an antinodal curve with $m = -4$. (b) Draw the wave pattern produced when the separation between the sources is reduced to 3λ. In your drawing, sketch all antinodal curves—that is, the curves on which $r_2 - r_1 = m\lambda$. Label each curve by its value of *m*. (c) In general, what determines the maximum (most positive) and minimum (most negative) values of the integer *m* that labels the antinodal lines? (d) Suppose the separation between the sources is increased to $7\frac{1}{2}\lambda$. How many antinodal curves will there be? To what values of m do they correspond? Explain your reasoning. (You should not have to make a drawing to answer these questions.)

Section 35.2 Two-Source Interference of Light

35.9 • Young's experiment is performed with light from excited helium atoms ($\lambda = 502$ nm). Fringes are measured carefully on a screen 1.20 m away from the double slit, and the center of the 20th fringe (not counting the central bright fringe) is found to be 10.6 mm from the center of the central bright fringe. What is the separation of the two slits?

35.10 •• Coherent light with wavelength 450 nm falls on a double slit. On a screen 1.80 m away, the distance between dark fringes is 4.20 mm. What is the separation of the slits?

35.11 •• Two slits spaced 0.450 mm apart are placed 75.0 cm from a screen. What is the distance between the second and third dark lines of the interference pattern on the screen when the slits are illuminated with coherent light with a wavelength of 500 nm?

35.12 •• If the entire apparatus of Exercise 35.11 (slits, screen, and space in between) is immersed in water, what then is the distance between the second and third dark lines?

35.13 •• Two thin parallel slits that are 0.0116 mm apart are illuminated by a laser beam of wavelength 585 nm. (a) On a very large distant screen, what is the *total* number of bright fringes (those indicating complete constructive interference), including the central fringe and those on both sides of it? Solve this problem without calculating all the angles! (*Hint:* What is the largest that $\sin\theta$ can be? What does this tell you is the largest value of m?) (b) At what angle, relative to the original direction of the beam, will the fringe that is most distant from the central bright fringe occur?

35.14 • Coherent light with wavelength 400 nm passes through two very narrow slits that are separated by 0.200 mm, and the interference pattern is observed on a screen 4.00 m from the slits. (a) What is the width (in mm) of the central interference maximum? (b) What is the width of the first-order bright fringe?

35.15 •• Two very narrow slits are spaced 1.80 μm apart and are placed 35.0 cm from a screen. What is the distance between the first and second dark lines of the interference pattern when the slits are illuminated with coherent light with $\lambda = 550$ nm? (*Hint:* The angle θ in Eq. (35.5) is *not* small.)

35.16 •• Coherent light that contains two wavelengths, 660 nm (red) and 470 nm (blue), passes through two narrow slits separated by 0.300 mm, and the interference pattern is observed on a screen 5.00 m from the slits. What is the distance on the screen between the first-order bright fringes for the two wavelengths?

35.17 •• Coherent light with wavelength 600 nm passes through two very narrow slits and the interference pattern is observed on a screen 3.00 m from the slits. The first-order bright fringe is at 4.84 mm from the center of the central bright fringe. For what wavelength of light will the first-order dark fringe be observed at this same point on the screen?

35.18 •• Coherent light of frequency 6.32×10^{14} Hz passes through two thin slits and falls on a screen 85.0 cm away. You observe that the third bright fringe occurs at ±3.11 cm on either side of the central bright fringe. (a) How far apart are the two slits? (b) At what distance from the central bright fringe will the third dark fringe occur?

Section 35.3 Intensity in Interference Patterns

35.19 •• In a two-slit interference pattern, the intensity at the peak of the central maximum is I_0. (a) At a point in the pattern where the phase difference between the waves from the two slits is 60.0°, what is the intensity? (b) What is the path difference for 480-nm light from the two slits at a point where the phase angle is 60.0°?

35.20 • Coherent sources A and B emit electromagnetic waves with wavelength 2.00 cm. Point P is 4.86 m from A and 5.24 m from B. What is the phase difference at P between these two waves?

35.21 • Coherent light with wavelength 500 nm passes through narrow slits separated by 0.340 mm. At a distance from the slits large compared to their separation, what is the phase difference (in radians) in the light from the two slits at an angle of 23.0° from the centerline?

35.22 • Two slits spaced 0.260 mm apart are placed 0.700 m from a screen and illuminated by coherent light with a wavelength of 660 nm. The intensity at the center of the central maximum ($\theta = 0°$) is I_0. (a) What is the distance on the screen from the center of the central maximum to the first minimum? (b) What is the distance on the screen from the center of the central maximum to the point where the intensity has fallen to $I_0/2$?

35.23 •• Points A and B are 56.0 m apart along an east-west line. At each of these points, a radio transmitter is emitting a 12.5-MHz signal horizontally. These transmitters are in phase with each other and emit their beams uniformly in a horizontal plane. A receiver is taken 0.500 km north of the AB line and initially placed at point C, directly opposite the midpoint of AB. The receiver can be moved only along an east-west direction but, due to its limited sensitivity, it must always remain within a range so that the intensity of the signal it receives from the transmitter is no less than $\frac{1}{4}$ of its maximum value. How far from point C (along an east-west line) can the receiver be moved and always be able to pick up the signal?

35.24 • Consider two antennas separated by 9.00 m that radiate in phase at 120 MHz, as described in Exercise 35.5. A receiver placed 150 m from both antennas measures an intensity I_0. The receiver is moved so that it is 1.8 m closer to one antenna than to the other. (a) What is the phase difference ϕ between the two radio waves produced by this path difference? (b) In terms of I_0, what is the intensity measured by the receiver at its new position?

Section 35.4 Interference in Thin Films

35.25 • What is the thinnest film of a coating with $n = 1.42$ on glass ($n = 1.52$) for which destructive interference of the red component (650 nm) of an incident white light beam in air can take place by reflection?

35.26 •• **Nonglare Glass.** When viewing a piece of art that is behind glass, one often is affected by the light that is reflected off the front of the glass (called *glare*), which can make it difficult to see the art clearly. One solution is to coat the outer surface of the glass with a film to cancel part of the glare. (a) If the glass has a refractive index of 1.62 and you use TiO_2, which has an index of refraction of 2.62, as the coating, what is the minimum film thickness that will cancel light of wavelength 505 nm? (b) If this coating is too thin to stand up to wear, what other thickness would also work? Find only the three thinnest ones.

35.27 •• Two rectangular pieces of plane glass are laid one upon the other on a table. A thin strip of paper is placed between them at one edge so that a very thin wedge of air is formed. The plates are illuminated at normal incidence by 546-nm light from a mercury-vapor lamp. Interference fringes are formed, with 15.0 fringes per centimeter. Find the angle of the wedge.

35.28 •• A plate of glass 9.00 cm long is placed in contact with a second plate and is held at a small angle with it by a metal strip

0.0800 mm thick placed under one end. The space between the plates is filled with air. The glass is illuminated from above with light having a wavelength in air of 656 nm. How many interference fringes are observed per centimeter in the reflected light?

35.29 •• A uniform film of TiO_2, 1036 nm thick and having index of refraction 2.62, is spread uniformly over the surface of crown glass of refractive index 1.52. Light of wavelength 520.0 nm falls at normal incidence onto the film from air. You want to increase the thickness of this film so that the reflected light cancels. (a) What is the *minimum* thickness of TiO_2 that you must *add* so the reflected light cancels as desired? (b) After you make the adjustment in part (a), what is the path difference between the light reflected off the top of the film and the light that cancels it after traveling through the film? Express your answer in (i) nanometers and (ii) wavelengths of the light in the TiO_2 film.

35.30 • A plastic film with index of refraction 1.85 is put on the surface of a car window to increase the reflectivity and thus to keep the interior of the car cooler. The window glass has index of refraction 1.52. (a) What minimum thickness is required if light with wavelength 550 nm in air reflected from the two sides of the film is to interfere constructively? (b) It is found to be difficult to manufacture and install coatings as thin as calculated in part (a). What is the next greatest thickness for which there will also be constructive interference?

35.31 • The walls of a soap bubble have about the same index of refraction as that of plain water, $n = 1.33$. There is air both inside and outside the bubble. (a) What wavelength (in air) of visible light is most strongly reflected from a point on a soap bubble where its wall is 290 nm thick? To what color does this correspond (see Fig. 32.4 and Table 32.1)? (b) Repeat part (a) for a wall thickness of 340 nm.

35.32 •• Light with wavelength 648 nm in air is incident perpendicularly from air on a film 8.76 μm thick and with refractive index 1.35. Part of the light is reflected from the first surface of the film, and part enters the film and is reflected back at the second surface, where the film is again in contact with air. (a) How many waves are contained along the path of this second part of the light in its round trip through the film? (b) What is the phase difference between these two parts of the light as they leave the film?

35.33 •• **Compact Disc Player.** A compact disc (CD) is read from the bottom by a semiconductor laser with wavelength 790 nm passing through a plastic substrate of refractive index 1.8. When the beam encounters a pit, part of the beam is reflected from the pit and part from the flat region between the pits, so these two beams interfere with each other (Fig. E35.33). What must the minimum pit depth be so that the part of the beam reflected from a pit cancels the part of the beam reflected from the flat region? (It is this cancellation that allows the player to recognize the beginning and end of a pit.)

Figure **E35.33**

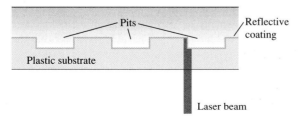

35.34 • What is the thinnest soap film (excluding the case of zero thickness) that appears black when illuminated with light with

wavelength 480 nm? The index of refraction of the film is 1.33, and there is air on both sides of the film.

Section 35.5 The Michelson Interferometer

35.35 • How far must the mirror M_2 (see Fig. 35.19) of the Michelson interferometer be moved so that 1800 fringes of He-Ne laser light ($\lambda = 633$ nm) move across a line in the field of view?

35.36 • Jan first uses a Michelson interferometer with the 606-nm light from a krypton-86 lamp. He displaces the movable mirror away from him, counting 818 fringes moving across a line in his field of view. Then Linda replaces the krypton lamp with filtered 502-nm light from a helium lamp and displaces the movable mirror toward her. She also counts 818 fringes, but they move across the line in her field of view opposite to the direction they moved for Jan. Assume that both Jan and Linda counted to 818 correctly. (a) What distance did each person move the mirror? (b) What is the resultant displacement of the mirror?

PROBLEMS

35.37 ••• The radius of curvature of the convex surface of a planoconvex lens is 68.4 cm. The lens is placed convex side down on a perfectly flat glass plate that is illuminated from above with red light having a wavelength of 580 nm. Find the diameter of the second bright ring in the interference pattern.

35.38 •• Newton's rings can be seen when a planoconvex lens is placed on a flat glass surface. For a particular lens with an index of refraction of $n = 1.50$ and a glass plate with an index of $n = 1.80$, the diameter of the third bright ring is 0.720 mm. If water ($n = 1.33$) now fills the space between the lens and the plate, what is the new diameter of this ring?

35.39 • **BIO** **Coating Eyeglass Lenses.** Eyeglass lenses can be coated on the *inner* surfaces to reduce the reflection of stray light to the eye. If the lenses are medium flint glass of refractive index 1.62 and the coating is fluorite of refractive index 1.432, (a) what minimum thickness of film is needed on the lenses to cancel light of wavelength 550 nm reflected toward the eye at normal incidence? (b) Will any other wavelengths of visible light be cancelled or enhanced in the reflected light?

35.40 •• **BIO** **Sensitive Eyes.** After an eye examination, you put some eyedrops on your sensitive eyes. The cornea (the front part of the eye) has an index of refraction of 1.38, while the eyedrops have a refractive index of 1.45. After you put in the drops, your friends notice that your eyes look red, because red light of wavelength 600 nm has been reinforced in the reflected light. (a) What is the minimum thickness of the film of eyedrops on your cornea? (b) Will any other wavelengths of visible light be reinforced in the reflected light? Will any be cancelled? (c) Suppose you had contact lenses, so that the eyedrops went on them instead of on your corneas. If the refractive index of the lens material is 1.50 and the layer of eyedrops has the same thickness as in part (a), what wavelengths of visible light will be reinforced? What wavelengths will be cancelled?

35.41 •• Two flat plates of glass with parallel faces are on a table, one plate on the other. Each plate is 11.0 cm long and has a refractive index of 1.55. A very thin sheet of metal foil is inserted under the end of the upper plate to raise it slightly at that end, in a manner similar to that discussed in Example 35.4. When you view the glass plates from above with reflected white light, you observe that, at 1.15 mm from the line where the sheets are in contact, the violet light of wavelength 400.0 nm is enhanced in this reflected light, but no visible light is enhanced closer to the line of contact.

(a) How far from the line of contact will green light (of wavelength 550 nm) and orange light (of wavelength 600.0 nm) first be enhanced? (b) How far from the line of contact will the violet, green, and orange light again be enhanced in the reflected light? (c) How thick is the metal foil holding the ends of the plates apart?

35.42 •• In a setup similar to that of Problem 35.41, the glass has an index of refraction of 1.53, the plates are each 8.00 cm long, and the metal foil is 0.015 mm thick. The space between the plates is filled with a jelly whose refractive index is not known precisely, but is known to be greater than that of the glass. When you illuminate these plates from above with light of wavelength 525 nm, you observe a series of equally spaced dark fringes in the reflected light. You measure the spacing of these fringes and find that there are 10 of them every 6.33 mm. What is the index of refraction of the jelly?

35.43 ••• Suppose you illuminate two thin slits by monochromatic coherent light in air and find that they produce their first interference *minima* at $\pm 35.20°$ on either side of the central bright spot. You then immerse these slits in a transparent liquid and illuminate them with the same light. Now you find that the first minima occur at $\pm 19.46°$ instead. What is the index of refraction of this liquid?

35.44 •• **CP CALC** A very thin sheet of brass contains two thin parallel slits. When a laser beam shines on these slits at normal incidence and room temperature (20.0°C), the first interference dark fringes occur at $\pm 32.5°$ from the original direction of the laser beam when viewed from some distance. If this sheet is now slowly heated up to 135°C, by how many degrees do these dark fringes change position? Do they move closer together or get farther apart? See Table 17.1 for pertinent information, and ignore any effects that might occur due to change in the thickness of the slits. (*Hint:* Since thermal expansion normally produces very small changes in length, you can use differentials to find the change in the angle.)

35.45 •• Two speakers, 2.50 m apart, are driven by the same audio oscillator so that each one produces a sound consisting of *two* distinct frequencies, 0.900 kHz and 1.20 kHz. The speed of sound in the room is 344 m/s. Find all the angles relative to the usual centerline in front of (and far from) the speakers at which *both* frequencies interfere constructively.

35.46 •• Two radio antennas radiating in phase are located at points *A* and *B*, 200 m apart (Fig. P35.46). The radio waves have a frequency of 5.80 MHz. A radio receiver is moved out from point *B* along a line perpendicular to the line connecting *A* and *B* (line *BC* shown in Fig. P35.46). At what distances from *B* will there be *destructive* interference? (*Note:* The distance of the receiver from the sources is not large in comparison to the separation of the sources, so Eq. (35.5) does not apply.)

Figure **P35.46**

35.47 •• One round face of a 3.25-m, solid, cylindrical plastic pipe is covered with a thin black coating that completely blocks light. The opposite face is covered with a fluorescent coating that glows when it is struck by light. Two straight, thin, parallel scratches, 0.225 mm apart, are made in the center of the black face. When laser light of wavelength 632.8 nm shines through the slits perpendicular to the black face, you find that the central bright fringe on the opposite face is 5.82 mm wide, measured between the dark fringes that border it on either side. What is the index of refraction of the plastic?

35.48 • A uniform thin film of material of refractive index 1.40 coats a glass plate of refractive index 1.55. This film has the proper thickness to cancel normally incident light of wavelength 525 nm that strikes the film surface from air, but it is somewhat greater than the minimum thickness to achieve this cancellation. As time goes by, the film wears away at a steady rate of 4.20 nm per year. What is the minimum number of years before the reflected light of this wavelength is now enhanced instead of cancelled?

35.49 •• Two speakers *A* and *B* are 3.50 m apart, and each one is emitting a frequency of 444 Hz. However, because of signal delays in the cables, speaker *A* is one-fourth of a period *ahead* of speaker *B*. For points far from the speakers, find all the angles relative to the centerline (Fig. P35.49) at which the sound from these speakers cancels. Include angles on *both* sides of the centerline. The speed of sound is 340 m/s.

Figure **P35.49**

35.50 ••• **CP** The electric fields received at point *P* from two identical, coherent wave sources are $E_1(t) = E\cos(\omega t + \phi)$ and $E_2(t) = E\cos \omega t$. (a) Use the trigonometric identities in Appendix B to show that the resultant wave is $E_P(t) = 2E\cos(\phi/2)\cos(\omega t + \phi/2)$. (b) Show that the amplitude of this resultant wave is given by Eq. (35.7). (c) Use the result of part (a) to show that at an interference maximum, the amplitude of the resultant wave is in phase with the original waves $E_1(t)$ and $E_2(t)$. (d) Use the result of part (a) to show that near an interference minimum, the resultant wave is approximately $\frac{1}{4}$ cycle out of phase with either of the original waves. (e) Show that the *instantaneous* Poynting vector at point *P* has magnitude $S = 4\epsilon_0 c E^2 \cos^2(\phi/2)\cos^2(\omega t + \phi/2)$ and that the *time-averaged* Poynting vector is given by Eq. (35.9).

35.51 •• **CP** A thin uniform film of refractive index 1.750 is placed on a sheet of glass of refractive index 1.50. At room temperature (20.0°C), this film is just thick enough for light with wavelength 582.4 nm reflected off the top of the film to be cancelled by light reflected from the top of the glass. After the glass is placed in an oven and slowly heated to 170°C, you find that the film cancels reflected light with wavelength 588.5 nm. What is the coefficient of linear expansion of the film? (Ignore any changes in the refractive index of the film due to the temperature change.)

35.52 ••• **GPS Transmission.** The GPS (Global Positioning System) satellites are approximately 5.18 m across and transmit two low-power signals, one of which is at 1575.42 MHz (in the UHF band). In a series of laboratory tests on the satellite, you put two 1575.42-MHz UHF transmitters at opposite ends of the satellite. These broadcast in phase uniformly in all directions. You measure the intensity at points on a circle that is several hundred meters in radius and centered on the satellite. You measure angles on this circle relative to a point that lies along the centerline of the satellite (that is, the perpendicular bisector of a line that extends from one transmitter to the other). At this point on the circle, the measured intensity is 2.00 W/m². (a) At how many other angles in the range $0° < \theta < 90°$ is the intensity also 2.00 W/m²? (b) Find the four smallest angles in the range $0° < \theta < 90°$ for which the intensity is 2.00 W/m². (c) What is the intensity at a point on the circle at an angle of 4.65° from the centerline?

35.53 •• Consider a two-slit interference pattern, for which the intensity distribution is given by Eq. (35.14). Let θ_m be the angular position of the mth bright fringe, where the intensity is I_0. Assume that θ_m is small, so that $\sin \theta_m \cong \theta_m$. Let $\theta_m{}^+$ and $\theta_m{}^-$ be the two angles on either side of θ_m for which $I = \frac{1}{2} I_0$. The quantity $\Delta \theta_m = |\theta_m{}^+ - \theta_m{}^-|$ is the half-width of the mth fringe. Calculate $\Delta \theta_m$. How does $\Delta \theta_m$ depend on m?

35.54 •• White light reflects at normal incidence from the top and bottom surfaces of a glass plate ($n = 1.52$). There is air above and below the plate. Constructive interference is observed for light whose wavelength in air is 477.0 nm. What is the thickness of the plate if the next longer wavelength for which there is constructive interference is 540.6 nm?

35.55 ••• A source S of monochromatic light and a detector D are both located in air a distance h above a horizontal plane sheet of glass and are separated by a horizontal distance x. Waves reaching D directly from S interfere with waves that reflect off the glass. The distance x is small compared to h so that the reflection is at close to normal incidence. (a) Show that the condition for constructive interference is $\sqrt{x^2 + 4h^2} - x = \left(m + \frac{1}{2}\right)\lambda$, and the condition for destructive interference is $\sqrt{x^2 + 4h^2} - x = m\lambda$. (*Hint:* Take into account the phase change on reflection.) (b) Let $h = 24$ cm and $x = 14$ cm. What is the longest wavelength for which there will be constructive interference?

35.56 •• **BIO** **Reflective Coatings and Herring.** Herring and related fish have a brilliant silvery appearance that camouflages them while they are swimming in a sunlit ocean. The silveriness is due to *platelets* attached to the surfaces of these fish. Each platelet is made up of several alternating layers of crystalline guanine ($n = 1.80$) and of cytoplasm ($n = 1.333$, the same as water), with a guanine layer on the outside in contact with the surrounding water (Fig. P35.56). In one typical platelet, the guanine layers are 74 nm thick and the cytoplasm layers are 100 nm thick. (a) For light striking the platelet surface at normal incidence, for which vacuum wavelengths of visible light will all of the reflections R_1, R_2, R_3, R_4, and R_5, shown in Fig. P35.56, be approximately in phase? If white light is shone on this platelet, what color will be most strongly reflected (see Fig. 32.4)? The surface of a herring has very many platelets side by side with layers of different thickness, so that *all* visible wavelengths are reflected. (b) Explain why such a "stack" of layers is more reflective than a single layer of guanine with cytoplasm underneath. (A stack of five guanine layers separated by cytoplasm layers reflects more than 80% of incident light at the wavelength for which it is "tuned.") (c) The color that is most strongly reflected from a platelet depends on the angle at which it is viewed. Explain why this should be so. (You can see these changes in color by examining a herring from different

Figure **P35.56**

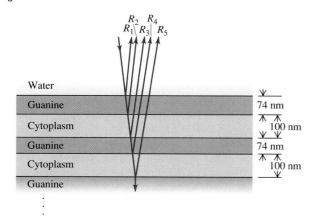

angles. Most of the platelets on these fish are oriented in the same way, so that they are vertical when the fish is swimming.)

35.57 • Two thin parallel slits are made in an opaque sheet of film. When a monochromatic beam of light is shone through them at normal incidence, the first bright fringes in the transmitted light occur in air at $\pm 18.0°$ with the original direction of the light beam on a distant screen when the apparatus is in air. When the apparatus is immersed in a liquid, the same bright fringes now occur at $\pm 12.6°$. Find the index of refraction of the liquid.

35.58 •• Red light with wavelength 700 nm is passed through a two-slit apparatus. At the same time, monochromatic visible light with another wavelength passes through the same apparatus. As a result, most of the pattern that appears on the screen is a mixture of two colors; however, the center of the third bright fringe ($m = 3$) of the red light appears pure red, with none of the other color. What are the possible wavelengths of the second type of visible light? Do you need to know the slit spacing to answer this question? Why or why not?

35.59 ••• In a Young's two-slit experiment a piece of glass with an index of refraction n and a thickness L is placed in front of the upper slit. (a) Describe qualitatively what happens to the interference pattern. (b) Derive an expression for the intensity I of the light at points on a screen as a function of n, L, and θ. Here θ is the usual angle measured from the center of the two slits. That is, determine the equation analogous to Eq. (35.14) but that also involves L and n for the glass plate. (c) From your result in part (b) derive an expression for the values of θ that locate the maxima in the interference pattern [that is, derive an equation analogous to Eq. (35.4)].

35.60 •• After a laser beam passes through two thin parallel slits, the first completely dark fringes occur at $\pm 19.0°$ with the original direction of the beam, as viewed on a screen far from the slits. (a) What is the ratio of the distance between the slits to the wavelength of the light illuminating the slits? (b) What is the smallest angle, relative to the original direction of the laser beam, at which the intensity of the light is $\frac{1}{10}$ the maximum intensity on the screen?

CHALLENGE PROBLEMS

35.61 ••• **CP** The index of refraction of a glass rod is 1.48 at $T = 20.0°C$ and varies linearly with temperature, with a coefficient of $2.50 \times 10^{-5}/C°$. The coefficient of linear expansion of the glass is $5.00 \times 10^{-6}/C°$. At 20.0°C the length of the rod is 3.00 cm. A Michelson interferometer has this glass rod in one arm, and the rod is being heated so that its temperature increases at a rate of 5.00 C°/min. The light source has wavelength $\lambda = 589$ nm, and the rod initially is at $T = 20.0°C$. How many fringes cross the field of view each minute?

35.62 ••• **CP** Figure P35.62 shows an interferometer known as *Fresnel's biprism.* The magnitude of the prism angle A is

Figure **P35.62**

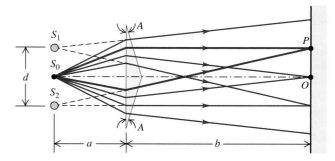

extremely small. (a) If S_0 is a very narrow source slit, show that the separation of the two virtual coherent sources S_1 and S_2 is given by $d = 2aA(n - 1)$, where n is the index of refraction of the material of the prism. (b) Calculate the spacing of the fringes of green light with wavelength 500 nm on a screen 2.00 m from the biprism. Take $a = 0.200$ m, $A = 3.50$ mrad, and $n = 1.50$.

Answers

Chapter Opening Question

The colors appear due to constructive interference between light waves reflected from the outer and inner surfaces of the soap bubble. The thickness of the bubble walls at each point determines the wavelength of light for which the most constructive interference occurs and hence the color that appears the brightest at that point (see Example 35.4 in Section 35.4).

Test Your Understanding Questions

35.1 Answer: (i) At any point P on the positive y-axis above S_1, the distance r_2 from S_2 to P is greater than the distance r_1 from S_1 to P by 4λ. This corresponds to $m = 4$ in Eq. (35.1), the equation for constructive interference. Hence all such points make up an antinodal curve.

35.2 Answer: (ii) Blue light has a shorter wavelength than red light (see Section 32.1). Equation (35.6) tells us that the distance y_m from the center of the pattern to the mth bright fringe is proportional to the wavelength λ. Hence all of the fringes will move toward the center of the pattern as the wavelength decreases, and the spacing between fringes will decrease.

35.3 Answer: (i), (iv), (ii), (iii) In cases (i) and (iii) we are given the wavelength λ and path difference $d\sin\theta$. Hence we use Eq. (35.14), $I = I_0\cos^2[(\pi d\sin\theta)/\lambda]$. In parts (ii) and (iii) we are given the phase difference ϕ and we use Eq. (35.10), $I = I_0\cos^2(\phi/2)$. We find:

(i) $I = I_0\cos^2[\pi(4.00 \times 10^{-7}\text{ m})/(5.00 \times 10^{-7}\text{ m})] = I_0\cos^2(0.800\pi\text{ rad}) = 0.655I_0$;

(ii) $I = I_0\cos^2[(4.00\text{ rad})/2] = I_0\cos^2(2.00\text{ rad}) = 0.173I_0$;

(iii) $I = I_0\cos^2[\pi(7.50 \times 10^{-7}\text{ m})/(5.00 \times 10^{-7}\text{ m})] = I_0\cos^2(1.50\pi\text{ rad}) = 0$;

(iv) $I = I_0\cos^2[(2.00\text{ rad})/2] = I_0\cos^2(1.00\text{ rad}) = 0.292I_0$.

35.4 Answers: (i) and (iii) Benzene has a larger index of refraction than air, so light that reflects off the upper surface of the benzene undergoes a half-cycle phase shift. Fluorite has a *smaller* index of refraction than benzene, so light that reflects off the benzene–fluorite interface does not undergo a phase shift. Hence the equation for constructive reflection is Eq. (35.18a), $2t = \left(m + \frac{1}{2}\right)\lambda$, which we can rewrite as $t = \left(m + \frac{1}{2}\right)\lambda/2 = \left(m + \frac{1}{2}\right)(400\text{ mm})/2 = 100$ nm, 300 nm, 500 nm, ...

35.5 Answer: yes Changing the index of refraction changes the wavelength of the light inside the compensator plate, and so changes the number of wavelengths within the thickness of the plate. Hence this has the same effect as changing the distance L_1 from the beam splitter to mirror M_1, which would change the interference pattern.

Bridging Problem

Answers: (a) 441 nm **(b)** 551 nm

36 DIFFRACTION

? The laser used to read a DVD has a wavelength of 650 nm, while the laser used to read a Blu-ray disc has a shorter 405-nm wavelength. How does this make it possible for a Blu-ray disc to hold more information than a DVD?

LEARNING GOALS

By studying this chapter, you will learn:

- What happens when coherent light shines on an object with an edge or aperture.

- How to understand the diffraction pattern formed when coherent light passes through a narrow slit.

- How to calculate the intensity at various points in a single-slit diffraction pattern.

- What happens when coherent light shines on an array of narrow, closely spaced slits.

- How scientists use diffraction gratings for precise measurements of wavelength.

- How x-ray diffraction reveals the arrangement of atoms in a crystal.

- How diffraction sets limits on the smallest details that can be seen with a telescope.

Everyone is used to the idea that sound bends around corners. If sound didn't behave this way, you couldn't hear a police siren that's out of sight around a corner or the speech of a person whose back is turned to you. What may surprise you (and certainly surprised many scientists of the early 19th century) is that *light* can bend around corners as well. When light from a point source falls on a straightedge and casts a shadow, the edge of the shadow is never perfectly sharp. Some light appears in the area that we expect to be in the shadow, and we find alternating bright and dark fringes in the illuminated area. In general, light emerging from apertures doesn't behave precisely according to the predictions of the straight-line ray model of geometric optics.

The reason for these effects is that light, like sound, has wave characteristics. In Chapter 35 we studied the interference patterns that can arise when two light waves are combined. In this chapter we'll investigate interference effects due to combining *many* light waves. Such effects are referred to as *diffraction*. We'll find that the behavior of waves after they pass through an aperture is an example of diffraction; each infinitesimal part of the aperture acts as a source of waves, and the resulting pattern of light and dark is a result of interference among the waves emanating from these sources.

Light emerging from arrays of apertures also forms patterns whose character depends on the color of the light and the size and spacing of the apertures. Examples of this effect include the colors of iridescent butterflies and the "rainbow" you see reflected from the surface of a compact disc. We'll explore similar effects with x rays that are used to study the atomic structure of solids and liquids. Finally, we'll look at the physics of a *hologram*, a special kind of interference pattern recorded on photographic film and reproduced. When properly illuminated, it forms a three-dimensional image of the original object.

36.1 Fresnel and Fraunhofer Diffraction

According to geometric optics, when an opaque object is placed between a point light source and a screen, as in Fig. 36.1, the shadow of the object forms a perfectly sharp line. No light at all strikes the screen at points within the shadow, and the area outside the shadow is illuminated nearly uniformly. But as we saw in Chapter 35, the *wave* nature of light causes effects that can't be understood with geometric optics. An important class of such effects occurs when light strikes a barrier that has an aperture or an edge. The interference patterns formed in such a situation are grouped under the heading **diffraction.**

Figure 36.2 shows an example of diffraction. The photograph in Fig. 36.2a was made by placing a razor blade halfway between a pinhole, illuminated by monochromatic light, and a photographic film. The film recorded the shadow cast by the blade. Figure 36.2b is an enlargement of a region near the shadow of the right edge of the blade. The position of the *geometric* shadow line is indicated by arrows. The area outside the geometric shadow is bordered by alternating bright and dark bands. There is some light in the shadow region, although this is not very visible in the photograph. The first bright band in Fig. 36.2b, just to the right of the geometric shadow, is considerably brighter than in the region of uniform illumination to the extreme right. This simple experiment gives us some idea of the richness and complexity of what might seem to be a simple idea, the casting of a shadow by an opaque object.

We don't often observe diffraction patterns such as Fig. 36.2 in everyday life because most ordinary light sources are neither monochromatic nor point sources. If we use a white frosted light bulb instead of a point source to illuminate the razor blade in Fig. 36.2, each wavelength of the light from every point of the bulb forms its own diffraction pattern, but the patterns overlap so much that we can't see any individual pattern.

Diffraction and Huygens's Principle

We can analyze diffraction patterns using Huygens's principle (see Section 33.7). This principle states that we can consider every point of a wave front as a source of secondary wavelets. These spread out in all directions with a speed equal to the speed of propagation of the wave. The position of the wave front at any later time is the *envelope* of the secondary wavelets at that time. To find the resultant displacement at any point, we combine all the individual displacements produced by these secondary waves, using the superposition principle and taking into account their amplitudes and relative phases.

36.1 A point source of light illuminates a straightedge.

Geometric optics predicts that this situation should produce a sharp boundary between illumination and solid shadow.

That's NOT what really happens!

DOESN'T HAPPEN

Point source

Area of illumination

Geometric shadow

Straightedge

Screen

36.2 An example of diffraction.

(a)

(b)

Photograph of a razor blade illuminated by monochromatic light from a point source (a pinhole). Notice the fringe around the blade outline.

Enlarged view of the area outside the geometric shadow of the blade's edge

Position of *geometric* shadow

In Fig. 36.1, both the point source and the screen are relatively close to the obstacle forming the diffraction pattern. This situation is described as *near-field diffraction* or **Fresnel diffraction,** pronounced "Freh-nell" (after the French scientist Augustin Jean Fresnel, 1788–1827). By contrast, we use the term **Fraunhofer diffraction** (after the German physicist Joseph von Fraunhofer, 1787–1826) for situations in which the source, obstacle, and screen are far enough apart that we can consider all lines from the source to the obstacle to be parallel, and can likewise consider all lines from the obstacle to a given point on the screen to be parallel. We will restrict the following discussion to Fraunhofer diffraction, which is usually simpler to analyze in detail than Fresnel diffraction.

Diffraction is sometimes described as "the bending of light around an obstacle." But the process that causes diffraction is present in the propagation of *every* wave. When part of the wave is cut off by some obstacle, we observe diffraction effects that result from interference of the remaining parts of the wave fronts. Optical instruments typically use only a limited portion of a wave; for example, a telescope uses only the part of a wave that is admitted by its objective lens or mirror. Thus diffraction plays a role in nearly all optical phenomena.

Finally, we emphasize that there is no fundamental distinction between *interference* and *diffraction.* In Chapter 35 we used the term *interference* for effects involving waves from a small number of sources, usually two. *Diffraction* usually involves a *continuous* distribution of Huygens's wavelets across the area of an aperture, or a very large number of sources or apertures. But both interference and diffraction are consequences of superposition and Huygens's principle.

Test Your Understanding of Section 36.1   Can *sound* waves undergo diffraction around an edge?   ❙

PhET: Wave Interference
ActivPhysics 16.6: Single-Slit Diffraction

36.2 Diffraction from a Single Slit

In this section we'll discuss the diffraction pattern formed by plane-wave (parallel-ray) monochromatic light when it emerges from a long, narrow slit, as shown in Fig. 36.3. We call the narrow dimension the *width,* even though in this figure it is a vertical dimension.

According to geometric optics, the transmitted beam should have the same cross section as the slit, as in Fig. 36.3a. What is *actually* observed is the pattern shown in Fig. 36.3b. The beam spreads out vertically after passing through the slit. The diffraction pattern consists of a central bright band, which may be much broader than the width of the slit, bordered by alternating dark and bright bands with rapidly decreasing intensity. About 85% of the power in the

36.3 (a) The "shadow" of a horizontal slit as incorrectly predicted by geometric optics. (b) A horizontal slit actually produces a diffraction pattern. The slit width has been greatly exaggerated.

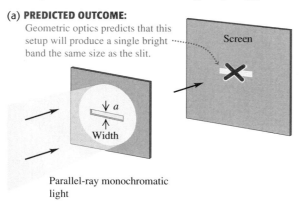

(a) **PREDICTED OUTCOME:**
Geometric optics predicts that this setup will produce a single bright band the same size as the slit.

Screen

↓ a
↑
Width

Parallel-ray monochromatic light

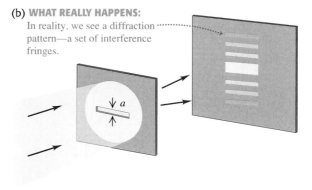

(b) **WHAT REALLY HAPPENS:**
In reality, we see a diffraction pattern—a set of interference fringes.

↓ a
↑

36.4 Diffraction by a single rectangular slit. The long sides of the slit are perpendicular to the figure.

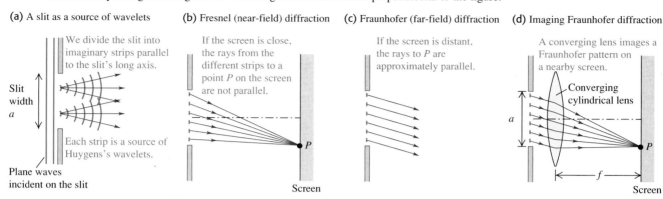

(a) A slit as a source of wavelets

We divide the slit into imaginary strips parallel to the slit's long axis.

Slit width a

Each strip is a source of Huygens's wavelets.

Plane waves incident on the slit

(b) Fresnel (near-field) diffraction

If the screen is close, the rays from the different strips to a point P on the screen are not parallel.

P

Screen

(c) Fraunhofer (far-field) diffraction

If the screen is distant, the rays to P are approximately parallel.

(d) Imaging Fraunhofer diffraction

A converging lens images a Fraunhofer pattern on a nearby screen.

Converging cylindrical lens

a

P

f

Screen

transmitted beam is in the central bright band, whose width is *inversely* proportional to the width of the slit. In general, the smaller the width of the slit, the broader the entire diffraction pattern. (The *horizontal* spreading of the beam in Fig. 36.3b is negligible because the horizontal dimension of the slit is relatively large.) You can observe a similar diffraction pattern by looking at a point source, such as a distant street light, through a narrow slit formed between your two thumbs held in front of your eye; the retina of your eye corresponds to the screen.

Single-Slit Diffraction: Locating the Dark Fringes

Figure 36.4 shows a side view of the same setup; the long sides of the slit are perpendicular to the figure, and plane waves are incident on the slit from the left. According to Huygens's principle, each element of area of the slit opening can be considered as a source of secondary waves. In particular, imagine dividing the slit into several narrow strips of equal width, parallel to the long edges and perpendicular to the page. Figure 36.4a shows two such strips. Cylindrical secondary wavelets, shown in cross section, spread out from each strip.

In Fig. 36.4b a screen is placed to the right of the slit. We can calculate the resultant intensity at a point P on the screen by adding the contributions from the individual wavelets, taking proper account of their various phases and amplitudes. It's easiest to do this calculation if we assume that the screen is far enough away that all the rays from various parts of the slit to a particular point P on the screen are parallel, as in Fig. 36.4c. An equivalent situation is Fig. 36.4d, in which the rays to the lens are parallel and the lens forms a reduced image of the same pattern that would be formed on an infinitely distant screen without the lens. We might expect that the various light paths through the lens would introduce additional phase shifts, but in fact it can be shown that all the paths have *equal* phase shifts, so this is not a problem.

The situation of Fig. 36.4b is Fresnel diffraction; those in Figs. 36.4c and 36.4d, where the outgoing rays are considered parallel, are Fraunhofer diffraction. We can derive quite simply the most important characteristics of the Fraunhofer diffraction pattern from a single slit. First consider two narrow strips, one just below the top edge of the drawing of the slit and one at its center, shown in end view in Fig. 36.5. The difference in path length to point P is $(a/2)\sin\theta$, where a is the slit width and θ is the angle between the perpendicular to the slit and a line from the center of the slit to P. Suppose this path difference happens to be equal to $\lambda/2$; then light from these two strips arrives at point P with a half-cycle phase difference, and cancellation occurs.

Similarly, light from two strips immediately *below* the two in the figure also arrives at P a half-cycle out of phase. In fact, the light from *every* strip in the top half of the slit cancels out the light from a corresponding strip in the bottom half.

36.5 Side view of a horizontal slit. When the distance x to the screen is much greater than the slit width a, the rays from a distance $a/2$ apart may be considered parallel.

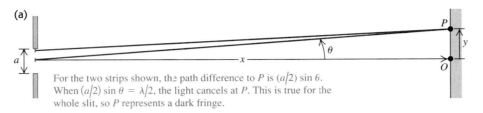

(a)

For the two strips shown, the path difference to P is $(a/2)\sin\theta$. When $(a/2)\sin\theta = \lambda/2$, the light cancels at P. This is true for the whole slit, so P represents a dark fringe.

(b) Enlarged view of the top half of the slit

θ is usually very small, so we can use the approximations $\sin\theta = \theta$ and $\tan\theta = \theta$. Then the condition for a dark band is

$$y_m = x\,\frac{m\lambda}{a}$$

Hence the combined light from the entire slit completely cancels at P, giving a dark fringe in the interference pattern. A dark fringe occurs whenever

$$\frac{a}{2}\sin\theta = \pm\frac{\lambda}{2} \quad\text{or}\quad \sin\theta = \pm\frac{\lambda}{a} \qquad (36.1)$$

The plus-or-minus $(\pm)$ sign in Eq. (36.1) says that there are symmetric dark fringes above and below point O in Fig. 36.5a. The upper fringe $(\theta > 0)$ occurs at a point P where light from the bottom half of the slit travels $\lambda/2$ farther to P than does light from the top half; the lower fringe $(\theta < 0)$ occurs where light from the *top* half travels $\lambda/2$ farther than light from the *bottom* half.

We may also divide the screen into quarters, sixths, and so on, and use the above argument to show that a dark fringe occurs whenever $\sin\theta = \pm 2\lambda/a$, $\pm 3\lambda/a$, and so on. Thus the condition for a *dark* fringe is

$$\sin\theta = \frac{m\lambda}{a} \quad (m = \pm 1,\ \pm 2,\ \pm 3,\dots) \qquad \begin{array}{l}\text{(dark fringes in single-}\\\text{slit diffraction)}\end{array} \qquad (36.2)$$

For example, if the slit width is equal to ten wavelengths $(a = 10\lambda)$, dark fringes occur at $\sin\theta = \pm\frac{1}{10},\ \pm\frac{2}{10},\ \pm\frac{3}{10},\dots$. Between the dark fringes are bright fringes. We also note that $\sin\theta = 0$ corresponds to a *bright* band; in this case, light from the entire slit arrives at P in phase. Thus it would be wrong to put $m = 0$ in Eq. (36.2). The central bright fringe is wider than the other bright fringes, as Fig. 36.3b shows. In the small-angle approximation that we will use below, it is exactly *twice* as wide.

With light, the wavelength λ is of the order of 500 nm $= 5 \times 10^{-7}$ m. This is often much smaller than the slit width a; a typical slit width is 10^{-2} cm $= 10^{-4}$ m. Therefore the values of θ in Eq. (36.2) are often so small that the approximation $\sin\theta \approx \theta$ (where θ is in radians) is a very good one. In that case we can rewrite this equation as

$$\theta = \frac{m\lambda}{a} \quad (m = \pm 1,\ \pm 2,\ \pm 3,\dots) \qquad \text{(for small angles } \theta)$$

where θ is in *radians*. Also, if the distance from slit to screen is x, as in Fig. 36.5a, and the vertical distance of the mth dark band from the center of the pattern is y_m, then $\tan\theta = y_m/x$. For small θ we may also approximate $\tan\theta$ by θ (in radians), and we then find

$$y_m = x\frac{m\lambda}{a} \qquad \text{(for } y_m \ll x\text{)} \qquad (36.3)$$

Figure 36.6 is a photograph of a single-slit diffraction pattern with the $m = \pm1$, ±2, and ±3 minima labeled.

CAUTION **Single-slit diffraction vs. two-slit interference** Equation (36.3) has the same form as the equation for the two-slit pattern, Eq. (35.6), except that in Eq. (36.3) we use x rather than R for the distance to the screen. But Eq. (36.3) gives the positions of the *dark* fringes in a *single-slit* pattern rather than the *bright* fringes in a *double-slit* pattern. Also, $m = 0$ in Eq. (36.2) is *not* a dark fringe. Be careful!

36.6 Photograph of the Fraunhofer diffraction pattern of a single horizontal slit.

$\leftarrow m = 3$
$\leftarrow m = 2$
$\leftarrow m = 1$

$\leftarrow m = -1$
$\leftarrow m = -2$
$\leftarrow m = -3$

Example 36.1 **Single-slit diffraction**

You pass 633-nm laser light through a narrow slit and observe the diffraction pattern on a screen 6.0 m away. The distance on the screen between the centers of the first minima on either side of the central bright fringe is 32 mm (Fig. 36.7). How wide is the slit?

SOLUTION

IDENTIFY and SET UP: This problem involves the relationship between the positions of dark fringes in a single-slit diffraction

36.7 A single-slit diffraction experiment.

Slit width = ?

32 mm

$x = 6.0$ m

Screen

pattern and the slit width a (our target variable). The distances between fringes on the screen are much smaller than the slit-to-screen distance, so the angle θ shown in Fig. 36.5a is very small and we can use Eq. (36.3) to solve for a.

EXECUTE: The first minimum corresponds to $m = 1$ in Eq. (36.3). The distance y_1 from the central maximum to the first minimum on either side is half the distance between the two first minima, so $y_1 = (32$ mm$)/2 = 16$ mm. Solving Eq. (36.3) for a, we find

$$a = \frac{x\lambda}{y_1} = \frac{(6.0 \text{ m})(633 \times 10^{-9} \text{ m})}{16 \times 10^{-3} \text{ m}} = 2.4 \times 10^{-4} \text{ m} = 0.24 \text{ mm}$$

EVALUATE: The angle θ is small only if the wavelength is small compared to the slit width. Since $\lambda = 633$ nm $= 6.33 \times 10^{-7}$ m and we have found $a = 0.24$ mm $= 2.4 \times 10^{-4}$ m, our result is consistent with this: The wavelength is $(6.33 \times 10^{-7} \text{ m})/(2.4 \times 10^{-4} \text{ m}) = 0.0026$ as large as the slit width. Can you show that the distance between the *second* minima on either side is $2(32$ mm$) = 64$ mm, and so on?

Test Your Understanding of Section 36.2 Rank the following single-slit diffraction experiments in order of the size of the angle from the center of the diffraction pattern to the first dark fringe, from largest to smallest: (i) wavelength 400 nm, slit width 0.20 mm; (ii) wavelength 600 nm, slit width 0.20 mm; (iii) wavelength 400 nm, slit width 0.30 mm; (iv) wavelength 600 nm, slit width 0.30 mm. ❙

36.3 Intensity in the Single-Slit Pattern

We can derive an expression for the intensity distribution for the single-slit diffraction pattern by the same phasor-addition method that we used in Section 35.3 to obtain Eqs. (35.10) and (35.14) for the two-slit interference pattern. We again imagine a plane wave front at the slit subdivided into a large number of strips. We superpose the contributions of the Huygens wavelets from all the strips at a point P on a distant screen at an angle θ from the normal to the slit plane (Fig. 36.8a). To do this, we use a phasor to represent the sinusoidally varying $\vec{E}$ field from

36.8 Using phasor diagrams to find the amplitude of the $\vec{E}$ field in single-slit diffraction. Each phasor represents the $\vec{E}$ field from a single strip within the slit.

(a)

Plane waves
incident on the slit

(b) At the center of the diffraction pattern (point O), the phasors from all strips within the slit are in phase.

(c) Phasor diagram at a point slightly off the center of the pattern; β = total phase difference between the first and last phasors.

(d) As in (c), but in the limit that the slit is subdivided into infinitely many strips

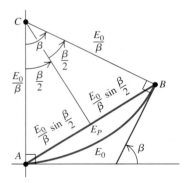

each individual strip. The magnitude of the vector sum of the phasors at each point P is the amplitude E_P of the total $\vec{E}$ field at that point. The intensity at P is proportional to $E_P{}^2$.

At the point O shown in Fig. 36.8a, corresponding to the center of the pattern where $\theta = 0$, there are negligible path differences for $x \gg a$; the phasors are all essentially *in phase* (that is, have the same direction). In Fig. 36.8b we draw the phasors at time $t = 0$ and denote the resultant amplitude at O by E_0. In this illustration we have divided the slit into 14 strips.

Now consider wavelets arriving from different strips at point P in Fig. 36.8a, at an angle θ from point O. Because of the differences in path length, there are now phase differences between wavelets coming from adjacent strips; the corresponding phasor diagram is shown in Fig. 36.8c. The vector sum of the phasors is now part of the perimeter of a many-sided polygon, and E_P, the amplitude of the resultant electric field at P, is the *chord*. The angle β is the total phase difference between the wave from the top strip of Fig. 36.8a and the wave from the bottom strip; that is, β is the phase of the wave received at P from the top strip with respect to the wave received at P from the bottom strip.

We may imagine dividing the slit into narrower and narrower strips. In the limit that there is an infinite number of infinitesimally narrow strips, the curved trail of phasors becomes an *arc of a circle* (Fig. 36.8d), with arc length equal to the length E_0 in Fig. 36.8b. The center C of this arc is found by constructing perpendiculars at A and B. From the relationship among arc length, radius, and angle, the radius of the arc is E_0/β; the amplitude E_P of the resultant electric field at P is equal to the chord AB, which is $2(E_0/\beta)\sin(\beta/2)$. (Note that β *must* be in radians!) We then have

$$E_P = E_0 \frac{\sin(\beta/2)}{\beta/2} \qquad \text{(amplitude in single-slit diffraction)} \qquad (36.4)$$

The intensity at each point on the screen is proportional to the square of the amplitude given by Eq. (36.4). If I_0 is the intensity in the straight-ahead direction where $\theta = 0$ and $\beta = 0$, then the intensity I at any point is

$$I = I_0 \left[\frac{\sin(\beta/2)}{\beta/2} \right]^2 \qquad \text{(intensity in single-slit diffraction)} \qquad (36.5)$$

We can express the phase difference β in terms of geometric quantities, as we did for the two-slit pattern. From Eq. (35.11) the phase difference is $2\pi/\lambda$ times the path difference. Figure 36.5 shows that the path difference between the ray from the top of the slit and the ray from the middle of the slit is $(a/2)\sin\theta$. The path difference between the rays from the top of the slit and the bottom of the slit is twice this, so

$$\beta = \frac{2\pi}{\lambda} a \sin\theta \qquad (36.6)$$

and Eq. (36.5) becomes

$$I = I_0 \left\{ \frac{\sin[\pi a(\sin\theta)/\lambda]}{\pi a(\sin\theta)/\lambda} \right\}^2 \qquad \text{(intensity in single-slit diffraction)} \qquad (36.7)$$

This equation expresses the intensity directly in terms of the angle θ. In many calculations it is easier first to calculate the phase angle β, using Eq. (36.6), and then to use Eq. (36.5).

Equation (36.7) is plotted in Fig. 36.9a. Note that the central intensity peak is much larger than any of the others. This means that most of the power in the wave remains within an angle θ from the perpendicular to the slit, where $\sin\theta = \lambda/a$ (the first diffraction minimum). You can see this easily in Fig. 36.9b, which is a photograph of water waves undergoing single-slit diffraction. Note also that the peak intensities in Fig. 36.9a decrease rapidly as we go away from the center of the pattern. (Compare Fig. 36.6, which shows a single-slit diffraction pattern for light.)

The dark fringes in the pattern are the places where $I = 0$. These occur at points for which the numerator of Eq. (36.5) is zero so that β is a multiple of 2π. From Eq. (36.6) this corresponds to

$$\frac{a \sin \theta}{\lambda} = m \qquad (m = \pm 1, \pm 2, \dots)$$

$$\sin \theta = \frac{m\lambda}{a} \qquad (m = \pm 1, \pm 2, \dots) \qquad (36.8)$$

This agrees with our previous result, Eq. (36.2). Note again that $\beta = 0$ (corresponding to $\theta = 0$) is *not* a minimum. Equation (36.5) is indeterminate at $\beta = 0$, but we can evaluate the limit as $\beta \to 0$ using L'Hôpital's rule. We find that at $\beta = 0$, $I = I_0$, as we should expect.

Intensity Maxima in the Single-Slit Pattern

We can also use Eq. (36.5) to calculate the positions of the peaks, or *intensity maxima,* and the intensities at these peaks. This is not quite as simple as it may appear. We might expect the peaks to occur where the sine function reaches the value ± 1—namely, where $\beta = \pm \pi$, $\pm 3\pi$, $\pm 5\pi$, or in general,

$$\beta \approx \pm(2m + 1)\pi \qquad (m = 0, 1, 2, \dots) \qquad (36.9)$$

This is *approximately* correct, but because of the factor $(\beta/2)^2$ in the denominator of Eq. (36.5), the maxima don't occur precisely at these points. When we take the derivative of Eq. (36.5) with respect to β and set it equal to zero to try to find the maxima and minima, we get a transcendental equation that has to be solved numerically. In fact there is *no* maximum near $\beta = \pm \pi$. The first maxima on either side of the central maximum, near $\beta = \pm 3\pi$, actually occur at $\pm 2.860\pi$. The second side maxima, near $\beta = \pm 5\pi$, are actually at $\pm 4.918\pi$, and so on. The error in Eq. (36.9) vanishes in the limit of large m—that is, for intensity maxima far from the center of the pattern.

To find the intensities at the side maxima, we substitute these values of β back into Eq. (36.5). Using the approximate expression in Eq. (36.9), we get

$$I_m \approx \frac{I_0}{\left(m + \frac{1}{2}\right)^2 \pi^2} \qquad (36.10)$$

where I_m is the intensity of the mth side maximum and I_0 is the intensity of the central maximum. Equation (36.10) gives the series of intensities

$$0.0450I_0 \qquad 0.0162I_0 \qquad 0.0083I_0$$

and so on. As we have pointed out, this equation is only approximately correct. The actual intensities of the side maxima turn out to be

$$0.0472I_0 \qquad 0.0165I_0 \qquad 0.0083I_0 \qquad \dots$$

Note that the intensities of the side maxima decrease very rapidly, as Fig. 36.9a also shows. Even the first side maxima have less than 5% of the intensity of the central maximum.

Width of the Single-Slit Pattern

For small angles the angular spread of the diffraction pattern is inversely proportional to the slit width a or, more precisely, to the ratio of a to the wavelength λ. Figure 36.10 shows graphs of intensity I as a function of the angle θ for three values of the ratio a/λ.

36.9 (a) Intensity versus angle in single-slit diffraction. The values of m label intensity minima given by Eq. (36.8). Most of the wave power goes into the central intensity peak (between the $m = 1$ and $m = -1$ intensity minima). (b) These water waves passing through a small aperture behave exactly like light waves in single-slit diffraction. Only the diffracted waves within the central intensity peak are visible; the waves at larger angles are too faint to see.

(a)

(b)

36.10 The single-slit diffraction pattern depends on the ratio of the slit width a to the wavelength λ.

(a) $a = \lambda$

If the slit width is equal to or narrower than the wavelength, only one broad maximum forms.

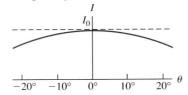

(b) $a = 5\lambda$

The wider the slit (or the shorter the wavelength), the narrower and sharper is the central peak.

(c) $a = 8\lambda$

With light waves, the wavelength λ is often much smaller than the slit width a, and the values of θ in Eqs. (36.6) and (36.7) are so small that the approximation $\sin\theta = \theta$ is very good. With this approximation the position θ_1 of the first minimum beside the central maximum, corresponding to $\beta/2 = \pi$, is, from Eq. (36.7),

$$\theta_1 = \frac{\lambda}{a} \tag{36.11}$$

This characterizes the width (angular spread) of the central maximum, and we see that it is *inversely* proportional to the slit width a. When the small-angle approximation is valid, the central maximum is exactly twice as wide as each side maximum. When a is of the order of a centimeter or more, θ_1 is so small that we can consider practically all the light to be concentrated at the geometrical focus. But when a is less than λ, the central maximum spreads over 180°, and the fringe pattern is not seen at all.

It's important to keep in mind that diffraction occurs for *all* kinds of waves, not just light. Sound waves undergo diffraction when they pass through a slit or aperture such as an ordinary doorway. The sound waves used in speech have wavelengths of about a meter or greater, and a typical doorway is less than 1 m wide; in this situation, a is less than λ, and the central intensity maximum extends over 180°. This is why the sounds coming through an open doorway can easily be heard by an eavesdropper hiding out of sight around the corner. In the same way, sound waves can bend around the head of an instructor who faces the blackboard while lecturing (Fig. 36.11). By contrast, there is essentially no diffraction of visible light through a doorway because the width a is very much greater than the wavelength λ (of order 5×10^{-7} m). You can *hear* around corners because typical sound waves have relatively long wavelengths; you cannot *see* around corners because the wavelength of visible light is very short.

36.11 The sound waves used in speech have a long wavelength (about 1 m) and can easily bend around this instructor's head. By contrast, light waves have very short wavelengths and undergo very little diffraction. Hence you can't *see* around his head!

Example 36.2 **Single-slit diffraction: Intensity I**

(a) The intensity at the center of a single-slit diffraction pattern is I_0. What is the intensity at a point in the pattern where there is a 66-radian phase difference between wavelets from the two edges of the slit? (b) If this point is 7.0° away from the central maximum, how many wavelengths wide is the slit?

SOLUTION

IDENTIFY and SET UP: In our analysis of Fig. 36.8 we used the symbol β for the phase difference between wavelets from the two edges of the slit. In part (a) we use Eq. (36.5) to find the intensity I at the point in the pattern where $\beta = 66$ rad. In part (b) we need to find the slit width a as a multiple of the wavelength λ so our target

variable is a/λ. We are given the angular position θ of the point where $\beta = 66$ rad, so we can use Eq. (36.6) to solve for a/λ.

EXECUTE: (a) We have $\beta/2 = 33$ rad, so from Eq. (36.5),

$$I = I_0\left[\frac{\sin(33\text{ rad})}{33\text{ rad}}\right]^2 = (9.2 \times 10^{-4})I_0$$

(b) From Eq. (36.6),

$$\frac{a}{\lambda} = \frac{\beta}{2\pi\sin\theta} = \frac{66\text{ rad}}{(2\pi\text{ rad})\sin 7.0°} = 86$$

For example, for 550-nm light the slit width is $a = (86)(550\text{ nm}) = 4.7 \times 10^{-5}$ m = 0.047 mm, or roughly $\frac{1}{20}$ mm.

EVALUATE: To what point in the diffraction pattern does this value of β correspond? To find out, note that $\beta = 66$ rad is approximately equal to 21π. This is an odd multiple of π, corresponding to the form $(2m + 1)\pi$ found in Eq. (36.9) for the intensity *maxima*. Hence $\beta = 66$ rad corresponds to a point near the tenth $(m = 10)$ maximum. This is well beyond the range shown in Fig. 36.9a, which shows only maxima out to $m = \pm 3$.

Example 36.3 Single-slit diffraction: Intensity II

In the experiment described in Example 36.1 (Section 36.2), the intensity at the center of the pattern is I_0. What is the intensity at a point on the screen 3.0 mm from the center of the pattern?

SOLUTION

IDENTIFY and SET UP: This is similar to Example 36.2, except that we are not given the value of the phase difference β at the point in question. We use geometry to determine the angle θ for our point and then use Eq. (36.7) to find the intensity I (the target variable).

EXECUTE: Referring to Fig. 36.5a, we have $y = 3.0$ mm and $x = 6.0$ m, so $\tan\theta = y/x = (3.0 \times 10^{-3} \text{ m})/(6.0 \text{ m}) = 5.0 \times 10^{-4}$. This is so small that the values of $\tan\theta$, $\sin\theta$, and θ (in radians) are all nearly the same. Then, using Eq. (36.7),

$$\frac{\pi a \sin\theta}{\lambda} = \frac{\pi(2.4 \times 10^{-4} \text{ m})(5.0 \times 10^{-4})}{6.33 \times 10^{-7} \text{ m}} = 0.60$$

$$I = I_0\left(\frac{\sin 0.60}{0.60}\right)^2 = 0.89 I_0$$

EVALUATE: Figure 36.9a shows that an intensity this high can occur only within the central intensity maximum. This checks out; from Example 36.1, the first intensity minimum ($m = 1$ in Fig. 36.9a) is $(32 \text{ mm})/2 = 16$ mm from the center of the pattern, so the point in question here at $y = 3$ mm does, indeed, lie within the central maximum.

Test Your Understanding of Section 36.3 Coherent electromagnetic radiation is sent through a slit of width 0.0100 mm. For which of the following wavelengths will there be *no* points in the diffraction pattern where the intensity is zero? (i) blue light of wavelength 500 nm; (ii) infrared light of wavelength 10.6 μm; (iii) microwaves of wavelength 1.00 mm; (iv) ultraviolet light of wavelength 50.0 nm.

36.4 Multiple Slits

In Sections 35.2 and 35.3 we analyzed interference from two point sources or from two very narrow slits; in this analysis we ignored effects due to the finite (that is, nonzero) slit width. In Sections 36.2 and 36.3 we considered the diffraction effects that occur when light passes through a single slit of finite width. Additional interesting effects occur when we have two slits with finite width or when there are several very narrow slits.

Two Slits of Finite Width

Let's take another look at the two-slit pattern in the more realistic case in which the slits have finite width. If the slits are narrow in comparison to the wavelength, we can assume that light from each slit spreads out uniformly in all directions to the right of the slit. We used this assumption in Section 35.3 to calculate the interference pattern described by Eq. (35.10) or (35.15), consisting of a series of equally spaced, equally intense maxima. However, when the slits have finite width, the peaks in the two-slit interference pattern are modulated by the single-slit diffraction pattern characteristic of the width of each slit.

Figure 36.12a shows the intensity in a single-slit diffraction pattern with slit width a. The *diffraction minima* are labeled by the integer $m_d = \pm 1, \pm 2, \ldots$ ("d" for "diffraction"). Figure 36.12b shows the pattern formed by two very narrow slits with distance d between slits, where d is four times as great as the single-slit width a in Fig. 36.12a; that is, $d = 4a$. The *interference maxima* are labeled by the integer $m_i = 0, \pm 1, \pm 2, \ldots$ ("i" for "interference"). We note that the spacing between adjacent minima in the single-slit pattern is four times as great as in the two-slit pattern. Now suppose we widen each of the narrow slits to the same width a as that of the single slit in Fig. 36.12a. Figure 36.12c shows the pattern

36.12 Finding the intensity pattern for two slits of finite width.

(a) Single-slit diffraction pattern for a slit width a

$m_d = -2 \quad m_d = -1 \quad 0 \quad m_d = 1 \quad m_d = 2$

(b) Two-slit interference pattern for narrow slits whose separation d is four times the width of the slit in (a)

$m_i = -8 \quad m_i = -4 \quad 0 \quad m_i = 4 \quad m_i = 8$

(c) Calculated intensity pattern for two slits of width a and separation $d = 4a$, including both interference and diffraction effects

Calculated intensity

"Envelope" of intensity function

(d) Actual photograph of the pattern calculated in (c)

For $d = 4a$, every fourth interference maximum at the sides ($m_i = \pm 4, \pm 8, ...$) is missing.

36.13 Multiple-slit diffraction. Here a lens is used to give a Fraunhofer pattern on a nearby screen, as in Fig. 36.4d.

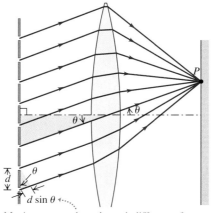

Maxima occur where the path difference for adjacent slits is a whole number of wavelengths: $d \sin\theta = m\lambda$.

from two slits with width a, separated by a distance (between centers) $d = 4a$. The effect of the finite width of the slits is to superimpose the two patterns—that is, to multiply the two intensities at each point. The two-slit peaks are in the same positions as before, but their intensities are modulated by the single-slit pattern, which acts as an "envelope" for the intensity function. The expression for the intensity shown in Fig. 36.12c is proportional to the product of the two-slit and single-slit expressions, Eqs. (35.10) and (36.5):

$$I = I_0 \cos^2\frac{\phi}{2} \left[\frac{\sin(\beta/2)}{\beta/2} \right]^2 \quad \text{(two slits of finite width)} \quad (36.12)$$

where, as before,

$$\phi = \frac{2\pi d}{\lambda}\sin\theta \qquad \beta = \frac{2\pi a}{\lambda}\sin\theta$$

Note that in Fig. 36.12c, every fourth interference maximum at the sides is *missing* because these interference maxima ($m_i = \pm 4, \pm 8, ...$) coincide with diffraction minima ($m_d = \pm 1, \pm 2, ...$). This can also be seen in Fig. 36.12d, which is a photograph of an actual pattern with $d = 4a$. You should be able to convince yourself that there will be "missing" maxima whenever d is an integer multiple of a.

Figures 36.12c and 36.12d show that as you move away from the central bright maximum of the two-slit pattern, the intensity of the maxima decreases. This is a result of the single-slit modulating pattern shown in Fig. 36.12a; mathematically, the decrease in intensity arises from the factor $(\beta/2)^2$ in the denominator of Eq. (36.12). This decrease in intensity can also be seen in Fig. 35.6 (Section 35.2). The narrower the slits, the broader the single-slit pattern (as in Fig. 36.10) and the slower the decrease in intensity from one interference maximum to the next.

Shall we call the pattern in Fig. 36.12d *interference* or *diffraction*? It's really both, since it results from the superposition of waves coming from various parts of the two apertures.

Several Slits

Next let's consider patterns produced by *several* very narrow slits. As we will see, systems of narrow slits are of tremendous practical importance in *spectroscopy,* the determination of the particular wavelengths of light coming from a source. Assume that each slit is narrow in comparison to the wavelength, so its diffraction pattern spreads out nearly uniformly. Figure 36.13 shows an array of eight narrow slits, with distance d between adjacent slits. Constructive interference occurs for rays at angle θ to the normal that arrive at point P with a path difference between adjacent slits equal to an integer number of wavelengths:

$$d\sin\theta = m\lambda \qquad (m = 0, \pm 1, \pm 2, ...)$$

This means that reinforcement occurs when the phase difference ϕ at P for light from adjacent slits is an integer multiple of 2π. That is, the maxima in the pattern occur at the *same* positions as for *two* slits with the same spacing. To this extent the pattern resembles the two-slit pattern.

But what happens *between* the maxima? In the two-slit pattern, there is exactly one intensity minimum located midway between each pair of maxima, corresponding to angles for which the phase difference between waves from the two sources is π, 3π, 5π, and so on. In the eight-slit pattern these are also minima because the light from adjacent slits cancels out in pairs, corresponding to the phasor diagram in Fig. 36.14a. But these are not the only minima in the eight-slit pattern. For example, when the phase difference ϕ from adjacent sources is $\pi/4$, the phasor diagram is as shown in Fig. 36.14b; the total (resultant) phasor is zero, and the intensity is zero. When $\phi = \pi/2$, we get the phasor diagram of Fig. 36.14c, and again both the total phasor and the intensity are zero. More

36.14 Phasor diagrams for light passing through eight narrow slits. Intensity maxima occur when the phase difference $\phi = 0, 2\pi, 4\pi, \ldots$. Between the maxima at $\phi = 0$ and $\phi = 2\pi$ are seven minima, corresponding to $\phi = \pi/4, \pi/2, 3\pi/4, \pi, 5\pi/4, 3\pi/2,$ and $7\pi/4$. Can you draw phasor diagrams for the other minima?

(a) Phasor diagram for $\phi = \pi$

(b) Phasor diagram for $\phi = \dfrac{\pi}{4}$

(c) Phasor diagram for $\phi = \dfrac{\pi}{2}$

$\phi = \pi = 180°$

$\phi = \dfrac{\pi}{4} = 45°$

$\phi = \dfrac{\pi}{2} = 90°$

generally, the intensity with eight slits is zero whenever ϕ is an integer multiple of $\pi/4$, *except* when ϕ is a multiple of 2π. Thus there are seven minima for every maximum.

Figure 36.15b shows the result of a detailed calculation of the eight-slit pattern. The large maxima, called *principal maxima,* are in the same positions as for the two-slit pattern of Fig. 36.15a but are much narrower. If the phase difference ϕ between adjacent slits is slightly different from a multiple of 2π, the waves from slits 1 and 2 will be only a little out of phase; however, the phase difference between slits 1 and 3 will be greater, that between slits 1 and 4 will be greater still, and so on. This leads to a partial cancellation for angles that are only slightly different from the angle for a maximum, giving the narrow maxima in Fig. 36.15b. The maxima are even narrower with 16 slits (Fig. 36.15c).

You should show that when there are N slits, there are $(N - 1)$ minima between each pair of principal maxima and a minimum occurs whenever ϕ is an integral multiple of $2\pi/N$ (except when ϕ is an integral multiple of 2π, which gives a principal maximum). There are small *secondary* intensity maxima between the minima; these become smaller in comparison to the principal maxima as N increases. The greater the value of N, the narrower the principal maxima become. From an energy standpoint the total power in the entire pattern is proportional to N. The height of each principal maximum is proportional to N^2, so from energy conservation the width of each principal maximum must be proportional to $1/N$. As we will see in the next section, the narrowness of the principal maxima in a multiple-slit pattern is of great practical importance.

Test Your Understanding of Section 36.4 Suppose two slits, each of width a, are separated by a distance $d = 2.5a$. Are there any missing maxima in the interference pattern produced by these slits? If so, which are missing? If not, why not? ❙

36.5 **The Diffraction Grating**

We have just seen that increasing the number of slits in an interference experiment (while keeping the spacing of adjacent slits constant) gives interference patterns in which the maxima are in the same positions, but progressively narrower, than with two slits. Because these maxima are so narrow, their angular position, and hence the wavelength, can be measured to very high precision. As we will see, this effect has many important applications.

An array of a large number of parallel slits, all with the same width a and spaced equal distances d between centers, is called a **diffraction grating.** The first one was constructed by Fraunhofer using fine wires. Gratings can be made by using a diamond point to scratch many equally spaced grooves on a glass or metal surface,

36.15 Interference patterns for N equally spaced, very narrow slits. (a) Two slits. (b) Eight slits. (c) Sixteen slits. The vertical scales are different for each graph; I_0 is the maximum intensity for a single slit, and the maximum intensity for N slits is $N^2 I_0$. The width of each peak is proportional to $1/N$.

(a) $N = 2$: two slits produce one minimum between adjacent maxima.

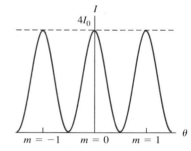

(b) $N = 8$: eight slits produce taller, narrower maxima in the same locations, separated by seven minima.

(c) $N = 16$: with 16 slits, the maxima are even taller and narrower, with more intervening minima.

36.16 A portion of a transmission diffraction grating. The separation between the centers of adjacent slits is d.

MasteringPHYSICS

ActivPhysics 16.4: The Grating: Introduction and Questions
ActivPhysics 16.5: The Grating: Problems

36.17 Microscopic pits on the surface of this DVD act as a reflection grating, splitting white light into its component colors.

or by photographic reduction of a pattern of black and white stripes on paper. For a grating, what we have been calling *slits* are often called *rulings* or *lines*.

In Fig. 36.16, GG' is a cross section of a *transmission grating;* the slits are perpendicular to the plane of the page, and an interference pattern is formed by the light that is transmitted through the slits. The diagram shows only six slits; an actual grating may contain several thousand. The spacing d between centers of adjacent slits is called the *grating spacing*. A plane monochromatic wave is incident normally on the grating from the left side. We assume far-field (Fraunhofer) conditions; that is, the pattern is formed on a screen that is far enough away that all rays emerging from the grating and going to a particular point on the screen can be considered to be parallel.

We found in Section 36.4 that the principal intensity maxima with multiple slits occur in the same directions as for the two-slit pattern. These are the directions for which the path difference for adjacent slits is an integer number of wavelengths. So the positions of the maxima are once again given by

$$d\sin\theta = m\lambda \qquad (m = 0, \pm1, \pm2, \pm3, \dots) \qquad \text{(intensity maxima, multiple slits)} \qquad (36.13)$$

The intensity patterns for two, eight, and 16 slits displayed in Fig. 36.15 show the progressive increase in sharpness of the maxima as the number of slits increases.

When a grating containing hundreds or thousands of slits is illuminated by a beam of parallel rays of monochromatic light, the pattern is a series of very sharp lines at angles determined by Eq. (36.13). The $m = \pm1$ lines are called the *first-order lines,* the $m = \pm2$ lines the *second-order lines,* and so on. If the grating is illuminated by white light with a continuous distribution of wavelengths, each value of m corresponds to a continuous spectrum in the pattern. The angle for each wavelength is determined by Eq. (36.13); for a given value of m, long wavelengths (the red end of the spectrum) lie at larger angles (that is, are deviated more from the straight-ahead direction) than do the shorter wavelengths at the violet end of the spectrum.

As Eq. (36.13) shows, the sines of the deviation angles of the maxima are proportional to the ratio λ/d. For substantial deviation to occur, the grating spacing d should be of the same order of magnitude as the wavelength λ. Gratings for use with visible light (λ from 400 to 700 nm) usually have about 1000 slits per millimeter; the value of d is the *reciprocal* of the number of slits per unit length, so d is of the order of $\frac{1}{1000}$ mm $= 1000$ nm.

In a *reflection grating,* the array of equally spaced slits shown in Fig. 36.16 is replaced by an array of equally spaced ridges or grooves on a reflective screen. The reflected light has maximum intensity at angles where the phase difference between light waves reflected from adjacent ridges or grooves is an integral multiple of 2π. If light of wavelength λ is incident normally on a reflection grating with a spacing d between adjacent ridges or grooves, the *reflected* angles at which intensity maxima occur are given by Eq. (36.13).

The rainbow-colored reflections from the surface of a DVD are a reflection-grating effect (Fig. 36.17). The "grooves" are tiny pits 0.12 μm deep in the surface of the disc, with a uniform radial spacing of 0.74 μm $= 740$ nm. Information is coded on the DVD by varying the *length* of the pits. The reflection-grating aspect of the disc is merely an aesthetic side benefit.

Example 36.4 **Width of a grating spectrum**

The wavelengths of the visible spectrum are approximately 380 nm (violet) to 750 nm (red). (a) Find the angular limits of the first-order visible spectrum produced by a plane grating with 600 slits per millimeter when white light falls normally on the grating.

(b) Do the first-order and second-order spectra overlap? What about the second-order and third-order spectra? Do your answers depend on the grating spacing?

SOLUTION

IDENTIFY and SET UP: We must find the angles spanned by the visible spectrum in the first-, second-, and third-order spectra. These correspond to $m = 1, 2,$ and 3 in Eq. (36.13).

EXECUTE: (a) The grating spacing is

$$d = \frac{1}{600 \text{ slits/mm}} = 1.67 \times 10^{-6} \text{ m}$$

We solve Eq. (36.13) for θ:

$$\theta = \arcsin \frac{m\lambda}{d}$$

Then for $m = 1$, the angular deviations θ_{v1} and θ_{r1} for violet and red light, respectively, are

$$\theta_{v1} = \arcsin\left(\frac{380 \times 10^{-9} \text{ m}}{1.67 \times 10^{-6} \text{ m}}\right) = 13.2°$$

$$\theta_{r1} = \arcsin\left(\frac{750 \times 10^{-9} \text{ m}}{1.67 \times 10^{-6} \text{ m}}\right) = 26.7°$$

That is, the first-order visible spectrum appears with deflection angles from $\theta_{v1} = 13.2°$ (violet) to $\theta_{r1} = 26.7°$ (red).

(b) With $m = 2$ and $m = 3$, our equation $\theta = \arcsin(m\lambda/d)$ for 380-mm violet light yields

$$\theta_{v2} = \arcsin\left(\frac{2(380 \times 10^{-9} \text{ m})}{1.67 \times 10^{-6} \text{ m}}\right) = 27.1°$$

$$\theta_{v3} = \arcsin\left(\frac{3(380 \times 10^{-9} \text{ m})}{1.67 \times 10^{-6} \text{ m}}\right) = 43.0°$$

For 750-nm red light, this same equation gives

$$\theta_{r2} = \arcsin\left(\frac{2(750 \times 10^{-9} \text{ m})}{1.67 \times 10^{-6} \text{ m}}\right) = 63.9°$$

$$\theta_{r3} = \arcsin\left(\frac{3(750 \times 10^{-9} \text{ m})}{1.67 \times 10^{-6} \text{ m}}\right) = \arcsin(1.35) = \text{undefined}$$

Hence the second-order spectrum extends from 27.1° to 63.9° and the third-order spectrum extends from 43.0° to 90° (the largest possible value of θ). The undefined value of θ_{r3} means that the third-order spectrum reaches $\theta = 90° = \arcsin(1)$ at a wavelength shorter than 750 nm; you should be able to show that this happens for $\lambda = 557$ nm. Hence the first-order spectrum (from 13.2° to 26.7°) does not overlap with the second-order spectrum, but the second- and third-order spectra do overlap. You can convince yourself that this is true for any value of the grating spacing d.

EVALUATE: The fundamental reason the first-order and second-order visible spectra don't overlap is that the human eye is sensitive to only a narrow range of wavelengths. Can you show that if the eye could detect wavelengths from 380 nm to 900 nm (in the near-infrared range), the first and second orders *would* overlap?

Grating Spectrographs

Diffraction gratings are widely used to measure the spectrum of light emitted by a source, a process called *spectroscopy* or *spectrometry*. Light incident on a grating of known spacing is dispersed into a spectrum. The angles of deviation of the maxima are then measured, and Eq. (36.13) is used to compute the wavelength. With a grating that has many slits, very sharp maxima are produced, and the angle of deviation (and hence the wavelength) can be measured very precisely.

An important application of this technique is to astronomy. As light generated within the sun passes through the sun's atmosphere, certain wavelengths are selectively absorbed. The result is that the spectrum of sunlight produced by a diffraction grating has dark *absorption lines* (Fig. 36.18). Experiments in the laboratory show that different types of atoms and ions absorb light of different wavelengths. By comparing these laboratory results with the wavelengths of absorption lines in the spectrum of sunlight, astronomers can deduce the chemical composition of the sun's atmosphere. The same technique is used to make chemical assays of galaxies that are millions of light-years away.

Figure 36.19 shows one design for a *grating spectrograph* used in astronomy. A transmission grating is used in the figure; in other setups, a reflection grating is used. In older designs a prism was used rather than a grating, and a spectrum was formed by dispersion (see Section 33.4) rather than diffraction. However, there is no simple relationship between wavelength and angle of deviation for a prism, prisms absorb some of the light that passes through them, and they are less effective for many nonvisible wavelengths that are important in astronomy. For these and other reasons, gratings are preferred in precision applications.

36.18 (a) A visible-light photograph of the sun. (b) Sunlight is dispersed into a spectrum by a diffraction grating. Specific wavelengths are absorbed as sunlight passes through the sun's atmosphere, leaving dark lines in the spectrum.

(a)

(b)

Resolution of a Grating Spectrograph

In spectroscopy it is often important to distinguish slightly differing wavelengths. The minimum wavelength difference $\Delta\lambda$ that can be distinguished by a spectrograph is described by the **chromatic resolving power** R, defined as

36.19 A schematic diagram of a diffraction-grating spectrograph for use in astronomy. Note that the light does not strike the grating normal to its surface, so the intensity maxima are given by a somewhat different expression than Eq. (36.13). (See Problem 36.64.)

① Light from telescope is sent along fiber-optic cables (not shown) and emerges here.

⑥ An electronic detector (like the one in a digital camera) records the spectrum.

② Light strikes concave mirror and emerges as a beam of parallel rays.

③ Light passes through diffraction grating.

④ Lenses direct diffracted light onto a second concave mirror.

⑤ Concave mirror reflects light to a focus.

$$R = \frac{\lambda}{\Delta\lambda} \qquad \text{(chromatic resolving power)} \qquad (36.14)$$

As an example, when sodium atoms are heated, they emit strongly at the yellow wavelengths 589.00 nm and 589.59 nm. A spectrograph that can barely distinguish these two lines in the spectrum (called the *sodium doublet*) has a chromatic resolving power $R = (589.00 \text{ nm})/(0.59 \text{ nm}) = 1000$. (You can see these wavelengths when boiling water on a gas range. If the water boils over onto the flame, dissolved sodium from table salt emits a burst of yellow light.)

We can derive an expression for the resolving power of a diffraction grating used in a spectrograph. Two different wavelengths give diffraction maxima at slightly different angles. As a reasonable (though arbitrary) criterion, let's assume that we can distinguish them as two separate peaks if the maximum of one coincides with the first minimum of the other.

From our discussion in Section 36.4 the mth-order maximum occurs when the phase difference ϕ for adjacent slits is $\phi = 2\pi m$. The first minimum beside that maximum occurs when $\phi = 2\pi m + 2\pi/N$, where N is the number of slits. The phase difference is also given by $\phi = (2\pi d \sin\theta)/\lambda$, so the angular interval $d\theta$ corresponding to a small increment $d\phi$ in the phase shift can be obtained from the differential of this equation:

$$d\phi = \frac{2\pi d \cos\theta \, d\theta}{\lambda}$$

When $d\phi = 2\pi/N$, this corresponds to the angular interval $d\theta$ between a maximum and the first adjacent minimum. Thus $d\theta$ is given by

$$\frac{2\pi}{N} = \frac{2\pi d \cos\theta \, d\theta}{\lambda} \qquad \text{or} \qquad d\cos\theta \, d\theta = \frac{\lambda}{N}$$

CAUTION **Watch out for different uses of the symbol d** Don't confuse the spacing d with the differential "d" in the angular interval $d\theta$ or in the phase shift increment $d\phi$! ❚

Now we need to find the angular spacing $d\theta$ between maxima for two slightly different wavelengths. We have $d\sin\theta = m\lambda$, so the differential of this equation gives

$$d\cos\theta \, d\theta = m \, d\lambda$$

According to our criterion, the limit or resolution is reached when these two angular spacings are equal. Equating the two expressions for the quantity $(d\cos\theta\,d\theta)$, we find

$$\frac{\lambda}{N} = m\,d\lambda \qquad \text{and} \qquad \frac{\lambda}{d\lambda} = Nm$$

If $\Delta\lambda$ is small, we can replace $d\lambda$ by $\Delta\lambda$, and the resolving power R is given by

$$R = \frac{\lambda}{\Delta\lambda} = Nm \tag{36.15}$$

The greater the number of slits N, the better the resolution; also, the higher the order m of the diffraction-pattern maximum that we use, the better the resolution.

Test Your Understanding of Section 36.5 What minimum number of slits would be required in a grating to resolve the sodium doublet in the fourth order? (i) 250; (ii) 400; (iii) 1000; (iv) 4000.

36.6 X-Ray Diffraction

X rays were discovered by Wilhelm Röntgen (1845–1923) in 1895, and early experiments suggested that they were electromagnetic waves with wavelengths of the order of 10^{-10} m. At about the same time, the idea began to emerge that in a crystalline solid the atoms are arranged in a regular repeating pattern, with spacing between adjacent atoms also of the order of 10^{-10} m. Putting these two ideas together, Max von Laue (1879–1960) proposed in 1912 that a crystal might serve as a kind of three-dimensional diffraction grating for x rays. That is, a beam of x rays might be scattered (that is, absorbed and re-emitted) by the individual atoms in a crystal, and the scattered waves might interfere just like waves from a diffraction grating.

The first **x-ray diffraction** experiments were performed in 1912 by Friederich, Knipping, and von Laue, using the experimental setup shown in Fig. 36.20a. The scattered x rays *did* form an interference pattern, which they recorded on photographic film. Figure 36.20b is a photograph of such a pattern. These experiments verified that x rays *are* waves, or at least have wavelike properties, and also that the atoms in a crystal *are* arranged in a regular pattern (Fig. 36.21). Since that time, x-ray diffraction has proved to be an invaluable research tool, both for measuring x-ray wavelengths and for studying the structure of crystals and complex molecules.

36.20 (a) An x-ray diffraction experiment. (b) Diffraction pattern (or *Laue pattern*) formed by directing a beam of x rays at a thin section of quartz crystal.

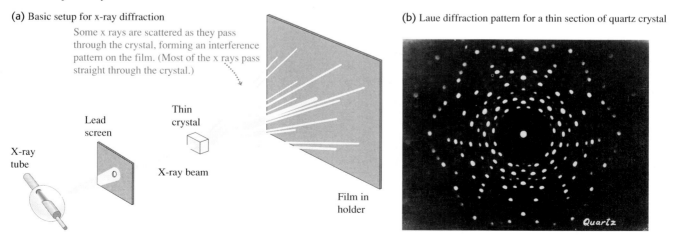

(a) Basic setup for x-ray diffraction

Some x rays are scattered as they pass through the crystal, forming an interference pattern on the film. (Most of the x rays pass straight through the crystal.)

Lead screen

Thin crystal

X-ray tube

X-ray beam

Film in holder

(b) Laue diffraction pattern for a thin section of quartz crystal

Quartz

36.21 Model of the arrangement of ions in a crystal of NaCl (table salt). The spacing of adjacent atoms is 0.282 nm. (The electron clouds of the atoms actually overlap slightly.)

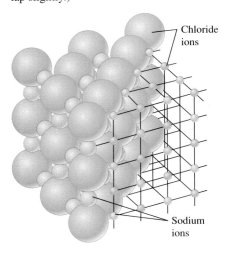

Chloride ions

Sodium ions

A Simple Model of X-Ray Diffraction

To better understand x-ray diffraction, we consider first a two-dimensional scattering situation, as shown in Fig. 36.22a, in which a plane wave is incident on a rectangular array of scattering centers. The situation might be a ripple tank with an array of small posts, 3-cm microwaves striking an array of small conducting spheres, or x rays incident on an array of atoms. In the case of electromagnetic waves, the wave induces an oscillating electric dipole moment in each scatterer. These dipoles act like little antennas, emitting scattered waves. The resulting interference pattern is the superposition of all these scattered waves. The situation is different from that with a diffraction grating, in which the waves from all the slits are emitted *in phase* (for a plane wave at normal incidence). Here the scattered waves are *not* all in phase because their distances from the *source* are different. To compute the interference pattern, we have to consider the *total* path differences for the scattered waves, including the distances from source to scatterer and from scatterer to observer.

As Fig. 36.22b shows, the path length from source to observer is the same for all the scatterers in a single row if the two angles θ_a and θ_r are equal. Scattered radiation from *adjacent* rows is *also* in phase if the path difference for adjacent rows is an integer number of wavelengths. Figure 36.22c shows that this path difference is $2d \sin \theta$, where θ is the common value of θ_a and θ_r. Therefore the conditions for radiation from the *entire* array to reach the observer in phase are (1) the angle of incidence must equal the angle of scattering and (2) the path difference for adjacent rows must equal $m\lambda$, where m is an integer. We can express the second condition as

$$2d \sin \theta = m\lambda \qquad (m = 1, 2, 3, \dots)$$

(Bragg condition for constructive interference from an array) (36.16)

CAUTION **Scattering from an array** In Eq. (36.16) the angle θ is measured with respect to the *surface* of the crystal, rather than with respect to the *normal* to the plane of an array of slits or a grating. Also, note that the path difference in Eq. (36.16) is $2d \sin \theta$, not $d \sin \theta$ as in Eq. (36.13) for a diffraction grating.

In directions for which Eq. (36.16) is satisfied, we see a strong maximum in the interference pattern. We can describe this interference in terms of *reflections* of the wave from the horizontal rows of scatterers in Fig. 36.22a. Strong reflection (constructive interference) occurs at angles such that the incident and scattered angles are equal and Eq. (36.16) is satisfied. Since $\sin \theta$ can never be greater than 1, Eq. (36.16) says that to have constructive interference the quantity $m\lambda$

36.22 A two-dimensional model of scattering from a rectangular array. Note that the angles in (b) are measured from the *surface* of the array, not from its normal.

(a) Scattering of waves from a rectangular array

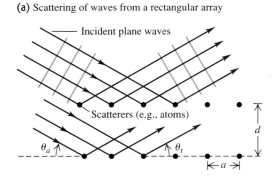

Incident plane waves

Scatterers (e.g., atoms)

(b) Scattering from adjacent atoms in a row
Interference from adjacent atoms in a row is constructive when the path lengths $a \cos \theta_a$ and $a \cos \theta_r$ are equal, so that the angle of incidence θ_a equals the angle of reflection (scattering) θ_r.

$a \cos \theta_a$ $a \cos \theta_r$

(c) Scattering from atoms in adjacent rows
Interference from atoms in adjacent rows is constructive when the path difference $2d \sin \theta$ is an integral number of wavelengths, as in Eq. (36.16).

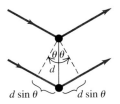

$d \sin \theta$ $d \sin \theta$

36.23 A cubic crystal and two different families of crystal planes. There are also three sets of planes parallel to the cube faces, with spacing a.

(a) Spacing of planes is $d = a/\sqrt{2}$.

(b) Spacing of planes is $d = a/\sqrt{3}$.

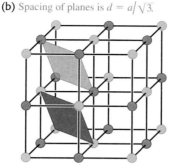

must be less than $2d$ and so λ must be less than $2d/m$. For example, the value of d in an NaCl crystal (see Fig. 36.21) is only 0.282 nm. Hence to have the mth-order maximum present in the diffraction pattern, λ must be less than $2(0.282\text{ nm})/m$; that is, $\lambda < 0.564$ nm for $m = 1$, $\lambda < 0.282$ nm for $m = 2$, $\lambda < 0.188$ nm for $m = 3$, and so on. These are all x-ray wavelengths (see Fig. 32.4), which is why x rays are used for studying crystal structure.

We can extend this discussion to a three-dimensional array by considering *planes* of scatterers instead of *rows*. Figure 36.23 shows two different sets of parallel planes that pass through all the scatterers. Waves from all the scatterers in a given plane interfere constructively if the angles of incidence and scattering are equal. There is also constructive interference between planes when Eq. (36.16) is satisfied, where d is now the distance between adjacent planes. Because there are many different sets of parallel planes, there are also many values of d and many sets of angles that give constructive interference for the whole crystal lattice. This phenomenon is called **Bragg reflection,** and Eq. (36.16) is called the **Bragg condition,** in honor of Sir William Bragg and his son Laurence Bragg, two pioneers in x-ray analysis.

CAUTION   **Bragg *reflection* is really Bragg *interference*** While we are using the term *reflection,* remember that we are dealing with an *interference* effect. In fact, the reflections from various planes are closely analogous to interference effects in thin films (see Section 35.4). |

As Fig. 36.20b shows, in x-ray diffraction there is nearly complete cancellation in all but certain very specific directions in which constructive interference occurs and forms bright spots. Such a pattern is usually called an x-ray *diffraction* pattern, although *interference* pattern might be more appropriate.

We can determine the wavelength of x rays by examining the diffraction pattern for a crystal of known structure and known spacing between atoms, just as we determined wavelengths of visible light by measuring patterns from slits or gratings. (The spacing between atoms in simple crystals of known structure, such as sodium chloride, can be found from the density of the crystal and Avogadro's number.) Then, once we know the x-ray wavelength, we can use x-ray diffraction to explore the structure and determine the spacing between atoms in crystals with unknown structure.

X-ray diffraction is by far the most important experimental tool in the investigation of crystal structure of solids. X-ray diffraction also plays an important role in studies of the structures of liquids and of organic molecules. It has been one of the chief experimental techniques in working out the double-helix structure of DNA (Fig. 36.24) and subsequent advances in molecular genetics.

36.24 The British scientist Rosalind Franklin made this groundbreaking x-ray diffraction image of DNA in 1953. The dark bands arranged in a cross provided the first evidence of the helical structure of the DNA molecule.

Example 36.5   X-ray diffraction

You direct a beam of 0.154-nm x rays at certain planes of a silicon crystal. As you increase the angle of incidence of the beam from zero, the first strong interference maximum occurs when the beam makes an angle of 34.5° with the planes. (a) How far apart are the planes? (b) Will you find other interference maxima from these planes at greater angles of incidence?

SOLUTION

IDENTIFY and SET UP: This problem involves Bragg reflection of x rays from the planes of a crystal. In part (a) we use the Bragg condition, Eq. (36.16), to find the distance d between adjacent planes from the known wavelength $\lambda = 0.154$ nm and angle of incidence $\theta = 34.5°$ for the $m = 1$ interference maximum. Given the value of d, we use the Bragg condition again in part (b) to find the values of θ for interference maxima corresponding to other values of m.

EXECUTE: (a) We solve Eq. (36.16) for d and set $m = 1$:

$$d = \frac{m\lambda}{2\sin\theta} = \frac{(1)(0.154 \text{ nm})}{2\sin 34.5°} = 0.136 \text{ nm}$$

This is the distance between adjacent planes.

(b) To calculate other angles, we solve Eq. (36.16) for $\sin\theta$:

$$\sin\theta = \frac{m\lambda}{2d} = m\frac{0.154 \text{ nm}}{2(0.136 \text{ nm})} = m(0.566)$$

Values of m of 2 or greater give values of $\sin\theta$ greater than unity, which is impossible. Hence there are *no* other angles for interference maxima for this particular set of crystal planes.

EVALUATE: Our result in part (b) shows that there *would* be a second interference maximum if the quantity $2\lambda/2d = \lambda/d$ were less than 1. This would be the case if the wavelength of the x rays were less than $d = 0.136$ nm. How short would the wavelength need to be to have *three* interference maxima?

Test Your Understanding of Section 36.6   You are doing an x-ray diffraction experiment with a crystal in which the atomic planes are 0.200 nm apart. You are using x rays of wavelength 0.100 nm. Will the fifth-order maximum be present in the diffraction pattern? |

ActivPhysics 16.7: Circular Hole Diffraction
ActivPhysics 16.8: Resolving Power

36.7 Circular Apertures and Resolving Power

We have studied in detail the diffraction patterns formed by long, thin slits or arrays of slits. But an aperture of *any* shape forms a diffraction pattern. The diffraction pattern formed by a *circular* aperture is of special interest because of its role in limiting how well an optical instrument can resolve fine details. In principle, we could compute the intensity at any point P in the diffraction pattern by dividing the area of the aperture into small elements, finding the resulting wave amplitude and phase at P, and then integrating over the aperture area to find the resultant amplitude and intensity at P. In practice, the integration cannot be carried out in terms of elementary functions. We will simply *describe* the pattern and quote a few relevant numbers.

The diffraction pattern formed by a circular aperture consists of a central bright spot surrounded by a series of bright and dark rings, as Fig. 36.25 shows.

36.25 Diffraction pattern formed by a circular aperture of diameter D. The pattern consists of a central bright spot and alternating dark and bright rings. The angular radius θ_1 of the first dark ring is shown. (This diagram is not drawn to scale.)

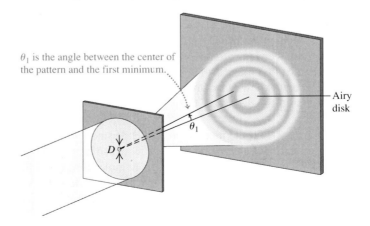

We can describe the pattern in terms of the angle θ, representing the angular radius of each ring. If the aperture diameter is D and the wavelength is λ, the angular radius θ_1 of the first *dark* ring is given by

$$\sin\theta_1 = 1.22\frac{\lambda}{D} \qquad \text{(diffraction by a circular aperture)} \qquad (36.17)$$

The angular radii of the next two dark rings are given by

$$\sin\theta_2 = 2.23\frac{\lambda}{D} \qquad \sin\theta_3 = 3.24\frac{\lambda}{D} \qquad (36.18)$$

Between these are bright rings with angular radii given by

$$\sin\theta = 1.63\frac{\lambda}{D}, \qquad 2.68\frac{\lambda}{D}, \qquad 3.70\frac{\lambda}{D} \qquad (36.19)$$

and so on. The central bright spot is called the **Airy disk,** in honor of Sir George Airy (1801–1892), Astronomer Royal of England, who first derived the expression for the intensity in the pattern. The angular radius of the Airy disk is that of the first dark ring, given by Eq. (36.17).

The intensities in the bright rings drop off very quickly with increasing angle. When D is much larger than the wavelength λ, the usual case for optical instruments, the peak intensity in the first ring is only 1.7% of the value at the center of the Airy disk, and the peak intensity of the second ring is only 0.4%. Most (85%) of the light energy falls within the Airy disk. Figure 36.26 shows a diffraction pattern from a circular aperture.

Diffraction and Image Formation

Diffraction has far-reaching implications for image formation by lenses and mirrors. In our study of optical instruments in Chapter 34 we assumed that a lens with focal length f focuses a parallel beam (plane wave) to a *point* at a distance f from the lens. This assumption ignored diffraction effects. We now see that what we get is not a point but the diffraction pattern just described. If we have two point objects, their images are not two points but two diffraction patterns. When the objects are close together, their diffraction patterns overlap; if they are close enough, their patterns overlap almost completely and cannot be distinguished. The effect is shown in Fig. 36.27, which presents the patterns for four very small "point" sources of light. In Fig. 36.27a the image of the left-hand source is well separated from the others, but the images of the middle and right-hand sources have merged. In Fig. 36.27b, with a larger aperture diameter and hence smaller Airy disks, the middle and right-hand images are better resolved. In Fig. 36.27c, with a still larger aperture, they are well resolved.

A widely used criterion for resolution of two point objects, proposed by the English physicist Lord Rayleigh (1842–1919) and called **Rayleigh's criterion,** is that the objects are just barely resolved (that is, distinguishable) if the center of one diffraction pattern coincides with the first minimum of the other. In that case the angular separation of the image centers is given by Eq. (36.17). The angular separation of the *objects* is the same as that of the *images* made by a telescope, microscope, or other optical device. So two point objects are barely resolved, according to Rayleigh's criterion, when their angular separation is given by Eq. (36.17).

The minimum separation of two objects that can just be resolved by an optical instrument is called the **limit of resolution** of the instrument. The smaller the limit of resolution, the greater the *resolution,* or **resolving power,** of the instrument. Diffraction sets the ultimate limits on resolution of lenses. *Geometric optics* may make it seem that we can make images as large as we like. Eventually, though, we always reach a point at which the image becomes larger but does not

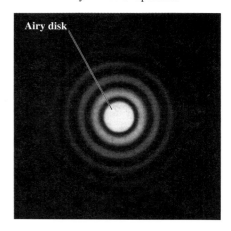

36.26 Photograph of the diffraction pattern formed by a circular aperture.

Airy disk

36.27 Diffraction patterns of four very small ("point") sources of light. The photographs were made with a circular aperture in front of the lens. **(a)** The aperture is so small that the patterns of sources 3 and 4 overlap and are barely resolved by Rayleigh's criterion. Increasing the size of the aperture decreases the size of the diffraction patterns, as shown in **(b)** and **(c)**.

(a) Small aperture

(b) Medium aperture

(c) Large aperture

gain in detail. The images in Fig. 36.27 would not become sharper with further enlargement.

CAUTION **Resolving power vs. chromatic resolving power** Be careful not to confuse the resolving power of an optical instrument with the *chromatic* resolving power of a grating (described in Section 36.5). Resolving power refers to the ability to distinguish the images of objects that appear close to each other, when looking either through an optical instrument or at a photograph made with the instrument. Chromatic resolving power describes how well different wavelengths can be distinguished in a spectrum formed by a diffraction grating.

Rayleigh's criterion combined with Eq. (36.17) shows that resolution (resolving power) improves with larger diameter; it also improves with shorter wavelengths. Ultraviolet microscopes have higher resolution than visible-light microscopes. In electron microscopes the resolution is limited by the wavelengths associated with the electrons, which have wavelike aspects (to be discussed further in Chapter 39). These wavelengths can be made 100,000 times smaller than wavelengths of visible light, with a corresponding gain in resolution. Resolving power also explains the difference in storage capacity between DVDs (introduced in 1995) and Blu-ray discs (introduced in 2003). Information is stored in both of these in a series of tiny pits. In order not to lose information in the scanning process, the scanning optics must be able to resolve two adjacent pits so that they do not seem to blend into a single pit (see sources 3 and 4 in Fig. 36.27). The blue scanning laser used in a Blu-ray player has a shorter wavelength (405 nm) and hence better resolving power than the 650-nm red laser in a DVD player. Hence pits can be spaced closer together in a Blu-ray disc than in a DVD, and more information can be stored on a disc of the same size (50 gigabytes on a Blu-ray disc versus 4.7 gigabytes on a DVD).

Example 36.6   Resolving power of a camera lens

A camera lens with focal length $f = 50$ mm and maximum aperture $f/2$ forms an image of an object 9.0 m away. (a) If the resolution is limited by diffraction, what is the minimum distance between two points on the object that are barely resolved? What is the corresponding distance between image points? (b) How does the situation change if the lens is "stopped down" to $f/16$? Use $\lambda = 500$ nm in both cases.

SOLUTION

IDENTIFY and SET UP: This example uses the ideas about resolving power, image formation by a lens (Section 34.4), and f-number (Section 34.5). From Eq. (34.20), the f-number of a lens is its focal length f divided by the aperture diameter D. We use this equation to determine D and then use Eq. (36.17) (the Rayleigh criterion) to find the angular separation θ between two barely resolved points on the object. We then use the geometry of image formation by a lens to determine the distance y between those points and the distance y' between the corresponding image points.

EXECUTE: (a) The aperture diameter is $D = f/(f\text{-number}) = (50\text{ mm})/2 = 25$ mm $= 25 \times 10^{-3}$ m. From Eq. (36.17) the angular separation θ of two object points that are barely resolved is

$$\theta \approx \sin\theta = 1.22\frac{\lambda}{D} = 1.22\frac{500 \times 10^{-9}\text{ m}}{25 \times 10^{-3}\text{ m}} = 2.4 \times 10^{-5}\text{ rad}$$

We know from our thin-lens analysis in Section 34.4 that, apart from sign, $y/s = y'/s'$ [see Eq. (34.14)]. Thus the angular separations of the object points and the corresponding image points are both equal to θ. Because the object distance s is much greater than the focal length $f = 50$ mm, the image distance s' is approximately equal to f. Thus

$$\frac{y}{9.0\text{ m}} = 2.4 \times 10^{-5} \qquad y = 2.2 \times 10^{-4}\text{ m} = 0.22\text{ mm}$$

$$\frac{y'}{50\text{ mm}} = 2.4 \times 10^{-5} \qquad y' = 1.2 \times 10^{-3}\text{ mm}$$

$$= 0.0012\text{ mm} \approx \tfrac{1}{800}\text{ mm}$$

(b) The aperture diameter is now $(50\text{ mm})/16$, or one-eighth as large as before. The angular separation between barely resolved points is eight times as great, and the values of y and y' are also eight times as great as before:

$$y = 1.8\text{ mm} \qquad y' = 0.0096\text{ mm} = \tfrac{1}{100}\text{ mm}$$

Only the best camera lenses can approach this resolving power.

EVALUATE: Many photographers use the smallest possible aperture for maximum sharpness, since lens aberrations cause light rays that are far from the optic axis to converge to a different image point than do rays near the axis. But as this example shows, diffraction effects become more significant at small apertures. One cause of fuzzy images has to be balanced against another.

Test Your Understanding of Section 36.7 You have been asked to compare four different proposals for telescopes to be placed in orbit, above the blurring effects of the earth's atmosphere. Rank the proposed telescopes in order of their ability to resolve small details, from best to worst. (i) a radio telescope 100 m in diameter observing at a wavelength of 21 cm; (ii) an optical telescope 2.0 m in diameter observing at a wavelength of 500 nm; (iii) an ultraviolet telescope 1.0 m in diameter observing at a wavelength of 100 nm; (iv) an infrared telescope 2.0 m in diameter observing at a wavelength of 10 μm. ❙

36.8 Holography

Holography is a technique for recording and reproducing an image of an object through the use of interference effects. Unlike the two-dimensional images recorded by an ordinary photograph or television system, a holographic image is truly three-dimensional. Such an image can be viewed from different directions to reveal different sides and from various distances to reveal changing perspective. If you had never seen a hologram, you wouldn't believe it was possible!

Figure 36.28a shows the basic procedure for making a hologram. We illuminate the object to be holographed with monochromatic light, and we place a photographic film so that it is struck by scattered light from the object and also by direct light from the source. In practice, the light source must be a laser, for reasons we will discuss later. Interference between the direct and scattered light leads to the formation and recording of a complex interference pattern on the film.

To form the images, we simply project light through the developed film (Fig. 36.28b). Two images are formed: a virtual image on the side of the film nearer the source and a real image on the opposite side.

Holography and Interference Patterns

A complete analysis of holography is beyond our scope, but we can gain some insight into the process by looking at how a single point is holographed and imaged. Consider the interference pattern that is formed on a sheet of photographic negative film by the superposition of an incident plane wave and a

36.28 (a) A hologram is the record on film of the interference pattern formed with light from the coherent source and light scattered from the object. (b) Images are formed when light is projected through the hologram. The observer sees the virtual image formed behind the hologram.

(a) Recording a hologram

(b) Viewing the hologram

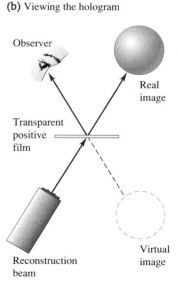

36.29 (a) Constructive interference of the plane and spherical waves occurs in the plane of the film at every point Q for which the distance b_m from P is greater than the distance b_0 from P to O by an integral number of wavelengths $m\lambda$. For the point Q shown, $m = 2$. (b) When a plane wave strikes a transparent positive print of the developed film, the diffracted wave consists of a wave converging to P' and then diverging again and a diverging wave that appears to originate at P. These waves form the real and virtual images, respectively.

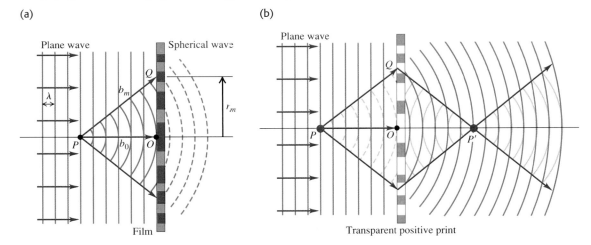

(a)   (b)

spherical wave, as shown in Fig. 36.29a. The spherical wave originates at a point source P at a distance b_0 from the film; P may in fact be a small object that scatters part of the incident plane wave. We assume that the two waves are monochromatic and coherent and that the phase relationship is such that constructive interference occurs at point O on the diagram. Then constructive interference will *also* occur at any point Q on the film that is farther from P than O is by an integer number of wavelengths. That is, if $b_m - b_0 = m\lambda$, where m is an integer, then constructive interference occurs. The points where this condition is satisfied form circles on the film centered at O, with radii r_m given by

$$b_m - b_0 = \sqrt{b_0^2 + r_m^2} - b_0 = m\lambda \qquad (m = 1, 2, 3, \dots) \quad \text{(36.20)}$$

Solving this for r_m^2, we find

$$r_m^2 = \lambda(2mb_0 + m^2\lambda)$$

Ordinarily, b_0 is very much larger than λ, so we neglect the second term in parentheses and obtain

$$r_m = \sqrt{2m\lambda b_0} \qquad (m = 1, 2, 3, \dots) \quad \text{(36.21)}$$

The interference pattern consists of a series of concentric bright circular fringes with radii given by Eq. (36.21). Between these bright fringes are dark fringes.

Now we develop the film and make a transparent positive print, so the bright-fringe areas have the greatest transparency on the film. Then we illuminate it with monochromatic plane-wave light of the same wavelength λ that we used initially. In Fig. 36.29b, consider a point P' at a distance b_0 along the axis from the film. The centers of successive bright fringes differ in their distances from P' by an integer number of wavelengths, and therefore a strong *maximum* in the diffracted wave occurs at P'. That is, light converges to P' and then diverges from it on the opposite side. Therefore P' is a *real image* of point P.

This is not the entire diffracted wave, however. The interference of the wavelets that spread out from all the transparent areas forms a second spherical wave that is diverging rather than converging. When this wave is traced back behind the film in Fig. 36.29b, it appears to be spreading out from point P. Thus the total diffracted wave from the hologram is a superposition of a spherical wave converging to form a real image at P' and a spherical wave that diverges as though it had come from the virtual image point P.

Because of the principle of superposition for waves, what is true for the imaging of a single point is also true for the imaging of any number of points. The film records the superposed interference pattern from the various points, and when light is projected through the film, the various image points are reproduced simultaneously. Thus the images of an extended object can be recorded and reproduced just as for a single point object. Figure 36.30 shows photographs of a holographic image from two different angles, showing the changing perspective in this three-dimensional image.

In making a hologram, we have to overcome two practical problems. First, the light used must be *coherent* over distances that are large in comparison to the dimensions of the object and its distance from the film. Ordinary light sources *do not* satisfy this requirement, for reasons that we discussed in Section 35.1. Therefore laser light is essential for making a hologram. (Ordinary white light can be used for *viewing* certain types of hologram, such as those used on credit cards.) Second, extreme mechanical stability is needed. If any relative motion of source, object, or film occurs during exposure, even by as much as a quarter of a wavelength, the interference pattern on the film is blurred enough to prevent satisfactory image formation. These obstacles are not insurmountable, however, and holography has become important in research, entertainment, and a wide variety of technological applications.

36.30 Two views of the same hologram seen from different angles.

Fresnel and Fraunhofer diffraction: Diffraction occurs when light passes through an aperture or around an edge. When the source and the observer are so far away from the obstructing surface that the outgoing rays can be considered parallel, it is called Fraunhofer diffraction. When the source or the observer is relatively close to the obstructing surface, it is Fresnel diffraction.

Single-slit diffraction: Monochromatic light sent through a narrow slit of width a produces a diffraction pattern on a distant screen. Equation (36.2) gives the condition for destructive interference (a dark fringe) at a point P in the pattern at angle θ. Equation (36.7) gives the intensity in the pattern as a function of θ. (See Examples 36.1–36.3.)

$$\sin\theta = \frac{m\lambda}{a} \quad (m = \pm1, \pm2, \dots) \quad (36.2)$$

$$I = I_0\left\{\frac{\sin[\pi a(\sin\theta)/\lambda]}{\pi a(\sin\theta)/\lambda}\right\}^2 \quad (36.7)$$

$I = 0.0083I_0 \quad m = 3$
$I = 0.0165I_0 \quad m = 2$
$I = 0.0472I_0 \quad m = 1$
O
$I = I_0 \quad \theta$
$m = -1$
$m = -2$
$m = -3$

Diffraction gratings: A diffraction grating consists of a large number of thin parallel slits, spaced a distance d apart. The condition for maximum intensity in the interference pattern is the same as for the two-source pattern, but the maxima for the grating are very sharp and narrow. (See Example 36.4.)

$$d\sin\theta = m\lambda$$
$$(m = 0, \pm1, \pm2, \pm3, \dots) \quad (36.13)$$

$N = 16$

$256I_0$

$m = -1 \quad m = 0 \quad m = 1$

X-ray diffraction: A crystal serves as a three-dimensional diffraction grating for x rays with wavelengths of the same order of magnitude as the spacing between atoms in the crystal. For a set of crystal planes spaced a distance d apart, constructive interference occurs when the angles of incidence and scattering (measured from the crystal planes) are equal and when the Bragg condition [Eq. (36.16)] is satisfied. (See Example 36.5.)

$$2d\sin\theta = m\lambda \quad (m = 1, 2, 3, \dots) \quad (36.16)$$

$d\sin\theta \qquad d\sin\theta$

Circular apertures and resolving power: The diffraction pattern from a circular aperture of diameter D consists of a central bright spot, called the Airy disk, and a series of concentric dark and bright rings. Equation (36.17) gives the angular radius θ_1 of the first dark ring, equal to the angular size of the Airy disk. Diffraction sets the ultimate limit on resolution (image sharpness) of optical instruments. According to Rayleigh's criterion, two point objects are just barely resolved when their angular separation θ is given by Eq. (36.17). (See Example 36.6.)

$$\sin\theta_1 = 1.22\frac{\lambda}{D} \quad (36.17)$$

Airy disk

BRIDGING PROBLEM   *Observing the Expanding Universe*

An astronomer who is studying the light from a galaxy has identified the spectrum of hydrogen but finds that the wavelengths are somewhat shifted from those found in the laboratory. In the lab, the H_α line in the hydrogen spectrum has a wavelength of 656.3 nm. The astronomer is using a transmission diffraction grating having 5758 lines/cm in the first order and finds that the first bright fringe for the H_α line occurs at $\pm 23.41°$ from the central spot. How fast is the galaxy moving? Express your answer in m/s and as a percentage of the speed of light. Is the galaxy moving toward us or away from us?

SOLUTION GUIDE

See MasteringPhysics® study area for a Video Tutor solution.

IDENTIFY and SET UP

1. You can use the information about the grating to find the wavelength of the H_α line in the galaxy's spectrum.
2. In Section 16.8 we learned about the Doppler effect for electromagnetic radiation: The frequency that we receive from a moving source, such as the galaxy, is different from the frequency that is emitted. Equation (16.30) relates the emitted frequency, the received frequency, and the velocity of the source (the target variable). The equation $c = f\lambda$ relates the frequency f and wavelength λ through the speed of light c.

EXECUTE

3. Find the wavelength of the H_α spectral line in the received light.
4. Rewrite Eq. (16.30) as a formula for the velocity v of the galaxy in terms of the received wavelength and the wavelength emitted by the source.
5. Solve for v. Express it in m/s and as a percentage of c, and decide whether the galaxy is moving toward us or moving away.

EVALUATE

6. Is your answer consistent with the relative sizes of the received wavelength and the emitted wavelength?

Problems

For instructor-assigned homework, go to www.masteringphysics.com

•, ••, •••: Problems of increasing difficulty. **CP**: Cumulative problems incorporating material from earlier chapters. **CALC**: Problems requiring calculus. **BIO**: Biosciences problems.

DISCUSSION QUESTIONS

Q36.1 Why can we readily observe diffraction effects for sound waves and water waves, but not for light? Is this because light travels so much faster than these other waves? Explain.

Q36.2 What is the difference between Fresnel and Fraunhofer diffraction? Are they different *physical* processes? Explain.

Q36.3 You use a lens of diameter D and light of wavelength λ and frequency f to form an image of two closely spaced and distant objects. Which of the following will increase the resolving power? (a) Use a lens with a smaller diameter; (b) use light of higher frequency; (c) use light of longer wavelength. In each case justify your answer.

Q36.4 Light of wavelength λ and frequency f passes through a single slit of width a. The diffraction pattern is observed on a screen a distance x from the slit. Which of the following will *decrease* the width of the central maximum? (a) Decrease the slit width; (b) decrease the frequency f of the light; (c) decrease the wavelength λ of the light; (d) decrease the distance x of the screen from the slit. In each case justify your answer.

Q36.5 In a diffraction experiment with waves of wavelength λ, there will be *no* intensity minima (that is, no dark fringes) if the slit width is small enough. What is the maximum slit width for which this occurs? Explain your answer.

Q36.6 The predominant sound waves used in human speech have wavelengths in the range from 1.0 to 3.0 meters. Using the ideas of diffraction, explain how it is possible to hear a person's voice even when he is facing away from you.

Q36.7 In single-slit diffraction, what is $\sin(\beta/2)$ when $\theta = 0$? In view of your answer, why is the single-slit intensity *not* equal to zero at the center?

Q36.8 A rainbow ordinarily shows a range of colors (see Section 33.4). But if the water droplets that form the rainbow are small enough, the rainbow will appear white. Explain why, using diffraction ideas. How small do you think the raindrops would have to be for this to occur?

Q36.9 Some loudspeaker horns for outdoor concerts (at which the entire audience is seated on the ground) are wider vertically than horizontally. Use diffraction ideas to explain why this is more efficient at spreading the sound uniformly over the audience than either a square speaker horn or a horn that is wider horizontally than vertically. Would this still be the case if the audience were seated at different elevations, as in an amphitheater? Why or why not?

Q36.10 Figure 31.12 (Section 31.2) shows a loudspeaker system. Low-frequency sounds are produced by the *woofer*, which is a speaker with large diameter; the *tweeter*, a speaker with smaller diameter, produces high-frequency sounds. Use diffraction ideas to explain why the tweeter is more effective for distributing high-frequency sounds uniformly over a room than is the woofer.

Q36.11 Information is stored on an audio compact disc, CD-ROM, or DVD disc in a series of pits on the disc. These pits are scanned by a laser beam. An important limitation on the amount of information that can be stored on such a disc is the width of the laser beam. Explain why this should be, and explain how using a shorter-wavelength laser allows more information to be stored on a disc of the same size.

Q36.12 With which color of light can the Hubble Space Telescope see finer detail in a distant astronomical object: red, blue, or ultraviolet? Explain your answer.

Q36.13 At the end of Section 36.4, the following statements were made about an array of N slits. Explain, using phasor diagrams, why each statement is true. (a) A minimum occurs whenever ϕ is an integral multiple of $2\pi/N$, except when ϕ is an integral multiple of 2π (which gives a principal maximum). (b) There are $(N-1)$ minima between each pair of principal maxima.

Q36.14 Could x-ray diffraction effects with crystals be observed by using visible light instead of x rays? Why or why not?

Q36.15 Why is a diffraction grating better than a two-slit setup for measuring wavelengths of light?

Q36.16 One sometimes sees rows of evenly spaced radio antenna towers. A student remarked that these act like diffraction gratings. What did she mean? Why would one want them to act like a diffraction grating?

Q36.17 If a hologram is made using 600-nm light and then viewed with 500-nm light, how will the images look compared to those observed when viewed with 600-nm light? Explain.

Q36.18 A hologram is made using 600-nm light and then viewed by using white light from an incandescent bulb. What will be seen? Explain.

Q36.19 Ordinary photographic film reverses black and white, in the sense that the most brightly illuminated areas become blackest upon development (hence the term *negative*). Suppose a hologram negative is viewed directly, without making a positive transparency. How will the resulting images differ from those obtained with the positive? Explain.

EXERCISES

Section 36.2 Diffraction from a Single Slit

36.1 •• Monochromatic light from a distant source is incident on a slit 0.750 mm wide. On a screen 2.00 m away, the distance from the central maximum of the diffraction pattern to the first minimum is measured to be 1.35 mm. Calculate the wavelength of the light.

36.2 • Parallel rays of green mercury light with a wavelength of 546 nm pass through a slit covering a lens with a focal length of 60.0 cm. In the focal plane of the lens the distance from the central maximum to the first minimum is 10.2 mm. What is the width of the slit?

36.3 •• Light of wavelength 585 nm falls on a slit 0.0666 mm wide. (a) On a very large and distant screen, how many *totally* dark fringes (indicating complete cancellation) will there be, including both sides of the central bright spot? Solve this problem *without* calculating all the angles! (*Hint:* What is the largest that $\sin\theta$ can be? What does this tell you is the largest that m can be?) (b) At what angle will the dark fringe that is most distant from the central bright fringe occur?

36.4 • Light of wavelength 633 nm from a distant source is incident on a slit 0.750 mm wide, and the resulting diffraction pattern is observed on a screen 3.50 m away. What is the distance between the two dark fringes on either side of the central bright fringe?

36.5 •• Diffraction occurs for all types of waves, including sound waves. High-frequency sound from a distant source with wavelength 9.00 cm passes through a slit 12.0 cm wide. A microphone is placed 8.00 m directly in front of the center of the slit, corresponding to point O in Fig. 36.5a. The microphone is then moved in a direction perpendicular to the line from the center of the slit to point O. At what distances from O will the intensity detected by the microphone be zero?

36.6 • **CP Tsunami!** On December 26, 2004, a violent earthquake of magnitude 9.1 occurred off the coast of Sumatra. This quake triggered a huge tsunami (similar to a tidal wave) that killed more than 150,000 people. Scientists observing the wave on the open ocean measured the time between crests to be 1.0 h and the speed of the wave to be 800 km/h. Computer models of the evolution of this enormous wave showed that it bent around the continents and spread to all the oceans of the earth. When the wave reached the gaps between continents, it diffracted between them as through a slit. (a) What was the wavelength of this tsunami? (b) The distance between the southern tip of Africa and northern Antarctica is about 4500 km, while the distance between the southern end of Australia and Antarctica is about 3700 km. As an approximation, we can model this wave's behavior by using Fraunhofer diffraction. Find the smallest angle away from the central maximum for which the waves would cancel after going through each of these continental gaps.

36.7 •• **CP** A series of parallel linear water wave fronts are traveling directly toward the shore at 15.0 cm/s on an otherwise placid lake. A long concrete barrier that runs parallel to the shore at a distance of 3.20 m away has a hole in it. You count the wave crests and observe that 75.0 of them pass by each minute, and you also observe that no waves reach the shore at ± 61.3 cm from the point directly opposite the hole, but waves do reach the shore everywhere within this distance. (a) How wide is the hole in the barrier? (b) At what other angles do you find no waves hitting the shore?

36.8 • Monochromatic electromagnetic radiation with wavelength λ from a distant source passes through a slit. The diffraction pattern is observed on a screen 2.50 m from the slit. If the width of the central maximum is 6.00 mm, what is the slit width a if the wavelength is (a) 500 nm (visible light); (b) 50.0 μm (infrared radiation); (c) 0.500 nm (x rays)?

36.9 •• **Doorway Diffraction.** Sound of frequency 1250 Hz leaves a room through a 1.00-m-wide doorway (see Exercise 36.5). At which angles relative to the centerline perpendicular to the doorway will someone outside the room hear no sound? Use 344 m/s for the speed of sound in air and assume that the source and listener are both far enough from the doorway for Fraunhofer diffraction to apply. You can ignore effects of reflections.

36.10 • **CP** Light waves, for which the electric field is given by $E_y(x, t) = E_{\max}\sin[(1.20 \times 10^7 \text{ m}^{-1})x - \omega t]$, pass through a slit and produce the first dark bands at $\pm 28.6°$ from the center of the diffraction pattern. (a) What is the frequency of this light? (b) How wide is the slit? (c) At which angles will other dark bands occur?

36.11 •• Parallel rays of light with wavelength 620 nm pass through a slit covering a lens with a focal length of 40.0 cm. The diffraction pattern is observed in the focal plane of the lens, and the distance from the center of the central maximum to the first minimum is 36.5 cm. What is the width of the slit? (*Note:* The angle that locates the first minimum is *not* small.)

36.12 •• Red light of wavelength 633 nm from a helium–neon laser passes through a slit 0.350 mm wide. The diffraction pattern is observed on a screen 3.00 m away. Define the width of a bright fringe as the distance between the minima on either side. (a) What is the width of the central bright fringe? (b) What is the width of the first bright fringe on either side of the central one?

Section 36.3 Intensity in the Single-Slit Pattern

36.13 •• Monochromatic light of wavelength 580 nm passes through a single slit and the diffraction pattern is observed on a screen. Both the source and screen are far enough from the slit for Fraunhofer diffraction to apply. (a) If the first diffraction minima are at $\pm 90.0°$, so the central maximum completely fills the screen, what is the width of the slit? (b) For the width of the slit as calculated in part (a), what is the ratio of the intensity at $\theta = 45.0°$ to the intensity at $\theta = 0$?

36.14 •• Monochromatic light of wavelength $\lambda = 620$ nm from a distant source passes through a slit 0.450 mm wide. The diffraction pattern is observed on a screen 3.00 m from the slit. In terms of the intensity I_0 at the peak of the central maximum, what is the intensity of the light at the screen the following distances from the center of the central maximum: (a) 1.00 mm; (b) 3.00 mm; (c) 5.00 mm?

36.15 •• A slit 0.240 mm wide is illuminated by parallel light rays of wavelength 540 nm. The diffraction pattern is observed on a screen that is 3.00 m from the slit. The intensity at the center of the central maximum ($\theta = 0°$) is 6.00×10^{-6} W/m². (a) What is the distance on the screen from the center of the central maximum to the first minimum? (b) What is the intensity at a point on the screen midway between the center of the central maximum and the first minimum?

36.16 • Monochromatic light of wavelength 486 nm from a distant source passes through a slit that is 0.0290 mm wide. In the resulting diffraction pattern, the intensity at the center of the central maximum ($\theta = 0°$) is 4.00×10^{-5} W/m². What is the intensity at a point on the screen that corresponds to $\theta = 1.20°$.

36.17 •• A single-slit diffraction pattern is formed by monochromatic electromagnetic radiation from a distant source passing through a slit 0.105 mm wide. At the point in the pattern 3.25° from the center of the central maximum, the total phase difference between wavelets from the top and bottom of the slit is 56.0 rad. (a) What is the wavelength of the radiation? (b) What is the intensity at this point, if the intensity at the center of the central maximum is I_0?

36.18 • Consider a single-slit diffraction experiment in which the amplitude of the wave at point O in Fig. 36.5a is E_0. For each of the following cases, draw a phasor diagram like that in Fig. 36.8c and determine *graphically* the amplitude of the wave at the point in question. (*Hint:* Use Eq. (36.6) to determine the value of β for each case.) Compute the intensity and compare to Eq. (36.5). (a) $\sin \theta = \lambda/2a$; (b) $\sin \theta = \lambda/a$; (c) $\sin \theta = 3\lambda/2a$.

36.19 •• Public Radio station KXPR-FM in Sacramento broadcasts at 88.9 MHz. The radio waves pass between two tall skyscrapers that are 15.0 m apart along their closest walls. (a) At what horizontal angles, relative to the original direction of the waves, will a distant antenna not receive any signal from this station? (b) If the maximum intensity is 3.50 W/m² at the antenna, what is the intensity at ±5.00° from the center of the central maximum at the distant antenna?

Section 36.4 Multiple Slits

36.20 •• **Diffraction and Interference Combined.** Consider the interference pattern produced by two parallel slits of width a and separation d, in which $d = 3a$. The slits are illuminated by normally incident light of wavelength λ. (a) First we ignore diffraction effects due to the slit width. At what angles θ from the central maximum will the next four maxima in the two-slit interference pattern occur? Your answer will be in terms of d and λ. (b) Now we include the effects of diffraction. If the intensity at $\theta = 0$ is I_0, what is the intensity at each of the angles in part (a)? (c) Which double-slit interference maxima are missing in the pattern? (d) Compare your results to those illustrated in Fig. 36.12c. In what ways is your result different?

36.21 • **Number of Fringes in a Diffraction Maximum.** In Fig. 36.12c the central diffraction maximum contains exactly seven

interference fringes, and in this case $d/a = 4$. (a) What must the ratio d/a be if the central maximum contains exactly five fringes? (b) In the case considered in part (a), how many fringes are contained within the first diffraction maximum on one side of the central maximum?

36.22 • An interference pattern is produced by eight parallel and equally spaced, narrow slits. There is an interference minimum when the phase difference ϕ between light from adjacent slits is $\pi/4$. The phasor diagram is given in Fig. 36.14b. For which pairs of slits is there totally destructive interference?

36.23 •• An interference pattern is produced by light of wavelength 580 nm from a distant source incident on two identical parallel slits separated by a distance (between centers) of 0.530 mm. (a) If the slits are very narrow, what would be the angular positions of the first-order and second-order, two-slit, interference maxima? (b) Let the slits have width 0.320 mm. In terms of the intensity I_0 at the center of the central maximum, what is the intensity at each of the angular positions in part (a)?

36.24 • Parallel rays of monochromatic light with wavelength 568 nm illuminate two identical slits and produce an interference pattern on a screen that is 75.0 cm from the slits. The centers of the slits are 0.640 mm apart and the width of each slit is 0.434 mm. If the intensity at the center of the central maximum is 5.00×10^{-4} W/m², what is the intensity at a point on the screen that is 0.900 mm from the center of the central maximum?

36.25 •• An interference pattern is produced by four parallel and equally spaced, narrow slits. By drawing appropriate phasor diagrams, show that there is an interference minimum when the phase difference ϕ from adjacent slits is (a) $\pi/2$; (b) π; (c) $3\pi/2$. In each case, for which pairs of slits is there totally destructive interference?

36.26 •• A diffraction experiment involving two thin parallel slits yields the pattern of closely spaced bright and dark fringes shown in Fig. E36.26. Only the central portion of the pattern is shown in the figure. The bright spots are equally spaced at 1.53 mm center to center (except for the missing spots) on a screen 2.50 m from the slits. The light source was a He-Ne laser producing a wavelength of 632.8 nm. (a) How far apart are the two slits? (b) How wide is each one?

Figure **E36.26**

1.53 mm

36.27 •• Laser light of wavelength 500.0 nm illuminates two identical slits, producing an interference pattern on a screen 90.0 cm from the slits. The bright bands are 1.00 cm apart, and the third bright bands on either side of the central maximum are missing in the pattern. Find the width and the separation of the two slits.

Section 36.5 The Diffraction Grating

36.28 •• Monochromatic light is at normal incidence on a plane transmission grating. The first-order maximum in the interference pattern is at an angle of 8.94°. What is the angular position of the fourth-order maximum?

36.29 • If a diffraction grating produces its third-order bright band at an angle of 78.4° for light of wavelength 681 nm, find (a) the number of slits per centimeter for the grating and (b) the angular location of the first-order and second-order bright bands. (c) Will there be a fourth-order bright band? Explain.

36.30 • If a diffraction grating produces a third-order bright spot for red light (of wavelength 700 nm) at 65.0° from the central maximum, at what angle will the second-order bright spot be for violet light (of wavelength 400 nm)?

36.31 • Visible light passes through a diffraction grating that has 900 slits/cm, and the interference pattern is observed on a screen that is 2.50 m from the grating. (a) Is the angular position of the first-order spectrum small enough for $\sin\theta \approx \theta$ to be a good approximation? (b) In the first-order spectrum, the maxima for two different wavelengths are separated on the screen by 3.00 mm. What is the difference in these wavelengths?

36.32 • The wavelength range of the visible spectrum is approximately 380–750 nm. White light falls at normal incidence on a diffraction grating that has 350 slits/mm. Find the angular width of the visible spectrum in (a) the first order and (b) the third order. (*Note:* An advantage of working in higher orders is the greater angular spread and better resolution. A disadvantage is the overlapping of different orders, as shown in Example 36.4.)

36.33 • When laser light of wavelength 632.8 nm passes through a diffraction grating, the first bright spots occur at $\pm 17.8°$ from the central maximum. (a) What is the line density (in lines/cm) of this grating? (b) How many additional bright spots are there beyond the first bright spots, and at what angles do they occur?

36.34 • (a) What is the wavelength of light that is deviated in the first order through an angle of 13.5° by a transmission grating having 5000 slits/cm? (b) What is the second-order deviation of this wavelength? Assume normal incidence.

36.35 • Plane monochromatic waves with wavelength 520 nm are incident normally on a plane transmission grating having 350 slits/mm. Find the angles of deviation in the first, second, and third orders.

36.36 • **Identifying Isotopes by Spectra.** Different isotopes of the same element emit light at slightly different wavelengths. A wavelength in the emission spectrum of a hydrogen atom is 656.45 nm; for deuterium, the corresponding wavelength is 656.27 nm. (a) What minimum number of slits is required to resolve these two wavelengths in second order? (b) If the grating has 500.00 slits/mm, find the angles and angular separation of these two wavelengths in the second order.

36.37 • A typical laboratory diffraction grating has 5.00×10^3 lines/cm, and these lines are contained in a 3.50-cm width of grating. (a) What is the chromatic resolving power of such a grating in the first order? (b) Could this grating resolve the lines of the sodium doublet (see Section 36.5) in the first order? (c) While doing spectral analysis of a star, you are using this grating in the *second* order to resolve spectral lines that are very close to the 587.8002-nm spectral line of iron. (i) For wavelengths longer than the iron line, what is the shortest wavelength you could distinguish from the iron line? (ii) For wavelengths shorter than the iron line, what is the longest wavelength you could distinguish from the iron line? (iii) What is the range of wavelengths you could *not* distinguish from the iron line?

36.38 • The light from an iron arc includes many different wavelengths. Two of these are at $\lambda = 587.9782$ nm and $\lambda = 587.8002$ nm. You wish to resolve these spectral lines in first order using a grating 1.20 cm in length. What minimum number of slits per centimeter must the grating have?

Section 36.6 X-Ray Diffraction

36.39 • X rays of wavelength 0.0850 nm are scattered from the atoms of a crystal. The second-order maximum in the Bragg reflection occurs when the angle θ in Fig. 36.22 is 21.5°. What is the spacing between adjacent atomic planes in the crystal?

36.40 • If the planes of a crystal are 3.50 Å ($1 \text{ Å} = 10^{-10} \text{ m} = 1$ Ångstrom unit) apart, (a) what wavelength of electromagnetic waves is needed so that the first strong interference maximum in the Bragg reflection occurs when the waves strike the planes at an angle of 15.0°, and in what part of the electromagnetic spectrum do these waves lie? (See Fig. 32.4.) (b) At what other angles will strong interference maxima occur?

36.41 • Monochromatic x rays are incident on a crystal for which the spacing of the atomic planes is 0.440 nm. The first-order maximum in the Bragg reflection occurs when the incident and reflected x rays make an angle of 39.4° with the crystal planes. What is the wavelength of the x rays?

Section 36.7 Circular Apertures and Resolving Power

36.42 • **BIO** If you can read the bottom row of your doctor's eye chart, your eye has a resolving power of 1 arcminute, equal to $\frac{1}{60}$ degree. If this resolving power is diffraction limited, to what effective diameter of your eye's optical system does this correspond? Use Rayleigh's criterion and assume $\lambda = 550$ nm.

36.43 • Two satellites at an altitude of 1200 km are separated by 28 km. If they broadcast 3.6-cm microwaves, what minimum receiving-dish diameter is needed to resolve (by Rayleigh's criterion) the two transmissions?

36.44 •• The VLBA (Very Long Baseline Array) uses a number of individual radio telescopes to make one unit having an equivalent diameter of about 8000 km. When this radio telescope is focusing radio waves of wavelength 2.0 cm, what would have to be the diameter of the mirror of a visible-light telescope focusing light of wavelength 550 nm so that the visible-light telescope has the same resolution as the radio telescope?

36.45 •• Monochromatic light with wavelength 620 nm passes through a circular aperture with diameter 7.4 μm. The resulting diffraction pattern is observed on a screen that is 4.5 m from the aperture. What is the diameter of the Airy disk on the screen?

36.46 • **Photography.** A wildlife photographer uses a moderate telephoto lens of focal length 135 mm and maximum aperture $f/4.00$ to photograph a bear that is 11.5 m away. Assume the wavelength is 550 nm. (a) What is the width of the smallest feature on the bear that this lens can resolve if it is opened to its maximum aperture? (b) If, to gain depth of field, the photographer stops the lens down to $f/22.0$, what would be the width of the smallest resolvable feature on the bear?

36.47 • **Observing Jupiter.** You are asked to design a space telescope for earth orbit. When Jupiter is 5.93×10^8 km away (its closest approach to the earth), the telescope is to resolve, by Rayleigh's criterion, features on Jupiter that are 250 km apart. What minimum-diameter mirror is required? Assume a wavelength of 500 nm.

36.48 • A converging lens 7.20 cm in diameter has a focal length of 300 mm. If the resolution is diffraction limited, how far away can an object be if points on it 4.00 mm apart are to be resolved (according to Rayleigh's criterion)? Use $\lambda = 550$ nm.

36.49 •• **Hubble Versus Arecibo.** The Hubble Space Telescope has an aperture of 2.4 m and focuses visible light (380–750 nm). The Arecibo radio telescope in Puerto Rico is 305 m (1000 ft) in diameter (it is built in a mountain valley) and focuses radio waves of wavelength 75 cm. (a) Under optimal viewing conditions, what is the smallest crater that each of these telescopes could resolve on our moon? (b) If the Hubble Space Telescope were to be converted to surveillance use, what is the highest orbit above the surface of the earth it could have and still be able to resolve the license plate (not the letters, just the plate) of a car on the ground? Assume optimal viewing conditions, so that the resolution is diffraction limited.

36.50 • **Searching for Starspots.** The Hale Telescope on Palomar Mountain in California has a mirror 200 in. (5.08 m) in diameter and it focuses visible light. Given that a large sunspot is about 10,000 mi in diameter, what is the most distant star on which this telescope could resolve a sunspot to see whether other stars have them? (Assume optimal viewing conditions, so that the resolution is diffraction limited.) Are there any stars this close to us, besides our sun?

PROBLEMS

36.51 •• BIO **Thickness of Human Hair.** Although we have discussed single-slit diffraction only for a slit, a similar result holds when light bends around a straight, thin object, such as a strand of hair. In that case, a is the width of the strand. From actual laboratory measurements on a human hair, it was found that when a beam of light of wavelength 632.8 nm was shone on a single strand of hair, and the diffracted light was viewed on a screen 1.25 m away, the first dark fringes on either side of the central bright spot were 5.22 cm apart. How thick was this strand of hair?

36.52 •• Suppose the entire apparatus (slit, screen, and space in between) in Exercise 36.4 is immersed in water ($n = 1.333$). Then what is the distance between the two dark fringes?

36.53 ••• Laser light of wavelength 632.8 nm falls normally on a slit that is 0.0250 mm wide. The transmitted light is viewed on a distant screen where the intensity at the center of the central bright fringe is 8.50 W/m². (a) Find the maximum number of totally dark fringes on the screen, assuming the screen is large enough to show them all. (b) At what angle does the dark fringe that is most distant from the center occur? (c) What is the maximum intensity of the bright fringe that occurs immediately before the dark fringe in part (b)? Approximate the angle at which this fringe occurs by assuming it is midway between the angles to the dark fringes on either side of it.

36.54 •• CP A loudspeaker having a diaphragm that vibrates at 1250 Hz is traveling at 80.0 m/s directly toward a pair of holes in a very large wall in a region for which the speed of sound is 344 m/s. You observe that the sound coming through the openings first cancels at $\pm 11.4°$ with respect to the original direction of the speaker when observed far from the wall. (a) How far apart are the two openings? (b) At what angles would the sound first cancel if the source stopped moving?

36.55 • **Measuring Refractive Index.** A thin slit illuminated by light of frequency f produces its first dark band at $\pm 38.2°$ in air. When the entire apparatus (slit, screen, and space in between) is immersed in an unknown transparent liquid, the slit's first dark bands occur instead at $\pm 21.6°$. Find the refractive index of the liquid.

36.56 • **Grating Design.** Your boss asks you to design a diffraction grating that will disperse the first-order visible spectrum through an angular range of 21.0° (see Example 36.4 in Section 36.5). (a) What must the number of slits per centimeter be for this grating? (b) At what angles will the first-order visible spectrum begin and end?

36.57 •• A slit 0.360 mm wide is illuminated by parallel rays of light that have a wavelength of 540 nm. The diffraction pattern is observed on a screen that is 1.20 m from the slit. The intensity at the center of the central maximum ($\theta = 0°$) is I_0. (a) What is the distance on the screen from the center of the central maximum to the first minimum? (b) What is the distance on the screen from the center of the central maximum to the point where the intensity has fallen to $I_0/2$?

36.58 ••• CALC The intensity of light in the Fraunhofer diffraction pattern of a single slit is

$$I = I_0 \left(\frac{\sin \gamma}{\gamma} \right)^2$$

where

$$\gamma = \frac{\pi a \sin \theta}{\lambda}$$

(a) Show that the equation for the values of γ at which I is a maximum is $\tan \gamma = \gamma$. (b) Determine the three smallest positive values of γ that are solutions of this equation. (*Hint:* You can use a trial-and-error procedure. Guess a value of γ and adjust your guess to bring $\tan \gamma$ closer to γ. A graphical solution of the equation is very helpful in locating the solutions approximately, to get good initial guesses.)

36.59 •• **Angular Width of a Principal Maximum.** Consider N evenly spaced, narrow slits. Use the small-angle approximation $\sin \theta = \theta$ (for θ in radians) to prove the following: For an intensity maximum that occurs at an angle θ, the intensity minima immediately adjacent to this maximum are at angles $\theta + \lambda/Nd$ and $\theta - \lambda/Nd$, so that the angular width of the principal maximum is $2\lambda/Nd$. This is proportional to $1/N$, as we concluded in Section 36.4 on the basis of energy conservation.

36.60 •• CP CALC In a large vacuum chamber, monochromatic laser light passes through a narrow slit in a thin aluminum plate and forms a diffraction pattern on a screen that is 0.620 m from the slit. When the aluminum plate has a temperature of 20.0°C, the width of the central maximum in the diffraction pattern is 2.75 mm. What is the change in the width of the central maximum when the temperature of the plate is raised to 520.0°C? Does the width of the central diffraction maximum increase or decrease when the temperature is increased?

36.61 • **Phasor Diagram for Eight Slits.** An interference pattern is produced by eight equally spaced, narrow slits. Figure 36.14 shows phasor diagrams for the cases in which the phase difference ϕ between light from adjacent slits is $\phi = \pi$, $\phi = \pi/4$, and $\phi = \pi/2$. Each of these cases gives an intensity minimum. The caption for Fig. 36.14 also claims that minima occur for $\phi = 3\pi/4$, $\phi = 5\pi/4$, $\phi = 3\pi/2$, and $\phi = 7\pi/4$. (a) Draw the phasor diagram for each of these four cases, and explain why each diagram proves that there is in fact a minimum. (*Note:* You may find it helpful to use a different colored pencil for each slit!) (b) For each of the four cases $\phi = 3\pi/4$, $\phi = 5\pi/4$, $\phi = 3\pi/2$, and $\phi = 7\pi/4$, for which pairs of slits is there totally destructive interference?

36.62 •• CP In a laboratory, light from a particular spectrum line of helium passes through a diffraction grating and the second-order maximum is at 18.9° from the center of the central bright fringe. The same grating is then used for light from a distant galaxy that is moving away from the earth with a speed of 2.65×10^7 m/s. For the light from the galaxy, what is the angular location of the second-order maximum for the same spectral line as was observed in the lab? (See Section 16.8.)

36.63 • What is the longest wavelength that can be observed in the third order for a transmission grating having 9200 slits/cm? Assume normal incidence.

36.64 •• (a) Figure 36.16 shows plane waves of light incident *normally* on a diffraction grating. If instead the light strikes the grating at an angle of incidence θ' (measured from the normal), show that the condition for an intensity maximum is *not* Eq. (36.13), but rather

$$d(\sin\theta + \sin\theta') = m\lambda \quad (m = 0, \pm 1, \pm 2, \pm 3, \dots)$$

(b) For the grating described in Example 36.4 (Section 36.5), with 600 slits/mm, find the angles of the maxima corresponding to $m = 0$, 1, and −1 with red light ($\lambda = 650$ nm) for the cases $\theta' = 0$ (normal incidence) and $\theta' = 20.0°$.

36.65 • A diffraction grating has 650 slits/mm. What is the highest order that contains the entire visible spectrum? (The wavelength range of the visible spectrum is approximately 380–750 nm.)

36.66 •• *Quasars*, an abbreviation for *quasi-stellar radio sources*, are distant objects that look like stars through a telescope but that emit far more electromagnetic radiation than an entire normal galaxy of stars. An example is the bright object below and to the left of center in Fig. P36.66; the other elongated objects in this image are normal galaxies. The leading model for the structure of a quasar is a galaxy with a supermassive black hole at its center. In this model, the radiation is emitted by interstellar gas and dust within the galaxy as this material falls toward the black hole. The radiation is thought to emanate from a region just a few light-years in diameter. (The diffuse glow surrounding the bright quasar shown in Fig. P36.66 is thought to be this quasar's host galaxy.) To investigate this model of quasars and to study other exotic astronomical objects, the Russian Space Agency plans to place a radio telescope in an orbit that extends to 77,000 km from the earth. When the signals from this telescope are combined with signals from the ground-based telescopes of the VLBA, the resolution will be that of a single radio telescope 77,000 km in diameter. What is the size of the smallest detail that this arrangement could resolve in quasar 3C 405, which is 7.2×10^8 light-years from earth, using radio waves at a frequency of 1665 MHz? (*Hint:* Use Rayleigh's criterion.) Give your answer in light-years and in kilometers.

Figure **P36.66**

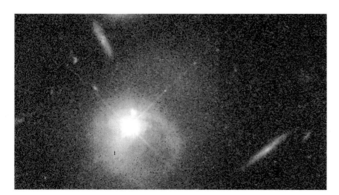

36.67 ••• **Phased-Array Radar.** In one common type of radar installation, a rotating antenna sweeps a radio beam around the sky. But in a *phased-array* radar system, the antennas remain stationary and the beam is swept electronically. To see how this is done, consider an array of N antennas that are arranged along the horizontal x-axis at $x = 0, \pm d, \pm 2d, \ldots, \pm(N-1)d/2$. (The number N is odd.) Each antenna emits radiation uniformly in all directions in the horizontal xy-plane. The antennas all emit radiation coherently, with the same amplitude E_0 and the same wavelength λ. The relative phase δ of the emission from adjacent antennas can be varied, however. If the antenna at $x = 0$ emits a signal that is given by $E_0 \cos \omega t$, as measured at a point next to the antenna, the antenna at $x = d$ emits a signal given by $E_0 \cos(\omega t + \delta)$, as measured at a point next to that antenna. The corresponding quantity for the antenna at $x = -d$ is $E_0 \cos(\omega t - \delta)$; for the antennas at $x = \pm 2d$, it is $E_0 \cos(\omega t \pm 2\delta)$; and so on. (a) If $\delta = 0$, the inter-

ference pattern at a distance from the antennas is large compared to d and has a principal maximum at $\theta = 0$ (that is, in the $+y$-direction, perpendicular to the line of the antennas). Show that if $d < \lambda$, this is the *only* principal interference maximum in the angular range $-90° < \theta < 90°$. Hence this principal maximum describes a beam emitted in the direction $\theta = 0$. As described in Section 36.4, if N is large, the beam will have a large intensity and be quite narrow. (b) If $\delta \neq 0$, show that the principal intensity maximum described in part (a) is located at

$$\theta = \arcsin\left(\frac{\delta\lambda}{2\pi d}\right)$$

where δ is measured in radians. Thus, by varying δ from positive to negative values and back again, which can easily be done electronically, the beam can be made to sweep back and forth around $\theta = 0$. (c) A weather radar unit to be installed on an airplane emits radio waves at 8800 MHz. The unit uses 15 antennas in an array 28.0 cm long (from the antenna at one end of the array to the antenna at the other end). What must the maximum and minimum values of δ be (that is, the most positive and most negative values) if the radar beam is to sweep 45° to the left or right of the airplane's direction of flight? Give your answer in radians.

36.68 •• **Underwater Photography.** An underwater camera has a lens of focal length 35.0 mm and a maximum aperture of $f/2.80$. The film it uses has an emulsion that is sensitive to light of frequency 6.00×10^{14} Hz. If the photographer takes a picture of an object 2.75 m in front of the camera with the lens wide open, what is the width of the smallest resolvable detail on the subject if the object is (a) a fish underwater with the camera in the water and (b) a person on the beach with the camera out of the water?

36.69 •• An astronaut in the space shuttle can just resolve two point sources on earth that are 65.0 m apart. Assume that the resolution is diffraction limited and use Rayleigh's criterion. What is the astronaut's altitude above the earth? Treat his eye as a circular aperture with a diameter of 4.00 mm (the diameter of his pupil), and take the wavelength of the light to be 550 nm. Ignore the effect of fluid in the eye.

36.70 •• BIO **Resolution of the Eye.** The maximum resolution of the eye depends on the diameter of the opening of the pupil (a diffraction effect) and the size of the retinal cells. The size of the retinal cells (about 5.0 μm in diameter) limits the size of an object at the near point (25 cm) of the eye to a height of about 50 μm. (To get a reasonable estimate without having to go through complicated calculations, we shall ignore the effect of the fluid in the eye.) (a) Given that the diameter of the human pupil is about 2.0 mm, does the Rayleigh criterion allow us to resolve a 50-μm-tall object at 25 cm from the eye with light of wavelength 550 nm? (b) According to the Rayleigh criterion, what is the shortest object we could resolve at the 25-cm near point with light of wavelength 550 nm? (c) What angle would the object in part (b) subtend at the eye? Express your answer in minutes (60 min = 1°), and compare it with the experimental value of about 1 min. (d) Which effect is more important in limiting the resolution of our eyes: diffraction or the size of the retinal cells?

36.71 •• A glass sheet is covered by a very thin opaque coating. In the middle of this sheet there is a thin scratch 0.00125 mm thick. The sheet is totally immersed beneath the surface of a liquid. Parallel rays of monochromatic coherent light with wavelength 612 nm in air strike the sheet perpendicular to its surface and pass through the scratch. A screen is placed in the liquid a distance of 30.0 cm away from the sheet and parallel to it. You observe that the first dark fringes on either side of the central bright fringe on the screen are 22.4 cm apart. What is the refractive index of the liquid?

36.72 •• **Observing Planets Beyond Our Solar System.** NASA is considering a project called *Planet Imager* that would give astronomers the ability to see details on planets orbiting other stars. Using the same principle as the Very Large Array (see Section 36.7), *Planet Imager* will use an array of infrared telescopes spread over thousands of kilometers of space. (Visible light would give even better resolution. Unfortunately, at visible wavelengths, stars are so bright that a planet would be lost in the glare. This is less of a problem at infrared wavelengths.) (a) If *Planet Imager* has an effective diameter of 6000 km and observes infrared radiation at a wavelength of $10 \mu m$, what is the greatest distance at which it would be able to observe details as small as 250 km across (about the size of the greater Los Angeles area) on a planet? Give your answer in light-years (see Appendix E). (*Hint:* Use Rayleigh's criterion.) (b) For comparison, consider the resolution of a single infrared telescope in space that has a diameter of 1.0 m and that observes $10 \text{-}\mu m$ radiation. What is the size of the smallest details that such a telescope could resolve at the distance of the nearest star to the sun, Proxima Centauri, which is 4.22 light-years distant? How does this compare to the diameter of the earth $(1.27 \times 10^4 \text{ km})$? To the average distance from the earth to the sun $(1.50 \times 10^8 \text{ km})$? Would a single telescope of this kind be able to detect the presence of a planet like the earth, in an orbit the size of the earth's orbit, around *any* other star? Explain. (c) Suppose *Planet Imager* is used to observe a planet orbiting the star 70 Virginis, which is 59 light-years from our solar system. A planet (though not an earthlike one) has in fact been detected orbiting this star, not by imaging it directly but by observing the slight "wobble" of the star as both it and the planet orbit their common center of mass. What is the size of the smallest details that *Planet Imager* could hope to resolve on the planet of 70 Virginis? How does this compare to the diameter of the planet, assumed to be comparable to that of Jupiter $(1.38 \times 10^5 \text{ km})$? (Although the planet of 70 Virginis is thought to be at least 6.6 times more massive than Jupiter, its radius is probably not too different from that of Jupiter. The reason is that such large planets are thought to be composed primarily of gases, not rocky material, and hence can be greatly compressed by the mutual gravitational attraction of different parts of the planet.)

CHALLENGE PROBLEMS

36.73 ••• **CALC** It is possible to calculate the intensity in the single-slit Fraunhofer diffraction pattern *without* using the phasor method of Section 36.3. Let y' represent the position of a point within the slit of width a in Fig. 36.5a, with $y' = 0$ at the center of the slit so that the slit extends from $y' = -a/2$ to $y' = a/2$. We imagine dividing the slit up into infinitesimal strips of width dy', each of which acts as a source of secondary wavelets. (a) The amplitude of the total wave at the point O on the distant screen in Fig. 36.5a is E_0. Explain why the amplitude of the wavelet from each infinitesimal strip within the slit is $E_0(dy'/a)$, so that the electric field of the wavelet a distance x from the infinitesimal strip is $dE = E_0(dy'/a) \sin(kx - \omega t)$. (b) Explain why the wavelet from each strip as detected at point P in Fig. 36.5a can be expressed as

$$dE = E_0 \frac{dy'}{a} \sin[k(D - y' \sin \theta) - \omega t]$$

where D is the distance from the center of the slit to point P and $k = 2\pi/\lambda$. (c) By integrating the contributions dE from all parts of the slit, show that the total wave detected at point P is

$$E = E_0 \sin(kD - \omega t) \frac{\sin[ka(\sin \theta)/2]}{ka(\sin \theta)/2}$$

$$= E_0 \sin(kD - \omega t) \frac{\sin[\pi a(\sin \theta)/\lambda]}{\pi a(\sin \theta)/\lambda}$$

(The trigonometric identities in Appendix B will be useful.) Show that at $\theta = 0$, corresponding to point O in Fig. 36.5a, the wave is $E = E_0 \sin(kD - \omega t)$ and has amplitude E_0, as stated in part (a). (d) Use the result of part (c) to show that if the intensity at point O is I_0, then the intensity at a point P is given by Eq. (36.7).

36.74 ••• **Intensity Pattern of N Slits.** (a) Consider an arrangement of N slits with a distance d between adjacent slits. The slits emit coherently and in phase at wavelength λ. Show that at a time t, the electric field at a distant point P is

$$E_P(t) = E_0 \cos(kR - \omega t) + E_0 \cos(kR - \omega t + \phi)$$
$$+ E_0 \cos(kR - \omega t + 2\phi) + \cdots$$
$$+ E_0 \cos(kR - \omega t + (N - 1)\phi)$$

where E_0 is the amplitude at P of the electric field due to an individual slit, $\phi = (2\pi d \sin \theta)/\lambda$, θ is the angle of the rays reaching P (as measured from the perpendicular bisector of the slit arrangement), and R is the distance from P to the most distant slit. In this problem, assume that R is much larger than d. (b) To carry out the sum in part (a), it is convenient to use the complex-number relationship

$$e^{iz} = \cos z + i \sin z$$

where $i = \sqrt{-1}$. In this expression, $\cos z$ is the *real part* of the complex number e^{iz}, and $\sin z$ is its *imaginary part*. Show that the electric field $E_P(t)$ is equal to the real part of the complex quantity

$$\sum_{n=0}^{N-1} E_0 e^{i(kR - \omega t + n\phi)}$$

(c) Using the properties of the exponential function that $e^A e^B = e^{(A+B)}$ and $(e^A)^n = e^{nA}$, show that the sum in part (b) can be written as

$$E_0 \left(\frac{e^{iN\phi} - 1}{e^{i\phi} - 1} \right) e^{i(kR - \omega t)}$$

$$= E_0 \left(\frac{e^{iN\phi/2} - e^{-iN\phi/2}}{e^{i\phi/2} - e^{-i\phi/2}} \right) e^{i[kR - \omega t + (N-1)\phi/2]}$$

Then, using the relationship $e^{iz} = \cos z + i \sin z$, show that the (real) electric field at point P is

$$E_P(t) = \left[E_0 \frac{\sin(N\phi/2)}{\sin(\phi/2)} \right] \cos[kR - \omega t + (N - 1)\phi/2]$$

The quantity in the first square brackets in this expression is the amplitude of the electric field at P. (d) Use the result for the electric-field amplitude in part (c) to show that the intensity at an angle θ is

$$I = I_0 \left[\frac{\sin(N\phi/2)}{\sin(\phi/2)} \right]^2$$

where I_0 is the maximum intensity for an individual slit. (e) Check the result in part (d) for the case $N = 2$. It will help to recall that $\sin 2A = 2 \sin A \cos A$. Explain why your result differs from Eq. (35.10), the expression for the intensity in two-source interference, by a factor of 4. (*Hint:* Is I_0 defined in the same way in both expressions?)

36.75 ••• **CALC** **Intensity Pattern of *N* Slits, Continued.** Part (d) of Challenge Problem 36.74 gives an expression for the intensity in the interference pattern of *N* identical slits. Use this result to verify the following statements. (a) The maximum intensity in the pattern is $N^2 I_0$. (b) The principal maximum at the center of the pattern extends from $\phi = -2\pi/N$ to $\phi = 2\pi/N$, so its width is inversely proportional to $1/N$. (c) A minimum occurs whenever ϕ is an integral multiple of $2\pi/N$, except when ϕ is an integral multiple of 2π (which gives a principal maximum). (d) There are $(N - 1)$ minima between each pair of principal maxima. (e) Halfway between two principal maxima, the intensity can be no greater than I_0; that is, it can be no greater than $1/N^2$ times the intensity at a principal maximum.

Answers

Chapter Opening Question

The shorter wavelength of a Blu-ray scanning laser gives it superior resolving power, so information can be more tightly packed onto a Blu-ray disc than a DVD. See Section 36.7 for details.

Test Your Understanding Questions

36.1 Answer: yes When you hear the voice of someone standing around a corner, you are hearing sound waves that underwent diffraction. If there were no diffraction of sound, you could hear sounds only from objects that were in plain view.

36.2 Answer: (ii), (i) and (iv) (tie), (iii) The angle θ of the first dark fringe is given by Eq. (36.2) with $m = 1$, or $\sin\theta = \lambda/a$. The larger the value of the ratio λ/a, the larger the value of $\sin\theta$ and hence the value of θ. The ratio λ/a in each case is (i) $(400\ \text{nm})/(0.20\ \text{mm}) = (4.0 \times 10^{-7}\ \text{m})/(2.0 \times 10^{-4}\ \text{m}) = 2.0 \times 10^{-3}$; (ii) $(600\ \text{nm})/(0.20\ \text{mm}) = (6.0 \times 10^{-7}\ \text{m})/(2.0 \times 10^{-4}\ \text{m}) = 3.0 \times 10^{-3}$; (iii) $(400\ \text{nm})/(0.30\ \text{mm}) = (4.0 \times 10^{-7}\ \text{m})/(3.0 \times 10^{-4}\ \text{m}) = 1.3 \times 10^{-3}$; (iv) $(600\ \text{nm})/(0.30\ \text{mm}) = (6.0 \times 10^{-7}\ \text{m})/(3.0 \times 10^{-4}\ \text{m}) = 2.0 \times 10^{-3}$.

36.3 Answers: (ii) and (iii) If the slit width a is less than the wavelength λ, there are no points in the diffraction pattern at which the intensity is zero (see Fig. 36.10a). The slit width is $0.0100\ \text{mm} = 1.00 \times 10^{-5}\ \text{m}$, so this condition is satisfied for (ii) $(\lambda = 10.6\ \mu\text{m} = 1.06 \times 10^{-5}\ \text{m})$ and (iii) $(\lambda = 1.00\ \text{mm} = 1.00 \times 10^{-3}\ \text{m})$ but not for (i) $(\lambda = 500\ \text{nm} = 5.00 \times 10^{-7}\ \text{m})$ or (iv) $(\lambda = 50.0\ \text{nm} = 5.00 \times 10^{-8}\ \text{m})$.

36.4 Answers: yes; $m_i = \pm5, \pm10, \ldots$ A "missing maximum" satisfies both $d\sin\theta = m_i\lambda$ (the condition for an interference maximum) and $a\sin\theta = m_d\lambda$ (the condition for a diffraction minimum). Substituting $d = 2.5a$, we can combine these two conditions into the relationship $m_i = 2.5m_d$. This is satisfied for $m_i = \pm5$ and $m_d = \pm2$ (the fifth interference maximum is missing because it coincides with the second diffraction minimum), $m_i = \pm10$ and $m_d = \pm4$ (the tenth interference maximum is missing because it coincides with the fourth diffraction minimum), and so on.

36.5 Answer: (i) As described in the text, the resolving power needed is $R = Nm = 1000$. In the first order ($m = 1$) we need $N = 1000$ slits, but in the fourth order ($m = 4$) we need only $N = R/m = 1000/4 = 250$ slits. (These numbers are only approximate because of the arbitrary nature of our criterion for resolution and because real gratings always have slight imperfections in the shapes and spacings of the slits.)

36.6 Answer: no The angular position of the mth maximum is given by Eq. (36.16), $2d\sin\theta = m\lambda$. With $d = 0.200\ \text{nm}$, $\lambda = 0.100\ \text{nm}$, and $m = 5$, this gives $\sin\theta = m\lambda/2d = (5)(0.100\ \text{nm})/(2)(0.200\ \text{nm}) = 1.25$. Since the sine function can never be greater than 1, this means that there is no solution to this equation and the $m = 5$ maximum does not appear.

36.7 Answer: (iii), (ii), (iv), (i) Rayleigh's criterion combined with Eq. (36.17) shows that the smaller the value of the ratio λ/D, the better the resolving power of a telescope of diameter D. For the four telescopes, this ratio is equal to (i) $(21\ \text{cm})/(100\ \text{m}) = (0.21\ \text{m})/(100\ \text{m}) = 2.1 \times 10^{-3}$; (ii) $(500\ \text{nm})/(2.0\ \text{m}) = (5.0 \times 10^{-7}\ \text{m})/(2.0\ \text{m}) = 2.5 \times 10^{-7}$; (iii) $(100\ \text{nm})/(1.0\ \text{m}) = (1.0 \times 10^{-7}\ \text{m})/(1.0\ \text{m}) = 1.0 \times 10^{-7}$; (iv) $(10\ \mu\text{m})/(2.0\ \text{m}) = (1.0 \times 10^{-5}\ \text{m})/(2.0\ \text{m}) = 5.0 \times 10^{-6}$.

Bridging Problem

Answers: 1.501×10^7 m/s or 5.00% of c; away from us

RELATIVITY

37

? At Brookhaven National Laboratory in New York, atomic nuclei are accelerated to 99.995% of the ultimate speed limit of the universe—the speed of light. Is there also an upper limit on the *kinetic energy* of a particle?

LEARNING GOALS

By studying this chapter, you will learn:

- The two postulates of Einstein's special theory of relativity, and what motivates these postulates.

- Why different observers can disagree about whether two events are simultaneous.

- How relativity predicts that moving clocks run slow, and that experimental evidence confirms this.

- How the length of an object changes due to the object's motion.

- How the velocity of an object depends on the frame of reference from which it is observed.

- How the theory of relativity modifies the relationship between velocity and momentum.

- How to solve problems involving work and kinetic energy for particles moving at relativistic speeds.

- Some of the key concepts of Einstein's general theory of relativity.

W hen the year 1905 began, Albert Einstein was an unknown 25-year-old clerk in the Swiss patent office. By the end of that amazing year he had published three papers of extraordinary importance. One was an analysis of Brownian motion; a second (for which he was awarded the Nobel Prize) was on the photoelectric effect. In the third, Einstein introduced his **special theory of relativity,** proposing drastic revisions in the Newtonian concepts of space and time.

The special theory of relativity has made wide-ranging changes in our understanding of nature, but Einstein based it on just two simple postulates. One states that the laws of physics are the same in all inertial frames of reference; the other states that the speed of light in vacuum is the same in all inertial frames. These innocent-sounding propositions have far-reaching implications. Here are three: (1) Events that are simultaneous for one observer may not be simultaneous for another. (2) When two observers moving relative to each other measure a time interval or a length, they may not get the same results. (3) For the conservation principles for momentum and energy to be valid in all inertial systems, Newton's second law and the equations for momentum and kinetic energy have to be revised.

Relativity has important consequences in *all* areas of physics, including electromagnetism, atomic and nuclear physics, and high-energy physics. Although many of the results derived in this chapter may run counter to your intuition, the theory is in solid agreement with experimental observations.

37.1 Invariance of Physical Laws

Let's take a look at the two postulates that make up the special theory of relativity. Both postulates describe what is seen by an observer in an *inertial frame of reference,* which we introduced in Section 4.2. The theory is "special" in the sense that it applies to observers in such special reference frames.

Einstein's First Postulate

Einstein's first postulate, called the **principle of relativity,** states: **The laws of physics are the same in every inertial frame of reference.** If the laws differed, that difference could distinguish one inertial frame from the others or make one frame somehow more "correct" than another. Here are two examples. Suppose you watch two children playing catch with a ball while the three of you are aboard a train moving with constant velocity. Your observations of the motion *of the ball,* no matter how carefully done, can't tell you how fast (or whether) the train is moving. This is because Newton's laws of motion are the same in every inertial frame.

Another example is the electromotive force (emf) induced in a coil of wire by a nearby moving permanent magnet. In the frame of reference in which the *coil* is stationary (Fig. 37.1a), the moving magnet causes a change of magnetic flux through the coil, and this induces an emf. In a different frame of reference in which the *magnet* is stationary (Fig. 37.1b), the motion of the coil through a magnetic field induces the emf. According to the principle of relativity, both of these frames of reference are equally valid. Hence the same emf must be induced in both situations shown in Fig. 37.1. As we saw in Chapter 29, this is indeed the case, so Faraday's law is consistent with the principle of relativity. Indeed, *all* of the laws of electromagnetism are the same in every inertial frame of reference.

Equally significant is the prediction of the speed of electromagnetic radiation, derived from Maxwell's equations (see Section 32.2). According to this analysis, light and all other electromagnetic waves travel in vacuum with a constant speed, now defined to equal exactly 299,792,458 m/s. (We often use the approximate value $c = 3.00 \times 10^8$ m/s, which is within one part in 1000 of the exact value.) As we will see, the speed of light in vacuum plays a central role in the theory of relativity.

Einstein's Second Postulate

During the 19th century, most physicists believed that light traveled through a hypothetical medium called the *ether,* just as sound waves travel through air. If so, the speed of light measured by observers would depend on their motion relative to the ether and would therefore be different in different directions. The Michelson-Morley experiment, described in Section 35.5, was an effort to detect motion of the earth relative to the ether. Einstein's conceptual leap was to recognize that if Maxwell's equations are valid in all inertial frames, then the speed of light in vacuum should also be the same in all frames and in all directions. In fact, Michelson and Morley detected *no* ether motion across the earth, and the ether concept has been discarded. Although Einstein may not have known about this negative result, it supported his bold hypothesis of the constancy of the speed of light in vacuum.

Einstein's second postulate states: **The speed of light in vacuum is the same in all inertial frames of reference and is independent of the motion of the source.**

Let's think about what this means. Suppose two observers measure the speed of light in vacuum. One is at rest with respect to the light source, and the other is moving away from it. Both are in inertial frames of reference. According to the principle of relativity, the two observers must obtain the same result, despite the fact that one is moving with respect to the other.

If this seems too easy, consider the following situation. A spacecraft moving past the earth at 1000 m/s fires a missile straight ahead with a speed of 2000 m/s (relative to the spacecraft) (Fig. 37.2). What is the missile's speed relative to the earth? Simple, you say; this is an elementary problem in relative velocity (see Section 3.5). The correct answer, according to Newtonian mechanics, is 3000 m/s.

37.1 The same emf is induced in the coil whether **(a)** the magnet moves relative to the coil or **(b)** the coil moves relative to the magnet.

(a)

(b)

Magnet moves ...

$\vec{v}$

N

Coil moves ...

N

S

$\vec{v}$

... same result

37.2 (a) Newtonian mechanics makes correct predictions about relatively slow-moving objects; (b) it makes incorrect predictions about the behavior of light.

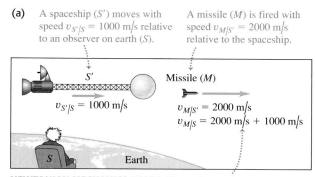

(a) A spaceship (S') moves with speed $v_{S'/S} = 1000$ m/s relative to an observer on earth (S). A missile (M) is fired with speed $v_{M/S'} = 2000$ m/s relative to the spaceship.

NEWTONIAN MECHANICS HOLDS: Newtonian mechanics tells us correctly that the missile moves with speed $v_{M/S} = 3000$ m/s relative to the observer on earth.

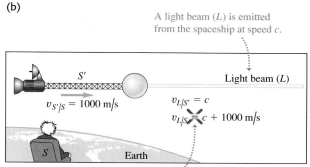

(b) A light beam (L) is emitted from the spaceship at speed c.

NEWTONIAN MECHANICS FAILS: Newtonian mechanics tells us *incorrectly* that the light moves at a speed greater than c relative to the observer on earth ... which would contradict Einstein's second postulate.

But now suppose the spacecraft turns on a searchlight, pointing in the same direction in which the missile was fired. An observer on the spacecraft measures the speed of light emitted by the searchlight and obtains the value c. According to Einstein's second postulate, the motion of the light after it has left the source cannot depend on the motion of the source. So the observer on earth who measures the speed of this same light must also obtain the value c, *not* $c + 1000$ m/s. This result contradicts our elementary notion of relative velocities, and it may not appear to agree with common sense. But "common sense" is intuition based on everyday experience, and this does not usually include measurements of the speed of light.

The Ultimate Speed Limit

Einstein's second postulate immediately implies the following result:

> **It is impossible for an inertial observer to travel at c, the speed of light in vacuum.**

We can prove this by showing that travel at c implies a logical contradiction. Suppose that the spacecraft S' in Fig. 37.2b is moving at the speed of light relative to an observer on the earth, so that $v_{S'/S} = c$. If the spacecraft turns on a headlight, the second postulate now asserts that the earth observer S measures the headlight beam to be also moving at c. Thus this observer measures that the headlight beam and the spacecraft move together and are always at the same point in space. But Einstein's second postulate also asserts that the headlight beam moves at a speed c relative to the spacecraft, so they *cannot* be at the same point in space. This contradictory result can be avoided only if it is impossible for an inertial observer, such as a passenger on the spacecraft, to move at c. As we go through our discussion of relativity, you may find yourself asking the question Einstein asked himself as a 16-year-old student, "What would I see if I were traveling at the speed of light?" Einstein realized only years later that his question's basic flaw was that he could *not* travel at c.

The Galilean Coordinate Transformation

Let's restate this argument symbolically, using two inertial frames of reference, labeled S for the observer on earth and S' for the moving spacecraft, as shown in Fig. 37.3. To keep things as simple as possible, we have omitted the z-axes. The x-axes of the two frames lie along the same line, but the origin O' of frame S' moves relative to the origin O of frame S with constant velocity u along the common x-x'-axis. We on earth set our clocks so that the two origins coincide at time $t = 0$, so their separation at a later time t is ut.

37.3 The position of particle P can be described by the coordinates x and y in frame of reference S or by x' and y' in frame S'.

Frame S' moves relative to frame S with constant velocity u along the common x-x'-axis.

Origins O and O' coincide at time $t = 0 = t'$.

CAUTION **Choose your inertial frame coordinates wisely** Many of the equations derived in this chapter are true *only* if you define your inertial reference frames as stated in the preceding paragraph. For instance, the positive *x*-direction must be the direction in which the origin O' moves relative to the origin O. In Fig. 37.3 this direction is to the right; if instead O' moves to the left relative to O, you must define the positive *x*-direction to be to the left

Now think about how we describe the motion of a particle P. This might be an exploratory vehicle launched from the spacecraft or a pulse of light from a laser. We can describe the *position* of this particle by using the earth coordinates (x, y, z) in S or the spacecraft coordinates (x', y', z') in S'. Figure 37.3 shows that these are simply related by

$$x = x' + ut \qquad y = y' \qquad z = z' \qquad \text{(Galilean coordinate transformation)} \qquad (37.1)$$

These equations, based on the familiar Newtonian notions of space and time, are called the **Galilean coordinate transformation.**

If particle P moves in the *x*-direction, its instantaneous velocity v_x as measured by an observer stationary in S is $v_x = dx/dt$. Its velocity v'_x as measured by an observer stationary in S' is $v'_x = dx'/dt$. We can derive a relationship between v_x and v'_x by taking the derivative with respect to t of the first of Eqs. (37.1):

$$\frac{dx}{dt} = \frac{dx'}{dt} + u$$

Now dx/dt is the velocity v_x measured in S, and dx'/dt is the velocity v'_x measured in S', so we get the *Galilean velocity transformation* for one-dimensional motion:

$$v_x = v'_x + u \qquad \text{(Galilean velocity transformation)} \qquad (37.2)$$

Although the notation differs, this result agrees with our discussion of relative velocities in Section 3.5.

Now here's the fundamental problem. Applied to the speed of light in vacuum, Eq. (37.2) says that $c = c' + u$. Einstein's second postulate, supported subsequently by a wealth of experimental evidence, says that $c = c'$. This is a genuine inconsistency, not an illusion, and it demands resolution. If we accept this postulate, we are forced to conclude that Eqs. (37.1) and (37.2) *cannot* be precisely correct, despite our convincing derivation. These equations have to be modified to bring them into harmony with this principle.

The resolution involves some very fundamental modifications in our kinematic concepts. The first idea to be changed is the seemingly obvious assumption that the observers in frames S and S' use the same *time scale*, formally stated as $t = t'$. Alas, we are about to show that this everyday assumption cannot be correct; the two observers *must* have different time scales. We must define the velocity v' in frame S' as $v' = dx'/dt'$, not as dx'/dt; the two quantities are not the same. The difficulty lies in the concept of *simultaneity,* which is our next topic. A careful analysis of simultaneity will help us develop the appropriate modifications of our notions about space and time.

Test Your Understanding of Section 37.1 As a high-speed spaceship flies past you, it fires a strobe light that sends out a pulse of light in all directions. An observer aboard the spaceship measures a spherical wave front that spreads away from the spaceship with the same speed c in all directions. (a) What is the shape of the wave front that *you* measure? (i) spherical; (ii) ellipsoidal, with the longest axis of the ellipsoid along the direction of the spaceship's motion; (iii) ellipsoidal, with the shortest axis of the ellipsoid along the direction of the spaceship's motion; (iv) not enough information is given to decide. (b) Is the wave front centered on the spaceship?

37.2 Relativity of Simultaneity

Measuring times and time intervals involves the concept of **simultaneity.** In a given frame of reference, an **event** is an occurrence that has a definite position and time (Fig. 37.4). When you say that you awoke at seven o'clock, you mean that two events (your awakening and your clock showing 7:00) occurred *simultaneously.* The fundamental problem in measuring time intervals is this: In general, two events that are simultaneous in one frame of reference are *not* simultaneous in a second frame that is moving relative to the first, even if both are inertial frames.

A Thought Experiment in Simultaneity

This may seem to be contrary to common sense. To illustrate the point, here is a version of one of Einstein's *thought experiments*—mental experiments that follow concepts to their logical conclusions. Imagine a train moving with a speed comparable to c, with uniform velocity (Fig. 37.5). Two lightning bolts strike a passenger car, one near each end. Each bolt leaves a mark on the car and one on the ground at the instant the bolt hits. The points on the ground are labeled A and B in the figure, and the corresponding points on the car are A' and B'. Stanley is stationary on the ground at O, midway between A and B. Mavis is moving with the train at O' in the middle of the passenger car, midway between A' and B'. Both Stanley and Mavis see both light flashes emitted from the points where the lightning strikes.

Suppose the two wave fronts from the lightning strikes reach Stanley at O simultaneously. He knows that he is the same distance from B and A, so Stanley concludes that the two bolts struck B and A simultaneously. Mavis agrees that the two wave fronts reached Stanley at the same time, but she disagrees that the flashes were emitted simultaneously.

Stanley and Mavis agree that the two wave fronts do not reach Mavis at the same time. Mavis at O' is moving to the right with the train, so she runs into the wave front from B' *before* the wave front from A' catches up to her. However, because she is in the middle of the passenger car equidistant from A' and B', her observation is that both wave fronts took the same time to reach her because both moved the same distance at the same speed c. (Recall that the speed of each wave front with respect to *either* observer is c.) Thus she concludes that the lightning bolt at B' struck *before* the one at A'. Stanley at O measures the two events to be simultaneous, but Mavis at O' does not! *Whether or not two events at different x-axis locations are simultaneous depends on the state of motion of the observer.*

You may want to argue that in this example the lightning bolts really *are* simultaneous and that if Mavis at O' could communicate with the distant points without the time delay caused by the finite speed of light, she would realize this. But that would be erroneous; the finite speed of information transmission is not the real issue. If O' is midway between A' and B', then in her frame of reference the time for a signal to travel from A' to O' is the same as that from B' to O'. Two signals arrive simultaneously at O' only if they were emitted simultaneously at A' and B'. In this example they *do not* arrive simultaneously at O', and so Mavis must conclude that the events at A' and B' were *not* simultaneous.

Furthermore, there is no basis for saying that Stanley is right and Mavis is wrong, or vice versa. According to the principle of relativity, no inertial frame of reference is more correct than any other in the formulation of physical laws. Each observer is correct *in his or her own frame of reference.* In other words, simultaneity is not an absolute concept. Whether two events are simultaneous depends on the frame of reference. As we mentioned at the beginning of this section, simultaneity plays an essential role in measuring time intervals. It follows that *the time interval between two events may be different in different frames of reference.* So our next task is to learn how to compare time intervals in different frames of reference.

37.4 An event has a definite position and time—for instance, on the pavement directly below the center of the Eiffel Tower at midnight on New Year's Eve.

37.5 A thought experiment in simultaneity.

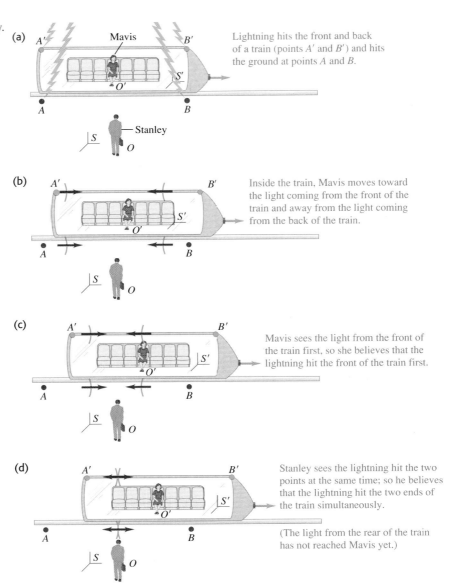

(a) Lightning hits the front and back of a train (points A' and B') and hits the ground at points A and B.

Mavis

(b) Inside the train, Mavis moves toward the light coming from the front of the train and away from the light coming from the back of the train.

(c) Mavis sees the light from the front of the train first, so she believes that the lightning hit the front of the train first.

(d) Stanley sees the lightning hit the two points at the same time; so he believes that the lightning hit the two ends of the train simultaneously.

(The light from the rear of the train has not reached Mavis yet.)

Test Your Understanding of Section 37.2 Stanley, who works for the rail system shown in Fig. 37.5, has carefully synchronized the clocks at all of the rail stations. At the moment that Stanley measures all of the clocks striking noon, Mavis is on a high-speed passenger car traveling from Ogdenville toward North Haverbrook. According to Mavis, when the Ogdenville clock strikes noon, what time is it in North Haverbrook? (i) noon; (ii) before noon; (iii) after noon.

MasteringPHYSICS

ActivPhysics 17.1: Relativity of Time

37.3 Relativity of Time Intervals

We can derive a quantitative relationship between time intervals in different coordinate systems. To do this, let's consider another thought experiment. As before, a frame of reference S' moves along the common x-x'-axis with constant speed u relative to a frame S. As discussed in Section 37.1, u must be less than the speed of light c. Mavis, who is riding along with frame S', measures the time interval between two events that occur at the *same* point in space. Event 1 is when a flash of light from a light source leaves O'. Event 2 is when the flash returns to O', having been reflected from a mirror a distance d away, as shown in Fig. 37.6a. We label the time interval Δt_0, using the subscript zero as a reminder that the apparatus is at rest, with zero velocity, in frame S'. The flash of light moves a total distance $2d$, so the time interval is

37.6 (a) Mavis, in frame of reference S', observes a light pulse emitted from a source at O' and reflected back along the same line. (b) How Stanley (in frame of reference S) and Mavis observe the same light pulse. The positions of O' at the times of departure and return of the pulse are shown.

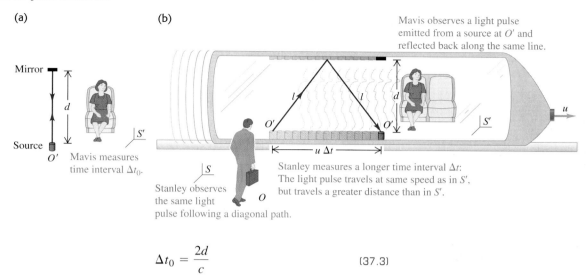

(a)

Mirror

d

Source

O' Mavis measures time interval Δt_0.

S'

(b)

Mavis observes a light pulse emitted from a source at O' and reflected back along the same line.

l l d

O' O'

$u\,\Delta t$

u

S'

S

Stanley observes the same light pulse following a diagonal path.

O

Stanley measures a longer time interval Δt: The light pulse travels at same speed as in S', but travels a greater distance than in S'.

$$\Delta t_0 = \frac{2d}{c} \tag{37.3}$$

The round-trip time measured by Stanley in frame S is a different interval Δt; in his frame of reference the two events occur at *different* points in space. During the time Δt, the source moves relative to S a distance $u\,\Delta t$ (Fig. 37.6b). In S' the round-trip distance is $2d$ perpendicular to the relative velocity, but the round-trip distance in S is the longer distance $2l$, where

$$l = \sqrt{d^2 + \left(\frac{u\,\Delta t}{2}\right)^2}$$

In writing this expression, we have assumed that both observers measure the same distance d. We will justify this assumption in the next section. The speed of light is the same for both observers, so the round-trip time measured in S is

$$\Delta t = \frac{2l}{c} = \frac{2}{c}\sqrt{d^2 + \left(\frac{u\,\Delta t}{2}\right)^2} \tag{37.4}$$

We would like to have a relationship between Δt and Δt_0 that is independent of d. To get this, we solve Eq. (37.3) for d and substitute the result into Eq. (37.4), obtaining

$$\Delta t = \frac{2}{c}\sqrt{\left(\frac{c\,\Delta t_0}{2}\right)^2 + \left(\frac{u\,\Delta t}{2}\right)^2} \tag{37.5}$$

Now we square this and solve for Δt; the result is

$$\Delta t = \frac{\Delta t_0}{\sqrt{1 - u^2/c^2}}$$

Since the quantity $\sqrt{1 - u^2/c^2}$ is less than 1, Δt is greater than Δt_0: Thus Stanley measures a *longer* round-trip time for the light pulse than does Mavis.

Time Dilation

We may generalize this important result. In a particular frame of reference, suppose that two events occur at the same point in space. The time interval between these events, as measured by an observer at rest in this same frame (which we call the *rest frame* of this observer), is Δt_0. Then an observer in a second frame moving with constant speed u relative to the rest frame will measure the time interval to be Δt, where

37.7 This image shows an exploding star, called a *supernova,* within a distant galaxy. The brightness of a typical supernova decays at a certain rate. But supernovae that are moving away from us at a substantial fraction of the speed of light decay more slowly, in accordance with Eq. (37.6). The decaying supernova is a moving "clock" that runs slow.

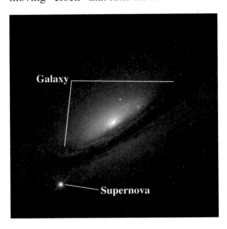

Galaxy

Supernova

37.8 The quantity $\gamma = 1/\sqrt{1 - u^2/c^2}$ as a function of the relative speed u of two frames of reference.

As speed u approaches the speed of light c, γ approaches infinity.

$$\gamma = \frac{1}{\sqrt{1 - u^2/c^2}}$$

Speed u

$$\Delta t = \frac{\Delta t_0}{\sqrt{1 - u^2/c^2}} \quad \text{(time dilation)} \tag{37.6}$$

We recall that no inertial observer can travel at $u = c$ and we note that $\sqrt{1 - u^2/c^2}$ is imaginary for $u > c$. Thus Eq. (37.6) gives sensible results only when $u < c$. The denominator of Eq. (37.6) is always smaller than 1, so Δt is always *larger* than Δt_0. Thus we call this effect **time dilation.**

Think of an old-fashioned pendulum clock that has one second between ticks, as measured by Mavis in the clock's rest frame; this is Δt_0. If the clock's rest frame is moving relative to Stanley, he measures a time between ticks Δt that is longer than one second. In brief, *observers measure any clock to run slow if it moves relative to them* (Fig. 37.7). Note that this conclusion is a direct result of the fact that the speed of light in vacuum is the same in both frames of reference.

The quantity $1/\sqrt{1 - u^2/c^2}$ in Eq. (37.6) appears so often in relativity that it is given its own symbol γ (the Greek letter gamma):

$$\gamma = \frac{1}{\sqrt{1 - u^2/c^2}} \tag{37.7}$$

In terms of this symbol, we can express the time dilation formula, Eq. (37.6), as

$$\Delta t = \gamma \, \Delta t_0 \quad \text{(time dilation)} \tag{37.8}$$

As a further simplification, u/c is sometimes given the symbol β (the Greek letter beta); then $\gamma = 1/\sqrt{1 - \beta^2}$.

Figure 37.8 shows a graph of γ as a function of the relative speed u of two frames of reference. When u is very small compared to c, u^2/c^2 is much smaller than 1 and γ is very nearly *equal* to 1. In that limit, Eqs. (37.6) and (37.8) approach the Newtonian relationship $\Delta t = \Delta t_0$, corresponding to the same time interval in all frames of reference.

If the relative speed u is great enough that γ is appreciably greater than 1, the speed is said to be *relativistic;* if the difference between γ and 1 is negligibly small, the speed u is called *nonrelativistic.* Thus $u = 6.00 \times 10^7$ m/s $= 0.200c$ (for which $\gamma = 1.02$) is a relativistic speed, but $u = 6.00 \times 10^4$ m/s $= 0.000200c$ (for which $\gamma = 1.00000002$) is a nonrelativistic speed.

Proper Time

There is only one frame of reference in which a clock is at rest, and there are infinitely many in which it is moving. Therefore the time interval measured between two events (such as two ticks of the clock) that occur at the same point in a particular frame is a more fundamental quantity than the interval between events at different points. We use the term **proper time** to describe the time interval Δt_0 between two events that occur *at the same point.*

CAUTION **Measuring time intervals** It is important to note that the time interval Δt in Eq. (37.6) involves events that occur *at different space points* in the frame of reference S. Note also that any differences between Δt and the proper time Δt_0 are *not* caused by differences in the times required for light to travel from those space points to an observer at rest in S. We assume that our observer is able to correct for differences in light transit times, just as an astronomer who's observing the sun understands that an event seen now on earth actually occurred 500 s ago on the sun's surface. Alternatively, we can use *two* observers, one stationary at the location of the first event and the other at the second, each with his or her own clock. We can synchronize these two clocks without difficulty, as long as they are at rest in the same frame of reference. For example, we could send a light pulse simultaneously to the two clocks from a point midway between them. When the pulses arrive, the observers set their clocks to a prearranged time. (But note that clocks that are synchronized in one frame of reference *are not* in general synchronized in any other frame.)

In thought experiments, it's often helpful to imagine many observers with synchronized clocks at rest at various points in a particular frame of reference. We can picture a frame of reference as a coordinate grid with lots of synchronized clocks distributed around it, as suggested by Fig. 37.9. Only when a clock is moving relative to a given frame of reference do we have to watch for ambiguities of synchronization or simultaneity.

Throughout this chapter we will frequently use phrases like "Stanley *observes* that Mavis passes the point $x = 5.00$ m, $y = 0$, $z = 0$ at time 2.00 s." This means that Stanley is using a grid of clocks in his frame of reference, like the grid shown in Fig. 37.9, to record the time of an event. We could restate the phrase as "When Mavis passes the point at $x = 5.00$ m, $y = 0$, $z = 0$, the clock at that location in Stanley's frame of reference reads 2.00 s." We will avoid using phrases like "Stanley *sees* that Mavis is a certain point at a certain time," because there is a time delay for light to travel to Stanley's eye from the position of an event.

37.9 A frame of reference pictured as a coordinate system with a grid of synchronized clocks.

The grid is three dimensional; identical planes of clocks lie in front of and behind the page, connected by grid lines perpendicular to the page.

Problem-Solving Strategy 37.1   Time Dilation

IDENTIFY *the relevant concepts:* The concept of time dilation is used whenever we compare the time intervals between events as measured by observers in different inertial frames of reference.

SET UP *the problem* using the following steps:
1. First decide what two events define the beginning and the end of the time interval. Then identify the two frames of reference in which the time interval is measured.
2. Identify the target variable.

EXECUTE *the solution* as follows:
1. In many problems, the time interval as measured in one frame of reference is the *proper* time Δt_0. This is the time interval between two events in a frame of reference in which the two events occur at the same point in space. In a second frame of reference that has a speed u relative to that first frame, there is a longer time interval Δt between the same two events. In this second frame the two events occur at different points. You will need to decide in which frame the time interval is Δt_0 and in which frame it is Δt.
2. Use Eq. (37.6) or (37.8) to relate Δt_0 and Δt, and then solve for the target variable.

EVALUATE *your answer:* Note that Δt is never smaller than Δt_0, and u is never greater than c. If your results suggest otherwise, you need to rethink your calculation.

Example 37.1   Time dilation at $0.990c$

High-energy subatomic particles coming from space interact with atoms in the earth's upper atmosphere, in some cases producing unstable particles called *muons*. A muon decays into other particles with a mean lifetime of 2.20 μs $= 2.20 \times 10^{-6}$ s as measured in a reference frame in which it is at rest. If a muon is moving at $0.990c$ relative to the earth, what will an observer on earth measure its mean lifetime to be?

SOLUTION

IDENTIFY and SET UP: The muon's lifetime is the time interval between two events: the production of the muon and its subsequent decay. Our target variable is the lifetime in your frame of reference on earth, which we call frame S. We are given the lifetime in a frame S' in which the muon is at rest; this is its *proper* lifetime, $\Delta t_0 = 2.20$ μs. The relative speed of these two frames is $u = 0.990c$. We use Eq. (37.6) to relate the lifetimes in the two frames.

EXECUTE: The muon moves relative to the earth between the two events, so the two events occur at different positions as measured in S and the time interval in that frame is Δt (the target variable). From Eq. (37.6),

$$\Delta t = \frac{\Delta t_0}{\sqrt{1 - u^2/c^2}} = \frac{2.20 \ \mu\text{s}}{\sqrt{1 - (0.990)^2}} = 15.6 \ \mu\text{s}$$

EVALUATE: Our result predicts that the mean lifetime of the muon in the earth frame (Δt) is about seven times longer than in the muon's frame (Δt_0). This prediction has been verified experimentally; indeed, this was the first experimental confirmation of the time dilation formula, Eq. (37.6).

Example 37.2 **Time dilation at airliner speeds**

An airplane flies from San Francisco to New York (about 4800 km, or 4.80×10^6 m) at a steady speed of 300 m/s (about 670 mi/h). How much time does the trip take, as measured by an observer on the ground? By an observer in the plane?

SOLUTION

IDENTIFY and SET UP: Here we're interested in the time interval between the airplane departing from San Francisco and landing in New York. The target variables are the time intervals as measured in the frame of reference of the ground S and in the frame of reference of the airplane S'.

EXECUTE: As measured in S the two events occur at different positions (San Francisco and New York), so the time interval measured by ground observers corresponds to Δt in Eq. (37.6). To find it, we simply divide the distance by the speed $u = 300$ m/s:

$$\Delta t = \frac{4.80 \times 10^6 \text{ m}}{300 \text{ m/s}} = 1.60 \times 10^4 \text{ s} \quad \text{(about } 4\tfrac{1}{2} \text{ hours)}$$

In the airplane's frame S', San Francisco and New York passing under the plane occur at the same point (the position of the plane). Hence the time interval in the airplane is a proper time, corresponding to Δt_0 in Eq. (37.6). We have

$$\frac{u^2}{c^2} = \frac{(300 \text{ m/s})^2}{(3.00 \times 10^8 \text{ m/s})^2} = 1.00 \times 10^{-12}$$

From Eq. (37.6),

$$\Delta t_0 = (1.60 \times 10^4 \text{ s})\sqrt{1 - 1.00 \times 10^{-12}}$$

The square root can't be evaluated with adequate precision with an ordinary calculator. But we can approximate it using the binomial theorem (see Appendix B):

$$(1 - 1.00 \times 10^{-12})^{1/2} = 1 - \left(\tfrac{1}{2}\right)(1.00 \times 10^{-12}) + \cdots$$

The remaining terms are of the order of 10^{-24} or smaller and can be discarded. The approximate result for Δt_0 is

$$\Delta t_0 = (1.60 \times 10^4 \text{ s})(1 - 0.50 \times 10^{-12})$$

The proper time Δt_0, measured in the airplane, is very slightly less (by less than one part in 10^{12}) than the time measured on the ground.

EVALUATE: We don't notice such effects in everyday life. But present-day atomic clocks (see Section 1.3) can attain a precision of about one part in 10^{13}. A cesium clock traveling a long distance in an airliner has been used to measure this effect and thereby verify Eq. (37.6) even at speeds much less than c.

Example 37.3 **Just when is it proper?**

Mavis boards a spaceship and then zips past Stanley on earth at a relative speed of $0.600c$. At the instant she passes him, they both start timers. (a) A short time later Stanley measures that Mavis has traveled 9.00×10^7 m beyond him and is passing a space station. What does Stanley's timer read as she passes the space station? What does Mavis's timer read? (b) Stanley starts to blink just as Mavis flies past him, and Mavis measures that the blink takes 0.400 s from beginning to end. According to Stanley, what is the duration of his blink?

SOLUTION

IDENTIFY and SET UP: This problem involves time dilation for two *different* sets of events measured in Stanley's frame of reference (which we call S) and in Mavis's frame of reference (which we call S'). The two events of interest in part (a) are when Mavis passes Stanley and when Mavis passes the space station; the target variables are the time intervals between these two events as measured in S and in S'. The two events in part (b) are the start and finish of Stanley's blink; the target variable is the time interval between these two events as measured in S.

EXECUTE: (a) The two events, Mavis passing the earth and Mavis passing the space station, occur at different positions in Stanley's frame but at the same position in Mavis's frame. Hence Stanley

measures time interval Δt, while Mavis measures the *proper* time Δt_0. As measured by Stanley, Mavis moves at $0.600c = 0.600(3.00 \times 10^8 \text{ m/s}) = 1.80 \times 10^8$ m/s and travels 9.00×10^7 m in time $\Delta t = (9.00 \times 10^7 \text{m})/(1.80 \times 10^8 \text{ m/s}) = 0.500$ s. From Eq. (37.6), Mavis's timer reads an elapsed time of

$$\Delta t_0 = \Delta t \sqrt{1 - u^2/c^2} = 0.500 \text{ s} \sqrt{1 - (0.600)^2} = 0.400 \text{ s}$$

(b) It is tempting to answer that Stanley's blink lasts 0.500 s in his frame. But this is wrong, because we are now considering a *different* pair of events than in part (a). The start and finish of Stanley's blink occur at the same point in his frame S but at different positions in Mavis's frame S', so the time interval of 0.400 s that she measures between these events is equal to Δt. The duration of the blink measured on Stanley's timer is the proper time Δt_0:

$$\Delta t_0 = \Delta t \sqrt{1 - u^2/c^2} = 0.400 \text{ s} \sqrt{1 - (0.600)^2} = 0.320 \text{ s}$$

EVALUATE: This example illustrates the relativity of simultaneity. In Mavis's frame she passes the space station at the same instant that Stanley finishes his blink, 0.400 s after she passed Stanley. Hence these two events are simultaneous to Mavis in frame S'. But these two events are *not* simultaneous to Stanley in his frame S: According to his timer, he finishes his blink after 0.320 s and Mavis passes the space station after 0.500 s.

The Twin Paradox

Equations (37.6) and (37.8) for time dilation suggest an apparent paradox called the **twin paradox.** Consider identical twin astronauts named Eartha and Astrid.

Eartha remains on earth while her twin Astrid takes off on a high-speed trip through the galaxy. Because of time dilation, Eartha observes Astrid's heartbeat and all other life processes proceeding more slowly than her own. Thus to Eartha, Astrid ages more slowly; when Astrid returns to earth she is younger (has aged less) than Eartha.

Now here is the paradox: All inertial frames are equivalent. Can't Astrid make exactly the same arguments to conclude that Eartha is in fact the younger? Then each twin measures the other to be younger when they're back together, and that's a paradox.

To resolve the paradox, we recognize that the twins are *not* identical in all respects. While Eartha remains in an approximately inertial frame at all times, Astrid must *accelerate* with respect to that inertial frame during parts of her trip in order to leave, turn around, and return to earth. Eartha's reference frame is always approximately inertial; Astrid's is often far from inertial. Thus there is a real physical difference between the circumstances of the two twins. Careful analysis shows that Eartha is correct; when Astrid returns, she *is* younger than Eartha.

Test Your Understanding of Section 37.3 Samir (who is standing on the ground) starts his stopwatch at the instant that Maria flies past him in her spaceship at a speed of 0.600c. At the same instant, Maria starts her stopwatch. (a) As measured in Samir's frame of reference, what is the reading on Maria's stopwatch at the instant that Samir's stopwatch reads 10.0 s? (i) 10.0 s; (ii) less than 10.0 s; (iii) more than 10.0 s. (b) As measured in Maria's frame of reference, what is the reading on Samir's stopwatch at the instant that Maria's stopwatch reads 10.0 s? (i) 10.0 s; (ii) less than 10.0 s; (iii) more than 10.0 s.

37.4 Relativity of Length

Not only does the time interval between two events depend on the observer's frame of reference, but the *distance* between two points may also depend on the observer's frame of reference. The concept of simultaneity is involved. Suppose you want to measure the length of a moving car. One way is to have two assistants make marks on the pavement at the positions of the front and rear bumpers. Then you measure the distance between the marks. But your assistants have to make their marks *at the same time*. If one marks the position of the front bumper at one time and the other marks the position of the rear bumper half a second later, you won't get the car's true length. Since we've learned that simultaneity isn't an absolute concept, we have to proceed with caution.

Lengths Parallel to the Relative Motion

To develop a relationship between lengths that are measured parallel to the direction of motion in various coordinate systems, we consider another thought experiment. We attach a light source to one end of a ruler and a mirror to the other end. The ruler is at rest in reference frame S', and its length in this frame is l_0 (Fig. 37.10a). Then the time Δt_0 required for a light pulse to make the round trip from source to mirror and back is

$$\Delta t_0 = \frac{2l_0}{c} \qquad (37.9)$$

This is a proper time interval because departure and return occur at the same point in S'.

In reference frame S the ruler is moving to the right with speed u during this travel of the light pulse (Fig. 37.10b). The length of the ruler in S is l, and the time of travel from source to mirror, as measured in S, is Δt_1. During this interval

MasteringPHYSICS

ActivPhysics 17.2: Relativity of Length

37.10 (a) A ruler is at rest in Mavis's frame S'. A light pulse is emitted from a source at one end of the ruler, reflected by a mirror at the other end, and returned to the source position. (b) Motion of the light pulse as measured in Stanley's frame S.

(a)

Source

Mirror

Mavis

l_0

S'

The ruler is stationary in Mavis's frame of reference S'. The light pulse travels a distance l_0 from the light source to the mirror.

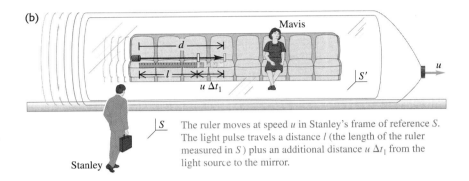

(b)

Mavis

d

l

$u\,\Delta t_1$

S'

u

S

Stanley

The ruler moves at speed u in Stanley's frame of reference S. The light pulse travels a distance l (the length of the ruler measured in S) plus an additional distance $u\,\Delta t_1$ from the light source to the mirror.

the ruler, with source and mirror attached, moves a distance $u\,\Delta t_1$. The total length of path d from source to mirror is not l, but rather

$$d = l + u\,\Delta t_1 \qquad (37.10)$$

The light pulse travels with speed c, so it is also true that

$$d = c\,\Delta t_1 \qquad (37.11)$$

Combining Eqs. (37.10) and (37.11) to eliminate d, we find

$$c\,\Delta t_1 = l + u\,\Delta t_1 \quad \text{or}$$

$$\Delta t_1 = \frac{l}{c - u} \qquad (37.12)$$

(Dividing the distance l by $c - u$ does *not* mean that light travels with speed $c - u$, but rather that the distance the pulse travels in S is greater than l.)

In the same way we can show that the time Δt_2 for the return trip from mirror to source is

$$\Delta t_2 = \frac{l}{c + u} \qquad (37.13)$$

The *total* time $\Delta t = \Delta t_1 + \Delta t_2$ for the round trip, as measured in S, is

$$\Delta t = \frac{l}{c - u} + \frac{l}{c + u} = \frac{2l}{c(1 - u^2/c^2)} \qquad (37.14)$$

We also know that Δt and Δt_0 are related by Eq. (37.6) because Δt_0 is a proper time in S'. Thus Eq. (37.9) for the round-trip time in the rest frame S' of the ruler becomes

$$\Delta t\sqrt{1 - \frac{u^2}{c^2}} = \frac{2l_0}{c} \qquad (37.15)$$

Finally, combining Eqs. (37.14) and (37.15) to eliminate Δt and simplifying, we obtain

$$l = l_0\sqrt{1 - \frac{u^2}{c^2}} = \frac{l_0}{\gamma} \qquad \text{(length contraction)} \qquad (37.16)$$

[We have used the quantity $\gamma = 1/\sqrt{1 - u^2/c^2}$ defined in Eq. (37.7).] Thus the length l measured in S, in which the ruler is moving, is *shorter* than the length l_0 measured in its rest frame S'.

CAUTION **Length contraction is real** This is *not* an optical illusion! The ruler really is shorter in reference frame S than it is in S'.

A length measured in the frame in which the body is at rest (the rest frame of the body) is called a **proper length;** thus l_0 is a proper length in S', and the length measured in any other frame moving relative to S' is *less than* l_0. This effect is called **length contraction.**

When u is very small in comparison to c, γ approaches 1. Thus in the limit of small speeds we approach the Newtonian relationship $l = l_0$. This and the corresponding result for time dilation show that Eqs. (37.1), the Galilean coordinate transformation, are usually sufficiently accurate for relative speeds much smaller than c. If u is a reasonable fraction of c, however, the quantity $\sqrt{1 - u^2/c^2}$ can be appreciably less than 1. Then l can be substantially smaller than l_0, and the effects of length contraction can be substantial (Fig. 37.11).

Lengths Perpendicular to the Relative Motion

We have derived Eq. (37.16) for lengths measured in the direction *parallel* to the relative motion of the two frames of reference. Lengths that are measured *perpendicular* to the direction of motion are *not* contracted. To prove this, consider two identical meter sticks. One stick is at rest in frame S and lies along the positive y-axis with one end at O, the origin of S. The other is at rest in frame S' and lies along the positive y'-axis with one end at O', the origin of S'. Frame S' moves in the positive x-direction relative to frame S. Observers Stanley and Mavis, at rest in S and S' respectively, station themselves at the 50-cm mark of their sticks. At the instant the two origins coincide, the two sticks lie along the same line. At this instant, Mavis makes a mark on Stanley's stick at the point that coincides with her own 50-cm mark, and Stanley does the same to Mavis's stick.

Suppose for the sake of argument that Stanley observes Mavis's stick as longer than his own. Then the mark Stanley makes on her stick is *below* its center. In that case, Mavis will think Stanley's stick has become shorter, since half of its length coincides with *less* than half her stick's length. So Mavis observes moving sticks getting shorter and Stanley observes them getting longer. But this implies an asymmetry between the two frames that contradicts the basic postulate of relativity that tells us all inertial frames are equivalent. We conclude that consistency with the postulates of relativity requires that both observers measure the rulers as having the *same* length, even though to each observer one of them is stationary and the other is moving (Fig. 37.12). So *there is no length contraction perpendicular to the direction of relative motion of the coordinate systems.* We used this result in our derivation of Eq. (37.6) in assuming that the distance d is the same in both frames of reference.

37.11 The speed at which electrons traverse the 3-km beam line of the SLAC National Accelerator Laboratory is slower than c by less than 1 cm/s. As measured in the reference frame of such an electron, the beam line (which extends from the top to the bottom of this photograph) is only about 15 cm long!

Beam line

37.12 The meter sticks are perpendicular to the relative velocity. For any value of u, both Stanley and Mavis measure either meter stick to have a length of 1 meter.

For example, suppose a moving rod of length l_0 makes an angle θ_0 with the direction of relative motion (the x-axis) as measured in its rest frame. Its length component in that frame parallel to the motion, $l_0 \cos\theta_0$, is contracted to $(l_0 \cos\theta_0)/\gamma$. However, its length component perpendicular to the motion, $l_0 \sin\theta_0$, remains the same.

Problem-Solving Strategy 37.2 | Length Contraction

IDENTIFY *the relevant concepts:* The concept of length contraction is used whenever we compare the length of an object as measured by observers in different inertial frames of reference.

SET UP *the problem* using the following steps:
1. Decide what defines the length in question. If the problem describes an object such as a ruler, it is just the distance between the ends of the object. If the problem is about a distance between two points in space, it helps to envision an object like a ruler that extends from one point to the other.
2. Identify the target variable.

EXECUTE *the solution* as follows:
1. Determine the reference frame in which the object in question is at rest. In this frame, the length of the object is its proper length l_0. In a second reference frame moving at speed u relative to the first frame, the object has contracted length l.
2. Keep in mind that length contraction occurs only for lengths parallel to the direction of relative motion of the two frames. Any length that is perpendicular to the relative motion is the same in both frames.
3. Use Eq. (37.16) to relate l and l_0, and then solve for the target variable.

EVALUATE *your answer:* Check that your answers make sense: l is never larger than l_0, and u is never greater than c.

Example 37.4 | How long is the spaceship?

A spaceship flies past earth at a speed of $0.990c$. A crew member on board the spaceship measures its length, obtaining the value 400 m. What length do observers measure on earth?

37.13 Measuring the length of a moving spaceship.

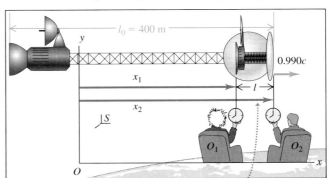

The two observers on earth (S) must measure x_2 and x_1 simultaneously to obtain the correct length $l = x_2 - x_1$ in their frame of reference.

SOLUTION

IDENTIFY and SET UP: This problem is about the nose-to-tail length of the spaceship as measured on the spaceship and on earth. This length is along the direction of relative motion (Fig. 37.13), so there will be length contraction. The spaceship's 400-m length is the *proper* length l_0 because it is measured in the frame in which the spaceship is at rest. Our target variable is the length l measured in the earth frame, relative to which the spaceship is moving at $u = 0.990c$.

EXECUTE: From Eq. (37.16), the length in the earth frame is

$$ l = l_0 \sqrt{1 - \frac{u^2}{c^2}} = (400 \text{ m})\sqrt{1 - (0.990)^2} = 56.4 \text{ m} $$

EVALUATE: The spaceship is shorter in a frame in which it is in motion than in a frame in which it is at rest. To measure the length l, two earth observers with synchronized clocks could measure the positions of the two ends of the spaceship simultaneously in the earth's reference frame, as shown in Fig. 37.13. (These two measurements will *not* appear simultaneous to an observer in the spaceship.)

Example 37.5 | How far apart are the observers?

Observers O_1 and O_2 in Fig. 37.13 are 56.4 m apart on the earth. How far apart does the spaceship crew measure them to be?

from O_1 to O_2 and is at rest in the earth frame in which the observers are at rest. Our target variable is the length l of this ruler measured in the spaceship frame, in which the earth and ruler are moving at $u = 0.990c$.

SOLUTION

IDENTIFY and SET UP: In this example the 56.4-m distance is the *proper* length l_0. It represents the length of a ruler that extends

EXECUTE: As in Example 37.4, but with $l_0 = 56.4$ m,

$$l = l_0 \sqrt{1 - \frac{u^2}{c^2}} = (56.4 \text{ m}) \sqrt{1 - (0.990)^2} = 7.96 \text{ m}$$

EVALUATE: This answer does *not* say that the crew measures their spaceship to be both 400 m long and 7.96 m long. As measured on earth, the tail of the spacecraft is at the position of O_1 at the same instant that the nose of the spacecraft is at the position of O_2. Hence the length of the spaceship measured on earth equals the 56.4-m distance between O_1 and O_2. But in the spaceship frame O_1 and O_2 are only 7.96 m apart, and the nose (which is 400 m in front of the tail) passes O_2 before the tail passes O_1.

How an Object Moving Near c Would Appear

Let's think a little about the visual appearance of a moving three-dimensional body. If we could see the positions of all points of the body simultaneously, it would appear to shrink only in the direction of motion. But we *don't* see all the points simultaneously; light from points farther from us takes longer to reach us than does light from points near to us, so we see the farther points at the positions they had at earlier times.

Suppose we have a rectangular rod with its faces parallel to the coordinate planes. When we look end-on at the center of the closest face of such a rod at rest, we see only that face. (See the center rod in computer-generated Fig. 37.14a.) But when that rod is moving past us toward the right at an appreciable fraction of the speed of light, we may also see its left side because of the earlier-time effect just described. That is, we can see some points that we couldn't see when the rod was at rest because the rod moves out of the way of the light rays from those points to us. Conversely, some light that can get to us when the rod is at rest is blocked by the moving rod. Because of all this, the rods in Figs. 37.14b and 37.14c appear rotated and distorted.

Test Your Understanding of Section 37.4 A miniature spaceship is flying past you, moving horizontally at a substantial fraction of the speed of light. At a certain instant, you observe that the nose and tail of the spaceship align exactly with the two ends of a meter stick that you hold in your hands. Rank the following distances in order from longest to shortest: (i) the proper length of the meter stick; (ii) the proper length of the spaceship; (iii) the length of the spaceship measured in your frame of reference; (iv) the length of the meter stick measured in the spaceship's frame of reference.

37.14 Computer simulation of the appearance of an array of 25 rods with square cross section. The center rod is viewed end-on. The simulation ignores color changes in the array caused by the Doppler effect (see Section 37.6).

(a) Array at rest

(b) Array moving to the right at 0.2c

(c) Array moving to the right at 0.9c

37.5 The Lorentz Transformations

In Section 37.1 we discussed the Galilean coordinate transformation equations, Eqs. (37.1). They relate the coordinates (x, y, z) of a point in frame of reference S to the coordinates (x', y', z') of the point in a second frame S'. The second frame moves with constant speed u relative to S in the positive direction along the common x-x'-axis. This transformation also assumes that the time scale is the same in the two frames of reference, as expressed by the additional relationship $t = t'$. This Galilean transformation, as we have seen, is valid only in the limit when u approaches zero. We are now ready to derive more general transformations that are consistent with the principle of relativity. The more general relationships are called the **Lorentz transformations.**

The Lorentz Coordinate Transformation

Our first question is this: When an event occurs at point (x, y, z) at time t, as observed in a frame of reference S, what are the coordinates (x', y', z') and time t' of the event as observed in a second frame S' moving relative to S with constant speed u in the $+x$-direction?

To derive the coordinate transformation, we refer to Fig. 37.15 (next page), which is the same as Fig. 37.3. As before, we assume that the origins coincide at the initial time $t = 0 = t'$. Then in S the distance from O to O' at time t is

37.15 As measured in frame of reference S, x' is contracted to x'/γ, so $x = ut + x'/\gamma$ and $x' = \gamma(x - ut)$.

Frame S' moves relative to frame S with constant velocity u along the common x-x'-axis.

Origins O and O' coincide at time $t = 0 = t'$.

The Lorentz coordinate transformation relates the spacetime coordinates of an event as measured in the two frames: (x, y, z, t) in frame S and (x', y', z', t') in frame S'.

still ut. The coordinate x' is a *proper length* in S', so in S it is contracted by the factor $1/\gamma = \sqrt{1 - u^2/c^2}$, as in Eq. (37.16). Thus the distance x from O to P, as seen in S, is not simply $x = ut + x'$, as in the Galilean coordinate transformation, but

$$x = ut + x'\sqrt{1 - \frac{u^2}{c^2}} \qquad (37.17)$$

Solving this equation for x', we obtain

$$x' = \frac{x - ut}{\sqrt{1 - u^2/c^2}} \qquad (37.18)$$

Equation (37.18) is part of the Lorentz coordinate transformation; another part is the equation giving t' in terms of x and t. To obtain this, we note that the principle of relativity requires that the *form* of the transformation from S to S' be identical to that from S' to S. The only difference is a change in the sign of the relative velocity component u. Thus from Eq. (37.17) it must be true that

$$x' = -ut' + x\sqrt{1 - \frac{u^2}{c^2}} \qquad (37.19)$$

We now equate Eqs. (37.18) and (37.19) to eliminate x'. This gives us an equation for t' in terms of x and t. We leave the algebraic details for you to work out; the result is

$$t' = \frac{t - ux/c^2}{\sqrt{1 - u^2/c^2}} \qquad (37.20)$$

As we discussed previously, lengths perpendicular to the direction of relative motion are not affected by the motion, so $y' = y$ and $z' = z$.

Collecting all these transformation equations, we have

$$x' = \frac{x - ut}{\sqrt{1 - u^2/c^2}} = \gamma(x - ut)$$

$$y' = y$$
$$z' = z \qquad \text{(Lorentz coordinate} \atop \text{transformation)} \qquad (37.21)$$

$$t' = \frac{t - ux/c^2}{\sqrt{1 - u^2/c^2}} = \gamma(t - ux/c^2)$$

These equations are the *Lorentz coordinate transformation*, the relativistic generalization of the Galilean coordinate transformation, Eqs. (37.1) and $t = t'$. For values of u that approach zero, the radicals in the denominators and γ approach 1, and the ux/c^2 term approaches zero. In this limit, Eqs. (37.21) become identical to Eqs. (37.1) along with $t = t'$. In general, though, both the coordinates and time of an event in one frame depend on its coordinates and time in another frame. *Space and time have become intertwined; we can no longer say that length and time have absolute meanings independent of the frame of reference.* For this reason, we refer to time and the three dimensions of space collectively as a four-dimensional entity called **spacetime,** and we call (x, y, z, t) together the **spacetime coordinates** of an event.

The Lorentz Velocity Transformation

We can use Eqs. (37.21) to derive the relativistic generalization of the Galilean velocity transformation, Eq. (37.2). We consider only one-dimensional motion along the x-axis and use the term "velocity" as being short for the "x-component of the velocity." Suppose that in a time dt a particle moves a distance dx, as measured in frame S. We obtain the corresponding distance dx' and time dt' in S' by taking differentials of Eqs. (37.21):

$$dx' = \gamma(dx - u\,dt)$$

$$dt' = \gamma(dt - u\,dx/c^2)$$

We divide the first equation by the second and then divide the numerator and denominator of the result by dt to obtain

$$\frac{dx'}{dt'} = \frac{\dfrac{dx}{dt} - u}{1 - \dfrac{u}{c^2}\dfrac{dx}{dt}}$$

Now dx/dt is the velocity v_x in S, and dx'/dt' is the velocity v'_x in S', so we finally obtain the relativistic generalization

$$v'_x = \frac{v_x - u}{1 - uv_x/c^2} \qquad \text{(Lorentz velocity transformation)} \qquad (37.22)$$

When u and v_x are much smaller than c, the denominator in Eq. (37.22) approaches 1, and we approach the nonrelativistic result $v'_x = v_x - u$. The opposite extreme is the case $v_x = c$; then we find

$$v'_x = \frac{c - u}{1 - uc/c^2} = \frac{c(1 - u/c)}{1 - u/c} = c$$

This says that anything moving with velocity $v_x = c$ measured in S also has velocity $v'_x = c$ measured in S', despite the relative motion of the two frames. So Eq. (37.22) is consistent with Einstein's postulate that the speed of light in vacuum is the same in all inertial frames of reference.

The principle of relativity tells us there is no fundamental distinction between the two frames S and S'. Thus the expression for v_x in terms of v'_x must have the same form as Eq. (37.22), with v_x changed to v'_x, and vice versa, and the sign of u reversed. Carrying out these operations with Eq. (37.22), we find

$$v_x = \frac{v'_x + u}{1 + uv'_x/c^2} \qquad \text{(Lorentz velocity transformation)} \qquad (37.23)$$

This can also be obtained algebraically by solving Eq. (37.22) for v_x. Both Eqs. (37.22) and (37.23) are *Lorentz velocity transformations* for one-dimensional motion.

CAUTION **Use the correct reference frame coordinates** Keep in mind that the Lorentz transformation equations given by Eqs. (37.21), (37.22), and (37.23) assume that frame S' is moving in the positive x-direction with velocity u relative to frame S. You should always set up your coordinate system to follow this convention.

When u is less than c, the Lorentz velocity transformations show us that a body moving with a speed less than c in one frame of reference always has a speed less than c in *every other* frame of reference. This is one reason for concluding that no material body may travel with a speed equal to or greater than that of light in vacuum, relative to *any* inertial frame of reference. The relativistic generalizations of energy and momentum, which we will explore later, give further support to this hypothesis.

Problem-Solving Strategy 37.3   **Lorentz Transformations**

IDENTIFY *the relevant concepts:* The Lorentz *coordinate* transformation equations relate the spacetime coordinates of an event in one inertial reference frame to the coordinates of the same event in a second inertial frame. The Lorentz *velocity* transformation equations relate the velocity of an object in one inertial reference frame to its velocity in a second inertial frame.

SET UP *the problem* using the following steps:
1. Identify the target variable.
2. Define the two inertial frames S and S'. Remember that S' moves relative to S at a constant velocity u in the $+x$-direction.
3. If the coordinate transformation equations are needed, make a list of spacetime coordinates in the two frames, such as x_1, x_1', t_1, t_1', and so on. Label carefully which of these you know and which you don't.
4. In velocity-transformation problems, clearly identify u (the relative velocity of the two frames of reference), v_x (the velocity of the object relative to S), and v_x' (the velocity of the object relative to S').

EXECUTE *the solution* as follows:
1. In a coordinate-transformation problem, use Eqs. (37.21) to solve for the spacetime coordinates of the event as measured in S' in terms of the corresponding values in S. (If you need to solve for the spacetime coordinates in S in terms of the corresponding values in S', you can easily convert the expressions in Eqs. (37.21): Replace all of the primed quantities with unprimed ones, and vice versa, and replace u with $-u$.)
2. In a velocity-transformation problem, use either Eq. (37.22) or Eq. (37.23), as appropriate, to solve for the target variable.

EVALUATE *your answer:* Don't be discouraged if some of your results don't seem to make sense or if they disagree with "common sense." It takes time to develop intuition about relativity; you'll gain it with experience.

Example 37.6   **Was it received before it was sent?**

Winning an interstellar race, Mavis pilots her spaceship across a finish line in space at a speed of $0.600c$ relative to that line. A "hooray" message is sent from the back of her ship (event 2) at the instant (in her frame of reference) that the front of her ship crosses the line (event 1). She measures the length of her ship to be 300 m. Stanley is at the finish line and is at rest relative to it. When and where does he measure events 1 and 2 to occur?

SOLUTION

IDENTIFY and SET UP: This example involves the Lorentz coordinate transformation. Our derivation of this transformation assumes that the origins of frames S and S' coincide at $t = 0 = t'$. Thus for simplicity we fix the origin of S at the finish line and the origin of S' at the front of the spaceship so that Stanley and Mavis measure event 1 to be at $x = 0 = x'$ and $t = 0 = t'$.

Mavis in S' measures her spaceship to be 300 m long, so she has the "hooray" sent from 300 m behind her spaceship's front at the instant she measures the front to cross the finish line. That is, she measures event 2 at $x' = -300$ m and $t' = 0$.

Our target variables are the coordinate x and time t of event 2 that Stanley measures in S.

EXECUTE: To solve for the target variables, we modify the first and last of Eqs. (37.21) to give x and t as functions of x' and t'. We do so in the same way that we obtained Eq. (37.23) from Eq. (37.22). We remove the primes from x' and t', add primes to x and t, and replace each u with $-u$. The results are

$$x = \gamma(x' + ut') \quad \text{and} \quad t = \gamma(t' + ux'/c^2)$$

From Eq. (37.7), $\gamma = 1.25$ for $u = 0.600c = 1.80 \times 10^8$ m/s. We also substitute $x' = -300$ m, $t' = 0$, $c = 3.00 \times 10^8$ m/s, and $u = 1.80 \times 10^8$ m/s in the equations for x and t to find $x = -375$ m at $t = -7.50 \times 10^{-7}$ s $= -0.750$ μs for event 2.

EVALUATE: Mavis says that the events are simultaneous, but Stanley says that the "hooray" was sent *before* Mavis crossed the finish line. This does not mean that the effect preceded the cause. The fastest that Mavis can send a signal the length of her ship is 300 m/$(3.00 \times 10^8$ m/s$) = 1.00$ μs. She cannot send a signal from the front at the instant it crosses the finish line that would cause a "hooray" to be broadcast from the back at the same instant. She would have to send that signal from the front at least 1.00 μs before then, so she had to slightly anticipate her success.

Example 37.7   **Relative velocities**

(a) A spaceship moving away from the earth at $0.900c$ fires a robot space probe in the same direction as its motion at $0.700c$ relative to the spaceship. What is the probe's velocity relative to the earth? (b) A scoutship is sent to catch up with the spaceship by traveling at $0.950c$ relative to the earth. What is the velocity of the scoutship relative to the spaceship?

SOLUTION

IDENTIFY and SET UP: This example uses the Lorentz velocity transformation. Let the earth and spaceship reference frames be S and S', respectively (Fig. 37.16); their relative velocity is $u = 0.900c$. In part (a) we are given the probe velocity $v_x' = 0.700c$ with respect to S', and the target variable is the velocity v_x of the

37.16 The spaceship, robot space probe, and scoutship.

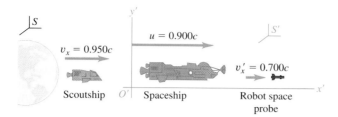

Scoutship O' Spaceship   Robot space probe

probe relative to S. In part (b) we are given the velocity $v_x = 0.950c$ of the scoutship relative to S, and the target variable is its velocity v'_x relative to S'.

EXECUTE: (a) We use Eq. (37.23) to find the probe velocity relative to the earth:

$$v_x = \frac{v'_x + u}{1 + uv'_x/c^2} = \frac{0.700c + 0.900c}{1 + (0.900c)(0.700c)/c^2} = 0.982c$$

(b) We use Eq. (37.22) to find the scoutship velocity relative to the spaceship:

$$v'_x = \frac{v_x - u}{1 - uv_x/c^2} = \frac{0.950c - 0.900c}{1 - (0.900c)(0.950c)/c^2} = 0.345c$$

EVALUATE: What would the Galilean velocity transformation formula, Eq. (37.2), say? In part (a) we would have found the probe's velocity relative to the earth to be $v_x = v'_x + u = 0.700c + 0.900c = 1.600c$, which is greater than c and hence impossible. In part (b), we would have found the scoutship's velocity relative to the spaceship to be $v'_x = v_x - u = 0.950c - 0.900c = 0.050c$; the relativistically correct value, $v'_x = 0.345c$, is almost seven times greater than the incorrect Galilean value.

Test Your Understanding of Section 37.5 (a) In frame S events P_1 and P_2 occur at the same x-, y-, and z-coordinates, but event P_1 occurs before event P_2. In frame S', which event occurs first? (b) In frame S events P_3 and P_4 occur at the same time t and the same y- and z-coordinates, but event P_3 occurs at a less positive x-coordinate than event P_4. In frame S', which event occurs first? ❚

37.6 The Doppler Effect for Electromagnetic Waves

An additional important consequence of relativistic kinematics is the Doppler effect for electromagnetic waves. In our previous discussion of the Doppler effect (see Section 16.8) we quoted without proof the formula, Eq. (16.30), for the frequency shift that results from motion of a source of electromagnetic waves relative to an observer. We can now derive that result.

Here's a statement of the problem. A source of light is moving with constant speed u toward Stanley, who is stationary in an inertial frame (Fig. 37.17). As measured in its rest frame, the source emits light waves with frequency f_0 and period $T_0 = 1/f_0$. What is the frequency f of these waves as received by Stanley?

Let T be the time interval between *emission* of successive wave crests as observed in Stanley's reference frame. Note that this is *not* the interval between the *arrival* of successive crests at his position, because the crests are emitted at different points in Stanley's frame. In measuring only the frequency f he receives, he does not take into account the difference in transit times for successive crests. Therefore the frequency he receives is *not* $1/T$. What is the equation for f?

During a time T the crests ahead of the source move a distance cT, and the source moves a shorter distance uT in the same direction. The distance λ between

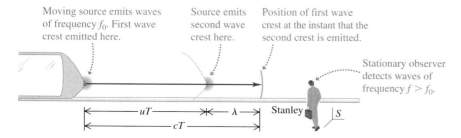

Moving source emits waves of frequency f_0. First wave crest emitted here.

Source emits second wave crest here.

Position of first wave crest at the instant that the second crest is emitted.

Stationary observer detects waves of frequency $f > f_0$.

Stanley

37.17 The Doppler effect for light. A light source moving at speed u relative to Stanley emits a wave crest, then travels a distance uT toward an observer and emits the next crest. In Stanley's reference frame S, the second crest is a distance λ behind the first crest.

successive crests—that is, the wavelength—is thus $\lambda = (c - u)T$, as measured in Stanley's frame. The frequency that he measures is c/λ. Therefore

$$f = \frac{c}{(c - u)T} \tag{37.24}$$

So far we have followed a pattern similar to that for the Doppler effect for sound from a moving source (see Section 16.8). In that discussion our next step was to equate T to the time T_0 between emissions of successive wave crests by the source. However, due to time dilation it is *not* relativistically correct to equate T to T_0. The time T_0 is measured in the rest frame of the source, so it is a proper time. From Eq. (37.6), T_0 and T are related by

$$T = \frac{T_0}{\sqrt{1 - u^2/c^2}} = \frac{cT_0}{\sqrt{c^2 - u^2}}$$

or, since $T_0 = 1/f_0$,

$$\frac{1}{T} = \frac{\sqrt{c^2 - u^2}}{cT_0} = \frac{\sqrt{c^2 - u^2}}{c}f_0$$

Remember, $1/T$ is not equal to f. We must substitute this expression for $1/T$ into Eq. 37.24 to find f:

$$f = \frac{c}{c - u}\frac{\sqrt{c^2 - u^2}}{c}f_0$$

Using $c^2 - u^2 = (c - u)(c + u)$ gives

$$f = \sqrt{\frac{c + u}{c - u}}f_0 \qquad \begin{array}{l}\text{(Doppler effect, electromagnetic} \\ \text{waves, source approaching observer)}\end{array} \tag{37.25}$$

This shows that when the source moves *toward* the observer, the observed frequency f is *greater* than the emitted frequency f_0. The difference $f - f_0 = \Delta f$ is called the Doppler frequency shift. When u/c is much smaller than 1, the fractional shift $\Delta f/f$ is also small and is approximately equal to u/c:

$$\frac{\Delta f}{f} = \frac{u}{c}$$

When the source moves *away from* the observer, we change the sign of u in Eq. (37.25) to get

$$f = \sqrt{\frac{c - u}{c + u}}f_0 \qquad \begin{array}{l}\text{(Doppler effect, electromagnetic waves,} \\ \text{source moving away from observer)}\end{array} \tag{37.26}$$

This agrees with Eq. (16.30), which we quoted previously, with minor notation changes.

With light, unlike sound, there is no distinction between motion of source and motion of observer; only the *relative* velocity of the two is significant. The last four paragraphs of Section 16.8 discuss several practical applications of the Doppler effect with light and other electromagnetic radiation; we suggest you review those paragraphs now. Figure 37.18 shows one common application.

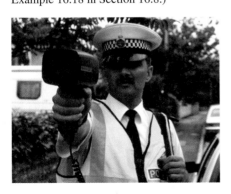

37.18 This handheld radar gun emits a radio beam of frequency f_0, which in the frame of reference of an approaching car has a higher frequency f given by Eq. (37.25). The reflected beam also has frequency f in the car's frame, but has an even higher frequency f' in the police officer's frame. The radar gun calculates the car's speed by comparing the frequencies of the emitted beam and the doubly Doppler-shifted reflected beam. (Compare Example 16.18 in Section 16.8.)

Example 37.8 **A jet from a black hole**

Many galaxies have supermassive black holes at their centers (see Section 13.8). As material swirls around such a black hole, it is heated, becomes ionized, and generates strong magnetic fields. The resulting magnetic forces steer some of the material into high-speed jets that blast out of the galaxy and into intergalactic space (Fig. 37.19). The light we observe from the jet in Fig. 37.19 has a

37.19 This image shows a fast-moving jet 5000 light-years in length emanating from the center of the galaxy M87. The light from the jet is emitted by fast-moving electrons spiraling around magnetic field lines (see Fig. 27.18).

frequency of 6.66×10^{14} Hz (in the far ultraviolet region of the electromagnetic spectrum; see Fig. 32.4), but in the reference frame of the jet material the light has a frequency of 5.55×10^{13} Hz (in the infrared). What is the speed of the jet material with respect to us?

IDENTIFY and SET UP: This problem involves the Doppler effect for electromagnetic waves. The frequency we observe is $f = 6.66 \times 10^{14}$ Hz, and the frequency in the frame of the source is $f_0 = 5.55 \times 10^{13}$ Hz. Since $f > f_0$, the jet is approaching us and we use Eq. (37.25) to find the target variable u.

EXECUTE: We need to solve Eq. (37.25) for u. We'll leave it as an exercise for you to show that the result is

$$u = \frac{(f/f_0)^2 - 1}{(f/f_0)^2 + 1} c$$

We have $f/f_0 = (6.66 \times 10^{14} \text{ Hz})/(5.55 \times 10^{13} \text{ Hz}) = 12.0$, so

$$u = \frac{(12.0)^2 - 1}{(12.0)^2 + 1} c = 0.986c$$

EVALUATE: Because the frequency shift is quite substantial, it would have been erroneous to use the approximate expression $\Delta f/f = u/c$. Had you done so, you would have found $u = c(\Delta f/f_0) = c(6.66 \times 10^{14} \text{ Hz} - 5.55 \times 10^{13} \text{ Hz})/(5.55 \times 10^{13} \text{ Hz}) = 11.0c$. This result cannot be correct because the jet material cannot travel faster than light.

37.7 Relativistic Momentum

Newton's laws of motion have the same form in all inertial frames of reference. When we use transformations to change from one inertial frame to another, the laws should be *invariant* (unchanging). But we have just learned that the principle of relativity forces us to replace the Galilean transformations with the more general Lorentz transformations. As we will see, this requires corresponding generalizations in the laws of motion and the definitions of momentum and energy.

The principle of conservation of momentum states that *when two bodies interact, the total momentum is constant,* provided that the net external force acting on the bodies in an inertial reference frame is zero (for example, if they form an isolated system, interacting only with each other). If conservation of momentum is a valid physical law, it must be valid in *all* inertial frames of reference. Now, here's the problem: Suppose we look at a collision in one inertial coordinate system S and find that momentum is conserved. Then we use the Lorentz transformation to obtain the velocities in a second inertial system S'. We find that if we use the Newtonian definition of momentum ($\vec{p} = m\vec{v}$), momentum is *not* conserved in the second system! If we are convinced that the principle of relativity and the Lorentz transformation are correct, the only way to save momentum conservation is to generalize the *definition* of momentum.

We won't derive the correct relativistic generalization of momentum, but here is the result. Suppose we measure the mass of a particle to be m when it is at rest relative to us: We often call m the **rest mass**. We will use the term *material particle* for a particle that has a nonzero rest mass. When such a particle has a velocity $\vec{v}$, its **relativistic momentum** $\vec{p}$ is

$$\vec{p} = \frac{m\vec{v}}{\sqrt{1 - v^2/c^2}} \qquad \text{(relativistic momentum)} \qquad (37.27)$$

37.20 Graph of the magnitude of the momentum of a particle of rest mass m as a function of speed v. Also shown is the Newtonian prediction, which gives correct results only at speeds much less than c.

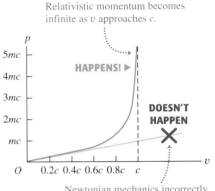

Relativistic momentum becomes infinite as v approaches c.

HAPPENS! ▶

DOESN'T HAPPEN

Newtonian mechanics incorrectly predicts that momentum becomes infinite only if v becomes infinite.

When the particle's speed v is much less than c, this is approximately equal to the Newtonian expression $\vec{p} = m\vec{v}$, but in general the momentum is greater in magnitude than mv (Fig. 37.20). In fact, as v approaches c, the momentum approaches infinity.

Relativity, Newton's Second Law, and Relativistic Mass

What about the relativistic generalization of Newton's second law? In Newtonian mechanics the most general form of the second law is

$$\vec{F} = \frac{d\vec{p}}{dt} \tag{37.28}$$

That is, the net force $\vec{F}$ on a particle equals the time rate of change of its momentum. Experiments show that this result is still valid in relativistic mechanics, provided that we use the relativistic momentum given by Eq. 37.27. That is, the relativistically correct generalization of Newton's second law is

$$\vec{F} = \frac{d}{dt} \frac{m\vec{v}}{\sqrt{1 - v^2/c^2}} \tag{37.29}$$

Because momentum is no longer directly proportional to velocity, the rate of change of momentum is no longer directly proportional to the acceleration. As a result, *constant force does not cause constant acceleration*. For example, when the net force and the velocity are both along the x-axis, Eq. 37.29 gives

$$F = \frac{m}{(1 - v^2/c^2)^{3/2}} a \qquad (\vec{F} \text{ and } \vec{v} \text{ along the same line}) \tag{37.30}$$

where a is the acceleration, also along the x-axis. Solving Eq. (37.30) for the acceleration a gives

$$a = \frac{F}{m} \left(1 - \frac{v^2}{c^2}\right)^{3/2}$$

We see that as a particle's speed increases, the acceleration caused by a given force continuously *decreases*. As the speed approaches c, the acceleration approaches zero, no matter how great a force is applied. Thus it is impossible to accelerate a particle with nonzero rest mass to a speed equal to or greater than c. We again see that the speed of light in vacuum represents an ultimate speed limit.

Equation (37.27) for relativistic momentum is sometimes interpreted to mean that a rapidly moving particle undergoes an increase in mass. If the mass at zero velocity (the rest mass) is denoted by m, then the "relativistic mass" m_{rel} is given by

$$m_{\text{rel}} = \frac{m}{\sqrt{1 - v^2/c^2}}$$

Indeed, when we consider the motion of a system of particles (such as rapidly moving ideal-gas molecules in a stationary container), the total rest mass of the system is the sum of the relativistic masses of the particles, not the sum of their rest masses.

However, if blindly applied, the concept of relativistic mass has its pitfalls. As Eq. (37.29) shows, the relativistic generalization of Newton's second law is *not* $\vec{F} = m_{\text{rel}}\vec{a}$, and we will show in Section 37.8 that the relativistic kinetic energy of a particle is *not* $K = \frac{1}{2}m_{\text{rel}}v^2$. The use of relativistic mass has its supporters and detractors, some quite strong in their opinions. We will mostly deal with individual particles, so we will sidestep the controversy and use Eq. (37.27) as the generalized definition of momentum with m as a constant for each particle, independent of its state of motion.

We will use the abbreviation

$$\gamma = \frac{1}{\sqrt{1 - v^2/c^2}}$$

We used this abbreviation in Section 37.3 with v replaced by u, the relative speed of two coordinate systems. Here v is the speed of a particle in a particular coordinate system—that is, the speed of the particle's *rest frame* with respect to that system. In terms of γ, Eqs. (37.27) and (37.30) become

$$\vec{p} = \gamma m \vec{v} \quad \text{(relativistic momentum)} \qquad (37.31)$$

$$F = \gamma^3 ma \quad (\vec{F} \text{ and } \vec{v} \text{ along the same line}) \qquad (37.32)$$

In linear accelerators (used in medicine as well as nuclear and elementary-particle physics; see Fig. 37.11) the net force $\vec{F}$ and the velocity $\vec{v}$ of the accelerated particle are along the same straight line. But for much of the path in most *circular* accelerators the particle moves in uniform circular motion at constant speed v. Then the net force and velocity are perpendicular, so the force can do no work on the particle and the kinetic energy and speed remain constant. Thus the denominator in Eq. (37.29) is constant, and we obtain

$$F = \frac{m}{(1 - v^2/c^2)^{1/2}} a = \gamma ma \quad (\vec{F} \text{ and } \vec{v} \text{ perpendicular}) \qquad (37.33)$$

Recall from Section 3.4 that if the particle moves in a circle, the net force and acceleration are directed inward along the radius r, and $a = v^2/r$.

What about the general case in which $\vec{F}$ and $\vec{v}$ are neither along the same line nor perpendicular? Then we can resolve the net force $\vec{F}$ at any instant into components parallel to and perpendicular to $\vec{v}$. The resulting acceleration will have corresponding components obtained from Eqs. (37.32) and (37.33). Because of the different γ^3 and γ factors, the acceleration components will not be proportional to the net force components. That is, *unless the net force on a relativistic particle is either along the same line as the particle's velocity or perpendicular to it, the net force and acceleration vectors are not parallel.*

Example 37.9   Relativistic dynamics of an electron

An electron (rest mass 9.11×10^{-31} kg, charge -1.60×10^{-19} C) is moving opposite to an electric field of magnitude $E = 5.00 \times 10^5$ N/C. All other forces are negligible in comparison to the electric-field force. (a) Find the magnitudes of momentum and of acceleration at the instants when $v = 0.010c$, $0.90c$, and $0.99c$. (b) Find the corresponding accelerations if a net force of the same magnitude is perpendicular to the velocity.

SOLUTION

IDENTIFY and SET UP: In addition to the expressions from this section for relativistic momentum and acceleration, we need the relationship between electric force and electric field from Chapter 21. In part (a) we use Eq. (37.31) to determine the magnitude of momentum; the force acts along the same line as the velocity, so we use Eq. (37.32) to determine the magnitude of acceleration. In part (b) the force is perpendicular to the velocity, so we use Eq. (37.33) rather than Eq. (37.32).

EXECUTE: (a) For $v = 0.010c$, $0.90c$, and $0.99c$ we have $\gamma = \sqrt{1 - v^2/c^2} = 1.00$, 2.29, and 7.09, respectively. The values of the momentum magnitude $p = \gamma mv$ are

$$p_1 = (1.00)(9.11 \times 10^{-31} \text{ kg})(0.010)(3.00 \times 10^8 \text{m/s})$$
$$= 2.7 \times 10^{-24} \text{ kg} \cdot \text{m/s at } v_1 = 0.010c$$

$$p_2 = (2.29)(9.11 \times 10^{-31} \text{ kg})(0.90)(3.00 \times 10^8 \text{ m/s})$$
$$= 5.6 \times 10^{-22} \text{ kg} \cdot \text{m/s at } v_2 = 0.90c$$

$$p_3 = (7.09)(9.11 \times 10^{-31} \text{ kg})(0.99)(3.00 \times 10^8 \text{ m/s})$$
$$= 1.9 \times 10^{-21} \text{ kg} \cdot \text{m/s at } v_3 = 0.99c$$

From Eq. (21.4), the magnitude of the force on the electron is

$$F = |q|E = (1.60 \times 10^{-19} \text{ C})(5.00 \times 10^5 \text{ N/C})$$
$$= 8.00 \times 10^{-14} \text{ N}$$

Continued

From Eq. (37.32), $a = F/\gamma^3 m$. For $v = 0.010c$ and $\gamma = 1.00$,

$$a_1 = \frac{8.00 \times 10^{-14}\,\text{N}}{(1.00)^3(9.11 \times 10^{-31}\,\text{kg})} = 8.8 \times 10^{16}\,\text{m/s}^2$$

The accelerations at the two higher speeds are smaller than the non-relativistic value by factors of $\gamma^3 = 12.0$ and 356, respectively:

$$a_2 = 7.3 \times 10^{15}\,\text{m/s}^2 \qquad a_3 = 2.5 \times 10^{14}\,\text{m/s}^2$$

(b) From Eq. (37.33), $a = F/\gamma m$ if $\vec{F}$ and $\vec{v}$ are perpendicular. When $v = 0.010c$ and $\gamma = 1.00$,

$$a_1 = \frac{8.00 \times 10^{-14}\,\text{N}}{(1.00)(9.11 \times 10^{-31}\,\text{kg})} = 8.8 \times 10^{16}\,\text{m/s}^2$$

Now the accelerations at the two higher speeds are smaller by factors of $\gamma = 2.29$ and 7.09, respectively:

$$a_2 = 3.8 \times 10^{16}\,\text{m/s}^2 \qquad a_3 = 1.2 \times 10^{16}\,\text{m/s}^2$$

These accelerations are larger than the corresponding ones in part (a) by factors of γ^2.

EVALUATE: Our results in part (a) show that at higher speeds, the relativistic values of momentum differ more and more from the nonrelativistic values calculated from $p = mv$. The momentum at $0.99c$ is more than three times as great as at $0.90c$ because of the increase in the factor γ. Our results also show that the acceleration drops off very quickly as v approaches c.

Test Your Understanding of Section 37.7 According to relativistic mechanics, when you double the speed of a particle, the magnitude of its momentum increases by (i) a factor of 2; (ii) a factor greater than 2; (iii) a factor between 1 and 2 that depends on the mass of the particle.

37.8 Relativistic Work and Energy

When we developed the relationship between work and kinetic energy in Chapter 6, we used Newton's laws of motion. When we generalize these laws according to the principle of relativity, we need a corresponding generalization of the equation for kinetic energy.

Relativistic Kinetic Energy

We use the work–energy theorem, beginning with the definition of work. When the net force and displacement are in the same direction, the work done by that force is $W = \int F\,dx$. We substitute the expression for F from Eq. (37.30), the applicable relativistic version of Newton's second law. In moving a particle of rest mass m from point x_1 to point x_2,

$$W = \int_{x_1}^{x_2} F\,dx = \int_{x_1}^{x_2} \frac{ma\,dx}{(1 - v^2/c^2)^{3/2}} \qquad (37.34)$$

To derive the generalized expression for kinetic energy K as a function of speed v, we would like to convert this to an integral on v. To do this, first remember that the kinetic energy of a particle equals the net work done on it in moving it from rest to the speed v: $K = W$. Thus we let the speeds be zero at point x_1 and v at point x_2. So as not to confuse the variable of integration with the final speed, we change v to v_x in Eq. 37.34. That is, v_x is the varying x-component of the velocity of the particle as the net force accelerates it from rest to a speed v. We also realize that dx and dv_x are the infinitesimal changes in x and v_x, respectively, in the time interval dt. Because $v_x = dx/dt$ and $a = dv_x/dt$, we can rewrite $a\,dx$ in Eq. (37.34) as

$$a\,dx = \frac{dv_x}{dt}\,dx = dx\frac{dv_x}{dt} = \frac{dx}{dt}\,dv_x = v_x\,dv_x$$

Making these substitutions gives us

$$K = W = \int_0^v \frac{mv_x\,dv_x}{(1 - v_x^2/c^2)^{3/2}} \qquad (37.35)$$

We can evaluate this integral by a simple change of variable; the final result is

$$K = \frac{mc^2}{\sqrt{1 - v^2/c^2}} - mc^2 = (\gamma - 1)mc^2 \qquad \text{(relativistic kinetic energy)} \qquad (37.36)$$

As v approaches c, the kinetic energy approaches infinity. If Eq. (37.36) is correct, it must also approach the Newtonian expression $K = \frac{1}{2}mv^2$ when v is much smaller than c (Fig. 37.21). To verify this, we expand the radical, using the binomial theorem in the form

$$(1 + x)^n = 1 + nx + n(n - 1)x^2/2 + \cdots$$

In our case, $n = -\frac{1}{2}$ and $x = -v^2/c^2$, and we get

$$\gamma = \left(1 - \frac{v^2}{c^2}\right)^{-1/2} = 1 + \frac{1}{2}\frac{v^2}{c^2} + \frac{3}{8}\frac{v^4}{c^4} + \cdots$$

Combining this with $K = (\gamma - 1)mc^2$, we find

$$K = \left(1 + \frac{1}{2}\frac{v^2}{c^2} + \frac{3}{8}\frac{v^4}{c^4} + \cdots - 1\right)mc^2$$

$$= \frac{1}{2}mv^2 + \frac{3}{8}\frac{mv^4}{c^2} + \cdots \qquad (37.37)$$

When v is much smaller than c, all the terms in the series in Eq. (37.37) except the first are negligibly small, and we obtain the Newtonian expression $\frac{1}{2}mv^2$.

Rest Energy and $E = mc^2$

Equation (37.36) for the kinetic energy of a moving particle includes a term $mc^2/\sqrt{1 - v^2/c^2}$ that depends on the motion and a second energy term mc^2 that is independent of the motion. It seems that the kinetic energy of a particle is the difference between some **total energy** E and an energy mc^2 that it has even when it is at rest. Thus we can rewrite Eq. (37.36) as

$$E = K + mc^2 = \frac{mc^2}{\sqrt{1 - v^2/c^2}} = \gamma mc^2 \qquad \begin{array}{l}\text{(total energy of} \\ \text{a particle)}\end{array} \qquad (37.38)$$

For a particle at rest ($K = 0$), we see that $E = mc^2$. The energy mc^2 associated with rest mass m rather than motion is called the **rest energy** of the particle.

There is in fact direct experimental evidence that rest energy really does exist. The simplest example is the decay of a neutral *pion*. This is an unstable subatomic particle of rest mass m_π; when it decays, it disappears and electromagnetic radiation appears. If a neutral pion has no kinetic energy before its decay, the total energy of the radiation after its decay is found to equal exactly $m_\pi c^2$. In many other fundamental particle transformations the sum of the rest masses of the particles changes. In every case there is a corresponding energy change, consistent with the assumption of a rest energy mc^2 associated with a rest mass m.

Historically, the principles of conservation of mass and of energy developed quite independently. The theory of relativity shows that they are actually two special cases of a single broader conservation principle, the *principle of conservation of mass and energy*. In some physical phenomena, neither the sum of the rest masses of the particles nor the total energy other than rest energy is separately conserved, but there is a more general conservation principle: In an isolated system, when the sum of the rest masses changes, there is always a change in $1/c^2$ times the total energy other than the rest energy. This change is equal in magnitude but opposite in sign to the change in the sum of the rest masses.

This more general mass-energy conservation law is the fundamental principle involved in the generation of power through nuclear reactions. When a uranium nucleus undergoes fission in a nuclear reactor, the sum of the rest masses of the resulting fragments is *less than* the rest mass of the parent nucleus. An amount of energy is released that equals the mass decrease multiplied by c^2. Most of this energy can be used to produce steam to operate turbines for electric power generators.

37.21 Graph of the kinetic energy of a particle of rest mass m as a function of speed v. Also shown is the Newtonian prediction, which gives correct results only at speeds much less than c.

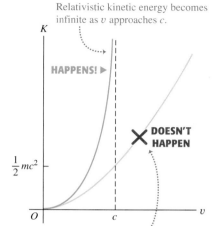

Relativistic kinetic energy becomes infinite as v approaches c.

HAPPENS! ▶

✗ **DOESN'T HAPPEN**

Newtonian mechanics incorrectly predicts that kinetic energy becomes infinite only if v becomes infinite.

Application **Monitoring Mass–Energy Conversion**
Although the control room of a nuclear power plant is very complex, the physical principle on which such a plant operates is a simple one: Part of the rest energy of atomic nuclei is converted to thermal energy, which in turn is used to produce steam to drive electric generators.

We can also relate the total energy E of a particle (kinetic energy plus rest energy) directly to its momentum by combining Eq. (37.27) for relativistic momentum and Eq. (37.38) for total energy to eliminate the particle's velocity. The simplest procedure is to rewrite these equations in the following forms:

$$\left(\frac{E}{mc^2}\right)^2 = \frac{1}{1 - v^2/c^2} \quad \text{and} \quad \left(\frac{p}{mc}\right)^2 = \frac{v^2/c^2}{1 - v^2/c^2}$$

Subtracting the second of these from the first and rearranging, we find

$$E^2 = (mc^2)^2 + (pc)^2 \quad \begin{array}{l}\text{(total energy, rest energy,} \\ \text{and momentum)}\end{array} \quad (37.39)$$

Again we see that for a particle at rest $(p = 0)$, $E = mc^2$.

Equation (37.39) also suggests that a particle may have energy and momentum even when it has no rest mass. In such a case, $m = 0$ and

$$E = pc \quad \text{(zero rest mass)} \quad (37.40)$$

In fact, zero rest mass particles do exist. Such particles always travel at the speed of light in vacuum. One example is the *photon*, the quantum of electromagnetic radiation (to be discussed in Chapter 38). Photons are emitted and absorbed during changes of state of an atomic or nuclear system when the energy and momentum of the system change.

Example 37.10   **Energetic electrons**

(a) Find the rest energy of an electron ($m = 9.109 \times 10^{-31}$ kg, $q = -e = -1.602 \times 10^{-19}$ C) in joules and in electron volts. (b) Find the speed of an electron that has been accelerated by an electric field, from rest, through a potential increase of 20.0 kV or of 5.00 MV (typical of a high-voltage x-ray machine).

SOLUTION

IDENTIFY and SET UP: This problem uses the ideas of rest energy, relativistic kinetic energy, and (from Chapter 23) electric potential energy. We use $E = mc^2$ to find the rest energy and Eqs. (37.7) and (37.38) to find the speed that gives the stated total energy.

EXECUTE: (a) The rest energy is

$$mc^2 = (9.109 \times 10^{-31} \text{ kg})(2.998 \times 10^8 \text{ m/s})^2$$
$$= 8.187 \times 10^{-14} \text{ J}$$

From the definition of the electron volt in Section 23.2, 1 eV = 1.602×10^{-19} J. Using this, we find

$$mc^2 = (8.187 \times 10^{-14} \text{ J})\frac{1 \text{ eV}}{1.602 \times 10^{-19} \text{ J}}$$
$$= 5.11 \times 10^5 \text{ eV} = 0.511 \text{ MeV}$$

(b) In calculations such as this, it is often convenient to work with the quantity $\gamma = 1/\sqrt{1 - v^2/c^2}$ from Eq. (37.38). Solving this for v, we find

$$v = c\sqrt{1 - (1/\gamma)^2}$$

The total energy E of the accelerated electron is the sum of its rest energy mc^2 and the kinetic energy eV_{ba} that it gains from the

work done on it by the electric field in moving from point a to point b:

$$E = \gamma mc^2 = mc^2 + eV_{ba} \quad \text{or}$$
$$\gamma = 1 + \frac{eV_{ba}}{mc^2}$$

An electron accelerated through a potential increase of $V_{ba} = 20.0$ kV gains 20.0 keV of energy, so for this electron

$$\gamma = 1 + \frac{20.0 \times 10^3 \text{ eV}}{0.511 \times 10^6 \text{ eV}} = 1.039$$

and

$$v = c\sqrt{1 - (1/1.039)^2} = 0.272c = 8.15 \times 10^7 \text{ m/s}$$

Repeating the calculation for $V_{ba} = 5.00$ MV, we find $eV_{ba}/mc^2 = 9.78$, $\gamma = 10.78$, and $v = 0.996c$.

EVALUATE: With $V_{ba} = 20.0$ kV, the added kinetic energy of 20.0 keV is less than 4% of the rest energy of 0.511 MeV, and the final speed is about one-fourth the speed of light. With $V_{ba} = 5.00$ MV, the added kinetic energy of 5.00 MeV is much greater than the rest energy and the speed is close to c.

CAUTION   **Three electron energies** All electrons have *rest* energy 0.511 MeV. An electron accelerated from rest through a 5.00-MeV potential increase has *kinetic* energy 5.00 MeV (we call it a "5.00-MeV electron") and *total* energy 5.51 MeV. Be careful to distinguish these energies from one another.

Example 37.11 **A relativistic collision**

Two protons (each with mass $M_p = 1.67 \times 10^{-27}$ kg) are initially moving with equal speeds in opposite directions. They continue to exist after a head-on collision that also produces a neutral pion of mass $M_\pi = 2.40 \times 10^{-28}$ kg (Fig. 37.22). If all three particles are at rest after the collision, find the initial speed of the protons. Energy is conserved in the collision.

37.22 In this collision the kinetic energy of two protons is transformed into the rest energy of a new particle, a pion.

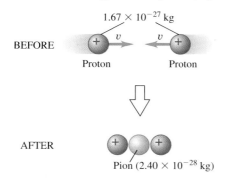

SOLUTION

IDENTIFY and SET UP: Relativistic total energy is conserved in the collision, so we can equate the (unknown) total energy of the two protons before the collision to the combined rest energies of the two protons and the pion after the collision. We then use Eq. (37.38) to find the speed of each proton.

EXECUTE: The total energy of each proton before the collision is $\gamma M c^2$. By conservation of energy,

$$2(\gamma M_p c^2) = 2(M_p c^2) + M_\pi c^2$$

$$\gamma = 1 + \frac{M_\pi}{2M_p} = 1 + \frac{2.40 \times 10^{-28} \text{ kg}}{2(1.67 \times 10^{-27} \text{ kg})} = 1.072$$

From Eq. (37.38), the initial proton speed is

$$v = c \sqrt{1 - (1/\gamma)^2} = 0.360c$$

EVALUATE: The proton rest energy is 938 MeV, so the initial kinetic energy of each proton is $(\gamma - 1)Mc^2 = 0.072Mc^2 = (0.072)(938 \text{ MeV}) = 67.5$ MeV. You can verify that the rest energy $M_\pi c^2$ of the pion is twice this, or 135 MeV. All the kinetic energy "lost" in this completely inelastic collision is transformed into the rest energy of the pion.

Test Your Understanding of Section 37.8 A proton is accelerated from rest by a constant force that always points in the direction of the particle's motion. Compared to the amount of kinetic energy that the proton gains during the first meter of its travel, how much kinetic energy does the proton gain during one meter of travel while it is moving at 99% of the speed of light? (i) the same amount; (ii) a greater amount; (iii) a smaller amount.

37.9 Newtonian Mechanics and Relativity

The sweeping changes required by the principle of relativity go to the very roots of Newtonian mechanics, including the concepts of length and time, the equations of motion, and the conservation principles. Thus it may appear that we have destroyed the foundations on which Newtonian mechanics is built. In one sense this is true, yet the Newtonian formulation is still accurate whenever speeds are small in comparison with the speed of light in vacuum. In such cases, time dilation, length contraction, and the modifications of the laws of motion are so small that they are unobservable. In fact, every one of the principles of Newtonian mechanics survives as a special case of the more general relativistic formulation.

The laws of Newtonian mechanics are not *wrong;* they are *incomplete.* They are a limiting case of relativistic mechanics. They are *approximately* correct when all speeds are small in comparison to c, and they become exactly correct in the limit when all speeds approach zero. Thus relativity does not completely destroy the laws of Newtonian mechanics but *generalizes* them. This is a common pattern in the development of physical theory. Whenever a new theory is in partial conflict with an older, established theory, the new must yield the same predictions as the old in areas in which the old theory is supported by experimental evidence. Every new physical theory must pass this test, called the **correspondence principle.**

The General Theory of Relativity

At this point we may ask whether the special theory of relativity gives the final word on mechanics or whether *further* generalizations are possible or necessary.

For example, inertial frames have occupied a privileged position in our discussion. Can the principle of relativity be extended to noninertial frames as well?

Here's an example that illustrates some implications of this question. A student decides to go over Niagara Falls while enclosed in a large wooden box. During her free fall she doesn't fall to the floor of the box because both she and the box are in free fall with a downward acceleration of 9.8 m/s². But an alternative interpretation, from her point of view, is that she doesn't fall to the floor because her gravitational interaction with the earth has suddenly been turned off. As long as she remains in the box and it remains in free fall, she cannot tell whether she is indeed in free fall or whether the gravitational interaction has vanished.

A similar problem occurs in a space station in orbit around the earth. Objects in the space station *seem* to be weightless, but without looking outside the station there is no way to determine whether gravity has been turned off or whether the station and all its contents are accelerating toward the center of the earth. Figure 37.23 makes a similar point for a spaceship that is not in free fall but may be accelerating relative to an inertial frame or be at rest on the earth's surface.

These considerations form the basis of Einstein's **general theory of relativity.** If we cannot distinguish experimentally between a uniform gravitational field at a particular location and a uniformly accelerated reference frame, then there cannot be any real distinction between the two. Pursuing this concept, we may try to represent *any* gravitational field in terms of special characteristics of the coordinate system. This turns out to require even more sweeping revisions of our space-time concepts than did the special theory of relativity. In the general theory of relativity the geometric properties of space are affected by the presence of matter (Fig. 37.24).

The general theory of relativity has passed several experimental tests, including three proposed by Einstein. One test has to do with understanding the rotation of the axes of the planet Mercury's elliptical orbit, called the *precession of the perihelion.* (The perihelion is the point of closest approach to the sun.) A second test concerns the apparent bending of light rays from distant stars when they pass near the sun. The third test is the *gravitational red shift,* the increase in wavelength of light proceeding outward from a massive source. Some details of the general theory are more difficult to test, but this theory has played a central role in investigations of the formation and evolution of stars, black holes, and studies of the evolution of the universe.

The general theory of relativity may seem to be an exotic bit of knowledge with little practical application. In fact, this theory plays an essential role in the

37.23 Without information from outside the spaceship, the astronaut cannot distinguish situation (b) from situation (c).

(a) An astronaut is about to drop her watch in a spaceship.

(b) In gravity-free space, the floor accelerates upward at $a = g$ and hits the watch.

$a = g$

(c) On the earth's surface, the watch accelerates downward at $a = g$ and hits the floor.

$a = 0$

Spaceship

g

37.24 A two-dimensional representation of curved space. We imagine the space (a plane) as being distorted as shown by a massive object (the sun). Light from a distant star (solid line) follows the distorted surface on its way to the earth. The dashed line shows the direction from which the light *appears* to be coming. The effect is greatly exaggerated; for the sun, the maximum deviation is only 0.00048°.

Actual position of star

Path of light from star

Sun

Earth

Apparent position

global positioning system (GPS), which makes it possible to determine your position on the earth's surface to within a few meters using a handheld receiver (Fig. 37.25). The heart of the GPS system is a collection of more than two dozen satellites in very precise orbits. Each satellite emits carefully timed radio signals, and a GPS receiver simultaneously detects the signals from several satellites. The receiver then calculates the time delay between when each signal was emitted and when it was received, and uses this information to calculate the receiver's position. To ensure the proper timing of the signals, it's necessary to include corrections due to the special theory of relativity (because the satellites are moving relative to the receiver on earth) as well as the general theory (because the satellites are higher in the earth's gravitational field than the receiver). The corrections due to relativity are small—less than one part in 10^9—but are crucial to the superb precision of the GPS system.

37.25 A GPS receiver uses radio signals from the orbiting GPS satellites to determine its position. To account for the effects of relativity, the receiver must be tuned to a slightly higher frequency (10.23 MHz) than the frequency emitted by the satellites (10.22999999543 MHz).

Invariance of physical laws, simultaneity: All of the fundamental laws of physics have the same form in all inertial frames of reference. The speed of light in vacuum is the same in all inertial frames and is independent of the motion of the source. Simultaneity is not an absolute concept; events that are simultaneous in one frame are not necessarily simultaneous in a second frame moving relative to the first.

Time dilation: If two events occur at the same space point in a particular frame of reference, the time interval Δt_0 between the events as measured in that frame is called a proper time interval. If this frame moves with constant velocity u relative to a second frame, the time interval Δt between the events as observed in the second frame is longer than Δt_0. (See Examples 37.1–37.3.)

$$\Delta t = \frac{\Delta t_0}{\sqrt{1 - u^2/c^2}} = \gamma \, \Delta t_0 \qquad (37.6), (37.8)$$

$$\gamma = \frac{1}{\sqrt{1 - u^2/c^2}} \qquad (37.7)$$

Length contraction: If two points are at rest in a particular frame of reference, the distance l_0 between the points as measured in that frame is called a proper length. If this frame moves with constant velocity u relative to a second frame and the distances are measured parallel to the motion, the distance l between the points as measured in the second frame is shorter than l_0. (See Examples 37.4 and 37.5.)

$$l = l_0 \sqrt{1 - u^2/c^2} = \frac{l_0}{\gamma} \qquad (37.16)$$

The Lorentz transformations: The Lorentz coordinate transformations relate the coordinates and time of an event in an inertial frame S to the coordinates and time of the same event as observed in a second inertial frame S' moving at velocity u relative to the first. For one-dimensional motion, a particle's velocities v_x in S and v_x' in S' are related by the Lorentz velocity transformation. (See Examples 37.6 and 37.7.)

$$x' = \frac{x - ut}{\sqrt{1 - u^2/c^2}} = \gamma(x - ut)$$

$$y' = y \qquad z' = z \qquad (37.21)$$

$$t' = \frac{t - ux/c^2}{\sqrt{1 - u^2/c^2}} = \gamma(t - ux/c^2)$$

$$v_x' = \frac{v_x - u}{1 - uv_x/c^2} \qquad (37.22)$$

$$v_x = \frac{v_x' + u}{1 + uv_x'/c^2} \qquad (37.23)$$

The Doppler effect for electromagnetic waves: The Doppler effect is the frequency shift in light from a source due to the relative motion of source and observer. For a source moving toward the observer with speed u, Eq. (37.25) gives the received frequency f in terms of the emitted frequency f_0. (See Example 37.8.)

$$f = \sqrt{\frac{c + u}{c - u}} f_0 \qquad (37.25)$$

Moving source emits light of frequency f_0. Stationary observer detects light of frequency $f > f_0$.

Relativistic momentum and energy: For a particle of rest mass m moving with velocity $\vec{v}$, the relativistic momentum $\vec{p}$ is given by Eq. (37.27) or (37.31) and the relativistic kinetic energy K is given by Eq. (37.36). The total energy E is the sum of the kinetic energy and the rest energy mc^2. The total energy can also be expressed in terms of the magnitude of momentum p and rest mass m. (See Examples 37.9–37.11.)

$$\vec{p} = \frac{m\vec{v}}{\sqrt{1 - v^2/c^2}} = \gamma m\vec{v} \qquad (37.27), (37.31)$$

$$K = \frac{mc^2}{\sqrt{1 - v^2/c^2}} - mc^2 = (\gamma - 1)mc^2 \qquad (37.36)$$

$$E = K + mc^2 = \frac{mc^2}{\sqrt{1 - v^2/c^2}} = \gamma mc^2 \qquad (37.38)$$

$$E^2 = (mc^2)^2 + (pc)^2 \qquad (37.39)$$

BRIDGING PROBLEM   Colliding Protons

In an experiment, two protons are shot directly toward each other. Their speeds are such that in the frame of reference of each proton, the other proton is moving at 0.500c. (a) What does an observer in the laboratory measure for the speed of each proton? (b) What is the kinetic energy of each proton as measured by an observer in the laboratory? (c) What is the kinetic energy of each proton as measured by the other proton?

SOLUTION GUIDE

See MasteringPhysics® study area for a Video Tutor solution.

IDENTIFY and SET UP

1. This problem uses the Lorentz velocity transformation, which allows us to relate the velocity v_x of a proton in one frame to its velocity v_x' in a different frame. It also uses the idea of relativistic kinetic energy.
2. Take the x-axis to be the line of motion of the protons, and take the +x-direction to be to the right. In the frame in which the left-hand proton is at rest, the right-hand proton has velocity $-0.500c$. In the laboratory frame the two protons have velocities

$-\alpha c$ and $+\alpha c$, where α (each proton's laboratory speed as a fraction of c) is our first target variable. Given this we can find the laboratory kinetic energy of each proton.

EXECUTE

3. Write a Lorentz velocity-transformation equation that relates the velocity of the right-hand proton in the laboratory frame to its velocity in the frame of the left-hand proton. Solve this equation for α. (*Hint:* Remember that α cannot be greater than 1. Why?)
4. Use your result from step 3 to find the laboratory kinetic energy of each proton.
5. Find the kinetic energy of the right-hand proton as measured in the frame of the left-hand proton.

EVALUATE

6. How much total kinetic energy must be imparted to the protons by a scientist in the laboratory? If the experiment were to be repeated with one proton stationary, what kinetic energy would have to be given to the other proton for the collision to be equivalent?

Problems

For instructor-assigned homework, go to www.masteringphysics.com

•, ••, •••: Problems of increasing difficulty. **CP**: Cumulative problems incorporating material from earlier chapters. **CALC**: Problems requiring calculus. **BIO**: Biosciences problems.

DISCUSSION QUESTIONS

Q37.1 You are standing on a train platform watching a high-speed train pass by. A light inside one of the train cars is turned on and then a little later it is turned off. (a) Who can measure the proper time interval for the duration of the light: you or a passenger on the train? (b) Who can measure the proper length of the train car: you or a passenger on the train? (c) Who can measure the proper length of a sign attached to a post on the train platform: you or a passenger on the train? In each case explain your answer.

Q37.2 If simultaneity is not an absolute concept, does that mean that we must discard the concept of causality? If event A is to *cause* event B, A must occur first. Is it possible that in some frames A appears to be the cause of B, and in others B appears to be the cause of A? Explain.

Q37.3 A rocket is moving to the right at $\frac{1}{2}$ the speed of light relative to the earth. A light bulb in the center of a room inside the rocket suddenly turns on. Call the light hitting the front end of the room event A and the light hitting the back of the room event B (Fig. Q37.3). Which event occurs first, A or B, or are they simultaneous, as viewed by (a) an astronaut riding in the rocket and (b) a person at rest on the earth?

Figure **Q37.3**

Q37.4 What do you think would be different in everyday life if the speed of light were 10 m/s instead of 3.00×10^8 m/s?

Q37.5 The average life span in the United States is about 70 years. Does this mean that it is impossible for an average person to travel a distance greater than 70 light-years away from the earth? (A light-year is the distance light travels in a year.) Explain.

Q37.6 You are holding an elliptical serving platter. How would you need to travel for the serving platter to appear round to another observer?

Q37.7 Two events occur at the same space point in a particular inertial frame of reference and are simultaneous in that frame. Is it possible that they may not be simultaneous in a different inertial frame? Explain.

Q37.8 A high-speed train passes a train platform. Larry is a passenger on the train, Adam is standing on the train platform, and David is riding a bicycle toward the platform in the same direction as the train is traveling. Compare the length of a train car as measured by Larry, Adam, and David.

Q37.9 The theory of relativity sets an upper limit on the speed that a particle can have. Are there also limits on the energy and momentum of a particle? Explain.

Q37.10 A student asserts that a material particle must always have a speed slower than that of light, and a massless particle must always move at exactly the speed of light. Is she correct? If so, how do massless particles such as photons and neutrinos acquire this speed? Can't they start from rest and accelerate? Explain.

Q37.11 The speed of light relative to still water is 2.25×10^8 m/s. If the water is moving past us, the speed of light we measure depends on the speed of the water. Do these facts violate Einstein's second postulate? Explain.

Q37.12 When a monochromatic light source moves toward an observer, its wavelength appears to be shorter than the value measured when the source is at rest. Does this contradict the hypothesis that the speed of light is the same for all observers? Explain.

Q37.13 In principle, does a hot gas have more mass than the same gas when it is cold? Explain. In practice, would this be a measurable effect? Explain.

Q37.14 Why do you think the development of Newtonian mechanics preceded the more refined relativistic mechanics by so many years?

EXERCISES

Section 37.2 Relativity of Simultaneity

37.1 • Suppose the two lightning bolts shown in Fig. 37.5a are simultaneous to an observer on the train. Show that they are *not* simultaneous to an observer on the ground. Which lightning strike does the ground observer measure to come first?

Section 37.3 Relativity of Time Intervals

37.2 • The positive muon (μ^+), an unstable particle, lives on average 2.20×10^{-6} s (measured in its own frame of reference) before decaying. (a) If such a particle is moving, with respect to the laboratory, with a speed of $0.900c$, what average lifetime is measured in the laboratory? (b) What average distance, measured in the laboratory, does the particle move before decaying?

37.3 • How fast must a rocket travel relative to the earth so that time in the rocket "slows down" to half its rate as measured by earth-based observers? Do present-day jet planes approach such speeds?

37.4 • A spaceship flies past Mars with a speed of $0.985c$ relative to the surface of the planet. When the spaceship is directly overhead, a signal light on the Martian surface blinks on and then off. An observer on Mars measures that the signal light was on for 75.0 μs. (a) Does the observer on Mars or the pilot on the spaceship measure the proper time? (b) What is the duration of the light pulse measured by the pilot of the spaceship?

37.5 • The negative pion (π^-) is an unstable particle with an average lifetime of 2.60×10^{-8} s (measured in the rest frame of the pion). (a) If the pion is made to travel at very high speed relative to a laboratory, its average lifetime is measured in the laboratory to be 4.20×10^{-7} s. Calculate the speed of the pion expressed as a fraction of c. (b) What distance, measured in the laboratory, does the pion travel during its average lifetime?

37.6 •• As you pilot your space utility vehicle at a constant speed toward the moon, a race pilot flies past you in her spaceracer at a constant speed of $0.800c$ relative to you. At the instant the spaceracer passes you, both of you start timers at zero. (a) At the instant when you measure that the spaceracer has traveled 1.20×10^8 m past you, what does the race pilot read on her timer? (b) When the race pilot reads the value calculated in part (a) on her timer, what does she measure to be your distance from her? (c) At the instant when the race pilot reads the value calculated in part (a) on her timer, what do you read on yours?

37.7 •• A spacecraft flies away from the earth with a speed of 4.80×10^6 m/s relative to the earth and then returns at the same speed. The spacecraft carries an atomic clock that has been carefully synchronized with an identical clock that remains at rest on earth. The spacecraft returns to its starting point 365 days (1 year) later, as measured by the clock that remained on earth. What is the difference in the elapsed times on the two clocks, measured in hours? Which clock, the one in the spacecraft or the one on earth, shows the shorter elapsed time?

37.8 • An alien spacecraft is flying overhead at a great distance as you stand in your backyard. You see its searchlight blink on for 0.190 s. The first officer on the spacecraft measures that the searchlight is on for 12.0 ms. (a) Which of these two measured times is the proper time? (b) What is the speed of the spacecraft relative to the earth expressed as a fraction of the speed of light c?

Section 37.4 Relativity of Length

37.9 • A spacecraft of the Trade Federation flies past the planet Coruscant at a speed of $0.600c$. A scientist on Coruscant measures the length of the moving spacecraft to be 74.0 m. The spacecraft later lands on Coruscant, and the same scientist measures the length of the now stationary spacecraft. What value does she get?

37.10 • A meter stick moves past you at great speed. Its motion relative to you is parallel to its long axis. If you measure the length of the moving meter stick to be 1.00 ft (1 ft = 0.3048 m)—for example, by comparing it to a 1-foot ruler that is at rest relative to you—at what speed is the meter stick moving relative to you?

37.11 •• **Why Are We Bombarded by Muons?** Muons are unstable subatomic particles that decay to electrons with a mean lifetime of 2.2 μs. They are produced when cosmic rays bombard the upper atmosphere about 10 km above the earth's surface, and they travel very close to the speed of light. The problem we want to address is why we see any of them at the earth's surface. (a) What is the greatest distance a muon could travel during its 2.2-μs lifetime? (b) According to your answer in part (a), it would seem that muons could never make it to the ground. But the 2.2-μs lifetime is measured in the frame of the muon, and muons are moving very fast. At a speed of $0.999c$, what is the mean lifetime of a muon as measured by an observer at rest on the earth? How far would the muon travel in this time? Does this result explain why we find muons in cosmic rays? (c) From the point of view of the muon, it still lives for only 2.2 μs, so how does it make it to the ground? What is the thickness of the 10 km of atmosphere through which the muon must travel, as measured by the muon? Is it now clear how the muon is able to reach the ground?

37.12 • An unstable particle is created in the upper atmosphere from a cosmic ray and travels straight down toward the surface of the earth with a speed of $0.99540c$ relative to the earth. A scientist at rest on the earth's surface measures that the particle is created at an altitude of 45.0 km. (a) As measured by the scientist, how much time does it take the particle to travel the 45.0 km to the surface of the earth? (b) Use the length-contraction formula to calculate the distance from where the particle is created to the surface of the earth as measured in the particle's frame. (c) In the particle's frame, how much time does it take the particle to travel from where it is created to the surface of the earth? Calculate this time both by the time dilation formula and from the distance calculated in part (b). Do the two results agree?

37.13 • As measured by an observer on the earth, a spacecraft runway on earth has a length of 3600 m. (a) What is the length of the runway as measured by a pilot of a spacecraft flying past at a speed of 4.00×10^7 m/s relative to the earth? (b) An observer on earth measures the time interval from when the spacecraft is directly over one end of the runway until it is directly over the other end. What result does she get? (c) The pilot of the spacecraft measures the time it takes him to travel from one end of the runway to the other end. What value does he get?

37.14 • A rocket ship flies past the earth at 85.0% of the speed of light. Inside, an astronaut who is undergoing a physical examination is having his height measured while he is lying down parallel to the direction the rocket ship is moving. (a) If his height is measured to be 2.00 m by his doctor inside the ship, what height would a person watching this from earth measure for his height? (b) If the earth-based person had measured 2.00 m, what would the doctor in the spaceship have measured for the astronaut's height? Is this a reasonable height? (c) Suppose the astronaut in part (a) gets up after the examination and stands with his body perpendicular to the direction of motion. What would the doctor in the rocket and the observer on earth measure for his height now?

Section 37.5 The Lorentz Transformations

37.15 · An observer in frame S' is moving to the right ($+x$-direction) at speed $u = 0.600c$ away from a stationary observer in frame S. The observer in S' measures the speed v' of a particle moving to the right away from her. What speed v does the observer in S measure for the particle if (a) $v' = 0.400c$; (b) $v' = 0.900c$; (c) $v' = 0.990c$?

37.16 · Space pilot Mavis zips past Stanley at a constant speed relative to him of $0.800c$. Mavis and Stanley start timers at zero when the front of Mavis's ship is directly above Stanley. When Mavis reads 5.00 s on her timer, she turns on a bright light under the front of her spaceship. (a) Use the Lorentz coordinate transformation derived in Example 37.6 to calculate x and t as measured by Stanley for the event of turning on the light. (b) Use the time dilation formula, Eq. (37.6), to calculate the time interval between the two events (the front of the spaceship passing overhead and turning on the light) as measured by Stanley. Compare to the value of t you calculated in part (a). (c) Multiply the time interval by Mavis's speed, both as measured by Stanley, to calculate the distance she has traveled as measured by him when the light turns on. Compare to the value of x you calculated in part (a).

37.17 ·· A pursuit spacecraft from the planet Tatooine is attempting to catch up with a Trade Federation cruiser. As measured by an observer on Tatooine, the cruiser is traveling away from the planet with a speed of $0.600c$. The pursuit ship is traveling at a speed of $0.800c$ relative to Tatooine, in the same direction as the cruiser. (a) For the pursuit ship to catch the cruiser, should the velocity of the cruiser relative to the pursuit ship be directed toward or away from the pursuit ship? (b) What is the speed of the cruiser relative to the pursuit ship?

37.18 · An extraterrestrial spaceship is moving away from the earth after an unpleasant encounter with its inhabitants. As it departs, the spaceship fires a missile toward the earth. An observer on earth measures that the spaceship is moving away with a speed of $0.600c$. An observer in the spaceship measures that the missile is moving away from him at a speed of $0.800c$. As measured by an observer on earth, how fast is the missile approaching the earth?

37.19 ·· Two particles are created in a high-energy accelerator and move off in opposite directions. The speed of one particle, as measured in the laboratory, is $0.650c$, and the speed of each particle relative to the other is $0.950c$. What is the speed of the second particle, as measured in the laboratory?

37.20 ·· Two particles in a high-energy accelerator experiment are approaching each other head-on, each with a speed of $0.9520c$ as measured in the laboratory. What is the magnitude of the velocity of one particle relative to the other?

37.21 ·· Two particles in a high-energy accelerator experiment approach each other head-on with a relative speed of $0.890c$. Both particles travel at the same speed as measured in the laboratory. What is the speed of each particle, as measured in the laboratory?

37.22 ·· An enemy spaceship is moving toward your starfighter with a speed, as measured in your frame, of $0.400c$. The enemy ship fires a missile toward you at a speed of $0.700c$ relative to the

enemy ship (Fig. E37.22). (a) What is the speed of the missile relative to you? Express your answer in terms of the speed of light. (b) If you measure that the enemy ship is 8.00×10^6 km away from you when the missile is fired, how much time, measured in your frame, will it take the missile to reach you?

Figure **E37.22**

Enemy   Starfighter

37.23 · An imperial spaceship, moving at high speed relative to the planet Arrakis, fires a rocket toward the planet with a speed of $0.920c$ relative to the spaceship. An observer on Arrakis measures that the rocket is approaching with a speed of $0.360c$. What is the speed of the spaceship relative to Arrakis? Is the spaceship moving toward or away from Arrakis?

Section 37.6 The Doppler Effect for Electromagnetic Waves

37.24 · Electromagnetic radiation from a star is observed with an earth-based telescope. The star is moving away from the earth with a speed of $0.600c$. If the radiation has a frequency of 8.64×10^{14} Hz in the rest frame of the star, what is the frequency measured by an observer on earth?

37.25 · **Tell It to the Judge.** (a) How fast must you be approaching a red traffic light ($\lambda = 675$ nm) for it to appear yellow ($\lambda = 575$ nm)? Express your answer in terms of the speed of light. (b) If you used this as a reason not to get a ticket for running a red light, how much of a fine would you get for speeding? Assume that the fine is \$1.00 for each kilometer per hour that your speed exceeds the posted limit of 90 km/h.

37.26 · A source of electromagnetic radiation is moving in a radial direction relative to you. The frequency you measure is 1.25 times the frequency measured in the rest frame of the source. What is the speed of the source relative to you? Is the source moving toward you or away from you?

Section 37.7 Relativistic Momentum

37.27 · A proton has momentum with magnitude p_0 when its speed is $0.400c$. In terms of p_0, what is the magnitude of the proton's momentum when its speed is doubled to $0.800c$?

37.28 · **When Should You Use Relativity?** As you have seen, relativistic calculations usually involve the quantity γ. When γ is appreciably greater than 1, we must use relativistic formulas instead of Newtonian ones. For what speed v (in terms of c) is the value of γ (a) 1.0% greater than 1; (b) 10% greater than 1; (c) 100% greater than 1?

37.29 · (a) At what speed is the momentum of a particle twice as great as the result obtained from the nonrelativistic expression mv? Express your answer in terms of the speed of light. (b) A force is applied to a particle along its direction of motion. At what speed is the magnitude of force required to produce a given acceleration twice as great as the force required to produce the same acceleration when the particle is at rest? Express your answer in terms of the speed of light.

37.30 · As measured in an earth-based frame, a proton is moving in the $+x$-direction at a speed of 2.30×10^8 m/s. (a) What force (magnitude and direction) is required to produce an acceleration in the $-x$-direction that has magnitude 2.30×10^8 m/s^2? (b) What magnitude of acceleration does the force calculated in part (a) give to a proton that is initially at rest?

37.31 • An electron is acted upon by a force of 5.00×10^{-15} N due to an electric field. Find the acceleration this force produces in each case: (a) The electron's speed is 1.00 km/s. (b) The electron's speed is 2.50×10^8 m/s and the force is parallel to the velocity.

37.32 • **Relativistic Baseball.** Calculate the magnitude of the force required to give a 0.145-kg baseball an acceleration $a = 1.00$ m/s^2 in the direction of the baseball's initial velocity when this velocity has a magnitude of (a) 10.0 m/s; (b) $0.900c$; (c) $0.990c$. (d) Repeat parts (a), (b), and (c) if the force and acceleration are perpendicular to the velocity.

Section 37.8 Relativistic Work and Energy

37.33 •• What is the speed of a particle whose kinetic energy is equal to (a) its rest energy and (b) five times its rest energy?

37.34 • If a muon is traveling at $0.999c$, what are its momentum and kinetic energy? (The mass of such a muon at rest in the laboratory is 207 times the electron mass.)

37.35 • A proton (rest mass 1.67×10^{-27} kg) has total energy that is 4.00 times its rest energy. What are (a) the kinetic energy of the proton; (b) the magnitude of the momentum of the proton; (c) the speed of the proton?

37.36 •• (a) How much work must be done on a particle with mass m to accelerate it (a) from rest to a speed of $0.090c$ and (b) from a speed of $0.900c$ to a speed of $0.990c$? (Express the answers in terms of mc^2.) (c) How do your answers in parts (a) and (b) compare?

37.37 • CP (a) By what percentage does your rest mass increase when you climb 30 m to the top of a ten-story building? Are you aware of this increase? Explain. (b) By how many grams does the mass of a 12.0-g spring with force constant 200 N/cm change when you compress it by 6.0 cm? Does the mass increase or decrease? Would you notice the change in mass if you were holding the spring? Explain.

37.38 • A 60.0-kg person is standing at rest on level ground. How fast would she have to run to (a) double her total energy and (b) increase her total energy by a factor of 10?

37.39 • **An Antimatter Reactor.** When a particle meets its antiparticle, they annihilate each other and their mass is converted to light energy. The United States uses approximately 1.0×10^{20} J of energy per year. (a) If all this energy came from a futuristic antimatter reactor, how much mass of matter and antimatter fuel would be consumed yearly? (b) If this fuel had the density of iron (7.86 g/cm^3) and were stacked in bricks to form a cubical pile, how high would it be? (Before you get your hopes up, antimatter reactors are a *long* way in the future—if they ever will be feasible.)

37.40 •• Electrons are accelerated through a potential difference of 750 kV, so that their kinetic energy is 7.50×10^5 eV. (a) What is the ratio of the speed v of an electron having this energy to the speed of light, c? (b) What would the speed be if it were computed from the principles of classical mechanics?

37.41 • A particle has rest mass 6.64×10^{-27} kg and momentum 2.10×10^{-18} kg·m/s. (a) What is the total energy (kinetic plus rest energy) of the particle? (b) What is the kinetic energy of the particle? (c) What is the ratio of the kinetic energy to the rest energy of the particle?

37.42 •• A 0.100-μg speck of dust is accelerated from rest to a speed of $0.900c$ by a constant 1.00×10^6 N force. (a) If the nonrelativistic mechanics is used, how far does the object travel to reach its final speed? (b) Using the correct relativistic treatment of Section 37.8, how far does the object travel to reach its final speed? (c) Which distance is greater? Why?

37.43 • Compute the kinetic energy of a proton (mass 1.67×10^{-27} kg) using both the nonrelativistic and relativistic expressions, and compute the ratio of the two results (relativistic divided by nonrelativistic) for speeds of (a) 8.00×10^7 m/s and (b) 2.85×10^8 m/s.

37.44 • What is the kinetic energy of a proton moving at (a) $0.100c$; (b) $0.500c$; (c) $0.900c$? How much work must be done to (d) increase the proton's speed from $0.100c$ to $0.500c$ and (e) increase the proton's speed from $0.500c$ to $0.900c$? (f) How do the last two results compare to results obtained in the nonrelativistic limit?

37.45 • (a) Through what potential difference does an electron have to be accelerated, starting from rest, to achieve a speed of $0.980c$? (b) What is the kinetic energy of the electron at this speed? Express your answer in joules and in electron volts.

37.46 • **Creating a Particle.** Two protons (each with rest mass $M = 1.67 \times 10^{-27}$ kg) are initially moving with equal speeds in opposite directions. The protons continue to exist after a collision that also produces an η^0 particle (see Chapter 44). The rest mass of the η^0 is $m = 9.75 \times 10^{-28}$ kg. (a) If the two protons and the η^0 are all at rest after the collision, find the initial speed of the protons, expressed as a fraction of the speed of light. (b) What is the kinetic energy of each proton? Express your answer in MeV. (c) What is the rest energy of the η^0, expressed in MeV? (d) Discuss the relationship between the answers to parts (b) and (c).

37.47 • The sun produces energy by nuclear fusion reactions, in which matter is converted into energy. By measuring the amount of energy we receive from the sun, we know that it is producing energy at a rate of 3.8×10^{26} W. (a) How many kilograms of matter does the sun lose each second? Approximately how many tons of matter is this (1 ton = 2000 lbs)? (b) At this rate, how long would it take the sun to use up all its mass?

PROBLEMS

37.48 • Inside a spaceship flying past the earth at three-fourths the speed of light, a pendulum is swinging. (a) If each swing takes 1.50 s as measured by an astronaut performing an experiment inside the spaceship, how long will the swing take as measured by a person at mission control on earth who is watching the experiment? (b) If each swing takes 1.50 s as measured by a person at mission control on earth, how long will it take as measured by the astronaut in the spaceship?

37.49 • After being produced in a collision between elementary particles, a positive pion (π^+) must travel down a 1.90-km-long tube to reach an experimental area. A π^+ particle has an average lifetime (measured in its rest frame) of 2.60×10^{-8} s; the π^+ we are considering has this lifetime. (a) How fast must the π^+ travel if it is not to decay before it reaches the end of the tube? (Since u will be very close to c, write $u = (1 - \Delta)c$ and give your answer in terms of Δ rather than u.) (b) The π^+ has a rest energy of 139.6 MeV. What is the total energy of the π^+ at the speed calculated in part (a)?

37.50 •• A cube of metal with sides of length a sits at rest in a frame S with one edge parallel to the x-axis. Therefore, in S the cube has volume a^3. Frame S' moves along the x-axis with a speed u. As measured by an observer in frame S', what is the volume of the metal cube?

37.51 ••• The starships of the Solar Federation are marked with the symbol of the federation, a circle, while starships of the Denebian Empire are marked with the empire's symbol, an ellipse whose major axis is 1.40 times longer than its minor axis ($a = 1.40b$ in Fig. P37.51). How fast, relative to an observer, does an empire ship have to travel for its marking to be confused with the marking of a federation ship?

Federation   Empire

37.52 •• A space probe is sent to the vicinity of the star Capella, which is 42.2 light-years from the earth. (A light-year is the distance light travels in a year.) The probe travels with a speed of 0.9930c. An astronaut recruit on board is 19 years old when the probe leaves the earth. What is her biological age when the probe reaches Capella?

37.53 • A particle is said to be *extremely relativistic* when its kinetic energy is much greater than its rest energy. (a) What is the speed of a particle (expressed as a fraction of c) such that the total energy is ten times the rest energy? (b) What is the percentage difference between the left and right sides of Eq. (37.39) if $(mc^2)^2$ is neglected for a particle with the speed calculated in part (a)?

37.54 •• **Everyday Time Dilation.** Two atomic clocks are carefully synchronized. One remains in New York, and the other is loaded on an airliner that travels at an average speed of 250 m/s and then returns to New York. When the plane returns, the elapsed time on the clock that stayed behind is 4.00 h. By how much will the readings of the two clocks differ, and which clock will show the shorter elapsed time? (*Hint:* Since $u \ll c$, you can simplify $\sqrt{1 - u^2/c^2}$ by a binomial expansion.)

37.55 • **The Large Hadron Collider (LHC).** Physicists and engineers from around the world have come together to build the largest accelerator in the world, the Large Hadron Collider (LHC) at the CERN Laboratory in Geneva, Switzerland. The machine will accelerate protons to kinetic energies of 7 TeV in an underground ring 27 km in circumference. (For the latest news and more information on the LHC, visit www.cern.ch.) (a) What speed v will protons reach in the LHC? (Since v is very close to c, write $v = (1 - \Delta)c$ and give your answer in terms of Δ.) (b) Find the relativistic mass, m_{rel}, of the accelerated protons in terms of their rest mass.

37.56 • **CP** A nuclear bomb containing 12.0 kg of plutonium explodes. The sum of the rest masses of the products of the explosion is less than the original rest mass by one part in 10^4. (a) How much energy is released in the explosion? (b) If the explosion takes place in 4.00 μs, what is the average power developed by the bomb? (c) What mass of water could the released energy lift to a height of 1.00 km?

37.57 • **CP Čerenkov Radiation.** The Russian physicist P. A. Čerenkov discovered that a charged particle traveling in a solid with a speed exceeding the speed of light in that material radiates electromagnetic radiation. (This is analogous to the sonic boom produced by an aircraft moving faster than the speed of sound in air; see Section 16.9. Čerenkov shared the 1958 Nobel Prize for this discovery.) What is the minimum kinetic energy (in electron volts) that an electron must have while traveling inside a slab of crown glass ($n = 1.52$) in order to create this Čerenkov radiation?

37.58 •• A photon with energy E is emitted by an atom with mass m, which recoils in the opposite direction. (a) Assuming that the motion of the atom can be treated nonrelativistically, compute the recoil speed of the atom. (b) From the result of part (a), show that the recoil speed is much less than c whenever E is much less than the rest energy mc^2 of the atom.

37.59 •• In an experiment, two protons are shot directly toward each other, each moving at half the speed of light relative to the laboratory. (a) What speed does one proton measure for the other

proton? (b) What would be the answer to part (a) if we used only nonrelativistic Newtonian mechanics? (c) What is the kinetic energy of each proton as measured by (i) an observer at rest in the laboratory and (ii) an observer riding along with one of the protons? (d) What would be the answers to part (c) if we used only nonrelativistic Newtonian mechanics?

37.60 •• Two protons are moving away from each other. In the frame of each proton, the other proton has a speed of 0.600c. What does an observer in the rest frame of the earth measure for the speed of each proton?

37.61 •• Frame S' has an x-component of velocity u relative to frame S, and at $t = t' = 0$ the two frames coincide (see Fig. 37.3). A light pulse with a spherical wave front is emitted at the origin of S' at time $t' = 0$. Its distance x' from the origin after a time t' is given by $x'^2 = c^2t'^2$. Use the Lorentz coordinate transformation to transform this equation to an equation in x and t, and show that the result is $x^2 = c^2t^2$; that is, the motion appears exactly the same in frame of reference S as it does in S'; the wave front is observed to be spherical in both frames.

37.62 • In certain radioactive beta decay processes, the beta particle (an electron) leaves the atomic nucleus with a speed of 99.95% the speed of light relative to the decaying nucleus. If this nucleus is moving at 75.00% the speed of light in the laboratory reference frame, find the speed of the emitted electron relative to the laboratory reference frame if the electron is emitted (a) in the same direction that the nucleus is moving and (b) in the opposite direction from the nucleus's velocity. (c) In each case in parts (a) and (b), find the kinetic energy of the electron as measured in (i) the laboratory frame and (ii) the reference frame of the decaying nucleus.

37.63 •• **CALC** A particle with mass m accelerated from rest by a constant force F will, according to Newtonian mechanics, continue to accelerate without bound; that is, as $t \to \infty$, $v \to \infty$. Show that according to relativistic mechanics, the particle's speed approaches c as $t \to \infty$. [*Note:* A useful integral is $\int (1 - x^2)^{-3/2} dx = x/\sqrt{1 - x^2}$.]

37.64 •• Two events are observed in a frame of reference S to occur at the same space point, the second occurring 1.80 s after the first. In a second frame S' moving relative to S, the second event is observed to occur 2.35 s after the first. What is the difference between the positions of the two events as measured in S'?

37.65 ••• Two events observed in a frame of reference S have positions and times given by (x_1, t_1) and (x_2, t_2), respectively. (a) Frame S' moves along the x-axis just fast enough that the two events occur at the same position in S'. Show that in S', the time interval $\Delta t'$ between the two events is given by

$$\Delta t' = \sqrt{(\Delta t)^2 - \left(\frac{\Delta x}{c}\right)^2}$$

where $\Delta x = x_2 - x_1$ and $\Delta t = t_2 - t_1$. Hence show that if $\Delta x > c\,\Delta t$, there is *no* frame S' in which the two events occur at the same point. The interval $\Delta t'$ is sometimes called the *proper time interval* for the events. Is this term appropriate? (b) Show that if $\Delta x > c\,\Delta t$, there is a different frame of reference S' in which the two events occur *simultaneously*. Find the distance between the two events in S'; express your answer in terms of Δx, Δt, and c. This distance is sometimes called a *proper length*. Is this term appropriate? (c) Two events are observed in a frame of reference S' to occur simultaneously at points separated by a distance of 2.50 m. In a second frame S moving relative to S' along the line joining the two points in S', the two events appear to be separated by 5.00 m. What is the time interval between the events as measured in S? [*Hint:* Apply the result obtained in part (b).]

37.66 •• **Albert in Wonderland.** Einstein and Lorentz, being avid tennis players, play a fast-paced game on a court where they stand 20.0 m from each other. Being very skilled players, they play without a net. The tennis ball has mass 0.0580 kg. You can ignore gravity and assume that the ball travels parallel to the ground as it travels between the two players. Unless otherwise specified, all measurements are made by the two men. (a) Lorentz serves the ball at 80.0 m/s. What is the ball's kinetic energy? (b) Einstein slams a return at 1.80×10^8 m/s. What is the ball's kinetic energy? (c) During Einstein's return of the ball in part (a), a white rabbit runs beside the court in the direction from Einstein to Lorentz. The rabbit has a speed of 2.20×10^8 m/s relative to the two men. What is the speed of the rabbit relative to the ball? (d) What does the rabbit measure as the distance from Einstein to Lorentz? (e) How much time does it take for the rabbit to run 20.0 m, according to the players? (f) The white rabbit carries a pocket watch. He uses this watch to measure the time (as he sees it) for the distance from Einstein to Lorentz to pass by under him. What time does he measure?

37.67 • One of the wavelengths of light emitted by hydrogen atoms under normal laboratory conditions is $\lambda = 656.3$ nm, in the red portion of the electromagnetic spectrum. In the light emitted from a distant galaxy this same spectral line is observed to be Doppler-shifted to $\lambda = 953.4$ nm, in the infrared portion of the spectrum. How fast are the emitting atoms moving relative to the earth? Are they approaching the earth or receding from it?

37.68 •• **Measuring Speed by Radar.** A baseball coach uses a radar device to measure the speed of an approaching pitched baseball. This device sends out electromagnetic waves with frequency f_0 and then measures the shift in frequency Δf of the waves reflected from the moving baseball. If the fractional frequency shift produced by a baseball is $\Delta f / f_0 = 2.86 \times 10^{-7}$, what is the baseball's speed in km/h? (*Hint:* Are the waves Doppler-shifted a second time when reflected off the ball?)

37.69 • **Space Travel?** Travel to the stars requires hundreds or thousands of years, even at the speed of light. Some people have suggested that we can get around this difficulty by accelerating the rocket (and its astronauts) to very high speeds so that they will age less due to time dilation. The fly in this ointment is that it takes a great deal of energy to do this. Suppose you want to go to the immense red giant Betelgeuse, which is about 500 light-years away. (A light-year is the distance that light travels in a year.) You plan to travel at constant speed in a 1000-kg rocket ship (a little over a ton), which, in reality, is far too small for this purpose. In each case that follows, calculate the time for the trip, as measured by people on earth and by astronauts in the rocket ship, the energy needed in joules, and the energy needed as a percentage of U.S. yearly use (which is 1.0×10^{20} J). For comparison, arrange your results in a table showing v_{rocket}, t_{earth}, t_{rocket}, E (in J), and E (as % of U.S. use). The rocket ship's speed is (a) 0.50c; (b) 0.99c; (c) 0.9999c. On the basis of your results, does it seem likely that any government will invest in such high-speed space travel any time soon?

37.70 •• A spaceship moving at constant speed u relative to us broadcasts a radio signal at constant frequency f_0. As the spaceship approaches us, we receive a higher frequency f; after it has passed, we receive a lower frequency. (a) As the spaceship passes by, so it is instantaneously moving neither toward nor away from us, show that the frequency we receive is not f_0, and derive an expression for the frequency we do receive. Is the frequency we receive higher or lower than f_0? (*Hint:* In this case, successive wave crests move the same distance to the observer and so they

have the same transit time. Thus f equals $1/T$. Use the time dilation formula to relate the periods in the stationary and moving frames.) (b) A spaceship emits electromagnetic waves of frequency $f_0 = 345$ MHz as measured in a frame moving with the ship. The spaceship is moving at a constant speed $0.758c$ relative to us. What frequency f do we receive when the spaceship is approaching us? When it is moving away? In each case what is the shift in frequency, $f - f_0$? (c) Use the result of part (a) to calculate the frequency f and the frequency shift $(f - f_0)$ we receive at the instant that the ship passes by us. How does the shift in frequency calculated here compare to the shifts calculated in part (b)?

37.71 • **CP** In a particle accelerator a proton moves with constant speed $0.750c$ in a circle of radius 628 m. What is the net force on the proton?

37.72 •• **CP** The French physicist Armand Fizeau was the first to measure the speed of light accurately. He also found experimentally that the speed, relative to the lab frame, of light traveling in a tank of water that is itself moving at a speed V relative to the lab frame is

$$v = \frac{c}{n} + kV$$

where $n = 1.333$ is the index of refraction of water. Fizeau called k the dragging coefficient and obtained an experimental value of $k = 0.44$. What value of k do you calculate from relativistic transformations?

CHALLENGE PROBLEMS

37.73 ••• **CALC Lorentz Transformation for Acceleration.** Using a method analogous to the one in the text to find the Lorentz transformation formula for velocity, we can find the Lorentz transformation for *acceleration*. Let frame S' have a constant x-component of velocity u relative to frame S. An object moves relative to frame S along the x-axis with instantaneous velocity v_x and instantaneous acceleration a_x. (a) Show that its instantaneous acceleration in frame S' is

$$a_x' = a_x \left(1 - \frac{u^2}{c^2} \right)^{3/2} \left(1 - \frac{uv_x}{c^2} \right)^{-3}$$

[*Hint:* Express the acceleration in S' as $a_x' = dv_x'/dt'$. Then use Eq. (37.21) to express dt' in terms of dt and dx, and use Eq. (37.22) to express dv_x' in terms of u and dv_x. The velocity of the object in S is $v_x = dx/dt$.] (b) Show that the acceleration in frame S can be expressed as

$$a_x = a_x' \left(1 - \frac{u^2}{c^2} \right)^{3/2} \left(1 + \frac{uv_x'}{c^2} \right)^{-3}$$

where $v_x' = dx'/dt'$ is the velocity of the object in frame S'.

37.74 ••• **CALC A Realistic Version of the Twin Paradox.** A rocket ship leaves the earth on January 1, 2100. Stella, one of a pair of twins born in the year 2075, pilots the rocket (reference frame S'); the other twin, Terra, stays on the earth (reference frame S). The rocket ship has an acceleration of constant magnitude g in its own reference frame (this makes the pilot feel at home, since it simulates the earth's gravity). The path of the rocket ship is a straight line in the +x-direction in frame S. (a) Using the results of Challenge Problem 37.73, show that in Terra's earth frame S, the rocket's acceleration is

$$\frac{du}{dt} = g \left(1 - \frac{u^2}{c^2} \right)^{3/2}$$

where u is the rocket's instantaneous velocity in frame S. (b) Write the result of part (a) in the form $dt = f(u)\,du$, where $f(u)$ is a function of u, and integrate both sides. (*Hint:* Use the integral given in Problem 37.63.) Show that in Terra's frame, the time when Stella attains a velocity v_{1x} is

$$t_1 = \frac{v_{1x}}{g\sqrt{1 - v_{1x}^2/c^2}}$$

(c) Use the time dilation formula to relate dt and dt' (infinitesimal time intervals measured in frames S and S', respectively). Combine this result with the result of part (a) and integrate as in part (b) to show the following: When Stella attains a velocity v_{1x} relative to Terra, the time t_1' that has elapsed in frame S' is

$$t_1' = \frac{c}{g}\operatorname{arctanh}\left(\frac{v_{1x}}{c}\right)$$

Here arctanh is the inverse hyperbolic tangent. (*Hint:* Use the integral given in Challenge Problem 5.124.) (d) Combine the results of parts (b) and (c) to find t_1 in terms of t_1', g, and c alone. (e) Stella accelerates in a straight-line path for five years (by her clock), slows down at the same rate for five years, turns around, accelerates for five years, slows down for five years, and lands back on the earth. According to Stella's clock, the date is January 1, 2120. What is the date according to Terra's clock?

37.75 ••• **CP** **Determining the Masses of Stars.** Many of the stars in the sky are actually *binary stars,* in which two stars orbit about their common center of mass. If the orbital speeds of the stars are high enough, the motion of the stars can be detected by the Doppler shifts of the light they emit. Stars for which this is the case are called *spectroscopic binary stars.* Figure P37.75 shows the simplest case of a spectroscopic binary star: two identical stars, each with mass m, orbiting their center of mass in a circle of radius R. The plane of the stars' orbits is edge-on to the line of sight of an observer on the earth. (a) The light produced by heated hydrogen gas in a laboratory on the earth has a frequency of 4.568110×10^{14} Hz. In the light received from the stars by a telescope on the earth, hydrogen light is observed to vary in frequency between 4.567710×10^{14} Hz and 4.568910×10^{14} Hz. Determine whether the binary star system as a whole is moving toward or away from the earth, the speed of this motion, and the orbital speeds of the stars. (*Hint:* The speeds involved are much less than c, so you may use the approximate result $\Delta f/f = u/c$ given in Section 37.6.) (b) The light from each star in the binary system varies from its maximum frequency to its minimum frequency and back again in 11.0 days. Determine the orbital radius R and the mass m of each star. Give your answer for m in kilograms and as a multiple of the mass of the sun, 1.99×10^{30} kg. Compare the value of R to the distance from the earth to the sun, 1.50×10^{11} m. (This technique is actually used in astronomy to determine the masses of stars. In practice, the problem is more complicated because the two stars in

Figure **P37.75**

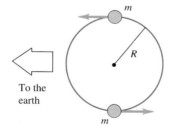

a binary system are usually not identical, the orbits are usually not circular, and the plane of the orbits is usually tilted with respect to the line of sight from the earth.)

37.76 ••• **CP CALC** **Relativity and the Wave Equation.** (a) Consider the Galilean transformation along the x-direction: $x' = x - vt$ and $t' = t$. In frame S the wave equation for electromagnetic waves in a vacuum is

$$\frac{\partial^2 E(x, t)}{\partial x^2} - \frac{1}{c^2}\frac{\partial^2 E(x, t)}{\partial t^2} = 0$$

where E represents the electric field in the wave. Show that by using the Galilean transformation the wave equation in frame S' is found to be

$$\left(1 - \frac{v^2}{c^2}\right)\frac{\partial^2 E(x', t')}{\partial x'^2} + \frac{2v}{c^2}\frac{\partial^2 E(x', t')}{\partial x'\partial t'} - \frac{1}{c^2}\frac{\partial^2 E(x', t')}{\partial t'^2} = 0$$

This has a different form than the wave equation in S. Hence the Galilean transformation *violates* the first relativity postulate that all physical laws have the same form in all inertial reference frames. (*Hint:* Express the derivatives $\partial/\partial x$ and $\partial/\partial t$ in terms of $\partial/\partial x'$ and $\partial/\partial t'$ by use of the chain rule.) (b) Repeat the analysis of part (a), but use the Lorentz coordinate transformations, Eqs. (37.21), and show that in frame S' the wave equation has the same form as in frame S:

$$\frac{\partial^2 E(x', t')}{\partial x^2} - \frac{1}{c^2}\frac{\partial^2 E(x', t')}{\partial t'^2} = 0$$

Explain why this shows that the speed of light in vacuum is c in both frames S and S'.

37.77 ••• **CP** **Kaon Production.** In high-energy physics, new particles can be created by collisions of fast-moving projectile particles with stationary particles. Some of the kinetic energy of the incident particle is used to create the mass of the new particle. A proton–proton collision can result in the creation of a negative kaon (K^-) and a positive kaon (K^+)

$$p + p \rightarrow p + p + \text{K}^- + \text{K}^+$$

(a) Calculate the minimum kinetic energy of the incident proton that will allow this reaction to occur if the second (target) proton is initially at rest. The rest energy of each kaon is 493.7 MeV, and the rest energy of each proton is 938.3 MeV. (*Hint:* It is useful here to work in the frame in which the total momentum is zero. But note that the Lorentz transformation must be used to relate the velocities in the laboratory frame to those in the zero-total-momentum frame.) (b) How does this calculated minimum kinetic energy compare with the total rest mass energy of the created kaons? (c) Suppose that instead the two protons are both in motion with velocities of equal magnitude and opposite direction. Find the minimum combined kinetic energy of the two protons that will allow the reaction to occur. How does this calculated minimum kinetic energy compare with the total rest mass energy of the created kaons? (This example shows that when colliding beams of particles are used instead of a stationary target, the energy requirements for producing new particles are reduced substantially.)

Answers

Chapter Opening Question

No. While the speed of light c is the ultimate "speed limit" for any particle, there is *no* upper limit on a particle's kinetic energy (see Fig. 37.21). As the speed approaches c, a small increase in speed corresponds to a large increase in kinetic energy.

Test Your Understanding Questions

37.1 Answers: (a) (i), (b) no You, too, will measure a spherical wave front that expands at the same speed c in all directions. This is a consequence of Einstein's second postulate. The wave front that you measure is *not* centered on the current position of the spaceship; rather, it is centered on the point P where the spaceship was located at the instant that it emitted the light pulse. For example, suppose the spaceship is moving at speed $c/2$. When your watch shows that a time t has elapsed since the pulse of light was emitted, your measurements will show that the wave front is a sphere of radius ct centered on P and that the spaceship is a distance $ct/2$ from P.

37.2 Answer: (iii) In Mavis's frame of reference, the two events (the Ogdenville clock striking noon and the North Haverbrook clock striking noon) are not simultaneous. Figure 37.5 shows that the event toward the front of the rail car occurs first. Since the rail car is moving toward North Haverbrook, that clock struck noon before the one on Ogdenville. So, according to Mavis, it is after noon in North Haverbrook.

37.3 Answers: (a) (ii), (b) (ii) The statement that moving clocks run slow refers to any clock that is moving relative to an observer. Maria and her stopwatch are moving relative to Samir, so Samir measures Maria's stopwatch to be running slow and to have ticked off fewer seconds than his own stopwatch. Samir and his stopwatch are moving relative to Maria, so she likewise measures Samir's stopwatch to be running slow. Each observer's measurement is correct for his or her own frame of reference. *Both* observers conclude that a moving stopwatch runs slow. This is consistent with the principle of relativity (see Section 37.1), which states that the laws of physics are the same in all inertial frames of reference.

37.4 Answer: (ii), (i) and (iii) (tie), (iv) You measure the rest length of the stationary meter stick and the contracted length of the moving spaceship to both be 1 meter. The rest length of the spaceship is greater than the contracted length that you measure, and so must be greater than 1 meter. A miniature observer on board the spaceship would measure a contracted length for the meter stick of less than 1 meter. Note that in your frame of reference the nose and tail of the spaceship can simultaneously align with the two ends of the meter stick, since in your frame of reference they have the same length of 1 meter. In the spaceship's frame these two alignments cannot happen simultaneously because the meter stick is shorter than the spaceship. Section 37.2 tells us that this shouldn't be a surprise; two events that are simultaneous to one observer may not be simultaneous to a second observer moving relative to the first one.

37.5 Answers: (a) P_1, (b) P_4 (a) The last of Eqs. (37.21) tells us the times of the two events in S': $t_1' = \gamma(t_1 - ux_1/c^2)$ and $t_2' = \gamma(t_2 - ux_2/c^2)$. In frame S the two events occur at the same x-coordinate, so $x_1 = x_2$, and event P_1 occurs before event P_2, so $t_1 < t_2$. Hence you can see that $t_1' < t_2'$ and event P_1 happens before P_2 in frame S', too. This says that if event P_1 happens before P_2 in a frame of reference S where the two events occur at the same position, then P_1 happens before P_2 in any other frame moving relative to S. (b) In frame S the two events occur at different x-coordinates such that $x_3 < x_4$, and events P_3 and P_4 occur at the same time, so $t_3 = t_4$. Hence you can see that $t_3' = \gamma(t_3 - ux_3/c^2)$ is greater than $t_4' = \gamma(t_4 - ux_4/c^2)$, so event P_4 happens before P_3 in frame S'. This says that even though the two events are simultaneous in frame S, they need not be simultaneous in a frame moving relative to S.

37.7 Answer: (ii) Equation (37.27) tells us that the magnitude of momentum of a particle with mass m and speed v is $p = mv/\sqrt{1 - v^2/c^2}$. If v increases by a factor of 2, the numerator mv increases by a factor of 2 *and* the denominator $\sqrt{1 - v^2/c^2}$ decreases. Hence p increases by a factor greater than 2. (Note that in order to double the speed, the initial speed must be less than $c/2$. That's because the speed of light is the ultimate speed limit.)

37.8 Answer: (i) As the proton moves a distance s, the constant force of magnitude F does work $W = Fs$ and increases the kinetic energy by an amount $\Delta K = W = Fs$. This is true no matter what the speed of the proton before moving this distance. Thus the constant force increases the proton's kinetic energy by the same amount during the first meter of travel as during any subsequent meter of travel. (It's true that as the proton approaches the ultimate speed limit of c, the increase in the proton's *speed* is less and less with each subsequent meter of travel. That's not what the question is asking, however.)

Bridging Problem

Answers: (a) $0.268c$ **(b)** 35.6 MeV **(c)** 145 MeV

APPENDIX A

THE INTERNATIONAL SYSTEM OF UNITS

The Système International d'Unités, abbreviated SI, is the system developed by the General Conference on Weights and Measures and adopted by nearly all the industrial nations of the world. The following material is adapted from the National Institute of Standards and Technology (**http://physics.nist.gov/cuu**).

Quantity	Name of unit	Symbol	
SI base units			
length	meter	m	
mass	kilogram	kg	
time	second	s	
electric current	ampere	A	
thermodynamic temperature	kelvin	K	
amount of substance	mole	mol	
luminous intensity	candela	cd	
SI derived units			**Equivalent units**
area	square meter	m^2	
volume	cubic meter	m^3	
frequency	hertz	Hz	s^{-1}
mass density (density)	kilogram per cubic meter	kg/m^3	
speed, velocity	meter per second	m/s	
angular velocity	radian per second	rad/s	
acceleration	meter per second squared	m/s^2	
angular acceleration	radian per second squared	rad/s^2	
force	newton	N	$kg \cdot m/s^2$
pressure (mechanical stress)	pascal	Pa	N/m^2
kinematic viscosity	square meter per second	m^2/s	
dynamic viscosity	newton-second per square meter	$N \cdot s/m^2$	
work, energy, quantity of heat	joule	J	$N \cdot m$
power	watt	W	J/s
quantity of electricity	coulomb	C	$A \cdot s$
potential difference, electromotive force	volt	V	J/C, W/A
electric field strength	volt per meter	V/m	N/C
electric resistance	ohm	Ω	V/A
capacitance	farad	F	$A \cdot s/V$
magnetic flux	weber	Wb	$V \cdot s$
inductance	henry	H	$V \cdot s/A$
magnetic flux density	tesla	T	Wb/m^2
magnetic field strength	ampere per meter	A/m	
magnetomotive force	ampere	A	
luminous flux	lumen	lm	$cd \cdot sr$
luminance	candela per square meter	cd/m^2	
illuminance	lux	lx	lm/m^2
wave number	1 per meter	m^{-1}	
entropy	joule per kelvin	J/K	
specific heat capacity	joule per kilogram-kelvin	$J/kg \cdot K$	
thermal conductivity	watt per meter-kelvin	$W/m \cdot K$	

Quantity	Name of unit	Symbol	Equivalent units
radiant intensity	watt per steradian	W/sr	
activity (of a radioactive source)	becquerel	Bq	s^{-1}
radiation dose	gray	Gy	J/kg
radiation dose equivalent	sievert	Sv	J/kg
SI supplementary units			
plane angle	radian	rad	
solid angle	steradian	sr	

Definitions of SI Units

meter (m)   The *meter* is the length equal to the distance traveled by light, in vacuum, in a time of 1/299,792,458 second.

kilogram (kg)   The *kilogram* is the unit of mass; it is equal to the mass of the international prototype of the kilogram. (The international prototype of the kilogram is a particular cylinder of platinum-iridium alloy that is preserved in a vault at Sévres, France, by the International Bureau of Weights and Measures.)

second (s)   The *second* is the duration of 9,192,631,770 periods of the radiation corresponding to the transition between the two hyperfine levels of the ground state of the cesium-133 atom.

ampere (A)   The *ampere* is that constant current that, if maintained in two straight parallel conductors of infinite length, of negligible circular cross section, and placed 1 meter apart in vacuum, would produce between these conductors a force equal to 2×10^{-7} newton per meter of length.

kelvin (K)   The *kelvin*, unit of thermodynamic temperature, is the fraction 1/273.16 of the thermodynamic temperature of the triple point of water.

ohm (Ω)   The *ohm* is the electric resistance between two points of a conductor when a constant difference of potential of 1 volt, applied between these two points, produces in this conductor a current of 1 ampere, this conductor not being the source of any electromotive force.

coulomb (C)   The *coulomb* is the quantity of electricity transported in 1 second by a current of 1 ampere.

candela (cd)   The *candela* is the luminous intensity, in a given direction, of a source that emits monochromatic radiation of frequency 540×10^{12} hertz and that has a radiant intensity in that direction of 1/683 watt per steradian.

mole (mol)   The *mole* is the amount of substance of a system that contains as many elementary entities as there are carbon atoms in 0.012 kg of carbon 12. The elementary entities must be specified and may be atoms, molecules, ions, electrons, other particles, or specified groups of such particles.

newton (N)   The *newton* is that force that gives to a mass of 1 kilogram an acceleration of 1 meter per second per second.

joule (J)   The *joule* is the work done when the point of application of a constant force of 1 newton is displaced a distance of 1 meter in the direction of the force.

watt (W)   The *watt* is the power that gives rise to the production of energy at the rate of 1 joule per second.

volt (V)   The *volt* is the difference of electric potential between two points of a conducting wire carrying a constant current of 1 ampere, when the power dissipated between these points is equal to 1 watt.

weber (Wb)   The *weber* is the magnetic flux that, linking a circuit of one turn, produces in it an electromotive force of 1 volt as it is reduced to zero at a uniform rate in 1 second.

lumen (lm)   The *lumen* is the luminous flux emitted in a solid angle of 1 steradian by a uniform point source having an intensity of 1 candela.

farad (F)   The *farad* is the capacitance of a capacitor between the plates of which there appears a difference of potential of 1 volt when it is charged by a quantity of electricity equal to 1 coulomb.

henry (H)   The *henry* is the inductance of a closed circuit in which an electromotive force of 1 volt is produced when the electric current in the circuit varies uniformly at a rate of 1 ampere per second.

radian (rad)   The *radian* is the plane angle between two radii of a circle that cut off on the circumference an arc equal in length to the radius.

steradian (sr)   The *steradian* is the solid angle that, having its vertex in the center of a sphere, cuts off an area of the surface of the sphere equal to that of a square with sides of length equal to the radius of the sphere.

SI Prefixes   To form the names of multiples and submultiples of SI units, apply the prefixes listed in Appendix F.

APPENDIX B

USEFUL MATHEMATICAL RELATIONS

Algebra

$$a^{-x} = \frac{1}{a^x} \qquad a^{(x+y)} = a^x a^y \qquad a^{(x-y)} = \frac{a^x}{a^y}$$

Logarithms: If $\log a = x$, then $a = 10^x$. $\quad \log a + \log b = \log(ab) \quad \log a - \log b = \log(a/b) \quad \log(a^n) = n \log a$

If $\ln a = x$, then $a = e^x$. $\quad \ln a + \ln b = \ln(ab) \qquad \ln a - \ln b = \ln(a/b) \qquad \ln(a^n) = n \ln a$

Quadratic formula: If $ax^2 + bx + c = 0$, $\quad x = \dfrac{-b \pm \sqrt{b^2 - 4ac}}{2a}$.

Binomial Theorem

$$(a + b)^n = a^n + na^{n-1}b + \frac{n(n-1)a^{n-2}b^2}{2!} + \frac{n(n-1)(n-2)a^{n-3}b^3}{3!} + \cdots$$

Trigonometry
In the right triangle ABC, $x^2 + y^2 = r^2$.

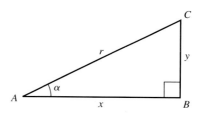

Definitions of the trigonometric functions:
$\sin \alpha = y/r \qquad \cos \alpha = x/r \qquad \tan \alpha = y/x$

Identities: $\quad \sin^2 \alpha + \cos^2 \alpha = 1 \qquad\qquad \tan \alpha = \dfrac{\sin \alpha}{\cos \alpha}$

$\sin 2\alpha = 2 \sin \alpha \cos \alpha \qquad\qquad \cos 2\alpha = \cos^2 \alpha - \sin^2 \alpha = 2\cos^2 \alpha - 1$
$$= 1 - 2\sin^2 \alpha$$

$\sin \tfrac{1}{2}\alpha = \sqrt{\dfrac{1 - \cos \alpha}{2}} \qquad\qquad \cos \tfrac{1}{2}\alpha = \sqrt{\dfrac{1 + \cos \alpha}{2}}$

$\sin(-\alpha) = -\sin \alpha \qquad\qquad\qquad \sin(\alpha \pm \beta) = \sin \alpha \cos \beta \pm \cos \alpha \sin \beta$

$\cos(-\alpha) = \cos \alpha \qquad\qquad\qquad \cos(\alpha \pm \beta) = \cos \alpha \cos \beta \mp \sin \alpha \sin \beta$

$\sin(\alpha \pm \pi/2) = \pm\cos \alpha \qquad\qquad \sin \alpha + \sin \beta = 2 \sin \tfrac{1}{2}(\alpha + \beta) \cos \tfrac{1}{2}(\alpha - \beta)$

$\cos(\alpha \pm \pi/2) = \mp\sin \alpha \qquad\qquad \cos \alpha + \cos \beta = 2 \cos \tfrac{1}{2}(\alpha + \beta) \cos \tfrac{1}{2}(\alpha - \beta)$

For *any* triangle $A'B'C'$ (not necessarily a right triangle) with sides a, b, and c and angles α, β, and γ:

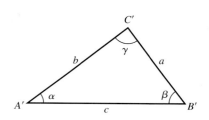

Law of sines: $\quad \dfrac{\sin \alpha}{a} = \dfrac{\sin \beta}{b} = \dfrac{\sin \gamma}{c}$

Law of cosines: $\quad c^2 = a^2 + b^2 - 2ab \cos \gamma$

Geometry

Circumference of circle of radius r: $\qquad C = 2\pi r \qquad\qquad$ Surface area of sphere of radius r: $\qquad A = 4\pi r^2$

Area of circle of radius r: $\qquad\qquad A = \pi r^2 \qquad\qquad$ Volume of cylinder of radius r and height h: $\quad V = \pi r^2 h$

Volume of sphere of radius r: $\qquad\qquad V = 4\pi r^3/3$

Calculus

Derivatives:

$$\frac{d}{dx}x^n = nx^{n-1}$$

$$\frac{d}{dx}\ln ax = \frac{1}{x}$$

$$\frac{d}{dx}e^{ax} = ae^{ax}$$

$$\frac{d}{dx}\sin ax = a\cos ax$$

$$\frac{d}{dx}\cos ax = -a\sin ax$$

Integrals:

$$\int x^n\, dx = \frac{x^{n+1}}{n+1} \quad (n \neq -1)$$

$$\int \frac{dx}{x} = \ln x$$

$$\int e^{ax}\, dx = \frac{1}{a}e^{ax}$$

$$\int \sin ax\, dx = -\frac{1}{a}\cos ax$$

$$\int \cos ax\, dx = \frac{1}{a}\sin ax$$

$$\int \frac{dx}{\sqrt{a^2 - x^2}} = \arcsin\frac{x}{a}$$

$$\int \frac{dx}{\sqrt{x^2 + a^2}} = \ln\left(x + \sqrt{x^2 + a^2}\right)$$

$$\int \frac{dx}{x^2 + a^2} = \frac{1}{a}\arctan\frac{x}{a}$$

$$\int \frac{dx}{(x^2 + a^2)^{3/2}} = \frac{1}{a^2}\frac{x}{\sqrt{x^2 + a^2}}$$

$$\int \frac{x\, dx}{(x^2 + a^2)^{3/2}} = -\frac{1}{\sqrt{x^2 + a^2}}$$

Power series (convergent for range of x shown):

$$(1 + x)^n = 1 + nx + \frac{n(n-1)x^2}{2!} + \frac{n(n-1)(n-2)}{3!}x^3$$
$$+ \cdots \quad (|x| < 1)$$

$$\sin x = x - \frac{x^3}{3!} + \frac{x^5}{5!} - \frac{x^7}{7!} + \cdots \quad (\text{all } x)$$

$$\cos x = 1 - \frac{x^2}{2!} + \frac{x^4}{4!} - \frac{x^6}{6!} + \cdots \quad (\text{all } x)$$

$$\tan x = x + \frac{x^3}{3} + \frac{2x^2}{15} + \frac{17x^7}{315} + \cdots \quad (|x| < \pi/2)$$

$$e^x = 1 + x + \frac{x^2}{2!} + \frac{x^3}{3!} + \cdots \quad (\text{all } x)$$

$$\ln(1 + x) = x - \frac{x^2}{2} + \frac{x^3}{3} - \frac{x^4}{4} + \cdots \quad (|x| < 1)$$

APPENDIX C

THE GREEK ALPHABET

Name	Capital	Lowercase	Name	Capital	Lowercase	Name	Capital	Lowercase
Alpha	A	α	Iota	I	ι	Rho	P	ρ
Beta	B	β	Kappa	K	κ	Sigma	Σ	σ
Gamma	Γ	γ	Lambda	Λ	λ	Tau	T	τ
Delta	Δ	δ	Mu	M	μ	Upsilon	Υ	υ
Epsilon	E	ϵ	Nu	N	ν	Phi	Φ	ϕ
Zeta	Z	ζ	Xi	Ξ	ξ	Chi	X	χ
Eta	H	η	Omicron	O	o	Psi	Ψ	ψ
Theta	Θ	θ	Pi	Π	π	Omega	Ω	ω

APPENDIX D

PERIODIC TABLE OF THE ELEMENTS

For each element the average atomic mass of the mixture of isotopes occurring in nature is shown. For elements having no stable isotope, the approximate atomic mass of the longest-lived isotope is shown in parentheses. For elements that have been predicted but not yet confirmed, no atomic mass is given. All atomic masses are expressed in atomic mass units ($1\ u = 1.660538782(83) \times 10^{-27}$ kg), equivalent to grams per mole (g/mol).

Group → Period ↓	1	2	3	4	5	6	7	8	9	10	11	12	13	14	15	16	17	18
1	1 **H** 1.008																	2 **He** 4.003
2	3 **Li** 6.941	4 **Be** 9.012											5 **B** 10.811	6 **C** 12.011	7 **N** 14.007	8 **O** 15.999	9 **F** 18.998	10 **Ne** 20.180
3	11 **Na** 22.990	12 **Mg** 24.305											13 **Al** 26.982	14 **Si** 28.086	15 **P** 30.974	16 **S** 32.065	17 **Cl** 35.453	18 **Ar** 39.948
4	19 **K** 39.098	20 **Ca** 40.078	21 **Sc** 44.956	22 **Ti** 47.867	23 **V** 50.942	24 **Cr** 51.996	25 **Mn** 54.938	26 **Fe** 55.845	27 **Co** 58.933	28 **Ni** 58.693	29 **Cu** 63.546	30 **Zn** 65.409	31 **Ga** 69.723	32 **Ge** 72.64	33 **As** 74.922	34 **Se** 78.96	35 **Br** 79.904	36 **Kr** 83.798
5	37 **Rb** 85.468	38 **Sr** 87.62	39 **Y** 88.906	40 **Zr** 91.224	41 **Nb** 92.906	42 **Mo** 95.94	43 **Tc** (98)	44 **Ru** 101.07	45 **Rh** 102.906	46 **Pd** 106.42	47 **Ag** 107.868	48 **Cd** 112.411	49 **In** 114.818	50 **Sn** 118.710	51 **Sb** 121.760	52 **Te** 127.60	53 **I** 126.904	54 **Xe** 131.293
6	55 **Cs** 132.905	56 **Ba** 137.327	71 **Lu** 174.967	72 **Hf** 178.49	73 **Ta** 180.948	74 **W** 183.84	75 **Re** 186.207	76 **Os** 190.23	77 **Ir** 192.217	78 **Pt** 195.078	79 **Au** 196.967	80 **Hg** 200.59	81 **Tl** 204.383	82 **Pb** 207.2	83 **Bi** 208.980	84 **Po** (209)	85 **At** (210)	86 **Rn** (222)
7	87 **Fr** (223)	88 **Ra** (226)	103 **Lr** (262)	104 **Rf** (261)	105 **Db** (262)	106 **Sg** (266)	107 **Bh** (264)	108 **Hs** (269)	109 **Mt** (268)	110 **Ds** (271)	111 **Rg** (272)	112 **Uub** (285)	113 **Uut** (284)	114 **Uuq** (289)	115 **Uup** (288)	116 **Uuh** (292)	117 **Uus** (294)	118 **Uuo**

Lanthanoids

57 **La** 138.905	58 **Ce** 140.116	59 **Pr** 140.908	60 **Nd** 144.24	61 **Pm** (145)	62 **Sm** 150.36	63 **Eu** 151.964	64 **Gd** 157.25	65 **Tb** 158.925	66 **Dy** 162.500	67 **Ho** 164.930	68 **Er** 167.259	69 **Tm** 168.934	70 **Yb** 173.04

Actinoids

89 **Ac** (227)	90 **Th** (232)	91 **Pa** (231)	92 **U** (238)	93 **Np** (237)	94 **Pu** (244)	95 **Am** (243)	96 **Cm** (247)	97 **Bk** (247)	98 **Cf** (251)	99 **Es** (252)	100 **Fm** (257)	101 **Md** (258)	102 **No** (259)

APPENDIX E

UNIT CONVERSION FACTORS

Length
1 m = 100 cm = 1000 mm = 10^6 μm = 10^9 nm
1 km = 1000 m = 0.6214 mi
1 m = 3.281 ft = 39.37 in.
1 cm = 0.3937 in.
1 in. = 2.540 cm
1 ft = 30.48 cm
1 yd = 91.44 cm
1 mi = 5280 ft = 1.609 km
1 Å = 10^{-10} m = 10^{-8} cm = 10^{-1} nm
1 nautical mile = 6080 ft
1 light year = 9.461×10^{15} m

Area
1 cm^2 = 0.155 $in.^2$
1 m^2 = 10^4 cm^2 = 10.76 ft^2
1 $in.^2$ = 6.452 cm^2
1 ft^2 = 144 $in.^2$ = 0.0929 m^2

Volume
1 liter = 1000 cm^3 = 10^{-3} m^3 = 0.03531 ft^3 = 61.02 $in.^3$
1 ft^3 = 0.02832 m^3 = 28.32 liters = 7.477 gallons
1 gallon = 3.788 liters

Time
1 min = 60 s
1 h = 3600 s
1 d = 86,400 s
1 y = 365.24 d = 3.156×10^7 s

Angle
1 rad = 57.30° = 180°/π
1° = 0.01745 rad = π/180 rad
1 revolution = 360° = 2π rad
1 rev/min (rpm) = 0.1047 rad/s

Speed
1 m/s = 3.281 ft/s
1 ft/s = 0.3048 m/s
1 mi/min = 60 mi/h = 88 ft/s
1 km/h = 0.2778 m/s = 0.6214 mi/h
1 mi/h = 1.466 ft/s = 0.4470 m/s = 1.609 km/h
1 furlong/fortnight = 1.662×10^{-4} m/s

Acceleration
1 m/s^2 = 100 cm/s^2 = 3.281 ft/s^2
1 cm/s^2 = 0.01 m/s^2 = 0.03281 ft/s^2
1 ft/s^2 = 0.3048 m/s^2 = 30.48 cm/s^2
1 mi/h·s = 1.467 ft/s^2

Mass
1 kg = 10^3 g = 0.0685 slug
1 g = 6.85×10^{-5} slug
1 slug = 14.59 kg
1 u = 1.661×10^{-27} kg
1 kg has a weight of 2.205 lb when g = 9.80 m/s^2

Force
1 N = 10^5 dyn = 0.2248 lb
1 lb = 4.448 N = 4.448×10^5 dyn

Pressure
1 Pa = 1 N/m^2 = 1.450×10^{-4} $lb/in.^2$ = 0.209 lb/ft^2
1 bar = 10^5 Pa
1 $lb/in.^2$ = 6895 Pa
1 lb/ft^2 = 47.88 Pa
1 atm = 1.013×10^5 Pa = 1.013 bar
      = 14.7 $lb/in.^2$ = 2117 lb/ft^2
1 mm Hg = 1 torr = 133.3 Pa

Energy
1 J = 10^7 ergs = 0.239 cal
1 cal = 4.186 J (based on 15° calorie)
1 ft·lb = 1.356 J
1 Btu = 1055 J = 252 cal = 778 ft·lb
1 eV = 1.602×10^{-19} J
1 kWh = 3.600×10^6 J

Mass–Energy Equivalence
1 kg $\leftrightarrow$ 8.988×10^{16} J
1 u $\leftrightarrow$ 931.5 MeV
1 eV $\leftrightarrow$ 1.074×10^{-9} u

Power
1 W = 1 J/s
1 hp = 746 W = 550 ft·lb/s
1 Btu/h = 0.293 W

APPENDIX F

NUMERICAL CONSTANTS

Fundamental Physical Constants*

Name	Symbol	Value
Speed of light in vacuum	c	2.99792458×10^8 m/s
Magnitude of charge of electron	e	$1.602176487(40) \times 10^{-19}$ C
Gravitational constant	G	$6.67428(67) \times 10^{-11}$ N·m^2/kg^2
Planck's constant	h	$6.62606896(33) \times 10^{-34}$ J·s
Boltzmann constant	k	$1.3806504(24) \times 10^{-23}$ J/K
Avogadro's number	N_A	$6.02214179(30) \times 10^{23}$ molecules/mol
Gas constant	R	$8.314472(15)$ J/mol·K
Mass of electron	m_e	$9.10938215(45) \times 10^{-31}$ kg
Mass of proton	m_p	$1.672621637(83) \times 10^{-27}$ kg
Mass of neutron	m_n	$1.674927211(84) \times 10^{-27}$ kg
Permeability of free space	μ_0	$4\pi \times 10^{-7}$ Wb/A·m
Permittivity of free space	$\epsilon_0 = 1/\mu_0 c^2$	$8.854187817\ldots \times 10^{-12}$ C^2/N·m^2
	$1/4\pi\epsilon_0$	$8.987551787\ldots \times 10^9$ N·m^2/C^2

Other Useful Constants*

Mechanical equivalent of heat		4.186 J/cal (15° calorie)
Standard atmospheric pressure	1 atm	1.01325×10^5 Pa
Absolute zero	0 K	-273.15°C
Electron volt	1 eV	$1.602176487(40) \times 10^{-19}$ J
Atomic mass unit	1 u	$1.660538782(83) \times 10^{-27}$ kg
Electron rest energy	$m_e c^2$	0.510998910(13) MeV
Volume of ideal gas (0°C and 1 atm)		22.413996(39) liter/mol
Acceleration due to gravity (standard)	g	9.80665 m/s^2

*Source: National Institute of Standards and Technology (**http://physics.nist.gov/cuu**). Numbers in parentheses show the uncertainty in the final digits of the main number; for example, the number 1.6454(21) means 1.6454 ± 0.0021. Values shown without uncertainties are exact.

Astronomical Data[†]

Body	Mass (kg)	Radius (m)	Orbit radius (m)	Orbit period
Sun	1.99×10^{30}	6.96×10^8	—	—
Moon	7.35×10^{22}	1.74×10^6	3.84×10^8	27.3 d
Mercury	3.30×10^{23}	2.44×10^6	5.79×10^{10}	88.0 d
Venus	4.87×10^{24}	6.05×10^6	1.08×10^{11}	224.7 d
Earth	5.97×10^{24}	6.38×10^6	1.50×10^{11}	365.3 d
Mars	6.42×10^{23}	3.40×10^6	2.28×10^{11}	687.0 d
Jupiter	1.90×10^{27}	6.91×10^7	7.78×10^{11}	11.86 y
Saturn	5.68×10^{26}	6.03×10^7	1.43×10^{12}	29.45 y
Uranus	8.68×10^{25}	2.56×10^7	2.87×10^{12}	84.02 y
Neptune	1.02×10^{26}	2.48×10^7	4.50×10^{12}	164.8 y
Pluto[‡]	1.31×10^{22}	1.15×10^6	5.91×10^{12}	247.9 y

[†]Source: NASA Jet Propulsion Laboratory Solar System Dynamics Group (**http://ssd.jpl.nasa.gov**), and P. Kenneth Seidelmann, ed., ***Explanatory Supplement to the Astronomical Almanac*** (University Science Books, Mill Valley, CA, 1992), pp. 704–706. For each body, "radius" is its radius at its equator and "orbit radius" is its average distance from the sun or (for the moon) from the earth.

[‡]In August 2006, the International Astronomical Union reclassified Pluto and other small objects that orbit the sun as "dwarf planets."

Prefixes for Powers of 10

Power of ten	Prefix	Abbreviation	Pronunciation
10^{-24}	yocto-	y	*yoc*-toe
10^{-21}	zepto-	z	*zep*-toe
10^{-18}	atto-	a	*at*-toe
10^{-15}	femto-	f	*fem*-toe
10^{-12}	pico-	p	*pee*-koe
10^{-9}	nano-	n	*nan*-oe
10^{-6}	micro-	μ	*my*-crow
10^{-3}	milli-	m	*mil*-i
10^{-2}	centi-	c	*cen*-ti
10^{3}	kilo-	k	*kil*-oe
10^{6}	mega-	M	*meg*-a
10^{9}	giga-	G	*jig*-a or *gig*-a
10^{12}	tera-	T	*ter*-a
10^{15}	peta-	P	*pet*-a
10^{18}	exa-	E	*ex*-a
10^{21}	zetta-	Z	*zet*-a
10^{24}	yotta-	Y	*yot*-a

Examples:

1 femtometer = 1 fm = 10^{-15} m

1 picosecond = 1 ps = 10^{-12} s

1 nanocoulomb = 1 nC = 10^{-9} C

1 microkelvin = 1μK = 10^{-6} K

1 millivolt = 1 mV = 10^{-3} V

1 kilopascal = 1 kPa = 10^{3} Pa

1 megawatt = 1 MW = 10^{6} W

1 gigahertz = 1 GHz = 10^{9} Hz

ANSWERS TO ODD-NUMBERED PROBLEMS

Chapter 21

21.1 a) 2.00×10^{10} b) 8.59×10^{-13}

21.3 2.1×10^{28}, -3.35×10^9 C

21.5 1.3 nC

21.7 3.7 km

21.9 a) $0.742\ \mu C$ on each b) $0.371\ \mu C$, $1.48\ \mu C$

21.11 1.43×10^{13}, away from each other

21.13 a) 2.21×10^4 m/s^2

21.15 0.750 nC

21.17 1.8×10^{-4} N, in the $+x$-direction

21.19 $x = -0.144$ m

21.21 $2.58\ \mu$N, in the $-y$-direction

21.23 a) 8.80×10^{-9} N, attractive
b) 8.22×10^{-8} N, about 10 times larger than the bonding force

21.25 a) 4.40×10^{-16} N b) 2.63×10^{11} m/s^2
c) 2.63×10^5 m/s

21.27 a) 3.30×10^6 N/C, to the left b) 14.2 ns
c) 1.80×10^3 N/C, to the right

21.29 a) $-21.9\ \mu C$ b) 1.02×10^{-7} N/C

21.31 a) 8740 N/C, to the right
b) 6540 N/C, to the right c) 1.40×10^{-15} N, to the right

21.33 a) 364 N/C b) no, $2.73\ \mu$m, downward

21.35 1.79×10^6 m/s

21.37 1.73×10^{-8} N, toward a point midway between the two electrons

21.39 a) $-\hat{\jmath}$ b) $\dfrac{\sqrt{2}}{2}\hat{\imath} + \dfrac{\sqrt{2}}{2}\hat{\jmath}$
c) $-0.39\hat{\imath} + 0.92\hat{\jmath}$

21.41 a) 633 km/s b) 15.9 km/s

21.43 a) 0
b) for $|x| < a$: $E_x = -\dfrac{q}{\pi\epsilon_0}\dfrac{ax}{(x^2 - a^2)^2}$;
for $x > a$: $E_x = \dfrac{q}{2\pi\epsilon_0}\dfrac{x^2 + a^2}{(x^2 - a^2)^2}$;
for $x < -a$: $E_x = -\dfrac{q}{2\pi\epsilon_0}\dfrac{x^2 + a^2}{(x^2 - a^2)^2}$

21.45 a) (i) 574 N/C, $+x$-direction (ii) 268 N/C, $-x$-direction (iii) 404 N/C, $-x$-direction
b) (i) 9.20×10^{-17} N, $-x$-direction
(ii) 4.30×10^{-17} N, $+x$-direction
(iii) 6.48×10^{-17} N, $+x$-direction

21.47 1.04×10^7 N/C, toward the -2.00-μC charge

21.49 a) $E_x = E_y = E = 0$ b) $E_x = 2660$ N/C, $E_y = 0$, $E = 2660$ N/C, $+x$-direction
c) $E_x = 129$ N/C, $E_y = 510$ N/C, $E = 526$ N/C, $284°$ counterclockwise from the $+x$-axis d) $E_x = 0$, $E_y = 1380$ N/C, $E = 1380$ N/C, $+y$-direction

21.51 a) $E_x = -4790$ N/C, $E_y = 0$, $E = 4790$ N/C, $-x$-direction b) $E_x = 2130$ N/C, $E_y = 0$, $E = 2130$ N/C, $+x$-direction c) $E_x = -129$ N/C, $E_y = -164$ N/C, $E = 209$ N/C, $232°$ counterclockwise from the $+x$-axis
d) $E_x = -1040$ N/C, $E_y = 0$, $E = 1040$ N/C, $-x$-direction

21.53 a) $(7.0\text{ N/C})\hat{\imath}$ b) $(1.75 \times 10^{-5}\text{ N})\hat{\imath}$

21.55 a) 1.14×10^5 N/C, toward the center of the disk b) 8.92×10^4 N/C, toward the center of the disk c) 1.46×10^5 N/C, toward the charge

21.57 a) 1.4×10^{-11} C $\cdot$ m, from q_1 toward q_2
b) 860 N/C

21.59 a) $\vec{p}$ is aligned in either the same or the opposite direction as $\vec{E}$. b) $\vec{p}$ is aligned in the same direction as $\vec{E}$.

21.61 a) 1680 N, from the $+5.00$-μC charge toward the -5.00-μC charge
b) 22.3 N $\cdot$ m, clockwise

21.63 b) $\dfrac{Q^2}{8\pi\epsilon_0 L^2}(1 + 2\sqrt{2})$, away from the center of the square

21.65 a) 3.17 nC b) $+x$-direction c) $x = -1.76$ m

21.67 a) $\dfrac{1}{2\pi}\sqrt{\dfrac{qQ}{\pi\epsilon_0 ma^3}}$ b) accelerates away from the origin along the y-axis

21.69 b) $2.80\ \mu C$ c) $39.5°$

21.71 a) 2.09×10^{21} N b) 5.90×10^{23} m/s^2
c) no

21.73 3.41×10^4 N/C, to the left

21.75 between the charges, 0.24 m from the 0.500-nC charge

21.77 a) $\dfrac{6q^2}{4\pi\epsilon_0 L^2}$, away from the vacant corner
b) $\dfrac{3q^2}{4\pi\epsilon_0 L^2}\left(\sqrt{2} + \dfrac{1}{2}\right)$, toward the center of the square

21.79 a) 6.0×10^{23}
b) 510 kN (electric), 4.1×10^{-31} N (gravitation)
c) yes for electric force, no for gravitation

21.81 a) ≈ 480 C b) 8.3×10^{13} N, repulsive

21.83 2190 km/s

21.85 a) 3.5×10^{20} b) 1.6 C, 2.3×10^{10} N

21.87 a) $\dfrac{mv_0^2\sin^2\alpha}{2eE}$ b) $\dfrac{mv_0^2\sin 2\alpha}{eE}$
d) 0.418 m, 2.89 m

21.89 a) $E_x = \dfrac{Q}{4\pi\epsilon_0 a}\left(\dfrac{1}{x - a} - \dfrac{1}{x}\right)$, $E_y = 0$
b) $\dfrac{qQ}{4\pi\epsilon_0 a}\left(\dfrac{1}{r} - \dfrac{1}{r + a}\right)\hat{\imath}$

21.91 a) $(-6110\text{ N/C})\hat{\imath}$ b) smaller c) 0.177 m

21.93 a) 1.56 N/C, $+x$-direction c) smaller
d) 4.7%

21.95 a) $-\dfrac{qQ}{2\pi\epsilon_0 a}\left(\dfrac{1}{y} - \dfrac{1}{\sqrt{a^2 + y^2}}\right)\hat{\imath}$
b) $\dfrac{qQ}{4\pi\varepsilon_0 a}\left(\dfrac{1}{x - a} + \dfrac{1}{x + a} - \dfrac{2}{x}\right)\hat{\imath}$

21.97 $E_x = E_y = \dfrac{Q}{2\pi^2\epsilon_0 a^2}$

21.99 a) 6.25×10^4 N/C, $225°$ counterclockwise from an axis pointing to the right at the point P
b) 1.00×10^{-14} N, opposite the electric field direction

21.101 a) 1.19×10^6 N/C, to the left
b) 1.19×10^5 N/C, to the left
c) 1.19×10^5 N/C, to the right

21.103 $\dfrac{\sigma}{2\epsilon_0}\left(-\dfrac{x}{|x|}\hat{\imath} + \dfrac{z}{|z|}\hat{k}\right)$

21.105 b) $q_1 < 0$, $q_2 > 0$ c) $0.843\ \mu C$ d) 56.2 N

21.107 a) $\dfrac{Q}{2\pi\epsilon_0 L}\left(\dfrac{1}{2x + a} - \dfrac{1}{2L + 2x + a}\right)$

Chapter 22

22.1 a) 1.8 N $\cdot$ m^2/C b) no c) (i) $0°$ (ii) $90°$

22.3 a) 3.53×10^5 N $\cdot$ m^2/C b) $3.13\ \mu C$

22.5 $\pi r^2 E$

22.7 0.977 N $\cdot$ m^2/C, inward

22.9 a) 0 b) 8.74×10^7 N/C
c) 2.60×10^7 N/C

22.11 a) 1.17×10^5 N $\cdot$ m^2/C b) no change

22.13 a) 4.50×10^4 N/C b) 918 N/C

22.15 0.0810 N

22.17 2.04×10^{10}

22.19 a) 6.47×10^5 N/C, $+y$-direction
b) 7.2×10^4 N/C, $-y$-direction

22.21 a) $5.73\ \mu$C/m^2 b) 6.47×10^5 N/C
c) -5.65×10^4 N $\cdot$ m^2/C

22.23 a) $0.260\ \mu$C/m^3 b) 1960 N/C

22.25 1.16 km/s

22.27 $23.6\ \mu$J

22.29 0 (outside the plates), σ/ϵ_0 (between the plates)

22.31 a) $2\pi R\sigma$ b) $\sigma R/\epsilon_0 r$ c) $\lambda/2\pi\epsilon_0 r$

22.33 a) yes, $+Q$ b) no c) yes d) no, no
e) no, yes, no

22.35 a) 750 N $\cdot$ m^2/C b) 0
c) 577 N/C, $+x$-direction d) charges both within and outside

22.37 a) -0.598 nC b) charges both within and outside

22.39 a) $\lambda/2\pi\epsilon_0 r$, radially outward b) $\lambda/2\pi\epsilon_0 r$, radially outward
d) $-\lambda$ (inner surface), $+\lambda$ (outer surface)

22.41 a) (i) $\dfrac{\alpha}{2\pi\epsilon_0 r}$, radially outward (ii) 0 (iii) 0
b) (i) $-\alpha$ (ii) 0

22.43 $10.2°$

22.45 a) $0\ (r < R)$; $\dfrac{1}{4\pi\epsilon_0}\dfrac{Q}{r^2}$ $(R < r < 2R)$, radially outward; $\dfrac{1}{4\pi\epsilon_0}\dfrac{2Q}{r^2}$ $(r > 2R)$, radially outward

22.47 a) (i) 0 (ii) 0 (iii) $\dfrac{q}{2\pi\epsilon_0 r^2}$, radially outward
(iv) 0 (v) $\dfrac{3q}{2\pi\epsilon_0 r^2}$, radially outward
b) (i) 0 (ii) $+2q$ (iii) $-2q$ (iv) $+6q$

22.49 a) (i) 0 (ii) 0 (iii) $\dfrac{q}{2\pi\epsilon_0 r^2}$, radially outward
(iv) 0 (v) $\dfrac{q}{2\pi\epsilon_0 r^2}$, radially inward
b) (i) 0 (ii) $+2q$ (iii) $-2q$ (iv) $-2q$

22.51 a) $\dfrac{qQ}{4\pi\epsilon_0 r^2}$, toward the center of the shell
b) 0

22.53 a) $\dfrac{\alpha}{2\epsilon_0}\left(1 - \dfrac{a^2}{r^2}\right)$
b) $q = 2\pi\alpha a^2$, $E = \dfrac{\alpha}{2\epsilon_0}$

22.55 $R/2$

22.57 $|x| > d$ (outside the slab): $\dfrac{\rho_0 d}{3\epsilon_0}\dfrac{x}{|x|}\hat{\imath}$; $|x| < d$ (inside the slab): $\dfrac{\rho_0 x^3}{3\epsilon_0 d^2}\hat{\imath}$

22.61 b) $\rho\vec{b}/3\varepsilon_0$

22.63 a) $-\dfrac{Q}{16\pi\epsilon_0 R^2}\hat{\imath}$ b) $\dfrac{Q}{72\pi\epsilon_0 R^2}\hat{\imath}$
c) 0 d) $\dfrac{5Q}{18\pi\epsilon_0 R^2}\hat{\imath}$

22.65 c) $\dfrac{Qr}{4\pi\epsilon_0 R^3}\left(4 - \dfrac{3r}{R}\right)$ e) $2R/3$, $\dfrac{Q}{3\pi\varepsilon_0 R^2}$

22.67 a) $\dfrac{480Q}{233\pi R^3}$

b) $r \leq R/2$: $E = \dfrac{180Qr^2}{233\pi\epsilon_0 R^4}$; $R/2 \leq r \leq R$:

$E = \dfrac{480Q}{233\pi\epsilon_0 r^2}\left[\dfrac{1}{3}\left(\dfrac{r}{R}\right)^3 - \dfrac{1}{5}\left(\dfrac{r}{R}\right)^5 - \dfrac{23}{1920}\right]$;

$r \geq R$: $E = \dfrac{Q}{4\pi\epsilon_0 r^2}$ c) 0.807

d) $E = \dfrac{180}{233}\dfrac{Q}{4\pi\epsilon_0 R^2}$

Chapter 23

23.1 -0.356 J
23.3 3.46×10^{-13} J $= 2.16$ MeV
23.5 a) 12.5 m/s b) 0.323 m
23.7 -1.42×10^{-18} J
23.9 a) 13.6 km/s b) 2.45×10^{17} m/s^2
23.11 $-q/2$
23.13 7.42 m/s, faster
23.15 a) 0 b) 0.750 mJ c) -2.06 mJ
23.17 a) 0 b) -175 kV c) -0.875 J
23.19 a) -737 V b) -704 V c) 8.2×10^{-8} J
23.21 b) $V = \dfrac{q}{4\pi\epsilon_0}\left(\dfrac{1}{|x|} - \dfrac{2}{|x-a|}\right)$

c) $x = -a, a/3$
23.23 a) 156 V b) -182 V
23.25 a) point b b) 800 V/m c) -48.0 μJ
23.27 a) (i) 180 V (ii) -270 V (iii) -450 V
 b) 719 V, inner shell
23.29 a) oscillatory b) 1.67×10^7 m/s
23.31 a) 94.9 nC/m b) less c) zero
23.33 a) 78.2 kV b) zero
23.35 0.474 J
23.37 a) 9.3×10^6 V/m, inward
 b) outer surface
23.39 a) 8.00 kV/m b) 19.2 μN c) 0.864 μJ
 d) -0.864 μJ
23.41 b) -20 nC c) no
23.43 -760 V
23.45 a) $E_x = -Ay + 2Bx$, $E_y = -Ax - C$, $E_z = 0$
 b) $x = -C/A$, $y = -2BC/A^2$, any value of z
23.47 a) (i) $V = \dfrac{q}{4\pi\epsilon_0}\left(\dfrac{1}{r_a} - \dfrac{1}{r_b}\right)$

 (ii) $V = \dfrac{q}{4\pi\epsilon_0}\left(\dfrac{1}{r} - \dfrac{1}{r_b}\right)$ (iii) $V = 0$

 d) 0 e) $E = \dfrac{q - Q}{4\pi\epsilon_0 r^2}$
23.49 a) cylinders coaxial with the given cylinder
 b) 2.90 cm, 4.20 cm, 6.08 cm
 c) get farther apart
23.51 a) -0.360 μJ b) $x = 0.074$ m
23.53 a) 7.66×10^{-13} J b) 5.17×10^{-14} m
23.55 a) -21.5 μJ b) -2.83 kV c) 35.4 kV/m
23.57 a) 7.85×10^4 V/m$^{4/3}$
 b) $E_x = -(1.05 \times 10^5$ V/m$^{4/3})x^{1/3}$
 c) 3.13×10^{-15} N, toward the positive anode
23.59 a) $-\dfrac{1.46q^2}{\pi\epsilon_0 d}$
23.61 a) -8.60×10^{-18} J $= -53.7$ eV
 b) 2.88×10^{-11} m
23.63 a) (i) $V = (\lambda/2\pi\epsilon_0)\ln(b/a)$
 (ii) $V = (\lambda/2\pi\epsilon_0)\ln(b/r)$ (iii) $V = 0$
 d) $(\lambda/2\pi\epsilon_0)\ln(b/a)$
23.65 a) 1.76×10^{-16} N, downward
 b) 1.93×10^{14} m/s^2, downward
 c) 0.822 cm d) 15.3° e) 3.29 cm
23.67 a) 97.1 kV/m b) 30.3 pC
23.69 a) $r > R$: $V_r = -\dfrac{\lambda}{2\pi\epsilon_0}\ln\left(\dfrac{r}{R}\right)$;

 $r < R$: $V_r = \dfrac{\lambda}{4\pi\epsilon_0}\left[1 - \left(\dfrac{r}{R}\right)^2\right]$

23.71 $\dfrac{3}{5}\left(\dfrac{Q^2}{4\pi\epsilon_0 R}\right)$

23.73 360 kV
23.75 b) yes c) no, no
23.77 $\dfrac{Q}{8\pi\epsilon_0 R}$
23.79 a) $\dfrac{Q}{4\pi\epsilon_0 a}\ln\left(\dfrac{x + a}{x}\right)$

 b) $\dfrac{Q}{4\pi\epsilon_0 a}\ln\left(\dfrac{a + \sqrt{a^2 + y^2}}{y}\right)$

 c) part (a): $\dfrac{Q}{4\pi\epsilon_0 x}$, part (b): $\dfrac{Q}{4\pi\epsilon_0 y}$

23.81 a) 1/3 b) 3
23.83 a) $E = \dfrac{Q_1}{4\pi\epsilon_0 R_1^2}$, $V = \dfrac{Q_1}{4\pi\epsilon_0 R_1}$

 b) $q_1 = \dfrac{Q_1 R_1}{R_1 + R_2}$, $q_2 = \dfrac{Q_1 R_2}{R_1 + R_2}$

 c) $V = \dfrac{Q_1}{4\pi\epsilon_0(R_1 + R_2)}$ for either sphere

 d) $E_1 = \dfrac{Q_1}{4\pi\epsilon_0 R_1(R_1 + R_2)}$,

 $E_2 = \dfrac{Q_1}{4\pi\epsilon_0 R_2(R_1 + R_2)}$
23.85 a) 7580 km/s b) 7260 km/s
 c) 2.3×10^9 K (protons), 6.4×10^9 K (helium)
23.87 a) 5.9×10^{-15} m b) 20.7 pJ
 c) 1.06×10^{15} J $= 253$ kilotons of TNT
23.89 1.01×10^{-12} m, 1.11×10^{-13} m, 2.54×10^{-14} m
23.91 c) 3, 0.507 μm

Chapter 24

24.1 a) 10.0 kV b) 22.6 cm^2 c) 8.00 pF
24.3 a) 604 V b) 90.8 cm^2 c) 1840 kV/m
 d) 16.3 μC/m^2
24.5 a) 120 μC b) 60 μC c) 480 μC
24.7 2.8 mm, yes
24.9 a) 1.05 mm b) 84.0 V
24.11 a) 4.35 pF b) 2.30 V
24.13 a) 15.0 pF b) 3.09 cm c) 31.2 kN/C
24.15 a) series b) 5000
24.17 a) $Q_1 = Q_2 = 22.4$ μC, $Q_3 = 44.8$ μC, $Q_4 = 67.2$ μC
 b) $V_1 = V_2 = 5.6$ V, $V_3 = 11.2$ V, $V_4 = 16.8$ V
 c) 11.2 V
24.19 a) $Q_1 = 156$ μC, $Q_2 = 260$ μC
 b) $V_1 = V_2 = 52.0$ V
24.21 a) 19.3 nF b) 482 nC c) 162 nC
 d) 25 V
24.23 57 μF
24.25 0.0283 J/m^3
24.27 a) $\dfrac{xQ^2}{2\epsilon_0 A}$ b) $\left(\dfrac{Q^2}{2\epsilon_0 A}\right)dx$ c) $\dfrac{Q^2}{2\epsilon_0 A}$

24.29 a) $U_p = 4U_s$ b) $Q_p = 2Q_s$ c) $E_p = 2E_s$
24.31 a) 24.2 μC b) $Q_{35} = 7.7$ μC, $Q_{75} = 16.5$ μC
 c) 2.66 mJ d) $U_{35} = 0.85$ mJ, $U_{75} = 1.81$ mJ
 e) 220 V for each capacitor
24.33 a) 1.60 nC b) 8.05
24.35 a) 3.60 mJ (before), 13.5 mJ (after)
 b) increased by 9.9 mJ
24.37 a) 0.620 μC/m^2 b) 1.28
24.39 0.0135 m^2
24.41 a) 2.31×10^{-11} C^2/N $\cdot$ m^2
 b) 4.0×10^4 V
 c) $\sigma = 4.6 \times 10^{-4}$ C/m^2, $\sigma_i = 2.8 \times 10^{-4}$ C/m^2
24.43 a) 10.1 V b) 2.25

24.45 a) $\dfrac{Q}{\epsilon_0 AK}$ b) $\dfrac{Qd}{\epsilon_0 AK}$ c) $K\dfrac{\epsilon_0 A}{d} = KC_0$
24.47 a) 421 J b) 0.054 F
24.49 a) 31 pF b) 0.37 nC c) 1.6 kV/m
 d) 2.2 nJ
24.51 133 kV/m
24.53 a) 0.0160 C b) 533 V c) 4.26 J d) 2.14 J
24.55 a) 158 μJ b) 72.1 μJ
24.57 a) 2.5 μF
 b) $Q_1 = 550$ μC, $Q_2 = 370$ μC, $Q_3 = Q_4 = 180$ μC, $Q_5 = 550$ μC; $V_1 = 65$ V, $V_2 = 87$ V, $V_3 = V_4 = 43$ V, $V_5 = 65$ V
24.59 $C_2 = 6.00$ μF, $C_3 = 4.50$ μF
24.61 a) 76 μC b) 1.4 mJ
 c) 11 V across each capacitor d) 1.3 mJ
24.63 a) 2.3 μF b) $Q_1 = 970$ μC, $Q_2 = 640$ μC
 c) 47 V
24.65 a) 3.91 b) 22.8 V
24.67 a) $C = 4\pi\epsilon_0 R$ b) 710 μF
24.69 a) 0.065 F b) 23,000 C
 c) 4.0×10^9 J
24.71 48.3 μF
24.73 0.185 μJ
24.75 b) 2.38 nF
24.77 a) $\dfrac{\epsilon_0 L}{D}[L + (K - 1)x]$

 c) $Q = \dfrac{\epsilon_0 LV}{D}[L + (K - 1)x]$

Chapter 25

25.1 1.0 C
25.3 a) 3.12×10^{19} b) 1.51×10^6 A/m^2
 c) 0.111 mm/s d) both J and v_d would decrease
25.5 a) 110 min b) 440 min c) $v_d \propto 1/d^2$
25.7 a) 330 C b) 41 A
25.9 9.0 μA
25.11 a) 1.06×10^{-5} $\Omega \cdot$ m
 b) 0.00105 (C°)$^{-1}$
25.13 a) 0.206 mV b) 0.176 mV
25.15 a) 1.21 V/m b) 0.0145 Ω c) 0.182 V
25.17 0.125 V
25.19 15 g
25.21 1.53×10^{-8} Ω
25.23 a) 11 A b) 3.1 V c) 0.28 Ω
25.25 a) 99.54 Ω b) 0.0158 Ω
25.27 a) 4.67×10^{-8} Ω b) 6.72×10^{-4} Ω
25.29 a) 27.4 V b) 12.3 MJ
25.31 a) zero b) 5.0 V c) 5.0 V
25.33 3.08 V, 0.067 Ω, 1.80 Ω
25.35 a) 1.41 A, clockwise b) 13.7 V c) -1.0 V
25.37 b) yes c) 3.88 Ω
25.39 a) 144 Ω b) 240 Ω c) 0.833 A, 0.500 A
25.41 a) 29.8 W b) 0.248 A
25.43 a) EJ b) ρJ^2 c) E^2/ρ
25.45 a) 300 W b) 0.90 J
25.47 a) 2.6 MJ b) 0.063 L c) 1.6 h
25.49 12.3%
25.51 a) 24.0 W b) 4.0 W c) 20.0 W
25.53 a) 26.7 Ω b) 4.50 A c) 453 W d) larger
25.55 a) 3.65×10^{-8} $\Omega \cdot$ m b) 172 A
 c) 2.58 mm/s
25.57 0.060 Ω
25.59 a) 2.5 mA b) 2.14×10^{-5} V/m
 c) 8.55×10^{-5} V/m d) 0.180 mV
25.61 42.0 s
25.63 a) 80 C° b) no
25.65 a) $\dfrac{\rho h}{\pi r_1 r_2}$
25.67 a) 0.057 Ω b) 3.34×10^{-8} $\Omega \cdot$ m
 c) 0.86 mm d) 0.00240 Ω
 e) 0.0011 (C°)$^{-1}$
25.69 a) 0.20 Ω b) 8.7 V
25.71 a) 1.0 kΩ b) 100 V c) 10 W
25.73 1.42 A
25.75 a) $I_A\left(1 + \dfrac{R_A}{r + R}\right)$ b) 0.0429 Ω
25.77 b) 8-gauge c) 106 W d) $19.25

25.79 a) 0.40 A   b) 1.6 W
c) 4.8 W, in the 12.0-V battery
d) 3.2 W, in the 8.0-V battery
25.81 a) 14.4 V   b) 2.59 MJ   c) 0.432 MJ
d) 0.96 Ω e) 1.73 MJ   f) 0.432 MJ
25.83 6.67 V
25.85 a) a/E b) aL/V_{bc} c) point c
d) 3.5×10^8 m/s²
25.87 a) $R = \dfrac{\rho_0 L}{A}\left(1 - \dfrac{1}{e}\right)$, $I = \dfrac{V_0 A}{\rho_0 L\left(1 - \dfrac{1}{e}\right)}$

b) $E(x) = \dfrac{V_0 e^{-x/L}}{L\left(1 - \dfrac{1}{e}\right)}$,

c) $V(x) = \dfrac{V_0\left(e^{-x/L} - \dfrac{1}{e}\right)}{1 - \dfrac{1}{e}}$

Chapter 26

26.1 $3R/4$
26.3 22.5 W
26.5 a) 3.50 A   b) 4.50 A   c) 3.15 A   d) 3.25 A
26.7 0.769 A
26.9 a) 8.80 Ω b) 3.18 A   c) 3.18 A   d) 5.09 V,
7.63 V, 15.3 V   e) 16.2 W, 24.3 W, 48.5 W
f) resistor with greater resistance
26.11 a) 8.00 A, 12.0 A   b) 84.0 V
26.13 5.00 Ω; $I_3 = 8.00$ A, $I_4 = 9.00$ A,
$I_6 = 4.00$ A, $I_{12} = 3.00$ A
26.15 a) $I_1 = 1.50$ A, $I_2 = I_3 = I_4 = 0.500$ A
b) $P_1 = 10.1$ W, $P_2 = P_3 = P_4 = 1.12$ W; R_1
glows brightest   c) $I_1 = 1.33$ A, $I_2 = I_3 = $
0.667 A   d) $P_1 = 8.00$ W, $P_2 = P_3 = 2.00$ W
e) R_1 glows less brightly; R_2 and R_3 glow
brighter
26.17 18.0 V, 3.00 A
26.19 a) 2 resistors in parallel and that combination
in series with 3 more resistors   b) 10 resistors
in parallel   c) 3 resistors in parallel
d) 2 resistors in parallel and that combination
in series with 4 resistors in parallel
26.21 a) 0.100 A   b) 4.0 W, 8.0 W   c) 12.0 W
d) 0.300 A, 0.150 A   e) 36.0 W, 18.0 W
f) 54.0 W   g) in series, the 800-Ω bulb is
brighter; in parallel, the 400-Ω bulb is brighter
h) parallel connection
26.23 1010 s
26.25 a) 2.00 A   b) 5.00 Ω c) 42.0 V
d) 3.50 A
26.27 a) 8.00 A   b) $\varepsilon_1 = 36.0$ V, $\varepsilon_2 = 54.0$ V
c) 9.00 Ω
26.29 a) 1.60 A, 1.40 A, 0.20 A   b) 10.4 V
26.31 a) 36.4 V   b) 0.500 A
26.33 a) 2.14 V, a is higher
b) 0.050 A, downward; 0
26.35 a) 0.641 Ω b) 975 Ω
26.37 a) 17.9 V   b) 22.7 V   c) 21.4%
26.39 a) 543 Ω b) 1.88 mA
c) 1824 Ω, 608 Ω, 203 Ω
26.41 a) 0.849 μF   b) 2.89 s
26.43 a) 4.21 ms   b) 0.125 A
26.45 192 μC
26.47 13.6 A
26.49 a) 0.937 A   b) 0.606 A
26.51 a) 133 μC   b) 8.87 V, 9.13 V
c) 8.87 V for both   d) 67.4 μC
26.53 900 W
26.55 12.1 Ω
26.57 a) 13.6 $\mu\Omega$ b) 2.14×10^{-8} $\Omega \cdot$m
26.59 a) 2.2 A, 4.4 V, 9.7 W   b) 16.3 W, brighter
26.61 a) 18.7 Ω b) 7.5 Ω
26.63 $I_1 = 0.848$ A, $I_2 = 2.14$ A, $I_3 = 0.171$ A
26.65 $I_2 = 5.21$ A, $I_4 = 1.11$ A, $I_5 = 6.32$ A
26.67 a) +0.22 V   b) 0.464 A
26.69 0.447 Ω (end-to-end), 0.423 Ω (in parallel)
26.71 a) 186 V, upper terminal positive
b) 3.00 A, upward   c) 20.0 Ω

26.73 a) $P_1 + P_2$ b) $\dfrac{P_1 P_2}{P_1 + P_2}$
26.75 a) 1.35 W   b) 8.31 ms   c) 0.337 W
26.77 a) −12.0 V   b) 1.71 A   c) 4.21 Ω
26.79 a) 114 V   b) 263 V   c) 266 V
26.81 b) 1897 Ω
26.83 a) 24.8 V, 65.2 V   b) 3840 Ω c) 62.6 V
d) no
26.85 1.7 MΩ, 3.1 μF
26.87 a) 19.4 s, 31.4 time constants   b) yes
26.89 a) $P = \dfrac{Q_0^2}{RC^2} e^{-2t/RC}$
26.93 b) 4 segments   c) 3.2 MΩ, 4.0×10^{-3}
d) 3.4×10^{-4} e) 0.88

Chapter 27

27.1 a) $(-6.68 \times 10^{-4}$ N$)\hat{k}$
b) $(6.68 \times 10^{-4}$ N$)\hat{i} + (7.27 \times 10^{-4}$ N$)\hat{j}$
27.3 a) positive   b) 0.0505 N
27.5 9490 km/s
27.7 a) $B_x = -0.175$ T, $B_z = -0.256$ T
b) B_y is not determined   c) 0, 90°
27.9 a) 1.46 T, in the xz-plane at 40° from the $+x$-axis
toward the $-z$-axis   b) 7.47×10^{-16} N, in the
xz-plane at 50° from the $-x$-axis toward the
$-z$-axis.
27.11 a) 3.05 mWb   b) 1.83 mWb   c) 0
27.13 −0.78 mWb
27.15 a) 0.160 mT, into the page   b) 0.111 μs
27.17 7.93×10^{-10} N, toward the south
27.19 a) 4.94×10^{-21} kg · m/s
b) 2.31×10^{-23} kg · m²/s
27.21 a) 835 km/s   b) 26.2 ns   c) 7.27 kV
27.23 a) 107 T   b) no
27.25 0.838 mT
27.27 a) $(1.60 \times 10^{-14}$ N$)\hat{j}$ b) yes
c) helix, no   d) 1.40 cm
27.29 a) 4.81 kN/C   c) yes
27.31 0.0445 T, out of the page
27.33 a) 4.92 km/s   b) 9.96×10^{-26} kg
27.35 2.0 cm
27.37 a) 13.4 kA, no
27.39 0.724 N, 63.4° below the direction of the
current in the upper wire segment
27.41 a) 817 V   b) 113 m/s²
27.43 a) $-ILB\hat{j}$ b) yes
27.45 b) $F_{cd} = 1.20$ N   c) 0.420 N · m
27.47 a) A_2 b) 290 rad/s²
27.49 −2.42 J
27.51 a) 1.13 A   b) 3.69 A   c) 98.2 V
d) 362 W
27.53 a) 4.7 mm/s   b) $+4.5 \times 10^{-3}$ V/m,
$+z$-direction   c) 53 μV
27.55 a) $-\dfrac{F_2}{qv_1}\hat{j}$ b) $F_2/\sqrt{2}$
27.57 a) 8.3×10^6 m/s   b) 0.14 T
27.59 3.45 T, perpendicular to the initial velocity of
the coin
27.61 a) 8.9×10^{-13} J = 5.5 MeV   b) 77 ns
c) 1.2 T   d) same as in (a)
27.63 a) −3.89 μC
b) $(7.60 \times 10^{14}$ m/s²$)\hat{i} +$
$(5.70 \times 10^{14}$ m/s²$)\hat{j}$
c) 2.90 cm   d) 2.88×10^7 Hz
e) (0.0290 m, 0, 0.874 m)
27.65 9τ
27.67 1.6 mm
27.69 $\dfrac{Mg \tan\theta}{LB}$, right to left
27.71 $B_r(r) = -\beta r/2$
27.73 a) 8.46 mT   b) 27.2 cm   c) 2.2 cm, yes
27.75 1.80 N, to the left
27.77 0.024 T, $+y$-direction
27.79 a) 0.0442 N · m, clockwise   b) stretched
c) 7.98 mJ
27.81 2.39 A
27.83 $-(0.444$ N$)\hat{j}$

27.85 b) (0, 0) to $(0, L)$: $\frac{1}{2}B_0 LI\hat{i}$
$(0, L)$ to (L, L): $-IB_0 L\hat{j}$
(L, L) to $(L, 0)$: $-\frac{1}{2}B_0 LI\hat{i}$
$(L, 0)$ to $(0, 0)$: 0
c) $-IB_0 L\hat{j}$
27.87 a) 2.52 m/s   b) 7.58 A   c) 0.198 Ω
27.89 a) 5.14 m   b) 1.72 μs   c) 6.08 mm
d) 3.05 cm

Chapter 28

28.1 a) $-(19.2 \mu$T$)\hat{k}$ b) 0   c) $(19.2 \mu$T$)\hat{i}$
d) $(6.79 \mu$T$)\hat{i}$
28.3 a) 60.0 nT, out of the page, at A and B
b) 0.120 μT, out of the page   c) 0
28.5 a) 0   b) $-(1.31 \mu$T$)\hat{k}$ c) $-(0.462 \mu$T$)\hat{k}$
d) $(1.31 \mu$T$)\hat{j}$
28.7 a) (i) $\dfrac{\mu_0 qv}{8\pi d^2}$, into the page   (ii) 0
(iii) $\dfrac{\mu_0 qv}{4\pi d^2}$, out of the page
b) $\dfrac{\mu_0 q^2 v' v}{16\pi d^2}$, attractive   c) 1.00×10^{-6}
28.9 $(97.5$ nT$)\hat{k}$
28.11 a) 0.440 μT, out of the page
b) 16.7 nT, out of the page   c) 0
28.13 a) $(5.00 \times 10^{-11}$ T$)\hat{j}$
b) $-(5.00 \times 10^{-11}$ T$)\hat{i}$
c) $(-1.77 \times 10^{-11}$ T$)(\hat{i} - \hat{j})$ d) 0
28.15 17.6 μT, into the page
28.17 a) 0.8 mT   b) 40 μT, 20 times larger
28.19 25 μA
28.21 a) 10.0 A
b) at all points directly above the wire
c) at all points directly east of the wire
28.23 a) $-(0.10 \mu$T$)\hat{i}$
b) 2.19 μT, at 46.8° from the x-axis to the
z-axis   c) $(7.9 \mu$T$)\hat{i}$
28.25 a) 0   b) 6.67 μT, toward the top of the page
c) 7.54 μT, to the left
28.27 a) 0   b) 0   c) 0.40 mT, to the left
28.29 a) at P: 41 μT, into the page; at Q: 25 μT, out
of the page   b) at P: 9.0 μT, out of the page;
at Q: 9.0 μT, into the page
28.31 a) 6.00 μN, repulsive   b) 24.0 μN
28.33 46 μN/m, repulsive, no
28.35 0.38 μA
28.37 $\dfrac{\mu_0|I_1 - I_2|}{4R}$, 0
28.39 a) 9.42 mT   b) 0.134 mT
28.41 18.0 A, counterclockwise
28.43 a) 305 A   b) -3.83×10^{-4} T · m
28.45 a) $\mu_0 I/2\pi r$ b) 0
28.47 $r = R/2$ and $2R$
28.49 a) 1790 turns/m   b) 63.0 m
28.51 a) 3.72 MA   b) 124 kA   c) 237 A
28.53 1.11 mT
28.55 a) 72.5 mA   b) 19.5 mA
28.57 a) (i) 1.13 mT   (ii) 4.68 MA/m   (iii) 5.88 T
28.59 a) 1.00 μT, into the page
b) $(7.49 \times 10^{-8}$ N$)\hat{j}$
28.61 a) in the plane of the wires, between them,
0.300 m from the 75.0-A wire
b) in the plane of the wires, 0.200 m from the
25.0-A wire and 0.600 m from the 75.0-A wire
28.63 a) 5.7×10^{12} m/s², away from the wire
b) 32.5 N/C, away from the wire   c) no
28.65 5.59×10^{-18} N
28.67 a) 2.00 A, out of the page
b) 2.13 μT, to the right   c) 2.06 μT
28.69 a) 11.1 μN/m, $-y$-direction
b) 11.1 μN/m, $+y$-direction
28.71 23.2 A

28.73 2.21×10^{-3} N·m

28.75 a) $\dfrac{\mu_0 N I a^2}{2} \left\{ \dfrac{1}{[(x + a/2)^2 + a^2]^{3/2}} + \dfrac{1}{[(x - a/2)^2 + a^2]^{3/2}} \right\}$

c) $\left(\dfrac{4}{5}\right)^{3/2} \dfrac{\mu_0 N I}{a}$ d) 20.2 mT e) 0, 0

28.77 a) $\dfrac{3I}{2\pi R^3}$ b) (i) $B = \dfrac{\mu_0 I r^2}{2\pi R^3}$ (ii) $B = \dfrac{\mu_0 I}{2\pi r}$

28.79 a) 0 b) $B = \dfrac{\mu_0 I}{2\pi r} \dfrac{r^2 - a^2}{b^2 - a^2}$ c) $B = \dfrac{\mu_0 I}{2\pi r}$

28.81 b) $B = \dfrac{\mu_0 I_0}{2\pi r}$ c) $\dfrac{I_0 r^2}{a^2}\left(2 - \dfrac{r^2}{a^2}\right)$

d) $B = \dfrac{\mu_0 I_0 r}{2\pi a^2}\left(2 - \dfrac{r^2}{a^2}\right)$

28.83 a) $B = \dfrac{1}{2}\mu_0 I n$, $+x$-direction

b) $B = \dfrac{1}{2}\mu_0 I n$, $-x$-direction

28.85 7.73×10^{-25} A·m^2 = $0.0834\mu_B$

28.87 b) $\dfrac{1}{2g}\left(\dfrac{\mu_0 Q_0^2}{4\pi \lambda R C d}\right)^2$

Chapter 29

29.1 a) 17.1 mV b) 28.5 mA
29.3 a) $Q = NBA/R$ b) no
29.5 a) 34 V b) counterclockwise
29.7 a) $\mu_0 i / 2\pi r$, into the page b) $\dfrac{\mu_0 i}{2\pi r} L \, dr$

c) $\dfrac{\mu_0 i L}{2\pi} \ln (b/a)$ d) $\dfrac{\mu_0 L}{2\pi} \ln (b/a) \dfrac{di}{dt}$

e) $0.506 \, \mu$V
29.9 a) 5.44 mV b) clockwise
29.11 a) bAv b) clockwise
c) bAv, counterclockwise
29.13 10.4 rad/s
29.15 a) counterclockwise b) clockwise
c) no induced current
29.17 a) a to b b) b to a c) b to a
29.19 a) clockwise b) no induced current
c) counterclockwise
29.21 13.2 mA, counterclockwise
29.23 a) 0.675 V b) point b c) 2.25 V/m, b to a
d) point b e) (i) 0 (ii) 0
29.25 46.2 m/s = 103 mph, no
29.27 a) 3.00 V b) b to a c) 0.800 N, to the right
d) 6.00 W for each
29.29 a) counterclockwise b) 42.4 mW
29.31 35.0 m/s, to the right
29.33 a) 2.55 V, point a b) 3.38 V, point a c) 0
d) 4.23 V
29.35 a) $\pi r_1^2 \dfrac{dB}{dt}$ b) $\dfrac{r_1}{2}\dfrac{dB}{dt}$ c) $\dfrac{R^2}{2r_2}\dfrac{dB}{dt}$

e) $\dfrac{\pi R^2}{4}\dfrac{dB}{dt}$ f) $\pi R^2 \dfrac{dB}{dt}$ g) $\pi R^2 \dfrac{dB}{dt}$
29.37 9.21 A/s
29.39 0.950 mV
29.41 2.34
29.43 a) 0.599 nC b) 6.00 mA c) 6.00 mA
29.45 a) 0.15 V/m b) 38 V/m·s
c) 3.4×10^{-10} A/m^2 d) 53.3 μT
29.47 a) $B = 0$, $\vec{M} = -(4.38 \times 10^4$ A/m$)\hat{\imath}$ 29.49
b) $\vec{B} = (15.0$ T$)\hat{\imath}$, $M = 0$
a) 3.7 A b) 1.33 mA c) counterclockwise
29.51 16.2 μV

29.53 a) $\dfrac{\mu_0 I a b v}{2\pi r (r + a)}$ b) clockwise

29.55 190 rpm
29.57 a) 17.9 mV b) a to b
29.59 b) $\dfrac{RF}{B^2 L^2}$

29.61 1.2 V
29.63 $\mu_0 I W/4\pi$
29.65 a) $\dfrac{\mu_0 I v}{2\pi} \ln (1 + L/d)$ b) point a c) 0
29.67 a) 0.165 V b) 0.165 V c) 0, 0.0412 V
29.69 a) $3^2 a^2 v/R$
29.71 point a: $\dfrac{qr}{2}\dfrac{dB}{dt}$, to the left; point b: $\dfrac{qr}{2}\dfrac{dB}{dt}$, toward the top of the page; point c: 0
29.73 5.0 s
29.75 a) 196 μA/m^2 b) 3.00 nA/m^2 c) 7.82 MHz
d) 90°
29.77 a) a to b b) $\dfrac{Rmg \tan \phi}{L^2 B^2 \cos \phi}$ c) $\dfrac{mg \tan \phi}{LB}$

d) $\dfrac{Rm^2 g^2 \tan^2\phi}{L^2 B^2}$ e) $\dfrac{Rm^2 g^2 \tan^2\phi}{L^2 B^2}$

Chapter 30

30.1 a) 0.270 V, yes b) 0.270 V
30.3 6.32 μH
30.5 a) 1.96 H b) 7.11 mWb
30.7 a) 1940 b) 800 A/s
30.9 a) 0.250 H b) 0.450 mWb
30.11 a) 4.68 mV b) point a
30.13 a) 1000 b) 2.09 Ω
30.15 b) 0.111 μH
30.17 2850
30.19 a) 0.161 T b) 10.3 kJ/m^3 c) 0.129 J
d) 40.2 μH
30.21 91.7 J
30.23 a) 2.40 A/s b) 0.800 A/s c) 0.413 A
d) 0.750 A
30.25 a) 17.3 μs b) 30.7 μs
30.27 a) 0.250 A b) 0.137 A c) 32.9 V, point c
d) 0.462 ms
30.29 a) $P = (4.50$ W$)(1 - e^{-(3.20 \, \text{s}^{-1})t})$

b) $P_R = (4.50$ W$)(1 - e^{-(3.20 \, \text{s}^{-1})t})^2$

c) $P_L = (4.50$ W$)(e^{-(3.20 \, \text{s}^{-1})t} - e^{-(6.40 \, \text{s}^{-1})t})$
30.33 a) 25.0 mH b) 90.0 nC c) 0.540 μJ
d) 5.58 mA
30.35 a) 105 rad/s, 0.0596 s b) 0.720 mC
c) 4.32 mJ d) -0.542 mC
e) -0.050 A, counterclockwise
f) $U_C = 2.45$ mJ, $U_L = 1.87$ mJ
30.37 a) 7.50 μC b) 15.9 kHz c) 0.0212 J
30.39 a) 298 rad/s b) 83.8 Ω
30.43 a) 0.288 μH b) 14.2 μV
30.47 20 km/s, about 30 times smaller
30.49 a) $\dfrac{\mu_0 i}{2\pi r}$ b) $\dfrac{\mu_0 i^2 l}{4\pi r}dr$ c) $\dfrac{\mu_0 i^2 l}{4\pi} \ln (b/a)$

d) $\dfrac{\mu_0 l}{2\pi} \ln (b/a)$
30.51 a) 5.00 H b) 31.7 m, no
30.53 a) 0.281 J b) 0.517 J c) 0.236 J
30.57 222 μF, 9.31 μH
30.59 13.0 mA, 184 A/s
30.61 a) 0 A, 20.0 V b) 0.267 A, 0 V
c) 0.147 A, 9.0 V
30.63 a) solenoid c) 50 V d) 3.5 A
e) 4.3 Ω, 43 mH
30.65 a) $A_1 = A_4 = 0.800$ A, $A_2 = A_3 = 0$;
$V_1 = 40.0$ V, $V_2 = V_3 = V_4 = V_5 = 0$
b) $A_1 = 0.480$ A, $A_2 = A_3 = 0.160$ A, $A_3 = 0.320$ A,
$A_4 = 0$; $V_1 = 24.0$ V, $V_2 = 0$, $V_3 = V_4 = V_5 =$
16.0 V c) 192 μC
30.67 a) $A_1 = A_4 = 0.455$ A, $A_2 = A_3 = 0$
b) $A_1 = 0.585$ A, $A_2 = 0.320$ A,
$A_3 = 0.160$ A, $A_4 = 0.107$ A
30.69 a) 50.0 V b) point a c) 60.0 V d) point c
e) -96.0 V f) point b g) 156 V h) point d
30.71 a) 0; $v_{ac} = 0$, $v_{cb} = 36.0$ V
b) 0.180 A; $v_{ac} = 9.0$ V, $v_{cb} = 27.0$ V
c) $i_0 = (0.180$ A$)(1 - e^{-t/(0.020 \, \text{s})})$

$v_{ac} = (9.0$ V$)(1 - e^{-t/(0.020 \, \text{s})})$,

$v_{cb} = (9.0$ V$)(3.00 + e^{-t/(0.020 \, \text{s})})$

30.75 a) $i_1 = \dfrac{\varepsilon}{R_1}$, $i_2 = \dfrac{\varepsilon}{R_2}(1 - e^{-R_2 t/L})$

b) $i_1 = \dfrac{\varepsilon}{R_1}$, $i_2 = \dfrac{\varepsilon}{R_2}$ c) $i = \dfrac{\varepsilon}{R_2}e^{-(R_1 + R_2)t/L}$

d) 21.2 Ω, 12.7 V e) 35.3 mA

30.77 a) $d = D\left(\dfrac{L - L_0}{L_f - L_0}\right)$

b) 0.63024 H, 0.63048 H, 0.63072 H, 0.63096 H
c) 0.63000 H, 0.62999 H, 0.62999 H, 0.62998 H
d) oxygen

30.79 a) $i_1 = \dfrac{\varepsilon}{R_1}(1 - e^{-R_1 t/L})$, $i_2 = \dfrac{\varepsilon}{R_2}e^{-t/R_2 C}$,

$q_2 = \varepsilon C(1 - e^{-t/R_2 C})$

b) $i_1 = 0$, $i_2 = 9.60$ mA c) $i_1 = 1.92$ A,
$i_2 = 0$ d) 1.6 ms e) 9.4 mA f) 0.22 s

Chapter 31

31.1 1.06 A
31.3 a) 31.8 V b) 0
31.5 a) 90°, leads b) 193 Hz
31.7 13.3 μF
31.9 a) 1510 Ω b) 0.239 H c) 497 Ω
d) 16.6 μF
31.11 a) (12.5 V) $\cos[(480$ rad/s$)t]$ b) 7.17 V
31.13 a) $i = (0.0253$ A$) \cos[(720$ rad/s$)t]$

b) 180 Ω
c) $v_L = -(4.56$ V$) \sin[(720$ rad/s$)t]$
31.15 a) 601 Ω b) 0.0499 A c) $-70.6°$, lags
d) 9.98 V, 4.99 V, 33.3 V
31.17 50.0 V
31.19 a) 40.0 W b) 0.167 A c) 720 Ω
31.21 b) 76.7 V
31.23 a) 45.8°, 0.697 b) 344 Ω c) 155 V
d) 48.6 W e) 48.6 W f) 0 g) 0
31.25 a) 0.302 b) 0.370 W c) 0.370 W, 0, 0
31.27 a) 113 Hz, 15.0 mA b) 7.61 mA, lag
31.29 a) 150 V b) 150 V, 1290 V, 1290 V
c) 37.5 W
31.31 a) 1.00 b) 75.0 W c) 75.0 W
31.33 a) 115 Ω b) 146 Ω c) 146 Ω
31.35 a) 10 b) 2.40 A c) 28.8 W d) 500 Ω
31.37 a) use a step-down transformer with $N_2/N_1 = \frac{1}{2}$
b) 6.67 A b) 36.0 Ω
31.39 0.124 H
31.41 3.59×10^7 rad/s
31.43 230 Ω
31.45 a) inductor b) 0.133 H
31.47 a) 0.831 b) 161 V
31.49 a) inductor: 1.15 A, 31.6 V; resistor: 1.15 A,
57.5 V; capacitor: 1.15 A, 14.6 V
b) all change; inductor: 0.860 A, 47.3 V; resistor:
0.860 A, 43.0 V; capacitor: 0.860 A, 5.46 V

31.51 $\dfrac{V_{out}}{V_s} = \sqrt{\dfrac{R^2 + \omega^2 L^2}{R^2 + \left(\omega L - \dfrac{1}{\omega C}\right)^2}}$

31.55 a) 102 Ω b) 0.882 A c) 270 V
31.57 b) yes c) 0 e) no
31.59 a) $I_R = V/R$, $I_C = V\omega C$, $I_L = V/\omega L$
d) 159 Hz e) 0.50 A
f) 0.50 A, 0.050 A, 0.050 A
31.61 a) L and C b) $\frac{1}{2}$ for each
31.63 a) 0.750 A b) 160 Ω c) 341 Ω, 619 Ω
d) 341 Ω
31.65 0, $I_0/\sqrt{3}$
31.67 a) decreases by $\frac{1}{2}$ b) increases by 2
c) decreases by $\frac{1}{2}$ d) no
31.69 a) $\dfrac{V}{\sqrt{R^2 + \dfrac{9L}{4C}}}$ b) $\sqrt{\dfrac{L}{C}} \dfrac{2V}{\sqrt{R^2 + \dfrac{9L}{4C}}}$

c) $\sqrt{\dfrac{L}{C}} \dfrac{V/2}{\sqrt{R^2 + \dfrac{9L}{4C}}}$ d) $\dfrac{2LV^2}{R^2 + \dfrac{9L}{4C}}$

e) $\dfrac{1}{2}\dfrac{LV^2}{R^2 + \dfrac{9L}{4C}}$

31.71 a) 75.8 V   b) 13.6 Ω
31.73 a) $V_R I/2$ b) 0   c) 0
31.75 a) 0.400 A   b) 36.9°   c) $(400 - 300i)\ \Omega$,
     500 Ω d) $(0.320 + 0.240i)$ A, 0.400 A
     e) 36.9°   f) $V_{R\text{-cpx}} = (128 + 96i)$V,
     $V_{L\text{-cpx}} = (-120 + 160i)$V,
     $V_{C\text{-cpx}} = (192 - 256i)$V

Chapter 32

32.1 a) 1.28 s   b) 8.15×10^{13} km
32.3 13.3 nT, $+y$-direction
32.5 3.0×10^{18} Hz, 3.3×10^{-19} s,
     6.3×10^{10} rad/m
32.7 a) 6.94×10^{14} Hz   b) 375 V/m   c) $E(x, t) =$
     $(375 \text{ V/m}) \cos [(1.45 \times 10^7 \text{ rad/m})x -$
     $(4.36 \times 10^{15} \text{ rad/s})t]$, $B(x, t) =$
     $(1.25\ \mu\text{T}) \cos [(1.45 \times 10^7 \text{ rad/m})x -$
     $(4.36 \times 10^{15} \text{ rad/s})t]$
32.9 a) (i) 60 kHz   (ii) 6.0×10^{13} Hz
     (iii) 6.0×10^{16} Hz   b) (i) 4.62×10^{-14} m $=$
     4.62×10^{-5} nm
     (ii) 508 m $= 5.08 \times 10^{11}$ nm
32.11 a) $+y$-direction   b) 0.149 mm   c) $\vec{B} =$
     $(1.03 \text{ mT})\hat{\imath} \cos [(4.22 \times 10^4 \text{ rad/m})y -$
     $(1.265 \times 10^{13} \text{ rad/s})t]$
32.13 a) 361 m   b) 0.0174 rad/m
     c) 5.22×10^6 rad/s   d) 0.0144 V/m
32.15 a) 0.381 μm   b) 0.526 μm   c) 1.38
     d) 1.90
32.17 a) 330 W/m²   b) 500 V/m, 1.7 μT
32.19 a) 11 μW/m²   b) 0.30 nT   c) 840 W
32.21 2.5×10^{25} W
32.23 12.0 V/m, 40.0 nT
32.25 850 kW
32.27 a) 0.18 mW   b) 274 V/m, 0.913 μT
     c) 0.18 mJ/s   d) 0.010 W/cm²
32.29 a) 637 W/m²   b) 693 V/m, 2.31 μT
     c) 2.12 μJ/m³
32.31 a) 30.5 cm   b) 2.46 GHz   c) 2.11 GHz
32.33 a) 7.10 mm   b) 3.55 mm
     c) 1.56×10^8 m/s
32.35 a) 4.38 mm   b) 4.38 mm   c) 4.38 mm
32.37 a) 0.375 mJ   b) 4.08 mPa
     c) 604 nm, 3.70×10^{14} Hz
     d) 30.3 kV/m, 101 μT
32.39 a) 71.6 MW/m²   b) 232 kV/m, 774 μT
     c) 35.8 MW/m²   d) 637 W/m²
32.41 a) 0.00602 W/m²   b) 2.13 V/m, 7.10 nT
     c) 1.20 pN, no
32.43 a) 840 V/m, 2.80 μT
     b) 1.56 μJ/m³ for each   c) 15.3 pJ
32.45 a) at $r = R$: 64 MW/m², 0.21 Pa; at $r = R/2$:
     260 MW/m², 0.85 Pa   b) no
32.47 3.89×10^{-13} rad/s²
32.49 a) $\rho I/\pi a^2$, in the direction of the current
     b) $\mu_0 I/2\pi a$, counterclockwise if the current is
     out of the page
     c) $\dfrac{\rho I^2}{2\pi^2 a^3}$, radially inward
     d) $\dfrac{\rho l I^2}{\pi a^2} = I^2 R$
32.51 a) 23.6 h   b) throw it
32.53 a) 9.75×10^{-15} W/m²
     b) 2.71 μV/m, 9.03×10^{-15} T, 67.3 ms
     c) 3.25×10^{-23} Pa
     d) 0.190 m
32.55 a) $\dfrac{4\rho G\pi MR^3}{3r^2}$ b) $\dfrac{LR^2}{4cr^2}$ c) 0.19 μm, no
32.57 b) 1.39×10^{-11} c) 2.54×10^{-8}

Chapter 33

33.1 39.4°
33.3 a) 2.04×10^8 m/s
     b) 442 nm
33.5 a) 1.55   b) 550 nm
33.7 a) 47.5°   b) 66.0°
33.9 2.51×10^8 m/s
33.11 a) 2.34   b) 82°
33.13 a) f, $n\lambda$, nv
     b) f, $(n/n')\lambda$, $(n/n')v$
33.15 71.8°
33.17 a) 51.3°   b) 33.6°
33.19 a) 58.1°   b) 22.8°
33.21 1.77
33.23 462 nm
33.25 0.6°
33.27 $0.375 I_0$
33.29 a) $I_0/2$, $0.125 I_0$, $0.0938 I_0$ b) 0
33.31 a) 1.40   b) 35.5°
33.33 $\arccos\left(\dfrac{\cos\theta}{\sqrt{2}}\right)$
33.35 6.38 W/m²
33.37 a) $I_0/2$, $0.250 I_0$, $0.125 I_0$, linearly polarized
     along the axis of each filter   b) $I_0/2$ linearly
     polarized along the axis of the filter; 0
33.41 a) 46.7°   b) 13.4°
33.43 72.1°
33.45 1.28
33.47 1.53
33.49 1.84
33.51 a) 48.6°   b) 48.6°
33.53 39.1°
33.55 0.23°, about the same
33.59 b) 38.9°   c) 5.0°
33.61 a) 35°   b) $I_p = 19.9$ W/m², $I_0 = 10.1$ W/m²
33.63 23.3°
33.67 a) $\Delta = 2\theta_a^A - 6 \arcsin\left(\dfrac{\sin\theta_a^A}{n}\right) + 2\pi$
     b) $\cos^2\theta_2 = \dfrac{n^2 - 1}{8}$
     c) violet: $\theta_2 = 71.55°$, $\Delta = 233.2°$;
     red: $\theta_2 = 71.94°$, $\Delta = 230.1°$

Chapter 34

34.1 39.2 cm to the right of the mirror, 4.85 cm
34.3 9.0 cm, tip of the lead
34.5 b) 33.0 cm to the left of the vertex, 1.20 cm,
     inverted, real
34.7 0.213 mm
34.9 18.0 cm from the vertex, 0.50 cm, erect, virtual
34.11 b) 28.0 cm, inverted   c) 8.00 cm
34.13 a) concave   b) 2.50 cm, 5.00 cm
34.15 2.67 cm
34.17 3.30 m
34.19 a) at the center of the bowl, 1.33   b) no
34.21 39.5 cm
34.23 8.35 cm to the left of the vertex, 0.326 mm,
     erect
34.25 a) 107 cm to the right of the lens, 17.8 mm,
     real, inverted   b) same as part (a)
34.27 71.2 cm to the right of the lens   b) -2.97
34.29 3.69 cm, 2.82 cm to the left of the lens
34.31 1.67
34.33 a) 18.6 mm   b) 19 mm from the cornea
     c) 0.61 mm, real, inverted
34.35 a) 36.0 cm to the right of the lens
     b) 180 cm to the left of the lens
     c) 7.20 cm to the left of the lens
     d) 13.8 cm to the left of the lens
34.37 26.3 cm from the lens, 12.4 mm, erect, same
     side
34.39 a) 200 cm to the right of the first lens, 4.80 cm
     b) 150 cm to the right of the second lens,
     7.20 cm
34.41 a) 53.0 cm   b) real   c) 2.50 mm, inverted
34.43 10.2 m
34.45 a) 1.4×10^{-4} b) 5.3×10^{-4}
     c) 1.5×10^{-3}

34.47 a) 85 mm   b) 135 mm
34.49 a) $f/11$ b) $1/480$ s $= 2.1$ ms
34.51 a) convex   b) 50 mm to 56 mm
34.53 a) 80.0 cm   b) 76.9 cm
34.55 49.4 cm, 2.02 diopters
34.57 -1.37 diopters
34.59 a) 6.06 mm   b) 4.12 mm
34.61 a) 640   b) 43
34.63 a) 8.37 mm   b) 21.4   c) -297
34.65 a) -6.33 b) 1.90 cm   c) 0.127 rad
34.67 a) 0.661 m   b) 59.1
34.69 7.20 m/s
34.71 $h/2$
34.73 a) 20.0 cm   b) 39.0 cm
34.75 a) 46 cm from the mirror, on the opposite side
     of the mirror, virtual   b) 29 mm, erect   c) no
34.77 51 m/s
34.79 b) 2.4 cm, -0.133
34.81 2.00
34.83 a) -3.3 cm   b) virtual
     c) 1.9 cm to the right of the vertex at the right-
     hand end of the rod   d) real, inverted, 1.06 mm
34.85 a) 58.7 cm, converging   b) 4.48 mm, virtual
34.87 a) 6.48 mm   b) no, behind the retina
     c) 19.3 mm from the cornea, in front of the retina
34.89 50.3 cm
34.91 10.6 cm
34.93 a) 0.24 m   b) 0.24 m
34.95 72.1 cm to the right of the surface vertex
34.97 0.80 cm
34.99 -26.7 cm
34.101 1.24 cm above the page
34.103 a) 46.7 m   b) 35.0 m
34.105 134 cm to the left of the object
34.107 a) 3.5 cm   b) 7.0 cm   c) 100 cm
     d) 57   e) no
34.109 4.17 diopters
34.111 a) 30.9 cm   b) 29.2 cm
34.113 d) 36.0 cm, 21.6 cm, $d = 1.2$ cm
34.115 a) 552   b) 25.8 cm
34.117 a) $4f$
34.119 b) 1.35 cm

Chapter 35

35.1 a) 14 cm, 48 cm, 82 cm, 116 cm, 150 cm
     b) 31 cm, 65 cm, 99 cm, 133 cm
35.3 b) 427 Hz   b) 0.796 m
35.5 0.75 m, 2.00 m, 3.25 m, 4.50 m, 5.75 m,
     7.00 m, 8.25 m
35.7 a) 2.0 m   b) constructively
     c) 1.0 m, destructively
35.9 1.14 mm
35.11 0.83 mm
35.13 a) 39   b) $\pm 73.3°$
35.15 12.6 cm
35.17 1200 nm
35.19 a) $0.750 I_0$ b) 80 nm
35.21 1670 rad
35.23 71.4 m
35.25 114 nm
35.27 0.0234°
35.29 a) 55.6 nm   b) (i) 2180 nm   (ii) 11.0
     wavelengths
35.31 a) 514 nm, green   b) 603 nm, orange
35.33 0.11 μm
35.35 0.570 mm
35.37 1.54 mm
35.39 a) 96.0 nm   b) no, no
35.41 a) 1.58 mm (green), 1.72 mm (orange)
     b) 3.45 mm (violet), 4.74 mm (green),
     5.16 mm (orange)   c) 9.57 μm
35.43 1.730
35.45 0°, 27.3°, 66.5°
35.47 1.57
35.49 above centerline: 3.14°, 15.9°, 29.5°, 45.4°,
     68.6°; below centerline: 9.45°, 22.5°, 37.0°, 55.2°
35.51 6.8×10^{-5} (C°)$^{-1}$
35.53 $\lambda/2d$, independent of m
35.55 b) 0.72 m
35.57 1.42

35.59 b) $I = I_0 \cos^2\left\{\dfrac{\pi[d\sin\theta + L(n-1)]}{\lambda_0}\right\}$

c) $\sin\theta = \dfrac{m\lambda_0 - L(n-1)}{d}$

35.61 14.0

Chapter 36

36.1 506 nm
36.3 a) 226 b) ±83.0°
36.5 9.07 m
36.7 a) 63.8 cm
    b) ±22.1°, ±34.3°, ±48.8°, ±70.1°
36.9 ±16.0°, ±33.4°, ±55.6°
36.11 0.920 μm
36.13 a) 580 nm b) 0.128
36.15 a) 6.75 mm b) 2.43 μW/m²
36.17 a) 668 nm b) $9.36 \times 10^{-5} I_0$
36.19 a) ±13.0°, ±26.7°, ±42.4°, ±64.1°
    b) 2.08 W/m²
36.21 a) 3 b) 2
36.23 a) 0.0627°, 0.125° b) $0.249I_0$, $0.0256I_0$
36.25 a) 1 & 3, 2 & 4 b) 1 & 2, 3 & 4
    c) 1 & 3, 2 & 4
36.27 15.0 μm (width), 45.0 μm (separation)
36.29 a) 4790 slits/cm b) 19.1°, 40.8° c) no
36.31 a) yes b) 13.3 nm
36.33 a) 4830 lines/cm b) ±37.7°, ±66.5°
36.35 10.5°, 21.3°, 33.1°
36.37 a) 17,500 b) yes
    c) (i) 587.8170 nm (ii) 587.7834 nm
    (iii) 587.7834 nm < λ < 587.8170 nm
36.39 0.232 nm
36.41 0.559 nm

36.43 1.85 m
36.45 92 cm
36.47 1.45 m
36.49 a) 77 m (Hubble), 1100 km (Arecibo)
    b) 1500 km
36.51 30.2 μm
36.53 a) 78 b) ±80.8° c) 555 μW/m²
36.55 1.68
36.57 a) 1.80 mm b) 0.796 mm
36.61 b) for $3\pi/2$: any two slits separated by one
    other slit; for the other cases: any two slits
    separated by three other slits
36.63 360 nm
36.65 second
36.67 c) ±2.61 rad
36.69 387 km
36.71 1.40

Chapter 37

37.1 bolt A
37.3 0.867c, no
37.5 a) 0.998c b) 126 m
37.7 1.12 h, in the spacecraft
37.9 92.5 m
37.11 a) 0.66 km b) 49 μs, 15 km c) 0.45 km
37.13 a) 3570 m b) 90.0 μs c) 89.2 μs
37.15 a) 0.806c b) 0.974c c) 0.997c
37.17 a) toward b) 0.385c
37.19 0.784c
37.21 0.611c
37.23 0.857c, away from
37.25 a) 0.159c b) 172 million dollars
37.27 $3.06p_0$
37.29 a) 0.866c b) 0.608c
37.31 a) 5.49×10^{15} m/s²

    b) 9.26×10^{14} m/s²
37.33 a) 0.866c b) 0.986c
37.35 a) 0.450 nJ b) 1.94×10^{-18} kg·m/s
    c) 0.968c
37.37 a) 3.3×10^{-13}% b) 4.0×10^{-13} g,
    increases, no
37.39 a) 1.11×10^3 kg b) 52.1 cm
37.41 a) 0.867 nJ b) 0.270 nJ c) 0.452
37.43 a) 5.34 pJ (nonrel), 5.65 pJ (rel), 1.06
    b) 67.8 pJ (nonrel), 331 pJ (rel), 4.88
37.45 a) 2.06 MV
    b) 0.330 pJ = 2.06 MeV
37.47 a) 4.2×10^9 kg = 4.6×10^6 tons
    b) 1.5×10^{13} y
37.49 a) $\Delta = 8.42 \times 10^{-6}$ b) 34.0 GeV
37.51 0.700c
37.53 a) 0.995c b) 1%
37.55 a) $\Delta = 9 \times 10^{-9}$ b) 7000m
37.57 0.168 MeV
37.59 a) $4c/5$ b) c c) (i) 145 MeV (ii) 625 MeV
    d) (i) 117 MeV (ii) 469 MeV
37.65 b) $\Delta x' = \sqrt{(\Delta x)^2 - c^2(\Delta t)^2}$ c) 14.4 ns
37.67 0.357c, receding
37.69 a) 1000 y, 866 y, 1.4×10^{19} J, 14%
    b) 505 y, 71 y, 5.5×10^{20} J, 550%
    c) 501 y, 7.1 y, 6.3×10^{21} J, 6300%
37.71 2.04×10^{-13} N
37.75 a) toward us at 13.1 km/s, 39.4 km/s
    b) 5.96×10^9 m, about 0.040 times the
    earth-sun distance; 5.55×10^{29} kg =
    $0.279\ m_{sun}$
37.77 a) 2494 MeV b) 2.526 c) 987.4 MeV

PHOTO CREDITS

About the Author Hugh D. Young; Roger Freedman

Chapter 21 Opener: iStockphoto; 21.5: Journal-Courier/The Image Works; 21.8a: Richard Megna/Fundamental Photographs; 21.29a: Reproduced from *PSSC Physics*, 2nd ed. (1965), D.C. Heath & Company with Education Development Center, Inc., Newton, Massachusetts; 21.30b: Tony Craddock/Photo Researchers, Inc.; App. 21.1 iStockphoto; App. 21.2: Albert Kok; P21.94: David Parker/Photo Researchers, Inc.

Chapter 22 Opener: U.S. Department of Energy; 22.10: AKG London Ltd.; 22.27b: Peter Terren/Tesladownunder.com; 22.28b: Russ Kinne/Comstock; App. 22.1a: Mark Webster/Photolibrary; App. 22.2: Dr. David Furness, Keele University/SPL/Photo Researchers, Inc.

Chapter 23 Opener: Ted Kurihara/Getty Images; 23.9: NASA/JPL/Caltech; 23.11: Lester V. Berman/Corbis; 23.17: Hulton Archive/Keystone/Getty Images; 23.22: iStockphoto; App. 23.1: iStockphoto; App. 23.2: 3D4Medical.com/Getty Images

Chapter 24 Opener: Shutterstock; 24.3: Shutterstock; 24.4: Andrew Lambert/Photo Researchers, Inc.; 24.7: Eric Schrader - Pearson Science; 24.11: Sandia National Laboratories; App. 24.1: iStockphoto; App. 24.2: H Heller, M Schaefer, & K Schulten, "Molecular dynamics simulation of a bilayer of 200 lipids in the gel and in the liquid-crystal phases," J. Phys. Chem. 97:8343-60, 1993.

Chapter 25 Opener: iStockphoto; 25.4: Eric Schrader - Pearson Science; 25.5: PhotoDisc/Getty Images; 25.8: iStockphoto; 25.12: iStockphoto; App. 25.1: Dr. David Furness, Keele University/Photo Researchers, Inc.; App. 25.2: Andrew J. Martinez/Photo Researchers, Inc.; 25.15 Richard Megna/Fundamental Photographs

Chapter 26 Opener: Maximilian Stock/Photo Researchers, Inc.; 26.2 Photos.com; 26.5: John P. Surey; 26.13: John P. Surey; App. 26.1: Dorling Kindersley Media Library; 26.18: Richard Megna/Fundamental Photographs; App. 26.2: Mehau Kulyk/Photo Researchers, Inc.; 26.25a: Banana Stock/Alamy; 26.25b: Wikipedia

Chapter 27 Opener: Simon Fraser/Photo Researchers, Inc.; 27.2b: Bill Aron/PhotoEdit Inc.; 27.14: Richard Megna/Fundamental Photographs; 27.17b: Sargent-Welch/VWR International; 27.20b: Shutterstock; 27.21: Lawrence Berkeley National Laboratory; 27.40: Jeremy Burgess/Photo Researchers, Inc.; App. 27.1: Robert Smith/Photolibrary; App. 27.2: iStockphoto

Chapter 28 Opener: CERN/European Organization for Nuclear Research; 28.8: Definitive Stock; 28.11: Jeremy Walker/Photo Researchers, Inc.; App. 28.1: iStockphoto; Test Your Understanding, page 941: Mark Antman/The Image Works; App. 28.2: Scarberry, K. E., Dickerson, E. B., Zhang, Z. J., Benigno, B. B. & McDonald, J. F., "Selective removal of ovarian cancer cells from human ascites fluid using magnetic nanoparticles." Nanomedicine: Nanotechnology, Biology and Medicine. 6, 399-408 (2010)

Chapter 29 Opener: iStockphoto; App. 29.1: Simon Fraser/University of Durham/Photo Researchers, Inc.; 29.9: Maximilian Stock Ltd./Photo Researchers, Inc.; 29.18a: Photodisc Red/Getty Images; 29.18b: Toyota Motor Sales USA; 29.18c: CIRRUS Design Corporation; App. 29.2: NASA/JPL/Caltech; 29.25: Ken Gatherum, Boeing Computer Services

Chapter 30 Opener: EschCollection/Getty Images; 30.2: Shutterstock; App. 30.1: Ron Chapple/Getty Images; 30.7: Photodisc/Getty Images; App. 30.2: SOHO/NASA; 30.10: John Walsh/Photo Researchers, Inc.

Chapter 31 Opener: John P. Surey & Caroline J. Robillard; 31.5: Rubberball/Getty Images; 31.14: Lawrence Migdale/Photo Researchers, Inc.; App. 31.1: Mauro Fermariello/Photo Researchers, Inc.; App. 31.2: iStockphoto; 31.22: Shutterstock; 31.23: Roger A. Freedman

Chapter 32 Opener: Shutterstock; 32.1: Bettmann/Corbis; 32.2a: iStockphoto; 32.2b: Malcolm Fife/Getty Images; App. 32.1: Ted Kinsman/Photo Researchers, Inc.; 32.16: The Image Bank/Getty Images; 32.18: iStockphoto; App. 32.2: Alexander Tsiaras/Photo Researchers, Inc.; 32.20: NASA/JPL-Caltech/E.Churchwell (University of Wisconsin-Madison); 32.23: iStockphoto

Chapter 33 Opener: Peter Aprahamian/Photo Researchers, Inc.; 33.1: iStockphoto; 33.2: National Institutes of Health/Photo Researchers, Inc.; 33.9: Roger A. Freedman; 33.10a: NASA/John F. Kennedy Space Center; 33.10b: iStockphoto; App. 33.1: Peter Herring/imagequestmarine.com; 33.13b: Susan Schwartzenberg, The Exploratorium; 33.16: VEM / Photo Researchers, Inc.; 33.17: iStockphoto; 33.20a: Randy O'Rourke/Corbis; 33.22a: Dougal Walters/Getty Images; 33.22b: Pixtal/AGE Fotostock; 33.26: Diane Hirsch/Fundamental Photographs; 33.31: Peter Aprahamian/Sharples Stress Engineers/Photo Researchers, Inc.; App. 33.2: iStockphoto; 33.33: Roger Freedman; 33.37a: K. Nomachi/Photo Researchers, Inc.

Chapter 34 Opener: Tek Image/Photo Researchers, Inc.; 34.8: Marshall Henrichs; 34.12a: NASA; 34.12b-c: NASA Headquarters; 34.23: iStockphoto; 34.27: Richard Megna/Fundamental Photographs; 34.34: PhotoDisc/Getty Images; 34.41a-c: Marshall Henrichs; App. 34.1: Shutterstock; 34.43c: THK Photo Products, Inc.; 34.44b: Omikron/Photo Researchers, Inc.; App. 34.2: Shutterstock; 34.52c: Jan Hinsch/Photo Researchers, Inc.; 34.54d: National Optical Astronomy Observatories

Chapter 35 Opener: iStockphoto; 35.4: Roger Freedman; 35.6: Pearson Education; 35.11b: Shutterstock; 35.16b: Bausch & Lomb Incorporated; 35.17: Bausch & Lomb Incorporated; App. 35.1, top: iStockphoto; App. 35.1, right and bottom: Peter Vukusic; App. 35.2: J. Reed and J.K.Gimzewski, UCLA California Nanosystems Institute, 2007

Chapter 36 Opener: Eric Schrader - Pearson Science; 36.2a-b: Pearson Education; 36.6: Pearson Education; 36.9b: Richard Megna/Fundamental Photographs; 36.11: Dane Hornsleth; 36.12d: Pearson Education; 36.17: iStockphoto; 36.18a: NSO/AURA/NSF; 36.18b: Physics Dept., Imperial College/Photo Researchers, Inc.; App.36.1: Tek Image/Photo Researchers, Inc.; 36.20b: Estate of Bertram Eugene Warren; 36.24: Science Photo Library/Photo Researchers, Inc.; 36.26: Pearson Education; 36.27a-c: Pearson Education; App. 36.2: National Radio Astronomy Observatory/Associated Universities, Inc./National Science Foundation; 36.30: Paul Silverman/Fundamental Photographs; P36.66: NASA

Chapter 37 Opener: Brookhaven National Laboratory/Corbis; 37.4: Shutterstock; 37.7: NASA/John F. Kennedy Space Center; App. 37.1: iStockphoto; 37.11: Jack Fields/Photo Researchers, Inc.; 37.18: Adam Hart-Davis/Photo Researchers, Inc.; 37.19: NASA and The Hubble Heritage Team (STScI/AURA); App. 37.2: Imaginechina/AP Images; 37.25: Thinkstock/Getty Images

INDEX

For users of the three-volume edition: pages 1–686 are in Volume 1; pages 687–1260 are in Volume 2; and pages 1223–1522 are in Volume 3. Pages 1261–1522 are not in the Standard Edition.